ANNUAL REVIEW OF PHYSIOLOGY

ANNUAL REVIEW OF PHYSIOLOGY

VICTOR E. HALL, *Editor*
University of California, Los Angeles

ARTHUR C. GIESE, *Associate Editor*
Stanford University

RALPH R. SONNENSCHEIN, *Associate Editor*
University of California, Los Angeles

VOLUME 30

1968
ANNUAL REVIEWS, INC.
4139 EL CAMINO WAY
PALO ALTO, CALIFORNIA, U.S.A.

ANNUAL REVIEWS, INC.
PALO ALTO, CALIFORNIA, U.S.A.

Library of Congress Catalogue Card Number: 39-15404

FOREIGN AGENCY

Maruzen Company, Limited
6 Tori-Nichome, Nihonbashi
Tokyo

PRINTED AND BOUND IN THE UNITED STATES OF AMERICA
BY GEORGE BANTA COMPANY, INC.

PREFACE

The publication of this volume of the *Annual Review of Physiology* marks the end of an era, for it will be the last to have been prepared under the general overseeing of Dr. James Murray Luck, who retires this year as Editor-in-Chief of Annual Reviews, Inc. It was he who, after the marked success which attended his founding of the *Annual Review of Biochemistry*, saw the possibility of a companion review in physiology. With his characteristic ability to gain the cooperation of fellow scientists in new projects, he persuaded the Board of Publication Trustees of the American Physiological Society, a group of hard-headed skeptics, to join with Annual Reviews, Inc. in founding the *Annual Review of Physiology*.

After many years of successful joint sponsorship of the *Annual Review* by Annual Reviews, Inc. and the American Physiological Society, in 1962 the Society withdrew from the arrangement for purely administrative reasons. Since then the *Review* has continued, changed only in that its Editorial Committee is appointed by Annual Reviews instead of the Society.

Dr. Luck thus became the first Editor of the *Annual Review* and established, virtually single-handedly, the policies, procedures, and formats which have served ever since. They have proved able to adapt interstitially to the enormous increase in the research output of physiologists without much external change, which is good evidence for the soundness of Dr. Luck's planning.

One of the keystones of the success of the Annual Reviews operation may not be obvious to outsiders: Dr. Luck's ability to recruit and maintain an office staff of unusually competent and dedicated people, who have made the work of the editors relatively light. In fact, the machinery for securing authors' consent to write, for handling manuscripts, and for seeing them through the press has been operated almost entirely by this staff under Dr. Luck's watchful eye.

It would then seem that now is the time for all of us related to the *Annual Review of Physiology* to express to him our gratitude and affectionate respect; and to wish him success and happiness in whatever new venture his outgoing inventive genius will next lead him to.

We wish particularly to mention, as typical, Dr. Luck's last nominee as Assistant Editor of the *Annual Review of Physiology*, Joann Huddleston, under whose care and feeding the present volume was developed. Again the George Banta Company has maintained its high standards of printing, for which our thanks.

V. E. H.
A. C. G.
R. R. S.

CONTENTS

A WORD ABOUT REPRINTS

The reader may be puzzled by the conspicuous number (1000 to 1016) aligned in the margin with the title of each review in this volume; it is a key for use in the ordering of reprints.

The sale of reprints of articles published in these *Reviews* has been initiated with this volume in the belief that reprints in individual copies, in sets covering stated topics, and in quantity for classroom use will have a special appeal to students and to teachers.

E. F. Adolph

PREFATORY CHAPTER: RESEARCH PROVIDES SELF-EDUCATION

By E. F. ADOLPH

The University of Rochester, Rochester, New York

I speak of research as a source of men's powers and not so much as a product of their endeavors. I speak of research as a mainspring of their educations, as a means of self-formation and self-renewal. I ignore men's specialties and their peak accomplishments. I suggest that the far reach of what men in all vocations do, depends considerably on their widespread experience in research modeled on the labors of scientists. It is their means of self-education.

Often education is conceived to be a formal pursuit by which a student gains knowledge and degrees. To me this view seems superficial and incidental. I think education comes mostly from within. The student, like the mature scholar, develops a project or idea. At first it seems his project poses problems that he cannot solve. In time, however, the forbidding becomes the familiar. He builds his own bridges between problem and answer; he no longer waits for bridges to be furnished by others. He becomes self-sufficient.

Is this student related to the scientist who spends his days in a laboratory clad in work-clothes? Yes, the scientist knows that manipulation and experiment get to the center of whatever problem he tackles. Notions that can be tested produce more satisfying answers than do vague ideas; testable ideas keep education itself footed in surety. Theory without continuous checking may fall to nothing. A built-in self-education treats part of every project as manipulative, whether or not it uses physical equipment.

The formal researches of those who spend most of their lives in organized scholarly effort represent the backbone of all learning. Meanwhile, the amateur researches of those who solve problems form part of their daily living, like breathing and eating. By these little researches many men live, while engaged in any occupation, even one that has no recognized place for research as a vocation. Such researches develop from everyday ideas and deepen the minds that work them out.

First I will talk about some aspects of research; then about its place in education.

MOTIVES IN RESEARCH

What impels scientists and others to do research? The usual motives mentioned are the advancement of knowledge, the public service, and the pursuit of a career. These are powerful urges but leave out the big benefit to the individual, namely his intellectual development.

Some ordinary problem faces the beginner; the problem has an available answer. He says, I will find an answer, and he succeeds in doing so. The second time he tries, he seems to know better than the first time how to seek an answer. Soon experience accumulates, and the reasoning processes, plus the searches in libraries and in laboratories, come more easily. Before he realizes it, he is launched in a type of endeavor that stays with him; the universe of self-education stands open to him. Later he finds his interests are cumulative, that one question leads to another. Already he is specializing, his efforts are channeled, and others look to him for certain types of answers. The exercise that started by accident may turn out to be intellectual.

Such prowess develops naturally in some beginning students. Maybe seeds were planted in preschool years, and sprouted into independent projects in days of unpressured adolescence. Individual effort becomes fun. Once such activity is tried, every success reinforces it. Soon the student can profit from the opportunity to live under his own initiative, free of the obligation to show accomplishments that are measured by conventional examinations.

Many instances of awakenings to the promise of self-education could be cited. The philosopher John Dewey, when a college student, first grasped the "excitement of the effort to understand the world" while he was attending a short course in textbook physiology. He suddenly saw what concrete scientific work could accomplish, and overnight changed from an indifferent student to a fiery one (1).

Research opportunity rarely came to college students, even in my day. Linked to a course given by G. H. Parker was an announced option of laboratory research. Though this option was meant for graduate students, I, a third-year undergraduate, applied for it and was accepted. Whether I wanted to test my choice of a career field, or to test my capacity to pursue an unknown kind of activity, I do not recall. In my research I managed to identify some sensory factors that led fruit flies to lay eggs. Later I wrote a manuscript describing my results, challenged to do so by Dr. Parker. Apparently he did not find my manuscript suitable for publication. Three years later he suggested that now was the time for me to write a definitive paper. This was published (2).

I believe the idea of research was already familiar to me through my associations with graduate students of varied interests, and earlier with teachers in school who delighted in guiding students into insect collecting, bird spying, and herbarium making. Those activities can arouse both questions and explorations.

Today opportunities for project-researches have become widely available to high school students. This movement toward early individual effort reflects a widespread realization that the young mind is often an inquiring mind, looking for an interest to latch onto. The opportunity to stir students who want to undertake their own projects also has brought new life to many teachers. Danger comes when students are pressed into an activity that they do not enjoy, for without enjoyment they shun involvement. The heart of the student is indispensable to a project, even as it proved to be in the days of "progressive" education that made a project out of every bit of instruction from kindergarten blocks onward. The notion that project education was the best education had great merit; fault lay in the attempt to press all education into a mold.

Experienced scholars will say: but research is intended for publication of results. I think publishable results do and will come out of only a small fraction of research activities. That fraction will be chiefly formal research. But much research is not of that kind; rather it is intended to benefit the doer.

However, formulation of results and implications is a part of every research. Only by careful analysis on paper will most decisions among possible interpretations be reached, and most intellectual values be realized. A news reporter gets his report straight by writing for an imagined reader. So the self-educating student writes for an imagined or real recipient and critic. The writing itself is an act of self-discipline; the words compel us to define our problem, arrange our evidence, and clarify our result. One's own censor is rarely a sufficient judge, hence one presents the results to a colleague or other willing listener, he serves as target of one's effort. He sees the work with a new eye, a fresh concept, and an independent judgment.

I hail the view that a specific research experience yields a general education, whether one ever again does formal research or not. A plausible basis for the view consists in the realization that no one can predict the type of problem or lack of knowledge that one will face a few years hence. To meet the unknown, one can be educated best by dealing with unknowns. When one gains self-confidence in solution of problems, a whole life stands to benefit.

At some stages, research may seem to be a self-centered way to obtain an education. But good stewardship will allow the self-educated person to become in turn an educator. He will help others to find a self-sufficiency, to stand alone.

So, while research can be a formal activity, perhaps designed in the public interest, it can also be designed as an individual activity. Sometimes individual activity develops into formal activity, little science into big science, amateur research into funded research. Hopefully the private rewards may be as great in one as in the other. For, once an individual is discovering that an answer gained to one question helps him to find the answer to another question, the individual needs no guidance, and perhaps advances best without guidance. He has become self-educating; he can enter any realm; he meets no authoritarian boundary to his explorations. Actually the amateur has one great advantage: formal research will usually limit him to "recognized" methods of thought and deed, while independence can lead him where there are no prescribed methods.

I think these characteristics and rewards of research activities hold in all departments of learning and of practical life; I can find no differences between one field of endeavor and another. Everywhere I observe that the outstanding benefit from research accrues to the doer himself. Research is his means of self-stimulation and of self-reward. He needles himself into intellectual effort. He advances his education and his capacities.

PATHWAYS IN RESEARCH

What path does the budding researcher follow? I do not believe that careers of scientists are predestined. But hindsight can usually make them appear so.

By a combination of advice and fortune, I decided to work for a doctorate with L. J. Henderson. He was a self-made intellectual in a university that valued individuals (3). Even his departmental ties were tenuous; but his determination to do what he liked was of unlimited strength. His researches were of great variety, both inside and outside of laboratories. Though superficially he might appear to wander, his persistence was intense and his probing was deep. I sometimes think his monument might be titled like Galileo's book (4) "Two new sciences". Henderson's sciences encompassed the concepts of (a) multivariate equilibria and (b) functional interactions. He had an intense faith in man's capacity to comprehend empirical systems, both inorganic and living and social (Fitness, Order, Interrelations). To me he became a shining example of the man who continually educated himself through research.

My first faculty position was in a university and department where research did not constitute part of one's job. But teaching was plentiful and was one's own responsibility. My problem became: how meet the task of heavy teaching and at the same time enlarge my horizon? For I already had an intensive urge to "get ahead" derived during graduate work and during a privileged year abroad. From the research viewpoint my efforts were fruitful, for publishable results emerged. Concurrently I was helpfully welcomed on a part-time basis in a laboratory (gas toxicology) of the U. S. Bureau of Mines and a laboratory (hot atmospheres) of the Society of Heating and Ventilating Engineers. Also I spent summers at Woods Hole, as I will mention below. These connections aided my efforts; how much initiative of mine was needed to form the connections I cannot estimate. Brashness and accident no doubt combined to make livable the self-imposed years of heavy teaching and tenuous research. In my case, self-education by means of research soon led to solid opportunities in both teaching and research.

In those years I found summer activities especially important. Research became possible to hundreds of biologists at the Marine Biological Laboratory (Woods Hole) and similar "biological stations". Most stations were actually founded to furnish work places for those who were otherwise isolated in one-man departments of colleges. Even in the earliest days, almost a century ago, it became apparent that the stations did much more than furnish the modest facilities; they were places where those of similar interests gathered. Biologists encouraged one another (5). Only in later years did many biologists pursue research at their own universities and form departments large enough to be self-contained. Fortunately, even today a remarkable number of biologists foregather at various biological stations each summer who otherwise would be unable to cultivate research interests. In my own development, four consecutive summers at Woods Hole allowed me to experiment with a variety of marine organisms. I taught part of a course that included observation of living aquatic animals.

It may be appropriate here to state how I once came to formulate a new research interest, that in Physiological Regulations. I reached a juncture where I craved a period of exploration. Were my past researches, I wondered, chosen by expediencies and short sight? In order to explore, I spent a few months in another university. I would not do experiments but would "doodle" on paper as I examined some speculative notions. Most of the speculative notions soon reached frustration stages. But one of them, an "equilibration diagram", that related either the water gain or the water loss of an animal to its bodily water content, yielded a pattern that I could apply. In the months and years following, this one concrete relationship led into successive studies of other aspects of regulatory arrangements (6) and the end is not yet. Yes, many physiologists had enunciated concepts of regulation; the truth is that their statements did not sink into me until I had developed concepts for myself; thereupon I noted similarities to theirs. Here I am not concerned with the novelty of the relationships visualized; I am concerned with what developed in my own mind. I learned in general that multiple ways of regarding physiological phenomena exist, and that I need not stay in customary paths.

How did I know that my work on equilibrations and physiological regulations was not illusory? I was well aware that colleagues believed physiological researches should be planned to elucidate mechanisms. I think my courage derived from an acute realization that in my new endeavor I was learning more than in previous periods of concentrated research; that I was now planning broadly; that I gained much, just by virtue of the fact that there were few models to follow. I had to work harder to interpret my results, and had to present them in an elementary and definitive fashion. Evidently the new path challenged me. Whether there is always a gain when one forsakes the familiar I do not know. Somehow one avoids frustrations and resolves doubts. I incline to think a well-worn path leaves too little room for play. At any rate, in the end my colleagues recognized that my path led to fruitful concepts. And it happened that cybernetics and transfer functions came along in time to make the field of regulatory physiology respected. My chief point here is that I clearly reaped a personal benefit even before my new effort could be recognized to be a contribution to physiology.

A life of research differs for each of its practitioners. Though no account of it can represent it adequately, one can view it with the same interest as one views biography. Little or big, research has its traits, sharply seen in the careers of others and eventually in the experiences of oneself.

ENJOYMENT OF RESEARCH

Research is for those who enjoy it. For a short while a student can be driven into research, for a longer while he can be led by a lure; but for enduring effort he thrives on what is within him. Where that inner urge came from can only be guessed; rather the urge (like love) seems to be special in each individual. Usually a moment of forceful conviction arrives and one says: research is what I want most to do.

What are some of the aspects of research that seem to furnish enjoyment? What are sources of this enjoyment? How does research, that seems to outsiders to be a detachment from life, hold warmth?

The kinds of satisfactions that scholars derive from their researches have been widely recognized. Some are: exercise of inquisitiveness, the chase, use of mind and hand, invention, exercise of skills, concentration of effort, framing of generalizations, competition in ideas, companionship in discussion, dispelling of superstitions, spicing of daily work, separation of fact from emotion, gain in reliability, and confidence in one's effort.

All these satisfactions tend to accumulate. They can be sources of pride so long as humility accompanies them. "Man needs to be convinced of the importance of the work he is doing" (Whitehead).

Of course, activities other than ostensible research can yield some of the same enjoyments. Fortunately, the researcher need not live without those other activities. However, research soon demands deep personal involvement; one may be warned in advance that by comparison many other activities will come to seem less enjoyable.

Here I do not propose to discuss each of these kinds of satisfaction. High quality is one's goal in every endeavor; slipshod work yields no satisfaction in research, big or little. Persistence of effort becomes indispensable; how can one rely on his observations unless he has repeated them often, and with variations of circumstances? How can one be confident that his concept will wear well unless he looks at it from many angles? Given solid quality in a report of research, only the fact that the same conclusions have been reached before will stand in the way of its publication. Therefore, to the individual, the quality of the work is the standard of his own satisfaction; to the fraternity of scholars, novelty of concept forms an additional criterion.

The human qualities of the researcher are revealed in his conversation. He has ideas to try out on his companions. He encourages his junior colleagues by shop talk, enchancing their devotion and cooperation. He heightens his own interest in how the results are coming out by arousing expectancy in others. He competes with colleagues for foresights and for vi-sions of possible significances. Such are the elements that make the difference between routine and enjoyment.

Ideas incite ideas, the self-educating scientist gains a habit of entertaining them. They do not come easily at first; he has to learn to be kind to them when they pop up. Further, ideas incite fresh ideas in others. There is something infectious about them. This is the scholar's highest function: to transmit to others the art of having thoughts based on realities, and to transmit the excitement that comes with them.

Satisfaction in one's efforts comes unawares. There is satisfaction in a meal, in a journey. A certain number of miles of travel satiates one. So it is with the activities of the scientist-scholar; a day's labor subconsciously demands a relaxation. But this metered satiety is only one of many satisfactions, and all of them together make up the measure of his believed accomplishment.

Perhaps some contrary mind would like to list the types of disappointment and frustration that come to researchers. Maybe the beginner can heed the difficulties he is likely to meet when he pursues elusive answers to his questions. For myself, the list of positive satisfactions in research here suffices.

What Is Self-Education?

I next mention some of the above characteristics of research activity, as they apply particularly to the education of university students. Everyone has aims in education, both for his own education and for the education of others.

I am unable to trace the various guidances, exposures, and frustrations that went into my early education. They, no doubt, determine my ideals of education, though their specific effects I do not recognize. What I do know is that somewhere and somehow I became self-educating. No longer did motives come from without but from within. In my own mind I link the attainment of self-education with the pursuit of research activities. Had it been otherwise, I suppose, this essay would not be written.

As a college student I was aware that I wanted to teach as well as research. I asked a faculty adviser whether I might learn about teaching in an education course. His reply was that when I had acquired something to teach I would be ready to present it to the students. This reply puzzled me, but years later it became plain that a teacher does his work by example and not by precept. He lives questioningly and transmits his questioning way of life.

Research is the greatest device for self-education invented by man, I judge. Research comes close to being a tool by which a man can lift himself intellectually by his own bootstraps. By it he cannot lose his present powers, but can increase them. He cannot stand still, he can only keep moving into new concepts and new understandings. He bares mistaken notions, amends hypotheses—and all by first-hand means. Bacon noted that "truth comes out of error more readily than out of confusion" (7). If one stands still he may only avoid errors; when one moves forward he tests his understanding. That process of education self-corrects itself.

The researcher becomes involved in what he does. Involvement is largely subconscious. The lures toward deed and thought take hold in both waking and sleeping hours. Stewing in a medium of notions and concepts seems indispensable to him who would reach a result. He feels excluded when involvement is prevented for a time, and comes back to commitment with pleasure. Hundreds of paths richly beckon. Some one of them seems satisfying. One says, this is what I was looking for. Actually one did not know what he was looking for, and when found, the new path satisfied an urge that one did not know existed.

Education and research both seem to say: You make the effort to frame answerable questions. You devise methods, such as experiments, suitable to answer them. If you take those steps, you will receive clear answers. This is a bargain that the universe offers. Few rules are known as to what kind of question is suitable—that is where experience counts most. But the scientist appears to have two advantages over the nonscientist: (a) He asks how, where, when, what; but not why. And (b) he can devise a decisive experiment.

Experience in extracting answers from an exacting universe creates attitudes in the student-researcher. He gains a faith, as did Empedocles, in the regularity of events. He embodies such faith in what some have called "scientific method". He acquires a feeling as to what "answerable" means. Sometimes he feels he can predict phenomena within narrow limits. He constructs hypotheses according to certain rules that he is almost unable to define. All this and more constitutes the research attitude.

Attitudes that develop in a research scientist are such as: He feels responsible for his work—thus, he cannot employ anyone to make decisions for him. He concentrates his effort, especially in the formation of concepts. He takes initiative in hard looking and hard thinking. He forces his portion of the universe to answer his questions wherever he thinks answers exist. Though he may flounder, and guess almost at random what to do next, he looks sharply for new directions.

Acquisition of such attitudes comes during the student's exposure to the thoughts and atmosphere of scholars at work. That exposure is today the basis of advanced education, and tomorrow perhaps of all education. The student "messes about" in experiments, books, and conversation. Something happens sooner or later to start him in pursuit of a notion. A special link latched his particular mind to a particular endeavor. Who could ever have prescribed that which would command his special motivations and capacities? From that moment of self-determination, self-education takes care of itself.

Occasionally one sees a junior colleague falteringly approach the boundary of self-confidence in his thinking. One wonders, is there some way in which I can encourage him to taste independence? Can he find an opportune release from conventional thinking? In my experience, the potential scholar can be drawn out by cautious questioning. He can be challenged to formulate inchoate questions that seethe in his mind. He will feel a need to dig deeper, and to found his inferences more accurately. Gradually he can define an area of thought where no one has previously penetrated. He forces himself into an independence he did not even seek. He makes his interest and effort visible to himself in the very act of trying to explain to me what he wants to do. What I describe here is the process that has gone on in "senior common rooms" and in "societies of fellows" for generations of scholars. I suggest that those doddering dons were not always purposeless when they made conversation.

The special quality of individual research lies in the motivation that results from raising one's own question. No question from another source will do so well. The limitation to any benefit in "problem-working" and in "teaching-machines" is that the student did not frame the problems.

The professor often thinks: the student will waste time arriving at a line of research endeavor and then it may not be a promising one. He won't know how to work at it, and I may not be interested in it. Let me save time by presenting to him one of my well-considered plans. Perhaps that represents a majority method of prodding the student into research. It may hasten one kind of productivity. But it may also deprive the student of exploration and decision-making at a critical stage in his career.

In my experience, each student or colleague with whom I associated in a research activity helped to educate me when he proposed a problem out of his own thinking. Not only did he learn as he drove himself to frame a question, but I learned a fresh approach, different from one I would have designed.

A widespread opinion is: the first research contributes most to one's education; after that, further research is largely repetition. But my personal experience indicates otherwise. The research I do today nets me just as many challenges as of old, not only because the immediate objectives are new, but because I look for more complex and comprehensive answers. I demand of myself a higher level of analysis and understanding. I have yet to enter a research that proceeded automatically to an anticipated conclusion. Always unexpected features and relationships appear; and they educate me.

My thought is that wherever someone raises a question, and follows through to an answer, that is research. And wherever research process and attitudes are learned by experience, that is education par excellence.

EDUCATION AND RESEARCH

The importance of self-impelled education varies with one's view of the purposes of education. Anciently education was used as an instrument of suppression, saying "don't". More recently education was used to purvey information, like news media. Here I am describing education that encourates personal independence, like research.

The world needs naïve research as means of education. It needs sophisticated research as advancement of public achievement and welfare. Sometimes naïve research develops into sophisticated research and hence serves doubly.

Questions to be investigated arise in all sorts of ways. Even experienced investigators may raise naïve ones; therefore the student need not feel ashamed of the ones that come naturally to him. For example, Slama & Williams (8) tried to raise sexually mature bugs of the family Pyrrhocoridae, and failed. But in other laboratories the insects reproduced regularly. Evidently conditions differed. Fifteen environmental factors were tested; finally paper of another kind was used to line the insect cages. Now the bugs bred. What effect could the paper have? It turned out that when the larvae touched the paper originally used, they absorbed juvenile hormone, which induced extra molts instead of metamorphosis to adult. Only bugs of the one family were prevented from maturing; others were not prevented. The particular analog of juvenile hormone present in the paper came from the balsam-fir wood from which this paper was made. From a chance failure of reproduction, identification of a series of hormones and their specificities unfolded.

When I noticed a rat running along the wall of an old flour mill, I wondered whether the rat was subsisting on the flour spilled in the dirt nearby. So I asked myself, how much can food material be diluted by dirt or water or other nonnutrient? This led to laboratory experiments on quantitative intakes of nonnutrient mixtures that showed how limited were the alimentary loads tolerated by laboratory rats (9).

Students sometimes become animated by reading or hearing what others have done. They prefer to hear what ordinary people did with a problem that arose spontaneously. What did a student in our own school make out of his own resources? Such an account, especially in the first person, strikes sparks most readily. Only secondarily do students take in the famous deeds of Pasteur with his microbes (10) and of Darwin (11) on his five-year voyage. During that voyage Darwin educated himself in framing questions and recording observations designed to provide answers. Many men have described how they pursued down-to-earth projects, such as the insect studies engagingly related by J. H. Fabre (12). Such descriptions only rarely come to the ears of students at the right moment, for no one can predict the man, the hearer, and the juncture that are to meet.

Scientists may feel uneasy when the uninitiated spend their efforts on problems that have already been satisfactorily solved. I do not decry repetitions of previous researches, providing they start from a question raised in the mind of the repeater. He has the choice of finding the answer in published work or of investigating for himself. He may prefer the latter! Only when the results come up for publication or when public funds allocated to research are being used, is there need for restraint of this preference.

I often wonder whether the teacher who pumps information into students does so because he is directed to do it, or because he believes that more information will develop the student's mind. Shall one suppose that every student's mind is empty, and that the duty of a teacher is to fill it with accepted facts and concepts?

I question whether each page of predigested input may smother the flame of the student's own motivations, preventing his effort to deploy what he already knows. Can we find ways of helping him so that he will not be stifled, but encouraged to examine his own ideas?

I believe that instead of being told, the student can be aroused. If he can raise a question, then I can help him to search for its answer. But the answer without the question is something he will generally ignore. The question already in his mind, however wild, carries a desire to understand. He will exercise whatever resources he has to analyse and to reason. The teacher's job is to help him discover that he has resources and can use them to his own satisfaction.

Though the student's questioning is often aroused in an individual conversation, yet group or class education also works to that end. The aroused student is not always the one who is conversing at the moment. A rhetorical question or a difficulty in another student's concept, may be the trigger. Intense moments in class teaching come unannounced. Suddenly someone feels: this is ideal teaching and learning, a satisfying experience. Why cannot all group gatherings intrigue me like this one? If the teacher knew how, all classes would be built accordingly; but the teacher cannot always design such moments of excitement. He can, however, welcome them when they appear.

Further pursuing the above notions, I wonder that laboratory instruction is so often an exercise in following directions. Maybe minute directions will produce a complete set of data. But will the designer of those data be the only one to appreciate them? I say: occasionally, at least, let the student pose a question to which a laboratory procedure can yield an answer. Manipulations will then have a self-determined aim. And the aim will be consummated when the student draws a reasoned conclusion from the information he himself has designedly obtained. A follow-up conference will later reveal the significances of the whole exercise. The exercise has now been modeled as a research project, and built into it are the potential benefits of research itself.

Perhaps teachers need renewed faith in the capacities of students to initiate intellectual ventures. Students prove of specific value to teacher-researchers through the questions they ask. They may ask: What will you gain when you understand this problem? How do you know that is so? What consequence follows from this particular result? Teachers might agree with St. Benedict (535 A.D.) (13) "that God often reveals what is better to the younger".

Customarily we deny to students the adventure of participation in the search and probe by saying: You must first complete such and such courses. But, how do we know that a requirement does not kill the very excitement and initiative that we cherish? Ignorance can be corrected by the student once he is motivated, while blunted motivation can never be compensated, I fear.

Research also develops and sustains the teacher. It supplies him with exercise for the mind, forcing him to work in depth. New questions are his weekly fare. Research furnishes the impetus to develop new powers and prowess. It allows the teacher to exemplify the qualities that instruction is designed to encourage in the student—qualities of independence, logic, aptitude, and creativeness.

Self-education is today largely limited to advanced students because teachers who have ventured in research are almost exclusively found in universities. But whenever those who have ventured find themselves in other schools and homes they may exert their full capacities to hold the unexplored universe and the questioning attitude before themselves and before their students. We do not know what age may be the best for arousing mental excitement. Could it be the kindergarten age? If so, that is the age at which to encourage questions that can be explored.

Research by teachers promotes teaching when it strengthens the atmosphere around the student. Questions and projects need not be hidden from students but aired to them. One's best teaching can be along paths of thought where oneself has concentrated most, providing one is willing to show the students a beginning instead of a completed phase. Actually, only rarely would the same old paths of thought need to be retraced, alternatives will inevitably be taken, and at times will shake one's own notions to their foundations.

The teacher-researcher can unify what he does instead of splitting his life into two parts. He does well to make abundantly clear to students that his research activity benefits those he teaches, through the freshness and accuracy that pervade him. Whatever might seem hidden about research can be spread to benefit many.

The reader recognizes that much of my essay is a counsel of perfection. I too have done loose teaching, isolated myself from students, and camouflaged my lack of thought. One revises his life in the light of mistakes; "men are moulded out of faults" (14); and such revision itself is self-education.

In summary, I suggest that from research activities the student is likely to profit in his initiative, questioning, reasoning, self-confidence, and persistence; and the teacher can profit in his freshness, vividness, accuracy, timing, and skill. Research and teaching have this in common: they are ever-renewing challenges.

Research Educates

I have pointed out that those who self-educate throughout life, may do so by some sort of research activity. Hence many men in many walks of life can profitably start their self-education early. Is not research as now practiced by scientists our one great contribution to educational method for all people? Students may be introduced to activity in, and feeling for, research in tender years. Also, teachers can share with students the benefits they derive from their own researches—especially the attitudes inculcated by them, and the modes of thinking and doing that they generate. Research activity may be encouraged wherever there is spontaneous curiosity. Its amateur uses may be as important as its sophisticated uses. Research can be a resource for all who capture its universal technique of question and answer.

LITERATURE CITED

1. Eastman, M. (J. Dewey) *Atlantic Monthly*, **168**, 671–85 (1941)
2. Adolph, E. F. *J. Exptl. Zool.*, **31**, 327–41 (1920)
3. Richards, D. W. (L. J. Henderson) *Physiologist*, **1**, ii, 32–7 (1958)
4. Galileo, G. *Dialogues Concerning Two New Sciences* (Crew, H., de-Salvio, A., Transl., Macmillan, New York, 1914)
5. Lillie, F. R. *The Woods Hole Marine Biological Laboratory*, Chap. 2 (Univ. of Chicago Press, Chicago, 1944)
6. Adolph, E. F. *Physiological Regulations* (Cattell, Lancaster, Pa., 1943)
7. Bacon, F. *The New Organon*, **ii**, XX, first sentence (1620)
8. Slama, K., Williams, C. M. *Proc. Natl. Acad. Sci.*, **54**, 411–14 (1965)
9. Adolph, E. F. *Am. J. Physiol.*, **151**, 110–25 (1947)
10. Vallery-Radot, R. *The Life of Pasteur* (Devonshire, R. L., Transl., Doubleday, New York, 1902)
11. Darwin, C. *Journal of Researches during the voyage of H. M. S. Beagle* (Murray, London, 1845)
12. Fabre, J. H. *The Hunting Wasps*, Chap. 1 (Teixiera de Mattos, A., Transl., Dodd Mead, New York, 1915)
13. Benedictus. *The Rule of Saint Benedict* (Gasquet, C., Transl., Chatto and Windus, London, 1936)
14. Shakespeare, W. *Measure for Measure*, V, i. 435

MEMBRANE PHENOMENA[1]

BY ASER ROTHSTEIN

School of Medicine and Dentistry, The University of Rochester
Rochester, New York

INTRODUCTION

Research in the field of membrane phenomena has continued at a high level of activity, covering an exceedingly diverse array of topics. In fact the only common thread to all of the studies is the membrane itself, and even in this respect the membranes under consideration are also diverse, ranging from purely theoretical concepts through a variety of physical models, numerous kinds of cell membranes, to complexes of membranes in epithelial systems. From a functional point of view, the research is concerned primarily with traffic regulation. All communication between the cell interior and the outside environment must pass through the membrane and must obey its traffic laws. For most physiologically important substances, special mechanisms in the membrane exert some control over the rate of flow. The nature of the mechanisms has been for some time and continues to be a central theme of membrane studies. Descriptions of the properties of these mechanisms have become more exact, but understanding of their nature has developed only slowly. For some substances the membrane plays a passive role in the sense that it offers a resistance to flow of material, but the force driving the flow is imposed across the membrane by an electrochemical gradient. In some cases, however, driving forces are exerted within the membrane by metabolically linked reactions; this results in movements against the external electrochemical gradient. Questions concerning metabolic reactions in the membrane, the enzymes involved, and the linkage to transport continue to stimulate a great deal of interest, but again progress has been slow.

The balance of inflows and outflows of materials through the membrane is one of the determining factors in the regulation of intracellular composition, and all of the factors that influence the flows will influence composition. From this point of view the membrane is an important control system for cellular processes. The cell exerts its control by a number of means. Some control is built into the nature of the membrane mechanisms, for example the transient changes in permeability during excitation in nerve. Others are exerted by the supply of energy from metabolic reactions, and still others by synthesis of new membrane components under stimulus of

[1] This study was carried out at the Atomic Energy Project, The University of Rochester, Rochester, New York, under contract with the United States Atomic Energy Commission.

inducers, with ultimate control vested in the genetic apparatus. The aspect of the membrane as a control system is receiving more attention and will become an increasingly important area of research.

The behavior of complexes of membranes in epithelial systems such as frog skin, toad bladder, intestine, and kidney will not be considered as a primary topic in this review. A number of studies of epithelial systems will be cited, however, because they throw some light on the behavior of the plasma membrane.

A great deal of emphasis is now placed on the chemistry of membranes, particularly of the membrane protein. Some of the studies are concerned with the basic structure of the membranes but most deal with specific components, carriers, and enzymes involved in particular functions. This is particularly true of studies of transport in mitochondria and chloroplasts, where previous work has clearly outlined the nature of the metabolic activities.

The diversity of membrane studies involving so many kinds of systems, and many approaches, anatomical, biochemical, biophysical, physiological, mathematical, etc., imposes difficulties in evolving a logical framework for a review. I have attempted to cover the work of the last year (May 1966 to May 1967) in the many topics of importance in membranology. The breadth of coverage has involved some sacrifice in terms of details in any one topic, but this was a conscious choice. Also in covering such a wide choice of topics, some of the literature may have been inadvertently overlooked. For this I apologize.

A good detailed summary of the status of membranology can be found in the published volume from the Symposium *Biological Membranes: Recent Progress, Annals of the New York Academy of Sciences,* 137, 403–1048. Most of these papers, as well as other reviews, are cited in appropriate places in the text.

STRUCTURE OF THE PLASMA MEMBRANE
GENERAL FEATURES

The newer techniques of electronmicroscopy, particularly negative staining and "freeze-etch", have demonstrated surface features of the membrane, often adding to the problems of interpretation of membrane structure as determined from the more classical techniques of electronmicroscopy and X-ray diffraction. The apertures of the transverse tubules in the striated muscle cell can be clearly seen, using the freeze-etch technique in parallel rows in the expected location in the membrane at the level of the Z-regions (1). On the other hand, sections of membrane fractions from various tissues, which look rather similar when prepared by fixing and sectioning, show marked differences in surface detail and internal structure when examined by negative staining technique with phosphotungstic acid (2). In some cases there are 50 Å surface globules and in others, membranous vesicles. Surface features of the membrane have been demonstrated in the form of a repeating subunit structure in certain cells of the blow fly (3). These subunits are confined to certain parts of the cells and may be involved in pinocytotic activity. Such subunit structures have now been demonstrated in a variety of cells. In one such cell, *Halobacterium halobium,* isolated membranes undergo deaggregation if placed in diluted salt solutions unless calcium is present (4). Apparently the calcium allows bridging between neighboring negative charges and stabilizes the subunits of the membrane. In the intact bacterium, calcium protects against transient changes in osmotic pressure, perhaps because of the same stabilizing effects.

The problem of interpretation of high-resolution microscopy of membranes is reviewed in (5). Numerous electronmicrographs have indicated some kind of substructure which can be interpreted in terms of subunits, but in the present paper these appearances are interpreted in terms of the "unit membrane" consisting of a lamellar bilayer of lipid with the variations in structure confined to the outside surface of the unit membrane, with only the nonlipid components involved. Questions are raised regarding interpretations of negative stained and dry preparations, and concerning the effect of the angle of cutting. The concept of the "unit membrane" is also supported by studies of low-angle X-ray diffraction patterns and by electronmicrographs obtained during careful dehydration of red cell ghosts and of myelin from brain (6). Dehydration in each case to the level of 10 to 20 per cent gave patterns that indicated close packing of laminar "unit structures" membrane with each membrane 100 Å thick. Further drying resulted in a change in the patterns which could be interpreted as a transition to an hexagonal structure, or a multifaced system.

On the other hand, serious questions are raised concerning the unit membrane concept on a number of grounds (7). They include: (*a*) The thickness of "unit membranes", even in the most carefully prepared sections, varies by 50 per cent. Recently cells have been found in intestinal epithelium in which the membrane is twice as thick as normal (8). (*b*) Osmium staining probably demonstrates protein structures rather than the molecular orientation and the location of the phospholipids in the original membrane. In *E. coli,* for example, there are no unsaturated fatty acids which are the groups in lipids that could bind osmium. Nevertheless, the "unit membrane" can be stained. (*c*) "Unit membranes" can be demonstrated in osmium-fixed mitochondria from which more than 90 per cent of the lipid has been removed by extraction. (For details see 9.) (*d*) The bimolecular leaflet structure formed spontaneously by phospholipid materials is not the only stable form. Furthermore, such lipid systems may be poor models for biological membranes since they contain no protein. (*e*) Subunit types of structures have been observed in membranes of the retina, yeast, bacteria, and mitochondria. (*f*) There is a wide spectrum of membrane composition with respect to both the relative amounts of protein and lipid and the composition of the lipids. (*g*) The physiological activities of different membranes are also hard to fit into the unit membrane concept, particularly the energy transductions, transport phenomena, pinocytosis, controlled growth, and cell division. The model of myelin is a poor one because it is metabolically inert and has only the function of an electrical insulator. (*h*) The mechanisms of biosynthesis of membranes are hard to rationalize with the unit membrane hypothesis. The cell would have to control an orderly synthesis of lipids to form a bilayer which would in turn specify the disposition of proteins. It is more reasonable to assume that the genetic information would control membrane protein synthesis and that the assembly of lipids would in turn be dictated by the amino acid sequences. The membranes would then be formed by aggregations of specific lipoproteins.

Specialized anatomical features of membranes in some cases are found at localized places in the junctions between cells. Previous studies on their anatomy and function have been reviewed (10) for cells of glands, kidney, urinary bladder, and liver. The junctions are highly permeable structures with conductance for ions far greater than that of nonjunctional membranes. They thereby form communicating systems of low diffusion resistance between cells but with no leakage to the exterior. Permability of the junctions seems to be controlled primarily by calcium. When the calcium concentration is increased, the junctional membranes become as impermeable as the nonjunctional ones and each cell is sealed off as a unit. The intercalated disks between cells of the heart cells also behave as the membrane junctions, having a low resistance to diffusion of potassium (11).

Specific Components

Lipids.—Little new work has appeared on the lipid composition of plasma membranes, but several reviews have been published. Comparisons of the lipid composition of different membranes are summarized in (12). Variations occur between species and classes, and among the membranes of different cells in the same organism and organelles of the same cells; they may even occur in the same cells under different physiological conditions. The lipid patterns vary among different animal and plant cells with respect to the total amount of phospholipid and its specific characteristics, the ratio between phosphoglyceride and sphingophospholipid, and the fatty acid constituents.

Interest in the relationships of membrane lipids to membrane function and properties has generated considerable information, much of it reviewed in (9) and (13), concerning the role of lipids in the structure and function of mitochondrial membranes. It is of particular interest that after extraction of lipids with loss of function, replacement of the lipids leads to reconstitution and a return of organized enzyme activities.

Acetylcholine increases turnover of lipids in the avian salt gland and also activates salt excretion, involving the Na-K-activated ATPase (14). But the increased turnover does not seem to be related to the activity of the Na-K-dependent ATPase, and its functional role in the secretory process is still an open question.

Changes in lipid content of the cell membrane occur when an L-form (a wall-less, dividing form) is derived from the protoplast of *Streptococcus pyogenes* (15). The L-form can no longer carry out biosynthesis of cell wall but has become stabilized so that its membrane is much more resistant to osmotic lysis than that of the protoplast. The total lipid content of the L-form membrane, while qualitatively similar, was twice as high as that of the protoplast, whereas the protein content was about the same.

Considerable information concerning lipid components has been gained through studies of the actions of chemical agents and drugs both on biological membranes and on model systems such as monolayers, bilayers, and micellar systems (16). Of particular interest are the polyene antibiotics, reviewed in (17), which act specifically as antifungicides. They intereact with the sterols of the cell membrane which leads to leakage of essential constituents and ultimately cell death. Bacterial resistance results from the near absence of sterols in their membranes. A rather dramatic indication of their mechanism of action has been demonstrated in the PPLO (pleuropneumonia-like organisms) *Mycoplasma laidlawii* which is normally insensitive to the polyenes and whose membrane contains no sterol. When, however, it is grown in the presence of sterol, sterols are incorporated into the membrane and sensitivity to the antibiotic develops. In monolayers and in bilayers of lipids, the presence of sterols is also a necessary condition for sensitivity to polyenes. The membranes of red blood cells lysed with polyenes show characteristic pits approximately 125 Å in diameter under negative staining.

Proteins.—Attempts to develop techniques for fractionating the protein components of the membrane continue. Purification and characterization have been severely hindered by the relatively high affinity for lipids and limited solubility in aqueous and organic solvents, and lack of reliable markers. Mixtures of 2-chloroethanol and water have been used to solubilize membranes of ascites cells, followed by separation on a Sephadex column (18). The proteins separate into two peaks, neither containing much lipid. The extraction procedure does not inhibit the activity of ribonuclease, which indicates minimal denaturation.

A problem in the fractionating of cell membrane is to find enzyme markers to differentiate the fractions from contaminating structures, as is discussed in (19), in relation to several cell types. The mitochondrion can be marked by succinate dehydrogenase and the endoplasmic reticulum by glucose-6-phosphatase activities. Preparations of plasma membranes from liver and kidney show contaminations on this basis, of 10 to 25 per cent. Alkaline phosphatase can be used as a marker for plasma membranes of kidney, but this enzyme is absent from the liver membranes. Some plasma membrane fractions can be marked by nucleotidase. The Na-K-ATPase was used as a marker for purification of plasma membrane of liver cells, cytochrome-*c* oxidase and several other enzymes for mitochondria, and glucose-6-phosphatase for the endoplasmic reticulum (20), supplemented by electronmicroscopy. After sonication of the purified membranes, the lipoproteins could be fractionated by flotation on a density gradient. In epithelial cells of intestine, Na-K-ATPase has also been used as a marker (21), showing a different distribution from alkaline phosphatase, cytochrome oxidase, invertase, and Mg-ATPase. With another procedure (22) 70 per cent of the membrane protein of liver cells was solubilized in .05 M K_2CO_3. After homogenization of the residue and addition of detergents, the protein could be separated by disk electrophoresis into fifteen distinct bands which showed the same mobilities on a second run. On Sephadex the membrane proteins showed considerable size heterogeneity.

In the protoplasts of the yeast *Candida utilis* (23) the proteins of the outer surface are not directly accessible to proteolytic enzymes, for these enzymes had no influence on membrane integrity. The protein content of isolated membranes is 40 per cent.

Specific membrane ligands.—Information concerning specific membrane ligands and their functional importance can be gained by use of specific agents added to cells or to purified membrane fractions. This has been particularly true of phosphoryl groups and sulfhydryl groups. The role of surface phosphoryl groups in sugar transport has been reviewed (24); a more recent study has also appeared (25). The phosphoryl groups located on the outer surface of the cell have a high affinity for extracellular ions such as UO_2^{++} and Ni^{++}. As a consequence of the metal binding, only those sugar transports involving metabolic intervention are disturbed. The phosphoryl sites are thought to be involved in uphill transport by maintenance of a high affinity of a carrier for certain sugars. In the presence of the heavy metals, the affinity is considerably lower, the rate of influx of the sugar is reduced, and only downhill movements can occur.

Sulfhydryl groups of membrane have been categorized by their reactivity to a variety of sulfhydryl agents and by the rate of penetration into the membrane structure to "sensitive" sites. Agents such as N-ethylmaleimide (NEM), which form irreversible covalent bonds, have also been used to label those sulfhydryl groups related to specific functions. The mercurial chloromercuribenzoate (PCMB) reacts rapidly with 14 per cent of the sulfhydryl groups of the red cell membrane, and more slowly with the remaining groups. The increased permeability and ultimate hemolysis are related to the faster-reacting groups (26). The sulfhydryl groups of the red cell have also been explored by using the slowly penetrating mercurial, *p*-chloromercuribenzyl sulfonate (PCMBS) (27). This agent acts rapidly on the small fraction (3 per cent) of the membrane sulfhydryl groups on the outside of the cell; the result is inhibition of sugar transfer. A small fraction of the sulfhydryl sites within the interior of the membrane reached slowly by the PCMBS are involved in alterations of the permeability to sodium and potassium. A slow spontaneous recovery occurs because of the release of sulfhydryl substances into the medium, binding the remaining agent. Concomitantly, much of the PCMBS bound to the membrane desorbs from the cell. From these and other experiments it is concluded that the sulfhydryl groups involved in the control of cation permeability are within the membrane structure separated from the medium and from the inside of the cell by permeability barriers to PCMBS.

Sulfhydryl groups are also involved in the transient changes in permeability to cations during the excitation process in axons (28). In the electroplax of electric eel, the sulfhydryl agent PCMB raises the threshold for acetylcholine but not the size of the response once elicited (29). Thus sulfhydryl groups are involved in the proteins of the acetylcholine-activated system. The sarcoplasmic membranes of skeletal muscles are also sensitive to sulfhydryl agents NEM or mersalyl (Salyrgan) (30). A specific fraction of the sulfhydryl groups is involved in calcium transport and calcium-activated ATPase. In the presence of ATP the calcium-activated ATPase is protected from the action of the agents. The protection afforded by ATP from inhibitory effects of NEM on the ATPase was used to label the Na-K-activated enzyme from red blood cells (31). The membrane preparation was first labeled with nonradioactive NEM in the presence of ATP, the membranes were then washed and re-incubated in labeled NEM in the absence of ATP; this was followed by fractionation. An upper estimate of the number of NEM sites is 60,000 per membrane.

Nature of the carriers and the carrier substrate reactions.—Progress in determining the chemical nature of the carrier and of the carrier-substrate complex has been slow and, except for the study on the Na-K-activated ATPase discussed at the end of the previous section (31), confined to sugar transport. The membrane protein (M-protein) involved in the permeation of galactosides in *E. coli* is assayed by the binding of radioactive NEM after treatment with cold NEM in the presence of substrate (TDG) which protects the permease sites (32). It is present in inducible strains only after induction. In one strain both the M-protein and the ability to transport galactosides are present in cells grown at 25° but not in those grown at 42°. The binding of NEM suggested at least 9000 subunits per cell. The M-protein can be separated from the membrane by treatment with detergents, which suggests that the bonding is through formation of lipoprotein.

Another factor in transport of galactosides in *E. coli* is related to a soluble heat-stable protein that is part of the phosphotransferase system (33). Cells subjected to osmotic shock lose ability to concentrate galactosides and, in parallel, lose much of their normal content of heat-stable protein. When the shocked cells are incubated with the purified heat-stable protein, the ability to accumulate the galactosides is retored if the cells have previously been induced to galactosides. The heat-stable protein is in the soluble fraction of the cell, but the enzyme responsible for transfer of phosphate from the heat-stable protein to sugars is in the membrane. The exact role of the heat-stable protein in the transport is not clear, nor is the relationship of this system to the M-protein.

In the brush borders of the epithelial cells, the binding of D-glucose, which is preferential but not dependent on sodium or ATP, may be the initial step in the transport (34). In red cell membranes the binding affinities for a variety of sugars to red cell ghosts are very similar to the K_m's for transport for the same sugars (35). Furthermore, in the case of the fat cells where insulin influences sugar transport by changing the binding parameters, the same is true for the effect of insulin on the binding of the sugars to the membrane fraction. It is suggested that the imine bond may be essential for the formation of the sugar-carrier complex. The sugars were found to be bound to lysine and to arginine.

The ATPases and related enzymes.—Most of the research in the active field of enzymes in the plasma membrane has been concerned with the number and kind of ATPases, their distribution, their function particularly in relation to cation transport, the nature of the cation activation, substrate specificity, the mechanism of the enzyme reaction, and purification and isolation. In mammalian tissues at least three different enzyme activities are recognized on the basis of cation activation and inhibition, sensitivity to cardiac glycosides, and substrate specificity. They are the magnesium-activated ATPase; the Na-K-Mg-activated ATPase which is sensitive to cardiac glycosides, often called the pump ATPase; and the calcium-activated ATPase. Other ATPases and less specific phosphatase activities are also found in the membranes. Most of the studies are done with crude membrane fractions. Thus the relationships between the activities in terms of the number of unique proteins are still an open question.

The widespread distribution of both the Mg-ATPase and the Na-K-ATPase is demonstrated by studies with a variety of tissues from a variety of sources (36–41). The pattern of stimulation by sodium and potassium, the requirement for magnesium, and the inhibition by calcium and ouabain are similar in all cases. In human striated muscle (38) the Na-K-enzyme is inhibited by the sulfhydryl agent PCMB as it is in red blood cells (31). In red blood cells from patients with hereditary spherocytosis (40) the Na-K-ATPase is increased, whereas the Mg-ATPase is decreased so that the ratio of ouabain-sensitive to -insensitive ATPase is much increased. In various marsupials (41) those that have red blood cells with high potassium have membranes with a relatively large amount of Na-K-ATPase, whereas those with low potassium have a low level (41). On the other hand, Mg-ATPase is the same in all of the species. Such a correlation between Na-K-ATPase and potassium content of red cells has been previously observed in low- and high-potassium sheep and in various other species. In detailed comparison of the Na-K-ATPase and Mg-ATPase from intestinal cells and red cells from the same animal, the rat (42), the substrate specificities and the activation kinetics for the various ions were found to be different for each of the enzymes, depending on its source (42). It is concluded, therefore, that tissue differentiation results in differences in the biochemical properties of both enzymes. Neither the Na-K-ATPase in red cells nor the cation transport is affected by dinitrophenol, but the Mg-ATPase is stimulated by this agent (43).

The activation of microsomal ATPase by both sodium and potassium has a maximum value (44), which confirms previous studies. The kinetic evidence indicates the presence of a sodium-specific and a potassium specific site but each of the ions competes for both sites; this produces competitive effects. Ouabain inhibits competitively with respect to both sodium and potassium (but probably only for the potassium-specific site) while oligomycin competes only with sodium. Calcium inhibits both the kidney cortex and the erythrocyte Na-K-ATPase (45). The inhibitory form is a calcium-ATP complex which acts as a competitive inhibitor for Mg-ATP. No competition was observed between calcium and sodium.

In addition to its inhibitory effect on the Na-K-ATPase, calcium can activate ATP splitting in red blood cell ghosts (42, 46). Magnesium, calcium, strontium, and barium can all activate ATPase with the greatest activation with strontium (43). Magnesium and calcium activate at different sites but there is an optimum concentration ratio because in addition to its activating effect, calcium can inhibit the magnesium site. Considerable evidence suggests that the Na-K-ATPase, Mg-ATPase, and Ca-ATPases are different enzymes. On the basis of studies with dinitrophenol it is suggested that the Ca-ATPase may be involved in regulation of passive permeability. A calcium-activated ATPase, demonstrated in the sarcoplasmic reticulum of muscle, is inhibited by sulfhydryl agents (30), stimulated by potassium (47), and seems to be involved in calcium transport.

The membrane ATPases of plant cells and microorganisms differ from those of the animal cells. In no case has an enzyme been demonstrated which is dependent on both potassium and sodium, and most reports indicate insensitivity to cardiac glycosides. In *E. coli* (48) the ATPase of the wild-type cell and of a potassium-defective mutant show no differences in activity. The enzyme is stimulated 20 per cent by sodium but potassium and strophanthin have no effect. In Mycoplasma (four different strains) an Mg-ATPase activity is found in the cell membrane, but it is not activated by sodium and potassium and not inhibited by ouabain or dinitrophenol (49). A cell wall fraction isolated from pea roots contains an ATPase that is stimulated by sodium, potassium, lithium, and ammonium ions but mixtures of sodium and potassium have no synergistic effects and magnesium can be replaced by calcium (50). An enzyme was also isolated from bean roots (51) that is strongly stimulated by both sodium and potassium but differs from transport ATPase in its solubility, ion activation, and sensitivity to ouabain.

A few studies have treated factors that control the amount of the Na-K-ATPase. For example, injury to the sciatic nerve of the cat results in a decrease in the Na-K-ATPase activity for eight days followed by an in-

crease in the degenerating nerve from sixteen to thirty-two days (52). The
Na-K-ATPase level of rat kidney seems to be under hormonal control because following adrenalectomy its activity is markedly reduced (53, 54). On
the other hand, administration of aldosterone in concentrations that restore
salt retention in the kidney does not restore the ATPase activity of the
membrane. Corticosterone in physiological doses does bring the level to
normal in two to three days. These changes in activity may, however, be
due to an inhibitory effect of Ca^{++} rather than a reduction in the amount
of enzyme. Thus in rats treated with aldactone, an aldosterone antagonist,
the reduced activity of ATPase can be restored by treating the membrane
preparations with EDTA (54).

The membrane ATPases are inhibited by many agents, some already
mentioned; these effects have been systematically determined (55, 56). The
Na-K-ATPase is inhibited by calcium, ouabain, cysteine, PCMB, NEM, oc-
tylguanidine, and oligomycin but none of these inhibits the Mg-ATPase.
Ultrasonic treatment, oleic acid, and deoxycholate inhibit both enzymes.
Saponin and preincubation at 37° activate the Mg-ATPase and inhibit the
Na-K-ATPase. The basal ATPase of the red blood cell is also activated by
low concentrations of sodium dodecyl sulfate (57). Although the stimulation is enhanced by either sodium or potassium it is not inhibited by ouabain. Inhibition of the Na-K-ATPase of brain by a variety of phenothi-
azines is correlated with the effects of these drugs on the central nervous system (58).

Na-K-ATPase has been found in membranes of virtually all mammalian
cells. In epithelial cells which are asymmetric in anatomy and in which the
activity of the cation transport system is polarized, the distribution of the
ATPase in different parts of the plasma membrane has been of some interest. A number of investigators have suggested that the transport of salt occurs into intercellular spaces through the lateral membranes, and evidence
has been presented in the case of the gall bladder that the lateral membranes are rich in ATPase (59). On the other hand, the brush borders are
particularly rich in Na-K-ATPase (21) and yet in the accepted model of
the epithelial cell the cation movements at that side of the cell are primarily
downhill with the active transport occurring in the lateral serosal membranes. Ability to demonstrate Na-K-ATPase by histochemical techniques
would be most useful in clearing up questions of localization. Unfortunately a systematic attempt to find a specific method was not very successful,
although nonspecific ATPase activity can be demonstrated (60).

Several attempts have been made to purify and isolate the components
of the Na-K-activated ATPase, but these continue to run into difficulties
(31, 56, 61–63).

Studies on the mechanism of the ATPase reaction have also continued.
As demonstrated previously, the system involves a transfer of phosphate
from ATP to protein followed by a dephosphorylation, the first step requiring sodium and the second, potassium. The phosphate remains in the pro-

tein fractions after neutral or acidic extraction, but is released by alkali and hydroxylamine (64). It is a high-energy phosphate and it can be transferred to aliphatic alcohols, behaving like an acylphosphate. Phosphate is also transferred to phosphorylserine but the kinetics of this transfer are different from those of the intermediate of the ATPase reaction. A phosphorylated intermediate of the Na-K-ATPase has been demonstrated in red blood cells (65), but only by working at 0° for very short periods of time to minimize the discharge of inorganic phosphate. Extraction of membranes from kidney with lipid solvents destroys the ATPase activity but not the ability to form labeled intermediates in the presence of sodium (66). The extraction inhibits the potassium-dependent dephosphorylation considerably more than the sodium-dependent phosphorylation process.

A number of enzyme reactions involving ATP, present in membranes, complicate the appraisal of ATP reactions involved in transport; for example, an exchange reaction between ATP and ADP occurs in a brain microsome fraction at rates similar to the liberation of inorganic phosphate by the Na-K-ATPase (67). It is not influenced by sodium, potassium, or ouabain, however, and it can be separated from the ATPase. Another ATP reaction in liver cells produces adenosine pyrophosphate (68). A protein phosphokinase has been partially purified (69) that can transfer phosphate from the phosphoprotein to ADP. It is activated by magnesium, is inhibited by calcium and PCMB, but is unaffected by ouabain or oligomycin.

Other enzymes.—In addition to the ATPases a number of other enzymes have been localized in the membranes of cells. For example, in erythrocytes much of the glycolytic machinery is located in the membrane. The effects of sulfate on glycolysis are determined by stimulation of the kinase reactions whereas inorganic phosphate stimulates both the kinase and the ATP-generating reactions (70). Also included in the ghost of the red blood cell is a system for metabolism of deoxyinosine that is different from that for inosine (71). In epithelial cells of the hamster intestine, invertase and maltase are located in knobs on the lumen surface of the plasma membrane (72). In yeast, invertase and phosphatases are located outside of the plasma membrane in the wall structure, held by either ionic bonding or disulfide bonding, with the degree of bonding varying among species and with the age of the culture (73). Also in a strain of yeast the utilization of several β-glucosides involves a β-glucosidase located on the cell membrane (74).

One subfraction of synaptic membranes, rich in acetylcholinesterase, binds cholinergic blocking agents and may contain the cholinergic receptors (75).

Components involved in mechanical properties.—A number of papers deal with the mechanical properties of the cell membranes and with the role of calcium. For example, inducers of pinocytosis in amoebae cause a large decrease in electrical resistance just prior to the formation of the pinocytotic vacuoles (76). This change in state seems to be related to a doubling of the thickness of the electron transparent core of the unit membrane and to the initial external concentration of calcium. Mechanical factors have also been demonstrated in ghosts of red blood cells washed with calcium-free saline, and treated with sodium fluoride to block ATP formation (46). A contraction can be demonstrated that depends on the presence of ATP and Ca^{++} inside the ghosts; Mg^{++}, on the other hand, is inhibitory. The effects of metabolic depletion on crenation, disk-sphere transformations, loss of membrane material, and hemolysis of red cells are consequences of depletion of ATP levels in the cell and an increase in its calcium content (77, 78). High internal Ca^{++} results in a contracted rigid membrane which undergoes mechanical fragmentation, a consequent loss of lipids and proteins, and a decreased critical hemolytic volume. Mechanical rigidity of membranes has also been inferred for the protoplast of *Bacillus megaterium* from shrinking and swelling curves (79).

A calcium-dependent contractile system in the membrane is also used to explain adhesion of cells (80, 81). Actomyosin-like proteins with ATPase activities have been isolated from membranes of cells, and glycerol-extracted cells can be made to contract in the presence of ATP. From parallel behavior of cell adhesion in relation to calcium, ATP, and ADP in comparison to the actomyosin system, it is proposed that the membrane has a contracting mechanism that is activated by calcium-ATP and inactivated by ADP or depletion of calcium, and that there is also a relaxing mechanism which involves magnesium. When the contractile system is predominant, infoldings result in the membrane, thereby changing the distribution of the charged groups that are responsible for adhesion.

Other components.—A variety of other components of membranes have been demonstrated; the most important is RNA. Although it has until now been demonstrated only in a few cells, its presence in membranes has important implications in regard to synthesis of membrane material. In protoplasts of *Candida utilis,* ribonuclease causes lysis, which suggests RNA as a membrane component, but it is not clear how much of the RNA was a cytoplasmic contamination (23). In mammalian reticulocytes, however, about half of the cellular RNA is closely associated with the cell membrane (82). The turnover of the membrane RNA was slower than that in the cytoplasm. Both forms of RNA disappear as the cells mature.

Carotenoids have been identified in the membranes of a wide variety of bacteria. Because they are markedly reduced in amount in the presence of diphenylamine without affecting cell growth or membrane formation (83), the large variations in the carotenoid components can be tolerated.

Polysaccharides associated with membrane structures of epithelial structures have been localized by electronmicrographic techniques (84). The polysaccharide is exterior to the osmophilic area and is interpreted to be associated with the protein of the outer surface of the membrane. It should therefore be regarded as a true part of the plasma membrane.

MODELS OF MEMBRANE SYSTEMS

Much effort has been devoted to the study of model systems in the optimistic hope that light would be shed on the behavior of biological membranes. Unfortunately the problems of comprehension at the level of the models seem to be almost as difficult as at the levels of the cellular membrane. Furthermore, relevance to biological systems is not always clear. Many kinds of physical and theoretical models have been studied. They include lipid monolayers, lipid bilayers, liquid crystals, and bulk-phase lipid solvents with dissolved liquid ion exchangers. In the theoretical field most studies are concerned with application of irreversible thermodynamics.

LIPID MONOLAYERS

Factors that contribute to the properties of the monolayers of various lipids have been determined in a number of studies, with the effects of calcium receiving most attention. The behavior of mixed cholesterol-phospholipid films is governed by Van Der Waal's interactions, configurational entropy effects, and alterations of the structure of water adjacent to the monolayers (85). These factors depend on chain length and degree of unsaturation. The presence of cholesterol and ions, particularly Ca^{++}, is an important factor as well. Stearic and palmitic acid monolayers react with Ca^{++} to produce solid condensed films that are rigid (86) with no measurable effect on surface viscosity. On the other hand, calcium changes the surface viscosity of phospholipid monolayers. Thus the saturated fatty acids are poor models for calcium interactions with the cell membrane. In the case of phosphatidyl serine, calcium produces a structural modification at approximately 1 mM or about one bound Ca^{++} for each phosphatidyl serine molecule (87). The interaction of calcium is greater with dipalmitoyl-lecithin monolayers than with sphingomyelin monolayers, producing a positive surface charge in the latter case (88) that can be explained in terms of the behavior of the ion dipole. More closely related to the behavior of cell membranes are careful re-estimates of the surface area of the human red cell lipids (89). From force–area curves, the ratio of lipid area to membrane area is 2:1 at low surface pressures and approaches 1:1 at collapse pressures. Thus if a bilayer exists in the red cell membrane, the lipids must be under low surface pressure.

BILAYERS OR "BLACK MEMBRANES"

Considerable research has been done on model bilayer membranes, often called "black membranes" because of their optical behavior. Most of the membranes are formed by painting lipids dissolved in nonaqueous solvents across a hole separating two aqueous compartments. Measurements are usually made of electrical resistance or potentials in the presence of various salts, but a number of studies of water fluxes have been made by tracer techniques as well as by osmotic methods. Membranes prepared from phosphatidyl choline have an electrical capacity indicating a membrane thickness of 70 ± 10 Å (90). The value is consistent with molecular models based on a 34 Å length for phosphatidyl choline with eighteen carbon chains. As in previous reports, the resistance in sodium or potassium chloride solutions is exceedingly high but it is reduced by a factor of 5000 when I$^-$ replaces Cl$^-$. The resistance of black membranes is also decreased by dinitrophenol with a half-maximal effect at .5 mM, but at higher concentrations of the agent the resistance is increased again (91). The resistance of the bilayers changes dramatically, by a factor of 10^5, on addition of the antibiotic valinomycin in the presence of potassium chloride (92). The membrane potentials are 54 to 58 mV per tenfold difference in salt concentrations, which indicates a very high selectivity for K$^+$ over Cl$^-$. The permeability to potassium becomes 400 times greater than for sodium and large biionic potentials can therefore be produced by putting sodium on one side and potassium on the other side of the membrane. Other polypeptides such as enniatins A and B, tetralactones, monactin, dinactin, and gramicidin A, B, and C are also effective. These compounds are all rings except for the gramicidins and even these may form rings. In synthetic valinomycins an increase in ring diameter of three to four units, or a decrease of two units depresses the effect. Increasing the lipophilic balance by substituting leucine for alanine increases the effectiveness and conversely, cyclic compounds with polar groups on the outer part of the ring as one finds in filipin, colimycin, and amphotericin were without effect. From an examination of molecular models, explanations for the observed effects are proposed.

The permeability of bilayer membranes to osmotic flow of water is constant over a wide range of gradients and concentrations of salts and nonelectrolytes (93). Furthermore, the value of the permeability constant is in the range of that found in biological membranes. Also, the bilayers resemble biological membranes inasmuch as measurements made by osmotic methods give permeability values higher than those determined by isotope measurements, but the discrepancy of eight- to tenfold is much greater in the models (94,95). The permeability coefficients measured osmotically depended on the particular phospholipid preparation used, whereas the isotopic fluxes were relatively independent of the phospholipid preparation. Interpretations of the results differ. The postulate of a pore structure used in biological membranes is difficult to reconcile with the high electrical resistance of the bilayers. The existence of relatively thick unstirred layers of aqueous solution adjacent to the membranes may account for a large part of the discrepancy (94, 95).

Bilayer membranes treated with proteins obtained from bacteria plus protamine display a variety of electrical phenomena including action potentials, thresholds, refractoriness, delayed rectification, and spontaneous rhythmic firing which is reversibly blocked by local anesthetics (96). Protein (albumin) also increases the ion conductance but with little specificity between Na⁺ and K⁺ (97). In this paper a different technique for making bilayers is described. A film of lipoprotein was formed on the interface between an aqueous solution of protein and a solution of phospholipid in heptane. A second film was brought up to the first one from the heptane side, allowing coalescence of the two films from the hydrophobic side. These membranes differ from those made by the usual technique inasmuch as the bilayer is formed from a lipoprotein complex rather than from lipids alone with proteins applied from the outside. Still another technique permits a rapid generation of fresh lipid water interfaces under constant conditions (98). The ensuing films have a calculated thickness of 50 Å.

LIQUID CRYSTALS

Suspensions of phospholipids in water form colloidal structures known as liquid crystals whose molecular arrangement has been analyzed by X-ray scattering (99). Depending on the particular conditions such as concentration and temperature, a variety of forms are found, including: a hexagonal array of cylinders with hydrocarbon chains filling the interior and the water outside; a laminar form with alternating sequence of planar layers of lipid in water; and a hexagonal form in which the water is in the interior of the cylinders with the hydrocarbon chains filling the gaps. Transitions occur which might allow the lipid structure to open and close randomly to form pores, and in one form narrow water channels exist which are lined with polar groups. Measurements of ion uptake by liquid crystals indicate that the energy of activation for diffusion of chloride into the crystals is low, whereas that of sodium and potassium is high (100). Furthermore, with increasing temperature, transitions in the behavior of the crystals toward ions occur. Calcium also has a pronounced effect on phosphatidyl serine, increasing the discrimination between potassium and sodium.

Toward water, the crystals behave as semipermeable membranes, swelling and shrinking in various concentrations of sucrose (101). They also recognize the size of the solute, with greater permeability for glycerol. Calcium does not change the amount of water inside the particle but does decrease the amount between the particles, presumably because of changes in surface charge.

BULK-PHASE MODELS

A bulk lipid solvent phase between two aqueous phases behaves like a carrier system toward ions, provided that a liquid ion exchanger is added (102). An organic molecule of molecular weight 300 to 600, sparingly soluble, with an ionic group, will act in this manner. The kinetics of ion transfer will display saturation, specificity, competition, and susceptibility to poisoning. The liquid ion exchangers markedly increase the partition of sodium and potassium in a variety of organic solvents (103), and phospholipids act to increase the transport of Ca⁺⁺ into chloroform (104). Furthermore,

greater cation selectivity is possible in lipid-water partition than in ion associations in aqueous media, but selectivity as high as that of the cell membrane has not been found. The effects of temperature on diffusion of ions
into butanol indicate that the discrimination between ions occurs at the interface (105). No pores of restrictive size have to be postulated.

Studies of the behavior of lipid-soluble carriers toward sugars have
been extended (106, 107). Dried glucose films were mixed with phospholipid extracts from red blood cells, and the resulting sugar-phospholipid complex was dissolved in hexane (107). The kinetics of the diffusion of sugars
and phospholipids into an aqueous phase were compatible with the premise
that the phospholipid-sugar complex must first occupy a site on the interfa-
cial boundary. The phospholipids from human and beef stroma have equal
abilities to carry glucose and mannitol into highly nonpolar solvents. Yet
human erythrocytes have a very much higher rate of glucose transfer. Furthermore, the amount of sugar bound by the extracted phospholipids greatly exceeds the number of functional transport sites in the intact cell. It
seems clear, therefore, that the phospholipids per se are not the physiological glucose carrier.

ION EXCHANGE MODELS

The behavior of ion exchange membranes has been extensively reviewed (108). Membranes can be classified in categories on the basis of the
mobility of the charged sites, the dissociation constants for the charged
groups, and the size of the pore structures. The physical chemical properties of these various ion exchange membranes are compared with those of
biological membranes, and it is clear that many of the properties of biological membranes can be mimicked. It is also clear, that much more must be
learned of the details of the ion permeation mechanisms in such membranes before their properties can be sufficiently defined to allow comparisons with biological phenomena. In ion exchange membranes with charged
pores, the kinetics of ion movement can resemble the carrier system proposed for biological membranes, with saturation phenomena competition,
specificity, and poisoning (102).

OTHER PHYSICAL MODELS

Two aqueous compartments connected by porous membrane with a constant flow of water in one, can discriminate between sodium and potassium
(109). The flow required, however, is larger than that found in biological
systems.

A model with three-dimensional electrical interconnections can mimic
the current spread within muscle bundles (110).

THEORETICAL MODELS

Most of the theoretical models are concerned with the flow through
fixed-charge membranes using irreversible thermodynamics, but some of
the models are based on specific biological systems. A liquid ion exchange

model with completely dissociated sites has a nonlinear current-voltage relationship, and exhibits finite limiting currents. The mobile sites rearrange under an applied electrical field to give a linear concentration profile and a logarithmic electrical potential profile at steady state (111, 112). Equations to deal with flows and potentials in ion exchange membranes under various assumptions have been developed (113–117). The problem of isotope interactions is also considered in aqueous and nonaqueous systems (118). Models of active transport have dealt with the problem of electrogenesis (119) and with the problem of distribution of local changes in the membrane in determining downhill and uphill directions in coupled-ion movements (120).

The behavior of specific biological systems is modeled for the squid axon (117, 120, 121) and the epithelial cell (122). An analog program for the Widdas model of sugar transport is also presented (123).

An anatomical model of lipoprotein units organized in a crystalline lattice is proposed to explain cooperative phenomena (124). It is patterned after the allosteric model for control of enzymic reactions. Changes in configurations of the lipoprotein subunits resulting from binding of ligands can explain both graded and all-or-none types of response.

Application of the principle of electrostatics to models of lipid membranes has allowed evaluation of the electrical field (125). The effects are important in the determination of the state of the bilayers and also in the behavior of macromolecules at distances up to 10^4 Å from the membrane. These factors may be important in determining the organization and the genesis of membranes.

TRANSPORT AND EXCITATION
TRANSPORT OF ALKALI METAL IONS

As usual, the largest numbers of papers have been concerned with the transport of the alkali metal cations. The studies focus on a number of problems, including (a) the nature of the driving forces which result in the ion movements, particularly whether the movements are downhill, or uphill supported by metabolic energy; (b) the mechanisms involved in the fluxes, such as carrier-mediated transfer or diffusional transfer through pores or a fixed charge matrix; (c) the cation specificity of the transferring mechanisms; (d) the relationship of fluxes to each other, particularly of sodium efflux to potassium influx; (e) the resulting steady-state distribution of ions; (f) the effects of particular conditions and of chemical agents on the various transfers and steady states; (g) the nature of the energy supply for the active transport systems; and (h) in the case of nerve, muscle, and algal cells, the nature of the transient changes in permeability during depolarization. Although this review is concerned primarily with cell membranes and transfers in and out of cells, some of the studies on epithelial systems contribute to our knowledge of cellular membranes and will be cited. The papers are organized according to the tissue studied.

Striated muscle.—A popular technique consists of preloading a muscle with sodium in potassium-free solutions, usually in the cold, and measuring the extrusion of sodium into warm solutions containing various cations. The technique has been used to determine the nature of the cation transport system, particularly the linkage between influx and efflux (126–130). In some cells the influx of K^+ is chemically linked to the efflux of Na^+ by an active transport system that is inhibited by cardiac glycosides, carries no net current, and is nonelectrogenic. In muscle, on the other hand, linkages of Na^+ and K^+ fluxes and sensitivity to cardiac glycosides have often been minimal, which suggests that the sodium-transport system is electrogenic. For example, in the reaccumulation of potassium in potassium-depleted, sodium-rich muscles the data on fluxes and potentials suggest that the potassium movements could be accounted for by the electrochemical driving force. On the other hand, in high-sodium muscles placed in 10 mM rubidium, the extruded sodium is replaced by rubidium whether the anion is chloride or sulfate (126). Measurements of the membrane potentials during the extrusion suggest that the sodium pump is electrogenic but that it also involves some degree of chemical linkage with Rb^+ (or K^+) influx. The large electrogenic component of the sodium transport is more sensitive to temperature, to ouabain, and to cocaine, than is the diffusion potential. From their own data and from other cited works, the authors conclude that the degree of linkage depends on many factors, the availability of ATP, the membrane potential, the specific ions present, and the internal sodium concentration. A similar partial linkage can be demonstrated with Cs^+ as the external cation (127). Cesium induces an extra extrusion of Na^+, which together with cesium-influx is inhibited by strophanthidin. The action of various diuretic agents on the cation fluxes also implies that the linkage of the sodium efflux-potassium influx is not obligatory (128). Some degree of linkage in smooth muscle has been proposed to explain the changes in cellular K^+ resulting from changes in external Ca^{++} and Na^+ (129).

Some of the difficulties in determining the linkage of sodium and potassium fluxes may be due to the effects of denervation (130). Thus the transport of sodium and potassium by sodium-rich muscles was found to increase when the muscles were innervated during the enrichment. Furthermore, in denervated muscle the addition of acetylcholine increased the transport, whereas blocking agents such as eserine inhibited. The membrane potential in denervated muscle was close to the potassium equilibrium potential, whereas in the innervated muscle it was significantly less. It is suggested that denervation makes the sodium pump more electrogenic, perhaps by decreasing the linked transport of potassium.

From the effects on sodium fluxes of various agents injected into single muscle fibers of the crab, it is concluded that in addition to a coupled sodium-potassium mechanism involving ATPase, another electrogenic Na pump is driven by respiration and possibly glycolysis (131).

The efflux of K^+, a downhill movement, is decreased either by addition of cysteine or serum albumin, or by extensive dialysis of the bathing solutions, probably due to removal of traces of heavy metals (132). The downhill fluxes of K^+ were also increased in smooth muscle by addition of nor-epinephrine (133); Na^+ fluxes, on the other hand, were increased by acetyl-choline and carbachol. These effects on permeability provide an explanation for the electrophysiological manifestations of the drugs. In heart muscle the membranes do not have a uniform permeability to K^+. The intercalated disks which form junctions between cells by modifications of the plasma membranes provide a low-resistance pathway for K^+ between the cells (134).

Not all investigators are convinced that the ion exchanges of muscle are necessarily membrane limited (135). On the basis of a technique called "influx profile analysis" using a theoretical model of diffusion into a closed system, it is suggested that the exchange of sodium is under some conditions a complex, bulk-phase limited process that involves adsorption sites in the cytoplasm. A variety of other substances including calcium, magnesium, amino acids, glucose, and water also behave as though they were bulk-phase limited, but K^+ acts as though it were membrane limited. The only adsorption sites present in high enough concentrations are the β-carboxyl groups of aspartic acid and the α-carboxyl groups of glutamic acid, and it is proposed that the specific binding of alkali metal ions by such sites, to-gether with an exclusion of potassium from certain regions in the protein matrix, is largely responsible for sodium-potassium discrimination. Bound sodium and potassium have also been estimated by use of ion-specific electrodes in barnacle muscle to be 38 and 84 per cent, respectively (136).

Red blood cells.—The concept of a ouabain-sensitive, linked sodium-potassium active transport system is well established in red blood cells, as is a strong correlation between the level of potassium in the cell and the activity of the transport systems. The responses of red cells from different animals to NH_4Cl provide an additional correlation (137). In low-potas-sium red blood cells such as those of the cat, responses were like that of a cation exchange resin but in the high potassium cells the responses were not, which indicates intervention of controlling systems for cations. In addi-tion to the ouabain-sensitive, sodium-potassium exchange pump, a second pump has been demonstrated that extrudes Na^+, but without a linked ex-change for K^+. It is ouabain insensitive, but is inhibited by ethacrynic acid, a diuretic (138). It has a higher affinity for sodium and is less dependent on metabolic depletion; therefore it predominates in cells with low internal sodium or in cells that are metabolically depleted.

Several studies have been concerned with downhill movements of ions. The limiting factor in the outflow into isosmotic solutions of low ionic strength is the cation permeability (139). At a given extracellular pH, fitting of the efflux data by a simplified form of the Goldman equation sug-gests that increased outflow at low ionic strength is due to the increased driving force rather than to a change in permeability. At exceedingly low ionic strengths, however, a reversible transition occurs to a new permeabil-ity about thirty times as high. The permeability is also increased by raising the pH in a manner that suggests control by positive fixed charges in the membrane, perhaps amino groups. The outflow of potassium is also markedly enhanced by sulfhydryl agents as discussed in the section on Specific Ligands (26, 27). The influx of sodium into red blood cells, also a downhill movement, can be measured only if the intracellular sodium trapped with the cells can be accurately estimated. Iodine-labeled serum albumin is often used as a reference substance, but its use gives an underestimate (140). Labeled sucrose also underestimates, but with a constant factor. Sodium itself gives better values, provided that the cells are separated rapidly or can be washed with sodium-free solutions. Values for cellular sodium are 6.5 to 6.9 meq/kg of cells, somewhat lower than previously reported. Using the above techniques, the kinetics of influx of sodium could be simulated by the use of models containing two compartments either in series or in parallel (141). Differences in the age of cells in the population could not account for the observed kinetics and it is proposed that the exchange across the membrane is followed by a slow diffusion into a convection-free interior.

Other mammalian cells.—In liver slices, 40 per cent of the sodium outflux is dependent on K^+ and is inhibited by ouabain (142). The addition of valinomycin inhibited the sodium efflux only slightly in the presence of potassium. Since this agent stimulates potassium accumulation by the mitochondria, this experiment does not support the idea of an involvement of mitochondrial potassium accumulation in the accumulation by the whole cell. Sodium extrusion from sodium-loaded slices of kidney cortex depends not only on the external potassium level but also on the external sodium concentration relative to internal sodium (143). Thus the concept of a critical energy barrier in terms of a maximal sodium gradient can be applied just as it has been applied to muscle; the critical barrier is somewhat lower in the kidney. Sodium-rich kidney slices from hibernating animals (144) have much higher capacity for transport at low temperature than those from nonhibernators, but the capacities are similar at normal temperature.

The permeability of cells to cations is dependent on Ca^{++}. For example, removal of calcium specifically caused a tenfold increase in the sodium influx of HeLa cells which was not inhibited by strophanthidin (145). As a consequence, in the absence of Ca^{++} the cells cannot retain a high potassium level. Conversely, a rapid component of the Ca^{++}-exchange involving 40 per cent of the cellular Ca^{++} is inhibited by sodium (145). Ca^{++} seems to act by competing for the sites involved in sodium permeability. Although Ca^{++} inhibits the Na-K-ATPase, no evidence of an effect on active sodium extrusion could be demonstrated.

In nerve cells most studies are concerned with depolarization phenomena, and these will be discussed in the next section, but in the resting cell an increase in external K^+ results not only in a decreased potential, but also in a decrease in the steady-state level of sodium (146).

In the cortical cells of the adrenal gland the membrane potential was dependent on external potassium with a tenfold change giving a potential change of 44 to 50 mV, but in the medullary cells the potentials were much less affected by potassium (147). Thus the potassium permeabilities of the two cell types are considerably different. A method for estimating extracellular space in kidney slices is based on efflux kinetics for various ions and nonelectrolytes (148).

Epithelial systems.—The salt and water movements through epithelial systems involve multiple compartments and multiple membranes. Many studies are concerned with the characteristics of fluid transport and with the location of the various activities in this complex structure. Much of the behavior of the epithelia, however, reflects the activities of cell membranes, and on this basis a brief summary of several papers will be given here.

In fluid transport by the gall bladder of the rabbit, a close linkage is observed between the transport of sodium and chloride ions (59, 149). In the absence of either ion the fluid transport slows or ceases. Ion transport apparently occurs in the lateral membranes of the cells into the spaces between the cells, leading to distention and to the bulk flow characteristics of the tissues. Experiments on frog skin using hypertonic solutions and histochemical techniques also suggest that sodium and fluid are transported through the lateral membranes into the spaces between the cells (150). In the frog skin, sodium and potassium can also migrate laterally from cell to cell; this reflects the presence of intercellular connections of low resistance. At low external sodium concentrations, sodium transport behaves as though a series arrangement of sodium compartments were present (151).

The sodium system in larval salamanders has a high specificity, lithium being able to substitute for Na^+, but not potassium, rubidium, calcium, or magnesium (152). Measurement of potentials following substitution of various cations has demonstrated that in kidney tubule cells the peritubular membrane has a high and specific permeability to potassium, whereas the luminal membrane is characterized by approximately equal permeabilities to sodium, potassium, and chloride (153). In the rumen of the sheep the potential was dependent on the potassium concentration on either side of the epithelium but not dependent on sodium concentration (154).

The flows of sodium, potassium, and chloride in the rat intestine under varied electrical and chemical and osmotic gradients are considered in terms of irreversible thermodynamic equations (155). Two channels across the tissue are proposed, one allowing only passive transport and the other only active. The passive channel is lined with negatively fixed charges and the predominant resistance is friction with water. The active channel, on the other hand, behaves like two membranes in series, the first being semipermeable but allowing active transport of sodium, and the second being similar to the passive channel. The spaces left by sloughed epithelial cells may provide the passive pathway. The amount of bound sodium in cells of frog skin has been estimated by nuclear magnetic resonance techniques to be about 60 per cent (156).

Microorganisms.—In yeast, the inward cation carrier can transport any of the alkali metal cations, but has the highest affinity for potassium. The transport of a given cation in the presence of another depends not only on the relative affinities for the transport site, but also on modification of the transport by a second cation-binding site (157). Certain ions such as hydrogen, cesium, and calcium, with a relatively higher affinity for the modifying site, reduce the maximal rate of transport to a degree depending on the cation being transported, with no change in the Michaelis constant. A considerably higher degree of discrimination of potassium over sodium occurs in the presence of Ca^{++} or at low pH. Yeast cells can be prepared in which much of the cation, normally potassium, is replaced by rubidium, cesium, lithium, or calcium (158). A mutant of *E. coli* was unable to accumulate potassium in the normal manner because of an increased outflow (159). Thus the defect is not in the active transport system, but is due to an increased permeability.

Plant cells.—Fluxes, steady-state distribution of ions, and potentials have been measured in various plant cells, particularly algae and roots. The large green algae offer particular advantages because the samples can be easily obtained from the vacuole, and because potential measurements are relatively easy. On the other hand, interpretation is more difficult because two membranes and three compartments are involved: the plasmalemma, the vacuolar membrane, the cytoplasm, the vacuole, and the external medium. Many of the studies are concerned with cation specificity, the number of transport systems, their location, and the energy supply. In algae the cation specificity for efflux favors sodium over rubidium and cesium, but for influx rubidium and potassium are favored over sodium as counter ions for the sodium extrusion (160). The balance of sodium extrusion and uptake is dependent on external phosphate. At low phosphate the extrusion predominates and the cell can be kept virtually free of sodium, but at high phosphate the uptake of sodium is also stimulated and the cells gain sodium. In the large marine alga *Chaetomorpha darwinii,* flux and potential measurements across the plasmalemma and vacuolar membranes indicate that sodium is specifically extruded and potassium selectively taken up at the plasmalemma (161). In addition a potassium pump works from the cytoplasm into the vacuole, accounting for the lower than expected concentration of potassium in the cytoplasm. Dinitrophenol reduces the active transport of cations (potassium in and sodium out), but not the downhill movement of sodium whose content in the cell rises rapidly. The effects of dinitrophenol may be related to the finding that the active inward transport of potassium into *Nitella* is dependent on ATP production (162). Comparisons of fluxes in summer and winter *Nitella* suggest that the transport of potassium from the cytoplasm to the vacuole is linked to chloride transport (163).

In higher plants the determinants of mechanisms of transport are more difficult to establish because the contributions of the two membranes, plasmalemma and vacuolar, are less easy to assess. From measurements of steady-state distributions of ions and of potentials, calculations using the Nernst equation have been made to determine which ions are at electrochemical equilibrium. In tissues of pea and oat seedlings (164) and in castor oil plants and roots (165), K^+ is close to electrochemical equilibrium, but the other ions are not. From the direction of the electrochemical gradients it can be assumed that Ca^{++}, Mg^{++}, and Na^+ are actively extruded, whereas anions are actively accumulated. An unequivocal appraisal of the system requires measurements of fluxes, steady-state concentrations, and potentials in each compartment and across each membrane. Such an analysis was attempted in barley roots (166). At the steady state, the ratio of potassium to sodium in the cells was 3 : 1 compared to 1 : 3 in the solution, but in the cytoplasm the ratio was very high, 11 :1. The selectivity for potassium thus appears to be primarily at the plasmalemma and it is the low sodium content of the cytoplasm that is responsible for the low sodium flux at the tonoplast. The pattern is very much like that found in algae. The simplest model would place an active anion pump into the vacuole and an active efflux of sodium and influx of potassium at the plasmalemma. Unlike the situation in animal cells, the sodium and potassium transports are not inhibited by ouabain. The characteristics of the cation influx mechanism have been explored in detail in barley roots (167, 168). The uptake of sodium follows two saturation curves with K_m of 0.05 and 10 mM. The first of these is inhibited competitively by low concentrations of calcium and potassium. Therefore, in the presence of potassium, the first mechanism is preempted, leaving sodium to be transported by the second. The latter system, which has a higher affinity for sodium than for potassium, shows a number of inflections, indicating a spectrum of overlapping affinities for the active sites.

Transport of substituted ammonium ions.—Substituted ammonium ions such as choline, often used in place of sodium and potassium in physiological solutions, are not incorporated in the phospholipids or converted to other metabolites, but they are taken up slowly by the red blood cell by two distinct mechanisms, one a saturable system and the other proportional to concentration (169). In brain slices choline is actually taken up against a concentration gradient by a process inhibited by dinitrophenol and requiring substrate. The maximum uptake depends on the presence of sodium but, because choline does not stimulate the Na-K-ATPase, it is probably not transported by the ATPase system (170). A variety of quarternary alkylammonium cations taken up by nerves of insects penetrate faster with increasing lipid solubility (171).

EXCITATION PHENOMENA

Depolarization phenomena continue as a focal point of research on membrane phenomena, much of it based on the Hodgkin-Huxley model. For example, the Hodgkin-Huxley equation for conduction has been modified to account for details of the change in excitation with temperature and external concentrations (172, 173).

The theory that the permeability cycle in excitable membranes is controlled by an acetylcholine system has been extensively reviewed (174). Much of the evidence is based on the action of inhibitors of the two components of the system, the receptor which is activated by acetylcholine and the esterase which breaks down the acetylcholine. Criticism of the hypothesis has been based largely on the relative insensitivity of depolarization phenomena to the inhibitors and to the time factors involved. Past failures to get predicted effects of acetylcholine and various inhibitors are explained by the presence of permeability barriers which can be overcome by pretreating the cells to render them permeable. Also, the concentration of organophosphate in the axoplasm is only 1/1000 that added. In all types of axons the actions of acetylcholine, esterase, acetylase, and receptor have been demonstrated. It is proposed that the reaction of acetylcholine with the receptor leads to a conformational change which results in the observed permeability changes.

Another interpretation of the mechanism of excitation is based on the asymmetric nature of the membrane, for example major differences in responses produced by internal and external applications of enzymes, salts, and organic molecules (175). This model involves a membrane structure of lipoproteins bound together by noncovalent bonds. It is subdivided into two layers, the outer one possessing a high negative charge. In the resting state its sites are occupied predominantly by divalent cations from the medium. The inner layer consists of low-density negative charges with potassium as the counter ion. Any decrease in the ratio of divalent to monovalent cations in the outer layer leads to a change of state and to an increased permeability. Thus an increase in outside potassium leads to displacement of Ca^{++} and depolarization. An increase in Ca^{++}, on the other hand, fills the sites with Ca^{++} resulting in stabilization. Transitions can also be produced electrically because the outward current drives the potassium from the interior of the axon into the outer layer, displacing divalent cations. The excitation terminates spontaneously because of a redistribution of ions that occurs after the membrane potential is re-established.

The depolarization produced by high external K^+ involves a change in membrane potential and in membrane permeability. If the voltage is clamped, external K^+ still causes an increased permeability and an increased efflux of K^+. The specific activity of the potassium that leaves the cell is the same as that remaining behind, which indicates a single mixed cellular compartment (176).

Considerable evidence has accumulated that the increased conductance to sodium and potassium on excitation involves two independent pathways whose properties are different from the permeability paths in the resting cell. Thus tetrodotoxin isolated from the puffer fish has been shown to be a specific blocking agent for the increased sodium conductance during excitation, with no effect, however, on the resting potential. On the basis of its specificity of action, its binding has been used as a measure of the number of sodium channels (177). They are rare on the surface, fewer than 13 per square micron. Tetrodotoxin has been used on squid axon (178), lobster nerve (177), and frog nerve (179), to differentiate sodium and potassium channels. Tarichatoxin, isolated from newt eggs, a compound similar to tetrodotoxin, also has a selective action on the sodium channel. The local anesthetics can also differentiate the excitation pathways and the resting permeability. At low concentrations they reduce the sodium conductance, whereas at high concentrations they also reduce the potassium conductance (179, 180) but do not change the resting potential. Cesium injected into axons has no effect on the potassium permeability in the resting cell, but inhibits the increase in potassium permeability during excitation (181, 182). Potassium is preferred by the conductance channel by nine to one over cesium. A related effect of cesium is a prolongation of the action potential which may be due to a delay in shutting off the sodium conductance. The potassium channels can be closed from the inside by injection of tetraethylammonium (183).

The sodium channel can accept lithium almost equally well, but potassium, rubidium, and cesium at reduced rates. On the other hand, in the resting state the permeabilities favor potassium and rubidium but tend to exclude sodium and lithium (184, 185). The fact that other cations can diffuse through the sodium channel, though at a reduced rate, explains why action potentials can occur in sodium-free solutions. Na^+ can be replaced by univalent cations, both inorganic and organic (186, 187), and by various bivalent cations (178, 188). That these ions indeed use the sodium pathway is suggested by the fact that the excitations are sensitive to tetrodotoxin which also blocks sodium conductance (178, 186) and because the product of the flux and membrane resistance are constant for all the cations tested, including sodium (187).

Normally an increase in external Ca^{++} stabilizes the membrane and adds only slightly to the conductance during excitation (189) but, if the axon is perfused with cesium fluoride or phosphate (188), Ca^{++} spikes can be produced. Treatment with pronase inside the axon makes the nerves sodium dependent again. Such results have been used to support a theory of excitation discussed at the beginning of this section (175).

The efflux of calcium follows a fast and slow exponential, the fast process being reported for the first time (190). The permeability of the axon to calcium, based on the rapid component, is twenty to thirty times larger than that of monovalent cations. This component may be surface-bound Ca^{++}.

The effects of Ca^{++} on permeability of cells in general have been of continuing interest. In the case of nerve cells, the relationship of calcium to the action of local anesthetics has been reviewed in some detail (180). Procaine and Ca^{++} compete for sites that are directly involved in control of sodium and potassium flows. Both Ca^{++} and procaine delay the turning on of sodium conductance (191); furthermore, both compete for binding to phospholipids. Lanthanum also behaves like Ca^{++} (192). In the junctional membrane, Ca^{++} and carbamylcholine also compete for common binding sites and Ca^{++} decreases sensitivity to the drug (193).

The studies of depolarization in muscle follow much the same patterns as in nerve. They are concerned primarily with the changes in sodium and potassium conductance and their relationships to potentials, the specificities of the ion pathways, the effects of Ca^{++} and agents that influence the conductance such as local anesthetics and tetrodotoxin, and with calcium fluxes.

The current-voltage relationships of crayfish muscle indicate that the membrane undergoes a number of independent reactions on excitation (194). One or another of these can be eliminated or modified by different procedures and agents. As previously demonstrated in other cells, the intracellular potentials recorded from heart fibers in the atrioventricular conducting system decreased when potassium was increased, somewhat less than predicted from the Nernst equation (195). The sodium concentration, although it had little effect on resting potential, determined the peak value of the action potential. The relationship of sodium to the overshoot of the action potential could be demonstrated in elasmobranch muscle by replacing the normal osmotic component, urea, with additional NaCl to achieve high salt concentrations (196). The rate of depolarization, the amplitude and duration of the action potential, and the overshoot all increased in direct proportion to the external sodium, which indicates that the initial part of the spike is due to the sodium conductance.

Changes in sodium permeability, rather than an effect on the cation pump, are proposed as an explanation for the rapid depolarizing effects of ouabain (197). Sodium permeability is also influenced by Ca^{++}. In crayfish muscle, sodium permeability increased when calcium was reduced, which led to large transient sodium-dependent depolarizations that could be blocked by tetrodotoxin (198). Repolarization is linked to replenishment of calcium in the membrane from internal stores. Thus a second depolarization can be produced by adding EDTA or by changing to fresh calcium-free medium. In the frog heart the size of the overshoot of the action potential is decreased if the external Na^+ is decreased or if the internal sodium is increased (199). Lithium can replace sodium. In the presence of atropine 75 per cent of the sodium can be replaced by choline with no change in the overshoot but the rate of rise is reduced. Calcium has a marked effect on relationship of overshoot to sodium concentration, particularly at low sodium concentrations, due probably to calcium influx. Indeed, a tenfold increase in the external Ca^{++} concentration results in an increase of 18 mV in the size of the overshoot due to the entry of Ca^{++}. Similar results were obtained with Sr^{++} but not Mg^{++} (200). In barnacle fibers, calcium spikes can be produced if the internal Ca^{++} is reduced by injection of chelating agents (201). At relatively low external Ca⁺⁺, the membrane behaves like a calcium electrode in terms of the overshoot, but at high external Ca⁺⁺, the size of the overshoot tends to reach a maximal value. It is, therefore, suggested that Ca⁺⁺, in addition to carrying inward current, combines with negative sites at the outer surface of the membrane, which results in reduced permeability to Ca⁺⁺.

In determining Ca⁺⁺ fluxes, the problem of interstitial space has been avoided by a technique using only the center part of the single muscle fiber (202). The resting influx of calcium is not sensitive to increases in Ca⁺⁺ above 1.8 mM but the stimulated influx is increased considerably at high external Ca⁺⁺. The efflux of half of the Ca⁺⁺ follows a single curve with a time constant of 125 minutes. The remainder followed a much slower time constant. An increased Ca⁺⁺ influx also accounts for the prolonged action potentials in procaine-treated crayfish muscle (203). Tetrodotoxin does not block the calcium influx. Thus the calcium channels are insensitive to tetrodotoxin and procaine, whereas the sodium channels are sensitive to both. Insensitivity of Ca⁺⁺ influx to tetrodotoxin and procaine during excitation has also been reported in barnacle muscle (204). In this study calcium spikes could be produced in the absence of sodium, provided the internal calcium was low. During the spike, Ca⁺⁺ enters the cell; the process is not suppressed by tetrodotoxin and is increased by procaine. Thus in this system the calcium channels seem different from the sodium and potassium channels. In this respect the muscles are different from nerve cells in which Ca⁺⁺ apparently flows into the cells via the sodium channels (see previous section).

In previous studies on algae, the action potentials were explained in terms of an initial increase in chloride efflux followed by an outflow of potassium. These conclusions were based on the changes in fluxes following a series of depolarizations. With a technique that allows determinations of ion efflux during a single action potential, the previous results were confirmed (205). The initial efflux of chloride with a single action potential could also be measured using a silver chloride electrode in a thin film of solution flowing over the surface of the cell (206). Quantitative relationships of chloride and potassium flows are difficult to establish because the cell wall space resists the flow of chloride more than it does the flow of potassium.

CALCIUM TRANSPORT

In the previous section on depolarization it was noted that the permeability to calcium may be increased considerably during excitation in nerve and muscle. In fact, under certain conditions, calcium can replace sodium as the conducting cation in the rising phase of the action potential. Active transport systems for Ca⁺⁺ have also been investigated, particularly in the intestine and in the sarcoplasmic reticulum of muscle.

In calcium transport across the intestinal mucosa two distinct steps are involved: first a net uptake at the mucosal surface to form a cellular reservoir, followed by transfer across the serosal membrane (207). The dependency of the second step on the presence of glucose (on the mucosal side) and of oxygen, and its inhibition by dinitrophenol suggest that it is the active or uphill step. This conclusion is supported by the finding that storage of Ca^{++} in the cells occurs only if the Ca^{++} is presented on the mucosal side (208). On the other hand, experiments with the short-circuit technique suggest that calcium transfer across the epithelium is a passive process (209). In the absence of phosphate no evidence of saturation of the calcium fluxes, or uphill transport was observed. In the presence of phosphate, calcium appears to move uphill, but it may be acting only as a counter ion for the uphill phosphate transport. Vitamin D increases the transfer of Ca^{++}, but in both directions, so its action may be mediated by an increase in permeability (210). Detergents also increase the transfer of cesium and strontium, presumably by increasing lipid solubility and thereby altering the rate of permeation (211, 212).

Calcium is the trigger substance in the excitation-contraction coupling in striated muscle. The sarcoplasmic reticulum plays a key role in the release and reaccumulation of Ca^{++} during the contraction-relaxation cycle. The finding that isolated fragments of the reticulum are capable of taking up large quantities of Ca^{++} has greatly stimulated the study of these phenomena. Several pertinent reviews have treated the anatomy and role of the transverse tubules which form the bridge between the outside and the reticulum (213), the role of Ca^{++} as a mediator (214), and the action of calcium on the contractile system and the role of the sarcoplasmic reticulum (215). A suspension of the reticular vesicles supplemented by ATP and magnesium can take up calcium in association with the splitting of ATP. The Ca^{++}-enhanced ATPase is inhibited by sulfhydryl reagents and protected by ATP. Furthermore, the rate of calcium uptake diminishes in parallel to the inhibition of the enzyme. The Ca^{++} activation is related to calcium in the external solution rather than inside the vesicles. The stoichiometry of transfer suggests two calciums pumped for one ATP split, with ATP breakdown coupled only to calcium influx and not to outflux (216). Both the calcium-activated ATPase and the calcium accumulation are accelerated by potassium (217), and inhibited to some degree by ouabain, especially in the presence of sodium (218).

Localization of the cations by staining reactions has demonstrated Ca^{++} in the reticulum (219) and sodium in the transverse tubules (220). The latter finding supports the concept that the tubules are connected to the outside.

Although the reticulum is involved in the distributions of Ca^{++} within the muscle, the plasma membrane must, in addition, regulate the total amount of Ca^{++} in the cell. For example, during contracture, produced by a number of procedures, the increased permeability to Ca^{++} leads to a large increase in cellular content, and on release of the contracture the Ca^{++}

levels return to normal (221). On denervation the Ca^{++} content of muscle is also increased but in this case a parallel increase in the sequestering ability of the reticulum occurs (222).

Although calcium inhibits the Na-K-ATPase of red cell ghosts, another ATPase is activated by calcium (220). If ghosts are hemolyzed in the presence of Mg-ATP, calcium efflux can be demonstrated against the electrochemical gradient. The movement was independent of the inorganic phosphate gradient and of sodium and was not inhibited by ouabain (223). Thus the calcium transport is independent of the sodium transport.

Transport of Anions

Halides.—In plant cells the steady-state distribution of anions relative to the potentials between the vacuole and the outside solution indicates that the anion distribution is maintained against the electrochemical gradient (164–166). In barley roots the accumulation of chloride reaches a steady-state level with influx equal to efflux (224). The pathways for cations and anions are independent of each other, involving, respectively, hydrogen and hydroxyl exchanges. When chloride and potassium are accumulated, they both mix rapidly throughout the roots. With cesium, however, the internal barriers in the root limit its movements. Its slow equilibration results in a slower equilibration of chloride, which acts as a counter ion.

In red blood cells the distribution of chloride is passive, obeying the Donnan equilibrium (225). Chloride ratios can, therefore, be used to calculate the membrane potentials from the Nernst equation. In the presence of an impermeant ion such as citrate, an inversion of the normal potential across the membrane results. In the ascites tumor cells replacement of chloride by sulfate resulted in changes in membrane potential because the membrane is permeable to chloride and less so to sulfate (226). The potential was greater than predicted from the Nernst equation and it was suggested that sodium diffusion may contribute.

Although in many animal cells chloride reaches an equilibrium distribution, which indicates that only downhill movements are involved, some epithelial systems are capable of transporting chloride uphill. In frog skin such a transport can be observed only at very low chloride concentrations because at higher concentrations the transport is masked by large passive transfer (227). Furthermore, the experiments should be done in sodium-free solutions because in the presence of sodium, only 5 per cent of the short-circuit current is carried by chloride. With sodium-free solutions and low Cl^-, a reversal of potential occurs at the mucosal membrane, due perhaps to the electrogenic character of the inward chloride transport. The turtle bladder also has a reverse potential in sodium-free media (228). Short-circuit experiments reveal an active transport of chloride independent of sodium transport, but as in frog skin, much smaller in magnitude. The isolated cornea of the frog transports chloride even in the presence of sodium (229). In fact, the short-circuit current indicates that the primary transport is of chloride with sodium behaving passively. The olfactory receptor in frogs produces a potential which is dependent on chloride, but this may be a diffusion potential (230). Evidence has also been presented that independent electrogenic chloride and hydrogen transport systems are located at separate sites in the gastric mucosa (231). Sulfate cannot substitute for chloride for transport. Thus in the presence of sulfate, the properties of the hydrogen-secreting system can be determined.

Fluoride can be transported uphill in the intestine of the rat but it moves in the opposite direction to the usual absorption—that is, from serosa to mucosa (232). The transport is dependent on the presence of calcium which seems to act to prevent the backflow from the mucosal side of the intestine.

The accumulation of iodide by the thyroid is inhibited by a variety of substances which have quite different effects on potassium levels and on incorporation of P^{32} (233). Thus the iodide mechanism is independent of the potassium concentration and of phosphate accumulation.

Sulfate.—Although animal cells tend to be relatively impermeable to, and are unable to transport sulfate, specific active transport systems have been demonstrated in microorganisms and in plants. In the roots of sunflower, sulfate first binds to anionic sites in the free space and then is taken up by a metabolically linked system (234, 235). When water transport is at a sufficiently high level, the sulfate transport is increased. A similar mechanism of binding in free space followed by an uptake is demonstrated in roots of wheat (236). The uptake is also influenced by increase in osmotic pressure with mannitol.

Inorganic sulfate is concentrated by the mycelium of *Penicillium chrysogenum* with the uptake influenced by temperature, energy sources, and pH, and regulated by the degree of sulfur deficiency (237). The kinetics of exchange suggest two intracellular pools. Sulfate transport is apparently regulated by a feedback inhibition with perhaps thiosulfate, a product of fungal sulfate reduction, as the inhibiting agent.

Phosphate.—Phosphate transfer across cell membranes has been studied in a variety of cells. In erythrocytes the kinetics of influx is first order and is proportional to the concentration with no inhibitory effect of sulfate or arsenate. The results suggest that phosphate movement is a simple diffusion process (238). In ascites tumor cells, however, the intracellular phosphorus distribution is highly controlled, with regulation determined not only by intracellular factors but by control over entrance and exit. The phosphate influx tends to show saturation, and the steady-state fluxes in both directions depend on extracellular phosphate, which indicates a high degree of exchange diffusion. Although the intracellular phosphate pool increases with the external phosphate concentration, a large fraction of the inorganic pool does not leak out even when the phosphate concentration is exceedingly low (239).

In microorganisms phosphate uptake is usually an active process. In a marine fungus the uptake is specifically stimulated by sodium (240). In phosphate-deprived *Euglena* a saturable phosphate-uptake system is inhibited by dinitrophenol, by low temperature, and competitively by arsenate (241). That an active transport is involved is clear, because the phosphate moves against the electrochemical gradient. A phosphatase on the outer surface may be involved in the transport system. It increases markedly in amount on phosphate depletion and the ability to accumulate phosphate appears at the same time as the induced phosphatase. The effects of arsenate on growth of *Streptococcus faecalis* are primarily from competition for a transport system for phosphate. As the cells become loaded with arsenate they lose their capacity to transport ions, including arsenate itself, by interference with metabolism (242). The influx and efflux of phosphate and arsenate have also been studied in yeast. In prestarved cells, phosphate once transported into the cells has a very low rate of efflux. After preincubation with glucose, however, a higher rate of both uptake and of efflux is observed. The efflux is inhibited by dinitrophenol and is proportional to the internal phosphate concentration. The rate of outflow seems to be controlled by metabolic factors involved in the maintenance of the inorganic phosphate pool. In a potassium-defective mutant of *E. coli* the phosphate uptake is reduced unless the potassium concentration is high. The enhanced phosphate uptake is probably related to the need for potassium as a counter ion (243).

Osmotic Properties, Water, and Nonelectrolytes

The equilibration of cells with changes in the osmotic pressure of the medium using different solutes provides information concerning penetration of water and of solutes, as well as nonosmotic factors that control cell size. Frog nerves immersed in solutions of different tonicity swell and shrink to equilibrium volumes following the Boyle—Van't Hoff relationship after correction for a large osmotically inactive fraction (244). Electrical properties were changed on swelling and shrinking, due to altered membrane permeability. All nerves are not alike, however, in osmotic properties. Lobster and squid nerve fibers respond differently when subjected to osmotic changes using NaCl and KCl (245). The swelling curves of lobster axon indicate that it is permeable to potassium and chloride but not to sodium, whereas those of the squid axon indicate relative impermeability to chloride. The nonosmotic volume was 20 per cent for lobster and 40 per cent for squid.

The responses of kidney (246) and heart muscle (247) to changes in external osmolarity, with nonelectrolytes such as mannitol and sucrose, do not follow simple osmometric behavior. The factors that may participate include the compensating action of the ion pumps, the loss of salts, the presence of bound cations and water inside the cell, and the mechanical behavior of the tissue. Bound water, measured by several techniques in the yeast cell, can be classified into four regions: the solution region (80 per cent), the gel region (10 per cent), the mobile adsorption region around polar groups (5 per cent), and the localization water region around highly charged sites (5 per cent) (248).

Swelling and shrinking due to changes in tonicity may also change the permeability of the membrane. This is true for frog nerve, as judged by electrical properties (244). In frog skin an unusual change has been reported after an increase in osmolarity (249). Sucrose flux increases, with a three-fold higher influx than efflux. This net inward movement proceeds in spite of sizable bulk flow of water in the opposite direction. The movement of the hyperosmotic agent down its concentration gradient may be the driving force.

Osmotic gradients can be used to increase the flow of water. In algae, the two ends of the cell behave as though they had different water permeabilities (250). In many membranes the flow of water under an osmotic gradient is greater than the diffusion of tritiated water under the same driving force. The discrepancy has been interpreted in terms of a pore structure. Gastric mucosa behaves as though it has pores of two different radii, with 88 per cent of the area available for diffusion, consisting of pores with radii smaller than 2.5 Å (251). Negatively charged pores are also suggested from experiments on electroosmotic flow in the squid axon (252). Solvent drag effects on urea in the intestine also suggest the presence of pores (253). On the other hand, the diffusional permeability in frog skin, measured with tritiated water, changed markedly with change in stirring rate, which indicates the presence of unstirred layers. The hydrolic conductivity, however, was independent of stirring rates. It is therefore suggested that all previous determinations of diffusional permeability are underestimates. If the values for diffusional permeability are extrapolated to infinite stirring rates, then the discrepancy between diffusional and hydrolic permeabilities in frog skin is about two, but conclusions concerning pores drawn from this ratio are considered questionable.

Most studies on nonelectrolytes are concerned with sugar permeability and transport, to be discussed in the next section, but a few are concerned with other substances. Urea penetration into elasmobranch red blood cells is presumed to be a carrier-mediated transport (254). Thiourea enters red cells by a facilitated mechanism that is inhibited by butanol (255). Permeability of red blood cells can be measured at constant volume by detecting volume changes photometrically, and compensating with added nonpenetrating solute (256). By this technique the penetration of glycerol in the beef erythrocyte seems to be a simple diffusion process. The permeabilities to several nonelectrolytes are almost doubled during stimulation of axons. The penetration is independent of sodium at rest but on stimulation the increased permeability is sodium dependent, possibly because of a drag effect.

Transport of Sugars and Amino Acids

Sugars.—Sugar transfer in most mammalian cells behaves like a carrier system but with net downhill movement, to yield a final equilibrium distribution. In epithelial cells of the intestine and kidney, however, sugars can be accumulated against their concentration gradients. These accumulations are related in some manner to sodium gradients or transport and they will be discussed in a section on sodium-dependent transport. In microorganisms, some sugars reach equilibrium distribution via a carrier system (permease), but others are accumulated against the gradient by active transport systems that are sometimes inducible and under genetic control. Recent studies have been concerned largely with a more detailed analysis of the characteristics of the carrier systems such as kinetics and specificity, a few studies with the chemical nature of the carrier and the chemical events in transport.

In muscle, xylose, arabinose, and glucose compete for common entry system but glucosides do not compete and do not penetrate rapidly (257). Xylosides also penetrate but by a different mechanism. The permeability of muscle to sugars is increased in the presence of nitrate (258), and after contracture with caffeine (259), the effects in each case being attributed to an increase in cellular Ca^{++}. In the squid axon, in contrast, the permeability to sucrose is not increased by excitation (260). The data suggest that a fraction of only 10^{-8} of the area of the squid axon membrane is open to free diffusion but this is sufficient to account for the leakage conductance of the axon.

The kinetics of sugar transfer across the red cell membrane have been examined in detail for many years. A recent analysis leads to the conclusion that the sugar-loaded carrier can reorient in the membrane or traverse the membrane more rapidly, by a factor of four, than can the unloaded carrier (261). The discrepancy is increased at low temperatures. The transport of a variety of sugars by yeast follows a pattern similar to that in red blood cells. A review of the available data, using Wilbrandt's model of transport kinetics, also suggests that the loaded and unloaded carriers must traverse the membrane at different rates (262). Another theory of transport, the dimer theory, has been re-examined in detail using twenty-one pairs of sugars (263). The data gave no support to the dimer theory but fitted the simple monovalent-carrier model. The carrier-mediated transport is retained in ghosts prepared from red cells (264).

Carrier kinetics have been demonstrated in a number of cells. In ascites cells, xylose transport, but not that of glucose, is a saturable system (265). In intestine, two routes for sugar transport have been identified, one, sensitive to uranyl ion, that is specific for glucose, and one, insensitive, that is shared by other sugars such as galactose and 3-methyl glucose (266). In *Neurospora crassa* an equilibrating carrier system is involved in transfer of sorbose (267). Glucose competitively inhibits and can induce counterflow. In yeast, analogs of glucose inhibit its metabolism by competing for the transport system (268). *Proteus mirabilis* transports sucrose by a carrier system that is energy dependent and inhibited by azide and dinitrophenol (269). *Micrococcus* possesses a carrier-mediated system for concentrating maltose but not glucose (270). Its specificity is related to the 1–4 linkages. The effects of a variety of substances on the influx and efflux of glucosides into *E. coli* support the conclusion that glucoside is transported by the glucose permease and that the inhibitory effects of metabolizable compounds are due to changes in the energy supply that control the exit reaction of the permease (271). The uphill transport of galactosides in *E. coli* is also dependent on a metabolically dependent reduction in affinity at the inner surface of the membrane (272). In the presence of inhibitors of metabolism the change in affinity is blocked and the efflux increases. Consequently the sugars will equilibrate rapidly but cannot be accumulated. In yeast, the transport of sugars is related to the Pasteur effect (273).

In spores of *Myrothecium verrucarria* two systems have been demonstrated for uptake of trehalose (274). One is constitutive and involves hydrolysis of trehalose by a surface trehalase with the resultant glucose transported into the cell. The second is an inducible uphill transport system for trehalose.

Several studies have been concerned with chemical parameters of transport of sugars. For example, isolated brush borders of intestinal epithelial cells show a specific binding for D-glucose (275). Furthermore, the binding of labeled phlorizin, a specific inhibitor of transport in the intestine, has been used to estimate the concentration of the carrier in kidney (276). Heavy metals with a high affinity for phosphoryl groups have been used in yeast to explore their role in transport (25). A series of such studies has been reviewed (24). Briefly, it is proposed that membrane phosphoryl groups are involved in uphill sugar transport by modifying the affinity of the carrier for certain sugars, but they are not involved in the equilibrating system which has a broader specificity. Two other studies are also discussed in the section on the Nature of Carriers and the Carrier-Substrate Reactions. In *E. coli*, a heat-stable protein, part of the phosphotransferase system has been isolated that restores the ability of osmotically shocked cells to transport galactosides (33). Also in *E. coli,* a membrane protein has been isolated that is involved in the transport of galactosides (32).

Amino acids.—Virtually all of the studies have been concerned with sorting out the various transport systems for different amino acids by determining either the degree of competition between various pairs of amino acids for influx, or the effect of one amino acid on the efflux of another. Nonutilizable amino acid analogs continue to be particularly useful in making flux measurements, avoiding complications of incorporation. The results are sometimes complicated because of overlapping specificities and because amino acids sometimes interfere with each other by mechanisms other than competition for a carrier. Furthermore, different cells have somewhat different patterns of amino acid transport.

The transport system for neutral amino acids has been characterized in diaphragm using the nonutilizable amino acids, AIB (α-aminoisobutyric acid) and cycloleucine (277). At least two transport systems for AIB and methionine seem to be involved in ascites cells, one sensitive and one insensitive to sodium (278). A further complication is reported for neutral amino acid transport in the intestine (279). A separate mechanism exists for several imino acids, but glycine is also transported by the system for neutral amino acids.

Valine transport has been studied in *Agrobacterium tumefaciens* in relation to ability to produce plant tumors (280). A nontumorogenic strain shows a typical accumulating system sensitive to metabolic inhibitors, with outward exchange produced by related amino acids. In the tumorogenic strain, however, the picture was different. The uptake of valine was rapid but not specific, being inhibited by structurally unrelated amino acids. The valine is converted into α-ketoisovaleric acid which rapidly leaves the cell.

The transport of dibasic amino acids has been extensively studied in relation to other amino acids. In the ascites cell the transport of lysine shows heterogeneity in terms of inhibition by other amino acids (281). One fraction is inhibited by phenylalanine, a second by the neutral amino acids, and the third is not inhibited by the neutral amino acids. One explanation proposes that lysine can be transported by three independent transporting systems, each with different affinities; a second is based on a common transport system with partial inhibition by other amino acids arising through adjacent sites and allosteric-like phenomena. The difficulties of determining the relationships on the basis of competition studies are pointed out.

The system for dibasic amino acids is more specific in the kidney than in other systems (282–284). For example, phenylalanine and histidine, which inhibit in other systems, have no effect on lysine accumulation in the kidney. Cystine and cysteine do not exchange with the dibasic amino acids and presumably are transported by a separate system. On the other hand, the dibasic amino acids inhibit cysteine efflux. In another study on kidney, it is pointed out that the dibasic amino acid, lysine, is transported by two systems with different affinities and capacities and that cystine may be transported by one of them (285). Although the carrier system for dibasic amino acids is not the same as that for neutral amino acids in intestine, an interrelationship of the transports in the form of a counterflow phenomenon can still occur (286). In yeast two systems for dibasic acids have been demonstrated, one being specific for arginine (287).

Dicarboxylic amino acid transport has been examined in some microorganisms. In *Mycobacterium,* L-glutamic acid and D-glutamic acid are taken up by different pathways (288). In *Streptococcus faecalis,* the uptake of glutamic acid is inhibited by actinomycin D, but the effect seems to be a direct one on transport rather than a block in protein synthesis (289). Glutamate uptake in *Hansenula* lags for twenty to forty minutes after addition of glucose, whereas glucose-pretreated cells showed no lag. Apparently some transport intermediate formed from glucose requires a period of time for synthesis.

The transport of tryptophan in *Neurospora* has saturation kinetics, a high temperature coefficient, and competition by leucine and phenylalanine (290). Work with a variety of analogs suggests a three-point attachment for the uptake site, an uncharged side chain and an α-amino group in addition to the carboxyl groups. Oocytes of frog also accumulate phenylalanine and tryptophan by a typical active transport system (291).

In *Pseudomonas* an inducible active transport system has been demonstrated for carnitine (292). In ascites cells, benzylamine is taken up by a system that is similar to that for catecholamines rather than the neutral amino acids (293).

Dependence of transport on sodium.—Most studies on the effects of sodium on sugar and amino acid transport have been carried out on the intestine, but similar effects have been demonstrated in kidney and in other cells. Sodium dependence has also been demonstrated in microorganisms but the mechanisms may be different. Interpretation of the sodium effects is rather difficult because of the complexity of the intestinal system.

The removal of sodium or the addition of ouabain, a specific inhibitor of the sodium transport system, results in an inability of the epithelial cells to concentrate the sugars and amino acids. Furthermore, the effects of sodium and ouabain on transport into the cell are parallel to the effects on transepithelial transport. Several prevalent hypotheses (294, 295) relate the effects to the difference between intracellular and extracellular sodium concentrations, to sodium-dependent changes in the affinity of the carriers for sugars, to formation of ternary-sugar-sodium-carrier complexes, and to effects of internal sodium on metabolic factors. The effects of glycosides on sugar transport are considered in some detail (296). Sodium dependence of sugar transport has been investigated in the chicken intestine (297, 298) and in the frog intestine (299, 300).

The connection between sodium and sugar transport reflects itself also in an effect of sugars on the transepithelial transport of sodium. Thus, in the presence of an actively transported sugar the absorption of salt and water is increased in the rat intestine (301). The effect is not due to increased substrate supply since it is produced with nonmetabolizable sugars. The increased sodium transport in the presence of transported sugars is sometimes measured indirectly in terms of the transepithelial potential which is a consequence of sodium transport. In rat intestine, the size of the potential shows saturation with respect to both sodium and sugar concentrations, which suggests that a sodium-sugar-carrier complex is formed (302). The degree of interaction of the cation and sugar binding sites is high in the rat but low in rabbit intestine. The increase in potential across the intestine of the tortoise, on addition of nonmetabolizable sugars, is shown by use of microelectrodes to be due to an increased potential across the serosal face of the cell (303). It is not influenced by varying the ionic composition. The conclusion follows that the increased potential difference is due to the action of an electrogenic pump in the serosal face of the epithelial cell. In a marine bacterium a sodium dependence has been demonstrated for both the induction and the functioning of a sugar-transporting system (304).

Sodium dependence and inhibition by ouabain of amino acid transport have been further demonstrated in the intestine of the rat (305) and fish (306), kidney (283, 284, 307), ascites cells (278), adipose tissue (308), and microorganisms (309–311). As with sugars, the ability of the cells to accumulate the amino acid against a concentration gradient is impaired, and in an epithelium it is the mucosal-to-serosal flux that is reduced in the absence of sodium. The kinetic evidence has sometimes been interpreted in terms of a direct link between amino acid and sodium transport (307). The transport of all amino acids is not equally affected by sodium. For example, the transport of cystine and of arginine is more dependent on sodium than is the transport of dibasic amino acids (283). The dependence seems to be related to the sodium content of the cells rather than a stoichiometric linkage of sodium and amino acid transports (284). In ascites cells ten amino acids enter by sodium-dependent pathways. The effect of sodium is on the K_m for the influx (278). For several amino acids, however, both sodium-dependent and sodium-independent systems can be identified.

Interaction between amino acid and sugar transport.—Additional observations have been made on the interactions between sugar and amino acid transports. Amino acids inhibit the transport of sugars (312, 313) and conversely sugars inhibit amino acid transport (313–315). Only the actively transported amino acids seem to be involved (314) but they can be nonmetabolizable substances (315) so that direct interference with metabolic pathways is not the cause. Flux analyses are difficult to interpret but it is suggested that sugars increase the efflux of amino acid at the mucosal membrane (314). Another possibility is a competition for a common source of energy for the two transport systems (315).

ENERGETICS

The energy sources for transport, the intermediates involved, and the energy balances have been of concern for many years. In some tissues, activity of the cation pump is associated with an extra increment of metabolism, glycolysis, or respiration. In other situations the metabolism is interfered with and the resultant effects on transport can be measured. In some cases ATP utilization can be directly measured. From the data conclusions can be drawn about the metabolic reactions that support the transport, the stoichiometry of transport in relation to substrate utilization, and the thermodynamic efficiency.

In red blood cells when the internal sodium is increased, both potassium

influx and lactate production are increased and become more sensitive to
ouabain (316). Thus the increased activity of the sodium-potassium pump
increases the rate of glycolysis. The effects of sodium on glycolysis by he-
molysates indicate that the membrane phosphoglycerate kinase is the point
at which the sodium-potassium transport system can influence the metabolic
rate. ADP, a product of the Na-K-ATPase, is a substrate for the kinase.

In contrast to red cells, energy production under anaerobic conditions is
insufficient to maintain the ion transport in liver (317). However, substrates which act as electron acceptors in the mitochondria, to allow ATP
production under anaerobic conditions, increased the ouabain-sensitive sodium-potassium transport to the aerobic levels. ATP produced in the mitochondria can, therefore, serve for sodium and potassium transport. The
role of mitochondria has also been explored in toad bladder using a variety
of inhibitors under short-circuit conditions (318). Uncouplers of phosphorylation and electron transfer inhibitors rapidly blocked the short-circuit
current, but energy transfer inhibitors produced only slow or partial inhibition. It is proposed that an intermediate formed in those energy transfer
reactions closest to the electron transfer chain is involved in transport.
These nonphosphorylating intermediates could be channeled either into
ATP synthesis or into support of active transport. This scheme, however,
does not account for the demonstrated direct role of ATP in cation transport.

The increased respiration associated with cation transport has been investigated in muscle (319), kidney (320), gall bladder (321), ascites cells
(322), nerve (323), and avian salt gland (324). The extra oxygen is inhibited by ouabain, a specific inhibitor of transport. In ascites cells made sodium rich by cooling, rewarming in media containing potassium results in a
sixfold larger respiration than in potassium-free media (322) and a much
more rapid extrusion of sodium. The increased respiration is dependent entirely on the potassium transported. In fact, the relationship between the
respiration rate and the external potassium follows a typical saturation-
curve. From the effects of inhibitors of mitochondrial metabolism it seems
clear that the energy source for the increased respiration is the mitochondrion.

In a number of tissues, the quantitative relationship between oxygen
consumption and sodium transport has been used to calculate the stoichiometric relationship of ATP and transport using known ratios of oxygen consumption and, high-energy phosphate production. In some cases
ATP utilization was measured directly. Na/P ratios of 2 to 4 have been
reported. Recently such measurements have been made in crab nerve loaded with sodium by tetanic stimuli (323). In the presence of external potassium, sodium is extruded and oxygen consumption is increased. The calculated Na/P ratios were between 1.9 and 3.4, in agreement with values
from direct measurements of high-energy phosphate utilization. The outside cation site has a high affinity for potassium and the inside site for so-

dium. It is therefore postulated that the ATP is used to maintain a difference in specificity by converting the sodium-preferring sites into potassium-preferring sites.

In the gall bladder of the rabbit a 1-to-1 linkage exists between active sodium and chloride transports (321). Oxygen consumption was depressed when chloride was replaced by a poorly transported anion or sodium by a poorly transported cation, or in the presence of ouabain. The oxygen consumption consists of three fractions; 9 per cent requires both sodium and chloride, is inhibited by ouabain, and is linked to sodium chloride transport; 36 per cent requires sodium and not chloride, is inhibited by ouabain, and may be linked to cellular potassium transport; and 55 per cent represents basal uptake. If the extra oxygen observed during transport supplies the energy for transport, then about 25 sodium plus 25 chloride are transported per oxygen or about four sodium and four chloride per high-energy phosphate (experimental values, 2.7 to 4.7). These figures agree with the ratios for other tissues for sodium except that the gall bladder pumps the equivalent number of chlorides as well. In other epithelia, however, the sodium transport sets up potential differences favoring chloride movement, and this electrical coupling insures the passive transport of one chloride ion per sodium ion to maintain electroneutrality. Thus the sum of ions transferred for each oxygen is the same as in the gall bladder and the total osmotic work is the same.

From the relationship between the reabsorbed sodium and oxygen consumption in the rabbit kidney, the efficiency of transport was calculated to be 75 per cent, assuming that the work was the sum of that performed at each cell membrane based on values for cellular sodium and potassium concentrations and on potential differences (320). If, as suggested, cellular sodium may be compartmentalized and separated from the transport stream, the calculated work done would be less.

In algal cells it is possible to separate the energy source for the active chloride transport from that for active potassium influx (162). In far-red light, in CO_2-free nitrogen, or in the presence of low concentrations of the inhibitor dichlorophenyldimethyl urea, chloride influx is inhibited but not potassium influx. On the other hand, in the presence of uncouplers of phosphorylation, potassium influx is inhibited but not chloride influx. It is suggested that potassium transport is dependent on ATP from phosphorylation reactions but that chloride transport is directly coupled to some electron transfer reaction, perhaps close to the second light reaction of photosynthesis. Phosphate uptake also is dependent on ATP production and proceeds by a pathway independent of the chloride transport system (325).

Effects of Calcium

Many of the effects of calcium, particularly on depolarization and permeability, have already been discussed, as have the transport of calcium and the activation of ATPase. The many effects of calcium on membranes have been reviewed (326): it acts as an adhesive between cells, increases the rigidity of the cytoplasmic surface, decreases the charge density at the membrane surface, reduces membrane permeability, and alters electrical properties. To break the membranes of the epithelial cells of the intestine apart, it is necessary to use chelating agents such as EDTA to remove calcium (327). Calcium competes with carbamylcholine for binding sites in muscle (193, 328), and with procaine in delaying the turning on of the sodium conductance mechanism in the axon and in binding to phospholipids (191). Calcium is a stabilizer of membranes of nerves (189, 192), influences permeability of muscle to sugar (258, 259), controls the passive permeability to sodium and potassium in frog oocytes (329), and inhibits the stimulation of respiration by ouabain in brain slices (330).

The effects of calcium on electrolyte metabolism have been studied in HeLa cells (145). When the concentration of calcium outside was increased, a reduction in sodium influx caused a decrease in sodium and an increase in potassium in the cell. No effect was seen on the active transport of sodium or on potassium efflux. Furthermore, when the external sodium was decreased the internal calcium increased. Thus, calcium may compete with sodium at the membrane for influx and thereby control the passive diffusion of sodium into the cell. Similar effects on cation balance have been reported in other cells, probably due also to a specific action of Ca^{++} on sodium permeability.

ACTIONS OF HORMONES

Aldosterone and corticosteroids.—The effects of aldosterone have been previously localized in the nucleus in epithelial cells of toad bladder. It binds to a receptor leading to a DNA-dependent synthesis of RNA, which in turn results in production of proteins. Recently the effect of aldosterone on crab muscle has also been shown to be mediated by RNA synthesis (331). The nature of the protein and its role in stimulating sodium transport is a matter of debate. One hypothesis suggests that aldosterone induces production of an enzyme in the tricarboxylic acid cycle that increases the production of ATP and thereby supports increased transport of sodium. A second proposes that aldosterone induces production of a protein that increases the supply of cellular sodium by increasing the sodium permeability of the mucosal membrane. Recent experiments support the first hypothesis (332, 333). In substrate-depleted bladders, aldosterone had no effect but vasopressin produced the usual rise in sodium transport. In substrate-enriched bladders, the absolute increase in response to vasopressin was greater after maximal stimulation by aldosterone. During maintained reverse flow of sodium, aldosterone produced a significant increase in the sodium flux ratio. These results support the concept that aldosterone increases the output of the sodium pump independently of any effect on the permeability of the mucosal surface. On the basis of the effects of an extensive series of substrates and their analogs, it is proposed that aldosterone acts by inducing synthesis of a protein involved in the tricarboxylic acid cycle. This concept is supported by the fact that substrate-aldosterone synergism is limited to oxaloacetate, precursors of oxaloacetate, and precursors of acetyl-CoA.

Evidence for the second hypothesis has been reviewed (334). The aldosterone-induced protein is presumed to act like a permease in facilitating the entry of sodium into the tissue from the mucosal side. The striking and specific effects of substrates in enhancing the transport are considered secondary to the action of the hormone in facilitating the entry of sodium. A similar mechanism has been proposed to explain the action of aldosterone on salt transport in the toad intestine (335).

After adrenalectomy, the level of Na-K-ATPase of kidney falls slowly for six to seven days (53, 54). Kinetic data suggest that this is due to a decrease in enzyme level rather than a change in any of the affinity constants. But administration of aldosterone in levels sufficient to give maximal sodium retention caused no change in ATPase after three hours. Corticosterone in physiological doses, on the other hand, returned the enzyme level to normal in two to three days. Thus it is corticosterone, not aldosterone, that is responsible for maintaining kidney ATPase, and the salt-level response of aldosterone is not related to the ATPase. The decrease in ATPase level is also found with the aldosterone antagonist aldactone; but EDTA added to the membrane preparation from aldactone-treated rats before dialysis, restores the ATPase. The effect of ouabain on the membrane preparation could also be reversed by addition of high concentrations of aldosterone and EDTA. These actions, which seem to be related to the calcium of the membrane, suggest that the ATPase level has not been reduced after adrenalectomy, but that its activity has been inhibited, perhaps by Ca^{++}.

Vasopressin and cyclic AMP.—Vasopressin, which must be added to the serosal side, has been presumed to act through production of cyclic AMP in the cell, leading to a general increase in permeability of the mucosal surface. This concept was tested in toad bladder with zero sodium transport established by diluting the mucosal membrane with isoosmotic sucrose until no transport occurred (336). The results suggest that vasopressin acts only on permeability barriers. The effects of vasopressin and of oxytocin on permeability were similar, but on sodium transport were quite different (337). Vasopressin and cyclic AMP both increase the net water movement and the diffusional permeability to water of isolated collecting tubules of the rabbit, but the permeability to urea is not changed (338). The response of the toad bladder to cyclic AMP depends on the cellular potassium content (339). The potassium-dependent step is subsequent to the production of cyclic AMP. Amphotericin, thought to interact with sterols in the membrane, increases the permeability to hydrophilic solutes but the tissue retains its low permeability to bulk water transport (340) and its responsiveness to vasopressin. Thus the two substances act at independent sites, one on diffusional permeability and the other on a system that controls bulk flow.

Acetylcholine.—The possible role of acetylcholine in excitation has been discussed in the section on depolarization (174). The basic idea is that the reaction of acetylcholine with the receptor results in configurational change and a transient shift in ion permeability. The acetylcholine is inactivated by the acetylcholine esterase during repolarization. The role of acetylcholine in junctional transmission is more clearly established. In the depolarization of single cell preparations from the electric eel, the effects of acetylcholine are inhibited by prior treatment with PCMB, which indicates that a protein component with a sulfhydryl group is involved in the acetylcholine-activated permeability system (29).

Norepinephrine.—In smooth muscle of the intestine depolarized by high potassium, norepinephrine increases both the inward and outward fluxes of potassium but has little effect on the fluxes of chloride (133). The electrical effects of norepinephrine, but not the effects on tension, can be explained by the increased passive permeability to potassium. The increased potential and short-circuit current in frog skin on electrical stimulation may be due to liberation of norepinephrine (341).

Membrane fragments prepared from turkey red blood cells increase their content of cyclic AMP on addition of epinephrine. Production of cyclic AMP, which occurs in the membrane, may be an intermediate in the action of epinephrine (342).

Insulin.—The amounts of various metabolic intermediates are altered in a variety of tissues after insulin treatment. The results can be explained by an increase in the size of the internal glucose pool of the cell, but the specific changes in particular cells depend on the kinetics of the various reactions (343). Previous studies show that insulin added to perfused liver causes a prompt uptake of potassium not accompanied by an immediate increase in uptake of glucose. Glucagon evokes an early release of potassium in the period of outflow of glucose. Retention of part of this potassium depends on insulin (344). The effects of ouabain and of insulin in stimulating glycogen synthesis and depressing lactate production are independent of each other. Thus the effects of insulin on cation transport are not directly related to those on glucose transport (345). Insulin causes an accumulation of potassium by frog muscle and also stimulates oxygen consumption; these responses are independent of the effects of calcium (346). Cyclic AMP increases the glucose uptake in striated muscle and may be a mediator of insulin action (347).

Addition of ouabain or omission of potassium stimulates insulin secretion by pieces of pancreas incubated *in vitro,* but not in the absence of sodium (348). The high level of sodium in the β-cell is considered to be the fundamental stimulus for insulin secretion.

SYNTHESIS OF MEMBRANE COMPONENTS

Most data on synthesis of membrane proteins are derived from the use of specific inhibitors of RNA or of protein synthesis. For example, the inducible membrane systems such as permeases are dependent on protein synthesis. More recently it has been found that the effects of aldosterone are mediated through synthesis of new proteins, but not necessarily of membrane protein (332–334). Data on turnover of lipid components have also been plentiful. A few recent papers have been concerned with membrane synthesis. For example, during adaptation of fish to different temperatures the transport capacity for amino acid is altered, apparently by synthesis of additional carrier molecules (306). In kidney cortex the addition of puromycin and cyclohexamide rapidly inhibits amino acid incorporation into protein, but inhibits amino acid transport only after a delay of two hours (349). The evidence suggests that the amino acid carrier has 50 per cent turnover time in a few hours. If protein synthesis is blocked the transport capacity decreases accordingly.

Sialic acid on the surface of cells was removed by digestion with neuraminidase (350). When glucosamine was supplied as a substrate, the regeneration of sialic acid was not sensitive to inhibitors of protein or RNA synthesis, but both actinomycin D and puromycin inhibited the production from an intracellular precursor. Once synthesized, the final emergence of the precursor could take place in the presence of the inhibitor of RNA synthesis.

From estimates of the fluxes of sodium and potassium in synchronously grown tissue culture cells, it was found that the transport and permeability sites were synthesized at a particular time in the cell division cycle, about the beginning of the S-period, rather than in parallel with the general increase in the total amount of membrane (351).

REGULATION OF MEMBRANE FUNCTIONS

Very few systematic studies of regulation have been carried out, but it is clear that regulation can be accomplished in a number of ways: by balance of influx and efflux (pumps and leaks), by control of metabolic factors, by the electrolyte environment particularly Ca^{++}, by the substrate concentrations relative to the affinities of the carrier, by hormones, perhaps by allosteric control systems, by substrate induction of carrier synthesis, and by genetic factors.

Environmental Control

The intestine of the rat, but not that of the hamster, responds to starvation by an increased active transport of sugars and amino acids (352). When a euryhaline fish, the flounder, is transferred from seawater to freshwater, an instantaneous 90 per cent reduction in sodium and chloride outflux is observed, due primarily to changes in the gill permeability (353).

About thirty minutes later a second progressive reduction occurs. The rapid regulation involves independent responses to low sodium and low chloride. The delayed reduction results from a progressive, sodium-dependent decrease in the amount of carrier available for ion exchange reactions. In contrast, when a marine fish, the perch, is transferred from salt- to freshwater, the rapid change involves only a 40 per cent reduction in outflux and no delayed response. Consequently the transfer of the marine fish is accompanied by heavy loss of electrolytes and death. In the oyster a regulatory mechanism adjusts the size of the amino acid pool to the external tonicity (354).

Internal Feedback

In *Salmonella typhimurium*, sulfate is accumulated against a concentration gradient (355). The entry process, but not the exit, requires energy. The uptake is thought to be controlled by a feedback inhibition system involving a compound, 3′-phosphoadenosine-5′-phosphosulfate, formed from sulfate during the course of transport.

The regulation of electrolyte content and volume during the cycle of division in tissue culture cells involves a complex of controls (351). The volume increases exponentially but the content of sodium and potassium fluctuates. About one and one-half hours after cell division a net loss of 20 per cent of the total potassium occurs. Thereafter the deficit is eliminated. The sodium content falls during the cell division, then rises when potassium content decreases, and falls again when potassium content increases. Very small changes in the balance of influx and efflux account for the changes in cation content. About two hours after the cell division burst, the unidirectional fluxes increase twofold. The increase in influx is balanced by increase in efflux, so that there are no dramatic changes in content. The control of the synthesis of the carrier must be closely coordinated with synthesis of the leakage pathway.

Genetic Control

In a number of previously discussed papers, genetic control over membrane functions was demonstrated. The most explored system is the galactose permease of *E. coli*. The induction of the galactose operon is influenced by the transport system (356). When the transport system is defective because of a mutation outside of the operon, the inducer for the operon cannot be retained in sufficient concentrations to activate it and the threshold for induction by external substrate is raised. In some cases the transport mutants cause the shutdown of the whole operon. The operon concept does not apply to the sucrose fermenting mutants in *Proteus mirabilis*. The gene for the specific transport system is not linked to the gene for β-fructofuranosidase, the enzyme that attacks sucrose (269).

A recessive mutation in sheep is characterized by red blood cells with a low content of potassium and of Na-K-ATPase. Low-potassium sheep were bled to induce production of new red blood cells which were then separated from older cells by means of density gradient centrifugation (357). In the young cells the active transport of potassium was four to five times greater than in cells drawn six days after bleeding. Thus, the loss of transport capacity occurs in the nondividing circulating red cells.

In man, two gene-controlled systems for transport of the imino acids have been demonstrated, one relatively nonspecific, the other with a much greater specificity but a lower capacity (358).

Regulation During Development

In the oocyte of the frog, measurements of membrane potentials in the presence of different external ions indicate that with low calcium, the membrane behaves as though it were permeable to sodium chloride but not potassium, whereas with high calcium it behaves as though it were permeable to potassium chloride but not sodium (329). After ovulation of the unfertilized egg the potassium selectivity and dependence on calcium disappears. Thus the mechanism of ovulation may involve the removal of the calcium regulation of ion permeability.

Ten days before hatching, the yolk sac of the chick can concentrate the amino acids, but not sugars (359). With increase in age the transport for sugars increases, and shortly before hatching the embryo is able to concentrate sugars as well as amino acids. Similar results were obtained for glucose transport by slices of embryonic intestine of chicks (360).

SUBCELLULAR STRUCTURE

Mitochondria

The only studies on mitochondria to be discussed are those concerned with the structure of the membranes and the localization within the membranes of the enzymatic and lipid components, and those concerned with the ion transports, their energy supply, and their possible mechanisms. The relationship between the structure and function of mitochondria has been reviewed, particularly the changes in structure produced by various treatments and evidence concerning the localization of the electron transfer chain and the structural protein (361).

The general structure of the mitochondrial membranes in relation to the concept of the "unit membrane" has also been reviewed (362). The relationship between lipids and membrane structure has been investigated by removal of 80 to 95 per cent of the lipids with solvents (9). The procedure demonstrates a separate inner membrane which appears to have stable cross-linkages between two protein layers and which is structurally different from the outer membrane. The two membranes differ in lipid composition in electronmicroscopic appearance after various treatments (363, 364), and in content of different enzyme systems (365–367). The inner membrane contains the complexes of the electron transfer chain and the ATPase, whereas the outer membrane contains the citric acid cycle and ancillary systems, but is devoid of electron transfer components. The outer membrane contains about 30 per cent of the total mitochondrial protein, and in each of the membranes about 40 to 50 per cent of the protein is structural, the rest consisting of about fifty enzymes. The soluble fraction of the outer membrane contains the enzymes of low molecular weight, whereas the insoluble fraction is rich in macromolecular dehydrogenating complexes and contains the enzymes involved in substrate phosphorylation and fatty acid oxidation.

Treatment using Fe^{++} results in peroxidation of lipids, a loss of 65 per cent of the protein and 39 per cent of the lipid with little change in the number or size of mitochondrial particles (368). The remaining structure or "ghost" contains a large proportion of the cytochrome systems and some flavine but exhibits no respiratory control or coupled phosphorylation.

The physiological anatomy of the mitochondria has been explored in terms of "spaces" determined by osmotic behavior and distribution of the various substances (369). Chloride and sucrose give the same space. If the potassium is assumed to be in the sucrose-free water its concentration would be 150 meq/liter.

Several reviews concerned with ion transport in mitochondria have appeared. The transport of calcium in relation to metabolism has been summarized (370). Two to five calcium ions were transported for each molecule of high-energy intermediate. One explanation of this finding involves a carrier with multiple sites and the other involves the separation of H^+ and OH^- across the membrane driven by the electron transport, with the transport involving a calcium for proton exchange. The accumulation of potassium and the necessary energy supply are the subjects of another review (371). The uptake of K^+ can be energized either by exogenous ATP or by intermediate precursors of ATP synthesis, but the maximal transport occurs in the presence of both ATP and substrates. Unlike the bivalent cations, potassium does not uncouple the respiration by competing with the phosphorylation cycle. A cyclic process, in which an oxidative phosphorylation limb and an ATPase limb are linked by the respiratory chain, may supply a high-energy intermediate for potassium uptake.

A more general review includes the following topics: the preparation of the mitochondria, passive movements of ions, energy-dependent movements of ions including potassium, sodium, and bivalent cations, and the relationships to oxidative phosphorylation (372). Isolated mitochondria can take up potassium against the concentration gradient with expenditure of energy, but it is not clear how the movements are related to the electrochemical gradients. The uptake can take place either in exchange for hydrogen ion or in association with a penetrating anion. Acetate, phosphate, and possibly substrate anions can penetrate but chloride, sulfate, and nitrate can penetrate only slowly. When respiration is blocked, potassium uptake ceases unless ATP is supplied externally. Oligomycin blocks uptake supported by ATP but not that supported by substrate metabolism. Valinomycin stimulates potassium uptake either by hydrogen exchange or with a penetrating anion. Bivalent cations are also taken up by energy-linked processes but the uphill nature of the process is even more questionable because the divalent ions may be sequestered in unionized forms so that it is not known whether the cations move against the electrochemical gradient.

The chemiosmotic hypothesis concerning ion transport in mitochondria and chloroplasts, recently summarized (373), is based on a coupling between electron flow and proton flow in an anisotropic membrane. The system consists of four parts, the proton translocating reversible ATPase system, the proton translocating oxidoreduction chain, the exchange diffusion systems, and the coupling of proton translocation to translocation of anions and cations in an ion-impermeable asymmetric membrane. The coupling between the oxidoreduction and phosphorylation can be described as a circulating proton current connecting the ATPase and the redox systems. The two systems would tend to come into equilibrium and allow some reversibility of both with respect to each other, accounting for respiratory control and reverse electron transport. The chemiosmotic theory is supported by recent investigations in which ATP synthesis was accomplished by forcing the passage of proton in the inward direction (374). Normally, hydrogen ion moves in the outward direction.

The accumulation of potassium by liver mitochondria is stimulated by small amounts of valinomycin, gramicidin, calcium, or acetate but larger quantities block, releasing accumulated potassium salts (375). Potassium uptake by liver mitochondria has also been measured under steady-state levels of potassium, with selective glass electrodes and an automatic titrator (376). The results are somewhat different from those obtained when the mitochondria are separated by filtration or centrifugation. The rate and direction of movement depend on the energy source, on the anion, and on the presence of calcium. With the induced potassium movement extra oxygen is consumed but the ratio of potassium to oxygen varies with the conditions, being as high as 24. There is a contrary movement of hydrogen ion. Valinomycin increases permeability to potassium and stimulates the accumulating mechanism. Ion-specific electrodes were also used in a detailed evaluation of the nature of the valinomycin-induced potassium transport (377). As reported in the previous paper, the mechanism of action of valinomycin involves an increased permeability and a stimulation of the transport. Potassium-to-high-energy phosphate ratios of 7 for ATP-supported accumulation, and of 3.2 for oxidizable substrate, were higher than those obtained for bivalent ions. It is suggested that the high ratios are not compatible with the substrate-derived proton (chemiosmotic) hypothesis. Also, mechanisms dependent on substrate-derived electrons are contraindicated by the ability of ATP to energize the ion transport when the electron transport is inhibited. As an alternative to the chemiosmotic hypothesis, a scheme is suggested in which the energy transfer pathway operates between the electron transport chain, ATP synthesis, and the ion transport system, all three systems being linked through a common component allowing interconversion between all of the systems. A carrier model is proposed for the transport of ions with each carrier being able to bind variable numbers of cations. In mitochondria from pigeon breast muscle, a significant discrimination in favor of potassium over sodium was demonstrated. As in liver mitochondria, potassium stimulates the respiration (378).

Uptake of bivalent cations is discussed in a number of papers (379–384). In the absence of permeant anions calcium is taken up initially with little change in internal pH until the buffer capacity is exceeded. Additional uptake leads to an alkaline reaction in the mitochondrial membrane which continues until a maximal gradient of about 1 pH unit is established (379–381). During calcium uptake protons are excreted, the maximal ratio of hydrogen to calcium being 2:1. With permeant anions such as phosphate or acetate, more calcium can be taken up. The pH gradient is considered to serve as a driving force for the accumulation of calcium and changes in internal pH to limit the extent of the reaction.

During uptake of calcium in the presence of ATP and magnesium, ATPase is stimulated, H^+ is ejected, and phosphate is also taken up (380). The mol ratio of calcium to hydrogen to phosphate and ATP hydrolyzed is 2:2:1:1. These findings indicate that utilization of a single high-energy intermediate or its equivalent, whether generated by ATP utilization or electron transport, can cause the accumulation of two calcium, ejection of two hydrogen, accumulation of 1.2 phosphate.

Calcium activation of respiration, uptake of calcium, and ejection of hydrogen are also demonstrated in another study (382). In low potassium, however, the calcium-hydrogen exchanges undergo oscillations that are maximal in media containing impermeant anions. They do not occur in the presence of ATP but seem to depend in part on reverse electron flow with some kind of feedback relationship between calcium influx and efflux. With strontium the maximal ratio of hydrogen ejected to cation absorbed is 2 but it may be lower, depending on the specific anions and buffers (383). The intramitochondrial pH which is dependent on the cation-anion transfer plays a primary role in the regulation of respiration. As with Ca^{++}, permeant anions such as phosphate and acetate stimulate cation uptake and respiration, probably by neutralization of the internal high pH. In contrast to Ca^{++} and Sr^{++}, Mn^{++} uptake produces only a small alkalinization in the absence of a permeant anion. If a trace of calcium is present, however, proton ejection is accelerated, manganese accumulation is more than doubled, and a large alkalinization occurs. Thus calcium activates the transport and proton exchange (384). The proton movement stimulated by calcium depends on the manganese and not the calcium uptake. The uptake of magnesium and potassium is stimulated by zinc (385, 386).

CHLOROPLASTS

Ion transport in chloroplasts is not nearly as extensively studied as in mitochondria but there are many resemblances. The volume changes that occur during ion transport have been reviewed (387). Illumination *in vitro* results in a rapid shrinkage and uptake of H^+, which are reversed in the dark. Thus the production of energy results in movements of water and of protons which are opposite in chloroplasts from those in mitochondria. Calcium and phosphate can be taken up by chloroplasts in a light-dependent process that requires ATP as well. Monovalent ions are not accumulated under light-triggered ATPase conditions but there is a light-induced potassium efflux. One of the factors in shrinkage may be a contractile process for it has been demonstrated that glycerinated chloroplasts contract in the presence of magnesium and ATP. The protons transported into chloroplasts by the light-dependent process lead to a decrease in internal pH that may cause many of the observed changes (388). The light-induced shrinkage is inhibited by mercurials and PMA stimulates the shrinkage even though cyclic and noncyclic photophosphorylation in NAD reduction are inhibited (389). Inorganic phosphate also enhances the shrinkage. A phosphorylated intermediate appears to be important in the shrinkage reaction. Volume changes can also be observed as a result of permeation of undissociated acids but the chloroplast is relatively impermeable to cations or anions (390).

The quantum requirement for the light-induced hydrogen uptake has a minimum of .2 quantum absorbed per H^+ taken up for both 700 and 710 mμ. illumination, and .4 quantum/hydrogen for 685 mμ. light (391). Also there is a constant ratio of five hydrogens per electron over the wavelength range 650 to 710. Thus one quantum transports five protons. If one electron is yielded by one quantum, then the H^+ electron ratio is 5:1 when system one is undergoing cyclical electron flow. The fact that the ratio of 5:1 is independent of wavelength is strong evidence that the hydrogen uptake is linked to electron transport. It is easier to explain a coupling ratio of 5:1 by postulating a membrane carrier with multiple sites than by the five redox couples in system one that would be required in the chemiosmotic theory.

OTHER SUBCELLULAR STRUCTURES

The uptake of sodium and potassium by liver microsomes has little selectivity (392). Nuclear membranes can be isolated in pieces with well-preserved double membranes (393). The annular pores, by negative staining, appear to be composed of globular subunits. Permeability measurements on nuclear membranes of salivary gland cells and egg cells have been determined by passing electric current across the membrane and measuring the impedance, which has a strong capacitative component (394). The membrane potential is 2 to 15 mV, but the membrane shows little or no rectification or excitation. The finding that the envelope has relatively high electrical resistance indicates that the diffuse electron-dense material filling the annular pores must provide a diffusion barrier.

LITERATURE CITED

1. Rayns, D. G., Simpson, F. O. *Science,* **156,** 656–57 (1967)
2. Cunningham, W. P., Crane, F. L. *Exptl. Cell Res.,* **44,** 31–45 (1966)
3. Gupta, B. L., Berridge, M. J. *J. Cell Biol.,* **29,** 376–82 (1966)
4. Soo-Hoo, T. S., Brown, A. D. *Biochim. Biophys. Acta,* **135,** 164–66 (1967)
5. Robertson, J. D. *Ann. N. Y. Acad. Sci.,* **137,** 421–40 (1966)
6. Finean, J. B., Coleman, R., Green, W. G., Limbrick, A. R. *J. Cell Sci.,* **1,** 287–96 (1966)
7. Korn, E. D. *Science,* **153,** 1491–98 (1966)
8. Hampton, J. C., Rosario, B. *Anat. Record,* **156,** 369–82 (1966)
9. Fleischer, S., Fleischer, B., Stoeckenius, W. *J. Cell Biol.,* **32,** 193–208 (1967)
10. Loewenstein, W. R. *Ann. N. Y. Acad. Sci.,* **137,** 441–72 (1966)
11. Weidmann, S. *Ann. N. Y. Acad. Sci.,* **137,** 540–42 (1966)
12. van Deenen, L. L. M. *Ann. N. Y. Acad. Sci.,* **137,** 717–30 (1966)
13. Green, D. E., Tzagologg, A. *J. Lipid Res.,* **7,** 587–602 (1966)
14. Hokin, M. R., Hokin, L. E. *J. Gen. Physiol.,* **50,** 793–812 (1967)
15. Cohen, M., Panos, C. *Biochemistry,* **5,** 2385–92 (July 1966)
16. Cuthbert, A. W. *Pharmacol. Rev.,* **19,** 59–105 (1967)
17. Kinsky, S. C., Luse, S. A., van Deenen, L. L. M. *Fed. Proc.,* **25,** 1503 (1966)
18. Zahler, P. H., Wallach, D. F. H. *Biochim. Biophys. Acta,* **135,** 371–74 (1967)
19. Finean, J. B., Coleman, R., Green, W. A. *Ann. N. Y. Acad. Sci.,* **137,** 414–20 (1966)
20. Barclay, M., Barclay, R. K., Essner, E. S., Skipski, V. P., Terebus-Kekish, O. *Science,* **156,** 665–67 (1967)
21. Berg, G. G., Chapman, B. *J. Cell. Comp. Physiol.,* **65,** 361–72 (1965)
22. Neville, D. M., Jr. *Biochim. Biophys. Acta,* **133,** 168–70 (1967)
23. Mendoza, C. G., Villanueva, J. R. *Biochim. Biophys. Acta,* **135,** 189–95 (1967)
24. Rothstein, A., VanSteveninck, J. *Ann. N. Y. Acad. Sci.,* **137,** 606–23 (1966)
25. Van Steveninck, J. *Biochim. Biophys. Acta,* **126,** 154–62 (1966)
26. Bide, R. W., Myers, D. K. *Can. J. Biochem.,* **45,** 19–29 (1967)
27. Sutherland, R. M., Rothstein, A., Weed, R. I. *J. Cell. Physiol.,* **69,** 185–98 (1967)
28. Hunees-Cox, F., Fernandez, H. L., Smith, B. H. *Biophys. J.,* **6,** 677 (September 1966)
29. Karlin, A., Bartels, E. *Biochim. Biophys. Acta,* **126,** 525–35 (1966)
30. Hasselbach, W., Seraydarian, K. *Biochem. Z.,* **345,** 159–72 (1966)
31. Tosteson, D. C. *Ann. N. Y. Acad. Sci.,* **137,** 577–90 (1966)
32. Fox, C. F., Carter, J. R., Kennedy, E. P. *Proc. Natl. Acad. Sci.,* **57,** 698–705 (1967)
33. Kundig, W., Kundig, F. D., Anderson, B., Roseman, S. *J. Biol. Chem.,* **241,** 3243–45 (1966)
34. Faust, R. G., Shih-Min, L. W., Faggard, M. L. *Science,* **155,** 1261–63 (1966)
35. Langdon, R. G., Sloan, H. R. *Proc. Natl. Acad. Sci.,* **57,** 401–8 (1967)
36. Hays, R. M., Barland, P. *J. Cell Biol.,* **31,** 209–14 (1966)
37. Modolell, J. B., Moore, R. O. *Biochim. Biophys. Acta,* **135,** 319–32 (1967)
38. Samaha, F. J., Gergely, J. *Arch. Biochem. Biophys.,* **144,** 481–87 (1966)
39. Quinn, D. J., Lane, C. E. *Comp. Biochem. Physiol.,* **19,** 533–43 (November 1966)
40. Nakao, K., Kurashina, S., Nakao, M. *Life Sci.,* **6,** 595–600 (1967)
41. Baker, E., Simmonds, W. J. *Biochim. Biophys. Acta,* **126,** 492–99 (1966)
42. Berg, G. G., Szekerczes, J. *J. Cell. Physiol.,* **67,** 487–500 (June 1966)
43. Laris, P. C., Letchworth, P. E. *J. Cell. Physiol.,* **69,** 143–50 (1967)
44. Ahmed, K., Judah, J. D., Scholefield, P. C. *Biochim. Biophys. Acta,* **120,** 351–60 (1966)
45. Epstein, F. H., Whittman, R. *Biochem. J.,* **99,** 232–38 (1966)
46. Wins, P., Schoffeniels, E. *Biochim. Biophys. Acta,* **120,** 341–50 (July 1966)
47. Duggan, P. F. *Life Sci.,* **6,** 561 (1967)
48. Gunther, T., Dorn, F. *Z. Naturforsch.,* **21,** 1076–81 (1966)
49. Rottem, S., Razin, S. *J. Bacteriol.,* **92,** 714–22 (1966)
50. Dodds, J. J. A., Ellis, R. J. *Biochem. J.,* **101,** 31 (1966)

51. Gruener, N., Neumann, J. *Physiol. Plantarum,* **19**, 678–82 (1966)
52. Bachelard, H. S., Silva, G. D. *Arch. Biochem. Biophys.,* **117**, 98 (9166)
53. Chignell, C. F., Titus, E. J. *Biol. Chem.,* **241**, 5083–89 (1966)
54. Landon, E. J., Jazab, N., Forte, L. *Am. J. Physiol.,* **211**, 1050–56 (1966)
55. Emmelot, P., Bos, C. J. *Biochim. Biophys. Acta,* **120**, 369–82 (1966)
56. Matsui, H., Schwartz, A. *Biochim. Biophys. Acta,* **128**, 380–90 (1966)
57. Chan, P. C. *Biochim. Biophys. Acta,* **135**, 53–60 (1967)
58. Davis, P. W., Brody, T. M. *Biochem. Pharmacol.,* **15**, 703–10 (1966)
59. Kaye, G. I., Wheeler, H. O., Whitlock, R. T., Lane, N. *J. Cell Biol.,* **30**, 237 (1966)
60. Tormey, J. M. *Nature,* **210**, 820–22 (1966)
61. Potter, H., Charnock, J. S., Opit, L. J. *Australian J. Exptl. Biol. Med. Sci.,* **44**, 503–18 (1966)
62. Cooper, J. R., McIlwain, H. *Biochem. J.,* **102**, 675–83 (1967)
63. Cooper, J. R., McIlwain, H. *Ibid.,* 20P
64. Hems, D. A. *Biochem. J.,* **102**, 15–16P (1967)
65. Blostein, R. *Biochem. Biophys. Res. Commun.,* **24**, 598 (1966)
66. Rendi, R. *Biochim. Biophys. Acta,* **128**, 394–96 (1966)
67. Stahl, W. L., Stattin, A., McIlwain, H. *Biochem. J.,* **99**, 404–12 (1966)
68. Lieberman, I., Lansing, A. I., Lynch, W. E. *J. Biol. Chem.,* **242**, 736–39 (1967)
69. Burnett, G. H., Conklin, R. L. *Biochim. Biophys. Acta,* **135**, 358–61 (1967)
70. Rizzo, S. C., Eckel, R. E. *Am. J. Physiol.,* **211**, 429–36 (1966)
71. Lionetti, F. J., Fortier, N. L. *Biochim. Biophys. Acta,* **119**, 462–69 (1966)
72. Johnson, C. F. *Science,* **155**, 1670–72 (1967)
73. Weimberg, R., Orton, W. L. *J. Bacteriol.,* **91**, 1–13 (1966)
74. Kaplan, J. G., Tacreiter, W. *J. Gen. Physiol.,* **50**, 9–24 (1966)
75. Lapetina, E. G., Soto, E. F., De-Robertis, E. *Biochim. Biophys. Acta,* **135**, 33–43 (1967)
76. Brandt, P. W., Freeman, A. R. *Science,* **155**, 582–85 (1967)
77. Weed, R. I., Bowdler, A. J. *J. Clin. Invest.,* **45**, 1137–49 (1966)
78. Weed, R. I., Reed, C. F. *Am. J. Med.,* **41**, 681–98 (1966)
79. Marquis, R. E. *Arch. Biochem. Biophys.,* **118**, 323–31 (1967)
80. Jones, B. M. *Nature,* **212**, 362–65 (1966)
81. Jones, P. C. T. *Nature,* **212**, 365–69 (1966)
82. Burka, E., Schreml, W., Kick, C. *Biochem. Biophys. Res. Commun.,* **26**, 334–38 (1967)
83. Salton, M. R. J., Schmitt, M. D. *Biochim. Biophys. Acta,* **135**, 196–207 (1967)
84. Pease, D. C. *J. Ultrastruct. Res.,* **15**, 555–88 (1966)
85. Demel, R. A., Van Deenen, L. L. M., Pethica, B. A. *Biochim. Biophys. Acta,* **135**, 11–19 (1967)
86. Deamer, D. W., Cornwell, D. G. *Biochim. Biophys. Acta,* **116**, 555–62 (1966)
87. Bangham, A. D., Papahadjopoulos, D. *Biochim. Biophys. Acta,* **126**, 181–84 (1966)
88. Shah, D. O., Schulman, J. H. *Biochim. Biophys. Acta,* **135**, 184–87 (1967)
89. Bar, R. S., Deamer, D. W., Cornwell, D. G. *Science,* **153**, 1010–12 (1966)
90. Lauger, P., Lesslauer, W., Marti, E., Richter, J. *Biochim. Biophys. Acta,* **135**, 10–32 (1967)
91. Bielawski, J., Thompson, T. E., Lehninger, A. L. *Biochem. Biophys. Res. Commun.,* **24**, 948–54 (1966)
92. Mueller, P., Rudin, D. O. *Biochem. Biophys. Res. Commun.,* **26**, 398–404 (1967)
93. Hanai, T., Haydon, D. A. *J. Theoret. Biol.,* **11**, 370–82 (1966)
94. Thompson, T. E., Huang, C. *Ann. N. Y. Acad. Sci.,* **137**, 740–44 (1966)
95. Hanai, T., Haydon, D. A., Redwood, W. R. *Ann. N. Y. Acad. Sci.,* **137**, 731–39 (1966)
96. Mueller, P., Rudin, D. O. *Nature,* **213**, 603–4 (1967)
97. Tsofina, L. M., Liberman, E. A., Babakov, A. V. *Nature,* **212**, 681–83 (1966)
98. Tien, H. T., Dawidowicz, E. A. *J. Colloid Interface Sci.,* **22**, 438–53 (1966)
99. Luzzati, V., Reiss-Husson, F., Rivas, E., Gulik-Krzywicki, T. *Ann. N. Y. Acad. Sci.,* **137**, 409–13 (1966)
100. Papahadjopoulos, D., Bangham, A.

D. *Biochim. Biophys. Acta,* **126,** 185–88 (1966)

101. Rendi, R. *Biochim. Biophys. Acta,* **135,** 333–46 (1967)
102. Shean, G. M., Sollner, K. *Ann. N. Y. Acad. Sci.,* **137,** 759–76 (1966)
103. Hyma, E. S. *Biophys. J.,* **6,** 405–10 (1966)
104. Nayler, W. G. *J. Pharmacol. Exptl. Therap.,* **153,** 479–84 (1966)
105. Ting, H. P., Bertrand, G. L., Sears, D. F. *Biophys. J.,* **6,** 813–23 (1966)
106. Hobson, H. D., Laris, P. C. *Biochim. Biophys. Acta,* **125,** 403–5 (1966)
107. LeFevre, P. G. *The Behavior of Phospholipid-Glucose Complexes at Hexane/Aqueous Interfaces Currents in Modern Biology* (North-Holland, Amsterdam, 1967)
108. Eisenman, G., Sandblom, J. P., Walker, J. L., Jr. *Science,* **155,** 765–74 (1967)
109. Rastas, J., Ekman, A., Salminen, S. *Nature,* **211,** 1152–54 (1966)
110. Tomita, T. *J. Theoret. Biol.,* **12,** 216 (1966)
111. Walker, J. L., Jr., Eisenman, G. *Ann. N. Y. Acad. Sci.,* **137,** 777–91 (1966)
112. Walker, J. L., Jr., Eisenman, G. *Biophys. J.,* **6,** 513–33 (1966)
113. Essig, A., Kedem, O., Hill, T. L. *J. Theoret. Biol.,* **13,** 72–89 (1966)
114. George, E. P., Simons, R. *Australian J. Biol. Sci.,* **19,** 459–70 (1966)
115. Ciani, S., Gliozzi, A. *Biophysik,* **3,** 281–99 (1967)
116. Ciani, S., Gliozzi, A. *Ibid.,* **3,** 22 (1966)
117. Botre, C., Borghi, S., Marchetti, M. *Biochim. Biophys. Acta,* **135,** 162–63 (1967)
118. Essig, A. *J. Theoret. Biol.,* **13,** 63–71 (1966)
119. Hoshiko, T., Lindley, B. D. *J. Gen. Physiol.,* **50,** 729–756 (1967)
120. Vaidhyanathan, V. S., Phillips, H. M. *J. Theoret. Biol.,* **13,** 32–47 (1966)
121. Fitzhugh, R. *J. Gen. Physiol.,* **49,** 989–1005 (1966)
122. Parsons, D. S., Prichard, J. S. *Biochim. Biophys. Acta,* **126,** 471–91 (1966)
123. Hempling, H. G. *Biochim. Biophys. Acta,* **135,** 355–58 (1967)
124. Changeux, J. P., Thiery, J., Tung, Y., Kittel, C. *Proc. Natl. Acad. Sci.,* **57,** 335 (1967)
125. Friedenberg, R., Blatt, A., Gallucci, V., Danielli, J. F., Shames, I. *J. Theoret. Biol.,* **11,** 465–77 (1966)

126. Adrian, R. H., Slayman, C. L. *J. Physiol. (London),* **184,** 970 (1966)
127. Sjodin, R. A., Beauge, L. A. *Science,* **156,** 1248–50 (1967)
128. Daniel, E. E. *Can. J. Physiol. Pharmacol.,* **45,** 149–59 (1967)
129. Goodford, P. J. *J. Physiol. (London),* **186,** 11 (1966)
130. Dockry, M., Kernan, R. P., Tangney, A. *J. Physiol. (London),* **186,** 187–200 (1966)
131. Bittar, E. E. *J. Physiol. (London),* **187,** 81–103 (1966)
132. Armstrong, W. McD., Knoebel, S. B. *J. Cell. Physiol.,* **67,** 211–16 (1966)
133. Jenkinson, D. H., Morton, I. K. M. *J. Physiol. (London),* **188,** 373–86 (1967)
134. Weidmann, S. *J. Physiol. (London),* **18,** 323–42 (1966)
135. Ling, G. N. *Ann. N. Y. Acad. Sci.,* **137,** 837–59 (1966)
136. McLaughlin, S. G. A., Hinke, J. A. M. *Can. J. Physiol. Pharmacol.,* **44,** 837–48 (1966)
137. Salminen, S., Manninen, V. *J. Cell. Physiol.,* **68,** 19–24 (1966)
138. Hoffman, J. F., Kregenow, F. W. *Ann. N. Y. Acad. Sci.,* **137,** 566–76 (1966)
139. LaCelle, P. L., Rothstein, A. *J. Gen. Physiol.,* **50,** 171–88 (1966)
140. Beilin, L. J., Knight, G. J., Munro-Faure, A. D., Anderson, J. *J. Gen. Physiol.,* **50,** 61–74 (1966)
141. Beilin, L. J., Eyeions, D., Hatcher, G., Knight, G. J., Munro-Faure, A. D., Anderson, J. *J. Gen. Physiol.,* **50,** 61–74 (1966)
142. Van Rossum, G. D. V. *Biochim. Biophys. Acta,* **122,** 323–32 (1966)
143. Smyth, H. *J. Physiol. (London),* **187,** 361–68 (1966)
144. Willis, J. S. *J. Gen. Physiol.,* **49,** 1221 (July 1966)
145. Morrill, G. A., Robbins, E. *J. Gen. Physiol.,* **50,** 781–92 (1967)
146. Wallin, G. *Nature,* **212,** 521–22 (1966)
147. Matthews, E. K. *J. Physiol. (London),* **189,** 139–48 (1967)
148. Kleinzeller, A., Knotkova, A. *Biochim. Biophys. Acta,* **126,** 604–5 (1966)
149. Diamond, J. M., Tormey, J. M. *Nature,* **210,** 817–20 (1966)
150. Ussing, H. H. *Ann. N. Y. Acad. Sci.,* **137,** 543–55 (1966)
151. Biber, T. U. L., Chez, R. A., Curran,

P. F. *J. Gen. Physiol.*, **49**, 1161–76 (1966)

152. Dietz, T. H., Kirschner, L. B., Porter, D. *J. Exptl. Biol.*, **46**, 85–96 (1967)
153. Giebisch, G., Malnic, G., Klose, R. M., Windhager, E. E. *Am. J. Physiol.*, **211**, 560–68 (1966)
154. Ferreira, H. G., Harrison, F. A., Keynes, R. D. *J. Physiol. (London)*, **187**, 631–44 (1966)
155. Clarkson, T. W. *J. Gen. Physiol.*, **50**, 695–727 (1967)
156. Rotunno, C. A., Kowalewski, V., Cereijido, M. *Biochim. Biophys. Acta*, **135**, 170–73 (1967)
157. Armstrong, W. M., Rothstein, A. *J. Gen. Physiol.*, **50**, 967–88 (1967)
158. Conway, E. J., Gaffney, H. M. *Biochem. J.*, **101**, 385–91 (1966)
159. Gunther, T., Dorn, F. *Z. Naturforsch.*, **21b**, 1082–88 (1966)
160. Kylin, A. *Plant Physiol.*, **41**, 579–84 (1966)
161. Dodd, W. A., Pitman, M. G., West, K. R. *Australian J. Biol. Sci.*, **19**, 341–54 (1966)
162. MacRobbie, E. A. C. *Australian J. Biol. Sci.*, **19**, 363–70 (1966)
163. MacRobbie, E. A. C. *Ibid.*, 371–83
164. Higinbotham, N., Etherton, B., Foster, R. J. *Plant Physiol.*, **42**, 37–46 (1967)
165. Bowling, D. J. F., Macklon, A. E. S., Spanswick, R. M. *J. Exptl. Biol.*, **17**, 410–16 (1966)
166. Pitman, M. G., Saddler, H. D. W. *Proc. Natl. Acad. Sci.*, **57**, 44–49 (1967)
167. Rains, D. W., Epstein, E. *Plant Physiol.*, **42**, 319–23 (1967)
168. Rains, D. W., Epstein, E. *Ibid.*, 314–18
169. Askari, A. *J. Gen. Physiol.*, **49**, 1147 (1966)
170. Schuberth, J., Sundwall, A., Sorbo, B. *Life Sci.*, **6**, 293–95 (1966)
171. Elderfrawi, M. E., O'Brien, R. D. *J. Exptl. Biol.*, **46**, 1–12 (1967)
172. Guttman, R. *J. Gen. Physiol.*, **49**, 1007–18 (1966)
173. Ehrenstein, G., Gilbert, D. *Biophys. J.*, **6**, 553 (1966)
174. Nachmansohn, D. *Ann. N. Y. Acad. Sci.*, **137**, 877–900 (1966)
175. Tasaki, I., Siger, I. *Ann. N. Y. Acad. Sci.*, **137**, 792–806 (1966)
176. Sjodin, R. A., Mullins, L. J. *J. Gen. Physiol.*, **50**, 533–49 (1967)
177. Moore, J. W., Narahashi, T., Shaw,

T. I. *J. Physiol. (London)*, **188**, 99–105 (1967)
178. Watanabe, A. *Science*, **155**, 95–97 (1967)
179. Hille, B. *Nature*, **210**, 1220–22 (1966)
180. Goldman, D. E., Blaustein, M. P. *Ann. N. Y. Acad. Sci.*, **137**, 967–81 (1966)
181. Adelman, W. J., Jr., Senft, J. P. *J. Gen. Physiol.*, **50**, 279–93 (1966)
182. Sjodin, R. A. *J. Gen. Physiol.*, **50**, 269–78 (1966)
183. Armstrong, C. M. *J. Gen. Physiol.*, **50**, 491–503 (1966)
184. Meves, H. *Ann. N. Y. Acad. Sci.*, **137**, 807–17 (1966)
185. Moore, J. W., Anderson, N., Blaustein, M., Takata, M., Lettvin, J. Y., Pickard, W. F., Berstein, T., Pooler, J. *Ann. N. Y. Acad. Sci.*, **137**, 818–29 (1966)
186. Tasaki, I., Singer, I., Watanabe, A. *Am. J. Physiol.*, **211**, 746–54 (1966)
187. Tasaki, I., Singer, I., Watanabe, A. *J. Gen. Physiol.*, **50**, 989–1007 (1967)
188. Tasaki, I., Watanabe, A., Singer, I. *Proc. Natl. Acad. Sci.*, **56**, 1116–22 (1966)
189. Narahashi, T. *Comp. Biochem. Physiol.*, **19**, 759–74 (1966)
190. Luxoro, M., Rissetti, S. *Biochim. Biophys. Acta*, **135**, 368–70 (1967)
191. Blaustein, M. P., Goldman, D. E. *J. Gen. Physiol.*, **49**, 1043–63 (1966)
192. Takata, M., Pickard, W. F., Lettvin, J. Y., Moore, J. W. *J. Gen. Physiol.*, **50**, 461–71 (1966)
193. Nastuk, W. L., Liu, J. H. *Science*, **154**, 266–67 (1966)
194. Ozeki, M., Freeman, A. R., Grundfest, H. *J. Gen. Physiol.*, **49**, 1335–49 (1966)
195. Kanno, T., Matsuda, K. *J. Gen. Physiol.*, **50**, 243–53 (1966)
196. Seyama, I., Irisawa, H. *J. Gen. Physiol.*, **50**, 505–17 (1967)
197. Casteels, R. *J. Physiol. (London)*, **184**, 131–42 (1966)
198. Reuben, J. P., Brandt, P. W., Girardier, L., Grundfest, H. *Science*, **155**, 1263–66 (1967)
199. Niedergerke, R., Orkand, R. K. *J. Physiol. (London)*, **184**, 291–311 (1966)
200. Weyne, J. *Arch. Intern. Physiol. Biochim.*, **74**, 461–75 (1966)

201. Hagiwara, S., Takahashi, K., *J. Gen. Physiol.*, **50**, 583–601 (1967)

202. Curtis, B. A. *J. Gen. Physiol.*, **50**, 255–67 (1966)

203. Takeda, K. *J. Gen. Physiol.*, **50**, 1049–74 (1967)

204. Hagiwara, S. *Ann. N. Y. Acad. Sci.*, **137**, 1015–24 (1966)

205. Haapanen, L., Skoglund, C. R. *Acta Physiol. Scand.*, **69**, 51–68 (1967)

206. Mailman, D. S., Mullins, L. J. *Australian J. Biol. Sci.*, **19**, 385–98 (1966)

207. Schachter, D., Kowarski, S., Finkelstein, J. D., Ma, R. I. W. *Am. J. Physiol.*, **211**, 1131–36 (1966)

208. Forte, J. G., Nauss, A. H. *Am. J. Physiol.*, **211**, 239–42 (1966)

209. Helbock, H. J., Forte, J. G., Saltman, P. *Biochim. Biophys. Acta*, **126**, 81–93 (1966)

210. Wasserman, R. H., Taylor, A. N., Kallfelz, F. A. *Am. J. Physiol.*, **211**, 419–23 (1966)

211. Webling, D., Holdsworth, E. S. *Biochem. J.*, **100**, 652–60 (1966)

212. Webling, D., Holdsworth, E. S. *Ibid.*, 661–63

213. Peachey, L. D. *Ann. N. Y. Acad. Sci.*, **137**, 1025–37 (1966)

214. Podolsky, R. J., Costantin, L. L. *Ann. N. Y. Acad. Sci.*, **137**, 1038–40 (1966)

215. Hasselbach, W. *Ann. N. Y. Acad. Sci.*, **137**, 1041–48 (1966)

216. Weber, A., Herz, R., Reiss, I. *Biochem. Z.*, **345**, 329–69 (1966)

217. Duggan, P. F. *Life Sci.*, **6**, 561–67 (1967)

218. Lee, K. S., Choi, S. J. *J. Pharmacol. Exptl. Therap.*, **153**, 114–20 (1966)

219. Philpott, C. W., Goldstein, M. A. *Science*, **155**, 1019–21 (1967)

220. Zadunaisky, J. A. *J. Cell Biol.*, **31**, C11–C16 (1966)

221. Pfaffman, M., Holland, W. *Am. J. Physiol.*, **211**, 400–2 (1966)

222. Howell, J. N., Fairhurst, A. S., Jenden, D. J. *Life Sci.*, **5**, 439–47 (1966)

223. Schatzmann, H. J. *Experientia*, **22**, 364–68 (1966)

224. Jackson, P. C., Edwards, D. G. *J. Gen. Physiol.*, **50**, 225–41 (1966)

225. Funder, J., Wieth, J. O. *Acta Physiol. Scand.*, **68**, 234–45 (1966)

226. Aull, F. *J. Cell. Physiol.*, **69**, 21–32 (1967)

227. Martin, D. W., Curran, P. F. *J. Cell. Physiol.*, **67**, 367–74 (1966)

228. Gonzalez, C. F., Shamoo, Y. E., Brodsky, W. A. *Am. J. Physiol.*, **212**, 641–50 (1967)

229. Zadunaisky, J. A. *Am. J. Physiol.*, **211**, 506–12 (1966)

230. Takagi, S. F., Wyse, G. A., Yajima, T. *J. Gen. Physiol.*, **50**, 473–89 (1966)

231. Rehm, W. S. *Ann. N. Y. Acad. Sci.*, **137**, 591–605 (1966)

232. Parkins, F. M., Hollifield, J. W., McCaslin, A. J., Wu, S. L., Faust, R. G. *Biochim. Biophys. Acta*, **126**, 513–24 (1966)

233. Larsen, P. R., Wolff, J. *Science*, **155**, 335–36 (1967)

234. Pettersson, S. *Physiol. Plantarum*, **19**, 459–92 (1966)

235. Petterson, S. *Ibid.*, 581–601

236. Ingelsten, B. *Physiol. Plantarum*, **19**, 563–79 (1966)

237. Yamamoto, L. A., Segel, I. H. *Arch. Biochem. Biophys.*, **114**, 523–38 (1966)

238. Chedru, J., Cartier, P. *Biochim. Biophys. Acta*, **126**, 500 (1966)

239. Levinson, C. *Biochim. Biophys. Acta*, **120**, 292–98 (1966)

240. Siegenthaler, P. A., Belsky, M. M., Goldstein, S. *Science*, **155**, 93–94 (1967)

241. Blum, J. J. *J. Gen. Physiol.*, **49**, 1125–37 (1966)

242. Harold, F. M., Baarda, J. R. *J. Bacteriol.*, **91**, 2257–62 (1966)

243. Damadian, R. *Biochim. Biophys. Acta*, **135**, 378–80 (1967)

244. Shapiro, H. *Comp. Biochem. Physiol.*, **19**, 225 (1966)

245. Freeman, A. R., Reuben, J. P., Brandt, P. W., Grundfest, H. *J. Gen. Physiol.*, **50**, 423–45 (1966)

246. Kleinzeller, A., Nedvidkova, J., Knotkova, A. *Biochim. Biophys. Acta*, **135**, 286–99 (1967)

247. Page, E., Storm, S. R. *J. Gen. Physiol.*, **49**, 641–53 (1966)

248. Koga, S., Echigo, A., Nunomura, K. *Biophys. J.*, **6**, 665–74 (1966)

249. Franz, T. J., VanBruggen, J. T. *J. Gen. Physiol.*, **50**, 933–49 (1967)

250. Tazawa, M., Kamiya, N. *Australian J. Biol. Sci.*, **19**, 399–449 (1966)

251. Altamirano, M., Martinoya, C. *J. Physiol. (London)*, **184**, 771–90 (1966)

252. Stallworthy, W. B., Fenson, D. S. *Can. J. Physiol. Pharmacol.*, **44**, 866–70 (1966)

253. Lippe, C., Cremaschi, D., Capraro, V. *Comp. Biochem. Physiol.*, **19**, 179–86 (1966)
254. Rabinowitz, L. *J. Cell. Physiol.*, **67**, 177–80 (1966)
255. Ospina, B., Hunter, F. R. *Nature*, **211**, 851 (1966)
256. Macey, R. I., Tolberg, A. B. *Biochim. Biophys. Acta*, **120**, 104–12 (1966)
257. Wong, H. A., Randle, P. J. *Biochem. J.*, **102**, 618–22 (1967)
258. Holloszy, J. O., Narahara, H. T. *Science*, **155**, 573–75 (1967)
259. Holloszy, J. O., Narahara, H. T. *J. Gen. Physiol.*, **50**, 551–62 (1967)
260. Mullins, L. J. *Ann. N. Y. Acad. Sci.*, **137**, 830–36 (1966)
261. Levine, M., Stein, W. D. *Biochim. Biophys. Acta*, **127**, 179–93 (1966)
262. Kotyk, A. *Biochim. Biophys. Acta*, **135**, 112–19 (1967)
263. LeFevre, P. G. *Biochim. Biophys. Acta*, **120**, 395–405 (1966)
264. Lacko, L. *J. Cell. Physiol.*, **67**, 501–6 (1966)
265. Saha, J., Coe, E. L. *Biochem. Biophys. Res. Commun.*, **26**, 441–46 (1967)
266. Newey, H., Sanford, P. A., Smyth, D. H. *J. Physiol. (London)*, **186**, 493–502 (1966)
267. Crocken, B., Tatum, E. L. *Biochim. Biophys. Acta*, **135**, 100–5 (1967)
268. Blakley, E. R., Myoda, T., Spencer, J. F. T. *Can. J. Biochem.*, **44**, 927–36 (1966)
269. Smit, J. A., Coetzee, J. N. *Nature*, **210**, 909–10 (1966)
270. Williams, P. J., McDonald, I. J. *Can. J. Microbiol.*, **12**, 1213–23 (1966)
271. Halpern, Y. S., Lupo, M. *Biochim. Biophys. Acta*, **126**, 163–67 (1966)
272. Winkler, H. H., Wilson, T. H. *J. Biol. Chem.*, **241**, 2200–11 (1966)
273. Kotyk, A., Kleinzeller, A. *Biochim. Biophys. Acta*, **135**, 106–11 (1967)
274. Mandels, G. R., Vitols, R. *J. Bacteriol.*, **93**, 159–67 (1967)
275. Faust, R. G., Wu, S. L., Faggard, M. L. *Science*, **155**, 1261–63 (1967)
276. Diedrich, D. F. *Am. J. Physiol.*, **211**, 581–87 (1966)
277. London, D. R., Segal, S. *Biochim. Biophys. Acta*, **135**, 179–80 (1967)
278. Inui, Y., Christensen, H. N. *J. Gen. Physiol.*, **50**, 203–24 (1966)
279. Munck, B. G. *Biochim. Biophys. Acta*, **120**, 97–103 (1966)
280. Behki, R. M., Hochster, R. M. *Can. J. Biochem.*, **44**, 1477–91 (1966)
281. Christensen, H. N., Liang, M. *J. Biol. Chem.*, **241**, 5542–51 (1966)
282. Schwartzman, L., Blair, A., Segal, S. *Biochim. Biophys. Acta*, **135**, 120–26 (1967)
283. Segal, S., Schwartzman, L., Blair, A., Bertoli, D. *Biochim. Biophys. Acta*, **135**, 127–35 (1967)
284. Schwartzman, L., Blair, A., Segal, S. *Biochim. Biophys. Acta*, **135**, 136–45 (1967)
285. Rosenberg, L. E., Albrecht, I., Segal, S. *Science*, **155**, 1426–27 (1967)
286. Munck, B. G. *Biochim. Biophys. Acta*, **120**, 282–91 (1966)
287. Grenson, M., Mousset, M., Wiame, J. M., Bechet, J. *Biochim. Biophys. Acta*, **127**, 325–38 (1966)
288. Yabu, K. *Biochim. Biophys. Acta*, **135**, 181–83 (1967)
289. Holden, J. T., Utech, N. M. *Biochim. Biophys. Acta*, **135**, 351–54 (1967)
290. Wiley, W. R., Matchett, W. H., *J. Bacteriol.*, **92**, 1698–1705 (1966)
291. Merriam, R. W. *Exptl. Cell Res.*, **42**, 340–47 (1966)
292. Kleber, H. P., Aurich, H. *Biochem. Biophys. Res. Commun.*, **26**, 255–59 (1967)
293. Christensen, H. N., Liang, M. *J. Biol. Chem.*, **241**, 5552–56 (1966)
294. Schultz, S. G., Fuisz, R. E., Curran, P. F. *J. Gen. Physiol.*, **49**, 849–66 (1966)
295. Lauterbach, F. *Biochim. Biophys. Acta*, **135**, 256–72 (1967)
296. Despopoulos, A. *Am. J. Physiol.*, **211**, 1329–33 (1966)
297. Alvarado, F., Monreal, J. *Comp. Biochem. Physiol.*, **20**, 471–88 (1967)
298. Alvarado, F. *Comp. Biochem. Physiol.*, **20**, 461–70 (1967)
299. Csáky, T. Z., Ho, P. M. *J. Gen. Physiol.*, **50**, 113 (1966)
300. Lassen, U. V., Csáky, T. Z. *J. Gen. Physiol.*, **49**, 1029–40 (1966)
301. Levinson, R. A., Schedl, H. P. *Am. J. Physiol.*, **211**, 939–42 (1966)
302. Lyon, I., Crane, R. K. *Biochim. Biophys. Acta*, **135**, 61–73 (1967)
303. Wright, E. M. *J. Physiol. (London)*, **185**, 486–500 (1966)
304. Rhodes, M. E., Payne, W. J. *Proc. Soc. Exptl. Biol. Med.*, **124**, 953–55 (1967)
305. Robinson, J. W. L., *Biochim. Biophys. Acta*, **126**, 61–72 (1966)
306. Mepham, T. B., Smith, M. W. *J. Physiol. (London)*, **186**, 619–31 (1966)
307. Thier, S. O., Blair, A., Fox, M.,

Segal, S. *Biochim. Biophys. Acta,* **135,** 300–5 (1967)

308. Goodman, H. M. *Am. J. Physiol.,* **211,** 815–20 (1966)

309. Stevenson, J. *Biochem. J.,* **99,** 257–60 (1966)

310. Drapeau, G. R., Matula, T. I., McLeod, R. A. *J. Bacteriol.,* **92,** 63–71 (1966)

311. Westlake, D. W. S., Horler, D. F., McConnell, W. B. *Biochem. Biophys. Res. Commun.,* **26,** 461–65 (1967)

312. Duthie, H. L., Hindmarsh, J. T. *J. Physiol. (London),* **187,** 195–200 (1966)

313. Hindmarsh, J. T., Kilby, D., Wiseman, G. *J. Physiol. (London),* **186,** 166–74 (1966)

314. Chez, R. A., Schultz, S. G., Curran, P. F. *Science,* **153,** 1012–13 (1966)

315. Bingham, J. K., Newey, H., Smyth, D. H. *Biochim. Biophys. Acta,* **130,** 281–83 (1966)

316. Parker, J. C., Hoffman, J. F. *J. Gen. Physiol.,* **50,** 893–916 (1967)

317. Seidman, I., Casarano, J. *Am. J. Physiol.,* **211,** 1165–70 (1966)

318. Hidalgo, C., Canessa-Fischer, M. *J. Cell. Physiol.,* **68,** 185–96 (1966)

319. Nissan, S., Aviram, A., Czaczkes, J. W., Ullmann, L., Ullmann, T. D. *Am. J. Physiol.* **210,** 1222–24 (1966)

320. Torelli, G., Milla, E., Faelli, A., Costantini, S. *Am. J. Physiol.,* **211,** 576–80 (1966)

321. Martin, D. W., Diamond, J. M. *J. Gen. Physiol.,* **50,** 295–315 (1966)

322. Levinson, C., Hempling, H. G. *Biochim. Biophys. Acta,* **135,** 306–18 (1967)

323. Baker, P. F., Connelly, C. M. *J. Physiol. (London),* **185,** 270–97 (1966)

324. Hokin, M. R. *Life Sci.,* **5,** 1829 (1966)

325. Smith, F. A. *Biochim. Biophys. Acta,* **126,** 94–99 (1966)

326. Manery, J. F. *Fed. Proc.,* **26,** 1804–10 (1966)

327. Millington, P. F., Critchley, D. R., Tovell, P. W. A. *J. Cell Sci.,* **1,** 415–24 (1966)

328. Manthey, A. A. *J. Gen. Physiol.,* **49,** 963–76 (1966)

329. Morrill, G. A., Rosenthal, J., Watson, D. E. *J. Cell. Physiol.,* **67,** 375–82 (1966)

330. Swanson, P. D., Ullis, K. *J. Phar-macol. Exptl. Therap.,* **153,** 321–28 (1966)

331. Bittar, E. E. *Biochem. Biophys. Res. Commun.,* **23,** 868 (1966)

332. Fanestil, D. D., Porter, G. A., Edelman, I. S. *Biochim. Biophys. Acta,* **135,** 74–88 (1967)

333. Fimognari, G. M., Porter, G. A., Edelman, I. *Biochim. Biophys. Acta,* **135,** 89–99 (1967)

334. Sharp, G. W. G., Leaf, A. *Physiol. Rev.,* **46,** 593–633 (1966)

335. Cofré, G., Crabbé, J., *J. Physiol. (London),* **188,** 177–90 (1967)

336. Civan, M. M., Kedem, O., Leaf, A. *Am. J. Physiol.,* **211,** 569–75 (1966)

337. Elliott, A. B. *Experientia,* **23,** 220–21 (1967)

338. Grantham, J. J., Burg, M. B. *Am. J. Physiol.,* **211,** 255–59 (1966)

339. Finn, A. L., Handler, J. S., Orloff, J. *Am. J. Physiol.,* **210,** 1279–84 (1966)

340. Lichtenstein, N. S., Leaf, A. *Ann. N. Y. Acad. Sci.,* **137,** 556–65 (1966)

341. González, C. S., Sánchez, J. O., Concha, J. B. *Biochim. Biophys. Acta,* **135,** 167–70 (1967)

342. Oye, I., Sutherland, E. W. *Biochim. Biophys. Acta,* **127,** 347–54 (1966)

343. Dailey, R. E., Hines, R. A., Roe, J. H. *Arch. Biochem. Biophys.,* **114,** 371–74 (1966)

344. Burton, S. D., Mondon, C. E., Ishida, T. *Am. J. Physiol.,* **212,** 261–66 (1967)

345. Clausen, T. *Biochim. Biophys. Acta,* **120,** 361 (1966)

346. O'Niell, K. E., Manery, J. F., Dryden, E. E. *J. Cell. Physiol.,* **68,** 35–44 (1966)

347. Edelman, P. M., Edelman, J. C., Schwartz, I. L. *Nature,* **210,** 1017–18 (1966)

348. Milner, R. D. G., Hales, C. N. *Biochim. Biophys. Acta,* **135,** 375–77 (1967)

349. Elsas, L. J., Rosenberg, L. E. *Proc. Natl. Acad. Sci.,* **57,** 371–78 (1967)

350. Kraemer, P. M. *J. Cell. Physiol.,* **69,** 199–208 (1967)

351. Jung, C., Rothstein, A. *J. Gen. Physiol.,* **50,** 917–32 (1967)

352. Hindmarsh, J. T., Kilby, D., Ross, B., Wiseman, G. *J. Physiol. (London),* **188,** 207–18 (1967)

353. Motais, R., Romeu, F. G., Maetz, J. *J. Gen. Physiol.,* **50,** 391–422 (1966)

354. Lynch, M. P., Wood, L. *Comp. Biochem. Physiol.*, **19**, 783–90 (1966)
355. Dreyfuss, J., Pardee, A. B. *J. Bacteriol.*, **91**, 2275–80 (1966)
356. Wu, H. C. P. *J. Mol. Biol.*, **24**, 213–23 (1967)
357. Lee, P., Woo, A., Tosteson, D. C. *J. Gen. Physiol.*, **50**, 379–90 (1966)
358. Scriver, C. R., Wilson, O. H. *Science*, **155**, 1428–30 (1967)
359. Holdsworth, C. D., Wilson, T. H. *Am. J. Physiol.*, **212**, 233–40 (1967)
360. Bogner, P. H., Braham, A. H., McLain, P. L., Jr. *J. Physiol. (London)*, **187**, 307–21 (1966)
361. Green, D. E., Perdue, J. F. *Ann. N. Y. Acad. Sci.*, **137**, 667–84 (1966)
362. Stoeckenius, W. *Ann. N. Y. Acad. Sci.*, **137**, 641–42 (1966)
363. Parsons, D. F., Yano, Y. *Biochim. Biophys. Acta*, **135**, 362–64 (1967)
364. Parsons, D. F., Williams, G. R., Chance, B. *Ann. N. Y. Acad. Sci.*, **137**, 643–66 (1966)
365. Bachmann, E., Allmann, D. W., Green, D. E. *Arch. Biochem. Biophys.*, **115**, 153–64 (1966)
366. Allmann, D. W., Backmann, E., Green, D. E. *Ibid.*, 165–71
367. Green, D. E., Bachmann, E., Allmann, D. W., Perdue, J. F. *Arch. Biochem. Biophys.*, **115**, 172–80 (1966)
368. McKnight, R. C., Hunter, F. E. *J. Biol. Chem.*, **241**, 2757–65 (1966)
369. Tarr, J. S., Jr., Gamble, J. L., Jr. *Am. J. Physiol.*, **211**, 1187–91 (1966)
370. Lehninger, A. L. *Ann. N. Y. Acad. Sci.*, **137**, 700–7 (1966)
371. Rotterberg, H., Solomon, A. K. *Ann. N. Y. Acad. Sci.*, **137**, 685–99 (1966)
372. Harris, E. J., Judah, J. D., Ahmed, K. *Current Topics Bioenerg.*, **1**, 255–77 (1966)
373. Mitchell, P. *Biol. Rev.*, **41**, 445–502 (1966)

374. Reid, R. A., Moyle, J., Mitchell, P. *Nature*, **212**, 257–58 (1966)
375. Lynn, W. S., Brown, R. H. *Arch. Biochem. Biophys.*, **114**, 260–70 (1966)
376. Harris, E. J., Cockrell, R., Pressman, B. C. *Biochem. J.*, **99**, 200–13 (1966)
377. Cockrell, R. S., Harris, E. J., Pressman, B. C. *Ibid.*, 2326–35
378. Marcus, G. J., Manery, J. F., Dryden, E. E. *Can. J. Biochem.*, **44**, 1133–44 (1966)
379. Chance, B., Yoshioka, T. *Biochemistry*, **5**, 3224–29 (1966)
380. Bielawski, J., Lehninger, A. L. *J. Biol. Chem.*, **241**, 4316–22 (1966)
381. Chance, B., Mela, L. *Nature*, **212**, 369–72 (1966)
382. Carafoli, E., Gamble, R. L., Lehninger, A. L. *J. Biol. Chem.*, **241**, 2644–52 (1966)
383. Wenner, C. E. *J. Biol. Chem.*, **241**, 2810–19 (1966)
384. Chance, B., Mela, L., *Biochemistry*, **5**, 3220–29 (1966)
385. Brierley, G. P., Bhattacharyya, R. N., Walker, J. G. *Biochem. Biophys. Res. Commun.*, **24**, 269–73 (1966)
386. Brierley, G. P., Bhattacharyya, R. N. *Ibid.*, **23**, 647–51 (1966)
387. Packer, L. *Ann. N. Y. Acad. Sci.*, **137**, 624–40 (1966)
388. Deamer, D. W., Crofts, A. R., Packer, L. *Biochim. Biophys. Acta*, **131**, 81–96 (1967)
389. Siegenthaler, P. A. *Physiol. Plantarum*, **19**, 437–47 (1966)
390. Crofts, A. R., Deamer, D. W., Packer, L. *Biochim. Biophys. Acta*, **131**, 97–118 (1967)
391. Dilley, R. A., Vernon, L. P. *Proc. Natl. Acad. Sci.*, **57**, 395–400 (1967)
392. Maude, D. L. *Biochim. Biophys. Acta*, **135**, 365–67 (1967)
393. Franke, W. W. *J. Cell Biol.*, **31**, 619–23 (1966)
394. Loewenstein, W. R., Kanno, Y., Ito, S. *Ann. N. Y. Acad. Sci.*, **137**, 708–16 (1966)

OSMOTIC AND IONIC REGULATION[1]   1001

BY W. T. W. POTTS

Department of Biology, University of Lancaster
Lancaster, England

INTRODUCTION

It is ten years since the last review on Osmotic and Ionic Regulation in Animals appeared in the *Annual Review of Physiology* (1). Since that time the field has been reviewed by Shaw (2), by Potts & Parry (3), and by Prosser & Brown (4). In addition a number of the more important groups of animals have been reviewed in the Academic Press series of books on the physiology of selected groups. In the light of these later works this review will be confined largely to the more recent papers on the subject.

It is difficult to define exactly the scope of this subject as it overlaps with the field of renal physiology, which is reviewed almost annually in this periodical, and also with transport through biological membranes reviewed by Rothstein (5) in the present volume. The limits covered in this review are defined in the last resort by the personal prejudices of the writer, but the main emphasis will be placed on the regulation of the salt and water balance of the whole animal. Active transport and excretory systems will be discussed from this point of view.

The material for this review has been arranged largely in a systematic fashion for the convenience of readers interested in particular groups. An exception has been made in the discussion of the fine structure of salt-transporting tissues where the number of papers is limited and interphyletic comparisons are more profitable.

FINE STRUCTURE STUDIES

The correlation of fine structure and ion transport is fraught with difficulties but the recent development of histochemical techniques to localise ions and enzymes on electronmicrographs should lead to rapid progress. A technique for the localisation of phosphatase activity has been described (6) and has been successfully applied to a number of tissues including amphibian epidermis (7). The localisation of chloride by precipitation as silver chloride and the localisation of sodium by precipitation as pyroantimonate have been attempted in the salt gland of the seagull *Larus argentatus* (8–11) and in the mammalian gall bladder (12). This method of localising sodium is open to the criticism that the small sodium ions will diffuse more rapidly than the large pyroantimonate ion and that therefore the precipitate will form along the diffusion channels of the pyroantimonate. As little is known about the localisation of sodium within cells, it is difficult to check

[1] The survey of literature for this review was concluded in May 1967.

73

the method empirically. However, Zadunaisky (13) has successfully used it
to demonstrate the local concentration of sodium in the transverse tubules
of skeletal muscle. As these tubules communicate with the extracellular
spaces, a high concentration of sodium is to be expected, and this is an interesting test of the reliability of the method. The demonstration by Kaye
et al. (12) that sodium is accumulated against the plasma membrane, in the
presence of ouabain, instead of in the intercellular spaces, has an inherent
logic which helps to confirm the technique. The identification of intracellular silver chloride granules by electron defraction is a further refinement
of these localising techniques (14).

   Sites of ultrafiltration.—In the vertebrate kidney, ultrafiltration takes
place through the basement membrane of the glomerulus which is directly
exposed to both the blood and the urine. The endothelium of the blood vessels is discontinuous and the epithelium of the glomerulus consists of podocytes which only make contact with the basement membrane over limited
areas (15). A striking analogy to the vertebrate glomerulus has been found
in the coelomosac of the crayfish *Astacus* (16). Here the epithelial cells are
also podocytes and are attached to the basement membrane only by long,
complex processes between which the basement membrane is directly exposed.

   Sites of ion transport.—In vertebrates and in many invertebrates, kidney tubules are generally the site of extensive ion resorption. Electronmicroscope studies of the tubular regions of a number of invertebrates show
an arrangement of β-cytomembranes and mitochondria similar to that
found in the vertebrates (17). The association of mitochondria with the
cell membrane suggests that the membrane is the site of some energy-con-
suming transfer process between the interior of the cell and the extracellular fluid. The function of this system is debatable as the vertebrate kidney is capable of both resorption and secretion. However, ion transfer
from the lumen of the kidney back to the blood takes place on such an extensive scale that it probably requires more energy than any secretary process. Micropuncture studies imply that the sodium is actively transported
from the interior of the cell into the peritubular fluid although it probably
enters the cell by diffusion (18–20). Chloride transfer is entirely passive.
It is therefore reasonable to correlate the system of β-cytomembranes and
associated mitochondria with a pump transferring sodium from the cell
lumen into the blood. Very similar systems have been described in the tubules of the crayfish antennary gland (21), the *Helix* kidney sac and ureter
(22), and the coxal glands of the scorpion (23).

   Significantly, very similar structures have been described by Copeland
(24) in the gills of brackish and freshwater crabs (*Carcinus* and *Callinectes*). In this case the basal folds and the associated mitochondria occupy the greater part of the cell, reaching almost to the distal surface. There
can be no doubt that these cells are the sites of active transport of ions
from the external medium into the blood. The outer surface of the cells is

thrown into evenly spaced folds. This is probably a device for increasing the surface area of the cell, analogous to the brush border found in the vertebrate proximal tubules and in the *Helix* kidney sac. Copeland believes that some pinocytosis occurs at the base of these surface folds though it is difficult to suggest what function this could have in an animal continuously gaining water by osmosis, unless ions are absorbed into the surface membrane and then "ingested". The inner or plasma surface of the cell of the anal papillae of the mosquito larvae (*Culex quinquefasciatus*), reared in freshwater, is connected to a complicated network of canaliculi (25). Pairs or occasionally triplets of thin flattened mitochondria enclosed flattened areas of the canaliculi. These structures Copeland has termed "mitochondrial pumps". They are sparsely distributed in the cells, but the fluxes of salt through the papillae must be very small in distilled water, although the concentration gradient will be very large. The canaliculi extend about halfway through the cell. The outer surface of the cell is tightly folded into a series of narrow parallel folds which have mitochondria lying parallel to the inner edges of the folds (25). The interpretation of these structures is difficult but the mitochondrial pumps may well be associated with the transport of material from the lumen of the cell into the plasma and are analogous to the β-cytomembrane of the kidney tubules. However, the system of folds and mitochondria at the outer surface may constitute an additional transport system at the outer surface of the cell. The external concentrations are so low that entry by diffusion into the cytoplasm would be negligible.

The fine structure of frog skin has been described on a number of occasions. Frog skin lacks β-cytomembranes or mitochondrial pumps, but the rate of ion transport per unit area is very low compared with that of the kidney. Recent localisation of ATPase in frog skin has confirmed that the active transport does not take place through the single continuous layer but through several layers arranged in series (7). This is an agreement with recent work on both sodium and potassium movement across the skin. Ussing (26) himself has suggested a similar modification of his frog skin model. Sodium probably enters the outer layer of cells by diffusion and is then pumped into the intercellular space whence it diffuses into the next layer. The correlation of fine structure and salt transport in the amphibian bladder is complicated by the presence of three types of cells in the mucosa (27). The mucosa contains what are termed "ordinary" epithelial cells, goblet cells, and mitochondria-rich cells. While the mitochondria-rich cells seem obvious candidates for the site of active transport, the sodium pool involved in transport is too large to be contained in these cells alone, and Keller (27) suggests that both the ordinary cells and the mitochondria-rich cells are involved. All three cell types possess basal membrane ATPase; the mitochondria-rich cells have more ATPase but the ordinary cells have the larger surface area (27, 28).

Sites of water transport.—Apart from the active uptake of water vapour by certain insects, water movement always appears to be the consequence of the active transport of solutes. The active transport of solutes will only be effective in transporting water if it leads to a local buildup of concentration. Curran (29) has proposed a simple double-membrane model depending on this principle to account for the transport of fluids across the gastric mucosa. The first, more selective, membrane is permeable to water but has a low permeability to solutes. The second, less selective, membrane is more permeable to both water and solutes. If the double membrane separates two similar solutions and solutes are transported into the confined space between the membranes, the solution will exert a higher osmotic pressure at the first, more selective membrane.

In the gall bladder water may be resorbed against an osmotic gradient. The lateral boundaries of the epithelial cells interdigitate and enclose an extensive system of intercellular spaces. Whitlock & Wheeler (30) suggest that these spaces correspond to the intermembrane space of Curran's model while the lateral plasma membrane of the epithelial cell corresponds to the less permeable membrane, and the basement membrane of the epithelium corresponds to the more permeable membrane. In agreement with this hypothesis the intercellular spaces are dilated during water transport (31), and contain a high concentration of sodium. When transport is blocked with ouabain, sodium is concentrated on the cytoplasmic surfaces of the lateral membranes of the cells.

Berridge & Gupta (32) have recently described the rectal papillae of the blowfly *Calliphora* and interpreted these in terms of the same model. The blowfly rectum can resorb water from solutions of xylose and trehalose hyperosmotic to the haemolymph. The epithelium cells of the papillae contain a complex system of intercellular spaces, arranged in arrays of parallel sacs, often associated with mitochondria, and communicating with an intercellular sinus draining ultimately into the haemocoele. Berridge & Gupta propose that the walls of the sacs constitute the more selective membrane, a basement lamina and various other structures the less selective. They suggest that ions, probably K^+ and Cl^-, are transported into the sacs until their osmotic pressure is sufficient to draw water in from the solutions in the rectum through the cytoplasm. As a corollary the cytoplasm of the epithelial cells must be isosmotic with the rectal contents.

The fine structures of a number of glands producing concentrated solutions have been described. Komnick & Komnick (11) have described the fine structure of the nasal gland of the sea gull *Larus argentatus* and after localising the sodium and chloride in both active and resting glands suggest that active sodium transport takes place through the basal and apical surfaces of the tubule cell, and possibly through the mitochondria, while chloride moves passively through the intercellular spaces. However, it is difficult to see how chloride could be transported or locally concentrated without an accompanying cation. Some further transport may take place in the epithelium of the collecting ducts. The secretory cells have deep lateral clefts and folds and the adjacent cells interdigitate so that the intercellular spaces are very complex and extensive although very narrow. They are closed to the lumen of the gland by desmosomes. The cytoplasm of the fields is rich in mitochondria and agranular endoplasmic reticulum. The base of the cell contains a complex of cytoplasmic folds and mitochondria.

The most remarkable feature of the salt gland of marine turtles *Caretta caretta* and *Chelone mydas* is the presence of a profusion of microvilli which interdigitate in the intercellular spaces, so that the lateral surface area of the cell is very extensive. The intercellular spaces between these villi contain a high concentration of a mucopolysaccharide. The cells are also rich in mitochondria but these lie in the cell bodies. Although the intercellular space is so elaborate, it is not confluent with the lumen of the gland, as the lumenal edges of adjacent cells are firmly joined by a complex system of desmosomes and terminal bars (33).

The rectal gland of the dogfish, which produces a sodium-rich fluid similar to that produced by the bird nasal gland, has been described by Bulger [(34) *Squalus acanthias*] and Doyle [(35, 36) *Urolophus*]. In the rectal gland the entire surface of the secretory cells is complex. The cells interdigitate in an elaborate manner so that each cell is deeply penetrated by lateral processes of adjacent cells. The intercellular spaces are narrow. The apical region of each cell contains large numbers of vesicles and multivesicular bodies (34).

It is not clear whether all these glands produce concentrated solutions directly or by the secretion of an isosmotic solution followed by water resorption. If the elaborate intercellular spaces in several of these glands function as part of a double membrane system the entire cytoplasm of the epithelium may be raised hyperosmotic to the blood.

Teleost and Artemia *gills.*—The fine structure of the chloride cell from a marine, brackish, and freshwater species of *Fundulus* adapted to various media has been described by Philpott & Copeland (38). In fish from seawater the chloride cell contains a conspicuous apical vacuole apparently fed by tubules of smooth endoplasmic reticulum. The distal surfaces of the chloride cells are almost entirely covered by the adjacent epithelium cells. The cytoplasm of the cells is rich in smooth endoplasmic reticulum and mitochondria but these are not arranged in any regular fashion. The apical vacuoles are filled with a granular material and evidently contain mucopolysaccharide (38) and chloride (14). In freshwater-adapted fish the apical vacuoles are absent and the cells are widely exposed to the external medium by the retraction of the surrounding epithelium. The transition from seawater- to freshwater-adapted forms occurs at a very low salinity (less than 8 per cent seawater) and vacuoles have been found in fish from hard freshwater. Presence of vacuoles in freshwater-adapted fish does not accord well with the theory of salt excretion because salt uptake rather than salt excretion should take place in solutions less concentrated than 30 per cent seawater.

The branchiopod *Artemia salina* can maintain itself in saturated salt solutions. The site of salt secretion has been localised by Croghan (39) on certain areas of the first ten pairs of branchiae, and the fine structure of the epithelium in these areas has been described by Copeland (40). The epithelium contains two groups of cells which again interdigitate and overlap in a complex fashion. Cells with a dark cytoplasm are surrounded by and largely overlain by cells with a light cytoplasm. The cells with a dark cytoplasm contain spectacular arrays of flattened saucer-shaped mitochondria arranged in stacks containing as many as twelve or even twenty mitochondria. The mitochondria are separated by thin flattened extensions of a canalicular system which opens on the plasma side of the cell and penetrates deeply into the cytoplasm. These structures are strikingly similar to the mitochondrial pumps described by Copeland in the anal papillae of the mosquito.

Certain features such as mitochondrial pumps, β-cytomembranes, and associated mitochondria, and lateral interdigitation and cells can be recognised in several different transporting tissues. β-Cytomembranes and associated mitochondria and Copeland's mitochondrial pumps are probably devices to associate a large surface area of the cell closely with the energy source. The elaborate intercellular spaces, at least in some cases, are devices for producing localised concentrations of ions to facilitate water movement.

Contractile vacuoles.—In *Paramecium* the contractile vacuole is fed by permanent nephridial canals. During diastole the canals are fed by fine nephridial tubules which connect peripherally to the endoplasmic reticulum (41). In contrast, in the Amoeba (42) there is no system of feeder canals and the vacuole swells by the irregular addition of minute droplets. In both cases the vacuole system is associated with mitochondria.

Protonephridia.—The protonephridium of the rotifer *Asplanchnodonta* has been well described. Each individual protonephridium consists of a syncytium enclosing the protonephridial tubules. Each protonephridium has four flame bulbs, drained by a tubule lying in a syncytium (43). In *Asplanchna priodonta* the flame bulbs project into the body fluids and the tubules surrounding the flames consist only of a very thin basement membrane supported by a double layer of slender rods. This is probably the site of ultrafiltration (43).

Osmotic and Ionic Regulation in Protozoa

The function of the contractile vacuole in osmotic regulation has long been studied but only ten years ago Beadle (1) could write " we have . . . practically no direct information regarding the chemical composition of the protoplasm of a protozoal cell". Today there is a growing body of information on the subject from which two facts stand out. First, the freshwater ciliates *Spirostomum* (44), *Paramecium* (45), and *Tetrahymena* (46–48), the marine ciliate *Uronema* (49), and the amoebas *Acanthamoeba* (50, 51) and *Chaos* (52, 53) all accumulate potassium. Secondly, the contractile vacuole, as in the ciliate *Tetrahymena* (54) and the amoeba *Chaos* (53), pumps sodium out of the cell. It seems likely that the primitive function of the sodium pump in all cells is to counteract the excess osmotic pressure produced by the Donnan equilibrium. Unlike the metazoans the ciliates *Spirostomum, Tetrahymena,* and *Paramecium* and the amoeba *Acanthamoeba* can also accumulate sodium when in dilute solutions. *Chaos* can also accumulate chloride above the environmental concentration by feeding or pinocytosis but the accumulation and turnover of chloride is slow and only apparent in long-term experiments. Whether or not this property is peculiar to *Chaos* requires investigation.

The internal potassium concentration varies between species and with conditions but usually lies in the range of 10–30 mE/liter. Potassium usually exchanges fairly freely although some portion is bound in *Acanthamoeba* (51). Potassium uptake is not linked to sodium output, at least in *Acanthamoeba* (51). The later may be confined to the contractile vacuole. The importance of the contractile vacuole in sodium output in the ciliates was demonstrated by Dunham & Stoner (54) who showed that in *Tetrahymena* the half-time of sodium exchange was greatly increased when the contractile vacuole was slowed down. From this experiment Dunham & Stoner calculated that the sodium concentration in the vacuole is up to eight times higher than in the cytoplasm and that saturation occurs beween 75 and 100 mE/liter. It may be relevant here that the vacuole in *A. proteus* is 20 mV positive with respect to the cytoplasm (55). Sodium is believed to enter the animal passively through a relatively impermeable surface.

Ionic regulation in the amoeba *Chaos chaos* differs in some respects from that in the ciliates. *Chaos chaos* contains about 20 mE Cl/liter even at low external chloride concentrations. Bruce & Marshall (53) conclude that this is taken in during feeding or by micropinocytosis and retained by a low permeability to chloride. Chapman-Andresen & Dick (52) showed that bromide exchange is very slow but with short-term experiments failed to find any halide ([82]Br) accumulation above the ambient. Brace & Marshall conclude that sodium and potassium accumulation, at least at low temperatures, is passive and due only to Donnan effects and at normal temperatures the contractile vacuole counteracts Donnan swelling by pumping out water and, selectively, sodium. Chapman-Andresen & Dick in contrast concluded that potassium uptake was active at normal temperatures. They also found that about 20 per cent of sodium uptake occurred by pinocytosis. The high accumulation of chloride 20 mE/liter, compared with only 0.4–0.6 mE Na/liter, suggests that the vacuole conserved chloride. Schmidt-Nielsen & Schrauger (56) found that in *Amoeba proteus* the vacuole has an osmotic pressure of 32 mOsm/liter, compared with 101 mOsm/liter in the cytoplasm.

COELENTERATES AND CTENOPHORES

It has long been known that the ionic composition of the mesogloea of pelagic medusae differs from that of seawater in containing fewer sulphate and magnesium ions and a slightly higher concentration of sodium and chloride but only recently has it been realised that this regulation has a buoyancy function (57). A reduction of 50 per cent in the concentration of sulphate alone will produce a buoyancy of 1 mg/ml. The medusae *Aequoria for skalia* and *Pelagia noctiluca* and the ctenophore *Beroë ovata* and *B. forskalia* all achieve rather better regulation and buoyancy than this.

Sodium, potassium, and chloride regulation has been examined in the hydroids *Tubularia crocea* (marine), *Cordylophora lacustris* (brackish), and *Hydra littoralis* and *Chlohydra viridissima* (freshwater) (58). All animals maintained a potassium concentration of a similar magnitude. *Hydra* and *Cordylophora* concentrate sodium and chloride in freshwater or dilute media but *Cordylophora* and *Tubularia* exclude both ions in more concentrated solutions. *Cordylophora* shows some similarities to *Tetrahymena* concentrating sodium in low concentrations, excluding it in high concentrations and maintaining an almost constant potassium content in a wide range of salinities. However, *Tetrahymena* possesses a contractile vacuole capable of expelling water when in hyposmotic media. The old problem of water balance in *Hydra* remains unsolved.

Annelids

The majority of polychaetes are marine and stenohaline but a few, e.g. *Arenicola marina,* are euryhaline, although isosmotic, and others are osmoregulators. Of the latter *Nereis diversicolor* and *N. limnicola* are found in freshwater. More remarkably Krishnamoorthy & Krishnaswany (59) have reported that the euryhaline species *Marphysa gravelyi* is hyposmotic in seawater.

Isosmotic cellular regulation is important in all euryhaline annelids. The adaptation of *Arenicola* to 50 per cent seawater is accompanied by a decline in the concentration of amino acids, mainly glycine and alanine, from 427 to 180 mmole/liter (60). A similar decline takes place in the sipunculid *Golfingia gouldii* (61). A detailed comparison of the water and salt permeabilities of *Nereis (Neanthes) succinea, N. diversicolor,* and *N. limnicola* (62, 63) shows that *N. diversicolor,* which can tolerate lower salinities than *N. succinea,* has a lower rate of salt loss following transfer to freshwater, while the freshwater *N. limnicola* suffers the least loss. There is considerable intraspecific variation, animals from the lowest salinities having the lowest rates of salt loss under standard conditions. The rates of swelling vary in the same order. However, the permeability to D_2O is similar in all three species. This indicates that the freshwater species has a more effective excretory system. The permeability to D_2O is equivalent to a rate of urine production of at least 10 per cent body weight per hour. The permeability to water does not change significantly with salinity as Jorgensen & Dales had suggested (64); Bogucki & Wojtczak (65) similarly concluded that the permeability of *N. diversicolor* to water remains constant.

A comparison of chloride fluxes in *Nereis vexillosa* (marine), *N. succinea* (brackish), and *N. limnicola* (freshwater), show that *N. limnicola* is the least permeable to chloride (66, 67). However, chloride influx remains almost proportional to the external concentration in *N. vexillosa* and *succinea* which suggests that chloride enters only by diffusion. In contrast, *N. diversicola* shows active uptake of sodium at low salinities (68). *N. limnicola* is even more remarkable in that it shows no evidence of chloride entry in solutions containing less than 200 mE Cl/liter. Oglesby suggests that all chloride influx is passive and the chloride loss is reduced in dilute solutions by the production of hyposmotic urine and a reduction of the permeability of the body wall, any losses being replaced from the food. If the permeability to salt does decline at low salinities then the linear relation between influx and external salinity is fortuitous and in fact indicates active uptake at low salinities. However, most of the results are only qualitative and this interesting work should be repeated on a quantitative basis. Although the nereids can osmoregulate, their powers are feeble and the blood concentration in freshwater is only one-fifth that in seawater. Once again tissue regulation includes drastic changes in the levels of free amino acids (69).

Earthworms live in damp or even waterlogged soil and are in many respects analogous to freshwater animals. Boroffka (70) has investigated the uptake of sodium and chloride ions in the nephridium of *Lumbricus terrestris* confirming and extending Ramsay's osmotic pressure measurements (71). The concentration of both sodium and chloride ions declines as the urine passes down the nephridium. Sodium and chloride ions are taken up from the urine but the permeability of the ducts to water is very low. From potential measurements across the nephridium it was concluded that sodium uptake was active while chloride followed passively. An endocrine factor in *Lumbricus* brain which influences salt and water balance in *Lumbricus* has been described by Kamemoto (72). Removal of the brain causes an increase in the water content and a decrease in the sodium concentration of the body which can be counteracted by transplantation of the brain or by the injection of brain homogenates.

MOLLUSCA

There have been a number of interesting developments in the last few years on the subject of salt and water balance in molluscs. Amongst these are: the recognition of a number of different mechanisms for developing buoyancy in marine molluscs, each depending on some form of ionic regulation; the elucidation of the basis of isosmotic tissue regulation in euryhaline molluscs; studies on water balance in terrestrial molluscs; and studies on the excretory systems of a variety of molluscs. In contrast the problem of the active uptake of ions by freshwater molluscs has been relatively neglected and the few studies in this field have dealt with calcium rather than sodium transport.

Marine molluscs are usually isosmotic with seawater but many pelagic species have well-developed powers of ionic regulation which aid buoyancy. In *Sepia* and in *Nautilus* buoyancy is maintained by the evacuation of water from the shell chambers. This is brought about by the active transport of salt from the chamber fluid until it is hyposmotic with the blood, the water then moves by osmosis into the blood against the hydrostatic pressure (73). As the osmotic concentration of seawater is approximately 1 M/liter this system would be effective to a depth of over twenty atmospheres or 600 feet. Many shell-less molluscs float by ionic regulation alone. Bathyscaphoid squids have greatly enlarged coelomic cavities filled with a solution isosmotic with seawater but in which the sodium is largely replaced by ammonium ions. As the solution of ammonium salts is less dense than that of seawater the whole animal has neutral buoyancy (74). The pelagic gasteropod *Pterotrachea coronata* produces some reduction of density by lowering the concentration of magnesium and sulphate ions in the blood, an interesting convergence with the coelenterates.

Euryhaline lamellibranchs such as *Mytilus, Ostrea,* and *Gryphaea* remain isosmotic with seawater and adapt their tissues to changing blood concentration by varying the concentration of free amino acids (75–78). Some euryhaline gasteropods can osmoregulate but their ability is limited and tissue regulation must take place on almost the same scale as in the lamellibranchs.

The blood concentrations of freshwater and terrestrial snails are low but they are able to tolerate concentrations up to twice normal. *Planorbis* and a number of other freshwater species survive well in diluted seawater up to 7‰ salinity and will tolerate 8‰, about twice their normal concentration (79). The mechanism of tissue tolerance to these changes is obscure; evidently the synthesis of free amino acids or other organic solutes, which would prevent exosmosis from the tissues as the blood concentration rose, is not important. Burton (80, 81) found that when *Helix pomatia* was desiccated the water content of the tissues varied inversely with the sodium content of the blood. However, as the blood sodium increased, the sodium content of the tissues rose and the greater part of the variation in total water content was due to variation in blood volume. Any penetration of blood solutes into the tissues will reduce the loss of tissue water at the expense of the blood volume. When salt loaded, *Helix pomatia* is slow to excrete the salt load (82, 83) but when desiccated, both *Helix aspersa* and *Otala lactata* can restore water balance very rapidly by crawling over a wet surface (81). Water balance is almost restored in the first hour, and afterwards remains constant. The basis of this rapid uptake is not clear. In addition to a facility for rapid water uptake, snails have a mechanism to reduce water loss. Water loss from the surface of active snails (*H. aspersa*) is almost equivalent to that from an open-water surface (84) but when a snail withdraws into the shell, evaporation from the exposed mantle is very low (85, 86). This reduced rate of evaporation is probably due to a layer of low water permeability situated on the collar surface. The permeability of the regulating mantle collar is only one fortieth of freshly killed tissue. The rate of water loss from aestivating Australian snails *Thermopipa* and *Pleuroscia* increases sharply above 25° and 35°C respectively which indicates some change of state in a water-resistant layer such as occurs in some insects (87). As a further means of withstanding desiccation some land snails store water in the mantle cavity (88).

The dynamics of calcium transport in freshwater molluscs have been studied by a number of workers. In both *Anodonta* and *Lymnaea* the body wall is very permeable to calcium. The isolated mantle of *Anodonta* is permeable to calcium ions in both directions but although the potential across the mantle is calcium dependent (89) there is no measurable active transport of calcium between isotonic salines. The inner surface of the mantle is less permeable than the outer (90). Only a small part of the calcium content of the mantle is involved in the exchange. The mantles of freshwater molluscs are less permeable than those of marine species (91). In *Anodonta* the rate of movement of calcium is much higher than that of sodium. When *Lymnaea stagnalis* is transferred to low calcium solutions, 1–25 mg/liter, a net loss of calcium takes place for several days but active uptake continues and gradually increases until there is a net influx once again (92, 93). The characteristics of the active uptake of sodium and calcium in freshwater molluscs remain to be defined.

Excretion in the molluscs has been reviewed recently (94).

ARACHNIDS

The arachnids are a neglected group compared with the crustaceans, but they present some interesting features. *Limulus polyphemus* is moderately euryhaline but remains isosmotic with the medium. The tissues show isosmotic regulation but unlike all other marine invertebrates they possess only a low concentration of free amino acids: 80 mmole/kg water. They contain a high concentration ($= 570$ mmoles/liter) of other nitrogen compounds. The concentration of these compounds declines with salinity but the compounds have not yet been identified (95). The scorpions are also unusual in possessing a high blood concentration compared with other terrestrial animals. The plasma of the scorpion *Androctonus* contains 263 mE Na/liter and 267 mE Cl/liter. The muscle contains 76 mmole/kg water of free amino acids, as high as in *Limulus* (96).

CRUSTACEA

Osmoregulation in crustaceans has been reviewed by Robertson (97) and Lockwood (98). Outstanding developments in this field in the last few years have been the analysis of the dynamics of salt balance in several crustacea, and the analysis of intracellular regulation by Florkin and his co-workers.

Regulation of cellular osmotic pressure.—In euryhaline species such as *Eriocheir* the concentration of free amino acids varies with the osmotic concentration of the blood (99, 100). In *Eriocheir* the adaptation involves an alteration in the concentrations of alanine and of glycine. Trimethylamine oxide also makes a substantial contribution to the osmotic pressure of seawater-adapted forms and declines similarly in freshwater. In *Carcinus* glycine and proline are the amino acids mainly involved (100). The total concentrations of inorganic ions vary in a similar ratio, but potassium ions are maintained at a relatively constant level while the intracellular concentrations of sodium and chloride change as much as fourfold (99, 101). Similar changes of amino acids occur in the euryhaline prawns *Leander serratus* and *L. sequilla* (102). Once again the major amino acids involved in adaptation are glycine, proline, and alanine.

Schoffeniels (103) demonstrated that a similar regulation of free amino acids could take place in isolated nerves of *Eriocheir sinensis*. The regulation is therefore not dependent on a hormonal mechanism and the amino acids must be of intracellular origin. Further experiments showed that osmotic pressure per se was not responsible for changes in the amino acid concentration but that the presence of sodium or potassium ions was necessary. Experiments with the isolated ventral nerve cord of the lobster *Hormarus vulgaris* showed that veretrine, cocaine, or electrical stimulation, all of which affected the ionic balance of the cells, also altered the amino acid content of the nerve cord (104, 105). Changes in the level of amino acid concentration within the tissue depend on the relative rates of synthesis and breakdown on free amino acids and Schoffeniels (106) has demonstrated the marked effects of various concentration of Na^+ and K^+ on glutamic acid dehydrogenase activity. Florkin & Schoffeniels (107) suggest that in stenohaline species, changes in the ionic concentration of the cell produce only a change in the rate of turnover of the amino acids, not in concentration, but in euryhaline forms, differential effects produce a change in the equilibrium level.

When *Carcinus maenas* and *Eriocheir sinensis* are transferred to dilute media, the rate of nitrogen excretion is increased for a while, as the result of the breakdown of free amino acids; when transferred to a more concentrated medium, nitrogen excretion is decreased while free amino acids are accumulated (107).

Osmotic regulation.—Comparative measurements of the permeability of various crustacea to ions are rare. Gross (108) measured the permeability of isolated pieces of exoskeleton to salts (mainly sodium chloride) and found that permeability was higher in marine species (e.g. *Pugettia producta*); lower in littoral and brackish species (e.g. *Hemigrapsus oregonensis, H. nudus,* and *Pachygrapsus crassipes*); and lowest in the freshwater crayfish *Cambarus clarkii.* Extrarenal sodium loss declines from 891 μE/hour in a 50 g *Carcinus* to 7.5 μE/hour in *Astacus* of the same weight (109, 110). The permeability to water is similarly higher in marine than in freshwater species. Werntz (111) found that the marine *Gammarus oceanicus* was twice as permeable to water as the freshwater *G.*

fasciatus. The rate constants for ^3H_2O exchange range from 2.4 h^{-1} in *Carcinus* to 0.20 h^{-1} in *Astacus* (112). The volume of urine produced is proportional to the osmotic gradient in hyposmotic solutions (111), a finding which confirms that the urine output is equivalent to the osmotic inflow. The origin of the water lost as urine in isosmotic or hyperosmotic media is obscure but *Artemia* drinks the medium like a teleost when in concentrated solutions (113), and oral and anal drinking have been widely reported in crustacea. The relative quantities of salt lost renally and extrarenally are highly variable. In the decapods renal losses are usually low, amounting to about 10 per cent of the total loss in *Astacus* (114–116) but in *Gammarus duebeni* the renal loss may account for 80 per cent of the total (117).

The salt lost, whether in the urine or by diffusion, must be replaced by active uptake. Shaw showed that in *Astacus,* and in other crustacea, the relationship between sodium uptake and external sodium concentration is similar to that between the rate of an enzymatic reaction and the substrate concentration, as defined by the Michaelis-Menten equation. At low concentrations uptake is proportional to concentration, but at high concentrations uptake tends to saturation. The external concentration at which uptake is half saturated will be a measure of the affinity of the carrier for the ion (109, 110). In brackish water animals this is fairly high, 70 mE/liter in *Carcinus maenas* and 10 mE/liter in *G. duebeni;* but such transport systems will be ineffective at low concentrations and freshwater animals have carrier systems with much higher affinities. In *Astacus* the transport system is saturated at an external concentration of 0.2 mE Na/liter (110) and at 0.1–0.15 mE Na/liter in *Gammarus pulex* (118). The problem is discussed in general terms by Shaw (109, 119). The chloride uptake systems have similar properties but sodium and chloride uptake can occur independently (120). In the crayfish sodium uptake is blocked by external ammonium ions and chloride uptake by external bicarbonate ions, this blockage suggesting that sodium uptake occurs in exchange for ammonium ions and chloride for bicarbonate ions, as in freshwater fish. However, such a system could not be effective in *Carcinus* as the sodium flux is much greater than that of ammonia and it is likely that sodium and chloride uptake are linked.

The regulation of the blood concentration in response to changes in the internal concentration is complex. A fall in the external concentration leads to an immediate fall in active uptake as a consequence of the properties of the transport system. As losses are initially unchanged the blood concentration declines and this stimulates an increased rate of uptake at the body surface. This is brought about by an increase in the quantity of carrier, not a change in its properties. The half-saturation concentration remains the same [(110) *Astacus;* (118, 121) *Gammarus*]. A fall in blood concentration leads directly to a reduction in the loss through the body surface and it also stimulates an increased uptake from the urine resulting in a further reduction of salt loss. The exact relationship between blood concentration and medium concentration depends on these interactions. The subject is reviewed by Shaw (119). A detailed survey of salt balance of the gammarids *Gammarus duebeni* (brackish water), and *G. pulex* and *G. lacustris* (freshwater), shows that the different parameters vary over an extremely wide range (118, 121, 122). In brackish water most of the salt loss from *G. duebeni* takes place in the urine. In freshwater urine loss becomes very small in all three species. The external concentration at which uptake is half saturated is twenty times higher in *G. duebeni* than in *G. pulex* but by suitable adjustments both can live in freshwater. Sutcliffe & Shaw (122) suggest that salt uptake from both the urine and the external medium is controlled by the same mechanism and that in general the work load is distributed fairly evenly between the body surface and the excretory organ.

The isolated gills of crayfish actively transport both sodium, potassium, and chloride ions although calcium and magnesium appear to be in approximate equilibrium [*Austropotamobius* (123); *Astacus leptodoclytus* (124)]. In distinction from frog skin, the interior is maintained strongly negative (about 60 mV) to the medium and the authors suggest that the sodium pump is situated at the inner surface of the epithelium, as in frog skin, but that in addition a powerful chloride pump is situated at the outer surface. Unlike frog skin the gills are more permeable to sodium than to chloride.

The active output of ions at the body surface in hyposmotic crustacea has been rather neglected. *Palaemonetes varians* maintains ion balance by the active output of sodium ions in more concentrated media, the chloride being close to passive equilibrium, while in hyposmotic media it takes up chloride activity and sodium is close to equilibrium (125). *Pachygrapsus crassipes* maintains a potential of only 2–3 mV in all media and must take up and put out both sodium and chloride ions (126).

Recent studies of crustacean excretory organs have confirmed that urine is produced by ultrafiltration and modified by resorption (127) but have clarified many of the details of the process and brought some interesting features to light. As the result of studies of the excretion of high molecular weight compounds in *Pacifastacus,* Kirschner & Wagner (128) conclude that the filtration volume is as high as 90 per cent of the blood entering the system. The resulting tenfold increase in blood protein concentration produces marked Donnan effects. As a result the ultrafiltrate contains a significantly lower sodium concentration than the blood. This is in agreement with Riegel's (129) micropuncture studies but Riegel (130) also found a lower concentration of chloride in the ultrafiltrate whereas a Donnan effect should increase the chloride concentration. Kirschner & Wagner (128) point out that the molecular weight of crayfish blood proteins is so large, 885,000, that the colloid osmotic pressure of the blood must be less than 1 mm Hg, thus allowing for ultrafiltration even after a tenfold increase in protein concentration. Picken (131) recorded a hydrostatic pressure of 15 mm Hg. The localisation of fluorescent labelled protein in the peritubular cells of the coelomosac suggests to Kirschner & Wagner that ultrafiltration occurs through the cells, in contrast to Kummel (16) who concluded that ultrafiltration occurred directly through the basement membrane between the feet of the podocytes, as in the mammal.

Micropuncture studies of crayfish (*Oronectes* and *Austropotamobius*) antennal gland by Riegel (129, 130) show that resorption of sodium, chloride, and potassium takes place in all parts of the gland, including the labyrinth and bladder. The inulin concentration in the coelomosac is only slightly higher in the blood, 116 per cent, but rises to 160–180 per cent at the distal end of the excretory organ, which indicates that some water is lost from the urine down the osmotic gradient (129). The bladder epithelium contains considerable cholinesterase activity, and ^{22}Na injected into the bladder appears in the blood. The cholinesterase inhibitor eserine blocks sodium uptake from the bladder (132).

Marine crustacea, even when isosmotic to seawater, generally maintain a low concentration of magnesium in the blood and a high concentration in the urine (133, 134). Gross & Capen (135) have demonstrated that in the euryhaline crab *Pachygrapsus,* magnesium is secreted into the bladder, largely in exchange for sodium. U/B ratios as high as ten were recorded although the U/B ratios for inulin did not reach two. Similarly U/B ratios as high as ten for magnesium were recorded in *Carcinus* after four days in air, while U/B ratios for inulin were only 2.5 (136). The longer the urine remained in the bladder the higher the magnesium concentrations achieved. As urine flow depended on the salinity of the medium, the relationships between the magnesium concentration of the blood and of the medium were complex. In addition to secreting magnesium the bladder is also the site of glucose resorption in *Pachygrapsus* (137).

Water balance in hyposmotic crustacea presents some problems. Although Croghan (113) showed that *Artemia* drank the medium like a marine teleost, Gross et al. (138) concluded that *Cardiosoma* did not drink the medium, 150 per cent seawater, in which it was hyporegulating. However, this conclusion was based only on the observation that the gut fluid was nearly isosmotic with the serum. More detailed analyses might lead to a different conclusion.

The development of the terrestrial habit depends on wide variety of mechanisms, both physiological and behavioural. A number of terrestrial crabs have the ability to take up water from moist sand [*Cardiosoma* (138); *Gecarcinus* (139)]. In *Gecarcinus* water is taken up through the pericardial sacs. These sacs are diverticulae of the pericardium and are particularly well developed in land crabs. In *Gecarcinus* they protrude into the branchial chambers and before ecdysis they bulge out from under the carapace, although they are still covered by the arthrodial membrane between the thorax and abdomen. The tip of the sac is covered by a tuft of setae which collects surface water and conducts it to a reservoir on the sac where it can be either absorbed or possibly transferred to the gills (139).

Copeland (personal communication) finds that "mitochondrial pumps", thought to be characteristic of salt transport, are confined to the posterior gills in contact with the sacs and Bliss et al. (140) observed that seawater was less readily absorbed than freshwater. This may indicate that salt and water are taken up by different routes. Before ecdysis the sacs become enormously extended to hold fluid, which is used to expand the new carapace. The coconut crab *Birgus* takes up water by drinking and keeps its gill chambers moist by placing water in them from small puddles (141).

Land or amphibious crabs also show behavioural adaptations including a preference for high humidities [*Potamon* (142)] and for waters of appropriate salinity [*Birgus* (141)]. The problem of salt balance in terrestrial crabs has not been fully elucidated. Most terrestrial and semiterrestrial crabs can regulate in both dilute and concentrated seawater although some of the more terrestrial species drown if totally immersed for some time (143). Salt balance presents few problems if freshwater or hyposmotic salines are available, as salt losses will be small on land and salt can be replenished by uptake through the gills as required. How regulation occurs when only seawater is available is still a mystery. If there is access to pools of seawater then no doubt some form of active excretion of salt can take place into the water but *Cardiosoma* can regulate hyposmotically when only seawater-dampened sand is available (138). Regulation should then lead to the production of a very concentrated solution of salt in the branchial chambers. How this is dealt with is not known. It may be significant that *Gecarcinus* can regulate in 150 per cent seawater when bulk water is available (138) but dies when only sand dampened with 150 per cent seawater is available (140). Urine in terrestrial crabs is never hyperosmotic to the blood and so can take no part in hyposmotic regulation although it may contain high concentrations of magnesium and thus play an important part in maintaining low blood magnesium (138).

The hormonal control of salt and water balance is now being investigated, and a complex picture is beginning to emerge. Several workers, including Kamemoto et al. (144) working on *Procambarus,* and Bliss, Wary & Marting (140) working on *Gecarcinus,* find evidence of a hormone released from the eyestalk which limits water uptake. Eyestalkless *Gecarcinus* show extra swelling of the pericardial sacs before moulting. Kamemoto et al. suggest that the hormone decreases the permeability of the body wall to water. Kamemoto shows that the hormone is produced in the brain, and released in the eyestalk. Bliss (139, 142) suggests that there is also a hormone favouring uptake and retention. In the semiterrestrial crab *Malagrapsus messon* it has been shown that the water-balance effect is mediated by a further hormone released from the thoracic ganglion under the influence of the eyestalk hormone. These are indications of other hormones controlling salt balance. Eyestalkless larvae of the decapod *Rithropanopeus harrisi* survive but are isosmotic over the salinity range 5 to 30‰ while intact larvae are hyperosmotic over the lower part of the range, but the eyestalkless larvae regulate and are hyposmotic to 40‰ while normal larvae are isosmotic at this concentration (145). Experiments by Lockwood with *Gammarus duebeni* suggest that in this animal the control of the salt uptake system can operate on changes of blood concentration rather than on absolute levels (146, 147).

Studies on calcium balance are not common and it is therefore worth mentioning that Dall (148) finds that in the prawn *Metapenaeus,* the gills are the main site of active uptake: 90 per cent of calcium uptake and 70 per cent of calcium loss take place across the gill; only 0.5 per cent of the loss takes place through the antennary gland.

Insects

No attempt will be made here to review all aspects of the physiology of salt and water balance in insects but two or three developments in this field must be mentioned.

The possibility of the active transport of water in physiological systems has often been discussed but in general more detailed analysis has shown that in the vertebrates and most invertebrates, water movement follows passively down concentration gradients established by the active transport of solutes, and the hypothesis of active water transport has been generally rejected. However, the active transport of water is now established in a number of insects and in certain ticks (149). The active transport of water takes place in the uptake of water vapour from air of low relative humidities (rh) Insect haemolymph is in equilibrium with an rh of about 99 per cent. A number of insects are able to take up water at rh of about 90 per cent, the rat flea *Xenopsylla* can take up water from air at 65 per cent rh (150), and the firebrat *Thermobia* can take it up from rh 50 per cent, or more precisely from a saturation deficit of 8 mm Hg (151). This is equivalent to an osmotic pressure difference of several hundred atmospheres. This process must require energy but the mechanism is unknown although Beament (152) has suggested a possible model, in which the driving force in cyclical changes is the degree of hydration of the underlying proteins while superficial lipids act as a valve.

Maddrell, giving the first detailed description of a water-balance hormone in the insects, has identified the site of production and release of a diuretic hormone in *Rhodnius prolixus* (153–157). The hormone is produced by neurosecretory cells lying in the posterior region of the mesothoracic ganglionic mass, and is released from axons lying in the proximal region of the abdominal nerves, close behind the ganglionic mass. The stimulus for the release of the hormone is the distention of the abdomen brought about by the swelling of the mid-gut following a meal. The stretch receptors probably responsible have been identified. The concentration of the hormone released is sufficient to bring about maximum diuresis within a few minutes. The hormone is destroyed by the Malpighian tubules and diuresis stops as soon as the distention of the abdomen is reduced. An antidiuretic factor produced by the corpora alata has been described in the cockroach *Periplaneta* (158). The hormone decreases the rate of secretion in the Malpighian tubules and increases resorption from the rectum. A further antidiuretic factor produced by the thoracic and last abdominal ganglia appears to reduce secretion but not rectal resorption.

The presence of a sodium-rich extracellular fluid was first demonstrated in central nervous tissues of the cockroach (159). The concentration of sodium is almost twice that in the haemolymph while the concentration of chloride is approximately half. Divalent ions, such as calcium, are even more concentrated, which suggests that the ions are in Donnan equilibrium with those in the haemolymph. The free anion groups causing the excess of cations in the extracellular fluid of the nervous system may be partially removed by desheathing. The extracellular fluid is accessible to inulin but not to trypan blue.

In the stick insect *Carausius morosus,* the haemolymph contains more potassium (33.7 mE/liter) than sodium (20.1 mE/liter), although the concentrations of these ions in the nerve cord tissues are similar to those of the cockroach, which possesses a sodium-rich haemolymph (160). Despite the very specialised ionic composition of the haemolymph in this species, the axons appear to be conventional in that production of action potentials is dependent on a relatively high concentration of sodium ions at the axon surfaces (161, 162). The dependence on magnesium ions demonstrated in this species (161) would appear not to involve a contribution of these ions in carrying the action current, but most probably a rôle in maintaining the stability of the axon membranes (162). The ability of the axons of *Carausius* to function with the extremely specialised haemolymph appears to be due to an appreciable regulation of the concentrations of inorganic cations at the axon surfaces. This regulation does not appear to result from any significant restriction in the accessibility of cations to the general extracellular system (160) but from a local regulation which appears to maintain a relatively high concentration of sodium ions at the axon surfaces by extrusion from the glial cells into the restricted extracellular spaces.

The physiology of the extracellular space in the insect nervous system in *Periplaneta* is reviewed by Treherne (163) who draws an illuminating analogy between this layer and the so-called blood-brain barrier of the vertebrates.

FISHES

Hagfishes.—Recent studies confirm Robertson's thesis (164) that *Myxine* is unique among the vertebrates in that its ancestors have never lived in freshwater. The blood is almost isosmotic with the medium and the osmotic pressure is due almost entirely to inorganic ions. The blood composition in some ways resembles that of the decapod crustacea in containing fewer divalent ions and more monovalent ions than seawater. This is probably a primitive feature (165). The urine is also almost isosmotic with the blood but contains correspondingly more divalent ions than the blood. The rate of urine production is low and the majority of individuals do not swallow seawater at all (166). The composition of the tissues also resembles that of marine invertebrates. Inorganic ions and organic phosphate together account for only 42 per cent of the total osmotic pressure of the muscle, whereas in the marine teleosts they account for over 70 per cent (167). Other constituents of *Myxine* muscle include 291 mmole/kg water of amino acids, mostly proline, 87 mmole of trimethylamine oxide, 87 mmole of betaine, 65 mmole of urea, and 72 mmole/kg water of lactate (168). The lactate concentration seems high for normal muscle.

All other marine vertebrates maintain a low salt content in their blood; their ancestors probably lived at one time in freshwater. Recent work has shown that there are only a limited number of ways in which these low concentrations are maintained, and it has become clear that each of these mechanisms has evolved several times independently. In the elasmobranchs, holocephali, and coelacanths and in certain brackish-water frogs, such as *Rana cancrivora,* the blood is made approximately isosmotic with seawater by maintaining a high concentration of urea and certain other organic compounds. In the lampreys, in teleosts, and in the tadpoles of *Rana cancrivora* (217) the osmotic pressure of the blood remains low and water balance is maintained by drinking the medium and secreting the salt extrarenally. The sturgeons, which also maintain a low blood concentration, probably maintain salt balance in the same way. Aquatic amniotes live in virtual isolation from the medium, although marine reptiles and birds possess salt-secreting glands to facilitate the removal of surplus salts.

Lampreys.—Lampreys regulate in hyperosmotic solutions in a manner similar to that of the teleosts. The rate of urine production is low and most of the chloride must be removed extrarenally (169). The skin is relatively permeable to electrolytes but cannot actively transport them (170). Tracer studies might show that in seawater additional large quantities of electrolytes are gained through the skin as well as through the gut. When freshwater-adapted lampreys were salt loaded, 75 per cent of the loss took place extrarenally, a fact again implying a high permeability to salts. In hyposmotic solutions urine flow is apparently proportional to the osmotic pressure difference between blood and medium. The urine flow in freshwater is 10 ml/kg/hour. The sodium concentration in the urine is fairly high, 20 mE/liter, and rises in more concentrated media (171).

Elasmobranchs.—Burger & Hess (172) demonstrated that the rectal gland in the dogfish *Squalus acanthias* secreted a fluid isosmotic with the blood but containing twice the concentration of sodium and chloride. In salt-loaded animals the rate of secretion averaged 1.9 ml/kg/hour. However, *Squalus acanthias* can maintain salt balance even after the removal of the gland although the salt content of the urine is increased (173). Recent measurements by Burger & Tosterson (174) showed that the rate of influx of sodium into the anterior end of *Squalus acanthias* is less than 1 mmole/kg/hour. The renal output was only 0.1 to 0.2 mE/kg/hour. Similarly, in *Scyliorhinus* the sodium turnover was only 700 µE/kg/hour although the chloride turnover was ten times as large. The renal loss of both sodium and chloride was about 60 µE/kg/hour, and the rectal gland loss about 30 µE/kg/hour. It is clear that most of the efflux of both ions must take place elsewhere (175). However, the total rate of influx indicates a very low permeability, the rate of influx into marine teleosts is between ten and twenty times as large as that into *S. acanthias*.

Holocephali.—Analyses of the blood of *Chaemera* (176) confirm that it also regulates like the elasmobranchs, although the concentration of sodium and chloride (341–393 µE/liter) is higher and the concentration of urea (244–287 mmole/liter) is rather lower than the elasmobranchs. The undoubtedly independent acquisition of a high blood urea in the amphibians and in the coelacanths adds weight to the suggestion that the holocephalans are not closely related to the elasmobranchs and may well have independently acquired this method of regulation (177).

Coelacanths.—Analyses of blood samples from a deep-frozen coelacanth indicate that the coelacanths also regulate in the same way. The blood contains a high concentration of urea (300–400 mmole/liter and a low concentration of sodium chloride ca. 200 mmole/liter, but the condition of the samples made it impossible to ascertain the original osmotic pressure of the blood exactly (178). The samples were slightly hyposmotic to seawater but this may be an artifact due to an accumulation of ice in the circulatory system during the freezing of the fish. It seems unlikely that the coelacanths would combine both a teleost and an elasmobranch method of osmotic regulation. Whatever the exact osmotic pressure of the blood, the problem of maintaining the salt balance remains.

Teleosts

After many years of comparative neglect, osmotic and ionic regulation in the teleosts is now the subject of intensive study. Over the last few years our picture of regulation has been dramatically altered by the recognition that a large part of the salt influx in seawater takes place through the body surface, not through the gut alone, as had previously been assumed. The hormonal control of salt balance in the teleosts is now being closely examined. Although no clear picture has emerged, it is certain that salt regulation in the teleosts differs in many ways from that in the tetrapods, in which by comparison regulation shows many similarities from group to group.

Regulation in hyperosmotic media.—Smith (179) showed that teleosts maintained water balance in the sea by drinking the water and by eliminating the divalent ions renally and the monovalent ions extrarenally. Keys (180) demonstrated that the extrarenal site of excretion was in the head region, most probably at the gills. Although a very large number of measurements of blood concentration have been published, dynamic studies of salt balance have been rather sparse until recently. Mullins (181) working with *Gasterosteus aculeatus,* House (182) with *Blennius pholis,* and Gordon (183) with *Salmo gairdneri* found that salt fluxes were much greater in seawater than in freshwater or brackish water. However, these workers all assumed that the influx in seawater took place through the gut. No measurements of drinking rates in teleosts were published between 1930 and 1964 when Motais & Maetz (184) showed that in the flounder *Platichthys flesus* only 20 per cent of the influx in seawater could be accounted for by the salt swallowed. The remaining 80 per cent must enter through the body surface. Similarly, in *Fundulus heteroclitus* (185, 186) the drinking accounts for only a minor part of the total influx of both sodium and chloride ions. In *Platichthys* the drinking averaged about 1 per cent of the body weight per hour and in *Serranus scriba* 0.5 per cent per hour (184). In the much smaller *F. heteroclitus* the drinking rate lies between 1.6 and 2.3 per cent of the body weight per hour. Recently, Hickman (187) has shown that in the flounder *Platichthys* the drinking rate averages about .5 per cent per hour. The intertidal blenny *Xiphister* drinks only 0.03 per cent per hour and practically all the influx takes place through the surface, most probably the gills (188). In the eel (*Anguilla*) the skin is impermeable to ions (189). The large extrarenal fluxes have some curious features. In *Fundulus* the greater part of the sodium flux across the gills take place by inward diffusion and outward active transport (186, 190). However, in *Fundulus* about 30 per cent of the fluxes in seawater are due to exchange diffusion. In many other fish a large part of the sodium flux in seawater is due to exchange diffusion so that transfer to an isotonic mannitol solution causes an instantaneous reduction in efflux. In *Uranoscopus, Serranus,* and *Xiphister* sodium outfluxes rapidly fall to 50 or 60 per cent of the outfluxes in seawater. In euryhaline fishes there is also a slower regulation extending over hours which finally reduces the effluxes to 1 or 2 per cent of their level in seawater. Once this slower regulation has taken place the fish maintains a low flux for many hours when returned to seawater. Motais, Garcia Romeu & Maetz (190) suggest that the exchange diffusion component is a valuable adaptation in procuring an instant reduction in flux on transfer to brackish water, but the value of a large flux in seawater in the first place is not explained. The exchange diffusion component varies with the external sodium concentration in a manner analogous to Michaelis-Menten kinetics. The half-saturated concentration is about 400 mmole Na/liter. It is noteworthy that marine teleosts always exchange 20 to 30 per cent of their total body sodium per hour, the greater part of this exchange taking place across the gills although in some cases the entry is due to exchange diffusion and in other cases to passive diffusion.

The value of this large exchange is even more inexplicable in the light of the fact that euryhaline fish adapted to freshwater and transferred back to seawater maintain a low permeability for many hours although apparently suffering no ill effects. This change in sodium permeability on transfer between seawater and freshwater in euryhaline fish is one of the most striking recent discoveries in this field.

Hickman (187), in the course of estimating drinking rates from a consideration of the rates of renal and enteric excretion of divalent ions, found that the greater part of the calcium ingested did not appear in either the urine or the rectum and is presumably also excreted through the gills.

The rate of urine flow in marine teleosts is low, 1.5 per cent of the body weight per day in the eel *Anguilla* (191), 1.4 per cent in *Platichthys* (192), 1 per cent body weight per day in *Fundulus kansae* (193), and only 0.34 per cent in *Xiphister* (188). Although most measurements show that the urine in marine teleosts is hyposmotic to the blood and the kidney lacks the loop of Henle, it was recorded by Stanley & Fleming (194) that during adaptation from freshwater to seawater, *Fundulus kansae* for a while produces urine remarkably hypertonic to the blood although not to the seawater. Some resorption of monovalent ions and water occurs in the bladder of the flounder (192). This is commonplace in the frog.

Because Keys (180) estimated chloride in his eel preparation by means of silver nitrate titration, the process of salt excretion in teleosts is often referred to as one of chloride excretion and cells possibly responsible for the process in the gill are usually referred to as "chloride cells". It is only a fortunate coincidence that potential measurements of House (182) showed that with the *Blennius pholis,* chloride secretion was in fact the primary process and sodium transport was facilitated by the potential produced by the active transport of chloride. More recently Maetz & Campanini (195) have found that the blood of the eel is also electrically positive with respect to seawater.

The rate of urine production in seawater is so low that it is not an important route for the output of sodium. The low rate is due primarily to a very low filtration rate, and Lahlou (192) has shown that only a proportion of the tubules in the kidney of the flounder function in seawater. In both the flounder (192) and *Fundulus kansae* (193) three quarters or more of the filtrate is resorbed.

The hormonal control of salt balance in seawater was until recently very obscure. Oxytocin was shown to increase the rate of exchange of sodium in seawater-adapted flounders and to speed the rate of adaptation from freshwater to seawater (196) but recently Motais & Maetz have shown that arginine vasotocin is more effective than oxytocin in facilitating adaptation to seawater (197). Cortisol is essential for normal sodium efflux in the eel. After adrenolectomy, efflux falls to one third of the normal level but cortisol restores it. Plasma sodium is increased by adrenolectomy and survival in seawater is limited (198).

Regulation in freshwater.—The rate of turnover of sodium and chloride in freshwater teleosts is of the order of 1 per cent or less of the body content per hour (196, 201). Urine output is large but the urine concentration is low and the greater part of the salt loss is extrarenal (202). In *Salmo gairdneri,* urine flow is of the order of 75–110 ml/kg/day (203, 204), except at smolting when the urine flow declines to about half. This reduction in urine flow is due to a reduction in the filtration rate. Holmes & Stanier (204) suggest that this related with changes in the level of adrenocortical hormones. However, the plasma concentration is similar if not marginally higher in the smolt than in pre-smolt and if the urine flow corresponds to the osmotic inflow of water then smolting must be accompanied by either a decrease in water permeability or a change in the body surface area. Similarly, Stanley & Fleming (205) showed that prolactin increased the urine flow but not the sodium loss in hypophysectomised *Fundulus* in freshwater and they suggest that it must act by increasing the water permeability. In both *Platichthys* (192) and in *Fundulus* (193) the filtration rate is two to four times the rate of urine production.

Sodium and chloride are both actively taken up at the gills. In the goldfish *Carassius* sodium can be taken up in exchange for ammonia ions. The addition of ammonium ions to the external media blocks sodium uptake but the intraperitoneal injection of ammonia facilitates it. Similarly chloride ions are taken up in exchange for bicarbonate ions. The sodium and chloride can be taken up independently (206, 207).

The hormonal control of salt balance in freshwater teleosts is obscure. Adrenalectomy reduces salt uptake in the eel but aldosterone restores it to normal (208). However, aldosterone cannot be detected in the eel (209) so the experiment is of doubtful significance. Cortisol, which does occur naturally in the eel (209), reduces sodium uptake. Isotocin stimulates sodium uptake in the goldfish *Carassius auratus,* oxytocin also increases uptake but simultaneously increases efflux from the gills. Arginine vasotocin has similar but less pronounced effects than oxytocin. Simultaneously arginine vasotocin and oxytocin, but not isotocin, have a diuretic effect leading to an increased salt loss (210). A variety of fish, including *Fundulus heteroclitus, Poecilia, Tilapia,* and *Xiphophorus* (210–213), cannot survive in freshwater after hypophysectomy although they will survive in isotonic saline. However, mammalian prolactin promotes survival in freshwater (214). The inability of hypophysectomised fish to survive is due to excessive salt loss which is reduced to normal by prolactin (185, 199). *Fundulus kansae* and the eel *Anguilla* can both survive in freshwater after hypophysectomy but salt losses are increased and plasma level is reduced (200, 212, 215, 216). The eel at least has a remarkably low permeability to salts in freshwater (208) and this reduces the limiting level of sodium in which it can survive below the level of most freshwaters (199). The increased loss following hypophysectomy in *F. heteroclitus* is probably extrarenal (185). Although Stanley & Fleming (202) suggested that it was mainly due to increased renal loss in *F. kansae,* later work (204) showed that the prolactin did not affect renal sodium loss in hypophysectomised *F. kansae*. It is worth noting that when transferred from seawater to freshwater, hypophysectomised *F. heteroclitus* can still reduce sodium loss by a considerable proportion so it must be concluded that other hormones are involved in the reduction of permeability during adaptation from seawater to freshwater.

Adaptation to changes of salinity.—The adaptation of the extrarenal fluxes to changes in salinity has been examined in a number of fishes by Motais, Garcia Romeu & Maetz (190). On transfer from seawater to freshwater any exchange diffusion component in the flux declines immediately to a negligible level. However, in several of the fish, for example the eel, the instantaneous decline in efflux is greater on transfer to freshwater than it is on transfer to isotonic mannitol and Motais et al. suggest that there may be an additional "osmotic" effect on the efflux. Although adrenalectomy reduces the efflux in seawater, transfer to freshwater causes a further small reduction in efflux even in adrenalectomised eels (198). After about thirty minutes in freshwater the efflux from euryhaline fish shows a progressive further decline. If the fish are transferred back to seawater at this stage the efflux does not return to its original level for several hours.

Transfer between seawater and freshwater is accompanied by rapid changes in renal function (191–193, 203). In both the eel *Anguilla* and the rainbow trout *Salmo gairdneri* the reduction of urine is due both to a decline in filtration and to a increase in tubular resorption (191, 218).

Osmotic and ionic regulation in fishes has been reviewed by Parry (37).

AMPHIBIA

Studies of salt and water regulation in amphibia continue in two fields: the study of the *in vitro* properties of frog skin and the study of whole animals. In general, there appears to be no correlation between workers in these two fields. Isolated frog skin has continued to be the subject of intense research as *in vitro* it constitutes an almost ideal sodium pump. More recently, similar studies have been extended to isolated preparations of the bladder (219), gut (220), and cornea (221) of the toad *Bufo marinus*. No attempt will be made here to review all the enormous output of papers on *in vitro* studies of frog skin but one or two recent developments with wider implications will be mentioned.

In Koefoed-Johnsen and Ussing's model for frog skin, chloride entered passively as the result of the potential created by the sodium pump. It was demonstrated by Krogh (22) that the intact frog would take up chloride ions against concentration gradients of 1000 to 1. In the model this would require a potential difference across the skin of 170 mV, much greater than that recorded. Recently evidence has been found in the frog *Leptadoctylus* of an additional chloride pump which facilitates chloride uptake at low external concentrations, although no active transport of chloride could be detected in the toad *Bufo arenaria* (223). It is possible that a similar pump will be found in *Rana*. This would reconcile Ussing's model with Krogh's observations.

The model has been modified recently in other respects. In the original model sodium entered the cells passively. At low external concentrations, the concentration of sodium in the cells would therefore be almost negligible. Biber, Chez & Curran (224) show that this is not the case and suggest that the active layer is more than one cell deep. This is supported by electronmicrographs of frog skin (7). Sodium concentration of the inner cells could be augmented by the activity of the outer cells in series with them.

Studies on whole animals have recently been concentrated on amphibia from extreme environments. The ability of certain frogs to regulate both like teleosts and like salachians in saline solutions at different periods of their life histories has been mentioned above. The elevation of urea as an adaptation to saline environments has been acquired independently more than once, even amongst the amphibians. The euryhaline species *Rana cancrivora* and *Bufo viridis* both can elevate urea while the stenohaline *Rana temporaria* and *Bufo bufo* cannot (225). *Bufo viridis* and *Bufo boreas* are osmo-conformers but can survive in 50 per cent seawater. In these conditions a considerable part of the tissue osmotic pressure is accounted for by free amino acids (ca. 150 mmole), as in marine invertebrates. Urea also accounts for about 50 mmole and is rather more concentrated in the tissues than in the blood (226). Amphibia from dry environments show a number of physiological adaptations. Thus the spadefoot toad *Scaphiopus couchi* can tolerate a loss of up to 60 per cent of the body water (227). During dehydration the urea content of the body may reach 300 mmole/liter. The high urea (comparable to that found in *Rana cancrivora* from saline environments) may have no survival value per se but the ability to tolerate it will conserve water which would otherwise be required for urine. Even the stenohaline frog *Rana temporaria* and the toad *Bufo bufo* may accumulate 40–60 mmole/urea/liter plasma· in dry air (225). Desert amphibia are usually capable of taking up water rapidly from dew or rain and storing it for later use in the bladder. The frog *Cyclorana* can store urine equivalent to 50 per cent of its body weight (219).

REPTILES

The most important development in this field in the last ten years has been the discovery of salt-secreting nasal and orbital glands in marine reptiles (228). These are now too well known to be reviewed here. More recently, Schmidt-Nielsen et al. (229) have shown that functional salt glands occur in completely terrestrial reptiles such as *Iguana iguana* and they suggest that they play a vital role in salt and water balance in many terrestrial forms. In *Iguana* the secretion contains up to 950 mE K/liter and lower concentrations of sodium. In this way the *Iguana* can eliminate salt with a minimal loss of water. In the absence of such a system the salt would have to be eliminated in the urine which would entail the loss of a much larger volume of water as the urine cannot be rendered hyperosmotic to the blood. Another recent development has been the demonstration by a number of workers that reptile skin, in spite of its appearance, is relatively permeable to water and to salts. The crocodile *Caimon sclerops,* in freshwater, gains 3.5 ml water/kg/hour, 70 per cent of it by osmosis through the skin, the rest by drinking. In 3.3 per cent sodium chloride it loses even more water through the skin. In air 75 per cent of the water loss takes place directly through the skin (230). Similarly, the desert tortoise *Gophorus agassazii* loses as much or more water through the skin as it does through the lungs (231). In two species of Australian lizard, *Anolis* and *Uta* (232), cutaneous loss amounted to 40 per cent of the total. The state of hydration of the skin affects its permeability which is reduced when the outside of the skin is dry (233). The skin may also be permeable to ions as well as water (234). Bentley et al. (235) suggest that most of the sodium influx in seawater into the diamondback terrapin *Malaclemys centrata* takes place directly through the skin. Freshwater terrapins can take up sodium directly through the skin of the pharynx which resembles frog skin in some respects (234).

Salt and water balance in the diamondback terrapin has been examined in seawater and in freshwater (235). In seawater, drinking was negligible, and extrarenal water loss was only 4 ml/kg/day, less than in most teleosts. The urine flow was low and it contained little salt although it was almost isosmotic with the blood. In freshwater, urine flow was higher but the total concentration was lower and the sodium content was negligible. The total sodium loss was 13 μE/kg/hour compared with a urine loss of only 0.7 μE Na/hour.

The effects of seawater and freshwater on the blood composition of the marine turtle *Caretta caretta* and of the freshwater terrapin *Clemmys leprosa* have been described by Schoffeniels & Tercafs (236). In both animals the blood contained a moderate concentration of urea (26–30 mmole/liter) when in seawater, less in freshwater (5–7 mmole/liter) but in neither case would the urea concentration significantly affect water balance. In the tortoise *Testudo hermanni* there was a considerable rise in both urea and electrolyte content of the blood during hibernation (237). In the chelonia the bladder may form a water store as in the anurans. In order to function in this way the permeability and transport properties of the bladder must be controlled, and isolated bladder preparations are now being studied. An interesting difference from the anuran bladder is that there is a transport system for chloride independent of the sodium pump (238).

The hormonal control of kidney function in the reptiles has been investigated in a range of animals. The naturally occurring ADH in reptiles as in other lower tetrapods is arginine vasotocin. This acts both by reducing the glomerular filtration rate and by increasing water permeability and salt resorption in the tubules. Such reduction may be due to a reduction in the number of functioning glomeruli (239, 240).

BIRDS AND MAMMALS

Studies of water balance in desert mammals and birds are reviewed by Schmidt-Nielsen (241). The mammals possess no extrarenal salt glands but desert mammals are generally capable of producing very concentrated urine. The grasshopper mouse *Onchomys torridus* can produce urine with an average concentration of 3180 mOsm/liter, maximum 4250 mOsm/liter, when salt and protein loaded (242, 4). Similar figures are recorded for a number of other mammals. As a result some small mammals can survive by drinking seawater (*Rheithrodomys*) (243) or without recourse to liquid water at all. The latter include the carnivorous mulgara *Dasycercus* (244) and the herbivorous kangaroo rat *Dipodomys* (245). In contrast the mountain beaver *Aplodonta rufa* can only produce urine with a maximal concentration of less than 800 mmole/liter (246). The monotreme *Echidna*, which lives in a dry habitat, can produce urine containing 2300 mOsm/liter, as high as that of eutherian mammals from similar habitats, a finding that further rebuffs the naive belief that morphologically primitive animals are also physiologically primitive (247).

LITERATURE CITED

1. Beadle, L. C. *Ann. Rev. Physiol.,* **19,** 329–58 (1957)
2. Shaw, J. In *Comp. Biochem.,* **2,** 471–518 (1960)
3. Potts, W. T. W., Parry G. In *Osmotic and Ionic Regulation in Animals* (Pergamon Press, Oxford, 1964)
4. Prosser, C. L., Brown, F. A. In *Comparative Animal Physiology* (2nd ed., Saunders, Philadelphia, 1962)
5. Rothstein, A. *Ann. Rev. Physiol.,* **30,** 15–72 (1968)
6. Goldfischer, S., Essner, E., Novikoff, A. B. *J. Histochem. Cytochem.,* **12,** 72–82 (1964)
7. Farquhar, M. G., Palade, G. E. *J. Cell Biol.,* **30,** 359–79 (1966)
8. Komnick, H. *Protoplasma,* **55,** 414–18 (1962)
9. Komnick, H. *Ibid.,* **56,** 605–36 (1963)
10. Komnick, H. *Ibid.,* **58,** 96–127 (1964)
11. Komnick, H., Komnick, U. *Z. Zellforsch. Mikroskop. Anat.,* **60,** 163–203 (1963)
12. Kaye, G. I., Lane, N., Cole, J. D., Donn, A. *Anat. Record,* **154,** 366 (Abstr.) (1966)
13. Zadunaisky, J. A. *J. Cell Biol.,* **31,** C11–C15 (1966)
14. Philpott, C. W. *Protoplasma,* **60,** 7–23 (1965)
15. Forster, R. P. *Cell,* **5,** 89–161 (1961)
16. Kummel, G. *Zool. Beitr.,* **10,** 227–52 (1964)
17. Sjostrand, F. *Intern. Rev. Cytol.,* **5,** 456–552 (1956)
18. Giebisch, G. *J. Gen. Physiol.,* **44,** 659–78 (1961)
19. Giebisch, G., Windhager, E. E. *J. Gen. Physiol.,* **44,** 679–87 (1961)
20. Giebisch, G., Windhager, E. E. *Am. J. Physiol.,* **204,** 387–91 (1963)
21. Beams, H. W., Anderson, E., Press, N. *Cytologia,* **21,** 50–57 (1956)
22. Bouillon, J. *Ann. Sci. Nat.,* **12,** 719–49 (1960)
23. Rasmont, R., Vandermeersche, G., Castiaux, R. *Nature,* **182,** 328–29 (1958)
24. Copeland, D. E. *Biol. Bull.,* **127,** 367–68 (1964)
25. Copeland, D. E. *J. Cell Biol.,* **23,** 253–63 (1964)
26. Ussing, H. H., Windhager, E. E. *Acta Physiol. Scand.,* **61,** 484–504 (1964)
27. Keller, A. R. *Anat. Record,* **147,** 367–77 (1963)
28. Choi, J. K. *J. Cell Biol.,* **16,** 53–72 (1963)

29. Curran, P. F. *J. Gen. Physiol.*, **43**, 1137–48 (1960)
30. Whitlock, R. T., Wheeler, H. O. *J. Clin. Invest.*, **43**, 2249–65 (1964)
31. Whitlock, R. T., Wheeler, H. O., Kayer, G. E., Lane, N. *Fed. Proc.*, **24**, 589 (1965)
32. Berridge, M. J., Gupta, B. L. *J. Cell Sci.*, **2**, 89–112 (1967)
33. Ellis, R. A., Abel, J. H., Jr., *Science*, **144**, 1340 (1964)
34. Bulger, R. E. *Anat. Record*, **147**, 95–107 (1963)
35. Doyle, W. L. *Anat. Record*, **142**, 228 (Abstr.) (1962)
36. Doyle, W. L. *Am. J. Anat.*, **111**, 223–38 (1962)
37. Parry, G. *Biol. Rev. Cambridge Phil. Soc.*, **41**, 392–444 (1966)
38. Philpott, C. W., Copeland, D. E. *J. Cell Biol.*, **18**, 389–404 (1963)
39. Croghan, P. C. *J. Exptl. Biol.*, **35**, 234–42 (1958)
40. Copeland, D. E. *Protoplasma* (In press) (1967)
41. Schneider, L. *J. Protozool.*, **7**, 75–90 (1960)
42. Mercer, E. H. *Proc. Roy Soc. B*, **150**, 216–32 (1959)
43. Braun, G., Kummel, G., Mangos, J. A. *Arch. Ges. Physiol.*, **289**, 141–54 (1966)
44. Carter, L. *J. Exptl. Biol.*, **34**, 71–84 (1957)
45. Yamaguchi, T. *Annot. Zool. Japon.*, **36**, No. 2, 55–65 (1963)
46. Andrus, W. DeW., Giese, A. C. *J. Cellular Comp. Physiol.*, **61**, 17–30 (1963)
47. Dunham, P. B., Child, F. M. *Biol. Bull.*, **121**, 129–40 (1961)
48. Dunham, P. B. *Biol. Bull.*, **126**, 373–90 (1964)
49. Kehlenbeck, E. K., Dunham, P. B., Holz, G. G. (Reprinted from *Excerpta Med. Intern. Cong. Ser. No. 91*. Abstr. Intern. Conf. Protozool., 2nd, London, August 1965)
50. Klein, R. L. *Exptl. Cell Res.*, **28**, 549–59 (1962)
51. Klein, R. L., Breland, A. P. *Comp. Biochem. Physiol.*, **17**, 39–48 (1966)
52. Chapman-Andresen, C., Dick, D. A. T. *Compt. Rend. Carlsberg*, **32**, 445–69 (1962)
53. Bruce, D. L., Marshall, J. M. *J. Gen. Physiol.*, **49**, 151–78 (1965)
54. Dunham, P. B., Stoner, L. C. *J. Protozool.*, **14** (In press)
55. Prusch, R. D., Dunham, P. B. *J. Gen. Physiol.*, **50**, 1083 (1967)
56. Schmidt-Nielsen, B., Schrauger, C. R. *Science*, **139**, 606 (1963)
57. Denton, E. J., Shaw, T. I. *J. Physiol. (London)*, **161**, 14P–15P (1962)
58. Steinbach, H. B. *Biol. Bull.*, **124**, 322–36 (1963)
59. Krishnamoorthy, B., Krishnaswamy, S. *Zool. Jahrb.*, **72**, 316–26 (1966)
60. Duchâteau-Bosson, Gh., Jeuniaux, Ch., Florkin, M. *Arch. Intern. Physiol. Biochim.*, **68**, 30–35 (1961)
61. Virkar, R. A., *Comp. Biochem. Physiol.*, **18**, 617–25 (1966)
62. Smith, R. I., *Biol. Bull.*, **125**, 332–43 (1963)
63. Smith, R. I. *Ibid.*, **126**, 142–49 (1964)
64. Jorgensen, C. B., Dales, R. P. *Physiol. Comp.*, **4**, 357–74 (1957)
65. Bogucki, M., Wojtczak, W. *Polsk. Arch. Hydrobiol.*, **25**, No. 1 (1964)
66. Oglesby, L. C. *Comp. Biochem. Physiol.*, **14**, 621–40 (1965)
67. Oglesby, L. C. *Ibid.*, **16**, 437–55
68. Fretter, V. *J. Marine Biol. Assoc. U.K.*, **34**, 151–60 (1955)
69. Jeuniaux, Ch., Duchâteau-Bosson, Gh., Florkin, M. *J. Biochem. Tokyo*, **49**, 427–531 (1961)
70. Boroffka, I. *Z. Vergleich. Physiol.*, **51**, 25–48 (1965)
71. Ramsay, J. *J. Exptl. Biol.*, **26**, 46–56 (1949)
72. Kamemoto, F. I. *Gen. Comp. Endocrinol.*, **4**, 420–26 (1964)
73. Denton, E. J. In *Physiology of Mollusca*, **I**, 425–34 (Wilbur, K. M., Yonge, C. M., Eds., Academic Press, New York, 1964)
74. Denton, E. J., Shaw, T. P., Gilpin-Brown, J. B. *Nature*, **182**, 1810–11 (1958)
75. Potts, W. T. W. *J. Exptl. Biol.*, **35**, 749–64 (1958)
76. Bricteux-Gregoire, S., Duchâteau-Bosson, Gh., Jeuniaux, Ch., Florkin, M. *Arch. Intern. Physiol. Biochim.*, **71**, 116–23 (1963)
77. Bricteux-Gregoire, S., Duchâteau-Bosson, Gh., Jeuniaux, Ch., Florkin, M. *Ibid.*, **72**, 267–75 (1964)
78. Bricteux-Gregoire, S., Duchâteau-Bosson, Gh., Jeuniaux, C., Florkin, M. *Ibid.*, 835–42
79. Klekowski, R. Z. *Polsk. Arch. Hydrobiol.*, **22**(9) (1961)
80. Burton, R. F. *Can. J. Zool.*, **42**, 1085–97 (1964)

81. Burton, R. F. *Comp. Biochem. Physiol.*, **17**, 1007–18 (1966)
82. Jullien, A., Ripplinger, J., Cardot, J., Duvernoy, J., Jolly, M. *Arch. Intern. Physiol. Biochim.*, **151**, 1214–17 (1958)
83. Jullien, A., Ripplinger, J., Cardot, J. *Arch. Intern. Physiol. Biochim.*, **152**, 634–36 (1958)
84. Machin, J. *J. Exptl. Biol.*, **41**, 759–69 (1964)
85. Machin, J. *Naturwissenschaften*, **52**, 18 (1965)
86. Machin, J. *J. Exptl. Biol.*, **45**, 267–78 (1966)
87. Warburg, M. R. *Malacol. Soc. London Proc.*, **36**, 297–305 (1965)
88. Blinn, W. C. *Physiol. Zool.*, **27**, 329–37 (1964)
89. Kirschner, L. B. *J. Gen. Physiol.*, **46**, 362A-63A (1963)
90. Istin, M., Maetz, J. *Biochim. Biophys. Acta*, **88**, 225–27 (1964)
91. Wilbur, K. M. In *Physiology of Molluscs*, **I**, 243–82 (Wilbur, K. M., Yonge, C. M., Eds., Academic Press, New York, 1964)
92. Van der Borght, O. *Arch. Intern. Physiol. Biochim.*, **70**, 611–23 (1962)
93. Van der Borght, O. *Ibid.*, **71**, 46–50 (1963)
94. Potts, W. T. W. *Biol. Rev. Cambridge Phil. Soc.*, **42**, 1–41 (1967)
95. Bricteux-Gregoire, S., Duchâteau-Bosson, Gh., Jeuniaux, Ch., Florkin, M. *Comp. Biochem. Physiol.*, **19**, 729–37 (1966)
96. Bricteux-Gregoire, S., Duchâteau-Bosson, Gh., Jeuniaux, Ch., Schoffeniels, E., Florkin, M. *Arch. Intern. Physiol. Biochim.*, **71**, 393–400 (1963)
97. Robertson, J. D. In *The Physiology of Crustacea* (Waterman, T. H., Ed., Academic Press, New York and London, 1960)
98. Lockwood, A. P. M. *Biol. Rev. Cambridge Phil. Soc.*, **37**, 257–305 (1962)
99. Bricteux-Gregoire, S., Duchâteau-Bosson, Gh., Jeuniaux, Ch., Florkin, M. *Arch. Intern. Physiol. Biochim.*, **70**, 273–86 (1962)
100. Duchâteau-Bosson, Gh., Florkin, M., Jeuniaux, Ch. *Arch. Intern. Physiol. Biochim.*, **67**, 489–93 (1959)
101. Shaw, J. *J. Exptl. Biol.*, **32**, 644–80 (1955)
102. Jeuniaux, Ch., Bricteux-Gregoire, S., Florkin, M. *Cahiero Biol. Mariner*, **2**, 373–79 (1961)
103. Schoffeniels, E. *Arch. Intern. Physiol. Biochim.*, **68**, 696–99 (1961)
104. Gilles, R., Schoffeniels, E. *Biochim. Biophys. Acta*, **82**, 518–24 (1964)
105. Gilles, R., Schoffeniels, E., *Ibid.*, 525–32
106. Schoffeniels, E. *Life Sci.*, **3**, 845–51 (1964)
107. Florkin, M., Schoffeniels, E. In *Studies in Comparative Biochemistry* (Munday, K. A., Ed., Pergamon Press, London, 1965)
108. Gross, W. J. *Biol. Bull.*, **112**, 43–62 (1957)
109. Shaw, J. *J. Exptl. Biol.*, **38**, 135–52 (1961)
110. Shaw, J. *Ibid.*, **36**, 126–44 (1959)
111. Werntz, H. O. *Biol. Bull.*, **124**, 225–39 (1962)
112. Rudy, P. R. *Comp. Biochem. Physiol.* (In press) (1967)
113. Croghan, P. C. *J. Exptl. Biol.*, **35**, 243–49 (1958)
114. Bryan, G. W. *J. Exptl. Biol.*, **37**, 83–99 (1960)
115. Bryan, G. W. *Ibid.*, 100–12
116. Bryan, G. W. *Ibid.*, 113–28
117. Lockwood, A. P. M. *J. Exptl. Biol.*, **42**, 59–69 (1963)
118. Sutcliffe, D. W. *J. Exptl. Biol.* (In press) (1967)
119. Shaw, J. *Symp. Soc. Exptl. Biol.*, **18**, 237–54 (1964)
120. Shaw, J. *J. Exptl. Biol.*, **37**, 557–72 (1960)
121. Sutcliffe, D. W. *J. Exptl. Biol.* (In press) (1967)
122. Sutcliffe, D. W., Shaw, J. *J. Exptl. Biol.* (In press) (1967)
123. Croghan, P. C., Curra, R. A., Lockwood, A. P. M. *J. Exptl. Biol.*, **42**, 463–74 (1965)
124. Bielawski, J. *Comp. Biochem. Physiol.*, **41**, 423–32 (1964)
125. Potts, W. T. W., Parry, G. *J. Exptl. Biol.*, **41**, 591–601 (1964)
126. Rudy, P. P. *Comp. Biochem. Physiol.*, **18**, 881–907 (1966)
127. Riegel, J. A., Kirschner, L. B. *Biol. Bull.*, **118**, 296–307 (1960)
128. Kirschner, L. B., Wagner, S. *J. Exptl. Biol.*, **43**, 385–95 (1965)
129. Riegel, J. A. *J. Exptl. Biol.*, **42**, 379–84 (1965)
130. Riegel, J. A. *Ibid.*, **40**, 487–92 (1963)
131. Picken, L. E. R. *J. Exptl. Biol.*, **13**, 309–28 (1936)
132. Kamemoto, F. I., Keister, S. M.,

Spalding, A. E. *Comp. Biochem. Physiol.*, **7**, 81–87 (1962)

133. Dehnel, P. A., Stone, D. *Biol. Bull.*, **126**, 354–72 (1964)

134. Dehnel, P. A., Carefoot, T. H. *Comp. Biochem. Physiol.*, **15**, 377–97 (1965)

135. Gross, W. J., Capen, R. L. *Biol. Bull.*, **131**, 272–91 (1966)

136. Riegel, J. A., Lockwood, A. P. M. *J. Exptl. Biol.*, **38**, 491–99 (1961)

137. Gross, W. J. *Comp. Biochem. Physiol.*, **20**, 313–18 (1967)

138. Gross, W. J., Lasiewski, R. C., Dennis, M., Rudy, P. P. *Comp. Biochem. Physiol.*, **17**, 641–60 (1966)

139. Bliss, D. E. In *Phylogeny and Evolution of Crustacea*, 59–78 (Museum of Comp. Zool., spec. publ., 1963)

140. Bliss, D. E., Wary, S. M. E., Marting, E. A. *Am. Zool.*, **6**, 197–212 (1966)

141. Gross, W. J. *Am. Naturalist*, **89**, 205–22 (1955)

142. Dandy, J. W. T., Ewer, D. W. *Trans. Roy. Soc. S. Africa*, **36**, 137–62 (1961)

143. Gross, W. J. *Biol. Bull.*, **126**, 54–68 (1964)

144. Kamemoto, F. I., Kato, K. N., Tucker, L. E. *Am. Zool.*, **6**, 213–19 (1966)

145. Kobler, F. A., Costlow, J. D. *Am. Zool.*, **6**, 221–29 (1966)

146. Lockwood, A. P. M. *J. Exptl. Biol.*, **38**, 647–58 (1961)

147. Lockwood, A. P. M. *Ibid.*, **41**, 447–58 (1964)

148. Dall, W. *Australian J. Marine Freshwater Res.*, **16**, 181–203 (1965)

149. Lees, A. D. *Proc. Intern. Congr. Acarology, 1st, Arologia*, **6**, 315–23 (1964)

150. Knülle, W. *J. Insect Physiol.*, **13**, 333–57 (1967)

151. Beament, J. W. L., Noble Nesbitt, J., Watson, J. A. L. *J. Exptl. Biol.*, **41**, 323–30 (1964)

152. Beament, J. W. L. *Symp. Soc. Exptl. Biol.*, **19**, 273–98 (1965)

153. Maddrell, S. H. P. *J. Exptl. Biol.*, **40**, 247–56 (1963)

154. Maddrell, S. H. P. *Ibid.*, **41**, 163–76 (1964)

155. Maddrell, S. H. P. *Ibid.*, 459–72 (1964)

156. Maddrell, S. H. P. *Ibid.*, **45**, 499–508 (1966)

157. Maddrell, S H. P. *Ibid.*, **44**, 59–68 (1966)

158. Wall, B. J. *J. Insect Physiol.*, **13**, 565–78 (1967)

159. Treherne, J. E. *J. Exptl. Biol.*, **39**, 193–218 (1962)

160. Treherne, J. E. *Ibid.*, **42**, 7–27 (1965)

161. Treherne, J. E. *Ibid.*, 1–6 (1965)

162. Treherne, J. E., Maddrell, S. H. P. *J. Exptl. Biol.* (In press) (1967)

163. Treherne, J. E. In *Studies in Comparative Biochemistry* (Munday, K. A., Ed., Pergamon Press, London, 1965)

164. Robertson, J. D. *Biol. Rev. Cambridge Phil. Soc.*, **32**, 156–87 (1957)

165. Munz, N. Z., McFarland, W. N. *Comp. Biochem. Physiol.*, **13**, 381–400 (1964)

166. Morris, R. *J. Exptl. Biol.*, **42**, 359–71 (1965)

167. Robertson, J. D. *J. Exptl. Biol.*, **37**, 879–88 (1960)

168. Robertson, J. D. In *Some Contemporary Studies in Marine Science*, 631–44 (Barnes, H., Ed., Allen & Unwin, London, 1966)

169. Morris, R. *J. Exptl. Biol.*, **35**, 649–65 (1958)

170. Bentley, P. J. *Comp. Biochem. Physiol.*, **6**, 95–97 (1962)

171. Bentley, P. J., Follett, F. K. *J. Physiol. (London)*, **169**, 902–918 (1963)

172. Burger, J. W., Hess, W. N. *Science*, **131**, 670–71 (1960)

173. Burger, J. W. *Physiol. Zool.*, **38**, 191–96 (1965)

174. Burger, J. W., Tosterson, D. C. *Comp. Biochem. Physiol.*, **19**, 649–53 (1966)

175. Maetz, J., Lahlou, B. *J. Physiol. (Paris)*, **58**, 249 (1966)

176. Fänge, R., Fugelli, K. *Nature*, **196**, 689 (1962)

177. Patterson, C. *Phil. Trans. Roy. Soc. B*, **249**, 101–219 (1965)

178. Pickford, G. E., Grant, F. B. *Science*, **155**, 568–70 (1967)

179. Smith, H. W. *Am. J. Physiol.*, **93**, 480–505 (1930)

180. Keys, A. B. *Z. Vergleich. Physiol.*, **15**, 364–88 (1931)

181. Mullins, L. J. *Acta Physiol. Scand.*, **21**, 303–14 (1950)

182. House, C. R. *J. Exptl. Biol.*, **40**, 87–104 (1963)

183. Gordon, M. S. *Biol. Bull.*, **124**, 45–54 (1963)

184. Motais, R., Maetz, J. *Compt. Rend. Acad. Sci.*, **261**, 532 (1965)

185. Potts, W. T. W., Evans, D. H. *Biol. Bull.*, **131**, 362–68 (1966)

186. Potts, W. T. W., Evans, D. H. *Ibid.* (In press) (1967)
187. Hickman, C. P. (In press) (1967)
188. Evans, D. H. *J. Exptl. Biol.* (In press) (1967)
189. Chester Jones, I., Phillips, J. G., Bellamy, D. *J. Comp. Endocrinol.*, (Suppl.) **1**, 36–47 (1962)
190. Motais, R., Garcia Romeu, F., Maetz, J. *J. Gen. Physiol.*, **50**, 391–423 (1966)
191. Sharratt, B. M., Chester Jones, I., Bellamy, D. *Comp. Biochem. Physiol.*, **11**, 9–18 (1964)
192. Lahlou, B. *Comp. Biochem. Physiol.*, **20**, 925–39 (1967)
193. Fleming, W. R., Stanley, J. G. *Am. J. Physiol.*, **209**, 1025–30 (1965)
194. Stanley, J. G., Fleming, W. R. *Science*, **144**, 63–64 (1964)
195. Maetz, J., Capanini, G. *J. Physiol. (Paris)*, **58**, 248 (1966)
196. Motais, R., Maetz, J. *Gen. Comp. Endocrinol.*, **4**, 210–24 (1964)
197. Motais, R., Maetz, J. *J. Physiol. (Paris)* (In press) (1967)
198. Mayer, N., Maetz, J., Chan, D. K. O., Forster, M., Chester Jones, I. *Nature* (In press) (1967)
199. Maetz, J., Sawyer, W. H., Pickford, G. E., Mayer, N. *Gen. Comp. Endocrinol.*, **8**, 163–77 (1967)
200. Maetz, J., Mayer, N., Chartier-Baraduc, M. M. *Gen. Comp. Endocrinol.*, **8**, 177–89 (1967)
201. Motais, R. *Compt. Rend. Acad. Sci.*, **257**, 724 (1961)
202. Stanley, J. G., Fleming, W. R. *Biol. Bull.*, **131**, 155–65 (1966)
203. Holmes, R. *Ann. Rept. Challenger Soc.*, **3**, 23 (1961)
204. Holmes, W. N., Stanier, M. *J. Exptl. Biol.*, **44**, 33–46 (1966)
205. Stanley, J. G., Fleming, W. R. *Comp. Biochem. Physiol.*, **20**, 199–208 (1967)
206. Maetz, J., Garcia Romeu, F. *J. Gen. Physiol.*, **47**, 1209–27 (1964)
207. Garcia Romeu, F., Maetz, J. *J. Gen. Physiol.*, **47**, 1195–1202 (1964)
208. Chester Jones, I., Henderson, I. W., Butler, D. G. *Arch. Anat. Microscop. Morphol. Exptl.*, **54**, 453–69 (1965)
209. Sandor, T., Vinson, G. P., Chester Jones, I., Whitehouse, B. J. *J. Endocrinol.*, **34**, 105–15 (1965)
210. Maetz, J., Bourguet, J., Lahlouh, B., Hourdry, J. *Gen. Comp. Endocrinol.*, **4**, 508–54 (1964)
211. Burden, C. *Biol. Bull.*, **110**, 8–28 (1956)
212. Handin, R. I., Nandi, J., Bern, H. A. *J. Exptl. Zool.*, **157**, 339–44 (1964)
213. Schneibman, M. P., Kallman, K. D. *Gen. Comp. Endocrinol.*, **6**, 144–55 (1966)
214. Pickford, G. E., Phillips, J. G. *Science*, **130**, 454 (1959)
215. Olivereau, M. *Gen. Comp. Endocrinol.*, **6**, 130–43 (1966)
216. Olivereau, M., Chartier-Baraduc, M. M. *Gen. Comp. Endocrinol.*, **7**, 27–36 (1966)
217. Gordon, M. S., Tucker, V. A. *J. Exptl. Biol.*, **42**, 437–46 (1965)
218. Holmes, W. N., and McBean, R. L. *J. Exptl. Biol.*, **40**, 335–41 (1963)
219. Bentley, P. J. *Biol. Rev. Cambridge Phil. Soc.*, **41**, 275–316 (1966)
220. Cafre, G., Crabbe, J. *J. Physiol. (London)*, **188**, 177–90 (1967)
221. Tercafs, R. R. *Arch. Intern. Physiol. Biochim.*, **73**, 762–73 (1965)
222. Krogh, A. *Skand. Arch. Physiol.*, **76**, 60–73 (1937)
223. Zadunaisky, J. A., Fisch, F. W. *Am. J. Physiol.*, **207**, 1010–14 (1964)
224. Biber, T. U. L., Chez, R. A., Curran, P. F. *J. Gen. Physiol.*, **49**, 1161–76 (1966)
225. Schoffeniels, E., Tercafs, R. R. *Ann. Soc. Roy. Zool. Belg.*, **96**, 23–40 (1966)
226. Gordon, M. S. *Biol. Bull.*, **128**, 218–29 (1965)
227. McClanahan, L. *Comp. Biochem. Physiol.*, **20**, 73–100 (1967)
228. Schmidt-Nielsen, K., Fänge, R. *Nature*, **182**, 783–85 (1958)
229. Schmidt-Nielsen, K., Borut, A., Lee, P., Crawford, E. *Science*, **142**, 1300–1 (1963)
230. Bentley, P. J., Schmidt-Nielsen, K. *J. Cellular Comp. Physiol.*, **66**, 303–10 (1966)
231. Schmidt-Nielsen, K., Bentley, P. J. *Science*, **154**, 911 (1966)
232. Claussen, D. L. *Comp. Physiol. Biochem.*, **20**, 115–30 (1967)
233. Tercafs, R. R., Schoffeniels, E. *Ann. Soc. Roy. Zool. Belg.*, **96**, 9–22 (1966)
234. Dunson, W. A. *Science*, **149**, 67–69 (1965)
235. Bentley, P. J., Bretz, W. L., Schmidt-Nielsen, K. *J. Exptl. Biol.*, **46**, 161–67 (1967)
236. Schoffeniels, E., Tercafs, R. R. *Ann.*

Soc. Roy. Zool. Belg., **96**, 1–8 (1966)

237. Gilles-Baillien, M., Schoffeniels, E. *Ann. Soc. Roy. Zool. Belg.*, **95**, 77–81 (1965)

238. Brodsky, W. A., Schilb, T. P. *Am J. Physiol.*, **210**, 987–96 (1966)

239. Dantzler, W. H. *Am. J. Physiol.*, **212**, 83–91 (1967)

240. Dantzler, W. H., Schmidt-Nielsen, B. *Am. J. Physiol.*, **210**, 198–210 (1966)

241. Schmidt-Nielsen, K. In *Desert Animals* (Clarendon Press, Oxford, 1964)

242. Schmidt-Nielsen, K., Haines, H. B. *Physiol. Zool.*, **37**, 259–65 (1964)

243. Haines, H. B. *Physiol. Zool.*, **37**, 266–72 (1964)

244. Schmidt-Nielsen, K., Newsome, A. E. *Am. J. Physiol.*, **196**, 625 (1962)

245. Schmidt-Nielsen, B., Schmidt-Nielsen, K. *J. Cellular Comp. Physiol.*, **38**, 165–81 (1951)

246. Nungesser, W. C., Pfeiffer, E. W. *Comp. Biochem. Physiol.*, **14**, 289–98 (1965)

247. Bentley, P. J., Schmidt-Nielsen, K. *Comp. Biochem. Physiol.*, **20**, 285–90 (1967)

RESPIRATION[1,2]

BY E. J. M. CAMPBELL

*Royal Postgraduate Medical School and Hammersmith Hospital
London, England*

THE RESPIRATORY MUSCLES AND THE MECHANICS OF BREATHING

Three subjects which were unknown or ignored ten years ago are now prominent: the proprioceptive control of the respiratory muscles; the intrinsic properties of these muscles; and the mechanics of the thoracic cage. The last year has seen the appearance of important work on the first and third of these topics.

Control.—The elucidation of this subject largely consists of fitting the respiratory muscles into the corpus of knowledge culled from study of the limb muscles in animals and it increasingly involves the same rules of evidence and jargon. Those who wish to follow developments will be helped by reviews written by neurophysiologists for respiratory physiologists (1–3).

The intercostal muscles and the diaphragm clearly differ. The intercostal muscles are rich in spindles, there is abundant evidence of fusimotor (γ) activity, and they are probably subject to more precise voluntary control. The γ- or fusimotor neurones supply the intrafusal muscle fibres whose contractions stretch the spindle and stimulate the spindle endings. Afferents from these endings pass to the anterior horn cells of the large or α-motor neurones which supply the main muscle fibres. This "α-γ linkage" is now known to be important not only in reflex excitation but in the initiation and control of muscular action. The existence of two functionally different types of intercostal γ-neurones has been confirmed. These are the "rhythmic" or "specifically respiratory" γ-neurones and the "tonic" γ-neurones. Rhythmic γ-activity appears to be closely linked to respiratory α-activity, but tonic γ-activity is more responsive to proprioceptive reflexes facilitated by movements of the chest wall as well as by other spinal and supraspinal reflexes (4, 5). There is now convincing evidence for a stretch reflex in the intercostals of both cat (6) and man (7) which strengthens the applicability of data obtained from the limb muscles of animals to the intercostals.

[1] I began to collect material for this review in June 1966, it took shape in March 1967 and was completed in May. When necessary, however, I have strayed outside these limits.

I have chosen subjects for this review which are at present of particular interest to my colleagues and myself. Unfortunately, these do not include such hardy annuals as the chemical control of breathing, pulmonary mechanics and gas exchange, or the pulmonary circulation.

[2] I am very grateful for help from Drs. R. D. Cohen, R. H. T. Edwards, S. Freedman, J. M. B. Hughes, N. L. Jones, G. Laszlo, J. Newsom Davis.

Selective voluntary control of the intercostals with total absence of diaphragmatic contraction appears to be a feature of singing (8) and may also be achieved by physiotherapists (9). Unequal excursion of the two domes of the diaphragm is a normal finding, the left usually being dominant. Unilateral paradoxical movement occurs on sniffing in 6 per cent of normal subjects and this test is therefore not totally reliable (10). The scalene are virtually ordinary muscles of breathing and they contract during inspiration, even during quiet breathing in the majority of subjects (11). During quiet breathing their contraction comes on sometime after the beginning of inspiration but as breathing is increased they contract progressively earlier until they anticipate the onset of inspiration. The sternomastoids are much more truly accessory muscles. Delhez & Petit (12) have comprehensively reviewed data obtained by electromyography of the respiratory muscles. Measurements of the movements of the chest in patients with strokes (13) suggest that the supramedullary influence on the respiratory muscles of man is asymmetrical.

The vagi.—Guz and his co-workers have described the effects of bilateral vagal block in conscious normal man (14–16). Apart from some increase in the randomness of frequency, there was no effect on resting breathing (14). The ventilatory response to carbon dioxide was diminished; this was chiefly the result of a failure of the frequency to increase (15). The same group has also described the effect of ipsilateral vagal block on unilateral lung inflation in anaesthetised man (16). The findings add to the evidence that the responses to changes in lung volume are not readily interpreted in terms of the classical Hering-Breuer reflexes.

In the rabbit whose accessory muscles have been cut, phrenic block reduces the tidal volume and the effect is increased by vagotomy (17). In Dial-anaesthetised cats, when the airway pressure during inspiration and expiration is elevated independently, the abdominal muscles respond selectively to pressure opposing expiration, whereas the diaphragm responds to pressures during both inspiration and expiration (18). Vagotomy abolishes the abdominal respiratory activity under all conditions as well as the inhibition of the diaphragm caused by positive pressure during inspiration, but does not interrupt the diaphragm augmentation in response to an expiratory load (18).

There has been an elegant exchange of evidence for (19) and against (20) the Head paradoxical reflex being an artifact. In cats, experimental pulmonary oedema increases the traffic in the vagal C-fibres but not in the A-fibres (21).

Clearly there is much more to be learned about the vagi. I hope that more attention will be devoted to the function of the information they transmit; too often an observation is attributed to some "reflex" and no further physiological interpretation is attempted.

Breathing movements of the chest wall.—The deformations of the chest wall during static respiratory efforts and during different patterns of breathing cycles have been studied by measuring the dorsoventral and lateral diameters of the rib cage (22). During inspiratory efforts the horizontal section of the rib cage becomes more elliptical, whereas during expiratory efforts it becomes more circular. During hyperventilation or breathing through resistances, the change of the dorsoventral diameter lags behind that of the lateral one and that of the lung volume. The phase shift increases as the load increases. Hence the force of the respiratory muscles acts mainly on the lateral part of the rib cage, whereas the frontal part is mainly driven by the pressure across it and by the movements of the lateral parts. The deformation occurring under load implies: first, that some muscles lengthen instead of shortening and vice versa; second, that the signals from muscle, joint, and lung receptors are out of phase with each other; and third, that the work of breathing is slightly larger than that calculated on the volume pressure diagram (22).

Konno & Mead (23) have found that the chest wall behaves as a system with two degrees of freedom made up of two parts separated by the costal margin. When the system is closed, i.e. when the airways are closed, the system has only one degree of freedom. Hence the volume change of the rib cage must be equal and opposite to that of the abdomen. In a very elegant analysis, they have shown that there is a unique relation between motion of the rib cage and that of the abdomen at a given lung volume; during breathing, particularly quiet breathing, the abdomen moves more and the rib cage less than if the relaxation characteristic of the chest wall and abdomen were followed. This means that the work done by the respiratory muscles on the respiratory system itself must be greater than previously thought, since more energy must be expended to produce a given volume change plus distortion from the relaxed configuration than to produce the same volume change without distortion. The greater the work done on the respiratory system itself, the smaller will be the influence on ventilation of an external load. In other words, it appears that the respiratory system operates with a greater internal impedance than hitherto supposed. The price is a somewhat greater energy expenditure and the reward, increased stability of ventilation (24).

When the relaxed rib cage is squeezed along the lateral diameter with a closed airway, there may be a negligible increase in the oesophageal pressure, notwithstanding the decrease of the rib cage cross section and the lack of muscular contraction (25). In other words, work is done on the chest which does not appear on the conventional pressure-volume diagram and is not measured when the oesophageal pressure is used. During the breathing cycle the deformation work may become appreciable when flow resistances are high. The gross distortions of the movements of the chest seen in patients with chronic lung disease suggest that this whole new rigorous approach should be very informative.

Capacity of the respiratory muscles.—Rindqvist (26) has produced an exhaustive thesis on the importance of the respiratory muscular forces in ventilatory capacity. It is based upon the careful delineation of the maximum voluntary expiratory and inspiratory pressure-volume curves in a large number of male and female subjects over a wide age range. He finds that over most of the normal vital capacity, only comparatively small variations occur in the maximum pressure that the inspiratory muscles can produce with maximal efforts. Thus, for example, between the respiratory levels of about 25 and 75 per cent of total lung capacity these variations are only of the order of 10 per cent. The expiratory curves have a steeper slope and this difference becomes more marked at respiratory levels further away from the levels of full inflation and full expiration. It is interesting that the lung volumes where the respiratory muscles create their largest pressures closely coincide with those at which the greatest demand for force is to be expected. Thus, in maximum efforts, the inspiratory muscles create the highest pressure at the resting end-expiratory level, i.e. the position from which inspiration normally starts. The expiratory muscles seem to be so arranged as to develop their largest forces at high lung volumes where expiratory flow is effort-dependent. Rindqvist's data also seem to indicate that variations in the respiratory muscular force between healthy subjects of different ages are large enough to cause some variation in the maximum voluntary ventilation. Instantaneous expiratory power may exceed 50 W (300 kpm/min) during forced expiration (27).

Eldridge (28) found that he could produce an elevation of the blood lactate by respiratory muscular work only by combining hyperventilation, added mechanical loads, and reduced concentration of inspired oxygen. Although this study indicates that the respiratory muscles are not a major source of lactate even during markedly increased breathing work, it does suggest that their aerobic working capacity may occasionally be exceeded. An indication of this capacity is provided by a study of healthy young men who exercised at 80 per cent of their aerobic working capacity and hyperventilated to 70–80 per cent of their maximum voluntary ventilation for fifteen minutes; they were still able to achieve 100 per cent maximum voluntary ventilation in a fifteen-second effort (29). As Otis pointed out some years ago, an implication of the oxygen cost curve of ventilation is that, for any subject, there is a critical level of ventilation above which the respiratory muscles use all the additional oxygen provided by further increasing ventilation; he estimated this ventilation to be about 140 liters per minute in young normal subjects. Shephard (30) has found a value of 120 liters per minute by extrapolation from measurements of the oxygen cost of breathing in sedentary men at submaximal exercise. This value was only 33 per cent above the ventilation at maximal exercise in these subjects.

The "sprint" maximum voluntary ventilation over a fifteen-second period is some 30–40 per cent greater than the sustained (four minute) maximum voluntary ventilation in normal subjects (31). In patients with chronic airway obstruction we have found that the sprint and sustained maximum voluntary ventilation are the same and are attained during exercise (in preparation). It seems, therefore, that the mechanical limit of the ventilatory capacity may be beyond the maximum aerobic working capacity of the respiratory muscles in normal subjects but not in some patients.

RESPIRATION SENSATION: BREATH-HOLDING

Wiley & Zechman (32) have expanded earlier studies on the ability of man to detect resistive loads added to the breathing. They found that normal subjects in the sitting position could detect an added load of about 0.6 cm H_2O liter^{-1} second^{-1}, or about a 25–30 per cent increase in the physiological nonelastic load. Various manoeuvres such as changes of posture and histamine-induced bronchoconstriction increased the threshold of detection, but left the ratio of the increased load to the internal load unchanged. Also, in patients with increased airways resistance the minimum detectable load was greater, but the ratio of the minimum detectable load to the internal load was of the same order. These findings are in accord with the Weber-Fechner "law" derived from studies of other somatic sensory modalities. Wiley & Zechman also report that a patient with a transection of the spinal cord at C5 could detect added resistance as well as a normal subject. Newsom Davis (33, 33a), on the other hand, found that most subjects with partial or complete transection of the lower cervical cord had an impaired ability to detect loads. He argues that receptors around thoracic joints are mainly responsible for the perception of added loads in healthy subjects and that the normal detection threshold of some subjects with cervical transection is due to their ability to sense changes in the upper airway. In support of this, Newsom Davis found that oropharyngeal mucosal anaesthesia impaired the ability of patients with partial cord transection to detect loads, but did not affect the ability of normal subjects to do so. It is unlikely that sensory information passing in the vagi is responsible for the sensation of an added load, because it is unaffected by bilateral vagal block (14). Wiley & Zechman emphasize that loads may be detected by various nervous pathways; the balance of evidence suggests that they are normally appreciated by mechanisms in the chest wall and can also be appreciated by mechanisms in the upper respiratory passages, but are not mediated by pulmonary afferents travelling in the vagi. Further observations of acute interruption of nervous pathways (the obvious choice would be spinal anaesthesia to block the intercostal nerves in otherwise normal subjects) are required to decide which pathways are normally used, because chronic loss of the normal pathway may lead to heightened sensitivity of another.

It is important to appreciate that information (whether from joints or elsewhere in the thoracic cage) about position, change of position, or rate of change of position alone (whether arising in single receptors or recognised by the pattern of impulses from many receptors) will not suffice for the detection of added loads because such information will not, by itself, distinguish a reduction of movement due to a load from that due to a reduction in the applied muscular force. Similarly, information from single receptors about tension will not distinguish an increase due to an increased hindrance from that due to increased muscular force. But information about the change in tension applied to one site in the cage as a function of time could distinguish between increased muscular force and increased load. So also could the instantaneous balance or pattern of information from two or more sites. The phase shifts between different parts of the rib cage discussed on page 107 could supply the gross mechanical basis for the sensations.

Breath-holding.—The conscious, apnoeic, respiratory physiologist (CARP) has long been a popular test bed, and the distressing sensation which produces the breaking point of breath-holding has given a number of clues to sensory mechanism. First, a brief recapitulation: when breathing is suppressed, there is a varying initial period of relative comfort after which an unpleasant sensation arises in the chest and increases in intensity until the subject can no longer suppress the desire to breathe. When he takes a breath the sensation is promptly relieved. The sensation is stronger and the duration of breath-holding time shorter at low lung volumes. Guz et al. (14) have shown that bilateral block of the vagus and glossopharyngeal nerves in two conscious, apnoeic subjects prolonged breath-holding time at all lung volumes and abolished the unpleasant sensation in the chest. These observations imply that the drive to inspiration during breath-holding is largely mediated by the ninth or, more probably, the tenth cranial nerve. They might also be taken to show that consciousness of the afferent activity in these nerves is the cause of the unpleasant sensation. An alternative explanation would be that the sensation arises because the normal responses to this afferent activity are being prevented, i.e. that the chest and lungs are not being allowed to move. Paralysis of the respiratory muscles by curarisation prolonged the tolerable duration of apnoea at functional residual capacity of two conscious, apnoeic subjects from about ninety seconds to over four minutes and abolished the unpleasant sensation (34). These findings suggest that the distress of breath-holding arises in sensory structures stimulated by contraction of the respiratory muscles and is not due to consciousness of stimuli arising in the lungs. It seems these sensory structures are functionally in series with the respiratory muscles and are stimulated when these muscles contract but the normal movement is prevented. The sensation is therefore absent either if contraction is prevented or if movement is permitted. In these paralysed subjects, chemoreceptors, pulmonary mechanical receptors, medullary respiratory neurones, and lower motor neurones were presumably all as active as in the controlled state—as apnoea was prolonged beyond the normal breath-holding time, these neural elements were probably more active. This activity caused no sensation. If confirmed, these observations strongly suggest that the chest wall is an essential common pathway for most if not all respiratory sensations other than those arising in the upper respiratory tract.

Dyspnoea in disease.—This was comprehensively discussed at the Manchester Symposium on Breathlessness (35). Since then Guz et al. (14, 15) have published fuller details about the effects of vagal block in man. Petit (36) has also published detailed studies of the mechanical changes associated with the onset of dyspnoea in patients with bronchial asthma. He found that the onset of dyspnoea was correlated most closely with the appearance of inequality of time constants (ventilatory asynchrony). This sensation could be vagally mediated but, bearing in mind the observations on paralysis, it may be that the distortion of the thoracic cage produces a sensation by changing the pattern arising in chest wall receptors.

ACID-BASE

At the Ciba Symposium on the Development of the Lung, Rahn (37) suggested that the interpretation of homeostasis of blood reaction is easier if we think not of $[H^+]$ or pH but of the $[OH^-]/[H^+]$ ratio. This ratio is dependent on changes in the ionisation constant of water, pKw (pKw = pH + pOH). pKw varies inversely with temperature so that, for example, the preservation of a normal $[OH^-]/[H^+]$ ratio during hypothermia requires a fall of $[H^+]$ (rise of pH). This elegant suggestion ran into criticism in the subsequent discussion on three grounds: first, some people regard intracellular fluid as a more relevant milieu than blood; second, the comparison of pH at different temperatures is not strictly possible; third, the suggestion implies a constancy of the chemical potential of H^+ which is not strictly true. Despite these criticisms the general idea has obvious attractions.

For some years there has been disagreement about the criteria by which respiratory and nonrespiratory changes in the acid-base composition of the body should be recognised. There have been two sources of confusion: semantic and physiological. The semantic confusion arises from the ambiguous use of the terms acidosis and alkalosis to refer either to a physiological disturbance or to a resultant chemical change in the blood. At an *ad hoc* meeting at the New York Academy of Sciences (38) there was general agreement that the terms acidosis and alkalosis should be used in a physiological and not a chemical sense; they should be used to imply a disturbance of mechanism, whatever the resultant pH. The physiological source of confusion has been about which titration curve or dissociation curve is relevant when evaluating physiological disturbances.

Blood, tissue, and body dissociation curves.—Lloyd & Michel (39) have derived an expression for the carbon dioxide dissociation curve of true plasma *in vitro* in terms of the plasma pH and plasma bicarbonate concentrations. McHardy (40) has derived both equations and graphs for the relationship between change in Pco_2 and changes of carbon dioxide content of whole blood of man. Both these formulations incorporate terms dependent upon haemoglobin concentration and saturation. None of the techniques which attempt to disentangle respiratory from nonrespiratory changes in acid-base composition *in vivo* by manipulating whole blood (e.g. alkali reserve, standard bicarbonate, carbon dioxide combining power, buffer base, base excess) is satisfactory because they all depend upon the *in vitro* titration characteristics of blood, which are not the same as those found *in vivo*. By this is meant the following: when the Pco_2 of blood is raised or lowered *in vitro* the changes in $[H^+]$ and $[HCO_3^-]$ are not the same as those which are found when the Pco_2 of the whole animal is raised or lowered and blood sampled at the different values of Pco_2. Hence, restoring the Pco_2 of blood *in vitro* to, say, 40 mm Hg does not restore the bicarbonate concentration of the plasma, the carbon dioxide content of the whole blood, or any of the other measurements to the value that would have obtained had the Pco_2 of the whole organism been 40 mm Hg.

Schwartz and his co-workers (41) have defined the acute whole-body carbon dioxide titration curve of normal man. This curve describes the changes in $[H^+]$ and bicarbonate that occur when the Pco_2 is raised or lowered and held there for a few hours. Various relationships were defined, notably:

$$\Delta H^+ = 0.77\Delta Pco_2 \text{ and } \Delta HCO_3^- = 0.1\Delta Pco_2$$

where H^+ is nanomolal and HCO_3^- is millimolar. These values imply that the whole-body dissociation curve is much flatter than that of the whole blood. Other workers have found slightly steeper dissociation curves (42, 43), but the implication is the same.

The explanation for the difference between the *in vivo* and *in vitro* carbon dioxide titration curves probably lies in the fact that haemoglobin is the predominant buffer for both blood and interstitial fluid. *In vivo* the bicarbonate ions generated from carbon dioxide are distributed not only in plasma but in the interstitial fluid as well. Thus "buffer base" in whole blood is reduced ($Hb^- \rightarrow HHb$) but not replaced by an equal amount of HCO_3^-. Armstrong et al. (44) have suggested that a good working approximation for the *in vivo* titration curve is to say that the curve for the body approximates that of blood with a haematocrit of 0.09 or haemoglobin of 3 g/100 ml and this value can then be used with the Singer-Hastings or Siggaard-Andersen-Astrup diagrams. If rigorously interpreted this approach would imply that there is no net shift of bicarbonate as opposed to H^+ ions across the cell membranes. This interpretation is compatible with Schwartz's results, but those of Michell and Prys-Roberts would suggest that there are some transcellular ionic shifts so that some HCO_3^- in the extracellular fluid represents intracellular buffering. These differences may well be technical because these studies rely upon small differences between large numbers. Full measurements not only of the concentration changes but also of the volumes of distribution of carbon dioxide and electrolytes are awaited with interest.

Particular attention has been paid to the effects of changes in Pco_2 on brain and muscle. In response to rapid changes of Pco_2, the buffer capacity of the brain appears to be similar to that of the blood (45-47). If a rise of Pco_2 is sustained for two hours, there is an upward shift of the *in vitro* dissociation curve which is not secondary to renal changes and which may well be related to those active mechanisms which raise the cerebrospinal fluid [HCO_3^-] (48).

The behaviour of muscle is less clear. Relman's earlier work on isolated living muscle would suggest either that the slope of the dissociation curve of muscle intracellular fluid is very steep or that it rapidly changes its position. Clancy & Brown (49), in a paper which discusses the problem very clearly, come to a similar conclusion. But studies of the intracellular pH of whole body, which must be dominated by muscle, suggest that the slope of the dissociation curve is flat and hence the rise in intracellular [H^+] produced by hypercapnia is large (50).

Attempts to clarify intracellular changes suffer from three handicaps: first, the application of the Henderson-Hasselbalch equation to multicompartmental systems of uncertain ionic strength (47–52); second, the theoretical basis of the weak acid (e.g. DMO) methods can be challenged for similar reasons (47–52; and see below); third, the delineation of the boundaries and measurement of the extra- and intracellular fluids are difficult (although this is not as important as is commonly thought). The measurement of intracellular pH is further discussed below.

A different experimental approach, using the whole organism but which bears on the same problems as those discussed above, examines the rate of rise in Pco_2 during breath-holding or rebreathing. This rise is surprisingly rapid and its rate is surprisingly constant which suggests that the large intracellular pool of muscle is an insignificant carbon dioxide "store" over short periods of time (53, 54). Whether or not this is due to the limitation of carbon dioxide mobility to muscle by the circulation or due to some other factor such as lack of carbonic-anhydrase-like activity in muscle remains an open question. The apparent carbon dioxide dissociation curve of man during exercise, estimated by both hyperventilation and rebreathing, appears to be about 1 ml kg^{-1} mm^{-1} (55) or twice that at rest.

The chronic "titration curve" of the organism depends, in addition to the factors already discussed, on the buffering of carbon dioxide by poorly accessible stores such as bone and also on the generation of HCO_3^- by the kidney. The curve is not known experimentally for man, but clinical data (56, 57) suggest that the relationships are similar to those found experimentally in the dog (58):

$$\Delta H^+ = 0.32 \Delta Pco_2; \quad \Delta HCO_3^- = 0.25 \Delta Pco_2$$

Mild or moderate hypoxaemia (arterial Po_2 45–55 mm Hg) does not affect the acid-base response of the dog to hypercapnia (59).

Intracellular pH.—In a very important paper, Carter et al. (52) describe how, by a technical tour de force, they have measured intracellular pH of resting muscle and transmembrane potential using microelectrodes. They found that the pH_i was determined by the transmembrane potential and blood pH. The average resting pH_i they report (6.0) is much lower than that found with previous direct measurements and with methods using the partition of weak acids (e.g. DMO) or bases. They produce evidence that the discrepancy is not technical.

It is extremely unlikely that there is any single homogeneous value for pH_i. The pH near the surface of a charged macromolecule (pH_s) may differ from that of the bulk phase. The electrodes measure chiefly the bulk phase pH whereas DMO may measure something in between. The discrepancies between the Dallas work, Caldwell's earlier studies, and the DMO data require further instrumental and experimental study. It is, however, to be hoped that time will not be wasted in dispute about whose pH is "correct"; let us remember alveolar gas and Haldane and Krogh. Perhaps one may forecast that the derived value conventionally referred to as "intracellular pH" will turn out not to have the same physicochemical meaning as pH in extracellular fluid, but to be nevertheless informative.

Miscellaneous.—There have been studies of the role of carbonic anhydrase in facilitating the diffusion of CO_2 in bicarbonate solutions (60, 61) and on the importance of carbamino-bound CO_2 in CO_2 transport and buffering (62).

An unsuspected and challenging observation is the apparent failure of complete CO_2 equilibration throughout the blood in the pulmonary capillaries when $O_2 : CO_2$ mixtures are rebreathed during exercise (63). It is suggested that molecular CO_2 is generated by the oxygenation of haemoglobin at a rate which exceeds the limits of either the chloride shift or (improbably) the hydration reaction. The "apparent" variation of the "apparent" pK of the $CO_2 : HCO_3^-$ system in blood from subjects with otherwise normal blood chemistry is about 0.025 (SD) (64, 65). In blood with abnormal electrolyte or protein concentrations the pK may be considerably different. The effects of gross hypercapnia (P_{CO_2} over 200 mm Hg) in man have been described and reviewed (66).

MORBID PHYSIOLOGY; PULMONARY FUNCTION TESTING

Respiratory function tests are now firmly established on the scene of medical practice and are moving from the stage of neglect to the stage of misuse. Unfortunately, many people continue to use them with the aim of diagnosing morbid changes of structure. Admittedly, they may sometimes help in this way, but their real place is in answering functional questions— and "how much trouble is there?" is often a more relevant question than "what is the cause of the trouble?" The fact that certain techniques and measurements have added to our general understanding of pathological processes does not mean that these measurements need be repeated in a given patient. We are now free to (*a*) dispense with measurements as superfluous, (*b*) advise that they be carried out as helpful for confirmation, or (*c*) insist upon them as essential for adequate management (67). Thus it is nowadays rarely necessary to measure lung compliance and certainly not to measure it repeatedly; the vital capacity is an adequate indication of what ones wishes to know.

Studies of carbon monoxide uptake are also finding their proper place now that clinicians recognise that these measurements do not tell all about the alveolar capillary membrane. I agree with Filley (67) that spirometry should be widely used and was dismayed to read a paper (68) which concludes that "simple ventilatory function testing yields results which are too scattered to be useful in the detection of pulmonary abnormality in the individual asymptomatic subject". Up to a point this is a fair comment but it will be misinterpreted as implying that these tests are not worth doing in people who are not very sick, whereas serial studies show that the ability to detect abnormality is almost doubled if one has prior information on a subject's ventilatory capacity (69). A similar case can be made about diffusing capacity (transfer factor) (70).

The most abused investigations for the next few years will probably be the blood gases. They have a dramatic quality which attracts the enthusiast who treats *them* rather than the patient.

A factor causing difficulty in the correct application of physiology in practice is the lack of a simple unequivocal terminology. Terminology should be such that statements about functional defects, about morbid anatomy, and about aetiology are clearly distinguishable. Functional defects should be referred to in terms unequivocally relating only to function. For broad clinical purposes the functional defects commonly observed in chronic bronchopulmonary disease can still be conveniently classified along lines similar to those suggested nearly thirty years ago by Cournand & Richards (71).

I do not like the expression of the results of measurements as "percentage normal" but I recognise that for those unfamiliar with the methods some attempt to convey the "clinical significance" is helpful. The comprehensive improvement index (72) is an ingenious attempt to express such significance of a change in a variable by relating it both to the normal range and to the extreme limit of abnormality.

A good review (73) and a new book (74) on respiratory failure both testify to the fact that physicians practising respiratory medicine need to be more than chest doctors with access to lung function tests.

Bronchitis and emphysema.—Respiratory physiology and emphysema have long been inextricably entwined and the relevance of function to structure is so often illustrated by a passing reference to emphysema that it has come as something of a shock to many physiologists to find that emphysema is a very untidy subject. Its definition in structural terms seems to be agreed upon and the subdivision into alveolar or panacinar and centrilobular or bronchiolar types seems worth making as a first approximation. Unfortunately, the criteria both for the recognition of emphysema (before or after death) and for distinguishing between the types are uncertain. Most unsettling of all has been the recognition of some patients with a long history of breathlessness and airways obstruction with increased residual volume and with ventilation:perfusion disturbances whose lungs at autopsy differ from those of "typical" (panacinar) emphysema. Some morbid anatomists find little or no emphysema; others say there is always some degree of centrilobular emphysema (see below). Although there have been occasional references to such patients over the years, they have become well recognised largely as a result of the work of Fletcher and his co-workers, who call them "type B" to distinguish them from patients with extensive emphysema ("type A"). This year several studies have added to this recognition (75–79).

Although not all groups use the same criteria or the same terms, the patients of type B share three challenging physiological features: 1. an obstructive ventilatory defect with little to find in the airways or parenchyma at autopsy; 2. a disturbance of gas exchange with little impairment of diffusing capacity (transfer factor) (80) during life or damage to the gas exchanging surface at autopsy; 3. hypercapnia disproportionate to the loss of ventilatory capacity.

1. Although evidence for excessive collapse of large airways in expiration continues to be found in some patients (81), the major pressure drop may be in small airways.

2. The defective gas exchange may be due to dilatation of small airways critically placed to hinder gaseous diffusion which is being re-established as the chief mechanism by which the inspired and alveolar gases are mixed (82–84). Another possibility is that the obstruction of small airways causes their peripheral airspaces to be ventilated collaterally.

3. Hypercapnia in patients with airways obstruction is usually attributed either to mechanical inadequacy of the chest or to lack of a central drive. In most patients with chronic lung disease, the total ventilation is normal or increased, but because of ventilation:perfusion trouble (an increased physiological dead space) the alveolar ventilation or alveolar clearance of carbon dioxide is reduced. Fishman et al. (85) suggest that a distinction should be made between *general* alveolar hypoventilation due to failure of the ventilatory apparatus and *net* alveolar hypoventilation due to ventilation:perfusion trouble. The chronic hypercapnia of patients with type B is chiefly due to a net alveolar hypoventilation rather than a general alveolar hypoventilation, but the problem of why they tolerate the hypercapnia remains. Perhaps they are not exposed to the same hypoxic drive during exercise as patients of type A (86). Perhaps they have lost some nonchemical drive from the lungs which persists or is increased in patients of type A. Perhaps patients of type B constitutionally come from the relatively insensitive end of the enormous range of ventilatory response to hypercapnia seen in normal subjects. [Those who think that an elevation of arterial Pco_2 is resisted nigh unto death should be given pause by the report by Jarrett (87) that the arterial Pco_2 of a trained diver may rise to 70 mm during work.]

The acute profound elevation of Pco_2 to narcotic levels when the acutely ill patient is given oxygen is also incompletely understood. Although conventionally attributed to removal of the chemoreceptor hypoxic drive, an acute deterioration in the distribution of the pulmonary blood flow may be important (88, 89).

Asthma.—In patients with asthma, changes in clinical severity may be accompanied by changes in lung volume rather than in FEV_1 (90). It is suggested that all subjects react to an increased airways resistance with increased residual volume, functional residual capacity, and total lung capacity, sometimes of considerable magnitude. In one patient during a remission, the total lung capacity, measured by He dilution, fell from eleven to about six liters. There are variable changes in the pattern of blood flow distribution (91) and the blood gases do not closely reflect either the clinical severity or the degree of airway obstruction as indicated by spirometry (92).

The administration of nebulised isoproterenol to asthmatics improves airway resistance and FEV_1 per cent but causes an increase in the alveolar-arterial Po_2 difference and a fall in the steady state Dco. These findings suggest that the bronchodilator increases the ventilation of already well-ventilated portions of the lungs but increases the unevenness of distribution of ventilation: blood flow ratios throughout the lung (93, 94).

Nonobstructive conditions.—No great principles or concepts have emerged but there has been much honest endeavour which has helped to expand and clarify understanding of morbid physiology in the following conditions: pregnancy (95)—ladies please forgive me—; farmer's lung (96); sarcoidosis (97); bagassosis (98); asbestosis (99); rheumatoid arthritis, systemic lupus erythematosus, scleroderma (100); pulmonary fibrosis and granulomatosis (101–104); pulmonary resection (105).

Most of these are uncommon, chronic conditions, but the availability of blood gas methods has shown a high incidence of defective gas exchange in acute common conditions such as myocardial infarction (106, 107), left ventricular failure (108) and the postoperative state after general surgery (109, 110, 110a).

The presence of a high alveolar-arterial Po_2 difference, when breathing oxygen is a feature of severe left ventricular failure and the postoperative period. Whether or not this represents infinitely low ventilation: perfusion ratios in open parts of lung, atelectasis, or precapillary shunting remains to be seen.

Dempsey et al. (111, 112) have published a most comprehensive study of the effects of obesity on cardiorespiratory function. This and other studies (113–117) have added to the evidence that the syndrome named after the Fat Boy of Pickwick Papers is not to be simply interpreted as a mechanical problem due to a mass of fat.

REGIONAL LUNG FUNCTION: THE EFFECTS OF GRAVITY

The different techniques employed in the study of regional lung function have been well reviewed in a collection of papers (118) from an international symposium held in Lund, Sweden. There are articles on the use of radio-active isotopes such as ^{133}Xe, ^{15}O, macroaggregates of labelled albumin and ^{85}Kr, on bronchospirometry, and on the use of the mass spectrometer. Of all methods ^{133}Xe has so far given the most information about regional ventilation and perfusion.

The xenon method has been used by Milic-Emili et al. (119) to show the expansion of different regions of the lung at various lung volumes [unless otherwise stated, all studies refer to the vertical (head up) lung since this position magnifies the pressure gradients within the lung and hence regional differences]. Two important findings were: first, at functional residual capacity the lower regions of the lung were expanded to only 30 per cent of their volume at total lung capacity while the upper zones were expanded to 60 per cent of their total lung capacity volume; second, during inspiration over the first 20 per cent of vital capacity starting from residual volume no gas entered the lower zones. A similar distribution has been recently shown by Dollfuss et al. (120) who injected boluses of xenon into the mouthpiece at different lung volumes. They also measured the subsequent expired xenon concentration at the mouth and found that during the last part of the expirate from about 20 per cent ventilatory capacity there was an abrupt change in concentration. This supports the notion that airways gradually close from base to apex as the residual volume is approached. The inversion of the distribution of ventilation in obese subjects (117) shows that the lower zones of their lungs are functioning close to residual volume.

All these results can be related to the known gradient of intrapleural pressure. Pleural pressure becomes progressively greater (or less negative) down the vertical lung from apex to base, and in the most dependent regions at low lung volumes may exceed atmospheric pressure and cause airways collapse. The importance of intrapleural pressure in the uneven distribution of ventilation has been shown by Zardini & West (121). In an isolated lung preparation, ventilation was found to be uniform when transpulmonary pressure was the same at all levels, and remained the same over a wide range of vascular pressures. Immersing the lung in egg albumin foam to simulate the gradient of pleural pressure caused uneven ventilation in a manner similar to that observed in the human lung. The gradient of pleural pressure extends from the upper to lower parts of the lung, depending on body position, and direct measurements have been made in the prone and supine positions (122) as well as the vertical. At normal lung volumes ventilation is greater in the dependent zones in normal subjects whatever their body position (123, 124). Increases in gravity (positive acceleration) increase these regional differences in ventilation in proportion to the magnitude of the acceleration (125).

Glazier et al. (126) have shown that the increase in intrapleural pressure from apex to base is accompanied by a decrease in alveolar size as intrapleural pressure becomes less negative. Alveolar size was measured using modern morphometric techniques after the lungs of dogs had been frozen intact within the chest. The volume of the apical alveoli was about four times that of the basal, most of the gradient in size being near the apex. In dogs frozen in the horizontal position a gradient of size was seen from left to right or ventral to dorsal, depending on position.

The distribution of blood flow varies, as expected, with body position (123). There are, however, other factors not related to gravity, which influence the distribution of pulmonary blood flow. Pain & West (127) showed that blood flow rose 4 cm higher when an isolated lung was inflated to a certain transpulmonary pressure than if it was deflated to the same pressure (vascular and alveolar pressure and lung volume being constant). This is presumably an effect of changes in the surface tension of the alveolar lining layer altering pericapillary pressure. In man the distribution of pulmonary perfusion at different lung volumes has been studied by Anthonisen & Milic-Emili (128). Xenon 133 was injected to reach the lung at residual volume, functional residual capacity, or total lung capacity; regional count rates were recorded after subsequent inspiration to total lung capacity. It is reasonable to assume that at total capacity alveoli throughout the lung are equal or almost equal in size; consequently, after correcting for lung volume, the differences in blood flow per alveolus at different levels in the lung can be obtained. Using this method Hughes et al. (129) made similar measurements with a scanning technique that allowed them to pay particular attention to the dependent zones of the lung. At functional residual capacity, blood flow per alveolus was observed to decrease over the lower third of the lung. This zone of increased vascular resistance varied in magnitude with lung volume, becoming less at total lung capacity but much more marked at residual volume. They consider that the added resistance to flow in the dependent zones lies in vessels outside the influence of alveolar pressure, and that interstitial pressure must be higher in the lower regions of the vertical lung in man. Other factors such as vasomotor tone have not yet been shown to play a significant part in determining the regional distribution of pulmonary blood flow in man. Oxygen breathing in normal man does not alter the distribution of perfusion or ventilation (130).

With xenon 133, measurements of regional ventilation and perfusion are usually taken separately after injection and inhalation. Anthonisen et al. (131) measured regional count rates during a constant intravenous infusion of xenon over a five-minute period and during subsequent rebreathing of xenon gas in closed circuit. They found that $\dot{V}A/\dot{Q}$ ratios decreased from apex to base but that it was more uniform over the basal regions than previously predicted.

Macroaggregates of human serum albumin tagged with ^{131}I or ^{99}Tc are now frequently used to assess the regional distribution of pulmonary blood flow in patients with disorders affecting the pulmonary circulation such as pulmonary embolism and mitral stenosis. Fred et al. (132) used macroaggregated radioiodinated albumin (^{131}I MAA) in conjunction with pulmonary angiography in the diagnosis of pulmonary embolism. Five out of 27 patients with angiographic evidence of thromboembolism had normal isotope scans, so that this isotope technique cannot be considered completely reliable. There is a good correlation between the ratio of apical to basal blood flow distribution in mitral stenosis and the height of mean left atrial pressure measured by transseptal catheterization (133). One of the disadvantages of macroaggregated albumin is that blood flow *per unit lung volume* is not readily obtainable. Friedman et al. (133) paid particular attention to their external scintillation technique in an effort to overcome this. Using macroaggregated albumin, studies of pulmonary blood flow after acceleration show that the distribution of pulmonary blood flow in supine man does not alter during transverse acceleration up to 8 G (134). This is perhaps surprising because a large increase in the gradient of transmural vascular pressures between the anterior and posterior parts of the lungs would have occurred during acceleration. On the other hand, extravascular pressures may have changed similarly and thus balanced the intravascular effects.

Exercise; Altitude

The physiology of exercise extends far beyond the confines of respiration, but respiratory physiologists are by tradition and inclination well suited to combine an integrative and an analytical approach. Although the broad outlines of the changes of respiratory function during exercise have long been known, the advent of more practicable and acceptable methods has facilitated further documentation of normal behaviour and of the factors affecting it. Two symposia offered much useful information (135, 135a).

Changes in various respiratory, circulatory, and other variables in exercise of varying intensity in the erect posture have been reported by a number of workers (136–145). The general impression is that the younger, fitter, bigger, but less obese subject, at any given work load the less the $\dot{V}o_2$, $\dot{V}co_2$, ventilation, cardiac output, heart rate, and lactate and the greater the ceiling many of these can reach. During maximal exercise with the arms, the $\dot{V}o_2$ attained is two thirds but the cardiac output is four fifths of that achieved in maximum leg work. Simultaneous work with arms and legs does not cause a higher $\dot{V}o_2$ or cardiac output than leg exercise alone (146). Two additional useful reviews of the circulatory response to exercise in man have come from Sweden (147, 148). The 90 per cent response time of the increase in $\dot{V}o_2$ and cardiac output at the onset of exercise is about 1½ minutes (149–151).

Metabolism.—The amounts, sources, and uses of energy in work and leisure have been reviewed (152) and a major technical advance has greatly increased understanding of the substrates of muscle metabolism during exercise (153, 153a). In this beautiful and very important work, biopsies from the thigh muscles of men before, during, and after exercise have shown that the muscle's own glycogen store is an important source of energy and may be a limiting factor in work capacity (153). McArdle's syndrome (myophosphorylase-b deficiency) is a unique "experiment of nature" because the breakdown of glycogen to lactic acid is impaired. Despite the lack of lactate accumulation, the muscles become stiff, there is a reactive hyperaemia and an oxygen debt. Heart rate and ventilation are disproportionate to the usual chemical stimuli (154). In the gastrocnemius of the dog, stimulated to contract at a rate above that producing maximum $\dot{V}o_2$, the lactate, after increasing, falls (155), which is reminiscent of Åstrand's observations in prolonged ski races. Perhaps the limiting factor causing fatigue in these situations is the availability of some other substrate, or perhaps it is the inability of the contractile mechanism to use the energy in whatever form it is provided. Changes in lactate and lactate-pyruvate ratio during "negative work" are compatible with the suggestion that energy is stored in, rather than dissipated from muscles when they resist downhill walking (156).

Bouhuys (157) has documented the metabolic acidosis during exercise in healthy males and he related the changes in gas exchange and various acid base variables to changes in the blood lactate concentration. The slope of the apparent dissociation curve of the body during exercise is about 1 ml $\times$ mm^{-1} $\times$ kg^{-1} (55). Use of this in a carbon dioxide balance (158) lessens some of the discrepancies between the observed changes in blood lactate and those that would be estimated from changes of the gas exchange as noted by Bouhuys. Rowell et al. (159) have examined the hepatic-splanchnic lactate and pyruvate uptake during exercise at 50–70 per cent of the maximum aerobic capacity. They found that splanchnic lactate uptake averaged 0.77 of the estimated total body lactate per minute or 46 per cent of the lactate removed in sixty minutes. Splanchnic carbon dioxide production could account for oxidation of only a small fraction of lactate removed by this region, thus gluconeogenesis is a likely major pathway. They conclude that the lactate-oxygen-debt relationship during exercise is time dependent while oxygen debt is not.

Altitude.—The forthcoming Olympic Games at Mexico City (2250 m; barometric pressure 575 mm Hg; equivalent to breathing 15.5 per cent oxygen at sea level) have heightened interest in those components of cardiorespiratory function which are particularly needed for distance running and are adversely affected by altitude (160, 161).

Acute exposure to altitudes of 3000–4000 m produces a predictable reduction in maximum $\dot{V}o_2$ and increases in ventilation, cardiac output etc., at submaximal work (162–165). Dill et al. (163) found that performance is more adversely affected in the first few days or weeks at altitude than in an acute exposure of thirty minutes. Pretreatment with carbonic anhydrase inhibitors may accelerate acclimatization by producing a metabolic acidosis to coincide with the respiratory alkalosis (166, 167). At the other extreme of "acclimatization", it appears that the young athlete of European ancestry who is born and raised in Leadville has an oxygen transport system no better than that of the athlete at sea level (168). It therefore seems that the national quest for Olympic medals should have started way back. It is uncertain whether or not acclimatization for a few weeks improves performance on returning to sea level (169, 170).

Working capacity.—There is continued interest in methods of measuring or estimating the maximum oxygen uptake as the best index of overall maximum cardiorespiratory power (170–175). A simple technique has been devised for estimating maximum (anaerobic) power by timing a sprint of a few steps up a staircase. The values reported are about three times the aerobic capacity (176–178).

All well-educated respiratory physiologists have, of course, read Barcroft's book on the *Architecture of Physiological Function* and are familiar with Murray and Morgan's graphical analysis of oxygen transport. They will therefore also enjoy two developments of the theme as applied to exercise: one for oxygen (176) and one for carbon dioxide (179).

METHODS

Physiological developments.—The following physiological (as opposed to instrumental) developments are particularly original. Four papers describe methods which are difficult to apply but are very illuminating in their approach and manipulation. First, an analysis of the relationship of lung elastic recoil and maximum expiratory flow (180); second, a method for considering oxygen exchange in the lungs using Bohr integral isopleths and ventilation: perfusion ratio isopleths superimposed on the oxygen dissociation curve (181); third, the analysis of the distribution of diffusing capacity in relation to blood flow using measurement of both Do_2 and Dco (182); fourth, the comparison of arterial and end-tidal concentrations of inert gases of differing solubility following intravenous infusion which provides another way of examining ventilation: perfusion relationships (183).

A more generally applicable trick is to modify the rebreathing method for studying the ventilatory response to carbon dioxide so as to produce "open loop" conditions, that is, no effect of response on stimulus (184, 185). A complete "carbon dioxide response curve" can be obtained in three to four minutes. Those who are skeptical about carbon dioxide responsiveness can use the method to study other aspects of breathing without the complication of a variable carbon dioxide stimulus (186).

A good review of heat and water exchanges in the respiratory tract includes a useful graphical method of calculation (187).

The availability of rapid gas analysers enables the composition of the mixed venous blood to be estimated using the lungs as a tonometer in a manner that would gladden the great men of the past (188–190).

Instrumentation.—Useful contributions to whole-body plethysmography (191–194) and impedance plethysmography (195–197), and a good review of methods for measuring forces, pressures, displacements, flows, etc. (198) have appeared. There has been much consolidation, evaluation, and refinement in the use of electrodes (199–207), and in the measurement of blood gas content (208–213). A nomogram for the effects of temperature on the blood gases has been published (214), and a new portable, manual, nonelectronic, solid-state analogue computer facilitates on-line severinghausmanship (215).

LITERATURE CITED

1. Buller, A. J. The muscle spindle and the control of movement. *Breathlessness,* 11–17 (Howell, J. B. L., Campbell, E. J. M., Eds., Blackwell, Oxford, 243 pp., 1966)

2. von Euler, C. The control of respiratory movement. *Breathlessness,* 19–32 (Howell, J. B. L., Campbell, E. J. M., Eds., Blackwell, Oxford, 243 pp., 1966)

3. Sears, T. A. The respiratory motoneurone: integration at spinal segmented level. *Breathlessness,* 33–47 (Howell, J. B. L., Campbell, E. J. M., Eds., Blackwell, Oxford, 243 pp., 1966)

4. Corda, M., von Euler, C., Lennerstrand, G. Reflex and cerebellar influences on α and on 'rhythmic' and 'tonic' γ activity in the intercostal muscle. *J. Physiol. (London),* **184,** 898–923 (1966)

5. von Euler, C., Peretti, G. Dynamic and static contributions to the rhythmic activation of primary and secondary spindle endings in external intercostal muscle. *J. Physiol. (London),* **187,** 501–16 (1966)

6. Glebovskii, V. D. Stretch reflexes of intercostal muscles. *Fed. Proc. Transl. Suppl. 25,* T937–42 (1966)

7. Newsom Davis, J., Sears, T. A. The effects of sudden alterations in load on human intercostal muscles during voluntary activation. *J. Physiol. (London),* 36–38P (1967)

8. Bouhuys, A., Proctor, D. F., Mead, J. Kinetic aspects of singing. *J. Appl. Physiol.,* **21,** 483–96 (1966)

9. Stigol, L. C., Cuello, A. C. Voluntary control of the diaphragm in one subject. *J. Appl. Physiol.,* **21,** 1911–12 (1966)

10. Alexander, C. Diaphragm movements and the diagnosis of diaphragmatic paralysis. *Clin. Radiol.,* **17,** 79–83 (1966)

11. Raper, A. J., Thompson, W. T., Jr., Shapiro, W., Patterson, W. J., Jr. Scalene and sternomastoid muscle function. *J. Appl. Physiol.,* **21,** 497–502 (1966)

12. Delhez, L., Petit, J. M. Donnees actuelles de l'electromyographie respiratoire chez l'homme normal. *Electromyography,* **VI,** 101–46 (1966)

13. Fluck, D. C. Chest movements in hemiplegia. *Clin. Sci.,* **31,** 383–88 (1966)

14. Guz, A., Noble, M. I. M., Widdicombe, J. G., Trenchard, D., Mushin, W. W., Makey, A. R. The role of vagal and glossopharyngeal afferent nerves in respiratory sensation, control of breathing and arterial pressure regulation in conscious man. *Clin. Sci.,* **30,** 161–70 (1966)

15. Guz, A., Noble, M. I. M., Widdicombe, J. G., Trenchard, D., Mushin, W. W. The effect of bilateral block of vagus and glossopharyngeal nerves on the ventilatory response to CO_2 of conscious man. *Respirat. Physiol.,* **1,** 206–10 (1966)

16. Guz, A., Noble, M. I. M., Trenchard, D., Smith, A. J., Makey, A. R. The Hering-Breuer inflation reflex in man: studies of unilateral lung inflation and vagus nerve block. *Respirat. Physiol.,* **1,** 382–89 (1966)

17. Sant'Ambrogio, G., Decandia, M., Provini, L. Diaphragmatic contribution to respiration in the rabbit. *J. Appl. Physiol.,* **21,** 843–47 (1966)

18. Bishop, B. Diaphragm and abdominal muscle responses to elevated airway pressure in the cat. *J. Appl. Physiol.,* **22,** 959–65 (1967)

19. Paintal, A. S. Re-evaluation of respiratory reflexes. *Quart. J. Exptl. Physiol.,* **51,** 151–63 (1966)

20. Widdicombe, J. G. Head's paradoxical reflex. *Quart. J. Exptl. Physiol.,* **52,** 44–50 (1967)

21. Frankstein, S. I., Sergeeva, Z. N. Tonic activity of lung receptors in normal and pathological states. *Nature*, **210,** 1054–55 (1966)

22. Agostoni, E., Mognoni, P. Deformation of the chest wall during breathing efforts. *J. Appl. Physiol.*, **21,** 1827–32 (1966)

23. Konno, K., Mead, J. Measurement of the separate volume changes of rib cage and abdomen during breathing. *J. Appl. Physiol.*, **22,** 407–22 (1967)

24. Mead, J. Mechanical factors in the control of breathing—three problems. *Breathlessness*, 139–46 (Howell, J. B. L., Campbell, E. J. M., Eds., Blackwell, Oxford, 243 pp., 1966)

25. Agostoni, E., Mognoni, P., Torri, G., Miserocchi, G. Forces deforming the rib cage. *Respirat. Physiol.*, **2,** 105–17 (1966)

26. Rindqvist, T. The ventilatory capacity in healthy subjects: an analysis of causal factors with special reference to the respiratory forces. *Scand. J. Clin. Lab. Invest. Suppl. No. 88,* 179 pp. (1966)

27. Bouhuys, A., Jonson, B. Alveolar pressure, airflow rate and lung inflation in man. *J. Appl. Physiol.*, **22,** 1086–1100 (1967)

28. Eldridge, F. Anaerobic metabolism of respiratory muscles. *J. Appl. Physiol.*, **21,** 853–57 (1966)

29. Shephard, R. J. The maximum sustained voluntary ventilation in exercise. *Clin. Sci.*, **32,** 167–76 (1967)

30. Shephard, R. J. The oxygen cost of breathing during vigorous exercise. *Quart. J. Exptl. Physiol.*, **51,** 336–50 (1966)

31. Freedman, S. Prolonged maximum voluntary ventilation. *J. Physiol. (London)*, **184,** 42–44P (1966)

32. Wiley, R. L., Zechman, F. W., Jr. Perception of added airflow resistance in humans. *Respirat. Physiol.*, **2,** 73–87 (1966)

33. Newsom Davis, J. *Respiratory Sensation in Man* (M.D. thesis, Cambridge, 103 pp., 1966)

33a. Newsom Davis, J. Contribution of somatic receptors in the chest wall to detection of added inspiratory airway resistance. *Clin. Sci.*, **33,** 249–60 (1967)

34. Campbell, E. J. M., Freedman, S., Clark, T. J. H., Robson, J. G., Norman, J. The effect of muscular paralysis induced by tubocurarine on the duration and sensation of breath-holding. *Clin. Sci.*, **32,** 425–32 (1967)

35. Howell, J. B. L., Campbell, E. J. M., Eds. *Breathlessness* (Blackwell, Oxford, 243 pp., 1966)

36. Petit, J. M. *Physiopathologie de la dyspnée chez l'asthmatique* (Editions Arscia S.A., Bruxelles, 1966)

37. Rahn, H. Gas transport from the external environment to the cell. *Development of the Lung*, 3–23 (Reuck, A. V. S. de, Porter, R., Eds., Churchill, London, 1967)

38. Current concepts of acid-base measurement. *Ann. N.Y. Acad. Sci.*, **133,** Art. 1 (1st April, 1–274 pp., 1966)

39. Lloyd, B. B., Michel, C. C. A theoretical treatment of the carbon dioxide dissociation curve of true plasma in vitro. *Respirat. Physiol.*, **1,** 107–20 (1966)

40. McHardy, G. J. R. The relationship between the differences in pressure and content of carbon dioxide in arterial and venous blood. *Clin. Sci.*, **32,** 299–309 (1967)

41. Brackett, N. C., Jr., Cohen, J. J., Schwartz, W. B. Carbon dioxide titration curve of normal man. *New Engl. J. Med.*, **272,** 6–12 (1965)

42. Michel, C. C., Lloyd, B. B., Cunningham, D. J. C. The in vivo carbon dioxide dissociation curve of true plasma. *Respirat. Physiol.*, **1,** 121–37 (1966)

43. Prys-Roberts, C., Kelman, G. R., Nunn, J. F. Determination of the in vivo carbon dioxide titration curve of anaesthetized man. *Brit. J. Anaesthesia*, **38,** 500–9 (1966)

44. Armstrong, B. W., Mohler, J. G., Jung, R. C., Remmers, J. The in vivo carbon dioxide titration curve. Estimation from measurements on a single sample of blood. *Lancet*, **I,** 759–61 (1966)

45. Ponten, U. Acid-base changes in rat brain tissue during acute respiratory acidosis and baseosis. *Acta Physiol. Scand.*, **68,** 152–63 (1966)

46. Ponten, U. Studies of acute respiratory acid-base changes in brain tissue and cerebrospinal fluid.

Acta Physiol. Scand., **68**, *Suppl.* 275, 19 pp. (1966)

47. Roos, A. Intracellular pH and intracellular buffering power of the cat brain. *Am. J. Physiol.*, **209**, 1233–46 (1965)

48. Kazemi, H., Shannon, D. C., Carvallo-Gil, E. Brain CO_2 buffering capacity in respiratory acidosis and alkalosis. *J. Appl. Physiol.*, **22**, 241–46 (1967)

49. Clancy, R. L., Brown, E. B. In vivo CO_2 buffer curves of skeletal and cardiac muscle. *Am. J. Physiol.*, **211**, 1309–12 (1966)

50. Manfredi, F. Effects of hypocapnia and hypercapnia on intracellular acid-base equilibrium in man. *J. Lab. Clin. Med.*, **69**, 304–12 (1967)

51. Siesjo, Bo K., Ponten, U. Intracellular pH. True parameter or misnomer? *Ann. N.Y. Acad. Sci.*, **133**, 78–86 (1966)

52. Carter, N. W., Rector, F. C., Jr., Campion, D. S., Seldin, D. W. Measurement of intracellular pH of skeletal muscle with pH sensitive glass microelectrodes. *J. Clin. Invest.*, **46**, 920–33 (1967)

53. Cherniack, N. S., Longobardo, G. S., Staw, I., Heymann, M. Dynamics of carbon dioxide stores changes following an alteration in ventilation. *J. Appl. Physiol.*, **21**, 785–93 (1966)

54. Nahas, G. G., Verosky, M. The storage of CO_2 during apneic oxygenation. *Ann. N.Y. Acad. Sci.*, **133**, 134–37 (1966)

55. Clode, M., Clark, T. J. H., and Campbell, E. J. M. The immediate CO_2 storage capacity of the body during exercise. *Clin. Sci.*, **32**, 161–65 (1967)

56. van Ypersele de Strihou, C., Brasseur, L., De Coninck, J. The "carbon dioxide response curve" for chronic hypercapnia in man. *New Engl. J. Med.*, **275**, 117–22 (1966)

57. Dulfano, M. J., Ishikawa, S. Quantitative acid-base relationships in chronic pulmonary patients during the stable state. *Am. Rev. Respirat. Diseases*, **93**, 251–56 (1966)

58. Schwartz, W. B. Defense of extracellular pH during acute and chronic hypercapnia. *Ann. N.Y. Acad. Sci.*, **133**, 125–31 (1966)

59. Sapir, D. G., Levine, D. Z., Schwartz, W. B. The effects of chronic hypoxemia on electrolyte and acid-base equilibrium: An examination of normocapneic hypoxemia and of the influence of hypoxemia on the adaptation to chronic hypercapnia. *J. Clin. Invest.*, **46**, 369–77 (1967)

60. Enns, T. Facilitation by carbonic anhydrase of carbon dioxide transport. *Science*, **155**, 44–47 (1967)

61. Longmuir, I. S., Forster, R. E., Woo, Chi-Yan. Diffusion of carbon dioxide through thin layers of solution. *Nature*, **209**, 393–94 (1966)

62. Rossi-Bernardi, L., Roughton, F. J. W. The specific influence of carbon dioxide and carbamate compounds on the buffer power and Bohr effects in human haemoglobin solutions. *J. Physiol. (London)*, **189**, 1–29 (1967)

63. Jones, N. L., Campbell, E. J. M., McHardy, G. J. R., Higgs, B. E., Clode, M. The estimation of carbon dioxide pressure of mixed venous blood during exercise. *Clin. Sci.*, **32**, 311–27 (1967)

64. Trenchard, D., Noble, M. I. M., Guz, A. Serum carbonic acid pK_1 abnormalities in patients with acid-base disturbances. *Clin. Sci.*, **32**, 189–200 (1967)

65. Sinclair, M., Hart, A., Pope, H., Campbell, E. J. M. The Henderson-Hasselbach equation: a most useful monument to human laziness *Clin. Chim. Acta* (In press)

66. Prys-Roberts, C., Smith, W. D. A., Nunn, J. F. Accidental severe hypercapnia during anaesthesia. A case report and review of some physiological effects. *Brit. J. Anaesthesia*, **39**, 257–67 (1967)

67. Filley, G. F. Pulmonary function tests: when superfluous, when helpful, when essential? *Am. Rev. Respirat. Diseases*, **93**, 280–83 (1966)

68. Sobol, B. J. Assessment of ventilatory abnormality in the asymptomatic subject: an exercise in futility. *Thorax*, **21**, 445–49 (1966)

69. Rosenzweig, D. Y., Arkins, J. A., Schrock, L. G. Ventilation studies on a normal population after a seven year interval. *Am. Rev. Respirat. Diseases*, **94**, 74–78 (1966)

70. Krumholz, R. A. Pulmonary mem-

brane diffusing capacity and pulmonary capillary blood volume. An appraisal of their clinical usefulness. *Am. Rev. Respirat. Diseases,* **94,** 195–200 (1966)

71. Scadding, J. G. Patterns of respiratory insufficiency. *Lancet,* **I,** 701–5 (1966)

72. Polgar, G., Glauser, S. C. Comprehensive index for physiological functions in longitudinal studies. *Arzneimittel-Forsch.,* **16,** 153–55 (1966)

73. Williams, M. H., Jr. Ventilatory failure. *Medicine,* **45,** 317–30 (1966)

74. Filley, G. F. *Pulmonary Insufficiency and Respiratory Failure* (Lea & Febiger, Philadelphia, Pa., 162 pp., 1967)

75. Burrows, B., Fletcher, C. M., Heard, B. E., Jones, N. L., Wootliff, J. S. The emphysematous and bronchial types of chronic airways obstruction. A clinicopathological study of patients in London and Chicago. *Lancet,* **I,** 830–35 (1966)

76. Jones, N. L., Burrows, B., Fletcher, C. M. Serial studies of 100 patients with chronic airway obstruction in London and Chicago. *Thorax,* **22,** 327–35 (1967)

77. Emmanuel, G. E., Moreno, F. Distribution of ventilation and blood flow during exercise in emphysema. *J. Appl. Physiol.,* **21,** 1532–44 (1966)

78. Filley, G. F. Emphysema and chronic bronchitis: clinical manifestations and their physiologic significance. *Med. Clin. N. Am.,* **51,** 283–92 (1967)

79. Vandenbergh, E., van de Woestijne, K. P., Gyselen, A. Chronische bronchitis en obstructief longemfyseem. Kliniek en evolutie. *Tijdschr. Geneesk.,* **22,** 24–45 (1966)

80. Bedell, G. N., Ostiguy, G. L. Transfer factor for carbon monoxide in patients with airways obstruction. *Clin. Sci.,* **32,** 239–48 (1967)

81. Tammeling, G. J., Berg, W. C., Sluiter, H. J. Estimation of the expiratory collapse of the intrathoracic airways. *Am. Rev. Respirat. Diseases,* **93,** 238–50 (1966)

82. Muir, D. C. F. Bulk flow and diffusion in the airways of the lung. *Brit. J. Diseases Chest,* **60,** 169–76 (1966)

83. Cumming, G. Gas mixing efficiency in the human lung. *Respirat. Physiol.,* **2,** 213–24 (1967)

84. Sikand, R., Cerretelli, P., Farhi, L. E. Effects of $\dot{V}_A$ and $\dot{V}_A/\dot{Q}$ distribution and of time on the alveolar plateau. *J. Appl. Physiol.,* **21,** 1331–37 (1966)

85. Fishman, A. P., Goldring, R. M., Turino, G. M. General alveolar hypoventilation: a syndrome of respiratory and cardiac failure in patients with normal lungs. *Quart. J. Med.,* **35,** 261–75 (1966)

86. Jones, N. L. Pulmonary gas exchange during exercise in patients with chronic airway obstruction. *Clin. Sci.,* **31,** 39–50 (1966)

87. Jarrett, A. S. Alveolar carbon dioxide tension at increased ambient pressures. *J. Appl. Physiol.,* **21,** 158–62 (1966)

88. Pain, M. C. F., Read, D. J. C., Read, J. Changes of arterial carbon dioxide tension in patients with chronic lung disease breathing oxygen. *Australasian Ann. Med.,* **14,** 195–204 (1965)

89. Howard, P., Penman, R. W. B. The effect of breathing 30% oxygen on pulmonary ventilation-perfusion inequality in normal subjects and patients with chronic lung disease. *Clin. Sci.,* **32,** 127–37 (1967)

90. Woolcock, A. J., Read, J. Lung volumes in exacerbations of asthma. *Am. J. Med.,* **41,** 259–73 (1966)

91. Woolcock, A. J., McRae, J., Morris, J. G., Read, J. Abnormal pulmonary blood flow distribution in bronchial asthma. *Australasian Ann. Med.,* **15,** 196–203 (1966)

92. Tai, E., Read, J. Blood gas tensions in bronchial asthma. *Lancet,* **I,** 644–46 (1967)

93. Knudson, R. J., Constantine, H. P. An effect of isoproterenol on ventilation-perfusion in asthmatic versus normal subjects. *J. Appl. Physiol.,* **22,** 402–6 (1967)

94. Field, G. B. The effects of posture, oxygen, isoproterenol and atropine on ventilation-perfusion relationships in the lung in asthma. *Clin. Sci.,* **32,** 279–88 (1967)

95. Gilbert, R., Auchincloss, J. H., Jr., Dyspnea of pregnancy: clinical and physiological observations. *Am.*

J. Med. Sci. **252,** 270–76 (1966)

96. Rankin, J., Kobayashi, M., Barbee, R. A., Dickie, H. A. Pulmonary granulomatoses due to inhaled organic antigens. *Med. Clin. N. Am.,* **51,** 459–82 (1967)

97. Holmgren, A., Svanborg, N. On the influence of body position on steady-state diffusing capacity during exercise, studied in patients with pulmonary sarcoidosis. *Acta Med. Scand.,* **179,** 703–14 (1966)

98. Weill, H., Buechner, H. A., Gonzalez, E., Herbert, S. J., Aucoin, E., Ziskind, M. Bagassosis: a study of pulmonary function in 20 cases. *Ann. Internal Med.,* **64,** 737–47 (1966)

99. Kleinfield, M., Messite, J., Kooyma, O., Sarfaty, J. Effects of asbestos dust inhalation on lung function. *Arch. Environ. Health,* **12,** 741–46 (1966)

100. Huang, Chin Tang, Lyons, H. A. Comparison of pulmonary function in patients with systemic lupus erythematosus, scleroderma and rheumatoid arthritis. *Am. Rev. Respirat. Diseases,* **93,** 865–75 (1966)

101. Daum, S., Levinsky, L. Diffusing capacity of the lungs and its components in interstitial idiopathic hamman-rich fibroses in adults. *Rev. Czech. Med.,* **12,** 188–200 (1966)

102. Bachofen, H., Scherrer, M. Lung tissue resistance in diffuse interstitial pulmonary fibrosis. *J. Clin. Invest.,* **46,** 133–40 (1967)

103. Sharp, J. T., Sweany, S. K., van Lith, P. Physiologic observations in diffuse pulmonary fibrosis and granulomatosis. *Am. Rev. Respirat. Diseases,* **94,** 316–31 (1966)

104. Sharp, J. T., van Lith, P., Sweany, S. K. Clinicophysiologic correlations in diffuse pulmonary fibroses and granulomatoses. *Am. Rev. Respirat. Diseases,* **94,** 332–39 (1966)

105. Meier-Sydow, J., Beck, W., Ehrenforth, U., Lang, U. Quels parametres fonctionnels respiratoires et cardiovasculaires faut-il mesurer avant resection pulmonaire? *Bull. Physio-Pathol. Resp.,* **2,** 69–81 (1966)

106. Valentine, P. A., Fluck, D. C., Mounsey, J. P. D., Reid, D., Shill-ingford, J. P., Steiner, R. E. Blood gas changes after acute myocardial infarction. *Lancet,* **II,** 837–41 (1966)

107. McNicol, M. W., Kirby, B. J., Bhoola, K. D., Fulton, P. M., Tattersfield, A. E. Changes in pulmonary function 6-12 months after recovery from myocardial infarction. *Lancet,* **II,** 1441–43 (1966)

108. Saunders, K. B. Physiological dead space in left ventricular failure. *Clin. Sci.,* **31,** 145–51 (1966)

109. Diament, M. L., Palmer, K. N. V. Postoperative changes in gas tensions of arterial blood and in ventilatory function. *Lancet,* **II,** 180–82 (1966)

110. Diament, M. L., Palmer, K. N. V. Venous/arterial pulmonary shunting as the principal cause of postoperative hypoxaemia. *Lancet,* **I,** 15–17 (1967)

110a. Georg, J., Hornum, I., Mellemgaard, K. The mechanism of hypoxaemia after laparotomy. *Thorax,* **22,** 382–86 (1967)

111. Dempsey, J. A., Reddan, W., Balke, B., Rankin, J. Work capacity determinants and physiologic cost of weight supported work in obesity. *J. Appl. Physiol.,* **21,** 1815–20 (1966)

112. Dempsey, J. A., Reddan, W., Rankin, J., Balke, B. Alveolar-arterial gas exchange during muscular work in obesity. *J. Appl. Physiol.,* **21,** 1807–14 (1966)

113. Scherrer, M. La fonction respiratoire chez les obeses. *J. Franc. Med. Chir. Thor.,* **20,** 77–101 (1966)

114. Atlan, G., Brille, D. Role d'un facteur bronchique associe, clinique ou latent, dans le mecanisme de l'hypoventilation alveolaire de l'obese. Interet du test a l'Acetylcholine. *J. Franc. Med. Chir. Thor.,* **20,** 229–34 (1966)

115. Duron, B., Tassinari, A. Syndrome de pickwick et syndrome cardiorespiratoire de l'obesite. A propos d'une observation. *J. Franc. Med. Chir. Thor.,* **20,** 207–22 (1966)

116. Galy, P., Brune, J., Lheureux, P., Wiesendanger, T., Brune, A. A propos des troubles respiratoires des obese. L'importance du facteur contamination veineuse. *J.*

Franc. Med. Chir. Thor., **20**, 195–200 (1966)

117. Holley, H. S., Milic-Emili, J., Becklake, M. R., Bates, D. V. Regional distribution of pulmonary ventilation and perfusion in obesity. *J. Clin. Invest.*, **46**, 475–81 (1967)

118. Regional Lung Function. An International Symposium. University of Lund, March 6, 1965. *Scand. J. Respirat. Diseases Suppl. 62*, 111 pp. (1966)

119. Milic-Emili, J., Henderson, J. A. M., Dolovich, M. B., Trop, D., Kaneko, K. Regional distribution of inspired gas in the lung. *J. Appl. Physiol.*, **21**, 749–59 (1966)

120. Dollfuss, R. E., Milic-Emili, J., Bates, D. V. Regional ventilation of the lung, studied with boluses of [133]xenon. *Respirat. Physiol.*, **2**, 234–46 (1967)

121. Zardini, P., West, J. B. Topographical distribution of ventilation in isolated lung. *J. Appl. Physiol.*, **21**, 794–801 (1966)

122. Rutishauser, W. J., Banchero, N., Tsakiris, A. S., Edmundowicz, A. C., Wood, E. H. Pleural pressures at dorsal and ventral sites in supine and prone body positions. *J. Appl. Physiol.*, **21**, 1500–10 (1966)

123. Kaneko, K., Milic-Emili, J., Dolovich, M. B., Dawson, A., Bates, D. V. Regional distribution of ventilation and perfusion as a function of body position. *J. Appl. Physiol.*, **21**, 767–77 (1966)

124. Glazier, J. B., DeNardo, G. L. Pulmonary function studied with xenon[133] scanning technique. Normal values and a postural study. *Am. Rev. Respirat. Diseases*, **94**, 188–94 (1966)

125. Bryan, A. C., Milic-Emili, J., Pengelly, D. Effect of gravity on the distribution of pulmonary ventilation. *J. Appl. Physiol.*, **21**, 778–84 (1966)

126. Glazier, J. B., Hughes, J. M. B., Maloney, J. E., Pain, M. C. F., West, J. B. Decreasing alveolar size from apex to base in the upright lung. *Lancet*, **II**, 203–4 (1966)

127. Pain, M. C. F., West, J. B. Effect of the volume history of the isolated lung on distribution of blood flow. *J. Appl. Physiol.*, **21**, 1545–50 (1966)

128. Anthonisen, N. R., Milic-Emili, J. Distribution of pulmonary perfusion in erect man. *J. Appl. Physiol.*, **21**, 760–66 (1966)

129. Hughes, J. M. B., Glazier, J. B., Maloney, J. E., West, J. B. Effect of interstitial pressure on pulmonary blood flow. *Lancet*, **I**, 192–93 (1967)

130. Holley, H. S., Dawson, A., Bryan, A. C., Milic-Emili, J., Bates, D. V. Effect of oxygen on the regional distribution of ventilation and perfusion in the lung. *Can. J. Physiol. Pharmacol.*, **44**, 89–93 (1966)

131. Anthonisen, N. R., Dolovich, M. B., Bates, D. V. Steady state measurements of regional ventilation to perfusion ratios in normal man. *J. Clin. Invest.*, **45**, 1349–56 (1966)

132. Fred, H. L., Burdine, J. A., Gonzalez, D. A., Lockhart, R. W., Peabody, C. A., Alexander, J. K. Arteriographic assessment of lung scanning in pulmonary thromboembolism. *New Engl. J. Med.*, **275**, 1025–32 (1966)

133. Friedman, W. F., Braunwald, E. Alterations in regional pulmonary blood flow in mitral valve disease studied by radioisotope scanning. A simple nontraumatic technique for estimation of left atrial pressure. *Circulation*, **34**, 363–76 (1966)

134. Hoppin, F. G., Jr., York, E., Kuhl, D. E., Hyde, R. W. Distribution of pulmonary blood flow as affected by transverse ($+G_X$) acceleration. *J. Appl. Physiol.*, **22**, 469–74 (1967)

135. Proceedings of the International Symposium on physical activity and cardiovascular health. Toronto, October 1966. *Can. Med. Assoc. J.*, **96**, 695–918 (1967)

135a. Chapman, C. B. Physiology of muscular exercise. *Circ. Res.*, **20**, *Suppl. 1*, 1–226 (1967)

136. Jones, N. L., McHardy, G. J. R., Naimark, A., Campbell, E. J. M. Physiological dead space and alveolar arterial gas pressure differences during exercise. *Clin. Sci.*, **31**, 19–29 (1966)

137. Higgs, B. E., Clode, M., McHardy,

G. J. R., Jones, N. L., Campbell, E. J. M. Changes in ventilation, gas exchange and circulation during exercise in normal subjects. *Clin. Sci.*, 32, 329–37 (1967)

138. Grimby, G., Saltin, B. Physiological analysis of physically well-trained middle-aged and old athletes. *Acta Med. Scand.*, 179, 513–26 (1966)

139. Grimby, G., Nilsson, N. J., Sanne, H. Repeated serial determination of cardiac output during 30 min. exercise. *J. Appl. Physiol.*, 21, 1750–56 (1966)

140. Wasserman, K., Van Kessel, A. L., Bruton, G. G. Interaction of physiological mechanisms during exercise. *J. Appl. Physiol.*, 22, 71–85 (1967)

141. Škranc, O., Havel, V. A comparison between 18 to 20 year old students with average physique and trained individuals. *Physiol. Bohemoslov.*, 15, 244–52 (1966)

142. Malmberg, R. Pulmonary gas exchange at exercise and different body postures in man. *Scand. J. Respirat. Diseases*, 47, 92–102 (1966)

143. Klausen, K. Cardiac output in man in rest and work during and after acclimatization to 3,800 m. *J. Appl. Physiol.*, 21, 609–16 (1966)

144. Damato, A. N., Galante, J. G., Smith, W. M. Hemodynamic response to treadmill exercise in normal subjects. *J. Appl. Physiol.*, 21, 959–66 (1966)

145. Adams, W. C. Influence of age, sex and body weight on the energy expenditure of bicycle riding. *J. Appl. Physiol.*, 22, 539–45 (1967)

146. Stenberg, J., Astrand, P.-O., Ekblom, B., Royce, J., Saltin, B. Hemodynamic response to work with different muscle groups, sitting and supine. *J. Appl. Physiol.*, 22, 61–70 (1967)

147. Carlsten, A., Grimby, G. *The circulatory response to muscular exercise in man* (Jokl, Ernst, Ed., Thomas, Springfield, Ill., 1966)

148. Stenberg, J. The significance of the central circulation for the aerobic work capacity under various conditions in young healthy persons. *Acta Physiol. Scand. Suppl. 273*, 26 pp. (1966)

149. Gilbert, R., Baule, G. H., Auchincloss, J. H., Jr. Theoretical aspects of oxygen transfer during early exercise. *J. Appl. Physiol.*, 21, 803–9 (1966)

150. Auchincloss, J. H., Jr., Gilbert, R., Baule, G. H. Effect of ventilation on oxygen transfer during early exercise. *J. Appl. Physiol.*, 21, 810–18 (1966)

151. Cerretelli, P., Sikand, R., Farhi, L. E. Readjustments in cardiac output and gas exchange during onset of exercise and recovery. *J. Appl. Physiol.*, 21, 1345–50 (1966)

152. Durnin, J. V. G. A., Passmore, R. *Energy, Work and Leisure* (Heinemann Educational Books Ltd., London, 166 pp., 1967)

153. Bergstrom, J., Hultman, E. The effect of exercise on muscle glycogen and electrolytes in normals. *Scand. J. Clin. Lab. Invest.*, 18, 16–20 (1966)

153a. Hultman, E. Studies on muscle metabolism of glycogen and active phosphate in man with special reference to exercise and diet. *Scand. J. Clin. Lab. Invest.*, 19, *Suppl. 94*, 1–63 (1967)

154. Porte, D., Jr., Crawford, D. W., Jennings, D. B., Aber, C., McIlroy, M. B. Cardiovascular and metabolic responses to exercise in a patient with McArdle's syndrome. *New Engl. J. Med.*, 275, 406–12 (1966)

155. Stainsby, W. N., Welch, H. G. Lactate metabolism of contracting dog skeletal muscle in situ. *Am. J. Physiol.*, 211, 177–83 (1966)

156. Armstrong, B. W., Hurt, H. H., Jr., Workman, J. M. Downhill walking as a possible form of negative work. *Am. J. Physiol.*, 211, 1264–68 (1966)

157. Bouhuys, A., Pool, J., Binkhorst, R. A., Van Leeuwen, P. Metabolic acidosis of exercise in healthy males. *J. Appl. Physiol.*, 21, 1040–46 (1966)

158. Clode, M. CO_2 balance during exercise. *J. Physiol. (London)*, 184, 49–50P (1966)

159. Rowell, L. B., Kraning, K. K. II, Evans, T. O., Kennedy, J. W., Blackmon, J. R., Kusumi, F. Splanchnic removal of lactate and pyruvate during prolonged exercise in man. *J. Appl. Physiol.*, 21, 1773–83 (1966)

160. Williams, D. A. Athletic performance

at high altitude. *Nature,* **211,** 753 (1966)

161. Kreuzer, F. Transfer of oxygen in moderate hypoxia at rest and at severe exercise. *Med. Thorac.,* **23,** 321–29 (1966)

162. Stenberg, J., Ekblom, B., Messin, R. Hemodynamic response to work at simulated altitude 4,000 m. *J. Appl. Physiol.,* **21,** 1589–94 (1966)

163. Dill, D. B., Myhre, L. G., Phillips, E. E., Jr., Brown, D. K. Work capacity in acute exposures to altitude. *J. Appl. Physiol.,* **21,** 1168–76 (1966)

164. Grover, R. F., Reeves, J. T. Exercise performance of athletes at sea level and 3,100 meters altitude. *Med. Thorac.,* **23,** 129–43 (1966)

165. Reeves, J. T., Grover, R. F., Cohn, J. E. Regulation of ventilation during exercise at 10,200 ft. in athletes born at low altitude. *J. Appl. Physiol.,* **22,** 546–54 (1967)

166. Cain, S. M., Dunn, J. E. II. Low doses of acetazolamide to aid accommodation of men to altitude. *J. Appl. Physiol.,* **21,** 1195–1200 (1966)

167. Mani, K. V., Weinstein, S. A. Effect of carbonic anhydrase inhibition on blood gas and acid base balance during hypoxia. *Bull. Johns Hopkins Hosp.,* **119,** 331–42 (1966)

168. Grover, R. F., Reeves, J. T., Grover, E. B., Leathers, J. E. Muscular exercise in young men native to 3100 m. altitude. *J. Appl. Physiol.,* **22,** 555–64 (1967)

169. Consolazio, C. F., Nelson, R. A., Matoush, Le R. O., Hansen, J. E. Energy metabolism at high altitude (3,475 m). *J. Appl. Physiol.,* **21,** 1732–40 (1966)

170. Klausen, K., Robinson, S., Michael, E. D., Myhre, L. G. Effect of high altitude on maximal working capacity. *J. Appl. Physiol.,* **21,** 1191–94 (1966)

171. Armstrong, B. W., Workman, J. M., Hurt, H. H., Jr., Roemich, W. R. Clinico-physiologic evaluation of physical working capacity in persons with pulmonary disease. Rationale and Application of a method based on estimating maximal oxygen-consuming capacity from MBC and O_{2V_E}. *Am. Rev. Respirat. Diseases,* **93,** 90–99 (Part 1), 223–33 (Part 2) (1966)

172. Teräslinna, P., Ismail, A. H., MacLeod, D. F. Nomogram by Astrand and Rhyming as a predictor of maximum oxygen intake. *J. Appl. Physiol.,* **21,** 513–15 (1966)

173. Kasch, F. W., Phillips, W. H., Ross, W. D., Carter, J. E. L., Boyer, J. L. A comparison of maximal oxygen uptake by treadmill and step test procedures. *J. Appl. Physiol.,* **21,** 1387–88 (1966)

174. Wyndham, C. H., Strydom, N. B., Leary, W. P., Williams, C. G. Studies of the maximum capacity of men for physical effort. Part I: A comparison of methods of assessing the maximum oxygen intake. *Intern. Z. Angew. Physiol.,* **22,** 285–95 (1966)

175. Wyndham, C. H., Strydom, N. B., Leary, W. P. Studies of the maximum capacity of men for physical effort. Part II: The maximum oxygen uptake of young, active Caucasians. *Intern. Z. Angew. Physiol.,* **22,** 296–303 (1966)

176. Margaria, R. Assessment of physical activity in oxidative and anaerobic maximal exercise. *Intern. Z. Angew. Physiol.,* **22,** 115–24 (1966)

177. Margaria, R. Assessment of physical activity in oxidative and anaerobic maximal exercise. *Fed. Proc.,* **25,** 1409–12 (1966)

178. Margaria, R., Aghemo, P., Rovelli, E. Measurement of muscular power (anaerobic) in man. *J. Appl. Physiol.,* **21,** 1662–64 (1966)

179. McHardy, G. J. R., Jones, N. L., Campbell, E. J. M. Graphical analysis of carbon dioxide transport during exercise. *Clin. Sci.,* **32,** 289–98 (1967)

180. Mead, J., Turner, J. M., Macklem, P. T., Little, J. B. Significance of the relationship between lung recoil and maximum expiratory flow. *J. Appl. Physiol.,* **22,** 95–108 (1967)

181. King, T. K. C., Briscoe, W. A. Bohr integral isopleths in the study of blood gas exchange in the lung. *J. Appl. Physiol.,* **22,** 659–74 (1967)

182. Hyde, R. W., Rynes, R., Power, G. G., Nairn, J. Determination of distribution of diffusing capacity in relation to blood flow in the human lung. *J. Clin. Invest.,* **46,** 463–74 (1967)

183. Rochester, D. F., Brown, R. A., Jr., Wichern, W. A., Jr., Fritts, H.

W., Jr. Comparison of alveolar and arterial concentrations of ^{80}Kr and ^{133}Xe infused intravenously in man. *J. Appl. Physiol.*, **22**, 423–30 (1967)

184. Read, D. J. C. A clinical method for assessing the ventilatory response to carbon dioxide. *Australasian Ann. Med.*, **16**, 20–32 (1967)

185. Clark, T. J. H., Clarke, B. G., Hughes, J. M. B. A simple technique for measuring changes in ventilatory response to carbon dioxide. *Lancet*, **II**, 368–71 (1966)

186. Read, D. J. C., Simon, H., Brandi, G., Campbell, E. J. M. Regulation of ventilation during rebreathing at imposed respiratory frequencies. *Respirat. Physiol.*, **2**, 88–98 (1966)

187. Houdas, Y., Colin, J. Echanges thermiques et hydriques par les voies respiratoires de l'homme. *Pathol.-Biol.*, **14**, 229–38 (1966)

188. Kim, T. S., Rahn, H., Farhi, L. E. Estimation of true venous and arterial P_{CO2} by gas analysis of a single breath. *J. Appl. Physiol.*, **21**, 1338–44 (1966)

189. Farhi, L. E., Haab, P. Mixed venous blood gas tensions and cardiac output by "bloodless" methods; recent developments and appraisal. *Respirat. Physiol.*, **2**, 225–33 (1967)

190. Jones, N. L., Campbell, E. J. M., McHardy, G. J. R., Higgs, B. E., Clode, M. The estimation of carbon dioxide pressure of mixed venous blood during exercise. *Clin. Sci.*, **32**, 311–27 (1967)

191. Bernstein, L., Shepard, R. H., Jr. High resolution display for variables in volume-displacement body plethysmography. *J. Appl. Physiol.*, **21**, 721–24 (1966)

192. Ingram, R. H., Jr., Schilder, D. P. Effect of gas compression on pulmonary pressure, flow, and volume relationship. *J. Appl. Physiol.*, **21**, 1821–26 (1966)

193. Guyatt, A. R., Alpers, J. H., Davies, E. E. Design of body plethylsmograph for use in field studies. *J. Appl. Physiol.*, **22**, 390–93 (1967)

194. Jonson, B., Bouhuys, A. Measurement of alveolar pressure. *J. Appl. Physiol.*, **22**, 1081–85 (1967)

195. Hill, R. V., Jansen, J. C., Fling, J. L. Electrical impedance plethylsmography: a critical analysis *J. Appl. Physiol.*, **22**, 161–68 (1967)

196. Logic, J. L., Maksud, M. G., Hamilton, L. H. Factors affecting transthoracic impedance signals used to measure breathing. *J. Appl. Physiol.*, **22**, 251–54 (1967)

197. Baker, L. E., Geddes, L. A., Hoff, H. E., Chaput, C. J. Physiological factors underlying transthoracic impedance variations in respiration. *J. Appl. Physiol.*, **21**, 1491–99 (1966)

198. Rushmer, R. F. *Methods in Medical Research*, **II** (Year Book Med. Publ., Chicago, 301 pp., 1966)

199. Berglund, E., Malmberg, R., Simonsson, B., Stenhagen, S. Different methods for estimating arterial oxygen tension in man. *Scand. J. Respirat. Diseases*, **47**, 209–14 (1966)

200. Bishop, J. M., Pincock, A. C., Hollyhock, A., Raine, J., Cole, R. B. Factors affecting the measurement of the partial pressure of oxygen in blood using a covered electrode system. *Respirat. Physiol.*, **1**, 225–37 (1966)

201. Fletcher, G., Barber, J. L. Effect of sampling technique on the determination of PaO_2 during oxygen breathing. *J. Appl. Physiol.*, **21**, 463–68 (1966)

202. Fletcher, E. C. Allowance for changes in oxygen saturation, pH, P_{CO2} and P_{O2} in blood drawn for analysis. *Brit. J. Diseases Chest*, **60**, 182–84 (1966)

203. Flenley, D. C., Millar, J. S., Rees, H. A. Accuracy of oxygen and carbon dioxide electrodes. *Brit. Med. J.*, **2**, 349–52 (1967)

204. Mayers, L. B., Forster, R. E. A rapid method for measuring blood oxygen content utilizing the oxygen electrode. *J. Appl. Physiol.*, **21**, 1393–96 (1966)

205. Moran, F., Kettel, L. J., Cugell, D. W. Measurement of blood P_{O2} with the microcathode electrode. *J. Appl. Physiol.*, **21**, 725–28 (1966)

206. Rhodes, P. G., Moser, K. M. Sources of error in oxygen tension measurement. *J. Appl. Physiol.*, **21**, 729–34 (1966)

207. Saunier, C., Colas, T. Intéret de la tonometrie du sang pour le contrôle des méthodes mésurant la pression partielle de CO_2 dans le sang artériel. *Bull. Physio-Pathol. Resp.*, **2**, 275–82 (1966)

208. Ayers, S. M., Criscitiello, A., Gian-

nelli, S., Jr. Determination of blood carbon monoxide content by gas chromatography. *J. Appl. Physiol.*, **21**, 1368–70 (1966)

209. Cole, P. V., Hawkins, L. H. The measurement of the oxygen content of whole blood. *Bio-med. Eng.*, **2**, 56–63 (1967)

210. Gambino, S. R., Schreiber, H. The measurement of CO_2 content with the Auto Analyzer. A comparison with 3 standard methods and a description of a new method (alkalinization) for preventing loss of CO_2 from open cups. *Am. J. Clin. Pathol.*, **45**, 406–11 (1966)

211. Lenfant, C., Aucutt, C. Measurement of blood gases by gas chromatography. *Respirat. Physiol.*, **1**, 398–407 (1966)

212. Ortega, F. G., Orie, S. A. M., Tammeling, G. J. Determination of carbon dioxide content of blood by infrared analysis. *J. Appl. Physiol.*, **21**, 1377–80 (1966)

213. Rispens, P., Van Assendelft, O. W., Brunsting, J. R., Zilstra, W. G., Van Kampen, E. J. A direct method for the determination of the HCO_3 concentration as total carbon dioxide in blood and plasma. *Clin. Chim. Acta,* **14**, 760–66 (1966)

214. Kelman, G. R., Nunn, J. F. Nomograms for correction of blood P_{O_2}, P_{CO_2}, pH and base excess for time and temperature. *J. Appl. Physiol.*, **21**, 1484–90 (1966)

215. Severinghaus, J. W. Blood gas calculator. *J. Appl. Physiol.*, **21**, 1108–16 (1966)

THE GASTROINTESTINAL CIRCULATION[1]   1003

By Eugene D. Jacobson

Department of Physiology, University of Oklahoma Medical Center
Oklahoma City, Oklahoma

Introduction

The legion of physiological investigators has swelled to proportions that prevent even neglected areas of research from remaining neglected. The gastrointestinal circulation has not been a field thronged by too many tillers; nevertheless, the accelerating flurry of current work and interest has precipitated several recent reviews (1–6). Still to be answered are such questions as: what intrinsic and extrinsic factors regulate the gastrointestinal circulation? what relationship does this vasculature bear to the major functions of its organs? what role does it play in overall circulatory dynamics during health and disease? what new technics will be needed?

I have elected to discuss certain publications dealing with the gastrointestinal circulation, judging these to be articles in the main stream of physiological research. Time may prove the necessary omission of other papers to have been serious. This is the risk of the review as opposed to the catalogue. The present chapter has been arranged to satisfy the traditional notions of a gastrointestinal physiologist, which stem from the conviction that gastrointestinal blood vessels belong to gastrointestinal organs and do not stand naked for the convenience of the circulatory scholar.

Salivary Glands

During the early part of the past decade, quiet prevailed on the salivary circulation front. The current textbook story reflects this lull between the controversies which have marked the stormy history of the subject. Recently, however, Schachter's group has challenged the entire kallikrein-bradykinin hypothesis and has reasserted the primacy of vasodilator nerves in the glands. The views from two camps are well presented in recent reviews (7, 8).

Morley, Schachter & Smaje (9) have shown that chorda stimulation in the rabbit produces salivation and vasodilation, and both responses are blocked by atropine (less than 0.25 mg/kg). In the rabbit, as opposed to the cat, there is no discrepancy between secretory and circulatory sensitivity to cholinergic blockade. It was precisely this discrepancy between the responses of gland cells and of blood vessels in the cat which initiated the great debate about vasodilator nerve fibers versus metabolic dilators in salivary glands at the turn of this century (4). Schachter's group has also investigated the sympathetic influence on circulation in the rabbit salivary

---

[1] The survey of literature for this review was concluded in May 1967.

gland, and found an initial vasoconstriction followed by a modest afterdilation with nerve stimulation. Adrenergic constriction is prevented by alpha-receptor blockade, and the vasodilation is absent after the administration of beta-adrenergic antagonists. These responses to sympathetic stimulation are unaffected by atropine. This work reaffirms the older explanation of circulatory regulation in the salivary glands. Vascular control is dominated by neural factors rather than metabolic.

Doubtless, the controversial topic of circulatory control in the salivary glands will run true to its past form. The anticipated rejoinder from the 'metabolists' is in the offing. Hilton & Torres (10) have utilized the technic of duct ligation to reduce the content of kinin-forming enzymes in the feline submandibular gland. The result is a heightened sensitivity of the glandular circulation to the dilator effects of injected bradykinin. Duct ligation also markedly depresses the dilator response of the gland to parasympathetic stimulation. It is, of course, a large step that carries us from a degenerating gland whose circulation is hyporesponsive during nerve stimulation to the metabolists' theory which claims so central a regulatory role for the kallikrein-bradykinin system.

There is a newcomer among candidates for the position of metabolic regulator of 'functional hyperemia' in salivary glands. Erjavec, Beaven & Brodie (11) have reported the presence of histamine in saliva of glands stimulated by the parasympathetic nerves. They have also reported that depletion of glandular histamine content with pilocarpine desensitizes the gland to further cholinergic stimulation. The only surprising finding here is that it has taken physiologists so long to incriminate the ubiquitous histamine in this century-old controversy.

STOMACH

Until several years ago there was little interest in the gastric circulation, but lately there has been fresh activity, and several laboratories are involved in the study of blood flow to the stomach (6). Jacobson, Eisenberg & Swan (12), and Swan & Jacobson (13) have used a combination of the electromagnetic flowmeter and a gastric clearance technic to study gastric hemodynamics in the conscious dog and have found that drugs which alter secretory rate also change gastric mucosal blood flow *pari passu* in the same direction. However, certain agents, such as isoproterenol, can induce vasodilation without changing secretory rate. On the other hand, little correlation has been noted between alterations in secretory rate and in total arterial inflow to the stomach (muscle and mucosa). Evidence has been presented for a shift in the distribution of blood flow from muscularis to mucosa during secretory stimulation. This group suggests that an increased gastric mucosal perfusion during stimulation of active secretion by a drug proceeds by three mechanisms: the direct vasodilator action of the drug, the production of vasodilator metabolites by secreting cells, and a redistribution of blood flow from quiescent muscle to the active glandular tissue.

The validity of these conclusions rests mainly with the confidence in the technics utilized to measure gastric blood flow in conscious animals. The authors are aware of some of the limitations of aminopyrine clearance as an estimate of gastric mucosal blood flow (14). Other investigators have raised serious doubts about the use of electromagnetic flowmeters (15).

The effects of histamine on the gastric circulation in the anesthetized dog have also been pursued. Moody (16) has found a direct correlation between secretory rate and blood flow in an exteriorized pedicle from the fundus. Over a wide dosage range there was a steady ratio of mucosal to total gastric blood flow. Naitove & Colby (17) have also investigated gastric hemodynamic responses to histamine. Vascular resistance falls in response to low doses of histamine administered by close intra-arterial injection. Large doses cause a vasoconstriction which is probably secondary to sympathetic overriding of the direct dilator effects of histamine on the stomach.

PANCREAS

Because of its inaccessibility and complexity, the circulation of the pancreas has not invited casual exploration. New technics have surmounted some of the difficulty, and an old unanswered question has been reopened: What is the relationship between secretion and blood flow in the pancreas?

Delaney & Grim (18) have used the isotopic clearance method to estimate pancreatic blood flow. A known quantity of Rb^{86} or K^{42} is injected into a dog, cardiac output is measured, and the animal is killed at a set interval after administration of the radioactive indicator. The ratio of isotope in the pancreatic tissue to total body isotope should be proportional to the ratio of pancreatic blood flow to cardiac output. The theoretical basis for this isotopic clearance technic is discussed in a recent review (19, 20). Delaney & Grim (18) have reported that unstimulated pancreatic tissue flow in conscious dogs is 0.61 ml min^{-1} g^{-1}. Agents which increase pancreatic perfusion significantly include secretin (Boots), norepinephrine, and cortisone. Epinephrine and vasopressin diminish pancreatic uptake of isotopes.

Since secretory studies are not reported by Delanay & Grim (18), only a limited interpretation of their data is possible in terms of a secretory-blood flow relationship. Their perplexing observation that norepinephrine increases and epinephrine decreases uptake of the radioactive indicators by the pancreas is precisely the opposite of what they have reported in the stomach using the same technic (21).

Mackowiak, Friedman & Horn (22) have measured pancreatic arterial inflow with an electromagnetic flowmeter and have determined the pancreatic secretory rate by cannulation of Santorini's duct in anesthetized dogs. They have found that doses of secretin which elicit submaximal secretory responses cause a 20–30 per cent increase in blood flow, with vasodilation preceding the onset of pancreatic secretion. Sympathomimetic amines producing a systemic pressor response are associated with vasoconstriction of the pancreas and inhibition of secretin-stimulated secretion.

Eichelter & Schenk (23) have utilized the electromagnetic blood flowmeter is anesthetized dogs to gauge pancreatic perfusion, and have also measured secretory rate and the arteriovenous oxygen uptake across the organ. Secretin (Boots), in doses which increase pancreatic secretion, also increases arterial inflow by about 70 per cent, while decreasing infrarenal aortic blood flow. At peak secretion venous oxyhemoglobin saturation rises slightly, while arterial values are unchanged, and pancreatic oxygen consumption increases as a function of the greater perfusion.

These three papers indicate an awakening of interest in the pancreatic circulation and its role in the exocrine secretion of that organ. The articles agree that secretin increases pancreatic blood flow and, where measured, secretion and oxygen consumption as well. This circulatory response of the gland to secretin was reported decades ago with technics devoid of electronics. Several requirements need to be met if there is to be some new order in the characterization of a physiologically meaningful secretory-circulatory relationship in the pancreas. Highly purified secretin or the recently synthesized polypeptide ought to be used in a systematic dose-response fashion to explore the full range of simultaneously measured secretory and blood flow values in conscious animals. A study satisfying these requirements should be possible with current gadgetry.

Hungarian workers (24) have employed Sapirstein's dilution-indicator technic (19) to measure pancreatic perfusion during biliary and trypsin-induced pancreatitis. Both disorders are accompanied by pancreatic ischemia due to combined local factors and shock.

SPLEEN

It has probably been by chance that many physiologists dealing with microcirculatory phenomena have elected to study some part of the splanchnic circulation in preference to limb, kidney, or brain vessels. A sufficient number of these physiologists have investigated the splanchnic bed, so that we seem to know more about microcirculatory events than about the ordinary hemodynamics of this region. Gillespie's group (25, 26) have studied the splenic circulation in the anesthetized cat in order to determine the behavior of circulating norepinephrine during vasoconstriction. They have found that tritium-labeled norepinephrine is retained by splenic tissue after close intra-arterial infusion which is released thereafter at a slow rate from the parenchyma in the form of metabolites. When the catecholamine is administered in doses which fail to constrict arterioles, the drug is localized radioautographically in adrenergic nerve endings within the spleen. Doses of norepinephrine producing constriction result in deposition of the drug not only in nerve terminals but also in vascular smooth muscle cells of the spleen. Drug in excess of the constricting doses can also be localized in fixed splenic reticuloendothelial cells. Differential centrifugation reveals that norepinephrine adheres to the membrane of adrenergic endings. Alpha-adrenergic blockade reduces vasoconstriction and diminishes uptake of infused norepinephrine by smooth muscle and reticuloendothelial cells. These findings suggest that adrenergic terminals are responsible not only for synthesis and release of catecholamines but also for conservation of the materials enabling subsequent reuse. The reticuloendothelial cells appear to be the safety valves of the system, taking up excess catecholamines.

Ross & Kolin (27) have observed that the responses of splenic artery blood flow to intra-arterial epinephrine depend on the dosage: an increase with small doses and a decrease with high doses. Norepinephrine produces arteriolar constriction with any dose. Beta-adrenergic blockade prevents the dilator response to low doses of epinephrine. Venous outflow can be augmented with high or low doses of either catecholamine with or without beta-adrenergic blockade. The authors conclude that beta-adrenergic receptors do not appear to be involved in the mechanism by which the spleen divests itself of stored blood. This may bear interesting implications for those who beat the drum for beta-adrenergic stimulation in the treatment of hemorrhagic or septic shock.

INTESTINE

The blood vessels of the gut continue to be the most widely studied portion of the gastrointestinal circulation. This large circulatory region is the avenue for roughly half the splanchnic flow that subsequently reaches the liver, its vessels and the organ are accessible for study, and the vasculature appears to play a unique role in certain pathological states. The major physiological problems of concern to investigators working with the mesenteric circulation include microcirculatory events, regulatory processes, the relationship of blood flow to intestinal absorption, and the role of this circulation in shock.

In the area of new technics, several laboratories are employing one or another variation of isotopic indicators to assess gut perfusion (19, 28–32). A novel application has been Bacaner's estimation of colonic mucosal blood flow in conscious man (28). A Geiger-Muller detector is inserted into the lumen of the large intestine to measure radioactivity in a shell of tissue located at a fixed distance from the detector. The source of radioactivity is $Na_2HP^{32}O_4$, which is completely cleared from arterial blood on a single pass through the organ. Calculated flow with this method differs by less than 10 per cent from measured flow under acute conditions in anesthetized animals. Human colonic flow has been determined to be 0.3 to 0.8 ml min^{-1} ml^{-1} tissue in several patients. Considerably more experience will be needed with this technic to assess any shortcomings; however, there is surprisingly little disagreement among three groups employing this general method (28–30).

Forster (33) has described the use of inert-gas uptake in estimating intestinal mucosal blood flow. Carbon monoxide has a greater effective solubility in the blood than in tissue and appears to be limited in its uptake by blood flow, once the partial pressure of the gas is high enough to saturate the hemoglobin of the capillaries. Flow determined in this manner is only one tenth of that reported using isotopic technics, which suggests that an undiscerned barrier to the gas may be present.

Steadman (34), using glass microelectrodes inserted into mesenteric arteriolar smooth muscle cells, has found a resting transmembrane potential of 40 mV. Rhythmic slow waves, lasting 5 sec each with an amplitude of up to 14 mV, have been recorded and could be distinguished from the larger action potentials associated with mechanical vasoactivity. Autonomic nervous mediators appear to influence mainly the frequency of action potential firing—adrenergic substances stimulating and cholinergic stimulation depressing electrical activity.

Intestinal microcirulatory investigations conducted in Göteborg over the past several years are well summarized in an article by Folkow (29). Ingenious use of the double-tracer technic has led to the inference of a countercurrent mechanism in the villus. Small lipid-soluble molecules can rapidly traverse the narrow tissue bridge between arteriole and venule in the villous base, thereby shortcircuiting the capillary bed. This explanation also shortcircuits the old controversy about the elusive anatomical arteriovenous shunts in the gut. A countercurrent mechanism can readily be invoked to account for the oxygen gradient that exists along the length of villi. Teleologically, the intestinal countercurrent, if present, might serve to dampen a too rapid absorption of small lipid-soluble materials from the lumen. Folkow also analyzes 'autoregulatory escape' in the intestinal vasculature. During prolonged nerve stimulation of constantly perfused gut, resistance vessels will relax. This militates against a metabolic explanation of autoregulation. Folkow's schema of regional circulatory adjustments suggests an exceedingly complex vasculature and raises issues which will provide grist for many future investigative mills.

Johnson has been a most ardent upholder of the myogenic theory of autoregulation in the intestinal microcirculation (35). He contends that blood flow in the gut is adjusted to meet tissue demands by an intrinsic response of arteriolar muscle to stretch. Thus, when intravascular pressure rises, thereby stretching the vessel walls, arteriolar smooth muscle contracts to offset the driving head of pressure, thereby keeping blood flow near a stable value. Johnson & Hanson (36) have utilized the isogravimetric technic to investigate other microcirculatory dynamics in the gut. This method involves determination of the weight of a gut segment after cessation of arterial inflow and variation of venous outflow pressure. Outflow pressure is varied by changing the elevation of a column of blood connected to the mesenteric vein. Thus, elevation of the column increases venous pressure, and the intestinal segment gains weight. Once weight has stabilized, pressure in the system can be equated with midcapillary pressure in accordance with tenets of the Starling-Landis hypothesis. A coefficient of fluid movement across capillary walls is then calculated from the ratio of filtration rate (estimated by change in gut weight) to changing capillary pressure. This capillary filtration coefficient indicates available endothelial filtration surface and is regulated by precapillary sphincter tone. Johnson & Hanson (36) have found that increasing venous outflow pressure from the gut induces a diminishing increase in filtration rate which reaches a limit at pressures greater than 10 mm Hg. Thus, the capillary filtration coefficient falls with increments in capillary pressure [0.37 ml min^{-1} (100 g)$^{-1}$ at a pressure of 10 mm Hg and 0.11 ml min^{-1} (100 g)$^{-1}$ at a pressure of 20 mm Hg]. The authors conclude that the smooth muscle of precapillary sphincters exhibits a myogenic autoregulatory response to increased intravascular pressure. The negative feedback implications of the postulated mechanism seem apparent: capillary filtration is being controlled within set limits both by the opposing forces of intravascular pressure and by the potency of autoregulating vascular smooth muscle.

Johnson (35) has pursued these studies by determining arteriolar diameters and flow velocities in the mesentery. These experiments suggest that changes in arteriolar smooth muscle may best be correlated with alterations in flow, not pressure, a conclusion differing from that of physiologists who have maintained that the intestinal circulation exhibits autoregulation which can be explained on a myogenic basis. This group has included Johnson himself. A second conclusion from this study points to a singularly important role for the smooth muscle of precapillary sphincters (35). This vascular muscle, as opposed to that of the arterioles, appears most responsive to intravascular pressure changes. If these implications of Johnson's work are confirmed by other investigations, the key sensor in microcirculatory autoregulation may turn out to be the rate of transcapillary filtration rather than parenchymal tissue metabolism.

Another interesting report by Hanson & Johnson (37) concerns colonic hemodynamics. In this paper arterial pressure has been varied over the usual range, and calculated vascular resistance across a segment of large intestine has been found to decrease with increasing arterial pressure. At first sight this suggests a passively distensible vascular bed, devoid of myogenic autoregulation. However, when venous outflow pressure increases, the increment in resistance is abolished by the smooth muscle poison, papaverine. The authors believe that the colon autoregulates myogenically and they suggest that arterial pressure changes may not be transmitted faithfully to the sensitive vascular muscle. Venous pressure changes, on the other hand, are not damped to the same extent and therefore initiate a more direct response to the tone of smooth muscle located in the precapillary sphincters. The abolition of vascular reactivity by papaverine suggests an active process in the smooth muscle, although the pathway by which the drug dilates arterioles is not established.

The implications of Hanson & Johnson's work seem far-reaching. At one time autoregulation in the circulation could be identified simply by pump-perfusing the arterial inflow of an organ and calculating the resistance response to alterations in the flow. On this basis the stomach was found to be free from autoregulation (38). Now it appears that one must perform additional tests to confirm autoregulation, including observation of circulatory responses to manipulation of venous outflow pressure and chemical interference with smooth muscle metabolism.

More traditional approaches to microcirculatory regulation have been used by Altura (39). He has reported that rat mesocecal vessels, directly visualized, exhibit an enhanced constrictor responsiveness to topically applied catecholamines after adrenalectomy. Since adrenalectomy induces elevated circulating concentrations of histamine, Altura's findings constitute evidence against the theory that adrenal corticosteroids regulate local blood flow by opposing the effects of induced histamine formation (40). Baez, Kopman & Orkin (41), using the same preparation, find that after adrenergic exclusion the mesenteric microcirculation undergoes persistent vasoconstriction and is hyperresponsive to topically applied epinephrine. They also describe a depression of spontaneous vasomotion following ganglionic blockade with pentolinium or preganglionic sympathetic blockade effected by spinal anesthesia. A particularly striking observation relates to precapillary sphincter tone which manifests spasticity leading to local ischemia. These findings suggest that pharmacological blockade of the sympathetic nervous system in shock may lead to further deprivation of oxygen in the very tissue for which therapy has been instituted.

Ultimately, the physiologist would hope that the performance of the mesenteric circulation could be correlated with various aspects of the major intestinal functions—digestion and absorption. This object has not received its rightful share of investigative effort, as evidenced by the paucity of studies on intestinal absorption in relation to blood flow. Kilmore et al. (42) have prepared dogs with chronic blood flow transducers on the cranial mesenteric and hepatic arteries and have measured flow as a function of the ingested diet. Mesenteric blood flow increases when the mass of the feed increases or when the proportion of fat in the diet decreases. By contrast, hepatic arterial blood flow seems unrelated to these dietary factors. Chou, King & Dabney (43) have collected the venous effluent of gut segments in anesthetized dogs; they found that introduction of glucose solutions of 5 per cent or less into the lumen fails to influence segmental blood flow. Raising the glucose concentration to hypertonic levels is accompanied by significant increases in blood flow.

Placing these findings into a slightly larger picture of certain reports (6) within the past few years indicates a probable correlation between intestinal absorption and blood flow. However, changes must be considerable for absorption to alter blood flow or the reverse.

A comparison of vascular reactivity to various ions in pump-perfused mesenteric and gastric vascular beds has been reported by Texter et al. (44). Magnesium, potassium, and sodium (least potent) dilate precapillary vessels of the stomach. In the gut, calcium is a constrictor and sodium has little effect, while potassium and magnesium behave as dilators. These results correspond with findings in the forelimb, coronary, and renal beds obtained by using the pump-perfused preparation. On the other hand, when intestinal blood flow is measured directly by collecting the venous effluent, calcium appears to be without effect on the intestinal circulation (45). Surprisingly, Texter et al. (44) report that calcium acts to dilate gastric arterioles, and speculate that this effect may be secondary to a relaxation of visceral smooth muscle in the wall of the stomach.

This line of thinking about interactions between visceral and vascular smooth muscle reactivity in the gut is amplified extensively in a review by Haddy et al. (46). They feel that the net action of a drug on the resistance vessels of the gut is a function of three mechanisms which proceed simultaneously: arteriolar muscle reactivity, local metabolism, and the tone of gut muscle. Conceptually, this approach may be helpful in explaining why otherwise potent vasoactive drugs sometimes produce minimal changes in intestinal blood flow. Thus, according to Haddy et al. (46), the direct constrictor effects of epinephrine on arterioles are offset by relaxation of the wall of the gut, providing no net change in calculated resistance in a pump-perfused vascular bed. However, Ross (47), measuring mesenteric blood flow directly with a flowmeter, has found that epinephrine induces an abrupt and transient constriction followed by a prolonged afterdilation. Furthermore, he reports that intestinal luminal pressure decreases initially by only a few mm Hg and remains constant thereafter with epinephrine, whereas arterial resistance undergoes wide fluctuations. Ross concludes that visceral muscle tone of the gut wall is an insignificant factor in the transmural pressure across intestinal arterial vessels.

Largely because of concepts espoused by Fine and his collaborators (48, 49), efforts have been made to block alpha-adrenergic receptors in shock states. According to Fine, in shock the villain of the piece is a persistent sympathetic constrictor activity which leads to splanchnic ischemia and a breakdown in the ability of the reticuloendothelial system to cope with absorbed endotoxin. Seemingly, the ideal spot in this schema to interrupt the pathophysiological process would be at the start with an alpha-adrenergic blocker, notably phenoxybenzamine. Baue, Johnson & Parkins (50) have observed that dogs in hemorrhagic shock undergo deeper hypotension and exaggeration of splanchnic hypoxemia following phenoxybenzamine. Grega, Kinnard & Buckley (51) have noted that treatment of dogs in hemorrhagic shock with phenoxybenzamine effected no improvement in survival rates. White et al. (52) report that rats in endotoxin shock that were pretreated with phenoxybenzamine suffer more severe mesenteric ischemia and show a diminished ability to withstand the lethal effects of endotoxin, compared with animals given endotoxin alone.

Hruza & Zweifach (53) have studied the mesenteric microcirculatory adaptations to traumatic shock. Rats made resistant to drum-shock by repeated exposure to trauma exhibit less venoconstriction and a raised arteriolar threshold to the effects of catecholamines compared with nonadapted rats. Furthermore, the adapted rat liver is better able to catabolize catecholamines. These adaptations seem to be of value to survival insofar as they prevent splanchnic pooling and subsequent deterioration in this vasculature.

The effect of hemorrhagic (54) and endotoxin shock (55) on mesenteric hemodynamics has been pursued in conscious dogs by means of electromagnetic flowmeters. In both shock states mesenteric blood flow is markedly reduced, and splanchnic pooling does not seem to play the central role given to it by investigators who have studied the anesthetized, laparotomized dog.

LIVER

In the usual menu the *paté de foie* comes first; in this chapter the hepatic circulation brings matters to a close. The anatomical separation of the hepatic vessels from the rest of the gastrointestinal system and the peculiar complexities of the circulatory bed of the liver tend to remove this regional vasculature from a general consideration of gastrointestinal hemodynamics. Yet, blood perfusing the splanchnic viscera must immediately exit through the liver. Lately, physiologists have been concerned primarily with the regulation of hepatic perfusion and the relationship between the portal venous and hepatic arterial avenues of liver flow.

Hanson & Johnson (56) have investigated hepatic autoregulation and the phenomenon known as "reciprocity of flow", a term describing a decrease in hepatic arterial or portal venous resistance to blood flow when there is a decline in flow through the reciprocal vessel. The authors report that a decrease in hepatic artery pressure is accompanied by a fall in vascular resistance, which indicates autoregulation. This response is minimized by diverting portal venous drainage away from the liver. Decreasing portal perfusion lowers hepatic arterial resistance; thus some of the essentials of "reciprocity of flow" are confirmed. Finally, Hanson & Johnson have increased hepatic venous outflow pressure; this results in an increased hepatic arterial resistance (venoarteriolar reflex?), which triggers a decrease in portal venous resistance (reciprocity of flow). No doubt, if measured, the intestinal microcirculation would also show an autoregulatory response to these changing hepatic hemodynamic events. Perhaps the most attractive possibility for research in the splanchnic circulation is the likelihood that we may be able to treat the several vascular pathways as interdependent circuits in series and in parallel which regulate one another through a variety of intrinsic and extrinsic servomechanisms.

Hanson & Johnson (56) feel that "reciprocity of flow" is a form of hepatic arterial autoregulation, a local phenomenon which depends upon intrinsic vascular smooth muscle responses to hemodynamic events (myogenic hypothesis) and not to the accumulation of metabolites or to extrinsic nervous intervention. The authors also stress that arterial resistance changes have a markedly higher sensitivity to alterations in hepatic or portal venous pressure than to alterations in arterial pressure itself. In their view the sensing site which sets arterial resistance is the hepatic sinusoid. Pressure changes of only a few mm Hg in the hepatic or portal veins are relayed without decrement to the sinusoid and initiate arteriolar autoregulation. On the other hand, resistance circuits damp driving pressure so effectively that the sinusoid experiences little of the fluctuations in arterial force. It has been calculated that a change of 1 mm Hg in outflow venous pressure produces an arteriolar resistance response equal to that following A 10 mm Hg change in arterial pressure.

Greenway & Lawson (57) have measured venous flow into and from the cat liver with the electromagnetic flowmeter. They find that the right heart receives 117 ml of blood per kilogram body weight each minute, of which one third emerges from the liver. In turn, two thirds of this hepatic vein flow originates in the portal vein. Hypotension induced by spinal anesthesia decreases venous return to the heart but has no selective action on the splanchnic region. Epinephrine, however, augments superior mesenteric artery and portal venous perfusion, thereby increasing the splanchnic share of venous return to the heart. Since these effects cannot be replicated with norepinephrine, it is doubtful that pressure changes per se play the major part. The place of beta-adrenergic vasodilation in these interesting events has, unfortunately, not been investigated by the authors, although it seems likely that this system is operative.

Angiussola et al. (58) have been concerned with another dilator system in the hepatic circulation. The vasodilator polypeptides eledoisin and bradykinin augment hepatic blood flow, increase wedge pressure, and decrease splanchnic resistance. These responses of the liver occur in the anesthetized dog and in conscious man.

Lymphatic drainage is a second route of fluid egress from the liver. Miller and his collaborators (59) have evaluated the role of lymphatics in producing pathological changes in the liver. Ligation of the thoracic duct leads to central hepatic venous congestion, dilated sinusoids, and minimal fibrosis. These hepatic changes can also be observed following superior vena caval obstruction. A combination of both lesions produces marked degrees of these pathological findings in the liver. The authors conclude that the similarity of the liver in chronic congestive cardiac failure to the liver in their studies suggests that lymphatic obstruction is involved in the natural disease.

Conclusions

Lessons learned elsewhere in cardiovascular physiology and a variety of technical innovations have been applied and give promise of helping to answer the many formidable questions about the gastrointestinal circulation. The descriptive phase of physiology has been supplanted by a concern with regulatory processes, and this concern is apparent in the reports discussed in this chapter. Ultimately we must know the determinants of smooth muscle activity in gastrointestinal vessels and the neurochemical interactions which take place in the microcirculation. The search should lead away from traditional physiological approaches to the levels of molecular biology and bioelectric phenomena. Progress in circulatory studies will be gauged by the rapidity with which these more profound approaches become *de rigueur*.

ACKNOWLEDGMENTS

The author is obliged to Drs. Edward D. Frohlich, Morton I. Grossman, and A. Kurt Weiss for their criticisms.

LITERATURE CITED

1. *Symposium on the Gastrointestinal Circulation*, September 5–8, 1966, Lake Arrowhead, California. *Gastroenterology*, **52**, 332–471 (1967)
2. Grayson, J., Mendel, D. *Physiology of the Splanchnic Circulation* (Williams & Wilkins, Baltimore, Md., 200 pp., 1965)
3. Grim, E. The mesenteric circulation. *Handbook of Physiology*, **2**, Sec. 2, 1439–64 (Am. Physiol. Soc., Washington, D.C., 1963)
4. Jacobson, E. D. Secretion and blood flow in the gastrointestinal tract. *Handbook of Physiology*, **1**, Sec. 6 (Am. Physiol. Soc., Washington, D.C., 1967) (In press)
5. Jacobson, E. D. *Gastroenterology*, **48**, 85–109 (1965)
6. Jacobson, E. D. *Ibid.*, **52**, 98–112 (1967)
7. Schachter, M., Beilenson, S. *Gastroenterology*, **52** (Part 2), 401–6 (1967)
8. Lewis, G. P. *Gastroenterology*, **52** (Part 2), 406–13 (1967)
9. Morley, J., Schachter, M., Smaje, L. H. *J. Physiol. (London)*, **187**, 595–602 (1966)
10. Hilton, S. M., Torres, S. H. *J. Physiol. (London)*, **189**, 69–71P (1967)
11. Erjavec, F., Beaven, M. A., Brodie, B. B. *Fed. Proc.*, **26**, 237–40 (1967)
12. Jacobson, E. D., Eisenberg, M. M., Swan, K. G. *Gastroenterology*, **51**, 466–72 (1966)
13. Swan, K. G., Jacobson, E. D. *Am. J. Physiol.*, **212**, 891–96 (1967)
14. Jacobson, E. D., Swan, K. G., Grossman, M. I. *Gastroenterology*, **52** (Part 2), 414–20 (1967)
15. Sellers, A. F., Dobson, A. *Gastroenterology*, **52** (Part 2), 374–78 (1967)
16. Moody, F. G. *Gastroenterology*, **52**, 216–23 (1967)
17. Naitove, A., Colby, E. D. Gastric hemodynamic responses to histamine. Presented at 68th Ann. Meeting Am. Gastroenterol. Assoc., May 25-27, 1967, Colorado Springs, Colo. *Gastroenterology*, **52**, 1139 (1967)
18. Delaney, J., Grim, E. *Am. J. Physiol.*, **211**, 1398–1402 (1966)
19. Sapirstein, L. A. *Gastroenterology*, **52** (Part 2), 365–70 (1967)
20. Pitts, R. F. *Gastroenterology*, **52** (Part 2), 371–73 (1967)
21. Delaney, J. P., Grim, E. *Am. J. Physiol.*, **208**, 353–58 (1965)
22. Mackowiak, R., Friedman, M. H. F., Horn, J. *Gastroenterology*, **52**, 1106 (1967)
23. Eichelter, P., Schenk, W. G., Jr. *Arch. Surg.*, **93**, 200–7 (1966)
24. Papp, M., Makara, G. B., Hajtman, B., Csaky, L. *Gastroenterology*, **51**, 524–28 (1966)
25. Gillespie, J. S., Hamilton, D. N. H., Hosie, R. J. A., Macadam, R. F., McCaffery, H. *J. Physiol. (London)*, **187**, 4–5P (1966)
26. Gillespie, J. S., Kirpekar, S. M. *J. Physiol. (London)*, **187**, 51–79 (1966)
27. Ross, G., Kolin, A. *Fed. Proc.*, **26**, 550 (1967)
28. Bacaner, M. B. *Gastroenterology*, **51** (Part 2), 764–77 (1966)
29. Folkow, B. *Gastroenterology*, **52** (Part 2), 423–34 (1967)
30. Selkurt, E. E., Wathen, R. L. *Gastroenterology*, **52** (Part 2), 387–90 (1967)
31. Meckeler, K. J. H., Malawar, S. J., Jackson, B. J. *Gastroenterology*, **52**, 42–49 (1967)
32. Winne, D. *Arch. Pharmacol. Exptl. Pathol.*, **254**, 199–224 (1966)
33. Forster, R. E. *Gastroenterology*, **52** (Part 2), 381–86 (1967)
34. Steadman, W. M. *J. Physiol. (London)*, **186**, 382–400 (1966)
35. Johnson, P. C. *Gastroenterology*, **52** (Part 2), 435–40 (1967)
36. Johnson, P. C., Hanson, K. M. *Circ. Res.*, **19**, 766–73 (1966)
37. Hanson, K. M., Johnson, P. C. *Am. J. Physiol.*, **212**, 574–78 (1967)
38. Jacobson, E. D., Scott, J. B., Frohlich, E. D. *Am. J. Digest. Diseases*, **7**, 779–85 (1962)
39. Altura, B. *Am. J. Physiol.*, **211**, 1393–97 (1966)
40. Schayer, R. W. *Progr. Allergy*, **7**, 187–212 (1963)
41. Baez, S., Kopman, A. F., Orkin, L. R. *Circ. Res.*, **20**, 328–36 (1967)
42. Kilmore, M. A., McCormick, J. T., Jr., Flentge, R. L., Calhoun, W. K. *Fed. Proc.*, **26**, 472 (1967)
43. Chou, C. C., King, P. N., Dabney, J. M. *Fed. Proc.*, **26**, 715 (1967)
44. Texter, E. C., Jr., Laureta, H. C.,

Frohlich, E. D., Chou, C. C. *Am. J. Physiol.*, **212**, 569–73 (1967)

45. Dabney, J. M., Scott, J. B., Chou, C. C. *Am. J. Physiol.*, **212**, 835–39 (1967)

46. Haddy, F. J., Chou, C. C., Scott, J. B., Dabney, J. M. *Gastroenterology*, **52** (Part 2), 444–51 (1967)

47. Ross, G. *Am. J. Physiol.*, **212**, 1037–42 (1967)

48. Fine, J., *Gastroenterology*, **52** (Part 2), 454–58 (1967)

49. Palmerio, C., Nahor, A., Minton, R., Fine, J. *Proc. Soc. Exptl. Biol. Med.*, **124**, 623–27 (1967)

50. Baue, A. E., Johnson, D. G., Parkins, W. M. *Am. J. Physiol.*, **211**, 354–60 (1966)

51. Grega, G. J., Kinnard, W. J., Buckley, J. P. *Circ. Res.*, **20**, 253–61 (1967)

52. White, F. N., Ross, G., Barajas, L., Jacobson, E. D. *Proc. Soc. Exptl. Biol. Med.*, **122**, 1025–29 (1966)

53. Hruza, Z., Zweifach, B. W. *Fed. Proc.*, **26**, 627 (1967)

54. Lintermans, J. P., Appel, A. J., Bloom, R. S., Mullins, G. L., Guntheroth, W. G. *Am. J. Physiol.*, **212**, 482–87 (1967)

55. Jacobson, E. D., Swan, K. G. *Clin. Res.*, **14**, 426 (1966)

56. Hanson, K. M., Johnson, P. C. *Am. J. Physiol.*, **211**, 712–20 (1966)

57. Greenway, C. V., Lawson, A. E. *J. Physiol. (London)*, **186**, 579–95 (1966)

58. Angiussola, A. B., Feruglio, F. S., Campus, S., Chiandussi, L., Pandolfo, G., Bert, G. In *Hypotensive Peptides*, 430–40 (Erdos, E. G., Back, N., Sicuteri, F., Eds., Springer-Verlag, New York, 721 pp., 1966)

59. Miller, A. J., Pick, R., Kline, I. K., Bahadori, A. *Proc. Soc. Exptl. Biol. Med.*, **122**, 1067–70 (1966)

SYSTEMIC CIRCULATION: LOCAL CONTROL[1,2,3] 1004

By Ralph R. Sonnenschein and Fred N. White

Department of Physiology, University of California School of Medicine
Los Angeles, California

In this review we intend to survey and analyze reports, generally exclusive of abstracts, dealing with those aspects of vertebrate peripheral circulation, except for the pulmonary circuit, that are especially related to local control mechanisms. The more general aspects of circulatory regulation such as reflex and systemic hormonal control are reserved for a review in next year's volume, while the subject of hemodynamics is treated in McDonald's chapter in this volume (1), and splanchnic and hepatic circulation are dealt with by Jacobson in his review of gastrointestinal circulation (2).

Except to the extent that such studies may be useful in understanding physiological mechanisms, we are not including reports of primarily pathological, pharmacological, or anatomical emphasis. We would, however, like to call the reader's attention to a symposium devoted to morphology and histochemistry of the vascular wall (3). The present review is necessarily limited to the framework of our interests and competence, and the papers included have been selected as representative of current trends.

Since the blood flow and its local regulation in tissues depend on the characteristics of the vascular elements, we shall consider first the general features of vascular smooth muscle and its innervation, next the characteristics of the microcirculation in its performance of the nutrition of tissues, and finally the peculiarities of local control of the various vascular beds.

VASCULAR SMOOTH MUSCLE AND ITS INNERVATION
Electrical and Contractile Activity

The relationship between electrical and contractile activity in vascular smooth muscle, a topic which until the past few years has received relatively little attention, is now being pursued actively. In some circumstances contraction is uniformly associated with the occurrence of action potentials as shown by Roddie (4) for the aorta and vena cava of the turtle, Steed-

[1] The survey of literature for this review was concluded in June 1967.

[2] Supported in part by USPHS grants HE-05157 and HE-10281.

[3] Supplementary bibliographic material (152 references) has been deposited as Document number 9618 with the ADI Auxiliary Publications Project, Photoduplication Service, Library of Congress, Washington, D.C. 20540. A copy may be procured by citing the Document number and by remitting $2.50 for photoprints, or $1.75 for 35 mm microfilm. Advance payment is required. Make checks or money orders payable to: Chief, Photoduplication Service, Library of Congress.

147

man (5, 6) for rat mesenteric arteries, Funaki (7), and Axelsson et al. (8) for the portal vein of the rat, and Keatinge (9) for the sheep carotid stimulated with vasoconstrictor agents. In contrast, no change in membrane potential occurs with contraction of the rabbit pulmonary artery elicited by sympathetic stimulation or norepinephrine [Su & Bevan (10)]. Similar dissociation of mechanical and electrical events was reported for angiotensin-induced contraction of rabbit aortic strips [Shibata & Briggs (11)] and norepinephrine contraction in rabbit mesenteric vein [Cuthbert (12)]. In this latter study the suggestion is made that norepinephrine may release membrane-bound calcium ions.

Depolarization followed by contraction appears to be a uniform phenomenon in response to elevated potassium ion concentration for vascular smooth muscle (9–11). Calcium-free solutions have been variously reported to produce depolarization with relaxation or no tension change (11), disappearance of spontaneous electrical and mechanical activity (8), or repetitive spike discharge (9). From the above observations it appears that a variable relationship exists between excitation and contraction in vascular smooth muscle as indicated by the occurrence, under some circumstances, of dissociation of electrical and mechanical events. Hopefully, further studies along these lines may elucidate such questions as the ability of vascular smooth muscle to maintain prolonged steady tension.

INNERVATION

The minimum distance between nerve terminals and smooth muscle cells in the pulmonary artery of the dog [Fillenz (13)] and rabbit [Verity & Bevan (14)] ranges from 1500 to 4000 Å, a fact correlated with the long latency of contraction following nerve stimulation [Bevan & Verity (15)]. In the dog pulmonary artery (13) and arterioles of sheep kidney [Simpson & Devine (16)] some of the smooth muscle cells come within 1000 to 1500 Å of adrenergic terminals where they send out processes toward the axon. Fillenz (13) suggests that these may be key cells in the nervous control since norepinephrine should reach them first and in highest concentration. Further spread may be by electrical transmission in muscle cells, diffusion of transmitter, or both. Roddie (4) has presented functional evidence for electrical transmission between smooth muscle cells in turtle vessels, while Funaki (7) observed, with the electronmicroscope, close junctions between smooth muscle cells across which conduction might occur. Keatinge's (17) observations indicate that up to 1300 smooth muscle cells may be activated by a single sympathetic fiber.

Studies of the distribution of adrenergic fibers within walls of arteries [Keatinge (17) and Ehinger et al. (18)] and veins [Holman & McLean (19)] indicate that nerve terminals extend only into the outer zone of the media. Such observations suggest either that smooth muscle conduction is responsible for activation of inner medial cells or that the latter are activated by an independent mechanism.

Intense constriction, presumably on the basis of adrenergic innervation, may occur in large arteries supplying the kidney, splanchnic viscera, and skeletal muscle of diving mammals during submersion [Elsner et al. (20) and Bron et al. (21)]. Similar constriction, as well as the presence of dense adrenergic innervation, was reported in the large arteries supplying skeletal muscle in the duck, but not in the turkey, a nondiving bird, or in the cat [Folkow et al. (22)]. A shift in distribution of ventricular output between systemic and pulmonary circuits during diving in the turtle suggests the possibility of neurogenic regulation of regional resistances in this form [White & Ross (23)].

MECHANICAL PROPERTIES

Mechanical properties of smooth muscle of the cat portal vein were analyzed by Alexander (24) who described dynamic tension-length relations, and showed that net work dissipation increases under the influence of constrictor agents. From the results of potassium ion effects, it appeared that the tonoactomyosin phenomenon is not involved in normal constrictor or dilator mechanisms.

Lundholm & Mohme-Lundholm (25) derived length-tension diagrams for bovine mesenteric arteries after determining a resting length in metabolically poisoned vessels. At this length, maximum tension was developed and maximal shortening of 25 per cent occurred, as in skeletal muscle. The series-elastic component was, however, greater than in skeletal muscle. The important question whether tonic activity involves a "catch" mechanism or a continuous active state is raised by these studies.

CHEMICAL CONTROL

Plasma levels of 5-hydroxytryptamine (serotonin) and histamine in the rabbit are apparently adequate to contract the isolated aortic strip [Wurzel & Zweifach (26)] and these agents may play a role in regulating vascular tone *in vivo;* similar evidence suggests that 5-HT, but not histamine, may be important in the dog. A detailed description of methods for assay of plasma vasoactive agents is presented in this paper.

Nayler et al. (27) and Dorevitch et al. (28) have further characterized the action of a plasma pressor fraction, which they have named kinekard, and maintain that it acts on adrenergic receptors but not through the release of endogenous catecholamines. Bohr & Johansson (29) described a constrictor action of plasma which cannot be accounted for on the basis of known agents. Whether this agent is identical to kinekard is unknown.

The well known contraction of the ductus arteriosus in response to elevation in oxygen tension was shown by Gillman & Burton (30) to involve also the preductal segment of the aorta in pigs, rabbits, and cats. Interestingly, increased oxygen tension did not constrict the ductus or aorta of neonatal dogs. Elevated partial pressure of oxygen was shown by Smith & Vane (31) to increase tension of the aorta of guinea pig and rat, and ca-

rotid artery of swine. The action was not altered by pharmacological blocking agents, which indicates a direct effect. These observations on isolated
vessels together with those on intact vascular beds (see sections on special
regions) suggest a role for local oxygen tension in normal vascular regulation.

MICROCIRCULATION
FILTRATION AND PERMEABILITY

According to the classical Starling concept, outward filtration of water
occurs mainly in the proximal part of the capillary where hydrostatic pressure is highest, with reabsorption occurring in the distal portion. The details of this concept need re-evaluation in the light of recent work.

Wiederhielm (32), using water-soluble dyes, showed that substantial
differences in permeability may exist in different regions of capillary beds,
with the nonmuscular venules having the highest permeability within the
microcirculation. This observation and the calculation showing that the
total cross-sectional area of the venules is much larger than that of the
capillaries strongly indicate that it is the venules that are most involved in
the exchange of water. Intaglietta & Zweifach (33, 34) arrived at essentially the same conclusion on the predominantly distal locale for filtration and
reabsorption. Their observations, based on the measurement of the trajec-
tory of red cells in occluded capillaries, indicated that net outward filtration
occurs in the dilated vascular bed, while reabsorption takes place during
vasomotion when intravascular hydrostatic pressure is lowered. Capillary
arteriovenous pressure difference was surprisingly small, 4 mm Hg. These
observations may imply, for the maximally dilated bed, that all filtered
water is reabsorbed by lymphatics rather than partly by more distal segments of the microcirculation. The Starling concept of the balance of hydrostatic and osmotic forces in the regulation of water exchange need not
be modified except that permeability for water along the capillary is not
uniform, and the site of most water exchange is in the vicinity of the venules where permeability is greatest. The permeability to solutes is an independent question which needs investigation in the light of the demonstrated
nonuniformity of water permeability in the microcirculation.

Guyton et al. (35) made a direct demonstration of the role of interstitial
hydrostatic pressure in the Starling equilibrium, using their technique of a
chronically implanted perforated capsule for determination of interstitial
pressure. With a similar technique Guyton et al. (36) showed that the
movement of fluid within the interstitial space is greatly impeded at low
interstitial pressures, but as pressure is increased to a certain critical level
(atmospheric or slightly above) the mobility rises markedly.

Capillary permeability does not appear to be affected by hypoxemia according to the study of Scott et al. (37) who measured arterial and venous
pressure and tissue weight in the perfused dog forelimb while varying the
oxygen tension of the arterial blood. Transcapillary water movement, as

judged by limb weight, bore no obvious relation to arterial oxygen tension. Since the gradient in precapillary resistance was not assessed, the possibility still exists that mean capillary pressure fell to such an extent that an increase in permeability was offset by a decline in hydrostatic pressure. Paralyzing the vascular smooth muscle, in this preparation, might serve to abolish any change in gradient due to variation in smooth muscle tone along the precapillary vascular segment and allow a more critical assessment of the effect of hypoxemia on permeability.

Through use of an isotope technique Appelgren at al. (38) showed that the permeability of capillaries to protein is apparently unaffected by venous congestion and exercise. Under the influence of histamine the protein concentration of capillary filtrate could rise to as much as 75 per cent of the plasma level.

In isolated dog forelimb with constant blood flow, Baker (39) observed changes in $Rb^{86}Cl$ uptake and limb volume during infusion of 48/80 preceding or following denervation. He concluded that the major way in which histamine (released by 48/80) increases capillary permeability is by decreasing the pre- to postcapillary resistance ratio, chiefly through venoconstriction, with subsequent increase in capillary hydrostatic pressure and stretching of the capillary wall. After denervation, a decrease in filtration and of $Rb^{86}Cl$ uptake occurred. This effect of sympathectomy may be related to the apparently near-maximal dilatation of precapillary vessels as judged from the flow data; the outcome of this maneuver in a nondilated bed might yield different results. The reduction of $Rb^{86}Cl$ uptake and of filtration after sympathectomy raises the question of coupling between diffusion and bulk exchange.

A thoughtful and useful analysis of capillary transport capacity (PS) and its relationship to vascular conductance during metabolic vasodilatation has been presented by Renkin et al. (40). The maximal increase in PS was 2 to 2.5-fold which corresponds with several previous estimates for the increase in number of open capillaries during exercise. Under some circumstances a dissociation between vascular conductance and PS occurred, indicating different control mechanisms for the major resistance vessels and precapillary sphincters. Renkin (41) has also published a general discussion of factors involved in transcapillary exchange. Johnson & Wilson's (42) model for capillary exchange points up the possible role of a shunt in the extracellular space, due to rapid extracellular diffusion. Their calculations indicate that, with high rates of diffusion, the intracapillary concentration of a solute is essentially equal to the tissue space concentration over most of the capillary length. To the extent that this is correct, it would indicate that most of the capillary length is not used for solute transfer.

The relationship of fine structure of capillary endothelium to transport of solute has been investigated by Wolff (43) whose evidence suggests that directed transport of substances does not involve vesiculation, which may however be related to vascular permeability. Casley-Smith (44) also suggests that the passage of ions through intercellular junctions is more important than movement via vesicles. Apparently, substances of molecular weight greater than 20,000 cannot pass through the intercellular junctions; this agrees with Pappenheimer's concept of intercellular "slits" of 4 mμ width. According to Luft (45) the porous nature of the intercellular cement makes the postulation of vesicular transport unnecessary. On the other hand, Jennings & Florey (46) found that ferritin is transported across endothelial cells, at least in part, by vesicles.

Lundgren & Mellander (42a) studied the effect of net transcapillary fluid movement on the rate of transfer of a number of solutes (I^{131}, Na^{24}, Rb^{86}, and Xe^{133}) in cat skeletal muscle. They demonstrated that net transcapillary fluid movement in the direction of either absorption or filtration was associated with increased solute transport from tissue to blood. In the lower ranges of fluid movement the rate of solute transfer increased progressively with rate of fluid movement. The authors suggest the possibility that the state of the precapillary circulation existing during a Starling equilibrium may be a factor controlling the normal rate of solute exchange between tissue and blood.

Control

The hypothesis that so-called endogenous histamine is involved in regulation of the microcirculatory bed has been further tested by Altura & Zweifach (47). They point out, in the first place, that one cannot infer evidence of the role of histamine in local vascular reactions from experiments with antihistamines alone because of their direct action, usually constrictor, on the micro vessels. Moreover (48), the *in vivo* formation of endogenous histamine is not regularly associated with dilatation of the micro vessels, nor do procedures which activate histidine decarboxylase always cause parallel changes in vessel diameters and smooth muscle reactivity. Obviously, the role of histamine in microvascular regulation is in doubt. On the other hand, Altura (49) suggests that glucocorticoids may act as modulators of local blood flow through enhancement of vascular reactivity to endogenous humoral vasoactive substances.

The interesting possibility that extracellular osmolarity may be involved in regulation of vascular tone is suggested by Frohlich's (50) findings that intravenous infusion of hypertonic sodium or urea, increasing plasma osmolarity up to 350 mOsm per liter, was associated with progressively decreasing forearm resistance; and by the similar observations of Navar et al. (51) on vasodilatation produced in the kidney by hypertonic solutions. These, together with Stainsby's (52) original report on the relation of plasma osmotic pressure to vascular resistance in skeletal muscle, may represent experimental situations simulating metabolic production of substances whose osmotic activity has a general role in regulation of microvascular tone. In the case of exercise hyperemia in skeletal muscle, if hyperosmolarity is to be implicated as a mediator, rather specific criteria must be fulfilled. These include dilatation of resistance vessels and precapillary sphincters, with no significant dilatation of the venous segment or change in capillary permeability. Mellander et al. (52a) have shown through these criteria that hyperosmolarity may indeed play an important role in exercise hyperemia, and have furthermore correlated observations on intact muscle with an analysis of hyperosmolarity on isolated blood vessels.

Intraluminal pressure was shown by Weidman (53) to be of importance in the regulation of arteriolar tone in the bat wing. These vessels responded by contraction to increased pressure whether or not they were denervated. Along the same line, Baez et al. (54) concluded, from observations on micro vessels of the rat mesentery after acute sympathetic denervation, that the apparent hypersensitivity to epinephrine of such vessels is primarily related to modification of wall tension accompanying the hypotension of sympathectomy.

Rodbard (55) has presented the thesis that regulation of blood flow, in nonemergency situations, may occur at the capillary level. This would take place through changes in the degree of compression of the soft-walled capillaries due to alterations in tissue pressure following changes in filtration. Such phenomena as autoregulation and postocclusion or metabolic hyperemia could be mimicked by artificial models have distensibility and permeability characteristics postulated for the microcirculatory bed. The extent to which these models and the concept as a whole may apply to the physiological situation is worth considering, since the concept is so basically in contrast to the usually accepted mechanisms of local vascular control. Certain apparent discrepancies with previous observations exist. For example, in the case of exercise hyperemia the dilatation, according to Rodbard's concept, would be associated with a decrease in tissue pressure, whereas the work of Cobbold et al. (56), among others, has indicated increased filtration during exercise.

SPECIAL REGIONS
Skeletal Muscle

Metabolic control.—The mechanism of metabolic or exercise hyperemia of muscle, one of the longest known and best characterized of vascular responses, is still elusive. The possibility that changes in tissue Po_2 accompanying the increased oxygen consumption during exercise may be an important factor has recently been proposed again by Walker & Guyton (57) and Carrier et al. (58). Alterations in arterial oxygen saturation produced changes in the pressure-flow curves of isolated hindlegs of dogs; this indicates adjustments close to what would be required to assure constant delivery of oxygen to the area (57). Isolated small arteries of skeletal muscle, as well as those of coronary and mesenteric beds, showed an increase in conductance of 75 per cent when the Po_2 of the bathing fluid was lowered from 100 to 30 mm Hg (58). Similar changes occurred when pH was decreased from 7.40 to 7.10. During oxygen breathing, a corresponding decrease in forearm blood flow occurred in Bird & Telfer's (59) studies on intact humans; the flows in skin and skeletal muscle were not determined separately.

While the local concentration of oxygen in the tissue may indeed play a role in regulating the vascular resistance, it is unlikely that it is the sole factor, as Skinner & Powell (60) have pointed out in a clear-cut demonstration of the reinforcing interaction between oxygen and potassium. Although these studies may bear on the situation during exercise when venous oxygen content decreases and potassium content tends to rise, in these experiments the composition of blood infused into resting muscle was altered; it remains to be shown that these maneuvers mimic quantitatively the changes occurring in the vicinity of the vascular smooth muscle during exercise. This point was specifically suggested by Kontos et al. (61) on the basis of their observations of Po_2 and Pco_2 in venous blood from exercising human muscle. The extent of vasodilatation could not be accounted for on the basis of the calculated local hypoxia and hypercapnia. These same workers (62) found that increased blood carbon dioxide tension induced a pronounced decrease in resistance of resting forearm blood vessels during adrenergic blockade, and suggested a role for carbon dioxide in the local regulation of blood flow.

In McArdle's syndrome there is a deficiency in phosphorylase in skeletal muscle. Barcroft et al. (63) have shown that even though no decrease in pH, increase in Pco_2, or increase in lactate occurred in the venous blood from exercising muscle in a patient with that disease, postexercise hyperemia was as great as that in normal subjects. While changes in pH, Pco_2, or lactate may play some role in exercise hyperemia of the normal individual, apparently none of them is essential for the response. Barcroft (64) also showed, in an excellent review of the mode of action of epinephrine on skeletal muscle, that epinephrine produces its usual pattern of vasodilatation in the patient with McArdle's disease in the absence of elevated venous lactate; thus it appears that lactate production is not essential for epinephrine dilatation as previously proposed by Lundholm.

In an attempt to simulate more closely the chemical changes which might occur in the interstitial space, Cross & Gimlette (65) injected solutions of KCl, ATP, cyclic AMP, and lactic acid into the extravascular fluid of small areas of muscle along with Xe^{133} to evaluate changes in local blood flow. Concentrations of these substances which had been reported to produce marked dilatation after intra-arterial injection produced only small increases in flow when given locally.

The possibility that bradykinin might be involved in exercise hyperemia, postocclusion hyperemia, or cholinergic sympathetic vasodilatation was tested by Webster et al. (66). Carboxypeptidase B, which blocked bradykinin dilatation, failed to influence any of the above vascular responses, an observation indicating the unlikelihood that kinins are involved.

A suggested role of local changes in tissue osmolarity in metabolic vasodilatation is discussed in the section on microcirculation.

Nervous control.—There is a differential effect of sympathetic constriction on various segments of the vasculature of dog skeletal muscle with the main constriction occurring in small vessels, both venous and arterial (67). When, as in diving animals, large supply arteries have a potent constrictor innervation (20–22), local metabolic dilator materials are apparently unable to overcome the effect of neurogenic vasoconstriction. This is in contrast to the cat where the major sympathetic innervation is to small vessels and in proximity to vasodilator metabolites which can override neurogenic vasoconstriction to a considerable extent. Such overriding was shown by Bond et al. (68) to overcome neurogenically induced vasoconstriction in hemorrhagic shock in the dog. On the other hand, Ardill et al. (69) concluded that vasoconstrictor activity could suppress the dilator influences involved in reactive hyperemia.

Although Brick et al. (70) demonstrated a dilator (beta-receptor) effect, in the human forearm, of infused norepinephrine, they (71) have shown that reflex stimulation of the sympathetic nerves leads only to constriction (alpha-receptor stimulation). Coffman & Kelly (72) presented pharmacological evidence for a beta-adrenergic component in the reflex dilatation, in the human calf, which accompanies hyperventilation. Epinephrine released from the adrenal may be involved in this response.

Bolme et al. (73) studied the interrelation between sympathetic adrenergic constriction and the cholinergic vasodilator response in skeletal muscle of the dog. Moderate levels of constrictor tone antagonized the dilator response to only a minor degree; the cholinergic dilatation could be significantly reduced only in the presence of quite intense sympathetic vasoconstriction.

Beck et al. (74) presented evidence for dilator nerves in the sympathetic chain of dogs which by pharmacological analysis are neither adrenergic, cholinergic, nor histaminergic and whose action is similar to that of prostaglandin E. Brody (75) failed to find, by direct assay, elevations in the histamine content in the venous blood of cat hindquarters during reflex vasodilatation induced by intravenous norepinephrine or by sympathetic nerve stimulation. Isotopically labeled histamine infused into muscle did, however, appear along with its metabolic product, methylhistamine, in the venous effluent during these maneuvers. Vasodilatation per se did not seem to be responsible for the release since the labels failed to appear during vasodilatation induced by glyceryl trinitrate. The release of labeled histamine, however, cannot be used as conclusive proof of the participation of histaminergic nerves in the reflex since other agents, such as bretylium (76), may be released from adrenergic terminals. The labeled histamine, by virtue of its being an amine, might be released from adrenergic nerve terminals rather than from histaminergic nerves. Tuttle (77) argued, on the basis of pharmacological data, for a histaminergic component in reflex dilatation of the cat's tail. These studies are interesting in themselves. Their physiological significance depends, among other things, on whether true "active" reflex vasodilatation occurs. The criteria for such active dilatation which these authors have used need to be re-examined.

Abboud & Eckstein (78) analyzed peripheral dilatation in man accompanying the Valsalva maneuver, application of ice to the forehead, or upright tilting. At least part of the response appeared to be mediated by cholinergic dilator nerves. To the extent that the response of the subjects did not involve emotional components, the results contrast with previous work, which indicates that the cholinergic dilator system is not involved in reflexes elicited from vascular sensory receptors. Uvnäs (79) found cholinergic vasodilator nerves in the skeletal muscle of fox, jackal, and mongoose, in addition to the previous demonstration in the dog and cat. He reported the absence of the system in a series of lemurs and Old World monkeys as well as in rabbit, hare, badger, and polecat. Uvnäs suggests that fundamental differences in vasomotor mechanisms exist in these species. An excellent review of evidence for active neurogenic vasodilatation in muscle and skin of man was presented by Greenfield (80).

Exercise-blood flow relations.—Kontos et al. (61) and Wahren (81) have presented evidence, from observations on the human forearm, that the increased oxygen consumption of exercise is satisfied primarily by increase in blood flow rather than by increased extraction of oxygen.

Stegall (82) analyzed the mechanical factors in venous return from exercising calf muscles in human subjects. Although abdominal contraction raised inferior caval pressure and impeded venous outflow from the legs, the calf muscles were able to pump blood past this functional obstruction and in so doing contributed over 30 per cent of the energy required to circulate blood during running. By studying the differential effects of section of the ventral roots and of the sciatic nerve, Hudlická (83) calculated that, in the cat gastrocnemius, muscle tone is responsible for about 25 per cent of the vascular resistance at rest. Grimby et al. (84) measured the elimination rate of Xe^{133} from the quadriceps of trained and untrained subjects performing work at various loads. These loads were rated in each case relative to the maximum work output of each subject as judged by his oxygen uptake. For equivalent work loads relative to the maxima, the mean values for muscle blood flow were the same for trained and untrained subjects.

Capillary filtration coefficient was measured in the forearm of human subjects by Brod et al. (85) and was found to increase during exercise but to be essentially unchanged when blood flow increased during mental arithmetic or intra-arterial administration of epinephrine, acetylcholine, or isoprenaline. This indicates a dissociation of control of the vessels responsible for the two functions, resistance and exchange, as Renkin et al. (40, see microcirculation) also pointed out. That arteriovenous shunts are responsible for the dissociation between the exchange function and the total blood flow in skeletal muscle is made less likely by the analysis of Tønnesen & Sejrsen (86) of washout curves of Xe^{133} from the isolated cat gastrocnemius. The Xe^{133} method was compared with direct monitoring of blood flow by a drop counter by these same authors and by Kjellmer et al. (87). The two were found to be closely correlated.

Shepherd (88) and Donald et al. (89) have reviewed the nervous and local factors operating to regulate blood vessels of skeletal muscle during exercise. Golenhofen (90) has presented an excellent review of his work on muscle blood flow. He develops the thesis of inherent rhythmicity of the skeletal muscle vessels and the idea that during exercise local regulatory factors predominate in regulation of vascular tone; the dilatation counters the myogenically regulated constriction that would be induced by a rise in arterial pressure.

BRAIN

Chemical and nervous control.—The role of carbon dioxide in cerebro-vascular regulation was investigated by Shapiro et al. (91). Rapid changes in arterial P_{CO_2} were produced by altering inspired CO_2. The plot of arterial P_{CO_2} against corresponding values for cerebral blood flow manifested hysteresis, and the calculated values for tissue P_{CO_2} corresponded more directly with blood flow than did arterial P_{CO_2}. Their interpretation was that tissue P_{CO_2}, rather than arterial P_{CO_2}, is the effective regulator of cerebro-vascular resistance. This is closely related to the conclusion of Severinghaus & Lassen (92) who postulated from similar studies that increased CO_2, as well as hypoxia, affects cerebral blood flow via changes in pH of the extracellular fluid of vascular smooth muscle. Severinghaus et al. (93) in their high-altitude studies found that, after an initial increase, brain blood flow returned to normal in three to five days even though arterial pH remained elevated and arterial P_{CO_2} was low. The pH of the cerebrospinal fluid had remained at a normal level throughout. The authors proposed that cerebral blood flow returned to normal, after the initial hypoxia was corrected by oxygen breathing, because the pH of the cerebrospinal fluid and of extracellular fluid surrounding vascular smooth muscle had been kept normal by a process of active transport across the blood-brain barrier.

Hypoxia and hypercapnia have additive dilator effects on cerebral vessels of man according to Shapiro et al. (94), a conclusion supported by the findings of Strumza et al. (95). Autoregulation of cerebral flow is blunted by hypercapnia (96–98) and abolished by hypoxia (96). According to Yoshida et al. (97), cerebral autoregulation, in anesthetized monkeys, occurs in two phases, one a rapidly occurring phase which appears to involve sympathetic innervation and myogenic reflexes, the other a delayed component which appears to be metabolic. These authors (97) also presented evidence that changes in intracranial pressure are not involved in autoregulation.

By direct observation of the pial vessels of the rabbit, Mchedlishvili et al. (99) obtained evidence that during metabolic dilatation it was mainly the pial arteries rather than the cortical vessels which dilated to increase blood supply of the cortex. These observations, performed with the animal's skull open, may include artifacts due to changed pressure relationships and should be controlled by similar experiments with the skull closed. Dilatation of the pial vessels produced by local application of strychnine is possibly due to an axon reflex, according to Owman et al. (100). They demonstrated two sets of noradrenergic fibers, one coursing along the pial arteries and into the superficial cortex, the other a network in deep cortical layers. Division of the superficial fibers led to abolition of the strychnine dilatation; the possible effect of trauma to the local vessels should be considered. The strychnine dilatation was still present seven to fourteen days following sympathectomy at a time when, presumably, the axons had degenerated. It is difficult to reconcile this observation with the postulate of an axon reflex.

Regional distribution and methods.—Häggendal et al. (101) determined Kr^{85} clearances in the dog and found a fast and slow component in the disappearance curve which they ascribed to flow in the cortex and in subcortical white matter, respectively. Xenon-133 inhalation studies in human subjects by Veall & Mallett (102) also revealed a two-component curve. Carbon dioxide breathing decreased the half-time of the fast component, but failed to change that of the slow component which the authors suggested included a contribution from tissue other than white matter. Obrist et al. (103) constructed a three-compartment model for the analysis of clearance of Xe^{133}. This yielded estimates of separate blood flows, in descending order of magnitude, for gray matter, white matter, and extracerebral tissue. An inhomogeneity in flow in the caudate nucleus of the cat is suggested by the hydrogen clearance studies of Bozzao et al. (104).

A comparison of the results of external monitoring of Xe^{133} administered either by inhalation or by injection into the internal carotid artery indicated that the latter was a more valid quantitative assessment of cerebral blood flow (105). Extracerebral radioactivity, partly from xenon trapped in air spaces, appeared to contaminate the inhalation clearance curve. Lassen & Høedt-Rasmussen (106) compared the Kety-Schmidt outflow detection method with measurement of tissue washout of Kr^{85} by external monitoring. Generally, data obtained by the two methods were closely correlated with each other. The authors suggested that the Kety-Schmidt method is most useful for study of total blood flow, and the residue detection method best for measuring flow in circumscribed regions of the organ and for resolving separate components of the flow. Isbister et al. (107) also obtained good correlation between external counting over the brain and venous sampling, after administration of Xe^{133}. Heat clearance curves which may be calibrated by simultaneous Kr^{85} clearance may be useful for the analysis of transient changes in regional cortical blood flow (108). Seylaz & Molnar (109) have described a refinement of the thermal conductivity method for following regional flow changes in unanesthetized animals. Using hydrogen gas as an indicator, Gotoh et al. (110) found good agreement with results obtained by the standard nitrous oxide technique for total cerebral flow.

HEART

The innervation of the coronary vessels of the canine myocardium was analyzed by Feigl (111) who demonstrated that stimulation of the stellate ganglion yielded vasoconstriction after treatment of the animal with propranolol. He found no evidence of a cholinergic vasodilator component in the sympathetic innervation by appropriate stimulation of the hypothalamus or sympathetic chain. In the experiments of Daggett et al. (112) vagal stimulation induced an increase in coronary blood flow, most likely secondary to mechanical factors, as might also be the case in Ross's (113) similar observation.

A further step in the demonstration of the role of adenosine as a mediator for hypoxic coronary dilatation was taken by Katori & Berne (114). Following inhibition of adenosine deaminase, they detected adenosine in the venous effluent from isolated cat and guinea pig hearts subjected to severe hypoxia. Epinephrine, added to oxygenated perfusate, yielded results similar to those obtained by hypoxia (114). This may account for the metabolic effect of epinephrine on coronary vessels reported by Glomstein et al. (115). The possibility that low oxygen tension or decreased pH may be, of themselves, regulators of coronary vessels is suggested by the observation of Carrier et al. (58) that either alteration can dilate isolated coronary arteries.

While under many circumstances coronary blood flow follows myocardial oxygen consumption, dissociation between the two has been shown during vagal stimulation (112) where coronary blood flow increased with no change in oxygen consumption. This increase may be due to changes in transmural pressure during the prolonged diastole. A similar mechanism may explain the rise in coronary flow accompanying a reduction in myocardial oxygen consumption during counterpulsation in dogs with normal systemic arterial pressure [Hirsch et al. (116)]. McKenna et al. (117) observed that after propranolol administration in dogs, coronary resistance rose while oxygen consumption was unchanged; the oxygen demand was satisfied by increased oxygen extraction. Badeer & Pinkston (118), using heart-lung-systemic and heart-lung-coronary preparations, observed a much higher coronary flow in the latter situation even though oxygen consumption was the same in the two. Since stroke volume was considerably lower in the heart-lung-coronary preparation, the decrease in coronary resistance may have come about through reduction in myocardial wall tension.

Ross (113) used an electromagnetic flowmeter to measure right coronary blood flow in both anesthetized and unanesthetized dogs and found the flow pattern to be similar to that of the left coronary artery. The isotopic rubidium method has been found by McHenry & Knoebel (119) to yield values of coronary flow comparable to those of the Fick method. Good agreement between the rubidium and nitrous oxide methods was found in the detailed analysis of Donato et al. (120), while Moir (121) reported that the rubidium technique yielded considerably lower values than those recorded by a rotameter.

KIDNEY

Among the several chemical factors which may be involved in renal blood flow regulation, moderate acidosis appears to have a direct local dilator effect while the vasoconstriction occurring with severe acidosis is likely due to some secondary, circulating humoral substance (122). The infusion of hypertonic solutions of NaCl, glucose, urea, or mannitol decreases renal vascular resistance and produces a passive pressure-flow curve for the kidney (51, 123).

Thurau (124) has reviewed his concept of the mechanism of "autoregulation". From his observations that infusion of NaCl into a single distal tubule was accompanied by reduction in glomerular filtration rate in the same nephron, he has postulated a role for sodium ion concentration in the macula densa in regulation of afferent arteriolar tone. The proposed mechanism is through release of renin and subsequent local action of angiotensin on the afferent arteriole. One would suppose that if this is an important mechanism, the infusion of hypertonic NaCl should raise renal resistance, whereas Navar et al. (51) have shown just the reverse effect. Moreover, the low renin content in the juxtamedullary region would, as Thurau implies, be associated with poor autoregulatory capacity of medullary flow. This is, however, contrary to the findings of Carriere et al. (125) that, in the face of hypotension, medullary flow is well maintained, and also Aukland's (126) demonstration of good medullary autoregulation.

Increasing the ureteral pressure up to 50 mm Hg resulted in a rise in renal venous resistance which was offset by a decrease in prevenous resistance (127). These adjustments, sufficient to maintain constancy of the total resistance, occurred in the isolated perfused kidney and hence did not depend on extrinsic factors. The absence of such regulation with increased ureteral pressure in the experiments of Gosk et al. (128) may have been associated with peculiarities of their experimental conditions. Ono et al. (129) made the interesting observation that the spontaneous deterioration of renal autoregulation, occurring over a protracted time, could be reversed by administration of dipyridamol, a potentiator of the vascular action of adenine nucleotides. The authors suggested a role of adenine nucleotide metabolism in regulating the tone in at least some specialized part of the renal vasculature.

Barger & Herd (130) summarized their results on the partitioning of renal flow into cortical and outer medullary components, as determined by the analysis of Kr^{85} disappearance curves. In a variety of situations, changes in these two are reciprocal. Medullary flow is apparently reduced by antidiuretic hormone in addition to the effect of the hormone in increasing water permeability of the collecting ducts (131). The increase in cortical resistance accompanying hemorrhagic hypotension may be neurogenic according to Carriere et al. (125) and Bell & Murray (132), while medullary.flow is maintained through the action of local factors (125). Filtration fractions (inulin and protein) were calculated by Nissen (133) for plasma supplying superficial cortex, and combined deep cortex and medulla. He concluded that the lower filtration fraction of deep cortex and medulla probably implies a bypass of plasma around the juxtamedullary glomeruli, on the assumption that the filtration fractions of outer and deep glomeruli are essentially the same. It is possible, however, that the filtration fractions are nonuniform.

The peculiarities of the medullary vasculature preclude the use of heat clearance techniques for the assessment of blood flow in this region because of complications introduced by countercurrent exchange (134).

OTHER REGIONS

Skin.—Through comparison of the total blood flow through human forearm skin, measured by capacitance plethysmography, with the "effective circulation" determined by clearance of locally injected NaI^{131} or $Na^{22}Cl$, Hyman & Greeson (135) adduced evidence for a functional bypass for flow during reflex hyperemia induced by indirect heating. Thus a functional shunt mechanism appears to exist in forearm skin as well as in the skin of the hands and digits. According to Edwards's (136) observations on the rate of removal of Na^{24} from the rabbit's foot, flow through arteriovenous anastamoses can explain all of the hyperemia associated with cold-induced vasodilatation and the dilatation accompanying rewarming following intense vasoconstriction. The initial phase of reactive hyperemia involves the anastamoses, in part, while the later period of hyperemia is entirely via the anastamoses.

Although local cold markedly constricts vessels in human extremities, vessels under this condition are no more sensitive to norepinephrine than are warm vessels (137). Gaskell & Hoeppner (138) induced inhibition of vasoconstrictor tone in the fingers by subjecting subjects to body heating. When one hand was warmed the resistance of its vessels fell, a reaction indicating the role of local warming in augmenting the dilatation that follows reflex inhibition of constrictor innervation. Chalmers & Korner (139) found a balance between local dilator and neurogenic constrictor factors participating in the determination of vascular tone of the skin of rabbits subjected to hypoxia. Sympathetic stimulation of the paw of the dog produced arterial and venous as well as small vessel vasoconstriction, and the constriction of arteries and veins was greater than that observed in skeletal muscle (67). Interestingly, after administration of bretylium, stimulation of the sympathetic chain induced dilatation of small vessels in the paw.

Adipose tissue.—Following the initial characterization by Orö et al. (140) of the circulatory and metabolic roles of the adrenergic innervation of adipose tissue, Ngai et al. (141) and Öberg & Rosell (142) have studied in detail the characteristics of the vasculature of the subcutaneous yellow fat in dogs. The rather high mean level of resting flow, 8 to 9 ml $(100 \text{ g})^{-1} \text{ min}^{-1}$, was markedly reduced by stimulation of the sympathetic innervation; the high resting capillary filtration coefficient was increased and net water absorption occurred. After alpha-blockade, sympathetic stimulation brought about an increase in flow to 25 to 30 ml $(100 \text{ g})^{-1} \text{ min}^{-1}$ and a small increase in capillary filtration coefficient and in venodilatation, and all these effects were abolished by propranolol. Vascular resistance in fat was unchanged by carotid occlusion or by hypothalamic stimulation of the sympathetic cholinergic nerves. Blood flow in human adipose tissue at rest, determined with radioactive xenon, has been variously reported as 2.6 [Larsen (143)] and 6.7 ml $(100 \text{ g})^{-1} \text{ min}^{-1}$ [Häggendal (144)]. In the latter study, blood flow was markedly reduced when ambient temperature was lowered to 15° C.

A most striking set of observations on blood flow in brown adipose tissue in the newborn rabbit was made by Heim & Hull (145). In contrast to the flows reported above for yellow adipose tissue of 3 to 9 ml $(100 \text{ g})^{-1}$ min^{-1} at rest and a maximum of 30 ml $(100 \text{ g})^{-1} \text{ min}^{-1}$ during neurogenic dilatation, the mean resting flow in the brown fat, measured by a direct venous outflow method, was about 90 ml $(100 \text{ g})^{-1} \text{ min}^{-1}$ which constituted one tenth of the cardiac output of the newborn rabbit. Following intravenous injection of norepinephrine, the flow rose to 360 ml $(100 \text{ g})^{-1} \text{ min}^{-1}$ (representing one fourth of the cardiac output) while Qo_2 increased from 9 to 60 ml O_2 $(100 \text{ g})^{-1} \text{ min}^{-1}$. Exposure to cold brought about a comparable increase in flow, to 304 ml $(100 \text{ g})^{-1} \text{ min}^{-1}$. Hypoxia, induced by breathing 10 per cent oxygen, partly prevented the increase in Qo_2 but not that of blood flow produced by norepinephrine. These relatively huge resting and maximum blood flows lend support to the important metabolic role of brown fat in thermoregulation.

Salivary glands.—Morley et al. (146) reported that the vasodilatation and secretion in the submaxillary gland of the rabbit which accompany parasympathetic nerve stimulation have a parallel sensitivity to atropine block, and from this they drew the conclusion that true vasodilator nerve fibers to the submaxillary gland exist in the chorda tympani of the rabbit. The role of bradykinin in functional vasodilatation in the cat's submandibular gland has been further analyzed by Hilton & Torres (147). They confirmed Schacter's previous observation that even though a marked reduction in kinin-forming enzyme occurs in glands whose ducts have been ligated, chorda stimulation still produces a large dilatation. Hilton & Torres showed, however, that the sensitivity of the vessels of these glands to bradykinin is considerably increased so that the response to chorda stimulation can still be explained quantitatively on the action of bradykinin as the principal mediator. Vasodilatation of the submandibular gland of the dog was observed by Funakoshi et al. (148) when pressure in the duct was raised by 40 to 68 mm Hg. This ipsilateral response was abolished by section of the ipsilateral chorda tympani but not by section of the sympathetic innervation of the gland. The authors suggested that this baroceptor reflex may be of importance in regulating the blood supply of the gland.

Bone.—Bone blood flow in the leg of the rabbit was shown by Shim et al. (149) to be increased by 5 to 45 per cent one to two weeks after section of the sciatic nerve. The change was thought by the authors to be due to interruption of a sympathetic vasomotor nerve supply. Pasternak et al. (150), using clearance of Sr^{85}, found that the blood flow in the tibias of immature dogs was roughly twice that in mature dogs. Oxygen consumption was correspondingly higher in bone of the immature animal. The authors' assertion that blood flow is the factor which controls metabolic rate is unwarranted since no evidence was presented that blood flow limited the oxygen uptake.

Uterus.—Uterine blood vessels in pregnant sheep appear to be widely dilated, showing a linear pressure-flow relationship (151) with low sympathetic constrictor tone (152). Under appropriate conditions the sympathetic innervation can produce marked vasoconstriction in the gravid uterus. No evidence for sympathetic cholinergic innervation of vessels of the gravid uterus was obtained.

Vasa vasorum.—Observations on the vasa vasorum of the baroceptor areas in the cat and dog and of human carotid sinus led Hughes (153) to suggest the existence of a "venous pump"; venous sinuses in the walls of baroceptor areas might be filled in diastole and emptied during expansion of the receptor area during systole.

COMMENTARY

Certain developments appear to us to be especially interesting. In the first place, considerable effort is being directed toward the relationships between mechanical and electrical activity in vascular smooth muscle. The demonstration, in a number of preparations, that mechanical activity may occur in the absence of membrane action potentials points to a fundamental dissociation of these processes. Continuing investigations along these lines may lead to elucidation of the mechanisms of the maintenance of steady tension and rhythmic activity.

Electronmicroscopic and histochemical observations are showing the anatomical correlates of vascular neuromuscular interrelationships; for example, a large neuromuscular gap distance is associated with a long latency. A lack of homogeneity of distribution of nerve terminals has been demonstrated radially and longitudinally within the media of vessels. It is to be hoped that such studies may lead to a clearer understanding of the nature of the spread of the excitatory process in vascular smooth muscle.

In the microcirculation, the observation of nonuniform permeability to water necessitates a re-evaluation of the Starling hypothesis. Vasomotion takes on a new significance in the process of reabsorption of water. The possibility of nonuniformity of permeability to solutes is raised by these considerations.

Despite continuing efforts, the nature of the "metabolic dilator substances" in the various organs is still elusive. These may be different in different organs, and in any one organ several factors may be involved. Is there any unitary factor that may account for the observed responses to the variety of physiologically active agents? Can interstitial osmolarity be the determinant?

LITERATURE CITED

1. McDonald, D. A. Systemic circulation: hemodynamics. *Ann. Rev. Physiol.*, **30**, 525–56 (1968)
2. Jacobson, E. D. The gastrointestinal circulation. *Ann. Rev. Physiol.*, **30**, 133–46 (1968)
3. Comèl, M., Laszt, L., Eds. Morphology and histochemistry of the vascular wall (Symposium). *Angiologica (Basel)*, **2**, 225–434 (1967)
4. Roddie, I. C. Electrical and mechanical activity in turtle arteries and veins. In *Symposium on Electrical Activity and Innervation of Blood Vessels. Bibliotheca Anat.*, **8**, 1–4 (1967)
5. Steedman, W. M. Microelectrode studies on small mammalian arteries. In *Symposium on Electrical Activity and Innervation of Blood Vessels. Bibliotheca Anat.*, **8**, 25–29 (1967)
6. Steedman, W. M. Micro-electrode studies on mammalian vascular muscle. *J. Physiol. (London)*, **186**, 382–400 (1966)
7. Funaki, S. Electrical and mechanical activity of isolated smooth muscle from the portal vein of the rat. In *Symposium on Electrical Activity and Innervation of Blood Vessels. Bibliotheca Anat.*, **8**, 5–10 (1967)
8. Axelsson, J., Johansson, B., Jonsson, O., Wahlström, B. The effects of adrenergic drugs on electrical and mechanical activity of the portal vein. In *Symposium on Electrical Activity and Innervation of Blood Vessels. Bibliotheca Anat.*, **8**, 16–20 (1967)
9. Keatinge, W. R., Role of electrical activity in controlling mechanical tone of mammalian arteries. In *Symposium on Electrical Activity and Innervation of Blood Vessels. Bibliotheca Anat.*, **8**, 21–24 (1967)
10. Su, C., Bevan, J. A. Electrical and mechanical responses of pulmonary artery muscle to neural and chemical stimulation. In *Symposium on Electrical Activity and Innervation of Blood Vessels. Bibliotheca Anat.*, **8**, 30–34 (1967)
11. Shibata, S., Briggs, A. H. The relationships between electrical and mechanical events in rabbit aortic strips. *J. Pharmacol. Exptl. Therap.*, **153**, 466–70 (1966)
12. Cuthbert, D. W. Electrical activity in mammalian veins. In *Symposium on Electrical Activity and Innervation of Blood Vessels. Bibliotheca Anat.*, **8**, 11–15 (1967)
13. Fillenz, M. Innervation of blood vessels of lung and spleen. In *Symposium on Electrical Activity and Innervation of Blood Vessels. Bibliotheca Anat.*, **8**, 56–59 (1967)
14. Verity, M. A., Bevan, J. A. A morphopharmacologic study of vascular smooth muscle innervation. In *Symposium on Electrical Activity and Innervation of Blood Vessels. Bibliotheca Anat.*, **8**, 60–65 (1967)
15. Bevan, J. A., Verity, M. A. Postganglionic sympathetic delay in vascular smooth muscle. *J. Pharmacol. Exptl. Therap.*, **152**, 221–30 (1966)
16. Simpson, F. O., Devine, C. E. The fine structure of autonomic neuromuscular contacts in arterioles of sheep renal cortex. *J. Anat.*, **100**, 127–37 (1966)
17. Keatinge, W. R. Electrical and mechanical responses of arteries to stimulation of sympathetic nerves. *J. Physiol. (London)*, **185**, 701–15 (1966)
18. Ehinger, B., Falck, B., Sporrong, B. Adrenergic fibers to the heart and to peripheral vessels. In *Symposium on Electrical Activity and*

Innervation of Blood Vessels.
Bibliotheca Anat., **8,** 35–45 (1967)

19. Holman, M. E., McLean, A. The innervation of sheep mesenteric veins. *J. Physiol. (London),* **190,** 55–70 (1967)

20. Elsner, R., Franklin, D. L., Van Citters, R. L., Kenney, D. W. Cardiovascular defense against asphyxia. *Science,* **153,** 941–49 (1966)

21. Bron, K. M., Murdaugh, H. V., Jr., Millen, J. E., Lenthall, R., Raskin, P., Robin, E. D. Arterial constrictor response in a diving mammal. *Science,* **152,** 540–43 (1966)

22. Folkow, B., Fuxe, K., Sonnenschein, R. R. Responses of skeletal musculature and its vasculature during "diving" in the duck: peculiarities of the adrenergic vasoconstrictor innervation. *Acta Physiol. Scand.,* **67,** 327–42 (1966)

23. White, F. N., Ross, G. Circulatory changes during experimental diving in the turtle. *Am. J. Physiol.,* **211,** 15–18 (1966)

24. Alexander, R. S., Contractile mechanics of venous smooth muscle. *Am. J. Physiol.,* **212,** 852–58 (1967)

25. Lundholm, L., Mohme-Lundholm, E. Length at inactivated contractile elements, length-tension diagram, active state and tone of vascular smooth muscle. *Acta Physiol. Scand.,* **68,** 347–59 (1966)

26. Wurzel, M., Zweifach, B. W. Contracting principles of arterial smooth muscle in rabbit and dog plasma. *Arch. Intern. Pharmacodyn.,* **162,** 1–19 (1966)

27. Nayler, W. G., Rosenbaum, M., McInnes, I. E., Race, D., Lowe, T. E. Effect of adrenergic antagonists on the peripheral constrictor action of kinekard, a cardioactive plasma fraction. *Circ. Res.,* **19,** 528–37 (1966)

28. Dorevitch, N., Nayler, W. G., Lowe, T. E. The action on isolated smooth muscle of kinekard, a cardioactive fraction isolated from human plasma. *J. Pharmacol. Exptl. Therap.,* **155,** 367–75 (1967)

29. Bohr, D. F., Johansson, B. Contraction of vascular smooth muscle in response to plasma: comparison with response to known vascoactive agents. *Circ. Res.,* **19,** 593–601 (1966)

30. Gillman, R. G., Burton, A. C. Constriction of the neonatal aorta by raised oxygen tension. *Circ. Res.,* **19,** 755–65 (1966)

31. Smith, D. J., Vane, J. R. Effects of oxygen tension of vascular and other smooth muscle. *J. Physiol. (London),* **186,** 284–94 (1966)

32. Wiederhielm, C. A. Transcapillary and interstitial transport phenomena in the mesentery. *Fed. Proc.,* **25,** 1789–98 (1966)

33. Intaglietta, M., Zweifach, B. W. Indirect method for measurement of pressure in blood capillaries. *Circ. Res.,* **19,** 199–205 (1966)

34. Zweifach, B. W., Intaglietta, M. Fluid exchange across the blood capillary interface. *Fed. Proc.,* **25,** 1784–88 (1966)

35. Guyton, A. C., Prather, J., Scheel, K., McGehee, J. Interstitial fluid pressure: IV. Its effect on fluid movement through the capillary wall. *Circ. Res.,* **19,** 1022–30 (1966)

36. Guyton, A. C., Scheel, K., Murphree, D. Interstitial fluid pressure: III. Its effect on resistance to tissue fluid mobility. *Circ. Res.,* **19,** 412–19 (1966)

37. Scott, J. B., Daugherty, R. M., Jr., Haddy, F. J. Effect of severe local hypoxemia on transcapillary water movement in dog forelimb. *Am. J. Physiol.,* **212,** 847–51 (1967)

38. Appelgren, L., Jacobsson, S., Kjellmer, I. Estimation of the protein concentration of the capillary filtrate by an isotope technique. *Acta Physiol. Scand.,* **66,** 353–61 (1966)

39. Baker, C. H. Vascular volume changes following histamine release in the dog forelimb. *Am. J. Physiol.,* **211,** 661–66 (1966)

40. Renkin, E. M., Hudlická, O., Sheehan, R. M. Influence of metabolic vasodilatation on blood-tissue diffusion in skeletal muscle. *Am. J. Physiol.,* **211,** 87–98 (1966)

41. Renkin, E. M. Capillary blood flow and transcapillary exchange. *Physiologist,* **9,** 361–66 (1966)

42. Johnson, J. A., Wilson, T. A. A model for capillary exchange. *Am. J. Physiol.,* **210,** 1299–1303 (1966)

42a. Lundgren, O., Mellander, S. Augmentation of tissue-blood transfer of solutes by transcapillary filtration and absorption. *Acta Physiol. Scand.,* **70,** 26–41 (1967)

43. Wolff, J. On the meaning of vesicula-

tion in capillary endothelium. *Angiologica*, **4**, 64–68 (1967)

44. Casley-Smith, J. R. An electron microscopical study of the passage of ions through the endothelium of lymphatic and blood capillaries, and through the mesothelium. *Quart. J. Exptl. Physiol.*, **52**, 105–13 (1967)

45. Luft, J. H. Fine structure of capillary and endocapillary layer as revealed by ruthenium red. *Fed. Proc.*, **25**, 1773–83 (1966)

46. Jennings, M. A., Florey, L. An investigation of some properties of endothelium related to capillary permeability. *Proc. Roy. Soc. B*, **167**, 39–63 (1967)

47. Altura, B. M., Zweifach, B. W. Influence of reserpine and guanethidine on vascular reactivity and antihistamine constrictor action in the microcirculation. *Angiology*, **17**, 493–502 (1966)

48. Altura, B. M., Zweifach, B. W. Endogenous histamine formation and vascular reactivity. *Am. J. Physiol.*, **212**, 559–64 (1967)

49. Altura, B. M. Role of glucocorticoids in local regulation of blood flow. *Am. J. Physiol.*, **211**, 1393–97 (1966)

50. Frohlich, E. D. Prolonged local and systemic hemodynamic effects of hyperosmotic solutions. *Arch. Intern. Pharmacodyn.*, **161**, 154–66 (1966)

51. Navar, L. G., Guyton, A. C. Langston, J. B. Effect of alterations in plasma osmolality on renal blood flow autoregulation. *Am. J. Physiol.*, **211**, 1387–92 (1966)

52. Stainsby, W. N. Plasma osmotic pressure and resistance to flow in dog skeletal muscle. *Fed. Proc.*, **23** (Part I), 111 (1964)

52a. Mellander, S., Johansson, B., Gray, S., Jonsson, O., Lundvall, J., Ljung, B. The effects of hyperosmolarity on intact and isolated vascular smooth muscle. Possible role in exercise hyperemia. *Angiologica*, **4**, 310–22 (1967)

53. Weidman, M. P. Contractile activity of arterioles in the bat wing during intraluminal pressure changes. *Circ. Res.*, **19**, 559–63 (1966)

54. Baez, S., Kopman, A. F., Orkin, L. R. Microvascular hypersensitivity subsequent to chemical denervation. *Circ. Res.*, **20**, 328–37 (1967)

55. Rodbard, S. Evidence that vascular conductance is regulated at the capillary. *Angiology*, **17**, 549–73 (1966)

56. Cobbold, A., Folkow, B., Kjellmer, I., Mellander, S. Nervous and local chemical control of pre-capillary sphincters in skeletal muscle as measured by changes in filtration coefficient. *Acta Physiol. Scand.*, **57**, 180–92 (1963)

57. Walker, J. R., Guyton, A. C. Influence of blood oxygen saturation on pressure-flow curve of dog hindleg. *Am. J. Physiol.*, **212**, 506–9 (1967)

58. Carrier, O., Walker, J. R., Guyton, A. C. Comparative effects of pH and hypoxemia on minute coronary, mesenteric and skeletal muscle arteries. *Angiology*, **17**, 488–92 (1966)

59. Bird, A. D., Telfer, A. B. M. The effect of oxygen at 1 and 2 atmospheres on resting forearm blood flow. *Surg. Gynecol. Obstet.*, **123**, 260–68 (1966)

60. Skinner, N. S., Jr., Powell, W. J., Jr. Action of oxygen and potassium on vascular resistance of dog skeletal muscle. *Am. J. Physiol.*, **212**, 533–40 (1967)

61. Kontos, H. A., Richardson, D. W., Patterson, J. L., Jr. Blood flow and metabolism of forearm muscle in man at rest and during sustained contraction. *Am. J. Physiol.*, **211**, 869–76 (1966)

62. Kontos, H. A., Richardson, D. W., Patterson, J. L., Jr. Effects of hypercapnia on human forearm blood vessels. *Am. J. Physiol.*, **212**, 1070–80 (1967)

63. Barcroft, H., Greenwood, B., McArdle, B., McSwiney, R. R., Semple, S. J. G., Whelan, R. F., Youlten, L. J. F. The effect of exercise on forearm blood flow and on venous blood pH, Pco_2 and lactate in a subject with phosphorylase deficiency in skeletal muscle (McArdle's syndrome). *J. Physiol. (London)*, **189**, 44P (1967)

64. Barcroft, H. Factors affecting arterial blood flow and its measurement. *Angiology*, **17**, 443–50 (1966)

65. Cross, R. B., Gimlette, T. M. D. The effect of intramuscular injections of K, ATP and lactic acid on muscle blood flow estimated by ^{133}Xe clearance from the point of

injection. *J. Physiol. (London)*, **189**, 43P (1967)

66. Webster, M. E., Skinner, N. S., Jr., Powell, W. J., Jr. Role of the kinins in vasodilatation of skeletal muscle of the dog. *Am. J. Physiol.*, **212**, 553–58 (1967)

67. Zimmerman, B. G. Influence of sympathetic stimulation on segmental vascular resistance before and after adrenergic neuronal blockade. *Arch. Intern. Pharmacodyn.*, **160**, 66–82 (1966)

68. Bond, R. F., Manley, E. S., Jr., Green, H. D. Cutaneous and skeletal muscle vascular responses to hemorrhage and irreversible shock. *Am. J. Physiol.*, **212**, 488–97 (1967)

69. Ardill, B. L., Bhatnagar, V. M., Fentem, P. H. The suppression of reactive hyperaemia by the action of sympathetic adrenergic nerves. *J. Physiol. (London)*, **187**, 24P (1966)

70. Brick, I., Hutchison, K. J., Roddie, I. C. The vasodilator properties of noradrenaline. *J. Physiol. (London)*, **185**, 43P (1966)

71. Brick, I., Hutchison, K. J., Roddie, I. C. A comparison of the effects of circulating noradrenaline and vasoconstrictor nerve stimulation on forearm blood vessels. *Ibid.*, **189**, 27P (1967)

72. Coffman, J. D., Kelly, P. Hyperventilation and human calf blood flow. *Am. J. Physiol.*, **211**, 1255–60 (1966)

73. Bolme, P., Ngai, S. H., Rosell, S. (Personal communication)

74. Beck, L., Pollard, A. A., Kayaalp, S. O., Weiner, L. M. Sustained dilatation elicited by sympathetic nerve stimulation. *Fed. Proc.*, **25**, 1596–1606 (1966)

75. Brody, M. J. Neurohumoral mediation of active reflex vasodilatation. *Fed. Proc.*, **25**, 1583–92 (1966)

76. Fischer, J. E., Weise, K., Kopin, I. J. Release of tritiated bretylium by sympathetic nerve stimulation. *Nature*, **209**, 778–79 (1966)

77. Tuttle, R. S. Evidence for histaminergic nerves in the pyramidal cat. *Am. J. Physiol.*, **211**, 903–10 (1966)

78. Abboud, F. M., Eckstein, J. W. Active reflex vasodilatation in man. *Fed. Proc.*, **25**, 1611–17 (1966)

79. Uvnäs, B. Cholinergic vasodilator nerves. *Fed. Proc.*, **25**, 1618–22 (1966)

80. Greenfield, A. D. M. Survey of the evidence for active neurogenic vasodilatation in man. *Fed. Proc.*, **25**, 1607–10 (1966)

81. Wahren, J. Quantitative aspects of blood flow and oxygen uptake in the human forearm during rhythmic exercise. *Acta Physiol. Scand.*, **67**, *Suppl. 269*, 5–93 (1966)

82. Stegall, H. F. Muscle pumping in the dependent leg. *Circ. Res.*, **19**, 180–90 (1966)

83. Hudlická, O. Blood flow and oxygen consumption in muscles after section of ventral roots. *Circ. Res.*, **20**, 570–77 (1967)

84. Grimby, G., Häggendal, E., Saltin, B. Local xenon clearance from the quadriceps muscle during exercise in man. *J. Appl. Physiol.*, **22**, 305–10 (1967)

85. Brod, J., Přerovsky, I., Ulrych, M., Linhart, J., Heine, H. Changes in capillary filtration coefficient in the forearm during emotional and post-exercise hyperemia and after intra-arterial adrenaline, acetylcholine, and isopropylnoradrenaline. *Am. Heart J.*, **72**, 771–83 (1966)

86. Tønnesen, K. H., Sejrsen, P. Inert gas diffusion method for measurement of blood flow: comparison of bolus injection to directly measured blood flow in the isolated gastrocnemius muscle. *Circ. Res.*, **20**, 552–64 (1967)

87. Kjellmer, I., Lindbjerg, I., Přerovsky, I., Tønnesen, K. H. The relation between blood flow in an isolated muscle measured with the Xe[133] clearance and a direct recording technique. *Acta Physiol. Scand.*, **69**, 69–78 (1967)

88. Shepherd, J. T. Behavior of resistance and capacity vessels in human limbs during exercise. *Circ. Res.*, **20**, *Suppl. I*, I-70–I-81 (1967)

89. Donald, K. W., Lind, A. R., McNicol, G. W., Humphreys, P. W., Taylor, S. H., Staunton, H. P. Cardiovascular responses to sustained (static) contractions. *Circ. Res.*, **20**, *Suppl. I*, I-15–I-30 (1967)

90. Golenhofen, K. Physiologische Bemerkungen zum peripheren Blut-

kreislauf unter besonderer Beruck-
sichtigung der menschlichen Mus-
keldurchblutung. *Hippokrates*, **37**,
2–12 (1966)

91. Shapiro, W., Wasserman, A. J., Patterson, J. L., Jr. Mechanism and
pattern of human cerebrovascular
regulation after rapid changes in
blood CO_2 tension. *J. Clin. Invest.*,
45, 913–22 (1966)

92. Severinghaus, J. W., Lassen, N.
Step hypocapnia to separate arterial from tissue P_{CO_2} in the regulation of cerebral blood flow. *Circ.
Res.*, **20**, 272–78 (1967)

93. Severinghaus, J. W., Chiodi, H.,
Eger, E. I., II, Brandstater, B.,
Horbein, T. F. Cerebral blood
flow in man at high altitude: role
of cerebrospinal fluid pH in nor-
malization of flow in chronic hypocapnia. *Circ. Res.*, **19**, 274–82
(1966)

94. Shapiro, W., Wasserman, A. J., Patterson, J. L., Jr. Human cerebro-
vascular response to combined hypoxia and hypercapnia. *Circ. Res.*,
16, 903–10 (1966)

95. Strumza, M.-V., Strumza, J.-M.,
Kamdoum, M. C., Delarue, Y.
Augmentation de l'irrigation cere-
brale au cours de l'hypoxie hypox-
ique hypocapnique par l'enrichiss-
ment en CO_2 de l'air inspire.
Compt. Rend. Acad. Sci., **264**,
625–27 (1967)

96. Häggendal, E., Johansson, B. Effects
of arterial carbon dioxide tension
and oxygen saturation on cerebral
blood flow autoregulation in dogs.
Acta Physiol. Scand., **66**, *Suppl.
258*, 27–53 (1965)

97. Yoshida, K., Meyer, J. S., Sakamoto,
K., Handa, J. Autoregulation of
cerebral blood flow: electromagnetic flow measurements during
acute hypertension in the monkey.
Circ. Res., **19**, 726–38 (1966)

98. Harper, A. M. Autoregulation of
cerebral blood flow: influence
of the arterial blood pressure on
the blood flow through the cerebral
cortex. *J. Neurol. Neurosurg. Psychiat.*, **29**, 398–403 (1966)

99. Mchedlishvili, G. I., Baramidze, D.
G., Nikolaishvili, L. S. Functional
behavior of pial and cortical arteries in conditions of increased
metabolic demand from the cerebral cortex. *Nature*, **213**, 506–7
(1967)

100. Owman, C., Falck, B., Mchedlishvili,

G. I. Adrenergic structures of the
pial arteries and their connections
with the cerebral cortex. *Fed.
Proc.* (Transl. Suppl.), **25**, 612–
14 (1966)

101. Häggendal, E., Nilsson, N. J., Nor-
bäck, B. On the components of
Kr^{85} clearance curves from the
brain of the dog. *Acta Physiol.
Scand.*, **66**, *Suppl. 258*, 1–25
(1965)

102. Veall, N., Mallett, B. L. Regional
cerebral blood flow determination
by ^{133}Xe inhalation and external
recording: the effect of recirculation. *Clin. Sci.*, **30**, 353–69 (1966)

103. Obrist, W. D., Thompson, H. K.,
Jr., King, C. H., Wang, H. S.
Determination of regional cerebral
blood flow by inhalation of 133-
xenon. *Circ. Res.*, **20**, 124–35
(1967)

104. Bozzao, L., Fieschi, C., Agnoli, A.,
Bartolini, A. Sulla non omogeneita'
del flusso sanguigno nelle strutture
profonde dell'encefalo del gatto.
(Osservazioni nel nucleo caudato).
Boll. Soc. Ital. Biol. Sper., **42**,
1713–16 (1966)

105. Jensen, K. B., Høedt-Rasmussen, K.,
Sveinsdottir, E., Stewart, B. M.,
Lassen, N. A. Cerebral blood flow
evaluated by inhalation of ^{133}Xe
and extracranial recording: a
methodological study. *Clin. Sci.*,
30, 485–94 (1966)

106. Lassen, N. A., Høedt-Rasmussen, K.
Human cerebral blood flow measured by two inert gas techniques:
comparison of the Kety-Schmidt
method and the intra-arterial
method. *Circ. Res.*, **19**, 681–88
(1966)

107. Isbister, W. H., Schofield, P. F.,
Torrance, H. B. Cerebral blood
flow estimated by ^{133}Xe clearance
technique. *Arch. Neurol. (Chicago)*, **14**, 512–21 (1966)

108. Betz, E., Ingvar, D. H., Lassen, N.
A., Schmahl, F. W. Regional
blood flow in the cerebral cortex
measured simultaneously by heat
and inert gas clearance. *Acta
Physiol. Scand.*, **67**, 1–9 (1966)

109. Seylaz, J., Molnar, L. Nouvelle technique pour l'enrigistrement syn-
chrone du débit sanguin et de
l'activité électrique du cerveau
chez les animaux vigiles. *Compt.
Rend. Soc. Biol.*, **160**, 258–62
(1966)

110. Gotoh, F., Meyer, J. S., Tomita, M.

Hydrogen method for determining cerebral blood flow in man. *Arch. Neurol. (Chicago)*, **15**, 549–59 (1966)

111. Feigl, E. O. Sympathetic control of the coronary circulation. *Circ. Res.*, **20**, 262–71 (1967)

112. Daggett, W. M., Nugent, G. C., Carr, P. W., Powers, P. C., Harada, Y. Influences of vagal stimulation on ventricular contractility, O_2 consumption, and coronary flow. *Am. J. Physiol.*, **212**, 8–18 (1967)

113. Ross, G. Blood flow in the right coronary artery of the dog. *Cardiovasc. Res.*, **1**, 138–44 (1967)

114. Katori, M., Berne, R. M. Release of adenosine from anoxic hearts: relationship to coronary flow. *Circ. Res.*, **19**, 420–25 (1966)

115. Glomstein, A., Hauge, A., Øye, I., Sinclair, D. Effects of adrenaline on coronary flow in isolated perfused rat hearts. *Acta Physiol. Scand.*, **69**, 102–10 (1967)

116. Hirsch, L. J., Lluch, S., Katz, L. N. Counterpulsation effects of coronary blood flow and cardiac oxygen utilization. *Circ. Res.*, **19**, 1031–40 (1966)

117. McKenna, D. H., Corliss, R. J., Sialer, S., Zarnstorff, W. C., Crumpton, C. W., Rowe, G. G. Effect of propranolol on systemic and coronary hemodynamics at rest and during simulated exercise. *Circ. Res.*, **19**, 520–27 (1966)

118. Badeer, H. S., Pinkston, J. O. Cardiac oxygen consumption in the heart-lung-coronary preparation. *Am. J. Physiol.*, **211**, 1467–71 (1966)

119. McHenry, P. L., Knoebel, S. B. Measurement of coronary blood flow by coincidence counting and a bolus of $^{84}RbCl$. *J. Appl. Physiol.*, **22**, 495–500 (1967)

120. Donato, L., Bartolomei, G., Federghi, G., Torreggiani, G. Measurement of coronary blood flow by external counting with radio-active rubidium: critical appraisal and validation of the method. *Circulation*, **33**, 708–18 (1966)

121. Moir, T. W. Measurement of coronary blood flow in dogs with normal and abnormal myocardial oxygenation and function: comparison of flow measured by a rotameter and by Rb^{86} clearance. *Circ. Res.*, **19**, 695–99 (1966)

122. Bersentes, T. J., Simmons, D. H. Effects of acute acidosis on renal hemodynamics. *Am. J. Physiol.*, **212**, 633–40 (1967)

123. Astoin, M. Particularités de l'hémodynamique rénale au cours des perfusions de mannitol. *J. Physiol. (Paris)*, **58**, 451–52 (1966)

124. Thurau, K. The nature of autoregulation of renal blood flow. *Abstr. Intern. Congr. Nephrol., Washington, D.C., Sept. 25–30, 1966*, 93–94

125. Carriere, S., Thorburn, G. D., O'-Morchoe, C. C. C., Barger, A. C. Intrarenal distribution of blood flow in dogs during hemorrhagic hypotension. *Circ. Res.*, **19**, 167–79 (1966)

126. Aukland, K. Study of renal circulation with inert gases. Measurement in tissue. *Abstr. Inter. Congr. Nephrol., Washington, D.C., Sept. 25–30, 1966*, 97–98

127. Yoshitoshi, Y., Honda, N., Morikawa, A., Aizawa, C., Seki, K. Alterations in the intrarenal hemodynamics following changes in ureteral pressure in the rabbit kidney. *Japan. Heart J.*, **8**, 32–41 (1967)

128. Gosk, A., Juzwa, W., Paradowski, A., Kurbiel, A. Blood flow in kidney during stop-flow diuresis. *Acta Physiol. Polon.*, **17**, 145–52 (1966)

129. Ono, H., Inagaki, K., Hashimoto, K. A pharmacological approach to the nature of the autoregulation of the renal blood flow. *Japan. J. Physiol.*, **16**, 625–33 (1966)

130. Barger, A. C., Herd, J. A. Study of renal circulation in the unanesthetized dog with inert gases 1) external counting. *Abstr. Intern. Congr. Nephrol., Washington, D.C., Sept. 25–30, 1966*, 95–96

131. Fourman, J., Kennedy, G. C. An effect of antidiuretic hormone on the flow of blood through the vasa recta of the rat kidney. *J. Endocrinol.*, **35**, 173–76 (1966)

132. Bell, G., Murray, H. A. The relationship between the blood flow through the renal cortex and the arterial blood pressure. *J. Physiol. (London)*, **187**, 22P (1966)

133. Nissen, O. I. The filtration fractions of plasma supplying the superficial and deep venous drainage area of the cat kidney. *Acta Physiol. Scand.*, **68**, 275–85 (1966)

134. Aukland, K. Renal medullary heat

clearance in the dog. *Circ. Res.*, **20**, 194–203 (1967)

135. Hyman, C., Greeson, T. P. Evidence for the presence of shunts in skin of forearm. *J. Invest. Dermatol.*, **47**, 363–65 (1966)

136. Edwards, M. A. The role of arteriovenous anastomoses in cold-induced vasodilation, rewarming, and reactive hyperemia as determined by ^{24}Na clearance. *Can. J. Physiol. Pharmacol.*, **45**, 39–48 (1967)

137. Gaskell, P., Broy, G. M. The effect of local cooling on the sensitivity to noradrenaline of vessels in the feet. *Can. J. Physiol. Pharmacol.*, **45**, 75–82 (1967)

138. Gaskell, P., Hoeppner, D. L. The relative influence of nervous control and of local warming on arteriolar muscle during indirect vasodilatation. *Can. J. Physiol. Pharmacol.*, **45**, 83–91 (1967)

139. Chalmers, J. P., Korner, P. I. Effects of arterial hypoxia on the cutaneous circulation of the rabbit. *J. Physiol. (London)*, **184**, 685–97 1967)

140. Orö, L., Rosell, S., Wallenberg, L. Circulatory and metabolic processes in adipose tissue in vivo. *Nature*, **205**, 178–79 (1965)

141. Ngai, S. H., Rosell, S., Wallenberg, L. R. Nervous regulation of blood flow in the subcutaneous adipose tissue in dogs. *Acta Physiol. Scand.*, **68**, 397–403 (1966)

142. Öberg, B., Rosell, S. Sympathetic control of consecutive vascular sections in canine subcutaneous tissue. *Acta Physiol. Scand.*, **71**, 8–15 (1967)

143. Larsen, O. A., Lassen, N. A., Quaade, F. Blood flow through human adipose tissue determined with radioactive xenon. *Acta Physiol. Scand.*, **66**, 337–45 (1966)

144. Häggendal, E., Steen, B., Svanborg, A. Measurement of blood flow

through human abdominal subcutaneous fat tissue by local injection of radioactive xenon. Preliminary report. *Acta Med. Scand.*, **181**, 215–18 (1967)

145. Heim, T., Hull, D. The blood flow and oxygen consumption of brown adipose tissue in the new-born rabbit. *J. Physiol. (London)*, **186**, 42–55 (1966)

146. Morley, J., Schachter, M., Smaje, L. H. Vasodilatation in the submaxillary gland of the rabbit. *J. Physiol. (London)*, **187**, 595–602 (1966)

147. Hilton, S. M., Torres, S. H. Bradykinin and functional vasodilatation in the submandibular salivary gland in the cat. *J. Physiol. (London)*, **189**, 69P (1967)

148. Funakoshi, M., Hamada, T., Kawamura, Y. The effect of pressure within the submandibular gland on the glandular blood circulation. *Japan. J. Physiol.*, **17**, 21–29 (1967)

149. Shim, S. S., Cobb, H., Patterson, F. P. Bone blood flow in the limb following complete sciatic section. *Surg. Gynecol. Obstet.*, **123**, 333–35 (1966)

150. Pasternak, H. S., Kelly, P. J., Owen, C. A. Estimation of oxygen consumption, and carbon dioxide production and blood flow of bone in growing and mature dogs. *Mayo Clin. Proc.*, **41**, 831–35 (1966)

151. Greiss, F. C., Jr. Pressure-flow relationship in the gravid uterine vascular bed. *Am. J. Obstet. Gynecol.*, **96**, 41–47 (1966)

152. Greiss, F. C., Jr., Gobble, F. L., Jr. Effect of sympathetic nerve stimulation on the uterine vascular bed. *Am. J. Obstet. Gynecol.*, **97**, 962–67 (1967)

153. Hughes, T. The microcirculation of baroceptor areas. *Angiology*, **17**, 833–41 (1966)

ADRENAL CORTEX[1,2]

By Edwin D. Bransome, Jr.

Unit of Experimental Medicine, Department of Nutrition and Food Science Massachusetts Institute of Technology, Cambridge, Massachusetts

INTRODUCTION

In the past several years, much of the investigation of adrenocortical physiology has been concerned with the mechanisms of steroid biosynthesis within the adrenocortical cell, and with the interaction of cellular metabolism and extracellular stimuli. A considerable amount of attention, for example, has been given to the "mechanism of action of ACTH". While it is still too soon in the progress of cellular physiology to comprehend many of the behavioral phenomena of differentiated cells, the recent progress in adrenocortical cell physiology has been truly remarkable.

The object of this review is to capitalize upon the opportunity which this progress offers: the vantage point from which to assess the relevance of current research to intracellular and extracellular controls of adrenocortical activity. The limitations of space have dictated that some important areas of progress (e.g., peripheral metabolism of steroids and phenolic steroids, fetal adrenal physiology) not be reviewed. The presence of Dr. McCann's review of the anterior pituitary would make any discussion of the control of ACTH secretion in this chapter redundant.

The selection and organization of subject matter is oriented toward the sequential process of corticosteroid biosynthesis. Several figures and a certain amount of background information given here will seem unnecessary to workers familiar with this field, but are included to present a coherent view of the adrenal cortex to readers not as familiar with the field as those actively involved in it.

It might be helpful to mention several recent and comprehensive reviews of areas pertinent to the following discussion. Dorfman & Ungar (1) have thoroughly reviewed steroid metabolism in the 1965 edition of their book *The Metabolism of Steroid Hormones*. The reader is advised to consult their excellent compendium for questions on steroid nomenclature and for detailed biosynthetic and degradative pathways. Hilf's (2) article on the mechanism of action of ACTH, which also appeared in 1965, provides a thorough summary of progress up to that time, particularly of the Haynes-Berthet hypothesis of ACTH action. Additional general background will be provided by the volume *The Adrenal Cortex* edited by Eisenstein (3) which contains comprehensive reviews by twenty-six author-

---

[1] Literature to June 1967 was reviewed.

[2] The preparation of this chapter and the work by the reviewer referred to in it were supported by grants from the American Cancer Society.

ities. Another book, *Functions of the Adrenal Cortex,* edited by McKerns (4), contains a number of articles submitted in late 1966 which individually summarize recent progress in understanding adrenocortical cell physiology; some contributions from that volume will be referred to here. Finally, a CIBA study group report on the human adrenal cortex (5), not yet inspected by the reviewer at the time of this writing, was also published in 1967.

BIOSYNTHESIS OF CORTICOSTEROIDS

Perusal of the concise summary by Samuels & Uchikawa (6) of the work leading to current knowledge of adrenal steroid biosynthesis, and inspection of Figures 1 and 2 should orient the reader not already intimate with adrenocortical physiology to recent considerations of the various synthetic steps and the influences of ACTH, angiotensin II, etc. The somewhat myopic tendency of recent years has been to regard the action of tropic hormones upon their specific target cells solely within the context of the most interesting effect of the hormone. Thus the "mechanism of action" of ACTH has been considered almost exclusively within the context of effects on steroidogenesis. In truth, there are some effects which as yet cannot be coherently related to the control of steroid biosynthesis, for example, effects of ACTH upon protein and nucleic acid metabolism. Where

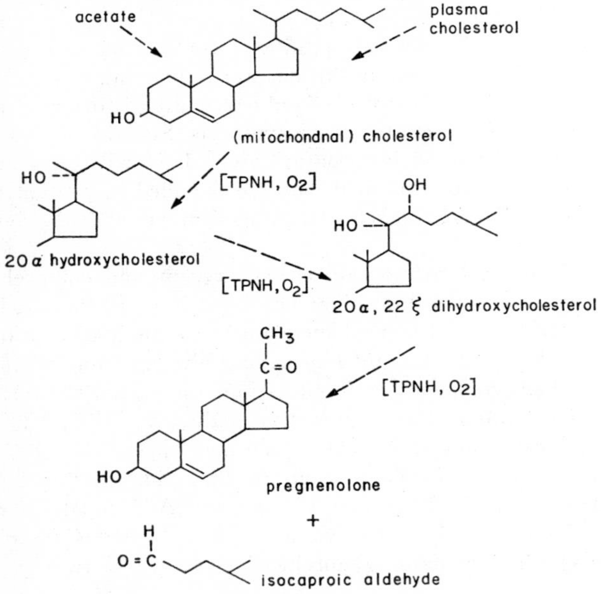

FIG. 1. Mechanism of cholesterol side-chain cleavage by adrenal cortex.

the interactions are not only unclear but ambiguous, they will be discussed in later sections.

CHOLESTEROL

Since the observation by Hechter et al. (7) that when acetate-C^{14} was incorporated into the perfused bovine adrenal, cortisol had a higher specific radioactivity than adrenal cholesterol, the question of whether cholesterol was an obligatory intermediate for the synthesis of adrenal steroids from acetate has been at issue. The existence of an alternate pathway has been suggested [e.g., by Goodman et al. (8)] but the observation by Werbin & Chaikoff (9) that the specific radioactivities of urine cortisol and adrenal cholesterol were equal after long-term feeding of cholesterol-4-C^{14} to guinea pigs suggested that cholesterol was indeed an obligatory intermediate. The explanation of the disparity in labeling by acetate consequently has supposed the existence of a small and at least partially restricted pool of adrenal cholesterol. Ichii & Kobayashi (10) recently reported that mitochondrial cholesterol radioactivity was higher than in the mitochondrial supernatant after incubation of rat adrenals with acetate-1-C^{14}, and that it was increased further after ACTH. Since the specific activity of corticosterone was still higher than that of mitochondrial cholesterol, it appeared that only a fraction of mitochondrial cholesterol was directly accessible for corticoid synthesis. Armstrong et al. (11) have made similar observations after incubating rat corpora lutea with acetate-1-C^{14} and luteinizing hormone. The existence of a restricted pool of adrenal cholesterol and the syn-

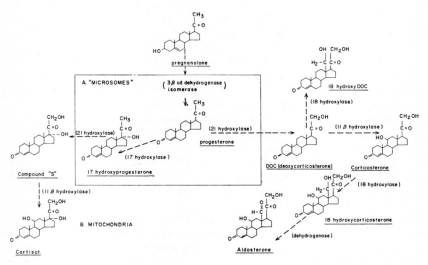

FIG. 2. Synthesis of adrenal corticoids from pregnenolone: major pathways.

thesis of at least a portion of it from acetate in adrenal cortex seem established by these *in vitro* experiments.

The adrenal cortex incorporates cholesterol esters as well as free plasma cholesterol; apparently the esters are hydrolyzed rapidly; the liberated free sterol mixes with free cholesterol pools only to be re-esterified, with esters becoming the predominant form (in contrast to other tissues). Shyamala et al. (12) have demonstrated that rat adrenal contains two enzymes, one in the mitochondria-rich fraction and one in the microsomal fraction, which esterify cholesterol. The microsomal enzyme requires ATP for its activity; the mitochondrial enzyme does not, but requires a lipid extract of cell sap. At least one of the possible mechanisms of the stimulatory effect of cell sap seems to be the provision of free cholesterol and fatty acids for esterification. The same workers found that the mitochondria-rich fraction of the Snell transplantable adrenocortical tumor 494-H was deficient in the capacity to esterify cholesterol (13). All of this is suggestive of a control system for esterification. At present, however, no more than a "storage" function has been postulated (6); and there does not yet seem to be any evidence of tight regulation of ester hydrolysis in the mitochondrial fraction.

The increased conversion of cholesterol to adrenocortical steroids is a well-known effect of ACTH. It has seemed logical that ACTH must enhance cholesterol deposition or synthesis in the adrenal cortex, at least by virtue of response to depletion of cholesterol precursor. Dexter et al. (14) have recently employed an approach which appears to have overcome the tendency of increased cholesterol utilization to obscure effects of ACTH upon cholesterol accumulation in the adrenal. They found, by using the drug aminoglutethimide to inhibit conversion of cholesterol to pregnenolone, that chronic ACTH administration to hypophysectomized rats almost doubled adrenal cholesterol. Robertson & Reddy (15) have recently reported studies of acetate 1-^{14}C incorporation into hydrocortisone, cholesterol, and mevalonate in calf adrenal cortex slices. Their work suggests several answers to the question of how much of the increase in adrenal cholesterol is a consequence of increased cholesterol synthesis and how much is due to increased uptake of plasma cholesterol. At low doses, ACTH increased acetate incorporation into cortisol, but at higher doses this effect declined (presumably as cholesterol synthesis was increased). The specific radioactivity of cholesterol was lower than that of hydrocortisone and was, as expected, depressed by all doses of ACTH. When mevalonate was introduced into the incubation medium, a decrease of acetate-1-C^{14} incorporation into mevalonate resulted, suggesting that the effect of ACTH upon cholesterol specific activity occurred at a synthetic step prior to mevalonate and that mevalonate was at least a major intermediate both in the synthesis of adrenal steroids and in the cholesterol which serves as steroid precursor. A decrease in adrenal cholesterol synthesis from exogenous acetate seems to be an acute effect of ACTH.

That net cholesterol synthesis may not be diminished at all is suggested by another observation of Robertson & Reddy (16) and a previous report by Macho & Palkovic (17). Increase in adrenal free fatty acid content parallels the steroid response to ACTH. Both a decrease in triglycerides (16, 17) and the rapid increase of adrenal lipase after ACTH *in vivo* (18) suggest that hydrolysis of triglycerides is the principal source of fatty acids. Endogenous acetate pools might be expected to expand, and dilution of added precursor would explain decreased cholesterol specific radioactivity after ACTH; free fatty acids released from triglycerides after activation of adrenal lipase might serve as an important source of acetoacetyl CoA and acyl CoA for steroid synthesis. These findings may be considered in the light of a study by Rudman & Garcia (21) which demonstrated triglycceride depletion in adrenal cortex after ACTH and perhaps, also, of the well-known extra-adrenal effect of ACTH upon adipose tissue lipolysis. The discrepancy *in vivo* between cholesterol and cortisol acetate-1-C^{14} incorporation may of course still be adequately explained by plasma cholesterol being less accessible to immediate steroid precursors than to the total of adrenal cholesterol pools.

The contribution of plasma cholesterol to cortisol, which must of course be assessed in addressing the effect of ACTH on adrenal cholesterol synthesis, cannot be comprehended by the *in vitro* studies of Robertson & Reddy and is probably equal in importance to cholesterol synthesis in the adrenal gland. Melby et al. (19) have found that after achievement of isotope equilibrium with 4-C^{14}-cholesterol and removal of endogenous ACTH, the specific radioactivity of canine adrenal vein cortisol dropped to 75 per cent of that of adrenal and plasma cholesterol, and they have concluded that extraction of plasma cholesterol was controlled by ACTH. They suggested that it is the plasma cortisol which is the principal precursor of cortisol. In a somewhat similar previous study, Krum et al. (20) found equivalent specific radioactivity in plasma and adrenal cholesterol-4-C^{14} and plasma cortisol. This suggested that exogenous cholesterol might completely account for cortisol precursors in the dog whereas Werbin & Chaikoff (9) had calculated that 40 per cent of guinea pig adrenal cholesterol was synthesized *de novo*. Even though the contribution of *de novo* cholesterol synthesis may be less in the dog than in the guinea pig adrenal cortex, the drop in specific radioactivity of cortisol after removal of ACTH is still consistent with a significant synthesis of cholesterol. It would seem that an examination of the effects of ACTH *in vivo* upon cholesterol and cortisol radioactivity after long-term ingestion of differentially labeled acetate and cholesterol, might go far to elucidate the relative contribution of adrenal cholesterol synthesis to the precursor pools in adrenal mitochondria.

CHOLESTEROL UTILIZATION

The pathway of cholesterol hydroxylation and side-chain cleavage is represented in Figure 1; please see Tchen (22) for an excellent brief summary. This step in corticosteroid biosynthesis is of particular importance because both ACTH and cyclic 3'5'-AMP appear to exert their principal effects on steroid biosynthesis at this "desmolase" step (23, 24). The actions of interstitial-cell-stimulating hormone (ICSH) on testicular testosterone synthesis and of ICSH and luteinizing hormone upon ovarian progesterone synthesis have been shown to occur at this step also by Hall (25), Koritz & Hall (26), and Channing & Villee (27). The product of side-chain cleavage has recently been shown to be isocaproaldehyde by Constantopoulos et al. (28) who employed unlabeled isocaproaldehyde as a trapping agent. Farese (29) has recently employed measurement of the aldehyde oxidation product, isocaproic acid, from cholesterol-26-C^{14}, to measure the effect of ACTH on side-chain cleavage. The soluble oxygenases in mitochondria, which oxidize cholesterol to $20\alpha22\xi$-hydroxycholesterol [see Tchen (22) and Sih et al. (30)], tolerate considerable variations in the side chain and require the presence of a reduced pyridine nucleotide.

Satoh et al. (31) have presented good evidence that NADPH (TPNH) rather than NADH (DPNH) is the nucleotide involved. The concentration of the latter required for enzymatic activity *in vitro* was much higher than estimates of *in situ* concentration *in vivo*. They also found that cyclic 3'5'-AMP had no direct effect on the soluble enzyme complex. There have been numerous reports dealing with the effects of extramitochondrial NADPH on conversion of cholesterol to pregnenolone, in general supporting the hypothesis of Haynes & Berthet (32) that the *in vivo* effect of ACTH is mediated through NADPH production. Koritz (33), however, has recently reported that succinate supports the formation of pregnenolone from endogenous precursors by bovine mitrochondria, and does so more efficiently than other Krebs-cycle intermediates. In addition, he found that amytal and seconal were inhibitory. Both observations suggested the involvement of energy-dependent reverse electron transport, and of transhydrogenation in the generation of the intramitochondrial NADPH required for the hydroxylation reaction. (See Figure 3.) There have also been a number of recent reports that the desmolase complex is inhibited by carbon monoxide and that the inhibition is reversed by 450 mμ light, a finding which indicates that the cytochrome P-450 is a cofactor [Bryson & Kaiser (34), Boyd & Simpson (35), Tchen (22)]. These reports suggest that Koritz is correct. The regulation of electron transport pathways then must be considered if NADPH is rate limiting. Please see below for further discussion of the electron transport pathways.

STIMULATION OF SIDE-CHAIN CLEAVAGE BY ACTH

Since the principal locus of stimulation of adrenal corticosteroid biosynthesis is at this step, consideration of various mechanisms proposed for the effect of the tropic hormone seems appropriate at this point. Decrease of endproduct inhibition, increased NADH formation, synthesis of a labile protein, uptake and extrusion of ions, increase in cyclic adenosine-3'5'-monophosphate, and antagonism of an inhibitory factor have all been in-

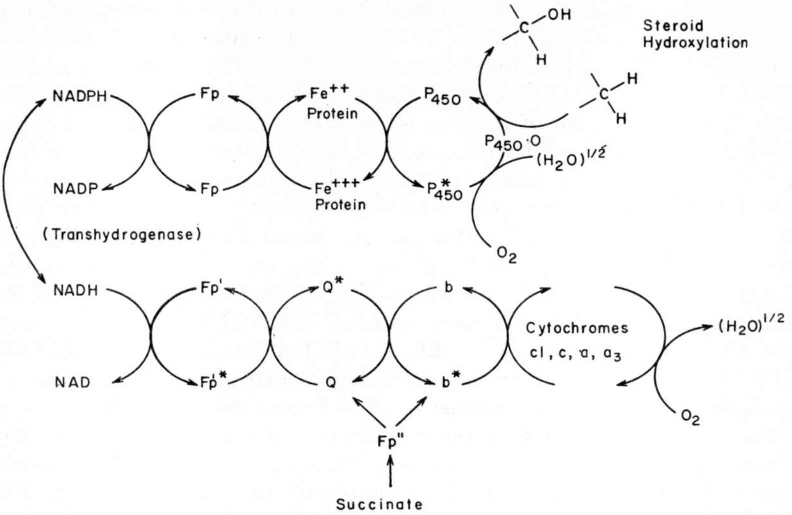

FIG. 3. The current concept of reversed electron transfer in steroid hydroxylations. Linkage of the P-450 chain to the respiratory chain through transhydrogenation.

criminated. It is not at all clear at present how these metabolic events are related to ACTH action, to steroid biosynthesis, or to each other; there is also the possibility that several may be artifacts of the experimental designs used to examine them.

The role of ions in corticosteroid biosynthesis.—Peron & McCarthy (36) have provided an excellent discussion of the effects *in vitro* of Ca^{++} upon the conversion of cholesterol. Indeed, substances in general which cause mitochondrial swelling have been found [see Koritz (37)] to stimulate pregnenolone synthesis in adrenal mitochondria and other subsequent mitochondrial hydroxylations; the presence of a stimulatory effect has been correlated with mitochondrial swelling. In addition, Peron et al. (38) and Harding et al. (39) found that there was little utilization of exogenous NADPH in rat adrenal and mitochondria. The possibility that Ca^{++} plays a role in 11β- and 18-hydroxylations that is not related to mitrochondrial swelling (and consequently increased permeability to exogenous NADPH) is discussed below.

Recent reports of extraction of corticosterone from rat adrenals under an applied electrical field without any ACTH, cyclin 3'5'-AMP, or NADPH (TPNH) by Cortes & Peron (40) raise additional possibilities of ionic influence upon steroid biosynthesis. Although Matthews & Saffran (41) have not found electrophysiological correlates of ACTH stimulation, the actions of ACTH and cyclic 3'5'-AMP still might primarily involve changes in ionic flux across adrenal cell membranes.

Endproduct inhibition by pregnenolone.—Koritz and associates (37) have found that, although there is a qualitative correlation between mitochondrial swelling and pregnenolone synthesis, the degree of swelling cannot be quantitatively correlated with increased side-chain cleavage. This suggests that alteration of internal mitochondrial membrane structure, and not swelling per se is of importance. The *in vitro* structural and stimulatory effects of Ca⁺⁺, fatty acids, sodium lauryl sulfate, and pronase are reversible. Hirshfield & Koritz (42) have found that ATP inhibits their effect, and have also found (43) that the increase in rat mitochondrial pregnenolone synthesis observed fifteen minutes after *in vivo* administration of ACTH could be prevented by adding ATP to the incubation medium. Because they noted little correlation between NADPH oxidation and pregnenolene synthesis, Koritz & Hirshfield (44) have concluded that NADPH (TPNH) entry into a more accessible mitochondrial structure is not of significance in the *in vitro* stimulation of pregnenolone synthesis.

The possibility that structural changes may govern side-chain cleavage by increasing the removal of pregnenolone is supported by other observations of Koritz & Hall (37, 45, 46) : that conversion of cholesterol to 20α-hydroxycholesterol is inhibited by pregnenolone. Because pregnenolone does not compete with cholesterol as a substrate and because 17α-hydroxypregnenolone, which has no effect on pregnenolone synthesis itself, can prevent the endproduct inhibition, they have suggested that pregnenolone influences the conformation of the hydroxylating enzyme. The description of "allosteric" transitions by Monod et al. (47) is quite consistent with the concept of pregnenolone as an "allosteric effect" and a blocking effect of its analogue 17α-hydroxypregnenolone.

Reports by Lever (48), Sabatini et al. (49), Nishikawa et al. (50), and Luse (51) of changes in zona fasciculata mitochondrial morphology after ACTH administration, including apparent increased exposure of membrane surface to the cell sap, lend credence to the hypothesis of Koritz (41) that ACTH (perhaps through cyclic 3'5'-AMP) may control steroidogenesis through increasing the egress of pregnenolone from intramitochondrial compartments. Appealing as this hypothesis is, its bases are experiments with cell-free extracts and electronmicroscopy: systems far removed from the adrenal *in situ*. More investigation is necessary before this ingenious and attractive explanation can be put into proper perspective.

"Steroidogenin-steroidohibin".—Farese (29, 52, 53) has recently reported that the enhancement of cholesterol side-chain cleavage in rat adrenal quarters after incubation with ACTH or cyclic 3'5'-AMP, which persists even when the influence of additional ACTH is blocked by puromycin(54) or chloramphenicol (55), does not seem to be attributable directly to ACTH, cyclic 3'5'-AMP, or supply of TPNH, but to an inductive process which can be blocked by puromycin. A 60,000 × *g* supernatant factor "steroidogenin" which increases corticosterone production and the rate of cholesterol side-chain cleavage appeared to be responsible. Its physicochemical behavior—

exclusion from Sephadex G-25, precipitation by $(NH_4)_2SO_4$, heat lability, and lability to trypsin—suggested that it was a protein at least in part. Control adrenal supernatants contained an acetone-precipitable factor "steroidohibin "which inhibited side-chain cleavage, was specifically from adrenal tissue, and also behaved like a protein. Since the effect of ACTH on side-chain cleavage (reflected by recovery of radioactivity from cholesterol-26-^{14}C in isocaproic acid; see Figure 1) was decreased to control levels by mild heating or trypsin treatment of 60,000 $\times$ g adrenal supernatant, the action of ACTH might seem attributable to a labile stimulatory factor, perhaps the labile protein suggested by several other investigators.

Arguments that the action of ACTH on steroid biosynthesis is the result of decrease in inhibition seem to be somewhat more persuasive at present. The stimulatory effect of ACTH-supernatant was best observed when inhibition by the controls was most obvious, and rarely increased the activity of the 60,000 $\times$ g pellet beyond that observed with no supernatant. Farese has thus tentatively proposed that ACTH may induce the synthesis of a labile protein which stimulates steroidogenesis by interfering with the action of another inhibitory protein on the conversion of cholesterol to pregnenolone.

Although he has observed a similar effect of supernatant from the adrenals of animals treated with ACTH *in vivo* (56), Farese has pointed out (29, 53) that it may still represent artifacts of his cell-free system, reflecting a highly artificial experimental design rather than physiological control. It is interesting to note, however, that the observations of Farese and of Koritz et al. (pregnenolone endproduct inhibition; see above), drawn from two very different experimental designs, and given different interpretations, are really not at all exclusive. Indeed, they are convergent, since neither scheme comprehends the mechanisms of inhibition or stimulation proposed by the other.

The role of NADPH (TPNH).—Except for the 3β-ol-dehydrogenase, isomerase step (see Figure 2 and below), steroidogenic enzymes in the adrenal cortex are known to utilize NADPH preferentially. It has been apparent from a report of Sweat & Lipscomb in 1955 (57), and from many others since, that optimum *in vitro* conditions for steroids usually involve the presence of NADPH (TPNH) or a generating system consisting of NADP and oxidizable substrates (glucose-6-phosphate, fumarate, malate, citrate, and α-ketoglutarate). These observations have led to investigations of how the level of this cofactor in adrenal cells might be regulated. That changes in proton availability probably cannot explain all of the effects of ACTH on steroid biosynthesis is suggested by Savard & Casey's observation (58) that NADPH had no effect upon acetate incorporation into adrenal corticoids.

McKerns (59–63) has reported a number of studies on adrenal homogenates concerning the activation of glucose-6-phosphate dehydrogenase by ACTH and the importance of glucose-6-phosphate as a substrate for the enzyme. He has stressed the importance of enzyme activity in determining NADPH concentration and has postulated that ACTH exerts its main influence on steroid biosynthesis at this point.

His experimental designs have been difficult for others to reproduce and there have been several recent reports that argue against significant changes in adrenal cell NADPH levels. Harding & Nelson (64) showed that the pyridine nucleotide concentrations of adrenocortical cells in the resting rat were very high and that although adrenal steroid secretion fell precipitously within thirty minutes of hypophysectomy, no change in adrenal NADPH or NADP was observed for seventy-two hours. The activities of the enzymes (65) which might be involved in NADPH generation (glucose-6-phosphate dehydrogenase, 6-phosphogluconate dehydrogenase, isocitrate dehydrogenase, NADPH-cytochrome-C reductase, glutathione reductase, and pyridine nucleotide transhydrogenase) were not significantly diminished within this period. In addition, Kuhn & Kissane (66) did not find any ACTH effect upon histochemically determined glucose-6-phosphate dehydrogenase or 6-phosphogluconate dehydrogenase. Peron & McCarthy (36) have attempted to determine the pyridine nucleotide content of rat adrenal mitochondria and have found the same patterns of content in cell fractions of normal animals, hypophysectomized animals, and animals treated with ACTH. Their data do not indicate any significant loss of accumulation of cytoplasmic or intramitochondrial NADPH, and suggest that the coenzyme concentration is not critical to corticosteroid hydroxylations.

Despite the evidence against the importance of NADPH concentration in the effect of ACTH upon cholesterol utilization or in other steroid hydroxylations, the concentration of cofactor could still be rate limiting in small and restricted mitochondrial compartments. McKerns (67) has some recent evidence for activation of a purified glucose-6-phosphate dehydrogenase preparation by ACTH; and the enzyme does provide a path for electron transfer to the P-450 chain through transhydrogenation.

Cyclic 3'5'-AMP.—The possibility of NADPH generation being important in adrenal corticosteroid biosynthesis, discussed above, drew attention to the pentose pathway. Ten years ago Haynes & Berthet (32) and Haynes (68) reported that ACTH stimulated α-glucan phosphorylase activity in bovine adrenal slices, an effect which would increase the availability of glucose-6-phosphate as a substrate for dehydrogenation. A rise in cyclic 3'5'-AMP concentration was thought to increase phosphorylase activity (through activation of phosphorylase-b kinase and/or decreased catabolism of the enzyme), and subsequently to glycogenolysis, increased glucose-6-phosphate production, and finally increased reduction of NADP (TPN) by glucose-6-phosphate dehydrogenase.

A number of findings since the formulation of this hypothesis suggest that it is incorrect. As noted elsewhere in the review, there are reasons to question whether NADPH is rate limiting for steroid side-chain cleavage. Oxidation of Krebs-cycle intermediates probably can fulfill the requirements of steroid hydroxylations for endogenous NADPH and subsequent reverse electron flow along the P-450 chain. Indeed, some of the energy requirements of steroid biosynthesis can probably be met by coupled oxidation of these substrates. Nor has it been possible to demonstrate a stimulatory effect of glucose-6-phosphate *in vitro* except under conditions which have almost certainly damaged adrenocortical cells and rendered them incapable of making endogenous NADPH available for a steroidogenic response to ACTH (36, 69). In addition it has been shown by Roberts & Creange (70 to 72) that the nucleotide can stimulate steroid hydroxylations regardless of the level of NADPH and in the absence of glycogen phosphorylation or endogenous precursor. Their observations of *in vitro* inhibition of microsomal C21-hydroxylation activity and of a stimulatory effect of 3'5'-AMP on cholesterol utilization in isolated adrenal mitochondria of the rat indicated that the nucleotide exerted a direct effect on steroid hydroxylations.

It has been evident, however, since the demonstration of a specific effect of cyclic 3'5'-AMP on rat adrenal steroidogenesis *in vitro* by Haynes et al. (73) and the demonstration by Hilton et al. (74) of an *in vivo* stimulatory effect, that the nucleotide had to be considered in the regulation of steroid biosynthesis. In the past few years, moreover, it has been incriminated as a chemical signal in the action of a large number of hormones on their target tissues [Sutherland et al. (75)]. The effects of cyclic 3'5'-AMP have been attributed to increased membrane permeability or to allosteric effects on enzyme protein conformation and activity. The reports by Roberts & Creange (70 to 72) of increased steroid hydroxylations by adrenal mitochondria are, as the paragraphs above indicate, not indicative of either mechanism. That direct enzymatic effects do occur is evident. For example, Huijing & Larner (76, 77) have suggested that cyclic 3'5'-AMP stimulates the rat heart kinase of UDPG, α-1,4-glucan α-4-glucosyl transferase, by increasing the affinity of the activating site of the enzyme for Mg^{++}. It will be interesting to see whether similar observations can be made with other enzymes activated by the nucleotide.

One of the problems in assessing the role of cyclic 3'5'-AMP is the relative impermeability of cell plasma membranes to the nucleotide. Pastan (78) has shown that the paucity of effects of exogenous nucleotide on thyroid cell metabolism was attributable to this problem, because a more soluble and less easily metabolized dibutyryl derivative had a very significant effect.

A convincing case for the involvement of cyclic 3'5'-AMP in mediation of the effects of ACTH has recently been made. The enzyme adenyl cyclase, which catalyzes the transformation of ATP to cyclic monophosphate, has been placed at the cell membrane of erythrocytes (79) and hepatocytes (80, 81) by Sutherland and associates. Reddy & Streeto (82) recently demonstrated not only that adenyl cyclase was present in adrenal membranes, but that there was a stimulatory effect of ACTH upon enzymatic activity.

Using a sensitive new double isotope-derivative method (83), they found a rapid and considerable increase in cyclic 3'5'-AMP. Grahame-Smith et al. (84) reported shortly afterwards that they too, using the older method of Butcher et al. (85), had found an increase of cyclic 3'5'-AMP *in vitro* within a minute, before any measurable effect of ACTH on corticoid biosynthesis appeared. They also reported that cycloheximide, which inhibited steroidogenesis, did not interfere with the increase in cyclic 3'5'-AMP, a fact suggesting that if protein synthesis does play a role in the effects of ACTH on steroidogenesis, it is after the activation of adenyl cyclase. Reddy & Streeto (82) found a small but significant stimulation of amino acid incorporation into protein when they added the nucleotide to rat adrenals— an observation consistent with, but not indicative of an effect on protein synthesis, as they have carefully pointed out.

Synthesis of a labile protein.—Stimulation of the adrenal by ACTH brings about an increased growth of adrenocortical cells and a commensurate increase of net protein synthesis. Farese & Reddy (86) showed that treatment of rats with depot-ACTH brought about a 50 per cent increase in protein content in sixteen hours. Bransome (87) has recently shown that adrenal protein was significantly elevated twenty-four hours after a single injection of ACTH into guinea pigs whose plasma cortisol had returned to normal after eight hours. Bransome & Reddy (88) had previously reported that *in vivo* amino acid incorporation into rat adrenal protein was significantly increased six hours after ACTH administration. Grower & Bransome (89) have since found a stimulation of leucine incorporation into adrenocortical protein *in vivo,* two hours after ACTH, principally into cytoplasmic supernatant protein fractions.

In assessing the role of protein synthesis as a mediator of the steroidogenic effect of ACTH, the rapidity of a response of increase in a specific protein is of paramount importance. Since Farese has not yet characterized "steroidogenin" he does not know whether that (presumed) protein is synthesized or activated as a result of ACTH administration, nor has he been able to determine whether it increases before corticosteroid production increases.

Experiments measuring the effect of ACTH *in vitro* on incorporation of labeled amino acids into protein, including a number of experiments performed by the reviewer, have yielded conflicting results. Reddy & Streeto (82) have provided some explanation for the findings of different investigators of ACTH stimulation, inhibition, or lack of effect. They have shown that the effects of ACTH on amino acid radioactivity of protein *in vitro* are extremely dependent upon whether precursor pools had been equilibrated, upon the presence of glucose, upon whether the labeled amino acid was given *in vivo* (ACTH *in vitro* then stimulated incorporation into protein), and upon the specific radioactivity of aminoacyl tRNA. They have concluded that the incorporation of labeled amino acid into protein cannot be considered indicative of protein synthesis unless specific activity of aminoacyl tRNA remains unchanged and the kinetics of amino acid incorporation in control and hormone-stimulated situations are identical. Such assumptions cannot be made; indeed, there is some evidence (88) that ACTH does affect the rate of equilibration of exogenous amino acids with precursor pools. Although Targovnik et al. (90) have reported that continuous protein synthesis is necessary for stimulation of steroid biosynthesis by ACTH in cultured adrenocortical tumor cells, Kowal (91) has reported that ACTH has no effect on amino acid incorporation into protein. The problems in examining protein synthesis within the context of rapid hormonal effects are obviously difficult. It appears now that interested investigators have no choice but to try to examine turnover and net quantitative changes of specific proteins, a laborious task at our present level of technology.

Ferguson's reports (54, 92) that puromycin prevented the steroidogenic effect of ACTH *in vitro* gave voice to the thesis that protein synthesis was necessary for ACTH action. He also found that the antibiotic prevented the steroidogenic response of rat adrenals *in vitro* to cyclic 3'5'-AMP but not to addition of an NADPH-generating system. Basal steroid production was unaffected by puromycin. Although Kittinger (93) later reported that the basal steroid production was diminished, the interpretation of his experiments may be questioned since they involved prolonged exposure to puromycin *in vitro*. Ferguson (94) recently has shown similar dose-response relationships for puromycin effects on amino acid incorporation into protein and inhibition of the effect of ACTH on steroids. Both he and his associates (94) and Farese (95) have shown that chloramphenicol and cycloheximide have *in vitro* actions similar to puromycin. The argument that a consistent correlation of inhibition of amino acid incorporation into protein with ACTH effect on steroid production indicates causation is somewhat weakened by the recent report of Halkerston et al. (96) that theophylline inhibits amino acid incorporation into adrenal protein *in vitro* without preventing the effect of ACTH on steroidogenesis.

Garren et al. (97) found that *in vivo* administration of puromycin and cycloheximide prevented the rapid action of ACTH on steroidogenesis in acutely hypophysectomized rats, and reached the similar conclusion that a labile protein was involved in ACTH action. Preliminary experiments by Farese (98), however, suggest that "steroidohibin" and its inhibition of steroid biosynthesis diminish promptly after hypophysectomy. Thus, interpretation not only of the effects of inhibitors, but also of the appropriateness of using acutely hypophysectomized animals becomes questionable. *In vivo* experiments with intact animals might be even harder to evaluate. Fiala & Fiala (99) reported that administration of cycloheximide to intact rats led to increased net synthesis of adrenal RNA and of corticosteroid production, presumably as a result of general stressful effects of the antibiotic and resultant ACTH secretion. They also showed that cortisol interferes with some cycloheximide actions.

Ferguson's (54) observation that puromycin added thirty minutes after ACTH did not prevent the *in vitro* steroidogenic effect of the hormone provides some reassurance, but only if the effect of puromycin was really an effect on protein synthesis. A number of reports have demonstrated many effects not related to specific interference with protein synthesis: glycogenolysis (100); inhibition of glycogen synthesis (101); interference with the insulin effect on epinephrine-stimulated fatty acid release from adipose tissue (102); increased adrenal phosphorylase activation after ACTH (54); decreased catabolism of cyclic 3′5′-AMP by phosphodiesterase and consequently increased adrenal levels (103); production of liver mitochondrial swelling (104); potentiation of ACTH-induced insulin release (105); cell necrosis not seen with cycloheximide (e.g. 106); inhibition of MeLa cell ribosome synthesis, reversed by cycloheximide (107); and interference with the retention phase of learning, also reversed by cycloheximide (108).

A more profound misgiving about simple interpretations of the experimental use of inhibitors is brought forth by the elegant experiments of Kenney (109) concerning the effect of cycloheximide and puromycin upon the turnover of rat liver tyrosine transaminase. He has reported that both drugs not only inhibit the synthesis of the enzyme but also inhibit its turnover. The assumption that the rate of synthesis alone governs the amount of a protein, is simply not a safe one. Schimke (110) and recently Rechcigl & Heston (111) have indicated that regulation of the rate of enzyme degradation can be of considerable significance in mammalian cells. The finding of Rosen & Milholland (112) that low doses of cycloheximide or actinomycin lead to increased liver transaminase levels, and several other reports (113, 114) of paradoxical increases in protein synthesis after prior inhibition by antibiotics raise another possible explanation for the effect of puromycin and similarly acting agents. The synthesis of another polypeptide, which could either catalyze or be a reactant in the process leading to removal of the protein under examination, might be preferentially inhibited by antibiotics. That synthetic mechanisms involved in enzyme removal may actually play an important role in modulating the response of the enzyme levels to various hormones is suggested by certain similarities in the behavior of tyrosine transaminase (108) to adrenocortical steroidogenesis. Inhibitors of protein synthesis in each case have no effect on baseline levels but only block hormonal induction.

The probability that there are two important facets of regulation rather than one, suggests an alternative to the hypothesis of a special very labile protein. If a labile stimulating factor is indeed important for steroidogenesis, ACTH may act through its stabilization, that is, through inhibiting the synthesis of proteins involved in removal of the factor. That this could indeed be the case is suggested by the hypothesis of "steroidohibin" and "steroidogenin" formulated by Farese (29, 52, 53). It would be interesting to discover whether both of Farese's labile factors lost their influence after exposure of adrenal cells to antibiotics: one might predict that a previously inhibited steroidogenic enzyme activity would be stabilized and that further changes in either direction would be prevented by the inhibition of protein synthesis.

It certainly seems that what appeared to be simple questions—whether a hormone rapidly increased amino acid incorporation into target cell protein, and whether inhibitors of protein synthesis prevented other actions of the hormone—are difficult to relate to the problem at issue, the role of protein synthesis in the hormone action. The paragraphs above indicate that with the present relative ignorance of the biochemistry of adrenocortical cells, the results of experiments designed to answer these questions cannot be interpreted with much confidence. After the behavior of individual proteins (cf. Farese's "steroidogenin" and "steroidohibin") has been assessed, evaluation of these experiments should be less open to debate.

FURTHER STEROID TRANSFORMATIONS

The synthesis of adrenal corticosteroids from cholesterol is dependent upon side-chain cleavage of cholesterol (two hydroxylations and followed by a "desmolase" reaction, discussed above) in the mitochondrial fraction (Figure 1). The transformation of pregnenolone to progesterone takes place outside of the mitochondrial membrane, enzymatic activity residing in endoplasmic reticulum (small "microsomes" on ultracentrifugation).

Subsequent conversions are shown in Figure 2; the major pathways to cortisol and aldosterone are shown. As perusal of Dorfman & Ungar's excellent volume (1) will indicate, there are other sequences of transformation to glucocorticoids: cortisol or corticosterone (in the rat); and the mineralocorticoid aldosterone. The paths shown here are quantitatively the most significant for higher vertebrates.

There are also many other steroids which are products of adrenocortical metabolism, including the physiologically important androgen, testosterone, which will not be discussed at much length in this review. The reader is referred to Dorfman & Ungar (1) and to several other recent reviews: one by Ibayashi et al. (115) on testosterone synthesis, an article by Lipsett et al. (116) on the metabolic transformations of androgens, and a very thorough review of the adrenogenital syndrome by Baulieu et al. (117). Except in instances of adrenocortical pathology, the small amount of estrogens (6) synthesized by the adrenal cortex has little physiological effect; adrenal synthesis of estrogens will not receive further attention in this review.

Recent elegant studies by Tait and associates (118) of superfused adrenal glands have confirmed the conclusions of others that "capsular" (zona glomerulosa) cells mainly produce the mineralocorticoid aldosterone, its important precursor 18-hydroxycorticosterone, and a small amount of corticosterone; that decapsulated adrenals (zona fasciculata and reticularis) produce 18-hydroxydeoxycorticosterone and corticosterone in the rat, or cortisol and a small amount of corticosterone in other higher vertebrates. The subcellular locations of the biosynthetic steps are indicated in Figure 2, as is the fact that there are three types of enzymes involved in steroid biosynthesis.

(*a*) Hydroxylase systems: mixed-function oxidases [Mason (119)], which require NADPH and molecular oxygen for activity.

(*b*) Dehydrogenases, which remove protons and which may utilize either NADH or NADPH as cofactors. Dehydrogenases are also involved in metabolic reduction of steroids and catalyze protonation. It is not clear whether a single enzyme can be truly reversible under physiological conditions. As the discussion below will illustrate, different enzyme proteins employed in different mechanisms of catalysis may behave quite similarly in substrate-to-product conversion.

(*c*) Isomerases, which catalyze the migration of the double bond. Only one such enzyme is involved in adrenal steroid biosynthesis and will be discussed below.

Steroid hydroxylases.—Most of the reactions in steroid biosynthesis (Figures 1 and 2) are hydroxylations. Considerable effort in the past several years has been expended in attempts to reconstitute the enzyme systems. Despite the fact that the hydroxylases exist in particulate form, and despite the fact that they are multiple-enzyme systems, considerable progress has been made in defining their composition. The tentative scheme shown in Figure 3 summarizes data from investigations of C11β- and 18-hydroxylations by adrenocortical mitochondria [Omura et al. (120), Nakamura et al. (121), Kimura & Suzuki (122), Kimura (123, 124), Cammer et al. (125), Harding et al. (126), Purvis et al. (127), Cooper et al. 128, 129)]; of microsomal C21-hydroxylations [Cooper et al. (130)]; and of cholesterol side-chain cleavage (see above).

The enzyme systems appear to consist of an oxidase which catalyzes the transfer of molecular oxygen—not yet characterized for any of these enzymatic activities—and a "reversed" electron transport chain which transports the proton for hydroxylation from NADPH. The upper part of Figure 3 represents this sequence: a flavoprotein (Fp) also called "adrenodoxin reductase" which functions as an NADPH reductase; a nonheme iron protein (Fe^{++}/$^{+++}$ protein) also called adrenodoxin (122–124); cytochrome P-450 which is probably in closest proximity to the oxidase. The lower part of Figure 3 represents a shorthand version of the "classical" electron transport chain and transhydrogenation from NADH (DPNH). The transhydrogenase step, NADH reductase (Fp'), coenzyme Q, and cytochrome B, all represent acceptor sites for protons from the oxidation of Krebs-cycle intermediates. A recent article by Chance et al. (131) is an excellent reference for a more extensive discussion of the classical mitochondrial electron transfer chain.

Although the transfer of electrons from the classical electron chain cannot be accurately located from present data, the work of Guerra et al. (132) and Harding & Nelson (126, 133) strongly suggests involvement of a transhydrogenase system. Krebs-cycle intermediates may however have other links with the P-450 chain. Cammer et al. (125, 134) and Purvis et al. (127) have shown that with succinate as substrate, adrenocortical mitochondria seem to be capable of utilizing energy generated by the classical chain. NAD (DPN) is reduced in an energy-requiring reversal of electron flow which supports reduction of the P-450 chain. Since they demonstrated a competition of this system with oxidative phosphorylation, Cammer & Estabrook (134) have also suggested that adrenocortical mitochondria may be adapted for the utilization of nonphosphorylated high-energy intermediates such as succinate, rather than ATP.

Since the same basic components appear to be present in all the adrenocortical hydroxylases so far examined, the question of the locus of specificity in the hydroxylase arises. Findings by Wilson et al. (135) that inhibition of 11β-hydroxylation in human adrenal mitochondria by methopyrapone (SU-4885) can be monitored by changes in the P-450 absorption spectrum suggest that there may be different cytochromes for each hydroxylation system. Burstein's (136) finding of a higher concentration of P-450 in adrenal microsomes from guinea pigs with greater ability to hydroxylate cortisol at C2α and C6β than in those from animals with low ability is also compatible with cytochrome specificity. There are several reports [Imai & Sato (137), Sladek & Mannering (138] suggesting that P-450 has multiple forms, and there is a great deal of precedent for genetic differences in cytochromes (139). The presumption of oxidase specificity is based upon the substrate specificity for different steroid oxygenations and the knowledge that congenital deficiencies (117) of all the human adrenocortical hydroxylation systems (except cholesterol side-chain cleavage which one might expect to be lethal) have been observed. One might wonder whether missing cytochromes might not be responsible for some of these syndromes.

The implications of this new information on the nature of hydroxylase systems for consideration of NADPH as a rate-limiting factor in steroid biosynthesis are discussed elsewhere in this review. It is still too early, especially since the specificity of hydroxylase components has not yet been adequately addressed, to correlate the achievement summarized in this section with the physiological control of steroid biosynthesis. The recent progress has, however, rekindled interest in a long-standing mystery: what function does ascorbic acid have in the adrenal cortex?

Ascorbic acid.—Despite the early prominence of ascorbic acid in the bioassay of ACTH [Sayers et al. (140)], the question of the function of this vitamin in the adrenal cortex has not been answered. The argument (141, 142) of whether ascorbic acid has any meaningful relationship to steroid biosynthesis has been renewed in recent years.

Cooper & Rosenthal (143) reported that ascorbic acid antagonized the stimulation of C21-hydroxylation in adrenal microsomes by norepinephrine, and suggested that a shift from adrenocortical cells might favor steroid biosynthesis *in vivo*. Stollar et al. (144) found that ascorbate added to adrenocortical tumor cell culture medium inhibited steroid production. Kitabchi (145) has also reported an inhibition of steroid C21-hydroxylase in beef adrenal microsomes associated with lipid peroxidation, and an inhibition of beef adrenal mitochondrial 11β-hydroxylase activity which is not associated with lipid peroxidation. He too theorized that ascorbic acid inhibited hydroxylase systems and that by stimulating its discharge, ACTH reversed the inhibition and allowed increased steroid biosynthesis.

On the other hand, Sweat & Bryson (146) found that ascorbic acid prevented the inhibition of 11β-hydroxylation by adrenochrome, which suggested that it might support steroid biosynthesis.

Harding et al. (126) have extended the observation of Harding & Nelson (147) that ascorbic acid could support steroid 11β-hydroxylation *in vitro*. They have demonstrated that ascorbic acid is capable of providing reducing equivalents to the steroid oxygenase system, and conclude that an ascorbate-supported reversal of electron flow, coupled to steroid hydroxylation, exists in adrenocortical mitochondria. Considering the rapid discharge of adrenal ascorbic acid in response to ACTH, there is a possibility that ACTH may exert its rapid effects on steroid biosynthesis through making ascorbic acid available to the mitochondrial electron transport chains. Thus ascorbic acid might enhance the stimulation of steroid biosynthesis by ACTH. It seems obvious that the continuing disagreement is in large part a product of our not knowing what *in vitro* systems and what experimental conditions are germane to *in vivo* adrenocortical cell physiology—a situation very much like that which pertains to the relationship of protein synthesis and the effect of ACTH on steroidogenesis.

CONVERSION OF PREGNENOLONE TO PROGESTERONE

The conversion of Δ^5-3β-hydroxysteroids to Δ^4-3-ketosteroids, first demonstrated in mammalian tissues by Samuels et al. (148), is important in the biosynthesis not only of adrenal corticosteroids but of the other biologically active ovarian and testicular steroids, progesterone, estradiol-17β, and testosterone. Two distinct enzymes are involved (6) : 3β-ol-dehydrogenase and Δ^5-3-ketosteroid isomerase. Products of the first enzymatic activity serve as substrates for the second isomerase step. (See Figure 2.) Both are found in the small particle of "microsomal" fraction prepared from adrenocortical endoplasmic reticulum. The principal substrate in the adrenal is Δ^5-pregnenolone released from mitochondria. Cheatum et al. have concluded that there is one distinct dehydrogenase site and one distinct isomerase site, each utilizing C19 and C21 substrates in both bovine ovary (149) and bovine adrenal cortex (150), although Ewald et al. (151, 152) had concluded that there were two isomerases in rat adrenals after observing differences in activity ratios with C19- and C21-isomerase substrates. Inasmuch as the proponents of either proposition were not able to obtain soluble enzyme preparations and therefore were not able to purify their extracts, the argument remains unsettled. Neither ACTH nor cyclic 3'5'-AMP has been shown to stimulate the conversion of pregnenolone to progesterone *in vitro*.

3β-ol-Dehydrogenase.—Current evidence supports the view that enzymatic hydroxylations of adrenal steroids are supported by NADPH, and recent reports also suggest transhydrogenation and reverse electron flow along a coenzymatic chain containing the cytochrome P-450 (see Figure 3 and elsewhere in this review). These hydroxylations are both mitochondrial and extramitochondrial. Both 3β-ol-dehydrogenase and isomerase activity, however, located in endoplasmic particles as are 17α- and 21-hydroxylase activities, appear to utilize NADH preferentially.

Inactivation of 3β-ol-dehydrogenase.—In 1961, Bongiovanni (153) reported that infants born with a rare form of congenital adrenal hyperplasia excreted large amounts of 3β-hydroxysteroidal androgens. Males had incomplete masculine development: severe hypospadias and shortening of the urogenital distance. Females were virilized: with clitoral hypertrophy and labial fusion. A deficiency in 3β-ol-dehydrogenase in the Leydig cells of an infant with this disorder led workers in Bongiovanni's laboratory to propose that a genetic deficiency in the enzyme was responsible for the adrenocortical hyperplasia, genital malformation, and abnormal steroid synthesis. A synthetic steroid, 2α-cyano-4,4,17α-trimethylandrost-5-en-17β-ol-3-one (cyanoketone), which had been shown to produce adrenal hypoplasia in rats through blocking glucocorticoids synthesis (154) was then employed by Goldman et al. (155) to produce a similar syndrome in rats. What was perhaps the most interesting finding in their study was that a single intramuscular injection of inhibitor, on either the thirteenth or fourteenth day of gestation when no fetal 3β-ol-dehydrogenase activity was detectable, produced the syndrome. The adrenocortical hyperplasia and clitoral hypertrophy could be prevented by the administration of corticosterone (156). The finding of a depot effect after intramuscular injection of cyanoketone (157) suggests that the inhibitor may have been present for more than a day, but the discrete effects produced on any one day suggest that the syndrome was not produced by free inhibitor beyond day fifteen of gestation. It is possible that the inhibitor may become tightly attached to inactive enzyme precursor. Binding of the inhibitor to the adult adrenal enzyme is rapid, persistent (158, 159) and appears to be noncompetitive for both *Pseudomonas testosteroni* (160, 161) and mammalian enzymes (161 and 163).

The possibility that the inhibitor or an inhibitor-enzyme protein complex may interfere with the synthesis of new enzyme is raised by continued deficiency in corticosterone production by both fetal and adult rat adrenals in the face of ACTH-induced hyperplasia of the cortex. If this latter mechanism of cyanoketone effect is shown in further experiments to account for some of the inhibition of steroid-3β-ol-dehydrogenase activity, a change in configuration of the enzyme protein effected by the tightly bound steroid would have to be considered responsible for repression of either translation or transcription of templates for the synthesis of new enzyme. The implications of such a finding would include the likelihood that more rapidly dissociating natural complexes of steroid and enzyme also play a role in regulating synthesis of enzymes involved in steroid biosynthesis.

Δ^5-3-Ketosteroid isomerase—The mechanism of action of Δ^5-3-ketosteroid isomerase ("isomerase" in Figure 2) was also initially investigated with an enzyme preparation from Pseudomonas testosteroni by Talalay and associates (164). Because there was no incorporation of isotope into the Δ^4-3-ketone product (cf. progesterone) (when the reaction took place in deuterium-labeled water), they concluded that the isomerization (Δ^5 to Δ^4) proceeded through a direct transfer of a hydrogen atom from C4 to C6 of the steroid nucleus. Further experiments with C4 and C6 deuterated Δ^5-3-ketosteroids by Malhotra & Ringold (165) suggested that loss of the 4β proton was rate limiting for the isomerization step.

Werbin & Chaikoff (166), however, found that when guinea pigs were fed a mixture of cholesterol-4-^{14}C and cholesterol-4β-(^{3}H), urinary cortisol had a reduced (^{3}H):(^{14}C) ratio, indicating loss of 4β-(^{3}H). Evidence that (^{3}H) was lost at the isomerase step came in in vitro experiments in which 4β-(^{3}H) was retained in pregnenolone but lost in progesterone. Oleinick & Koritz (167) have recently added proof to this indication that mammalian adrenal isomerase catalysis is via a mechanism different from that reported for the P. testosteroni enzyme. When androst-5-ene-3,17-dione was isomerized in a D_2O medium by a rat adrenal microsomal fraction, incorporation of isotope into the C6β position of the steroid nucleus occurred. Because Malhotra & Ringold (165) showed that protonation of the $\Delta^{3,5}$-dienol took place almost completely at C6β, the occurrence of deuterium at C4 suggested that an enolate anion was the intermediate. In suggesting a mechanism for the mammalian isomerase, Oleinick & Koritz (167) pointed out that although protonation of C6 was not direct, the rate-limiting step might be the same as that for bacterial enzyme: removal of the C4β proton. Their elegant exposition of the difference between a bacterial and a mammalian enzyme provides a lesson to be remembered in considering not only 3β-ol-dehydrogenase activity, but other enzymes as well. Mechanisms of enzyme activity may be quite different, even though substrate specificity and conversion rates may be similar. Detailed models drawn from experiments with bacterial enzymes should therefore not be tacitly assumed for mammalian enzymes.

The coenzyme requirements of the isomerase step are not yet clear. Although in vitro stimulation of isomerase activity in microsomal preparations from rat, mouse, and guinea pig adrenals by NAD$^+$ and NADH has also been reported by Oleinick & Koritz (168), only a small effect on beef adrenal cortex enzyme was observed. It should be evident from the discussion of steroid hydroxylations in this review that the effects of exogenous pyridine nucleotides upon subcellular fractions may not be wholly indicative of the mechanisms for proton transfer *in vivo*.

Specificity of stimulatory or inhibitory effects on these two enzymatic activities has not, to my knowledge, been reported. The lack of any preparation in which one of these enzymes is free from the other may be part of the problem. That specificity may exist is suggested by the reports of Steinetz et al. (169), Kowal et al. (170), and Villee (171) that progesterone exerts a product inhibition on steroid biosynthesis steps prior to progesterone formation.

SYNTHESIS OF GLUCOCORTICOIDS FROM PROGESTERONE

The major pathway for the synthesis of glucocorticoids through progesterone (1, 6) is shown in Figure 2. In all vertebrates some progesterone is hydroxylated at C21 to form 11-deoxycorticosterone (DOC); in most species, except rodents, birds, and reptiles (which lack much 17α-hydroxylation activity), this is a minor reaction. Most progesterone undergoes (microsomal) 17α-hydroxylation first, then 21-hydroxylation to 11-deoxycortisol (compound S of Reichstein), and finally 11β-hydroxylation to cortisol. The major glucocorticoid of rats and some other animals, corticosterone, is derived from 11β-hydroxylation of DOC. Since the report in 1959 of 17α-hydroxypregnenolone in canine adrenal vein blood by Carstensen et al. (172), there have been a number of investigations (reviewed in references 1, 6) showing the existence of a second pathway to cortisol from 17α-hydroxypregnenolone. Mulrow et al. (173) have suggested that more than a third of human adrenal cortisol may be synthesized by this route.

17α- and 21-hydroxylation.—C17-hydroxylation is presumed to share the properties of other C21-hydroxylation which has been relatively well studied, but not much attention has been paid to it in the last several years. The proposal of Berliner et al. (174) that C17-hydroxylation occurred exclusively in pericapillary reticuloendothelial cells has received little critical examination. Only very recently has any physiological specificity of this enzyme been proposed. Fevold (175, 176) found increased 17α-hydroxylase activity in rabbits after chronic ACTH administration, which favored pregnenolone as a substrate rather than progesterone. He proposed that ACTH increased cortisol synthesis by the alternate pathway mentioned above. It is thus difficult to place in perspective the observation of Pankov (177) that NADH in adrenal homogenates stimulated corticoid production but proportionately decreased 17α-hydroxylation.

C21-hydroxylation has not yet had such specificity proposed for it, although it has been extensively studied. A genetic block in its production is, however, the most common explanation for virilizing congenital adrenocortical hyperplasia (117).

Biglieri et al. (178) recently reported the first case of 17α-hydroxylation deficiency in a woman who also had a defect in aldosterone biosynthesis. Goldsmith et al. (179) have since reported another female patient with

increased adrenal and ovarian progesterone synthesis and decreased cortisol, estrogen, and testosterone production as the result of a single 17α-hy-
droxylation block.

11β-Hydroxylation.—C11-hydroxylation is also discussed above (re hydroxylases). Biochemical studies by Griffiths et al. (180) concerning functional zonation of the human adrenal cortex after four days of ACTH administration suggested that the principal effects upon steroid biosynthesis
were in clear cells at the border of the zona fasciculata and zona reticularis, and that 11β-hydroxylase activity in these cells was increased. A more
recent report by Griffiths & Glick (181) suggests that ACTH also stimulates 11β-hydroxylase in the fasciculoreticular border of the rat adrenal
cortex. Kowal (91, 182), using a monolayer culture of mouse adrenocortical tumor cells, has reported that not only ACTH, but cyclic 3'5'-AMP
and ATP stimulated a progressive increase in 11β-hydroxylation after
twelve to seventy-two hours. Vermeulen et al. (183), however, studying
steroid production rates in man, have not found that ACTH increases 11β-
hydroxylase efficiency.

Other effects on 11β-hydroxylase have been described. Peron & Mc-
Carthy (184, 36) have described *in vitro* proof of substrate specificity. They
also found that Ca^{++} had a stimulatory effect on C11-hydroxylation that was
not related to the swelling of rat adrenal mitochondria: progesterone C11β-
hydroxylation occurred at a greater rate with Ca^{++} present than if DOC
was absent. If DOC was present, the formation of 11β-hydroxyprogesterone
was inhibited at all Ca^{++} concentrations; only at high Ca^{++} levels did progesterone compete with DOC. Spatz & Hofmann (185) have shown in
studies with intact guinea pig adrenal mitochondria that NADPH did not
stimulate 11β-hydroxylation but did stimulate cholesterol side-chain cleavage, C21-hydroxylation, and reduction of cortisol. Instead an endogenous
cofactor, probably a Krebs-cycle intermediate, was involved. Also Williamson & O'Donnell (186) have recently reported that dicoumarol inhibits
C11-hydroxylation while stimulating NADPH oxidation.

The actions of exogenous substances on 11β-hydroxylation include a
somewhat unique stimulatory effect of ouabain, an 11α-hydroxyl cardiac
glucoside, shown recently by Tsao & King (187).

Since the introduction of (CIBA) SU-4885 or methopyropone
(2-methyl-1,2-bis(3-pyridyl)-1-propanone) as an inhibitor of steroid C11β-
hydroxylation, the drug has been found to be an inhibitor of C18- and
C19-hydroxylations also. It has been employed in a clinical test (188) of
"pituitary-adrenal reserve" based on adrenocortical stimulation by increased endogenous ACTH resulting from depressed production of cortisol.
Dominguez & Samuels (189) showed that the inhibition of 11β-hydroxy-
lase by methopyrapone was competitive. Williamson & O'Donnell (190)
have found that the drug's affinity for the enzyme was 56 times that of
DOC in beef adrenal mitochondrial extracts, and that at low levels of inhibitor, NADPH oxidation was increased. Recent evidence [Sanzari &

Peron (191), Wilson et al. (135)] of methopyrapone effect on cytochrome P-450 strengthens Williamson & O'Donnell's suggestion that the inhibitor is itself reduced to an inactive compound. Estrogens diminish the affinity of the enzyme for inhibitor.

BIOSYNTHESIS OF ALDOSTERONE

The synthesis of the physiologic mineralocorticoid by the zona glomerulosa of the adrenal cortex and its physiologic control have received considerable attention in the past few years. Excellent recent reviews by Davis (192), Pasqualini (193), and Bartter et al. (194) will take the reader beyond the following brief summary.

Figure 2 indicates that the principal pathway of aldosterone synthesis is through 18-hydroxycorticosterone. Nicolis & Ulick (195) have recently shown that the more efficient conversion of corticosterone *in vitro* is attributable to the fact that 18-hydroxyl and 20-ketone groups of 18-hydroxycorticosterone tend to form a cyclic hemiketal which tends to resist oxidation. Most recent reports have supported the importance of the 18-hydroxylation of corticosterone, which along with "18-ol-dehydrogenase" is located in the mitochondrial fraction [Raman et al. (196), Psychoyos et al. (197)].

Dorfman and his associates (196, 198) have shown that calcium stimulates 18-hydroxylation *in vitro,* and may be important *in vivo* as well; the suppression of aldosterone biosynthesis by heparin can probably be explained by its making calcium unavailable. They found that high sodium levels *in vitro* inhibited aldosterone synthesis (198). Current evidence from *in vivo* experiments suggests, however, that although low sodium levels may increase aldosterone biosynthesis [Davis et al. (199), Vecsei et al. (200), Blair-West et al. (201), Marusic & Mulrow (202)], high sodium levels have no immediate inhibitory effect [Blair-West et al. (201)] on steroid biosynthesis. The difficulty of correlating ingenious experimental use of cell-free systems with physiology is again apparent.

Greengard and associates (197, 203, 204) have made a compelling summary of the evidence that 18-hydroxylation of corticosterone is very much like the other mitochondrial steroid hydroxylation at C11. It seems to involve a reduction of endogenous NADP which is best supported by oxidation of Krebs-cycle intermediates and reverse electron flow to a cytochrome-P-450 chain. They have in addition suggested that the enzyme fumarase is a stimulatory supernatant (cell sap) factor, implying that conversion to malate is important for NADP reduction. The physiologic relevance of this *in vitro* phenomenon also remains to be seen. Raman et al. (196) have reported that methopyrapone (SU 4885, CIBA), best known as an 11β-hydroxylase inhibitor, and 3-(1,2,3,4-tetrahydro-1-oxo-2-napthyl) pyridine (SU 9055, CIBA), an inhibitor of 17α-hydroxylation, and 18-hydroxycorticosterone itself, inhibit 18-hydroxylation of corticosterone. There is simply not enough information available to reach any conclusion as to whether 18-hydroxylase is subject to feedback inhibition *in vivo*. Inborn errors involving both enzymes have been described. Salt-losing syndromes without virilization have been attributable to 18-hydroxylase deficiency [Visser & Cost (205), Degenhart et al. (206)] and to deficiency in dehydrogenation of 18-hydroxycorticosterone [Ulick et al. (207)].

Convincing evidence of another pathway of aldosterone biosynthesis, albeit a minor one, has been presented by Fazekas and associates (208–210). They found that rabbit adrenal homogenates carried out not only the expected *in vitro* transformation of progesterone to 18-hydroxycorticosterone and aldosterone but also to the 11-ketosteroids, 18-hydroxy-11-dehydrocorticosterone and 11-dehydroaldosterone. The formation of the 11-keto-18-hydroxysteroid had been described by others [e.g., Raman et al. (196)] but the proof that 11-dehydrocorticosterone can be hydroxylated at C18 and subsequently converted to aldosterone had not been presented.

Regulation of aldosterone biosynthesis.—The physiology of alterations in aldosterone biosynthesis has involved a great deal of work and no small amount of contention over the past few years. The interpretation of data derived from complicated experimental designs has as usual been the principal source of difficulty. The reviews cited at the beginning of this section (192–194) will provide the reader with a representative variation in interpretations. It seems sufficient in this chapter to summarize briefly a few recent findings.

The production of aldosterone by adrenals *in vitro* and *in vivo* is stimulated by salt depletion, a high concentration of potassium ions, angiotensin II, and ACTH.

The main influence of salt depletion appears not to be related to hyponatremia. Newsome & Bartter (211) have shown that volume changes correlate much better than sodium concentration with changes in aldosterone production *in vivo*. As indicated above, direct effects of decreases in sodium concentration upon steroid enzymology [Vecsei et al. (200), Marusic & Mulrow (202)] are hard to evaluate. Since the zona glomerulosa enlarges within a few days [e.g., Hartcroft & Eisenstein (212)], increases in net synthesis of enzyme proteins may occur, rather than enzyme activation. The specific stimulation of aldosterone biosynthesis by angiotensin II and potassium has been demonstrated *in vivo* [e.g., Cannon et al. (214)]. Although the lack of changes in glucocorticoid production suggests effects on C18-hydroxylation or dehydrogenation, Müller (213) has shown that substrate availability rather than enzyme activity is increased. The influence of angiotensin II and potassium appears to be exerted on cholesterol side-chain cleavage, the specificity residing in the cells of the zona glomerulosa.

Administration of angiotensin II, like sodium depletion, is capable of inducing hyperplasia of the zona glomerulosa and enlargement of its cells [Lamberg et al. (215)] but has been shown to have little effect on steroid synthesis in sodium-loaded animals [Spät & Sturcz (216), Davis et al. (217)]. Potentiation of the effects of angiotensin II and ACTH on aldosterone production by salt depletion, described by many investigators, is probably attributable to increased plasma renin levels. Ganong et al. (218), after noting that renin levels were increased during salt depletion, found that injections of renin for five days brought about a greater aldosterone output when dogs were subsequently infused with ACTH or angiotensin II. Renin did not increase 17-hydroxycorticosteroid levels, or cause salt depletion by itself. There is still no coherent explanation for the limitation of aldosterone response to ACTH administration since an abrupt decrease in response occurs after one day of treatment with ACTH.

There are several bits of evidence which suggest that the current list of aldosterone stimuli may be incomplete. Davis et al. (219) recently described a new syndrome in man of bilateral hyperplasia of the zona glomerulosa, and increased aldosterone secretion which was insensitive to sodium load. Renin levels were low and cortisol production was normal, which makes both angiotensin II and ACTH unlikely stimuli. Ganong et al. (220) have reported that aldosterone production in hypophysectomized dogs does not respond normally to angiotensin II. Palmore & Mulrow (221) have also concluded that a pituitary factor other than ACTH is responsible for increased aldosterone synthesis in sodium-depleted rats.

OTHER INFLUENCES ON CORTICOSTEROID BIOSYNTHESIS

Less immediate, but nonetheless physiologically important effects on adrenocortical cell physiology and steroid production have been proposed. Included are direct negative effects of the corticosteroid endproduct, the influence of the status of adrenocortical growth, and the various effects of gonadal hormones. Despite the considerable effects of exogenous thyroid on the adrenal cortex [e.g. Burstein & Fajer (222)] and despite the concern of older literature (223) with the effects of gonadotropins and growth hormone on adrenocortical function, a lack of recent progress excludes them from the present review.

Endproduct Inhibition of Corticosteroid Synthesis

The possibility that the presence of pregnenolone inhibits its further synthesis in adrenocortical mitochondria is discussed above. A number of reports also suggest that one of the loci of glucocorticoid feedback inhibition of the pituitary-adrenal axis is the adrenal cortex itself. It is not yet clear whether exogenous corticoids really interfere [Birmingham & Kurlents (224), Lucius et al. (225), Black et al. (226)], or do not interfere [Peron et al. (227)] with adrenal steroid biosynthesis under physiological circumstances. A recent report by Vinson (228) demonstrates that corticosterone produced *in vitro* is not just a reflection of rate of synthesis but also reflects extensive metabolism of corticosterone by the adrenal tissue. He found that progesterone hydroxylation was unaffected by exogenous corticosterone and that when he took metabolism into account, there was no inhibition of corticosteroid production.

An alternate possibility, that glucocorticoids may directly diminish adrenocortical sensitivity to ACTH, has been suggested by Bohus (229) who found that a cortisone-induced suppression of the adrenals of rats given two units of ACTH per 100 g body weight per day was broken through when four units were given. In other (230 to 232) reports which demonstrated a decreased response to ACTH, previous adrenocortical deprivation of endogenous ACTH was not properly taken into account. His thesis should be interpreted with caution, however, for the effects of 2.5 mg of cortisone, a foreign steroid, upon the rat may be pharmacologic and have no relevance to physiologic mechanisms.

Recently Ferguson et al. (233) found that 0.03 mM corticosterone inhibited *in vitro* incorporation of precursors into rat adrenal protein and RNA fractions. They have suggested that corticosterone may repress the synthesis of rate-limiting enzymes involved in steroidogenesis, and that ACTH may act as a derepressor. Morrow et al. (234) have reported similar observations of inhibition of amino acid incorporation into adrenal protein *in vitro* by corticosterone. They also found that testosterone in rather high concentration ($6.9 \times 10^{-4} M$) was as effective as puromycin in inhibiting "protein synthesis", and like puromycin, blocked the stimulation of corticosterone synthesis by ACTH without affecting baseline steroid production. They suggested that androgens might interfere with the synthesis of an adrenal protein necessary for the effect of ACTH in a manner not dependent on glucocorticoid feedback. It seems difficult to know what to make of these latter studies: as indicated above, it is not yet clear whether corticosterone really exerts a feedback effect *in vivo;* that interpretation of *in vitro* amino acid incorporation is uncertain has also been noted in this review. In addition, Kitay et al. (235) have reported that low doses of testosterone given *in vivo* to male rats actually stimulated steroid production *in vitro*. Large amounts of either gonadal hormone inhibited adrenocortical steroid biosynthesis.

Aldosterone has not been suggested to inhibit its own synthesis. Indeed, Sturcz et al. (236) looked for and did not find such an *in vitro* effect on rat adrenal slices.

ADRENOCORTICAL GROWTH

This review has so far been concerned with the recent considerable advances of adrenal corticosteroid biosynthesis, its intracellular controls, and the loci of interaction with extracellular controls. It is quite evident however that tropic influences have other important effects which have received less attention: they act to maintain the number of cells and cellular contents so that the characteristic rapid responses of steroid biosynthesis to stimuli—ACTH, angiotensin II, etc.—may take place without rate limitation by inadequate amounts of steroidogenesis, enzyme proteins, or other cell constitutents. Because aldosterone production and the growth of the zona glomerulosa have so far been subjected to phenomenological observation and not much more, current information concerns the responses of adrenal cortex to ACTH, which for the most part involve the zona fasciculata and zona reticularis.

If endogenous ACTH is eliminated by hypophysectomy or by suppression of the pituitary adrenal axis with exogenous corticosteroid, the sensitivity of adrenocortical steroid biosynthesis to ACTH stimulation is diminished. A larger amount of ACTH and a longer period of exposure to ACTH effect are necessary to achieve a corticosteroid response equal to that obtained in normal animals [Ohsawa (237), Bransome (87)]. The additional time necessary for restoration of normal adrenocortical sensitivity to endogenous ACTH appears to be related to the extent of previous suppression [Graber et al. (238)]. What critical restoration takes place during this time is not known. Bransome's observation (87) that one or two successive injections of ACTH result in a supranormal increase in net protein and nucleic acid synthesis in suppressed adrenals, suggests that a growth response may be important. His additional finding (239, 240) of increased sensitivity of guinea pig adrenal cortisol production to ACTH during recovery from the toxic effects of actinomycin D suggests, as might be suspected, that the requirements for a sensitivity of steroid biosynthesis to ACTH are relatively specific.

Protein synthesis.—That certain classes of proteins may play a particular role in governing steroid biosynthesis is implicit in the postulation of labile proteins as mediators of ACTH action. A recent demonstration by Levine et al. (241) that there is a distinction between steroid synthesis and steroid release in the adrenals of newborn rats; the apparent differences (discussed above) in the response of steroidogenic enzymes to ACTH; and the change of adrenal 17-ketosteroid excretion pattern in adolescence recently noted by Eberlein et al. (242) all provide evidence that there is a considerable differential in the response of adrenocortical protein synthesis. That ACTH promptly increases adrenal protein synthesis is indisputable [Farese (52), Bransome (87), Reddy & Streeto (82)], despite some paradoxical findings in experiments *in vitro*. That the synthesis of some proteins and not others is favored is suggested by the discovery of Grower & Bransome (89) of early effects on specific acrylamide gel-electrophoretic fractions of soluble protein. It is obvious that fractionation and identification of adrenocortical proteins needs much more attention before the role of protein synthesis either in the acute response of steroidogenesis to ACTH or in the readiness of the gland to respond can be properly assessed.

The question of how ACTH affects adrenal protein synthesis was first examined by Farese & Reddy (243) with adrenal cell fractions. Further work by Scriba & Reddy (244) and Scriba & Fries (245) has confirmed the initial discovery that a factor in the 105,000 × *g* supernatant was rate limiting for *in vitro* adrenal protein synthesis and was increased after ACTH administration, and has supported the hypothesis that the factor was aminoacyl transferase. Farese (246) found that after continued treatment with ACTH the protein synthetic activity of adrenal polysomes also was significantly increased.

RNA synthesis.—The latency of ACTH effect on polysomes, and the improbability that transcription of RNA templates for steroidogenic enzyme proteins plays an important part in rapid regulation in differentiated cells, suggest that RNA synthesis does not play an immediate role in ACTH action. The lack of interference with steroidogenesis by actinomycin [Ferguson and associates (54, 94, 247), Ney et al. (248), Farese (249)] except in bovine adrenal [Farese (249)] is additional evidence, but actinomycin has been found (Bransome 240) to have many side effects. As with puromycin, its administration may stablize a protein rather than inhibit its synthesis [e.g., Kenney (109), Thompson et al. (250)].

The stimulation of adrenal RNA synthesis by ACTH is unquestionable, although there have been problems with *in vitro* experimental design similar to those which have complicated protein synthesis [Farese & Schnure (251), Bransome (87)]. Farese & Schnure have shown an increase in RNA-polymerase after ACTH. Bransome & Chargaff (252) and Bransome (253, 254) have shown that there are rapid ACTH effects on labile RNAs in adrenocortical nuclei and cytoplasm which do not yet, unfortunately, have any known function (253).

Control of growth.—Bransome (255) recently demonstrated that one injection of ACTH stimulated the synthesis of rapidly labeled RNA and the net synthesis of guinea pig adrenal DNA, RNA, and protein. Gland weight was significantly increased within twenty-four hours. The sensitivity of adrenal growth response to ACTH was proportionately greater in dexamethasone-suppressed animals than normals. In both groups the adrenal growth response to a second injection of ACTH was, however, inhibited by effects of the first injection. Inhibition of radioactive precursor uptake by rapidly labeled RNAs was even more dramatic. This diminished sensitivity to ACTH of nucleic acid and protein synthesis, observed as steroidogenic response increased, could be overcome by further treatment with ACTH. The effect of ACTH upon adrenal growth is biphasic, stimulatory effects on net synthesis having less duration than the increased activity of regulatory mechanisms which inhibit RNA, DNA, and protein synthesis. During recovery from actinomycin toxicity, the regulatory mechanisms may be at low ebb, for the rate of protein and nucleic acid synthesis is increased [Bransome (239, 240)]. It would appear from these findings that adrenocortical growth is not only stimulated by ACTH but limited by it as well.

EFFECTS OF GONADAL HORMONES

The synthesis by the adrenal cortex of testosterone and steroids which may be peripherally converted to testosterone has been briefly referred to above. The adrenal undeniably contributes a significant amount of androgens in males as well as females.

Except for an *in vitro* study by Vinson & Jones (256) there had been no clear-cut demonstration of estrogen synthesis by other than pathological adrenocortical tissue [see Goldzieher (257)] until a recent report by Kase & Cohn (258) of a significant estrogen production in an ovariectomized woman. There is considerable evidence, on the other hand, that gonadal hormones have an important influence on adrenocortical function. Two recent reviews thoroughly summarize differences between sexes in adrenocortical morphology [Parkes & Deanesly (259)] and function [Kitay (261)]. Estrogens tend to increase plasma corticosteroid levels, adrenal size, the reactivity of adrenal steroid production to ACTH, and the synthesis of ACTH by the pituitary. In the last several years it has become quite apparent that the mechanisms of gonadal hormone influence on the adrenal cortex are numerous and that no unitary hypothesis is yet plausible. Progress in understanding the effects of gonadal hormones has nonetheless been significant, at least re estrogens.

ACTH.—Richard (262) has recently shown that extremely small amounts of estrogen may directly stimulate ACTH synthesis through influences on the hypothalamus and anterior pituitary, bolstering the evidence from Kitay (260, 261), McCann and associates (263, 264), and Telegdy et al. (265) of an effect on adrenocortical stimulation. The physiological importance of an effect on ACTH is not clear, however, because there are also direct effects on steroid synthesis and upon the peripheral metabolism and binding of glucocorticoids.

Corticosteroid-binding globulin.—Glucocorticoids are bound in the plasma by an α-globulin fraction, corticosteroid-binding globulin (CBG), which increases after estrogen administration or during pregnancy. For thorough reviews, see Daughaday (266), Sandberg (267), and Seal & Doe (268). Increased plasma cortisol of corticosterone measurements are found under these circumstances, but protein-bound glucocorticoid is essentially inactive. Recently Gala & Westphal (269) reviewed the fluctuations of CBG occurring with changes in the endocrine state of the rat. They pointed out that estrogen enhancement of CBG activity is not observed in hypophysectomized animals and suggested that the increase of CBG after estrogen treatment or adrenalectomy and the decrease of CBG with glucocorticoid administration are all mediated through the thyrotropin-thyroid system. Depression of CBG activity by testosterone seemed to involve another mechanism.

Steroid biosynthesis.—In 1963 Kitay (260) demonstrated that large doses of estrogen inhibited steroid secretion, whereas smaller doses were stimulatory. At the same time, Mestman & Nelson (270) reported that patients receiving estrogen had a steroidogenic diminished response to methopyropone (an inhibitor of 11β-hydroxylation) but retained their sensitivity to ACTH. Vermeulen et al. (183) have shown that estrogens increase the resistance of 11β-hydroxylase enzyme to inhibition by the drug and that the smaller rise in 11-deoxycortisol (Compound S) secretion is normal if the lesser degree of inhibition is taken into account. Nelson and associates (271) found that doses of estrogen high enough to inhibit rat adrenal corticosterone synthesis actually increase 11β-hydroxylase activity and they have demonstrated a stimulation of succinate (but not malate)-supported 11β-hydroxylation in adrenal homogenates after estrogen administration *in vivo* or *in vitro*. They have suggested that estrogens inhibit the classical respiratory chain and divert electron flow to the P-450 chain (see Figure 3 and the Steroid hydroxylases section above).

Steroid metabolism.—Kitay (261) has recently reviewed the small amount of information concerning the effect of estrogens on peripheral corticosteroid metabolism. He and his associates (272, 273) have presented convincing evidence for estrogen-stimulated corticosterone metabolism in rat adrenal cortex, of a magnitude compatible with physiological significance. ACTH, or gonadectomy of either sex decreased adrenal 5α-reductase activity and the ratio of an inactive corticosterone metabolite, 3β,5-allotetrahydrocorticosterone, to corticosterone. Estrogen or testosterone increased reductase activity (and subsequent 3β-ol-dehydrogenase action on 5-allo-dihydrocorticosterone) without affecting cholesterol side-chain cleavage or total corticoid production. Kitay has postulated that this intra-adrenal transformation of glucocorticoid to an inactive metabolite may be an important means of controlling steroid output. This discovery of a new regulatory mechanism makes the effects of estrogens on adrenal cortex seem a bit more coherent: increased sensitivity of corticosteroid production to ACTH and increased 11β-hydroxylase efficiency are offset by increased inactivation of glucocorticoids through binding to CBG and reduction of ring A by adrenal and peripheral tissues.

For more general considerations of corticoid metabolism which limitations of space exclude from this chapter several recent reviews are recommended: Dorfman & Ungar (1), Rosenfeld et al. (274), Luetscher et al. (275), Berstein et al. (276), and Dollefeld & Breuer (277).

LITERATURE CITED

1. Dorfman, R. I., Ungar, F. *The Metabolism of Steroid Hormones* (Academic Press, New York, 716 pp., 1965)
2. Hilf, R. The mechanism of action of ACTH. *New Engl. J. Med.,* **273,** 798–811 (1965)
3. *The Adrenal Cortex* (Eisenstein, A. B., Ed., Little-Brown, Boston, 685 pp., 1967)
4. *Functions of the Adrenal Cortex* (McKerns, K., Ed., Appleton-Century-Crofts, New York, 1967) (In press)
5. *The Human Adrenal Cortex.* CIBA Foundation Study Group. No. 27 (Little-Brown, Boston, 350 pp., 1967)
6. Samuels, L. T., Uchikawa, T. Biosynthesis of adrenal steroids. In *The Adrenal Cortex* (See Ref. 3), 61–102
7. Hechter, O., Solomon, M. M., Zaffaron, A., Pincus, G. Transformation of cholesterol and acetate to adrenal cortical hormones. *Arch. Biochem.,* **46,** 201–14 (1953)
8. Goodman, D. S., Avigan, J., Wilson,

H. The *in vitro* metabolism of desmosterol with adrenal and liver preparations. *J. Clin. Invest.*, **41**, 2135–41 (1962)

9. Werbin, H., Chaikoff, I. L. Utilization of adrenal gland cholesterol for synthesis of cortisol by the intact normal and the ACTH-treated guinea pig. *Arch. Biochem.*, **93**, 476–82 (1961)

10. Ichii, S., Kobayashi, S. Studies on the biosynthesis of sterol and corticosterone in rat adrenal gland. *Endocrinol. Japon.*, **13**, 39–45 (1966)

11. Armstrong, D. T., O'Brien, J., Greep, R. O. Effects of luteinizing hormone on progestin biosynthesis in the luteinized rat ovary. *Endocrinology*, **75**, 488–500 (1964)

12. Shyamala, G., Lossow, W. J., Chaikoff, I. L. Esterification of cholesterol by rat adrenal gland homogenates and subcellular components. *Biochim. Biophys. Acta*, **116**, 543–54 (1966)

13. Shyamala, G., Lossow, W. J., Chaikoff, I. L. Cholesterol esterification by the mitochondria-rich fraction of the Snell adrenal cortical tumor 494-H and the normal adrenal gland. *Cancer Res.*, **26**, 2485–87 (1966)

14. Dexter, R. N., Fishman, L. M., Ney, R. L., Liddle, G. W. An effect of ACTH on adrenal cholesterol accumulation. *49th Meeting Endocrine Soc., Miami, Florida, June 1967, Abstr. No. 76*

15. Robertson, G. L., Reddy, W. J. The site of ACTH-induced suppressors of the specific activity of cholesterol formed from acetate-1-C¹⁴ by adrenal cortex. *49th Meeting Endocrine Soc., Miami, Florida, June 1967, Abstr. No. 75*

16. Robertson, G. L., Reddy, W. J. ACTH effect on adrenal free fatty acids. *Fed. Proc.*, **26**, 423 (1967)

17. Macho, L., Palkovic, M. The effect of corticotrophin on free fatty acid content in rat adrenals. *Experientia*, **21**, 464–65 (1965)

18. Palkovic, H., Macho, L. The *in vivo* effect of ACTH on the activity of lipase in the rat adrenal. *Naturwissenschaften*, **54**, 168–69 (1967)

19. Melby, J. C., Egdahl, R. H., Dale, S. L. Role of circulating free cholesterol of plasma in adrenal steroidogenesis. *Clin. Res.*, **15**, 264 (1967)

20. Krum, A. A., Morris, M. D., Bennett, L. I. Role of cholesterol in the *in vivo* biosynthesis of adrenal steroids by the dog. *Endocrinology*, **74**, 543–47 (1964)

21. Rudman, D., Garcia, L. A. Effect of acrenocorticotropin on the concentration of triglyceride in the adrenal gland of the hypophysectomized rat. *Endocrinology*, **78**, 1087–88 (1966)

22. Tchen, T. T. Conversion of cholesterol to pregnenolone in the adrenal cortex: enzymology and regulation. In *Functions of the Adrenal Cortex* (See Ref. 4)

23. Stone, D., Hechter, O. Studies on ACTH action in perfused bovine adrenals: the site of action of ACTH in corticosteroidogenesis. *Arch. Biochem. Biophys.*, **51**, 457–69 (1954)

24. Karaboyas, G. C., Koritz, S. B. Identity of the site of action of 3'5' adenosine monophosphate and adrenocorticotrophic hormone in corticosteroidogenesis in rat adrenal and beef adrenal cortex slices. *Biochemistry*, **4**, 462–68 (1965)

25. Hall, P. F. On the stimulation of testicular steroidogenesis in the rabbit by interstitial cell-stimulating hormone. *Endocrinology*, **78**, 690–98 (1966)

26. Koritz, S. B., Hall, P. F. Further studies on the locus of action of interstitial cell-stimulating hormone. *Biochemistry*, **4**, 2740–47 (1965)

27. Channing, C. P., Villee, C. A. Stimulation of cholesterol metabolism in the luteinized rat ovary by luteinizing hormone. *Biochim. Biophys. Acta*, **127**, 1–17 (1966)

28. Constantopoulos, G., Carpenter, A., Satoh, P. S., Tchen, T. T. Formation of isocaproaldehyde in the enzymatic cleavage of cholesterol side chain by adrenal extract. *Biochemistry*, **5**, 1650–52 (1966)

29. Farese, R. V. ACTH-induced changes in steroidogenic activity of adrenal cell free systems. *Fed. Proc.*, **26**, 423 (1967)

30. Sih, C. J., Wang, K. C., Tai, H. H. C₂₂ acid intermediates in the microbiological cleavage of the cholesterol side chain. *J. Am. Chem. Soc.*, **89**, 1956–57 (1967)

31. Satoh, P., Constantopoulos, G., Tchen, T. T. Cleavage of cholesterol side chain by adrenal cortex. IV. Effect

of phosphate and various nucleotides on a soluble enzyme system. *Biochemistry,* **5,** 1646–49 (1966)

32. Haynes, R. C., Jr., Berthet, L. Studies on the mechanism of action of the adrenocorticotropic hormone. *J. Biol. Chem.,* **225,** 115–24 (1957)

33. Koritz, S. B. The energy linked synthesis of pregnenolone in beef adrenal cortex mitochondria. *Biochem. Biophys. Res. Commun.,* **23,** 485–89 (1966)

34. Bryson, M. J., Kaiser, I. H. Cleavage of cholesterol side chain by adrenal mitochondrial components containing cytochrome P-450 and non-heme iron protein. *Fed. Proc.,* **25,** 494 (1966)

35. Boyd, G. S., Simpson, E. R. Δ⁵Pregnenolone and progesterone synthesis. In *Functions of the Adrenal Cortex* (See Ref. 4)

36. Peron, F. G., McCarthy, J. L. Corticosteroidogenesis in the rat adrenal gland. In *Functions of the Adrenal Cortex* (See Ref. 4)

37. Koritz, S. B. On the regulation of pregnenolone synthesis. In *Functions of the Adrenal Cortex* (See Ref. 4)

38. Peron, F. G., Guerra, F., McCarthy, J. L. The influence of Ca²⁺ substrates, and electron transport inhibitors on corticosteroidogenesis in rat adrenal mitochondria. *6th Pan-Am. Congr. Endocrinol. Excerpta Med. Intern. Congr. Ser. 99, Abstr. No. 176,* E82 (1965)

39. Harding, B. W., Wilson, L. D., Wong, S. H., Nelson, D. H. Electron carriers of the rat adrenal and the 11β-hydroxylating system. *Steroids, Suppl. II,* 51–77 (1965)

40. Cortes, J. M., Peron, F. G. Direct extraction of corticosterone from rat adrenal glands under an applied electrical field I. *Biochim. Biophys. Acta,* **126,** 43–53 (1966)

41. Matthews, E. K., Saffran, M. Measurement of the resting membrane potential in the adrenal cortex and its relation to adrenocortical function. In *Functions of the Adrenal Cortex* (See Ref. 4)

42. Hirshfield, I. N., Koritz, S. B. Pregnenolone synthesis stimulation in the large particles from bovine adrenal cortex and bovine corpus luteum. *Endocrinology,* **78,** 165–68 (1966)

43. Hirshfield, I. N., Koritz, S. B. The stimulation of pregnenolone synthesis in the large particles from the adrenals of rats administered adrenocorticotropin *in vivo. Biochim. Biophys. Acta,* **111,** 313–17 (1965)

44. Koritz, S. B., Hirshfield, I. N. Studies on the control of pregnenolone synthesis. *2nd Intern. Congr. Hormonal Steroids. Excerpta Med. Intern. Congr. Ser. 111,* 36–37 (1966)

45. Koritz, S. B., Hall, P. F. End-product inhibition of the conversion of cholesterol to pregnenolone in an adrenal extract. *Biochemistry,* **3,** 1298–1304 (1964)

46. Koritz, S. B., Hall, P. F. Feedback inhibition by pregnenolone: a possible mechanism. *Biochim. Biophys. Acta,* **93,** 215–17 (1964)

47. Monod, J., Changeux, J. P., Jacob, F. Allosteric proteins and cellular control systems. *J. Mol. Biol.,* **6,** 306–29 (1963)

48. Lever, J. D. Physiologically induced changes in adrenocortical mitochondria. *J. Biophys. Biochem. Cytol.,* **2** (Suppl.), 313–18 (1956)

49. Sabatini, D. D., DeRobertis, E. D. P., Bleichman, H. B. Submicroscopic study of the pituitary action on the adrenal cortex of the rat. *Endocrinology,* **70,** 390–406 (1962)

50. Nishikawa, M., Murone, I., Sato, T. Electron microscopic examinations of the adrenal cortex. *Endocrinology,* **72,** 197–209 (1963)

51. Luse, S. Fine structure of adrenal cortex, In *The Adrenal Cortex* (See Ref. 3), 1–59

52. Farese, R. V. Regulation of adrenal growth and steroidogenesis by ACTH. In *Functions of the Adrenal Cortex* (See Ref. 4)

53. Farese, R. V. ACTH-induced changes in the steroidogenic activity of adrenal cell-free preparations (Submitted for publication, 1967)

54. Ferguson, J. J., Jr. Protein synthesis and adrenocorticotropin responsiveness. *J. Biol. Chem.,* **238,** 2754–59 (1963)

55. Farese, R. V. Inhibition of the steroidogenic effect of ACTH and incorporation of amino acid into rat adrenal protein *in vitro* by chloramphenicol. *Biochim. Biophys. Acta,* **87,** 699–701 (1964)

56. Farese, R. V. (Personal communication, 1967)

57. Sweat, M. L., Lipscomb, M. D. A transhydrogenase and reduced triphosphopyridine nucleotide involved in the oxidation of desoxycorticosterone to corticosterone by adrenal tissue. *J. Am. Chem. Soc.,* **77,** 5185–87 (1955)

58. Savard, K., Casey, P. J. Effects of pituitary hormones and NADPH on acetate utilization in ovarian and adrenocortical tissue. *Endocrinology,* **74,** 599–610 (1964)

59. McKerns, K. Mechanism of action of adrenocorticotropic hormone through activation of glucose-6-phosphate dehydrogenase. *Biochim. Biophys. Acta,* **90,** 357–71 (1964)

60. McKerns, K. Additional studies on the mechanism of action of ACTH. *Can. J. Biol. Chem.,* **43,** 923–32 (1965)

61. McKerns, K. The pentose-phosphate pathway, steroidogenesis and protein synthesis. *Biochim. Biophys. Acta,* **100,** 612–15 (1965)

62. McKerns, K. Hormone regulation of the genetic potential through the pentose phosphate pathway. *Biochim. Biophys. Acta,* **121,** 207–9 (1966)

63. McKerns, K. Mechanism of ACTH regulation of the adrenal cortex. In *Functions of the Adrenal Cortex* (See Ref. 4)

64. Harding, B. W., Nelson, D. H. Effect of hypophysectomy on NADP, and NADPH concentration and corticosteroid secretion in the rat adrenal. *Endocrinology,* **75,** 501–13 (1964)

65. Harding, B. W., Nelson, D. H. Effect of hypophysectomy on several rat adrenal NADPH-generating and oxidizing systems. *Endocrinology,* **75,** 506–14 (1964)

66. Kuhn, C., Kissane, J. M. Quantitative histochemistry of glucose-6-phosphate dehydrogenase and 6-phosphogluconate dehydrogenase in rat adrenal cortex: Effect of ACTH, cortisone and sodium deprivation. *Endocrinology,* **75,** 741–46 (1964)

67. McKerns, K. (Personal communication)

68. Haynes, R. C., Jr. The activation of adrenal phosphorylase by the adrenocorticotropic hormone. *J. Biol. Chem.,* **233,** 1220–22 (1958)

69. Halkerston, I.D.K. Whole cell preparations of adrenals for studies on the mechanism of action of ACTH. In *Functions of the Adrenal Cortex* (See Ref. 4)

70. Creange, J. E., Roberts, S. Studies on the mechanism of action of cyclic 3′5′-adenosine monophosphate on steroid hydroxylations in adrenal homogenates. *Biochem. Biophys. Res. Commun.,* **19,** 73–78 (1965)

71. Creange, J. E., Roberts, S. Stimulation of steroid C-11β and C-18 hydroxylations in rat adrenal homogenates by adenosine 3′5′ phosphate via a mechanism not requiring endogenous precursor, glycogen phosphorylation or NADPH generation. *Steroids, Suppl. II,* 13–28 (1965)

72. Roberts, S., Creange, J. E. The role of 3′5′-adenosine phosphate in the subcellular localization of regulatory processes in corticosteroidogenesis. In *Functions of the Adrenal Cortex* (See Ref. 4)

73. Haynes, R. C., Koritz, S. B., Peron, F. G. Influence of adenosine-3′5′-monophosphate on corticoid production by rat adrenal glands. *J. Biol. Chem.,* **234,** 1421–23 (1959)

74. Hilton, J. G., Kruesi, O. R., Nedeljkovic, R. I., Scian, L. F. Adrenocortical and medullary response to adenosine 3′5′-monophosphate. *Endocrinology,* **68,** 908–13 (1961)

75. Sutherland, E. W., Øye, I., Butcher, R. W. The action of epinephrine and the role of the adenyl cyclase system in hormone action. *Recent Progr. Hormone Res.,* **21,** 623–46 (1965)

76. Huijing, F., Larner, J. On the effect of adenosine-3′5′-cyclophosphate on the kinase of UDPG: β-1,4-glucan, α-4-glucosyl transferase. *Biochem. Biophys. Res. Commun.,* **23,** 259–63 (1966)

77. Huijing, F., Larner, J. On the mechanism of action of adenosine 3′5′ cyclophosphate. *Proc. Natl. Acad. Sci.,* **56,** 647–53 (1966)

78. Pastan, I. The effect of dibutyryi cyclic 3′5′-AMP on the thyroid. *Biochem. Biophys. Res. Commun.,* **25,** 14–16 (1966)

79. Davoren, P. R., Sutherland, E. W. The cellular location of adenyl cyclase in the pigeon erythrocyte. *J. Biol. Chem.,* **238,** 3016–23 (1963)

80. Sutherland, E. W., Rall, T. W.,

Menon, T. Adenyl cyclase I. Distribution, preparation and properties. *J. Biol. Chem.*, **237**, 1220–27 (1962)

81. Makman, M. H., Sutherland, E. W. Use of adenyl cyclase for assay of glucagon in human gastrointestinal tract and pancrease. *Endocrinology*, **75**, 127–34 (1964)

82. Reddy, W. J., Streeto, J. M. Adenosine 3′5′-monophosphate and the adrenal cortex. In *Functions of the Adrenal Cortex* (See Ref. 4)

83. Streeto, J. M., Reddy, W. J. An assay for adenyl cyclase. *Anal. Biochem.* (In press) (1967)

84. Grahame-Smith, D. G., Butcher, R. W., Ney, R. L., Sutherland, E. W. Adenosine-3′5′-monophosphate (cyclic AMP) as the mediator of the action of ACTH on the adrenal cortex. *Clin. Res.*, **15**, 259 (1967)

85. Butcher, R. W., Ho, R. J., Meng, H. C., Sutherland, E. W. Adenosine 3′5′-monophosphate in biological materials II. The measurement of adenosine 3′5′-monophosphate in tissues and the role of the cyclic nucleotide in the lipolytic response of fat to epinephrine. *J. Biol. Chem.*, **240**, 4515–23 (1965)

86. Farese, R. V., Reddy, W. J. Observations on the interrelations between adrenal protein, RNA and DNA during prolonged ACTH administration. *Biochim. Biophys. Acta*, **76**, 148–51 (1963)

87. Bransome, E. D., Jr. Regulation of adrenal growth: differences in the effects of ACTH in normal and dexamethasone suppressed guinea pigs (Submitted for publication, 1967)

88. Bransome, E. D., Jr., Reddy, W. J. Incorporation of amino acids into rat adrenal protein *in vivo*: effects of adrenocorticotropin and growth hormone. *Endocrinology*, **74**, 495–97 (1964)

89. Grower, M., Bransome, E. D., Jr. (In preparation)

90. Targovnik, J., Buonassisi, V., Ueda, K., Meiss, H., Sato, G. Studies on the mechanism of action of ACTH. *Fed. Proc.*, **25**, 380 (1966)

91. Kowal, J. The stimulation of IIβ-hydroxylation in cultured adrenal cells. *49th Meeting Endocrine Soc. Miami, Florida, June 1967, Abstr. No. 74*

92. Ferguson, J. J., Jr. Puromycin and adrenal responsiveness to adreno-corticotropic hormone. *Biochim. Biophys. Acta*, **57**, 616–17 (1962)

93. Kittinger, G. W. Puromycin inhibition of *in vitro* cortical hormone production by the rat adrenal gland. *Steroids*, **4**, 539–40 (1964)

94. Ferguson, J. J., Jr. Metabolic inhibitors and adrenal function. In *Functions of the Adrenal Cortex* (See Ref. 4)

95. Farese, R. V. Inhibition of the steroidogenic effect of ACTH and incorporation of amino acid into rat adrenal protein *in vitro* by chloramphenicol. *Biochim. Biophys. Acta*, **87**, 699–701 (1964)

96. Halkerston, I. D. K., Feinstein, M., Hechter, O. An anomalous effect of theophylline on ACTH and adenosine 3′5′-monophosphate stimulation. *Proc. Soc. Exptl. Biol. Med.*, **122**, 896–900 (1966)

97. Garren, L. D., Ney, R. L., Davis, W. W. Studies on the role of protein synthesis in the regulation of corticosterone production by adreno-ocorticotropic hormone *in vivo*. *Proc. Natl. Acad. Sci.*, **53**, 1443–50 (1965)

98. Farese, R. V. (Personal communication, 1967)

99. Fiala, S., Fiala, E. Hormonal dependence of actidione (cyclohexamide) action. *Biochim. Biophys. Acta*, **103**, 699–701 (1965)

100. Hofert, J., Boutwell, R. K. Puromycin-induced glycogenolysis as an event independent from inhibited protein in mouse liver: Effects of puromycin analogs. *Arch. Biochem. Biophys.*, **103**, 338–44 (1963)

101. Søvik, O. Effect of puromycin and puromycin analogues on glycogen synthesis in the isolated rat diaphragm. *Acta Physiol. Scand.*, **66**, 307–15 (1966)

102. Korner, A., Raben, M. S. Effect of amino-nucleoside and puromycin on insulin and epinephrine control of fatty acid release from adipose tissue. *Nature*, **203**, 1287–89 (1964)

103. Appleman, M. M., Kemp, R. G. Puromycin: a potent metabolic effect independent of protein synthesis. *Biochem. Biophys. Res. Commun.*, **24**, 564–68 (1966)

104. Greif, R. L., Song, C. S., Chipkin, D. Administered puromycin and mitochondrial swelling. *Endocrinology*, **77**, 223–25 (1965)

105. Lebovitz, H., Pooler, K. Puromycin

potentiation of corticotropin-induced insulin release. *Endocrinology,* **80,** 656–62 (1967)

106. Estensen, R. D., Baserga, R. Puromycin-induced necrosis of crypt cells of the small intestine of mouse. *J. Cell Biol.,* **30,** 13–22 (1966)

107. Soeiro, R., Vaughn, M., Darnell, J. Effect of puromycin or amino acid starvation on ribosome synthesis in HeLa cells. *Fed. Proc.,* **27,** 286 (1967)

108. Barondes, S. H. (Personal communication)

109. Kenney, F. T. Turnover of rat liver tyrosine transaminase : stabilization after inhibition of protein synthesis. *Science,* **156,** 525–27

110. Schimke, R. T. The importance of both synthesis and degradation in the control of arginase level in rat liver. *J. Biol. Chem.,* **239,** 3808–17 (1964)

111. Rechcigl, M., Jr., Heston, W. E. Genetic regulation of enzyme activity in mammaliam system by the alteration of the rates of enzyme degradation. *Biochem. Biophys. Res. Commun.,* **27,** 119–24 (1967)

112. Rosen, F., Milholland, R. J. Selective effects of cycloheximide on the adaptive enzymes tyrosine-α-ketoglutarate transaminase (TT) and tryptophan pyrrolase (TP). *Fed. Proc.,* **25,** 285 (1966)

113. Jondorff, W. R., Simon, D. C., Avniemelech, M. Further studies on the stimulation of L-(^{14}C)-amino acid incorporation with cycloheximide. *Mol. Pharmacol.,* **2,** 506–17 (1967)

114. MacKintosh, F. R., Bell, E. Stimulation of protein synthesis in unfertilized sea urchin eggs by prior metabolic inhibition. *Biochem. Biophys. Res. Commun.,* **27,** 425–30 (1967)

115. Ibayashi, H., Nakamura, M., Yamaji, T., Tanioka, T., Murakawa, S., Motohashi, K. Effect of LH and ACTH on production and excretion of testosterone *in vivo.* In *Steroid Dynamics,* 91–114 (Pincus, G., Nakao, T., Tait, J. F., Eds., Academic Press, New York, 577 pp., 1966)

116. Lipsett, M. B., Korenman, S. G., Wilson, H., Bardin, C. W. The effects of metabolic transformations of androgens. In *Steroid Dynamics,* 117–29 (Pincus, G.,

Nakao, T., Tait, J. F., Eds., Academic Press, New York, 577 pp., 1966)

117. Baulieu, E. E., Peillon, F., Migeon, C. J. Adrenogenital Syndrome. In *The Adrenal Cortex* (See Ref. 3), 553–638

118. Baniukiewicz, S., Brodie, A., Flood, C., Motta, M., Okamoto, M., Tait, J. F., Tait, S. A. S., Blair-West, J. R., Coghlan, J. P., Denton, D. A., Goding, J. R. Scoggins, B. A., Wintour, M., Wright, R. D. Adrenal biosynthesis of steroids *in vitro* and *in vivo* using continuous superfusion and infusion procedures. In *Functions of the Adrenal Cortex* (See Ref. 4)

119. Mason, H. S. Mechanisms of oxygen metabolism. *Advan. Enzymol.,* **19,** 79–223 (1957)

120. Omura, T., Sanders, E., Estabrook, R. W., Cooper, D. Y., Rosenthal, O. Isolation from adrenal cortex of a non heme iron protein and a flavo protein functional as a reduced triphosphopyridine nucleotide-cytochrome P-450 reductase. *Arch. Biochem. Biophys.,* **117,** 660–73 (1966)

121. Nakamura, Y., Otsuka, H., Tamaoki, B. I. Requirement of a new flavoprotein and a non-heme iron containing protein in the steroid IIβ- and 18-hydroxylase system. *Biochim. Biophys. Acta,* **122,** 34–42 (1966)

122. Kimura, T., Suzuki, K. Components of the electron transport system in adrenal steroid hydroxylase. *J. Biol. Chem.,* **242,** 485–91 (1967)

123. Kimura, T. Redox components of adrenal steroid hydroxylase. In *Biological and Chemical Aspects of Oxygenases,* 179–91 (Bloch, K., Hayaishi, O., Eds., Maruzen Co., Ltd., Tokyo, 1966)

124. Kimura, T. Electron transfer system of steroid hydroxylases in adrenal mitochondria. In *Functions of the Adrenal Cortex* (See Ref. 4)

125. Cammer, W., Cooper, D. Y., Estabrook, R. W. Electron transport reactions for steroid hydroxylation by adrenal cortex mitochondria. In *Functions of the Adrenal Cortex* (See Ref. 4)

126. Harding, B. W., Bell, J. J., Oldham, S. B., Wilson, L. D. Corticosteroid biosynthesis in adrenal cortical mitochondria. In *Functions of the Adrenal Cortex* (See Ref. 4)

127. Purvis, J. L., Battu, R. G., Peron, F. G. The generation and utilization of reducing power in the conversion of 11-deoxycorticosterone to corticosterone in rat adrenal mitochondria. In *Functions of the Adrenal Cortex* (See Ref. 4)

128. Cooper, D. Y., Novack, D., Foroff, O., Slade, A., Saunders, S., Narasimhulu, S., Rosenthal, O. Photochemical action spectrum of reconstituted steroid 11β hydroxylase of bovine adrenocortical mitochondria. *Fed. Proc.*, **26**, 341 (1967)

129. Estabrook, R. W., Cooper, D. Y., Rosenthal, O. The light reversible carbon monoxide inhibition of the steroid C-21-hydroxylase system of the adrenal cortex. *Biochem. Z.*, **338**, 741–55 (1963)

130. Cooper, D. Y., Narasimhulu, S., Rosenthal, O., Estabrook, R. W. Studies on the mechanism of C-21 hydroxylation. In *Functions of the Adrenal Cortex* (See Ref. 4)

131. Chance, B., Ernster, L., Garland, P. B., Lee, C.-P., Light, P. A., Ohnishi, T., Ragan, C. I., Wong, D. Flavoproteins of the mitochondrial respiratory chain. *Proc. Natl. Acad. Sci.*, **57**, 1498–1505 (1967)

132. Guerra, F., Peron, F. G., McCarthy, J. L. Further studies on corticosteroidogenesis III. Effect of biological substrates and electron transport dependence in rat adrenal mitochondria. *Biochim. Biophys. Acta*, **117**, 433–49 (1966)

133. Harding, B. W., Nelson, D. H. Electron carriers of the bovine adrenal cortical respiratory chain and hydroxylating pathways. *J. Biol. Chem.*, **241**, 2212–19 (1966)

134. Cammer, W., Estabrook, R. W. Energy-linked reactions for steroid hydroxylations by adrenal mitochondria. *Fed. Proc.*, **25**, 281 (1966)

135. Wilson, L., Oldham, S., Donovan, A., Harding, B. Evidence for the participation of cytochrome P-450 in 11β hydroxylation in human adrenal. *49th Meeting Endocrine Soc., Miami, Florida, June 1967, Abstr. No. 73*

136. Burstein, S. Cytochrome P-450 concentrations in adrenal and liver microsomes from guinea pigs with genetic differences in cortisol hydroxylation. *Biochem. Biophys. Res. Commun.*, **26**, 697–703 (1967)

137. Imai, Y., Sato, R. Evidence for two forms of P-450 hemoprotein in microsomal membranes. *Biochem. Biophys. Res. Commun.*, **23**, 5–11 (1966)

138. Sladek, W. E., Mannering, G. J. Evidence for a new P-450 hemoprotein in hepatic microsomes from methylcholanthrene treated rats. *Biochem. Biophys. Res. Commun.*, **24**, 668–74 (1966)

139. *The Metabolic Basis of Inherited Disease* (Stanbury, J. B., Wyngaarden, J. B., Frederickson, D. F., Eds., McGraw-Hill, New York, 1434 pp., 2nd ed., 1966)

140. Sayers, G., Sayers, M. A., Lewis, H. L., Long, C. N. H. Effect of adrenocorticotropic hormone on ascorbic acid and cholesterol content of the adrenal. *Proc. Soc. Exptl. Biol. Med.*, **55**, 238–39 (1944)

141. Hayano, M., Saba, N., Dorfman, R. I., Hechter, O. Some aspects of the biogenesis of adrenal steroid hormones. *Recent Progr. Hormone Res.*, **XII**, 79–123 (1956)

142. Kersten, H., Kersten, W., Staudinger, H. Mechanism of ascorbic acid activity. I. Isolation from adrenal microsomes of an ascorbic acid dependent reduced diphosphopyridine nucleotide oxidase. *Biochim. Biophys. Acta*, **27**, 598–608 (1958)

143. Cooper, D. Y., Rosenthal, O. Action of noradrenaline and ascorbic acid on C-21 hydroxylation of steroid by adrenocortical microsomes. *Arch. Biochem.*, **96**, 331–35 (1962)

144. Stollar, V., Buonassisi, V., Sato, G. Studies on hormone secreting adrenocortical tumor in tissue culture. *Exptl. Cell Res.*, **35**, 608–16 (1964)

145. Kitabchi, A. E. Inhibitory effect of ascorbic acid on steroid hydroxylase systems of beef adrenal cortex. *Fed. Proc.*, **26**, 484 (1967)

146. Sweat, M. L., Bryson, M. J. Steroid 11β oxygenation, ascorbic acid, epinephrine, and adrenochrome interrelations in the adrenal gland. *Endocrinology*, **76**, 773–75 (1965)

147. Harding, B. W., Nelson, D. H. Electron transport in bovine adrenal cortical 11β hydroxylation reactions. *6th Pan-Am. Congr. Endocrinol. Excerpta Med. Intern. Congr. Ser. 99*, E85 (1965)

148. Samuels, L. T., Helmreich, M. L., Lasater, M. B., Reich, H. An en-

zyme in endocrine tissues which oxidizes Δ^5-3-hydroxysteroids to α,β unsaturated ketones. *Science,* **113,** 490–91 (1951)

149. Cheatum, S. G., Warren, J. C. Purification and properties of 3β-hydroxysteroid dehydrogenase and Δ^5-3-ketosteroid isomerase from bovine corpora lutea. *Biochim. Biophys. Acta,* **122,** 1–13 (1966)

150. Cheatum, S. G., Douville, A. W., Warren, J. C. Site specificity of bovine adrenal 3β-hydroxysteroid dehydrogenase and Δ^5-3-ketosteroid isomerase. *Biochim. Biophys. Acta,* **137,** 172–78 (1967)

151. Ewald, W., Werbin, H., Chaikoff, I. L. Evidence for two substrate-specific Δ^5-3-ketosteroid isomerases in beef adrenal glands and their separation from 3β hydroxysteroid dehydrogenase. *Biochem. Biophys. Acta,* **81,** 199–201 (1964)

152. Ewald, W., Werbin, H., Chaikoff, I. L. Partial separation of beef adrenal Δ^5-3-ketosteroid isomerases; androst-5-ene-3,17-dione isomerase and pregn-5-ene-3,20-dione isomerase. *Steroids,* **4,** 759–76 (1964)

153. Bongiovanni, A. M. Unusual steroid pattern in congenital adrenal hyperplasia: Deficiency of 3β-hydroxy dehydrogenase *J. Clin. Endocrinol. Metab.,* **21,** 860–62 (1961)

154. Harding, H. R., Potts, G. O. The blocking effect of cyanotrimethyl-androstenolone on the induction of liver tryptophan pyrrolase (TPO) activity by ACTH. *Fed. Proc.,* **23,** 356 (1964)

155. Goldman, A. S., Bongiovanni, A. M., Yakovac, W. C. Production of congenital adrenal cortical hyperplasia hypospadias, and clitoral hypertrophy (adrenogenital syndrome) in rats by inactivation of 3β-hydroxysteroid dehydrogenase. *Proc. Soc. Exptl. Biol. Med.,* **121,** 757–66 (1966)

156. Goldman, A. S., Yakovac, W. C. Experimental congenital adrenal cortical hyperplasia: prevention of adrenal hyperplasia and clitoral hypertrophy by corticosterone. *Proc. Soc. Exptl. Biol. Med.,* **122,** 1214–1216 (1966)

157. Potts, G. O. (Personal communication, 1967)

158. Goldman, A. S., Yakovac, W. C., Bongiovanni, A. M. Persistent effects of a synthetic androstene

derivative on activities of 3β hydroxysteroid dehydrogenase and glucose-6-phosphate dehydrogenase in rats. *Endocrinology,* **77,** 1105–18 (1965)

159. McCarthy, J. L., Rietz, C. W., Wesson, L. K. Inhibition of adrenal corticosteroidogenesis in the rat by cyanotrimethyl androstenolone, a synthetic androstene. *Endocrinology,* **79,** 1123–29 (1966)

160. Goldman, A. S. Inhibition of 3β-hydroxysteroid dehydrogenase from Pseudomonas testosteroni by various estrogenic and progestinic steroids. *J. Clin. Endocrinol. Metab.,* **27,** 320–24 (1964)

161. Goldman, A. S. Stoichometric inhibition of various 3β-hydroxysteroid dehydrogenases by a substrate analogue. *J. Clin. Endocrinol. Metab.,* **27,** 325–32 (1967)

162. Neville, A. M., Engel, L. L. Inhibition of 3β- and 3α-hydroxysteroid dehydrogenases and of steroid-isomerase by anabolic steroids. *49th Meeting Endocrine Soc., Miami, Florida, June 1967, Abstr. No. 78*

163. Gagliano, R. G., Wesson, L., McCarthy, J. L. (Submitted for publication, 1967)

164. Wang, S.-F., Kawahara, F. S., Talalay, P. The mechanism of the Δ^5-3-ketosteroid isomerase reaction: absorbtion and fluorescence spectra of enzyme-steroid complexes. *J. Biol. Chem.,* **238,** 576–85 (1963)

165. Malhotra, S. K., Ringold, H. J. Chemistry of conjugate anions and enols V. Stereochemistry, kinetics and mechanism of the acid- and enzymatic-catalyzed isomerization of Δ^5-3-oxo steroids. *J. Am. Chem. Soc.,* **87,** 3228–36 (1965)

166. Werbin, H., Chaikoff, I. L. Fate of the 4β-hydrogen of cholesterol during its conversion to steroid hormones. *Biochim. Biophys. Acta,* **82,** 581–94 (1964)

167. Oleinick, N. L., Koritz, S. B. Studies on the mechanism of action of the Δ^5-3-ketosteroid isomerase from rat adrenal small particles. *Biochemistry,* **5,** 3400–5 (1966)

168. Oleinick, N. L., Koritz, S. B. The activation of the Δ^5-3-ketosteroid isomerase in rat adrenal small particles by diphosphopyridine nucleotides. *Biochemistry,* **5,** 715–24 (1966)

169. Steinetz, B. G., Beach, V. L., DiPasquale, G., Battista, J. V. Effects of

different gestogenic steroid types on plasma free corticosteroid level in ACTH-treated rats. *Steroids,* **5,** 93–108 (1965)

170. Kowal, J., Forchielli, E., Dorfman, R. I. The Δ^5-3β-hydroxy-steroid dehydrogenases of corpus luteum and adrenal II. Interaction of C_{19} and C_{21} substrates and products. *Steroids,* **4,** 77–100 (1964)

171. Villee, D. B. The role of progesterone in the development of adrenal enzymes. *2nd Intern. Congr. Hormonal Steroids. Excerpta Med. Intern. Congr. Ser. 111,* 65 (1966)

172. Carstensen, H., Oertel, G. W., Eik-Nes, K. B. Secretion of 17α-hydroxy-Δ^5-pregnenolone by the canine adrenal gland during stimulation with adrenocorticotropin. *J. Biol. Chem.,* **234,** 2570–77 (1959)

173. Mulrow, P. J., Cohn, G. L., Koljian, A. Conversion of 17-hydroxypregnenolone to cortisol by normal and hyperplastic human adrenal slices. *J. Clin. Invest.,* **41,** 1584–90 (1962)

174. Berliner, D. L., Nabors, C. J., Dougherty, T. F. The role of hepatic and adrenal reticuloendothelial cells in steroid biotransformation. *J. Reticuloendothel. Soc.,* **1,** 1–17 (1964)

175. Fevold, H. R. *In vitro* corticosteroid biosynthesis by adrenal tissue from ACTH stimulated rabbits. *Fed. Proc.,* **26,** 423 (1967)

176. Fevold, H. R. Regulation of the adrenal cortex secretory pattern by adrenocorticotropin. *Science,* **156,** 1753–55 (1967)

177. Pankov, Y. A. Effect of nicotinamide adenine dinucleotide on the ratio of 17-hydroxycorticotrosteroids and 17-desoxycorticosteroids synthesized by homogenates of pig adrenal cortex. *Fed. Proc.,* **25,** T268–70 (1966) ; *Transl. Probl. Endokrinol. Gormonoterap.,* **11,** 71 (1965)

178. Biglieri, E. G., Herron, M. A., Brust, N. 17-Hydroxylation deficiency in man. *J. Clin. Invest.,* **45,** 1946–54 (1966)

179. Goldsmith, O., Solomon, D. H., Horton, R. 17α Hydroxylation defect involving both adrenal and gonad. *49th Meeting Endocrine Soc., Miami, Florida, June 1967, Abstr. No. 7*

180. Griffiths, K., Grant, J. K., Symington, T. A biochemical investigation of the functional zonation of the adrenal cortex in man. *J. Clin. Endocrinol. Metab.,* **23,** 776–85 (1963)

181. Griffiths, K., Glick, D. Determination of the 11β hydroxylase activity in microgram samples of tissue: its quantitative histological distribution in the rat adrenal and the influence of corticotrophin. *J. Endocrinol.,* **35,** 1–12 (1966)

182. Kowal, J. The effect of ACTH and 3'5' AMP on steroidogenesis and 11β hydroxylation in cultured adrenal cells. *Clin. Res.,* **15,** 262 (1967)

183. Vermeulen, H., Verdonck, G., Van der Straeten, M., Daneels, R. Evaluation of the efficiency of 11β hydroxylation of 11-deoxycortisol in human subjects. *J. Clin. Endocrinol. Metab.,* **27,** 365–70 (1967)

184. McCarthy, J., Peron, F. G. The 11β hydroxylation of progesterone and deoxycorticosterone by rat adrenal mitochondria. *Biochemistry,* **6,** 25–31 (1967)

185. Spatz, L., Hofmann, F. G. Effects of NADPH and other cofactors on the *in vitro* metabolism of steroids by guinea pig adrenal glands. *Endocrinology,* **79,** 971–90 (1966)

186. Williamson, D. G., O'Donnell, V. J. Dicoumarol: a novel inhibitor of steroid 11β hydroxylation. *Can. J. Biochem.,* **45,** 340–44 (1967)

187. Tsao, D. P. N., King, T. E. Effect of cardiac glycosides on 11-hydroxylation of the adrenal system. *Arch. Biochem. Biophys.,* **118,** 259–60 (1967)

188. Liddle, G. W., Estep, H. L., Kendall, J. W., Williams, W. C., Townes, H. W. Clinical application of a new test of pituitary reserve. *J. Clin. Endocrinol. Metab.,* **19,** 875–94 (1959)

189. Dominguez, O. V., Samuels, L. T. Mechanism of inhibition of adrenal steroid 11β-hydroxylase by methopyrapone. *Endocrinology,* **73,** 304–9 (1963)

190. Williamson, D. G., O'Donnell, V. J. Mechanism of metopirone inhibition of a soluble adrenal steroid 11β-hydroxylase. *Can. J. Biochem.,* **45,** 153–63 (1967)

191. Sanzari, N. P., Peron, F. G. Influence of metopirone on substrate-supported hydroxylation of DOC by rat adrenal mitochondria. *Steroids,* **8,** 929–45 (1966)

192. Davis, J. O. The regulation of aldosterone secretion. In *The Adrenal Cortex*, 203–48 (Eisenstein, A. B., Ed., Little, Brown, Boston, 685 pp., 1967)

193. Pasqualini, J. R. Biogenese et metabolisme de l'aldosterone et des 18-hydroxy-corticosteroides. *Rev. Franc. Etudes Clin. Biol.*, 11, 139–54 (1966)

194. Bartter, F. C., Burwell, L. R., Davis, W. W. Studies on the biogenesis of aldosterone. In *Functions of the Adrenal Cortex* (See Ref. 4)

195. Nicolis, G. L., Ulick, S. Role of 18-hydroxylation in the biosynthesis of aldosterone. *Endocrinology*, 76, 514–21 (1965)

196. Raman, P. B., Sharma, D. C., Dorfman, R. I. Studies on aldosterone biosynthesis *in vivo*. *Biochemistry*, 5, 1795–1804 (1966)

197. Psychoyos, S., Tallan, H. H., Greengard, P. Aldosterone synthesis by adrenal mitochondria. *J. Biol. Chem.*, 241, 2949–56 (1966)

198. Sharma, D. C., Nerenberg, C., Dorfman, R. I. Effect of certain metal ions and heparin on aldosterone biosynthesis *in vitro*. *49th Meeting Endocrine Soc., Miami, Florida, June 1967, Abstr. No. 11*

199. Davis, J. O., Urquhart, J., Higgins, J. T., Jr. The effects of alterations of plasma sodium and potassium concentration on aldosterone secretion. *J. Clin. Invest.*, 42, 597–609 (1963)

200. Vecsei, P., Lommer, D., Steinacker, H. G., Wolff, H. P. Changes of 18-hydroxycorticosterone and aldosterone synthesis in rat adrenals *in vitro* after renal hypertension, nephrectomy and variation of sodium intake *in vivo*. *European J. Steroids*, 1, 91–93 (1966)

201. Blair-West, J. R., Coghlan, J. P., Denton, D. A., Goding, J. R., Wintour, M., Wright, R. D. The direct effect of increased sodium concentration in adrenal arterial blood on corticosteroid secretion in sodium deficient sheep. *Australian J. Exptl. Biol. Med. Sci.*, 44, 455–74 (1966)

202. Marusic, E. T., Mulrow, P. J. Stimulation of aldosterone biosynthesis in adrenal mitochondria by sodium depletion. *57th Meeting Am. Soc. Clin. Invest., May 1967, Atlantic City, N.J.*

203. Tallan, H. H., Psychoyos, S., Greengard, P. Aldosterone synthesis by adrenal mitochondria II. The effect of citric acid cycle intermediates: identification of the soluble stimulatory factor as fumarase. *J. Biol. Chem.*, 242, 1912–14 (1967)

204. Greengard, P., Tallan, H. H., Psychoyos, S. Biosynthesis of aldosterone by cell-free systems. In *Functions of the Adrenal Cortex* (See Ref. 4)

205. Visser, H. K. A., Cost, W. S. A new hereditary defect in the biosynthesis of aldosterone: urinary C_{21} corticosteroid pattern in three related patients with a salt-losing syndrome suggesting an 18-oxidation defect. *Acta Endocrinol.*, 47, 589–612 (1964)

206. Degenhart, H. J., Frankena, L., Visser, H. K. A., Cost, W. S., van Seters, A. P. Further investigation of a new hereditary defect in the biosynthesis of aldosterone: evidence for a defect in 18-hydroxylation of corticosterone. *Acta Physiol. Pharmacol. Neerl.*, 14, 1–2 (1966)

207. Ulick, S., Gautier, E., Vetter, K. K., Markello, J. R., Yaffe, S., Lowe, C. U. An aldosterone biosynthetic defect in a salt losing disorder. *J. Clin. Endocrinol. Metab.*, 24, 669–72 (1964)

208. Fazekas, A. G., Kokai, K. Biosynthesis of oxygenated corticosteroids by rabbit adrenals *in vitro*. *Steroids*, 9, 177–91 (1967)

209. Fazekas, A. G., Webb, J. L. Conversion of $(1,2-^3H)$-11-dehydrocorticosterone and aldosterone by rabbit adrenal. *European J. Steroids*, 1, 389–90 (1966)

210. Fazekas, A. G., Webb, J. L. Steroid biosynthetic studies with rabbit adrenal tissue. Metabolism of progesterone-4-^{14}C, deoxycorticosterone-1,2-^{3}H, corticosterone-1,2-^{3}H, and 11-dehydrocorticosterone-1,2-^{3}H. *Acta Biochim. Biophys. Acad. Sci. Hung.*, 1, 369–78 (1966)

211. Newsome, H. H., Bartter, F. C. Predominance of volume changes over sodium concentration in control of plasma renin. *49th Meeting Endocrine Soc., Miami, Florida, June 1967, Abstr. No. 2*

212. Hartcroft, P. M., Eisenstein, A. B. Alterations in the adrenal cortex of the rat induced by sodium de-

ficiency. Correlation of histologic changes with steroid hormone secretion. *Endocrinology*, **60**, 641–51 (1957)

213. Müller, J. Aldosterone stimulation in vitro III. Site of action of different aldosterone-stimulating substances. *Acta Endocrinol.*, **52**, 515–26 (1966)

214. Cannon, P. J., Ames, R. P., Laragh, J. H. Relation between potassium balance and aldosterone secretion in normal subjects and in patients with hypertensive or renal tubular disease. *J. Clin. Invest.*, **45**, 865–79 (1966)

215. Lamberg, B.-H., Pettersson, T., Gordin, A., Karlsson, R. The effect of synthetic angiotensin-II-amide and methopyrone (SU 4885) on the histochemistry of the adrenal cortex of intact and hypophysectomized rats. *Acta Endocrinol.*, **54**, 428–38 (1967)

216. Spät, A., Sturcz, J. Untersuchung als Angiotensin-Aldosteron-Systems an natriumbelasteten Ratten. *Endokrinologie*, **50**, 179–82 (1966)

217. Davis, W. W., Burwell, L. R., Bartter, F. C. Loss of stimulation of aldosterone secretion by angiotensin in the sodium-loaded dog. *Clin. Res.*, **15**, 258 (1967)

218. Ganong, W. F., Boryczka, A. T., Shackelford, R. Effect of renin on adrenocortical sensitivity to ACTH and angiotensin II in dogs. *Endocrinology*, **80**, 703–6 (1967)

219. Davis, W. W., Newsome, H. H., Wright, L. D., Hammond, W. G., Easton, J., Bartter, F. C. Bilateral adrenal hyperplasia as a cause of primary aldosteronism with hypertension, hypokalemia, and suppressed renin activity. *Am. J. Med.*, **42**, 642–47 (1967)

220. Ganong, W. F., Pemberton, D. L., Van Brunt, E. E. Adrenocortical responsiveness to ACTH and angiotensin II in hypophysectomized dogs and dogs treated with glucocorticoids. *49th Meeting Endocrine Soc., Miami, Florida, June 1967, Abstr. No. 8*

221. Palmore, W. P., Mulrow, P. J. A non-ACTH effect of the pituitary on aldosterone secretion. *49th Meeting Endocrine Soc., Miami, Florida, June 1967, Abstr. No. 9*

222. Burstein, S., Fajer, A. B. Effect of thyroxine on urinary corticosteroid patterns in guinea pigs. *Endocrinology*, **77**, 361–65 (1965)

223. Bransome, E. D., Jr., Reddy, W. J. Studies of adrenal nucleic acids: The influence of ACTH, unilateral adrenalectomy and growth hormone upon adrenal RNA and DNA in the dog. *Endocrinology*, **69**, 997–1008 (1961)

224. Birmingham, M. K., Kurlents, E. Inactivation of ACTH by isolated rat adrenals and inhibition of corticoid formation by adrenocortical hormones. *Endocrinology*, **62**, 47–60 (1958)

225. Lucius, R., Carballeira, A., Venning, E. H. Biotransformation of progesterone-4-C^{14} and 11-deoxycorticosterone-4-^{14}C by rat adrenal glands *in vitro*. *Steroids*, **6**, 737–56 (1965)

226. Black, W. C., Crampton, R. S., Verdesca, A. S., Nedeljkovic, R. I., Hilton, J. G. Inhibitory effect of hydrocortisone and analogues on adrenocortical secretion in dogs. *Am. J. Physiol.*, **201**, 1057–60 (1961)

227. Peron, F. G., Moncloa, F., Dorfman, R. I. Studies on the possible inhibitory effect of corticosterone on corticosteroidogenesis at the adrenal level in the rat. *Endocrinology*, **67**, 379–88 (1960)

228. Vinson, G. P. The relationship between corticosterone synthesis from endogenous precursors and from added radioactive precursors by rat adrenal tissue *in vitro*. *J. Endocrinol.*, **36**, 231–38 (1966)

229. Bohus, B. Feedback effect of corticosteroids at the adrenal level. *Acta Physiol. Acad. Sci. Hung.*, **29**, 203–8 (1966)

230. Endröczi, E., Lissak, K. Data on the specific functional adaptation of the adrenal cortex. *Acta Physiol. Acad. Sci. Hung.*, **15**, 25–26 (1959)

231. Langecker, H., Lurie, R. Die Hemmung der Corticotropin-sekretion durch Steroide. *Acta Endocrinol.*, **25**, 54–59 (1957)

232. Fekete, G., Gorog, P. The inhibitory action of natural and synthetic glucocorticoids on adrenal steroidogenesis at the adrenal level. *J. Endocrinol.*, **27**, 123–26 (1963)

233. Ferguson, J. J., Jr., Morita, Y., Mendelsohn, L. Incorporation *in vitro* of precursor into protein and RNA of rat adrenal. *Endocrinology*, **80**, 521–26 (1967)

234. Morrow, L. B., Burrow, G. W., Mulrow, P. J. Inhibition of adrenal

protein synthesis by steroids *in vitro*. *Endocrinology*, **80**, 883–88 (1967)

235. Kitay, J. I., Coyne, M. D., Nelson, R., Newsom, W. Relation of the testis to adrenal enzyme activity and adrenal corticosterone production in the rat. *Endocrinology*, **78**, 1061–66 (1966)

236. Sturcz, J., Spät, A., Szigeti, R. Effect of local aldosterone concentration on aldosterone production in incubated adrenals. *Acta Physiol. Acad. Sci. Hung.*, **30**, 125–28 (1966)

237. Ohsawa, N. Effect of administration of ACTH on adrenal responsiveness of hypophysectomized rats. *Endocrinology*, **77**, 461–66 (1965)

238. Graber, A. L., Ney, R. L., Nicholson, W. E., Island, D. P., Liddle, G. W. Natural history of pituitary-adrenal recovery following long term suppression with corticosteroids. *J. Clin. Endocrinol. Metab.*, **25**, 11–16 (1965)

239. Bransome, E. D., Jr. Caution in the use of actinomycin in investigating hormone action. *49th Meeting Endocrine Soc., Miami, Florida, June 1967, Abstr. No. 70*

240. Bransome, E. D., Jr. Actinomycin D and adrenal cortex: damage, recovery and cortisol production (Submitted for publication)

241. Levine, S. O., Glick, D., Nakane, P. K. Adrenal and plasma corticosterone and vitamin A in rat adrenal glands during postnatal development. *Endocrinology*, **80**, 910–14 (1967)

242. Eberlein, W. R., Bongiovanni, A. M., Rosenfield, R. L. Plasma 17-ketosteroids during adolescence. *57th Meeting Am. Soc. Clin. Invest., Atlantic City, N.J., May 1967*

243. Farese, R. V., Reddy, W. J. Effect of adrenocorticotrophin on adrenal protein synthesis. *Endocrinology*, **73**, 294–303 (1963)

244. Scriba, P. C., Reddy, W. J. Adrenocorticotrophin and adrenal protein synthesis. *Endocrinology*, **76**, 745–52 (1965)

245. Scriba, P. C., Fries, M. Aminoacyl transferase stimulation of protein synthesis by pig adrenal polysomes. *Nature*, **214**, 91–92 (1967)

246. Farese, R. V. Early effects of ACTH on adrenal protein synthesis. *Endocrinology*, **78**, 125–36 (1966)

247. Ferguson, J. J., Jr., Morita, Y. RNA synthesis and adrenocorticotropin responsiveness. *Biochim. Biophys. Acta*, **87**, 348–50 (1964)

248. Ney, R. L., Davis, W. W., Garren, L. D. Heterogeneity of template RNA in adrenal glands. *Science*, **153**, 896–97 (1966)

249. Farese, R. V. Effects of actinomycin D on ACTH-induced corticosteroidogenesis. *Endocrinology*, **78**, 929–36 (1966)

250. Thompson, E. B., Peterkofsky, B., Tomkins, G. M. Super-induction of tyrosine transaminase in ATC cells by inhibitors of RNA synthesis. *Fed. Proc.*, **26**, 347 (1967)

251. Farese, R. V., Schnure, J. J. Effects of ACTH on adrenal RNA synthesis. *Endocrinology*, **80**, 872–82 (1967)

252. Bransome, E. D., Jr., Chargaff, E. Synthesis of ribonucleic acids in the adrenal cortex: early effects of adrenocorticotropic hormone. *Biochim. Biophys. Acta*, **91**, 180–82 (1964)

253. Bransome, E. D., Jr. Chemical information in a mammalian cell: how many kinds of RNA are there? In *Progress in Biomedical Engineering*, 7–28 (Fogel, L. J., George, F. W., Eds., Spartan Books, Washington, D.C., 1967)

254. Bransome, E. D., Jr. The effects of ACTH on rapidly labeled adrenal cytoplasmic RNA (In preparation)

255. Bransome, E. D., Jr. Stimulation and inhibition of adrenal RNA synthesis by ACTH. *Current Mod. Biol.*, **1**, 21–23 (1967)

256. Vinson, G. P., Jones, I. C. The *in vitro* production of estrogens from progesterone by mouse adrenal glands. *J. Endocrinol.*, **29**, 185–91 (1964)

257. Goldzieher, J. W. Oestrogens in congenital adrenal hyperplasia. *Acta Endocrinol.*, **54**, 51–62 (1967)

258. Kase, N., Cohn, G. L. Clinical implications of extragonadal estrogen production. *New Engl. J. Med.*, **276**, 28–31 (1967)

259. Parkes, A. S., Deanesly, R. Relation between the gonads and the adrenal glands. In *Marshall's Physiology of Reproduction*, **III**, 1064–1111 (Parkes, A. S., Ed., Longmans, London, 1966)

260. Kitay, J. I. Pituitary-adrenal function in the rat after gonadectomy and gonadal hormone replacement. *Endocrinology*, **73**, 253–60 (1963)

261. Kitay, J. I. Effects of estrogen and androgen on the adrenal cortex of the rat. In *Functions of the Adrenal Cortex* (See Ref. 4)

262. Richard, R. Estrogen effects on pituitary-adrenal function via the hypothalamus and hypophysis. *Neuroendocrinology,* **1,** 322–32 (1966)

263. Ramirez, V. D., Moore, D., McCann, S. M. Independence of luteinizing hormone and adrenocorticotrophin secretion in the rat. *Proc. Soc. Exptl. Biol. Med.,* **118,** 169–73 (1965)

264. Chowers, I., McCann, S. M. The effects on ACTH and gonadotrophin secretion of implants of gonadal steroids in the hypothalamo-hypophyseal region. *Israel Med. J.,* **22,** 420–32 (1963)

265. Telegdy, G., Schreiberg, G., Endröczi, E. Effect of estrogens implanted into the hypothalamus on the activity of the pituitary adrenocortical system. *Acta Physiol. Acad. Sci. Hung.,* **25,** 229–34 (1964)

266. Daughaday, W. H. The binding of corticosteroids by plasma protein. In *The Adrenal Cortex* (See Ref. 3), 385–403

267. Sandberg, A. A. Protein-steroid interactions. In *Steroid Dynamics,* 1–59 (Pincus, G., Nakao, T., Tait, J. F., Eds., Academic Press, Inc., New York, 577 pp., 1966)

268. Seal, U. S., Doe, R. P. Corticosteroid-binding globulin: biochemistry, physiology, and phylogeny. In *Steroid Dynamics,* 63–87 (Pincus, G., Nakao, T., Tait, J. R., Eds., Academic Press, New York, 577 pp., 1966)

269. Gala, R. R., Westphal, U. Further studies on the corticosteroid-binding globulin of the rat: proposed endocrine control. *Endocrinology,* **79,** 67–75 (1966)

270. Mestman, J. H., Nelson, D. H. Inhibition by estrogen administration of adrenal-pituitary response to methopyrapone. *J. Clin. Invest.,* **42,** 1529–34 (1963)

271. Nelson, D. H. Some effects of estrogens on the metabolic action and secretion of the adrenal steroids, In *Functions of the Adrenal Cortex* (See Ref. 4)

272. Kitay, J. I. Adrenal biosynthesis of tetrahydrocortisone regulated by estrogen and androgen. *Fed. Proc.,* **25,** 551 (1966)

273. Kitay, J. I. Control of adrenal steroid secretion. *2nd Intern. Congr. Hormonal Steroids. Excerpta Med. Intern. Congr. Ser. 111,* 210 (1966)

274. Rosenfeld, R. S., Fukushima, D. K., Gallagher, T. F. Metabolism of adrenal cortical hormones. In *The Adrenal Cortex* (See Ref. 3), 103–32

275. Luetscher, J. A., Camargo, C. H., Cheville, R. H., Hancock, E. W., Dowdy, A. J., Nokes, G. W. Conjugation and excretion of aldosterone: testing of models with an analog computer. In *Steroid Dynamics,* 341–53 (Pincus, G., Nakao, T., Tait, J. F., Eds., Academic Press, New York, 577 pp., 1966)

276. *Steroid Conjugates* (Berstein, S., Contrall, E., Dusza, J. P., Joseph, P. J., Eds., Chem. Abstr. Serv., Am. Chem. Soc., Washington, D.C., 1966)

277. Dollefeld, E., Breuer, H. Vorkommen, Biogenese, und Stoffwechsel von Steroidsulfaten. *Z. Vitamin-Hormon- Fermentforsch.,* **14,** 194–298 (1966)

THE THYROID[1,2,3] 1006

By Sidney C. Werner and Janusz A. Nauman

*College of Physicians and Surgeons of Columbia University, New York, N.Y.
and Postgraduate Medical College, Warsaw, Poland*

An effort has been made to review the research of the past three years
since the previous survey on the thyroid (1). The product was then reduced to the required space and number of citations. Since the literature
during this period is practically endless, and since the numerous specialized
areas within the field provide long backgrounds of their own which relate
to present work, only a few areas of perhaps more active or personal interest have been surveyed. Comprehensive reviews have been cited, whenever
possible. Where articles are related, the earlier ones generally have not
been listed, in order to keep the number of references within bounds.

Several major conceptual changes arose in the time under consideration. Among these the thyroid emerged as a dual endocrine structure, concerned not only with the production of the traditional thyroid hormones
thyroxine and triiodothyronine but also with the fabrication and release of
a calcium-lowering principle, thyrocalcitonin. A physiological role of this
latter in man, though still not settled, seems probable (2). This subject,
which properly belongs with the calcium and phosphorus regulation of the
body, has been carefully reviewed (3), and so will not be treated further
here. Measurement of total and dialyzable triiodothyronine in serum was
achieved (4) and, together with kinetic data from radioactive triiodothyronine disappearance studies (5), suggested a metabolic role for triiodothyronine approximately equal to that of thyroxine (4). The startling concept
that hyperthyroidisim (Graves' disease) may be autoimmune in origin
(6–9) arose from a body of circumstantial evidence.

Control of Thyroid Function

Continuing efforts to establish suprahypothalamic centers in the central
nervous system concerned with thyroidal regulation were made, but failed
to utilize the more reliable indices of thyroid function, such as thyroid and

[1] The survey of literature for this review was concluded in June 1967.

[2] Abbreviations used in the paper include: immunoglobulin G (IgG); thyroxine
(T4); triiodothyronine (T3); iodide (I); thyrotropin-releasing factor (TRF).
Radioactive compounds are indicated by *, e.g. I*, but for a specific isotope, T4 ^{131}I,
for example; thyroxine-binding globulin (TBG); thyroxine-binding prealbumin
(TBPA).

[3] Aided in part by grants AM-00008 (C18 and 19) and International Postdoc-
toral Fellowship (J.A.N.) (2-F05-TW-843-01) United States Public Health Service.

renal clearances and absolute iodine uptake. An excellent review of the
subject of neural control was published by Reichlin (10), as well as in a
British Symposium (11). Evidence for the existence of a thyrotropin-releasing factor (TRF) of hypothalamic origin was summarized by Guillemin (12).

HYPOTHALAMUS

The hypothalamus appears to establish the "set point" of response of
the pituitary to changes in blood levels of thyroid hormones (10). Responsiveness at any given set point, however, is not altered (10). For example,
transplantation of the rat pituitary into the anterior chamber of the eye diminished but did not abolish either the unique ability of the gland to mono-
deiodinate radioactive thyroxine to radioactive triiodothyronine or its
ability to increase this capacity following thyroidectomy (13). Similarly,
thyrotropin release in response to propylthiouracil in hypophysectomized
rats was augmented when the pituitary was placed in direct contact with
the median eminence rather than in other sites (14). Purves and group
(15) suggested that the ectopic rat pituitary developed a hypersensitivity to
thyroxine with undue inhibition of the feedback system and hence of thyrotropin release as a result.

Effects of temperature and altitude.—The effects of temperature, and
presumably of barometric pressure, are probably hypothalamic mediated
(10). A symposium upon this topic was held recently (16). Hemoconcentra-
tion, however, probably accounted for the changes attributed to altered thyroid function seen in men exposed to cold (17) or to altitude (18), although in rats, thyroid function was decreased with exposure (19). Hemo-
concentration could also explain the increases in protein-bound iodine levels reported in human subjects in winter over summer levels (20). Rats
showed an inverse relationship between thyroid activity and ambient temperature (30, 24, and 5° C) in a double-label experiment (21). The suggestion that fecal loss of thyroid hormones resulted in compensatory thyroid
activation of rats exposed to cold (22) probably does not apply to man, in
view of the limited enterohepatic recirculation of thyroxine (23). Thyroidal response of the rat to hyperbaric conditions was attributed to stress
(24.)

Thyrotropin-releasing factor (TRF).—Since Guillemin has detailed
the subject of hypothalamic-releasing factors (12), only a few points need
be mentioned here. On the basis of a highly purified ovine TRF which contained less than 5–8 per cent by weight as amino acids, he and co-workers
suggested that TRF may not be a polypeptide, although they did not exclude the possibility of an unusual peptide structure (12). Schally (25) and
co-workers claimed 600,000-fold purification of porcine TRF (25). They
concluded that TRF is not a simple polypeptide but they emphasized persistence throughout purification of histidine, glutamic acid, and proline (25).

In vitro, TRF increased both thyrotropin synthesis and release by the mouse pituitary (26); *in vivo*, injection of the factor resulted within five minutes in depletion of pituitary thyrotropin content, whereas vasopressin and cerebral cortex extracts as controls were ineffective; histamine and stress, on the other hand, increased pituitary thyrotropin content but did not induce release (27). Treatment with thyroxine did not alter hypothalamic TRF content of mice but blocked pituitary response to TRF (28). Block was overcome by actinomycin D or cycloheximide, which suggests that TRF does not act through acute synthesis of protein, but that thyroxine may cause synthesis at the pituitary level of a labile substance that inhibits TRF effect (29). Response to TRF was also blocked by pretreatment with vasopressin but not with melanocyte-stimulating hormone (28).

Thyrotropin

Since this hormone was mainly employed to study thyroid hormone synthesis and release (see below), only a few general facts are presented here. A review is available (30).

Mechanism of action.—Scott and co-workers (31) pointed out that the metabolic effects on the thyroid of pituitary thyrotropin and of the circulating long-acting thyroid stimulator of Graves' disease resembled the changes produced when other tissues were activated by stimulatory mechanisms: alterations in membrane permeability, protein secretion, sodium transport, transmission of nerve impulses, and phagocytosis (or pinocytosis). Thus, thyrotropin initiated pinocytosis within the follicular lumen, followed by hydrolysis of lysosomal enzymes (32). Scott et al. concluded that if long-acting thyroid stimulator and thyrotropin act on the cell membrane, they share common receptor sites; but since chemically different sites may have been involved as well, differences in effects on intermediary metabolism would be explained (31) (see also below).

Pastan and Roth have demonstrated that thyrotropin was almost instantaneously bound by surface sites in the cell membrane of thyroid cell slices *in vitro* (33). Antithyrotropin serum or trypsin completely blocked thyrotropin activation of $^{14}CO_2$ production from glucose-1-^{14}C up to fifteen minutes after binding was permitted but only partially (40 per cent block) at one hour (33). Pastan and group (34) also isolated an ammonium sulfate-precipitated bacterial protein from the growth medium of *Clostridium perfringens* which acted like thyrotropin on dog or beef thyroid slices in increasing glucose-1-^{14}C oxidation and ^{32}P incorporation into phospholipids. "Bacterial thyroid stimulator" *in vivo* in chicks induced pseudopod formation, intracellular colloid droplets, and ^{131}I release; and it appeared to be a protein of molecular weight about 30,000, which was inactivated by exposure to 100°C and to pronase but displayed no enzymatic activity of its own (34).

Thyrotropin preferentially promoted secretion of radioactive triiodothyronine when given repeatedly to two subjects (35). This is in line with the implication from kinetic data that triiodothyronine may be preferentially secreted by the thyroid (4). Iodide caused an abrupt decrease in the output of radioactive triiodothyronine by the thyroid, and in the proportion of it in the blood (35).

Soderberg's hypothesis that the vasoactive amine, serotonin, has a role in thyrotropin action on the thyroid was confirmed by Clayton & Szego (36). Enhancement of thyroidal blood flow in the rat and decline of the normally high serotonin content of the thyroid were seen within minutes of intravenous administration of thyrotropin along with an increase in thyroid water. However, iodide discharge did not correlate well with increases in blood flow in the past studies so the significance of their observation is not entirely clear. Histamine liberated by serotonin release was postulated to regulate local circulation of the thyroid (37), though not in any specific relation to thyrotropic action.

Bioassay.—Two reviews of bioassay of thyrotropin are available (38, 39). The marked variability inherent in the methods for either thyrotropin or serum long-acting thyroid stimulator of Graves' disease continued to be a major problem, not only within a given system (40, 41), but among different systems (42). Circadian variation, and a drop in level of thyrotropin in the mouse within minutes after handling, injection, or other stimuli, were observed (43). Differences in sources of the same diet (44), in strain of mouse (44), or in substrain (45) greatly affected the outcome.

Sakiz & Guillemin (40) removed some of the heterogeneity in the raw data from the McKenzie assay for thyrotropin by logarithmic transformation of the initial and response counts followed by analysis of the log response counts with the log initial count as a covariant. McKenzie (41) adapted this procedure to assay for long-acting thyroid stimulator. In contrast, Becktel (46) confirmed Levy's claim that only minor gain in precision resulted from covariance analysis with thyrotropin in the mouse assay and found too in mouse and chick that the logarithm of the ratio of response count to initial count used by Levy was roughly but satisfactorily proportional to the width of the confidence intervals.

Good & Stenhouse (47) proposed a new assay design to minimize variability in the data, in which the mice were reused randomly 24 hours later. With logarithmic transformation of the data, they claimed to have detected thyrotropin in normal rat blood for the first time. Codeine and, earlier, morphine were used to suppress release of thyotropin as a factor (48), and dexamethasone-21-PO_4 has been similarly employed in thyrotropin-releasing factor and hence thyrotropin, bioassay experiments (29). Averill avoided thyroxine administration but used phenobarbital and an increase in ambient temperature to 34°C to depress endogenous pituitary thyrotropin secretion in the mouse (49). He showed that infusion of thyrotropin, as opposed to a single injection, quadrupled the response to the same dose and prolonged the response (48). Intraperitoneal injection was recommended for thyrotropin (50) and for assay for long-acting thyroid stimulator (51); and an *in vitro* assay was proposed for both, using measurement of ^{131}I release from the ^{131}I-labeled whole mouse thyroid lobe (52).

Immunoassay.—Biologic variability in assay can be avoided by immunoassay. Since thyrotropin is relatively species specific, thyrotropin of the species to be tested is customarily used as an antigen. Nonetheless, human thyrotropin was assayed with antibovine thyrotropin sera (53). Immunoassay depends on displacement of labeled thyrotropin previously reacted with antithyrotropin by unlabeled exogenous or endogenous thyrotropin. For assay in man, Utiger employed a double antibody technique (54) to measure the liberated unbound fraction, whereas Odell used the differential solubility in 55 per cent alcohol-5 per cent NaCl of human thyrotropin and human thyrotropin-antibody complex (55).

No correction was made for antibodies to contaminating serum proteins, since only thyrotropin was found antigenic, but cross-reaction with human chorionic gonadotropin and luteinizing hormone led Odell to absorb out human chorionic gonadotropin antibody (55). Formation of sensitizing antibody specifically against bovine thyrotropin was seen in man in response to a previous injection of a commercial bovine thyrotropin preparation (56). Despite the potential sources of error just indicated, immunoassay gave values corresponding to those expected.

Control of thyrotropin release.—Reichlin & Utiger (57) used immunoassay to establish that plasma thyrotropin concentration is a curvilinear function of either total or free thyroxine concentrations. A relation was suggested between deiodination of thyroid hormones and suppression of thyrotropin release (58), in line with an earlier hypothesis currently under contention concerning thyroxine action in general (59, 60). With triiodothyronine, no correlation between deiodination and potency was evident (58). However, antithyroid agents were used to block peripheral deiodination, so that altered pituitary responsiveness to thyroid hormones may possibly have resulted also and conditioned the result.

The well-known inhibition of thyrotropin release by acute stressing procedures was prevented in rats by antecedent chronic stress of minor intensity and by chronic reserpine administration; elevation of basal thyrotropin levels was also noted (61).

Chemical nature.—Inactivation of biological activity and of immunological competence of purified bovine thyrotropin by irradiation with a 2-meV electron beam (62) indicated that biological activity is impaired by ionization anywhere in the molecule whereas immunologic competence is damaged by ionization in a smaller part of the molecule (62). Efforts at purification of thyrotropin have been reviewed by Bates & Condliffe (63). More recently, Jakoby (64) crystallized bovine thyrotropin from weak ammonium sulfate concentrations.

Long-Acting Thyroid Stimulator

Excellent surveys of work with this agent present in the blood of patients with Graves' disease, are available as mentioned above (6–9). Apart from a later onset, and more prolonged duration, of effect, few if any other differences in responses to long-acting thyroid stimulator and thyrotropin

were known. Unlike thyrotropin, however, the stimulator failed to act on
the thyroid of the stasis tadpole or chick (65); and its effect was neutralized by anti-IgG but not by unconcentrated antithyrotropin serum whereas
thyrotropin was neutralized by antithyrotropin and not by anti-IgG serum
(11). A "short-acting" stimulator similarly neutralized by anti-IgG but not
antithyrotropin serum was identified in serum together with the long-acting
stimulator following ^{131}I treatment (66).

Pathogenetic role in hyperthyroidism.—The long-acting thyroid stimulator stimulated the human thyroid (67). Nonetheless, the percentage of positive assays in patients with hyperthyroidism was relatively low, particularly
in the absence of eye changes (68). This may be due to inadequate sensitivity of the mouse assay method, to frequently toxic serum, or to nonspecific
responses. A 40 per cent incidence of positive responses in active thyrotoxicosis was increased to 80 per cent by 7–15-fold concentration of IgG (11).
Normal human sera similarly concentrated gave negative responses.

Similarly low incidences of stimulator were found by Kriss and his
group. They observed that, although 17 of 24 patients with Graves' disease
had no demonstrable long-acting thyroid stimulator either before or after
[131]I treatment, the stimulator appeared after therapy in three of the remaining seven, together with worsening of the eye changes (68). This group
reaffirmed the earlier suggestion by others that the stimulator was related
to the eye changes rather than to thyroidal hyperfunctioning. Nonetheless,
negative stimulator titers were obtained in two patients wih extremely advanced severe eye changes of Graves' disease (69).

Perhaps the most telling argument for long-acting thyroid stimulator as
a pathogenetic agent for all the manifestations of Graves' disease is the
fact that neonatal hyperthyroidism includes the eye changes; and activity
waxes as the stimulator titer in the neonate reaches its peak, and wanes
shortly after birth as the titer subsides; transplacental passage of the stimulator seems certain in view of this course and of the consistent presence
of the stimulator in the maternal blood (70). Nonetheless, thyroid stimulation was found at autopsy thirteen weeks after birth of an infant with only
minimal stimulator levels at birth (71), a fact somewhat inconsistent with
an estimated half-life of six to seven days (72) for long-acting thyroid
stimulator.

Antibody nature.—This subject has been well summarized (9). Activity
of long-acting thyroid stimulator remains closely associated with the IgG
fraction of the serum proteins despite concentration, even to 30-fold (73).
Dorrington & Munro's claim that such activity was associated with immunoglobulin A (IgA) was retracted (9), although in an antigen-antibody
system, overlap was to be expected.

Long-acting thyroid stimulator behaved like an antibody upon fractionation with papain (9) with change from a long-acting to a short-acting substance, although the activity, found only in the Fab fragment of the split
IgG remaining after hydrolysis, still was not neutralized by antithyrotropin

but only by anti-IgG serum (9). The likelihood of a thyrotropin-like substance bound to an antibody molecule seems small, despite the report of long-acting effects from a mixture of thyrotropin with antithyrotropin serum (74), results perhaps explained by slow splitting off of thyrotropin from antibody.

Thyroidal antigen.—A possible antigen responsible for long-acting thyroid stimulator production was suggested. The stimulator was maximally removed from serum by whole thyroid homogenates, by the thyroid microsomal fraction as opposed to other subcellular particles, and by thyroid endoplasmic reticulum (9). However, ^{131}I-labeled normal IgG was absorbed by thyroid subcellular fractions to the same extent as similarly labeled stimulator IgG (75).

There was one report of failure to absorb out long-acting thyroid stimulator activity by incubation with human thyroid slices or cell membranes (76). A possible explanation may come from the description of a stimulator "protector" by Adams & Kennedy (77). A saline extract of human thyrotoxic thyroid tissue adsorbed out stimulator activity from positive sera (77) but adsorption was blocked by addition of serum from a stimulator-negative thyrotoxic patient. The agent protecting against adsorption, "protector", was postulated to be an incomplete or blocking stimulator-type antibody.

Seemingly complete removal of the thyroidal "antigen" by total surgical thyroidectomy was accomplished in two patients and only a minute fragment was left in another two; there resulted a transient decrease in long-acting thyroid stimulator titer, a sustained drop in antithyroglobulin tanned red cell titer, but no corresponding improvement in the eye changes (78).

Efforts to induce formation of stimulator in rabbits by injection of whole human thyroid homogenates and microsomal fraction met with variable success (6). McKenzie (79) maintained stimulator production, together with antithyroglobulin antibody for six months with suggestive increase in uptake by the thyroid and in protein-bound iodine although thyroiditis was a complicating factor. Lymphocytes from patients with Graves' disease were grown with phytohemagglutinin and released long-acting stimulator (6) neutralized by anti-IgG serum (80). Minimal amounts, only, were present despite assay of concentrated medium. Similar concentration of the medium alone occasionally produced positive assay responses in the same range as from the lymphocytes (81). Lymphoid tissue itself gave a negative response for long-acting thyroid stimulator (6), and a battery of immunologic tests gave no evidence of a conventional antigen-antibody response (82).

Mechanism of action.—The failure of long-acting stimulator to act on the thyroid of lower forms has already been mentioned (65). Differences among mammalian responses have also emerged. Stimulator and thyrotropin augmented *in vitro* oxidation of glucose and ^{32}P incorporation into phospholipids in both sheep (31) and dog (83) thyroid slices. The former stimulated ^{32}P incorporation into lecithin and monophosphatidylinositol equally, thyrotropin mainly into the latter; in contrast to thyrotropin, stimulator increased labeling of neutral lipids from U-^{14}C glucose although both agents decreased the labeled triglyceride/diglyceride ratio (31). Field (83) noted that the same lag occurred before stimulator effect *in vitro* as *in vivo*. McKenzie could not demonstrate antibody injury to the thyroid cell or inhibition of an intrathyroidal suppressor gene (6).

MISCELLANEOUS THYROTROPIC FACTORS

Four thyrotropin-like factors were under investigation.

Heterothyrotrope factor.—Fontaine observed a heterothyrotrope factor in some fractions of mammalian pituitary extracts, which showed low thyrotropin activity in mice but high activity in fish (84). This material appeared closely related to mammalian thyrotropin in molecular weight and amino acid composition, which suggests it might be an incomplete thyrotropin.

Exophthalmos-producing substance.—This substance was questioned as an entity. Winland (85) could not separate pituitary extracts into thyrotropin and exophthalmos-producing substance. Chemically, Horster and group (86) localized the substance into the third or small peptide fraction eluting from a Sephadex G-200 column. Water retention from such peptides could be reflected by proptosis in the fish, in response to changes in osmotic pressure.

Chorionic and tumor thyrotropins.—Kock (87) found the thyrotropin-like substance, shown by others in choriocarcinoma, to be present in pregnancy with hydatidiform mole. Hennen (88) obtained a weak thyrotropin-like response from normal placental extracts, and characterized a similar material in the serum of several patients with bronchogenic carcinoma.

Unclassified pituitary thyrotropin of Graves' disease.—A substance was extracted from the pituitaries of four hyperthyroid patients, three actively thyrotoxic at death, which behaved like thyrotropin upon bioassay and in Bates' percolation method, but which did not concentrate long-acting thyroid stimulator and which was not neutralized by antithyrotropin sera (89). Further elucidation is necessary.

HORMONAL SYNTHESIS AND RELEASE

The role of the nucleus, or of particular chromosomes within the nucleus, of the thyroid cell has remained unclarified. Al Saadi et al. (90) suggested that chromosome 15 might carry genetic information concerned with the regulation of orderly thyroid cell growth, upon finding that one of the chromosomes of this pair was lost in some thyroid tumors induced by iodine deficiency in Fisher rats.

Knowledge of the function of the thyroid cell nucleic acids also has remained limited. Exogenous or endogenous stimulation of the rat thyroid did not alter DNA concentration per wet weight of tissue (91). In mammals, total thyroid DNA compared either to the relative decrease in RNA content, or to the increase in gland protein concentration, decreased relatively little with increasing body size (92). Thyroid RNA content, together with ^{32}P and uridine-^{14}C incorporation, was significantly augmented by thyrotropin stimulation in the chick (93) and rat (91), a seemingly specific effect since uridine phosphorylase and uridine kinase each became more than twice as active as before treatment whereas the liver enzyme activities were unaffected (94).

Stimulation of messenger RNA has long been suggested as a possible primary action of thyrotropin with enhanced synthesis of specific enzymes or proteins resulting in hormonal biosynthesis. In this direction, actinomycin D abolished thyrotropin effect on both thyroidal ^{131}I uptake and organic iodine formation in hypophysectomized rats. Actinomycin D and puromycin administered 24–48 hours before thyrotropin injection reduced responsiveness to thyrotropin and long-acting stimulator in the McKenzie assay (51) but smaller doses of either actinomycin D or puromycin did not inhibit thyrotropin effect upon uptake or release when infused directly into the thyroid of intact rabbits (25, 96). The latter workers explained the discrepancy by the fact that the former group used high systemic concentrations of both antibiotics with consequent toxicity (96).

Hormone Synthesis

The discussion follows the major recognized "steps" in hormonal synthesis.

Iodide transport.—Iodide transport is considered to be "active" and energy dependent, with an intact cell membrane a prerequisite for concentration. The lipid nature of membranes in general led Schneider & Wolff (97) to investigate various phospholipids isolated from thyroid cells. Some, characterized by unsaturated lecithins or choline plasmogens, bound iodide (98). Binding was reversible and univalent anions (CLO_4^- ReO_4^- SCN^- Br^- NO_3^-) displaced iodide from the binding sites in the same sequence as in thyroid cell slices (97). A phospholipid concept was also supported by the fact that phospholipases A, C, and D abolished the iodine-concentrating ability of beef thyroid slices. Nonetheless, two protein fractions free of phospholipase A activity were since found which strongly inhibited iodide transport (98).

A role for ouabain-sensitive ATPase in active thyroid iodide transport remains doubtful. Increases in endogenous thyrotropin augmented thyroidal ouabain-sensitive ATPase activity and enhanced T/S (thyroid/serum) ratio; but when the T/S ratio was depressed by triiodothyronine administration or hypophysectomy, no consistent decrease in enzyme activity followed, nor an increase after the ratio was elevated by a short period of treatment with prophylthiouracil (99) or with cystamine or cysteamine (100). Finally, amphotericin B did not alter thyroidal ouabain-sensitive ATPase although iodide transport was inhibited in beef thyroid slices *in vitro,* T/M (thyroid/medium) ratio reduced, thyroid potassium concentration lowered, and sodium concentration elevated (101). Nonetheless, the possibility remains that a minute, and presently not identifiable, fraction of total nonspecific ATPase may be ouabain-sensitive ATPase and involved in iodide transport; or ouabain may have interfered with iodide retention by, but not with entry of iodide into, the thyroid (102).

Incorporation.—Oxidation of trapped iodide and incorporation of active iodide into tyrosine is generally considered to be a peroxidase-mediated step; available evidence has been recently reviewed (103). The source of H_2O_2 *in vivo* remains unknown. Peroxidase, purified from hog thyroid mitochondria and microsomes, contained iron, mostly in heme; and addition of hematine stimulated both oxidation of iodide and incorporation (104). It was thus held that the peroxidase may exist mainly as holoenzyme and the rest as apoenzyme (104). However, dissociation into apoenzyme and an iron-porphyrin prosthetic group was not demonstrated (105); and Yip (106) separated the peroxidase into two fractions, one of which contained no heme but which was nevertheless highly active in iodinating tyrosine residues and in oxidizing $NADH_2$ although unable to catalyze peroxidation of O-dianisidine. The hemoprotein in the second fraction, to the contrary, was less active in respect to tyrosine iodination, but very active in O-dianisidine peroxidation (107). Thus, the nature of enzyme has not been established and it is possible that the particulate material from thyroid extracts contains several peroxidases.

The importance of NADH or NADPH, and the flavin nucleotides, has generally been emphasized (108). Schulz et al. (109), on the other hand, investigated oxidation of tyramine catalyzed by a monoamine oxidase as the source of thyroidal H_2O_2 and postulated, as well, an internal regulatory mechanism through formation of 3-iodotyramine from iodotyrosines by the same thyroidal enzyme. The enzyme was present in the nonparticulate fraction of bovine thyroid glands, catalyzed decarboxylation of tyrosine, monoiodotyrosine, and phenylalanine, and was highly specific for aromatic amino acids (109).

After trapping, iodination of tyrosine probably takes place in tyrosine residues in thyroglobulin rather than in the free amino acid. Organification of iodide, with formation of newly iodinated thyroglobulin, occurred within seconds of ^{131}I or ^{125}I administration (110). Although thyroglobulin iodination was localized both to the follicular lumen (111) and to the thyroid cell proper (112), autoradiography revealed that shortly after ^{125}I administration, all protein-bound radioactivity was localized in the follicular colloid in close association with the microvilli (113). This suggested that the iodination mechanism may be at the surface of these structures (113). Moreover, purified sRNA from thyroid did not accept mono- or diiodotyrosine, a finding contrary to the theory that there is iodination of free tyrosine; and puromycin, which almost completely inhibits incorporation of tyrosine-^{14}C or leucine-^{14}C into thyroid protein, had no effect on iodine organification (95, 96, 114).

Coupling reaction.—The coupling reaction responsible for iodothyronine formation from iodotyrosines has been discussed (106). The type of enzyme involved, if any, and the intermediate or intermediates needed for the reaction to take place, remain unelucidated. Fisher et al. (115) extracted an enzyme system from beef thyroid microsomes which catalyzed *in vitro* the synthesis of 3,3'-diiodothyronine from monoiodotyrosine, and of thyroxine from diiodotyrosine. The reaction required manganese ion and pyridoxal or its phosphate for completion. Liunggren (116) obtained thyroxine upon oxidation of diiodotyrosine by an H_2O_2-generating system employing horse-radish peroxidase. He suggested that 4-hydroxy-3,5-diiodophenyl pyruvic acid might be the intermediate. However, no known H_2O_2 generating system has been linked to the coupling reaction *in vivo,* unless possibly the system involved in organification of iodide is available for this purpose as well.

Thyroglobulin.—A review of the chemical, physical, and immunological properties of thyroglobulin is available (117). Subsequent to this review, two distinct carbohydrate units were identified in thyroglobulin (118, 119). One, molecular weight 1050, consisted of five residues of mannose and one residue of glucosamine; the other, molecular weight 3200, consisted of sialic acid, fructose, galactose, mannose, and glucosamine. Nine smaller units and fourteen larger units were identified per molecule of thyroglobulin. Particulate systems also were identified which were active in the synthesis of both carbohydrate and peptide moieties (119).

The transport of amino acids into the thyroid cell as studied by means of nonmetabolized amino acids, α-aminoisobutyric acid, and cycloleucine as models has shown that concentration of these amino acids in thyroid slices was a function of time, and was partially, but not entirely, dependent on oxidative metabolism (120). Intracellular binding sites appeared to be involved in the transport.

After transport, the synthesis of thyroglobulin followed the steps generally accepted for protein synthesis in general, a sequence demonstrated in thyroid cell-free preparations (121). Neither deoxyribonuclease nor actinomycin D affected synthesis for the first 24 hours, which indicates considerable stability of thyroid mRNA (121). Synthesis of thyroid protein was inhibited by both iodide and thyroxine administration whereas iodine deficiency increased incorporation of valine-^{14}C by rat thyroid slices and a thyroid cell-free amino acid-incorporating system (122). The largest increase occurred in the supernatant and microsomal fractions. Contrariwise, protein synthesis was reduced by the addition of thyroxine to the incubation mixture. Since thyroxine is a product of iodinated thyroglobulin degradation, the possibility was raised that a feedback mechanism specifically inhibited thyroglobulin synthesis (122, 123).

The site of synthesis was localized by autoradiography and electronmicroscopy to the ribosomes of the endoplasmic reticulum (113, 124). The protein moiety, still uniodinated, migrated through the cisternae of the ergoplasm to the Golgi zone and then, in the form of vesicles, to the apical region of the cells for secretion into the colloid of the lumen (113, 124). Four iodoproteins were distinguished in the thyroid by ultracentrifugation, 12S, 19S, and 27S (111), plus a small percentage of 4S iodoprotein (125). The 12S and 27 iodoproteins had the same solubility properties and electrophoretic mobility as 19S thyroglobulin, and most likely have the same primary structure. The 12S component is believed to be the immediate precursor (126) ; the 27S component probably to be either a dimer of 19S or a mixture of equimolecular amounts of 19S, 12S, and 6S proteins, with the same amino acid composition and common immunological properties (127).

As already indicated, synthesis and iodination of thyroglobulin are independent processes (113, 127, 128), and iodination can take place in 12S protein as well as in 19S. An uniodinated 17S protein was isolated from sheep thyroid, with synthesis but not iodination shown in both thyroid slices and a cell-free system (125). This indicates that a high degree of polymerization can be attained in the thyroid without iodination. Chemical iodination of the 17S protein yielded 19S thyroglobulin (125).

Proteolysis of thyroglobulin within the cell was traced to a series of coordinated steps. Follicular luminal colloid migrated by pinocytosis through the cell toward the capillaries in the form of colloid droplets or vesicles (32, 113, 124). Lysis of thyroglobulin probably occurred within droplets from proteolytic enzymes contributed either by lysosomes (32, 113, 129) or by the plasma membrane surrounding the vesicle during pinocytosis (113). The nature of the proteolytic enzymes involved is obscure: the peak activities of the many so far isolated from thyroid tissue have been at an unphysiological pH. Deiss et al. (130) demonstrated peak activity for lysis of thyroglobulin in dog thyroid homogenates at pH 3.5–4.0, the optimum for lysosomal cathepsin. Peak enzyme activity was at pH 5.0–6.0 when thyrotropin was injected before the thyroid was removed, which suggests that *in vivo* this enzyme system may be active at a physiological pH (130). A proteolytic enzyme from thyroid rat homogenates which did catalyze lysis at physiological pH proved to be of thyroid mast cell origin (37).

Intrathyroidal deiodinase.—Iodotyrosine deiodinase (ITDase), which catalyzes deiodination of iodotyrosines liberated during hydrolysis of thyroglobulin, has been found in thyroid subcellular fractions: 90 per cent in the mitochondrial and microsomal fractions and 10 per cent in the soluble fractions (131). Upon electrophoresis, the ITDase in the particulate fractions migrated cathodally whereas that in the soluble fraction migrated toward the anode. The existence of two isozymic forms of ITDase was suggested, although extrathyroidal ITDase and the intrathyroidal enzyme are probably identical. Liver enzyme activity behaved like that of the thyroid, on partitioning, whereas only the particulate fraction was active in kidney material (131).

Energy production.—The close relationship between the intermediary metabolism of the thyroid and energy production for thyroid synthesis and secretion has been detailed (132, 133). Despite all, no direct relationship between cell respiration and the iodination and coupling reactions has been established. Iodide transport was blocked by agents which uncouple oxidative phosphorylation, yet carbohydrate utilization and the Krebs-cycle enzymes were not inhibited by methimazole and $KClO_4$, agents which also suppress iodide transport (134). Bishydroxycoumarin, too, had no effect on cell respiration but almost completely arrested iodination (133, 134). NADPH distribution in the thyroid was correlated with oxidation of glucose through the pentose shunt, whereas NADH and ATP were correlated with glucose oxidation via the Embden-Myerhof pathway and Krebs cycle (132). Oxidation via the former pathway exceeded that via the latter (135), though almost all the necessary enzymes for both pathways were found in thyroid slices and sheep isolated thyroid cells (136). These enzymes and the electron transport enzymes present in the primary respiratory chain in mitochondria, microsomes, and homogenates of calf thyroid were identical with those from other tissues (137, 138), except for a somewhat greater content of NADP-dependent isocitrate dehydrogenase and glucose-6-phosphate dehydrogenase in thyroid over liver (137). Presumably NADPH is thus in plentiful supply. A thyroidal DT-diaphorase enzyme system capable of transferring electrons from reduced pyridine nucleotide to flavin nucleotide was also identified, but no physiological role was revealed (139).

The relation between thyrotropin and energy production for hormone formation has remained unsettled. Thyrotopin increased glucose accumulation by thyroid tissue *in vitro* and oxidation of both carbons 1 and 6 of glucose in proportion to the dose (140). It also stimulated in calf thyroid slices the incorporation of ^{14}C-formate, glycine-2-^{14}C, and adenine-8-^{14}C into ribonucleic acids and purines. Other pituitary hormones were ineffective (141). Since glucose alone produced a similar effect, the possibility was raised that glucose and thyrotropin act by increasing available ribose and hence 5-phosphoribosyl-1-pyrophosphate (141).

Thyrotropin injected intravenously in normal rats increased total NADP content and NADPH:NADP ratio, which suggests that it not only increases pyridine nucleotide content but also promotes reduction, or inhibits oxidation, of this material (142). However, the purity of the thyrotropin preparations used may have influenced the outcome, inasmuch as crude, and more purified thyrotropin affected the dog thyroid differently *in vitro* (143). Moreover, the lag between thyrotropin administration and effect on rat thyroid oxidative enzymes was greater than with other thyrotropin-mediated changes, particularly glucose utilization (140). The mechanism of action of thyrotropin on pyridine nucleotides as well as on ATP (144) remains unknown.

Thyroidal intermediary metabolism is significantly influenced by inorganic iodide. Stimulation of labeled pyruvate, acetate, and palmitate oxidation occurred in beef thyroid slices when 0.1 mM iodide was added to the glucose-enriched medium (145). However, inhibitory effects appeared at 50 mM concentration, including decreased oxidation of labeled glucose, decreased oxygen consumption, and decreased aerobic glycolysis. Inhibition by thyroxine and triiodothyronine *in vitro* of iodination of tyrosine residues reported (146). These inhibitory actions of high concentrations of iodide or of thyroid hormones could possibly reflect the presence of mechanisms for thyroidal autoregulation.

Miscellaneous thyroidal iodoproteins.—In one study of other proteins beside thyroglobulin synthesized by the thyroid, iodoalbumin was isolated from both normal and pathological glands (147). The protein constituted less than 4 per cent of the total radioactive protein-bound iodine of normal glands, although values to 21 per cent were obtained, and yielded only iodotyrosines upon enzymatic hydrolysis (147). A protein-particulate insoluble iodoprotein was also found in normal and abnormal thyroids associated with all three particulate subcellular fractions (148). These insoluble iodoproteins, presumably heterogeneous, had a much higher mono- to diiodotyrosine ratio than thyroglobulin, comprised about 10–20 per cent of the total thyroidal protein-bound iodine, and had a very slow turnover (149); their physiological significance remains obscure.

Isolated Thyroid Cells; Organ Culture

Continuous-flow trypsinization was the most common technique employed to prepare bovine, ovine, and rat isolated thyroid cells (150). The rat cells were able to form normal appearing and functioning follicles in culture and on implantation *in vivo* (152, 153); but unlike thyroid tissue slices, the isolated thyroid cells retained their capacity to transport and accumulate radioiodine and to incorporate it into thyroglobulin-bound iodotyrosines and iodothyronines (150). The cells responded also to thyrotropin, by exit of radioiodine from bovine cells (30 per cent decrease) in the first hour of exposure and then by a 130–200 per cent rise over control values in the next five hours (151). Thyrotropin also augmented in isolated thyroid cells the synthesis of thyroglobulin and the release of iodine even when iodide transport was abolished. This confirmed Halmi's earlier suggestion from *in vivo* studies that incorporation is not secondary to increased intracellular radioiodine accumulation (150). Incorporation was not interrupted by puromycin which caused a 98 per cent block to protein, and hence enzyme, synthesis, or by 2-deoxyglucose which blocked both glucose oxidation and protein synthesis (150). Thus, the prevailing concept was confirmed, namely that iodination and coupling reactions occur only in preformed thyroglobulin.

Tong and co-workers suggested from this series of studies that thyrotropin acts at the site of protein iodination, namely, the cell surface. It stimulated incorporation of radioiodine into both 3–8S proteins, and thyroglobulin of bovine isolated thyroid cells was increased by H_2O_2 added to the medium (154). They also concluded that inhibition of organification occurred at the cellular level since isolated thyroid cells had no colloid, yet iodoamino acid synthesis was blocked by I⁻ concentrations per unit of tissue comparable to those blocking synthesis by thyroid slices (155).

Specialized function was progressively lost by bovine isolated thyroid cells grown in monolayer culture—over a period of seven to fourteen days in one study, three days in another, and with lamb cells, not before twenty to thirty days as judged histochemically (156). No effect of aging on organelles was observed except for increased lysosome activity. Unexpectedly, rat thyroid tissue in organ culture lost much of its viability in two hours, and slices were more vulnerable than whole lobes (157). In contrast, 2 mm cubes of rhesus thyroid in a steel grid maintained histological characteristics, organ-specific cytoplasmic antigen, and thyroglobulin content for two weeks, and somewhat longer with addition of thyrotropin (158). Thin human thyroid slices, similarly treated, preserved their histology and function for one week, including thyroxine release in response to thyrotropin and block to incorporation from methimazole (159).

A role of other hormones in thyrotropin action has been implied. In fetal rat glands cultured for four days, insulin potentiated thyrotropin-induced I* incorporation of radioiodine into radioactive diiodotyrosine and thyroxine (160). The effect was presumably at a step after I⁻ transport, inasmuch as perchlorate did not block insulin enhancement whereas methimazole did (160).

Hormonal Transport

Although almost all the circulating thyroxine is considered to be bound to thyroxine-binding proteins, doubt was raised as to whether triiodothyronine *in vivo* circulates in bound form (161). The concept of a single thyroxine-binding globulin was also challenged (162).

Thyroxine-binding globulin.—Two thyroxine-binding globulin (TBG) bands were identified with starch-gel electrophoresis, one termed "fast" and the other "slow" (163). TBG-like behavior of both components was demonstrated by displacement of thyroxine from its binding sites by diphenylhydantoin (162, 163) and by stable thyroxine loading (163). Only one band occurred in analbuminemic serum but two bands were reproduced by adding a normal concentration of serum albumin to this serum or to separated "slow" or "fast" TBG (162). Splitting thus probably represents the influence of a protein-protein interaction on a single species of TBG protein (162). Despite this evidence, only one TBG was found by other groups using a similar buffer system and technique of electrophoresis (164); or agar (165) or polyacrylamide (166) gel electrophoresis for protein separation.

The chemical nature of thyroxine-binding globulin is not known. The previous suggestion of a lipoprotein character has been denied (161). No TBG was present in the major human serum lipoprotein fractions isolated by several methods, whereas serum subfractions rich in thyroxine-binding globulin contained no significant concentration of lipids (161).

Thyroxine-binding prealbumin.—Two types of this substance, too, have been reported (167). Upon vertical starch-block electrophoresis of human serum, both moieties were different in their affinities and capacities for thyroxine. However, the thyroxine-binding prealbumin-like nature of the unconventional material was not verified by dialysis, or immunologically. It is thus possible that the thyroxine peak migrating with this second prealbumin area represented free rather than bound thyroxine (166). Human thyroxine-binding prealbumin was recently isolated (168). The material was electrophoretically identical with conventional prealbumin; had a molecular weight approximately 73,000, extinction coefficient, 13.6, and tryptophan content, 3.15 (168); and had one binding site per molecule (168, 169) which indicates the high specificity of this protein as a thyroxine carrier.

Thyroxine binding by albumin.—Human serum albumin, although of relatively minor importance in the physiological transport of thyroid hormones, is available in high purity and so was frequently employed in quantitative investigations of protein-hormone interactions. With fluorescence quenching, a single binding site of high affinity, and three or more weak sites, were demonstrated (170). The binding constant at pH 7.4 with a single molecule of thyroxine was 1.6×10^6, whereas the value for triiodothyronine was 3.8×10^5, although at pH 8.6 (170). Maximal binding by human serum albumin of thyroxine depends on the presence of the diphenylether structure of thyroxine, the number of iodine atoms, and the alanine side chain (particularly its carboxyl group) (171). These latter presumably interact with cationic groupings on the albumin molecule (171).

Physiological changes in thyroxine-binding proteins.—A change in distribution of thyroxine among thyroxine-binding proteins was found with aging (172). A relatively large proportion of thyroxine was bound to thyroxine-binding globulins in the youngest age groups, decreasing in middle age and increasing again in older age in correspondence with maximal thyroxine-binding capacities. The maximal binding capacities of thyroxine-binding prealbumin and the proportions of thyroxine associated with it behaved reciprocally to thyroxine-binding globulin. The relative thyroxine content of albumin remained constant.

A sex difference in thyroid hormones binding has been observed (173). Binding capacity of thyroxine-binding globulins for thyroxine was significantly higher for females whereas the capacity of thyroxine-binding prealbumin was significantly higher for males. These differences were reflected by changes in thyroxine distribution. Despite the age and sex-related changes in thyroxine-binding globulin and prealbumin, protein-bound iodine, percentage and absolute concentrations of free thyroxine, and *in vitro* resin uptake of triiodothyronine were constant (172, 173). The physiologic difference between males and females could be mimicked by administration of the corresponding gonadal steroids in pharmacological dosages (174, 175), but the progressive slowing of peripheral turnover of thyroxine from childhood through senescence could not be related to changes in thyroxine-binding globulin and prealbumin (173). Prednisone in large doses decreased the amount of added radioactive thyroxine bound to the globulin and increased the amount bound to the prealbumin in hyperthyroid patients, which suggests a reciprocal relationship between the two carriers (8). Subsequent work suggested that increased synthesis of the prealbumin and decreased formation of the globulin had occurred in response to the prednisone as suggested by their respective maximal binding capacities (176). Similar reciprocal behavior has been noted in acromegaly (177) but not after surgery when a significant decrease in thyroxine-binding prealbumin in capacity and concentration was observed early postoperatively but without change in either protein-bound iodine or binding capacity of thyroxine-binding globulin (178).

Unbound or "free" hormones.—It is generally accepted that small amounts of "free" or unbound thyroid hormones exist in plasma and that these are in reversible equilibrium with the binding proteins of the plasma and the binding sites within the tissue cells (see Kinetics). Actually, not much is known about intracellular binding proteins, although a protein capable of binding thyroxine was identified in heart muscle (179). Thyroxine-binding prealbumin can be considered most likely as a physiologically labile source of unbound thyroxine since its metabolism is very rapid and its synthesis easily affected (180). Thyroxine-binding globulin represents a stable reservoir for both hormones.

As stated above, the establishment of methods for the determination of total and "free" triiodothyronine indicated that its metabolic significance is about equal to that of thyroxine (4). Thus, the binding of triiodothyronine is of interest. In the chicken where serum albumin is the principal carrier and where both hormones are equally active, one strong and eight weak binding sites were demonstrated for thyroxine (181). For triiodothyronine, a large number of binding sites of low association constant were noted, which suggests that no specific binding had occurred (181). The situation in man is also not well understood. With agar gel electrophoresis at pH 7.4, most of the triiodothyronine was found to be bound to thyroxine-binding globulin, a small per cent to albumin (182, 183). With paper electrophoresis, a second carrier for triiodothyronine in the beta-globulin region was claimed (184). *In vivo,* either no, or minor binding of triiodothyronine by thyroxine-binding globulin has been postulated (161). However, the study was conducted in the nonequilibrated part of the disappearance curve shortly after radioactive triiodothyronine was administered. The half-time of its disappearance from the circulation was found identical to that of radioactive thyroxine (161), although from whole-body counting, about a fifth that of radioactive thyroxine (5) as determined in other studies (185). Also, with idiopathic lack of thyroxine-binding globulin or diphenylhydantoin intravenously, the former workers found marked decrease in thyroxine half-time but no change in triiodothyronine half-time (161).

Since direct determination of the minute amounts of unbound, or dialyzable, thyroid hormones in plasma is not possible, indirect methods have been developed utilizing equilibrium dialysis or ultrafiltration techniques (4, 187–189). Error may result from contamination with radioiodine of commercial ^{125}I or ^{131}I labeled thyroxine (T4) or triiodothyronine (T3) added to the test serum prior to dialysis, since radioiodine easily passes the semipermeable membrane (4, 189). Less attention has been paid to the error resulting from contamination of radioactive thyroxine by other labeled iodocompounds (190, 191). Thus a minute amount of radioactive triiodothyronine influenced the apparent per cent free radioactive thyroxine (PFT4) since unbound radioactive triiodothyronine concentration was almost ten times as great as that of unbound radioactive thyroxine whether dialysis was performed with diluted or undiluted serum (192). However, a decrease in PFT4 or PFT3 (per cent free triiodothyronine) over undiluted serum was stated to result from dilution (4, 189, 192) despite the claim for thyroxine, a strong ligand, to the contrary (193). Triiodothyronine is a weak ligand. The use of bacteriostatic agents such as Merthiolate or antibiotics to prevent bacterial growth during dialysis may also cause significant error, especially with diluted sera, from displacement of thyroid hormones from binding sites (192).

Normal values for serum PFT4 ranged from 0.030–0.050 per cent (187–189, 193). PFT3 values were about nine to ten times higher (4, 189). Absolute concentration of free thyroxine values ranged from 3.0–4.5 mμg per 100 ml (183, 189) and absolute concentration of free triiodothyronine averaged 1.5 mμg per 100 ml (4).

KINETIC STUDIES OF IODINE METABOLISM

DeGroot (194) has summarized the more common methods and definitions used in kinetic analysis; Rall et al. (195) have reviewed the peripheral metabolism of labeled thyroxine.

Mathematical models.—The most commonly used model has been a three-compartment one with iodine in the plasma taken up by the thyroid, released back into the circulation as thyroid hormone, and then degraded for recirculation or excretion. Berman and co-workers proposed for futher testing a more complex model with three special features: 1. three thyroidal phases: rapid initial, delay, and storage; 2. iodide feedback from the thyroid; 3. release of thyroxine, but also of triiodothyronine, from each of the three thyroidal phases (196). T3 was generally omitted from consideration, but its contribution is now estimated (see below) to be highly significant (4).

A four-compartment model was proposed to account for the pattern of plasma disappearance and excretion of radioactive thyroxine by normal subjects (197). Cavalieri & Searle (198) employed a two-compartment model, with no restriction on behavior of the plasma compartment, to study rate of exchange of radioactive thyroxine between plasma and extravascular space of the liver in humans without thyroid or hepatic disease, as did

Oppenheimer and group in a study of overall exchange of radioactive thyroxine with the tissues (199).

Anbar and group (200) proposed a double isotope procedure for measuring thyroxine deiodination rate as an index of thyroxine disappearance. The general concept was confirmed but Woeber et al. (201) concluded that Anbar and group's calculations were incorrect because they did not account for the greater dilution of plasma radioiodine relative to that of radioactive thyroxine due to different volumes of distribution. Theoretically, also, Anbar and group's initial differential equation 4 and solution equation 5 are seen to be in error for the same reason.

T4 secretory rates in steady and non-steady states were estimated by thin-layer chromatography to determine T4 specific activity, T4 ^{131}I, and T4 ^{127}I, with measurements made at t_o and at t_d in days (202).

Thyroidal iodine "leak".—The possibility of an iodine "leak" from the thyroid was first suggested in 1954 by Hickey and Brownell. Ermans and group (203) found in endemic goiter: specific activity (S.A.) of urinary I-/S.A. of serum I- remained > 1; urinary ^{131}I excretion consistently exceeded that predicted; and renal iodide excretion did not correspond to protein-bound ^{131}I. In normal subjects and in patients with thyroid disease, DeGroot (194) observed that release of nonhormonal iodine, i.e. iodine not identified as hormonal iodine, approximated closely the rate of hormonal iodine release (194). Fisher & Oddie, and later Nagataki et al. (204), also concluded that the thyroid adapted to increased iodine intake by I- spillage to plasma, since the thyroid organified ^{131}I, and since more ^{127}I was evidently organified than secreted as hormone on a diet rich in iodine. Iodine storage in the gland was not excluded other than by the inference that the subjects were in iodine equilibrium. Beckers et al. (205) found no iodine leak in adolescents on a normal iodine intake.

These analyses omitted the possibility that significant amounts of triiodothyronine might be secreted by the thyroid. With a mean stable concentration in normal human serum of 3.3 μg/liter in a small series (4), an approximation of secretion rate was calculated (4). Oddie and Fisher determined by whole-body counting a T3* distribution space of 30 liters and a fractional turnover rate constant, 0.5 (5). The extrathyroidal triiodothyronine pool thus was estimated at about 100 μg and the T3 as T3 degraded per day, 50 μg (4). This compares with a T4* distribution space of 10 liters, a fractional turnover rate constant 0.1, and a plasma T4 concentration of 60 μg/liter, or about 100 μg T4 as T4 degraded daily from an extrathyroidal pool of 600 μg (4, 186). Preferential secretion of T3 by the thyroid was also suggested, in view of the gland's normal 4:1 T4:T3 content (4). A level of T3 secretion equal to that degraded could account for all of the "iodine leak" by the thyroid, or part, i.e. in addition to glandular release of iodine, iodotyrosines, or even of iodoprotein. Materials indistinguishable from mono- and diiodotyrosine were found in normal human serum, specifically in the albumin fraction, and constituted about a quarter of the normal human serum iodine (206). Their origin is unknown. Schussler & Vance (207) claimed an effect of triiodothyronine on thyroxine kinetics since thyroxine disappearance was accelerated.

Effects of age, sex, body weight, and level of iodine intake.—Oddie and group have been adapting published kinetic data to the computer in an effort to better predictability from any given set of data. Of the three factors apart from thyroidal clearance that determine the plasma inorganic iodide level (PII) in the individual subject, dietary iodine intake, body weight (W), and renal excretion rate (K_2), at least two, W and K_2, were found sex dependent (208). Thyroidal average fractional iodide clearance rate (K_1) decreased with increasing dietary iodine intakes. Calculated iodine intake was about a third greater for males than females (208).

Thyroidal homeostasis, as expected, kept constant daily thyroidal iodide accumulation (A) at levels of dietary low iodine intake, whereas, at high levels, A increased (209). Nonetheless, a block to organic binding of iodide was found when a carrier I^- dose of the order of 750 µg was given and a serum I^- level of 30–38 µg/liter established (210). The I^- dose was lower when the gland was hyperfunctional; and correlation was observed with PII, and hence presumably intracellular iodide concentration (210). These data were interpreted, with the observation in the rat that a single dose of iodide decreased absolute amount of iodide binding when the amount of administered ^{127}I exceeded a minimum inhibitory level (210), to indicate inhibition of organic binding and not saturation of binding capacity. The latter would have resulted in a constant maximum rate of binding. Whether these findings have a physiological autoregulatory implication is not clear.

The problems involved in the measurement of the absolute iodide uptake by the thyroid (AIU) have been summarized: cervical extrathyroid activity during measurement of radioactive uptake, especially at low levels; loss of iodide in stools, sweat and urinary residue in the bladder; variation in renal clearance during the day; proportionality between the volume of the iodide space and body weight; presence of organically bound iodine in the urine; and the rapid output in hormonal form of a proportion of radioiodide taken up by the thyroid (211). Akerman and group (211) took advantage of a log-log relationship between early radioiodide uptake and thyroid clearance and assumed relative constancy of the renal iodide excretion rate constant, to devise a rapid and accurate procedure to measure AIU*. Koutras and co-workers (212), following the earlier suggestion of Ingbar, subdivided thyroidal clearance into "unidirectional clearance" at two to twenty minutes after intravenous injection of ^{131}I, and "net clearance" at two hours or more when loss of unbound I^* was complete (212). About 55 per cent of earlier trapped I^* remained in the normal gland at two hours, but only 7 per cent in Pendred's syndrome with defective I^- organification.

Free thyroxine concentrations were compared in maternal and cord bloods and were found equal; dialyzable fraction (DF) of thyroxine was elevated in the newborn but was compensated for by a decrease in protein-bound iodine (213). It was increased during the first two weeks of life, protein-bound ^{131}I for somewhat longer; thyroidal uptake was mostly normal and the iodide pump was highly active (213). Absolute iodine uptake during the first six months of life was estimated at tenfold that of the adult, and total iodide disposal rate at two to threefold (214). The large iodide pool of the infant was attributed to milk intake and the stimulation of the iodide pump at birth, to iodine want secondary to the increased renal excretion of pregnancy (215).

Beckers et al. (205) observed that values for thyroid secretion and thyroxine utilization expressed per unit of body weight or surface area decreased progressively as age advanced, and were intermediate in adolescence between those reported for young children and for adults. Adolescents had a T4* half-life of 6 days compared to 6.7 days in adults and 9.25 days in old age. Gregerman & Solomon (217) noted that the decreased thyroxine turnover in old age is due to altered mechanisms for hormone disposal or utilization, or both, rather than to lessened thyroid secretory capacity.

Oddie and group (216) obtained a formula to predict thyroxine iodine levels at ages 0.1 to 20 years, and included a sex factor. Body weight had a significant influence on thyroxine distribution space (216). The mean level decreased progressively to about fourteen years of age, and then rose progressively to the constant adult level by the third decade (218). Malvaux et al., to the contrary, found no difference in protein-bound iodine between adolescents and young adults though mean dialyzable fraction was clearly reduced in adolescence. Free thyroxine values were reduced in this age group compared to young adults (219). Braverman et al. (172) found that thyroxine binding increased with older age.

Previous work indicated that methyltestosterone decreased thyroxine globulin binding without significant change in thyroxine prealbumin binding (220). Norethandrolone, an androgenic-anabolic steroid, also decreased TBG T4-binding capacity but may have increased TBPA synthesis, inasmuch as the fractional or absolute rate of degradation of ^{125}I-labeled TBPA was unchanged (221). A mixture of norethandrolone and mestranol, primarily an estrogen, had no effect on 24-hour ^{131}I uptake or thyroxine kinetics (222).

Pregnancy.—Net thyroxine turnover and thyroid hormone requirements were not changed in normal human pregnancy (223). Net normal turnover in pregnant women was identical to that of nonpregnant women when expressed as daily turnover per square meter of body surface area (223), although pregnant monkeys showed increased thyroxine utilization (224). A sudden decrease in thyroid secretion rate at term appeared to exclude the iodine depletion of pregnancy due to renal loss (215) as a factor, and led to the proposal that chorionic tissue secretes a thyrotropin-like material.

Plasma-tissue flux.—Oppenheimer and associates (199) used the differential exit of ^{131}I thyroxine and ^{125}I albumin from plasma during the first four hours after simultaneous administration to analyze the size and kinetic characteristics of the total intracellular (extra-albumin) compartment of exchangeable thyroxine. With a closed two-compartment model, they calculated approximately 37 per cent of injected radioactive thyroxine to be distributed to the intracellular compartment of normal subjects, a clearance of 43 ml/min.

Plasma-liver flux.—Cavalieri & Searle (198) quantitated the rate of exchange of radioactive thyroxine between plasma and liver in subjects with neither thyroid nor hepatic disease, and some with an idiopathic decrease of thyroxine-binding globulin. A threefold hepatic concentration over plasma was seen at equilibrium four hours after injection, which suggested actual binding of radioactive thyroxine. A thyroxine flux into the liver from plasma of 118 µg/hour was estimated, with a loss of less than 5 per cent by a combination of biliary clearance (mostly as sulfate or glucuronide conjugates), deiodination, and escape via the liver lymphatics. This left 95 per cent to return unchanged to the plasma. They concluded, like Osorio and Myant for the monkey, that free rather than bound thyroxine determined the entry of hormone into the liver; and that the radioactive form binds reversibly to sites on or within the cell. This is consistent with the decreased hepatic thyroxine space and pool size noted in patients with cirrhosis and hepatitis but with normal thyroxine-binding globulin capacity and free thyroxine levels (199). The problem in liver disease is further complicated by changes which occur in thyroxine-binding proteins. Nonetheless, despite all the various alterations, absolute concentration of free thyroxine and absolute hormone disposal remain normal in cirrhosis of the liver (225, 226).

The bidirectionality of thyroid hormone flow was confirmed by rat liver perfusion *in vitro* (227). The smooth endoplasmic reticulum has been implicated in this process. Bernstein and group (228) increased hepatic accumulation of radioactive thyroxine in the rat with phenobarbital and chlordane which stimulate the formation of smooth endoplasmic reticulum, but not with 3-4-benzypyrine which does not.

Gorman and co-workers (227) proposed that the liver acts as a buffer against abrupt changes in plasma thyroxine concentration, such as occur during stress, anesthesia and operation, and disease (180). Nonetheless, the limited amounts of thyroxine in the enterohepatic circulation in man (15 per cent of total T4* excretion in ten days) as opposed to the rat and dog (50 per cent of total T4* excretion in three days) should be recalled (23). However, higher figures for man have been reported (229). A possible indirect role of the liver in human thyroidal regulation was also indicated since free fatty acids are potent anions and when increased, as after a fatty meal, decrease thyroxine binding to thyroxine-binding proteins with consequent rise in FT4 and FT3 levels (230).

HORMONAL ACTION AND PERIPHERAL HORMONAL METABOLISM

The effects of thyroid hormones on the thyroid cell were reviewed and, because of space requirements, will not be included in this paper (231).

The site and mode of action, as well as the metabolism of thyroid hormones, have remained elusive. Thyroxine-^{125}I was localized within kidney cells growing in tissue culture, mainly to the nuclei (231). The physiological significance of this finding is unclear since biologically active compounds are not necessarily concentrated at the site of action.

Cellular binding of thyroid hormones.—The stereochemical configuration of thyroid hormones was tested in relation to binding by cell receptors. Barker and group (233) held that the bulky iodine atoms in positions 3 and 5 positioned the outer ring of iodothyronine, and the iodine atoms, together with the methylene group of the alanine side chain, enhanced the binding characteristics of the inner ring to a hypothetical cellular receptor by contributing electrons. They also postulated that the ability of the outer ring to position its 3'-iodine atom in relation to the 4'-hydroxyl of the inner ring permitted interaction with a functional receptor and hence was responsible for biological activity (232). Alkyl substitutions were made on the phenolic benzene ring and yielded a compound, 3'-isopropyl-3,5-diiodothyronine, which was physiologically active by several criteria when administered to rats in 1/6 to 1/8 equimolar doses of thyroxine (233), as well as an iodine-free analogue, 3'-isopropyl-3,5-dibromothyronine, which was twice as active physiologically as thyroxine (234).

From these (233, 234) and other (232, 235) studies, the following generalizations were made about maintenance of physiological activity: (*a*) halogens (but not necessarily iodine) are required at carbon atoms 3 and 5 of the inner ring of thyroxine; (*b*) a substitution at the 3' position in the outer ring is also necessary, although bulk groupings on the second aromatic ring, such as in isopropyl or naphthyl derivatives, are at least as effective as the corresponding iodine atoms; (*c*) a linkage between the outer and inner rings is very important in permitting coordinated shifts of electrons. Unfortunately, doubt has been raised by the fact that the results were different when another endpoint, amino acid incorporation into protein, was used (236). Here, with cell-free preparations from rat liver, the degree of iodination, only, was related to the extent of stimulation.

Effects on cellular oxidative processes.—Until recently, the oxidative processes were thought to represent the primary locus of action of thyroid hormones and the subject has been fully reviewed (237, 238). Oxidation of so many substrates was stimulated that terminal electron transport was suggested as a common denominator. However, although intracellular cytochrome and cytochrome oxidase concentrations respond to changes in levels of thyroid hormone, the concentrations of the enzymes is normally too great for any variation to be likely to be rate determining. Also against the electron transport concept is the long lag period *in vivo* before response to thyroid hormone, too long for a primary action. Finally, direct stimulation of electron transport capacity occurred without concomitant change in metabolic rate (239). Thyroxine was injected into thyroidectomized rats whose liver mitochondria had lost nearly half their normal electron transport capacity, and restored normal capacity within three hours; recovery was not associated with synthesis of new respiratory assemblies (239). This effect would have been seen if previous postulates were correct (237). The reaction involved appeared to concern energy conservation during succinate oxidation (239).

Effects on oxidative phosphorylation.—Another popular concept, that thyroid hormones control cellular respiration through uncoupling of, or loosely coupled, oxidative phosphorylation, has been abandoned (238). Too great concentrations of the hormone were required to produce this effect (238). Thyroxine added in a concentration of 2.5×10^{-5} M to medium containing normal rat liver mitochondria and $MgCl_2$ in physiological concentration caused a reduction in efficiency of oxidative phosphorylation but with associated inhibition of terminal phosphate-transfer and slowing of rate of substrate oxidation (240). The relation between uncoupling and mitochondrial swelling was also examined (241). Thyroxine induced mitochondrial swelling at high levels of ATP but not under conditions suitable for phosphorylation. However, different results were obtained when liver mitochondria were suspended in an equal volume of deionized water and sucrose, or were pretreated with deionized water (242). Pretreatment enhanced this induced swelling when ADP or ATP was added to the medium; however, the effect from ATP occurred after a longer latent period than with that from ADP (242). Thyroxine increased the rate of succinate oxidation of pretreated mitochondria but not of untreated mitochondria, and this was followed by a decrease in respiratory control, by stimulation of ATPase activity, and by mitochondrial swelling (242). These studies illustrate again the influence of the procedure itself on the outcome.

The effect of thyroxine on mitochondria was also examined *in vivo*. A single subcalorigenic dose (5.2 ng per gram body weight) almost completely restored the ability to respond to 2,4-dinitrophenol of liver mitochondria from hypothyroid rats (243). It was suggested that thyroxine altered the permeability of the mitochondrial membrane, and that mitochondrial function was regulated through altered rate of entry and exit of substances involved in respiratory activity and energy transfer (243). In line with this, thyroxine and triiodothyronine *in vitro* altered the release of NADH-diaphorase and proteins from rat liver mitochondria but only at higher than physiological concentrations (244). Similarly, mitochondria from rats given toxic amounts of triiodothyronine *in vivo* released NADH-diaphorase and proteins (244).

Effects on protein synthesis.—The possibility was tested that thyroxine may activate genes by promoting the separation of complementary strands of specific segments of the DNA double helix prior to transcription (245), in line with the hormonal activation of many structural genes. No effect of thyroxine incubated with DNA from human placental nuclei was seen on the melting point of DNA (245).

The suggestion was therefore made that only mitochondrial RNA responds to thyroid hormones. *In vivo,* triiodothyronine doubled incorporation of radioactive amino acids into protein of liver mitochondria from thyroidectomized rats (246); *in vitro,* thyroxine in 10^{-5} or 10^{-6} M concentration, as well as some thyroxine analogues, stimulated amino acid incorporation into protein of liver mitochondria from intact rats within three minutes of incubation (247). Similar stimulation was induced in the microsomal fraction of skeletal muscle, but only in the presence of mitochondria; other ATP-generating systems were ineffective (248). The extent of stimulation of protein synthesis was proportional to hormone concentration until toxic amounts of thyroxine were reached (247, 248). Protein synthesis was then inhibited, possibly from uncoupling of oxidative phosphorylation or formation of $T4-Mg^{2+}$ complexes (247, 248). Nonetheless, the view that thyroid hormones may act primarily on protein synthesis was opened to question by the finding that a metabolic effect occurred despite block to protein synthesis by actinomycin D (237). Thus, acceleration by thyroid hormones of transfer of acyl sRNA to ribosomal protein, increase in RNA polymerase activity, and enhancement of mRNA synthesis, may reflect only one of many actions of these hormones at the cellular level.

The effect of thyroid hormones on tissue enzyme synthesis has been reviewed (249). Among others, mitochondrial alpha-glycerophosphate dehydrogenase (GPD) has excited interest. Desiccated thyroid fed to normal rats increased GPD activity, particularly in those tissues in which oxidative rate is increased by thyroid hormones. Thyroidectomy decreased GPD activity in liver, kidney, and heart (250). The response to thyroxine of GPD activity was greater and more sensitive than that of metabolic rate, but thyroxine stimulation of GPD was blocked by thiouracil and propylthiouracil whereas that of triiodothyronine was not (251). The major mechanism of action of thyroid hormones thus could be induction of synthesis of a series of enzymes related to GPD: 1. enhancement of oxidation of glycerol phosphate with response of lipid biosynthesis, mobilization, and metabolism; 2. action of this substrate as a "shuttle" for the transport of hydrogen from cytoplasmic NADH to the mitochondrial electron transport chain with lowering of the NADH:NAD ratio in the cytoplasm; and finally, 3. consequent stimulation of carbohydrate degradation (251).

To summarize, it is likely that the mitochondrion is the primary locus of thyroid hormonal effect, but no single mechanism of action has been identified.

ACKNOWLEDGMENT

The authors wish to acknowledge the kindness of the following investigators who permitted us to see manuscripts in press: Drs. S. Reichlin, P. L. Munson, R. Guillemin, A. V. Schally, J. M. McKenzie, J. Oppenheimer, K. Sterling, and T. H. Oddie; and to thank Mrs. Vera Ortynsky for generous assistance in the library and Mrs. Helen C. Smith for secretarial help.

LITERATURE CITED

1. Rosenberg, I. N., Bastomsky, C. H. *Ann. Rev. Physiol.*, **27**, 71–106 (1965)
2. Williams, G. A., Hargis, G. K., Galloway, W. B., Henderson, W. J. *Proc. Soc. Exptl. Biol. Med.*, **122**, 1273–76 (1966)
3. Munson, P. L., Hirsch, P. F. *Clin. Orthopaed. Related Res.*, **49**, 209–32 (1966)
4. Nauman, J. A., Nauman, A., Werner, S. C. *J. Clin. Invest.*, **46**, 1346–55 (1967)
5. Fisher, D. A., Oddie, T. H. *J. Clin. Endocrinol.*, **24**, 733–39 (1964)
6. McKenzie, J. M. *Recent Progr. Hormone Res.*, **23**, 1–40 (1967)
7. Adams, D. D. *Brit. Med. J.*, **1**, 1015–19 (1965)
8. Werner, S. C., Platman, S. R. *Lancet*, **2**, 751–55 (1965)
9. Dorrington, K. J., Munro, D. S. *Clin. Pharmacol. Therap.*, **7**, 788–806 (1966)
10. Reichlin, S. In *Neuroendocrinology* (Martin, L., Ganong, W. F., Eds., Academic Press, New York, 1966)
11. Harris, G. W., Ed. The Hypothalamus. *Brit. Med. Bull.*, **22** (September 1966)
12. Guillemin, R. *Ann. Rev. Physiol.*, **29**, 313–49 (1967)
13. Reichlin, S., Volpert, E. M., Werner, S. C. *Endocrinology*, **78**, 302–6 (1966)
14. Greer, M. A., Matsuda, K., Stott, A. K. *Endocrinology*, **78**, 389–95 (1966)
15. Purves, H. D., Sirett, N. E., Griesbach, W. E. *Neuroendocrinology (Switz.)*, **1**, 276–92 (1965-66)
16. Proc. Intern. Symp. on Temperature and Altitude. *Fed. Proc.*, **25**, 1151–1433 (1966)
17. Wilson, D. *Fed. Proc.*, **25**, 1357–62 (1966)
18. Surks, M. I. Beckwitt, H. J., Chidsey, C. A. *J. Clin. Endocrinol.*, **27**, 789–99 (1967)
19. Surks, M. I. *Endocrinology*, **78**, 307–15 (1966)
20. DuRuisseau, J. P. *J. Clin. Endocrinol.*, **25**, 1513–15 (1965)
21. Schindler, W. J., McHorse, T. S., Krause, D. M. *Endocrinology*, **79**, 281–88 (1966)
22. Heroux, D., Brauer, R. *J. Appl. Physiol.*, **20**, 597–606 (1965)
23. Furth, E., Hurley, J., Nunez, E.,

Becker, D. V. *Clin. Res.*, **15**, 258 (1967) Abstr.
24. Sjostrand, J. *Acta Physiol. Scand.*, **62**, 94–100 (1964)
25. Schally, A. V., Bowers, C. Y., Redding, T. W., Barrett, J. F. *Biochem. Biophys. Res. Commun.*, **25**, 165–69 (1966)
26. Sinha, D. K., Meites, J. *Endocrinology*, **78**, 1002–6 (1966)
27. Redding, T. W., Schally, A. V. *Endocrinology* (In press) (1967)
28. Redding, T. W., Bowers, C. Y., Schally, A. V. *Endocrinology*, **79**, 229–36 (1966)
29. Vale, W., Burgus, R., Guillemin, R. Program, 49th Meeting Endocrine Soc., 89 (1967)
30. Condliffe, P., Robbins, J. In *Hormones in Blood* (Gray, C. H., Bacharach, A. L., Eds., Academic Press, New York) (In press) (1967)
31. Scott, T. W., Good, B. F., Ferguson, K. A. *Endocrinology*, **79**, 949–54 (1966)
32. Wetzel, B. K., Spicer, S. S., Wollman, S. H. *J. Cell Biol.*, **25**, 593–618 (1965)
33. Pastan, I., Roth, J., Macchia, V. *Proc. Natl. Acad. Sci.*, **56**, 1802–9 (1966)
34. Pastan, I. Macchia, V., Bates, R. W. Program, 59th Annual Meeting Am. Soc. Clin. Invest., 82 (1967)
35. Wynn, J. Program, 59th Annual Meeting Am. Soc. Clin. Invest., 115 (1967)
36. Clayton, J. A., Szego, C. M. *Endocrinology*, **80**, 689–98 (1967)
37. Pastan, I., Almquist, S. *Endocrinology*, **78**, 361–66 (1966)
38. Bell, E. T. *Vitamins Hormones*, **24**, 96–102 (1966)
39. Kirkham, K. E. *Vitamins Hormones*, **24**, 173–266 (1966)
40. Sakiz, E., Guillemin, R. *Proc. Soc. Exptl. Biol. Med.*, **115**, 856–60 (1964)
41. McKenzie, J. M., Williamson, A. *J. Clin. Endocrinol.*, **26**, 518–26 (1966)
42. Bakke, J. *Current Topics in Thyroid Research*, 503–12 (Cassano, C., Andreoli, M., Eds., Academic Press, New York, 1965)
43. Ducommun, P., Sakiz, E., Guillemin, R. *Proc. Soc. Exptl. Biol. Med.*, **121**, 921–23 (1966)

44. Eayrs, J. T., Williams, E. D. *J. Endocrinol.*, **34**, 277–79 (1966)
45. Lee, N. D., Durovic, D. *J. Clin. Endocrinol.* (In press) (1967)
46. Becktel, J. M. *Proc. Soc. Exptl. Biol. Med.*, **124**, 999–1000 (1967)
47. Good, B. F., Stenhouse, N. S. *Endocrinology*, **78**, 429–39 (1966)
48. Redding, T. W., Schally, A. V. *Endocrinology*, **79**, 229–36 (1966)
49. Averill, R. L. W. *Endocrinology*, **80**, 359–60 (1967)
50. El Kabir, D. J. *J. Physiol. (London)*, **182**, 51P-52P (1966)
51. Kriss, J. P., Pleshakov, V., Chien, J. R. *J. Clin. Endocrinol.*, **24**, 1005–28 (1966)
52. Brown, J., Munro, D. S. *J. Physiol. (London)*, **182**, 9P–10P (1966)
53. LeMarchand-Beraud, Th., Scazziga, B. R. Vannotti, A. *Schweiz. Med. Wochschr.*, **95**, 718–22 (1966)
54. Utiger, R. D. *J. Clin. Invest.*, **44**, 1277–86 (1965)
55. Odell, W. D., Wilber, J. F., Paul, W. E. *J. Clin. Endocrinol.*, **25**, 1179–88 (1965)
56. Sherman, W. B., Werner, S. C. *J. Am. Med. Assoc.*, **190**, 244–45 (1964)
57. Reichlin, S., Utiger, R. D. *J. Clin. Endocrinol.*, **27**, 251–55 (1967)
58. Mouriz, J., Morreale de Escobar, G., Escobar del Rey, F. *Endocrinology*, **79**, 248–60 (1966)
59. Galton, V. A., Ingbar, S. H. *Endocrinology*, **77**, 169–76 (1965)
60. Anbar, M., Inbar, M., Tata, J. R. *Acta Endocrinol.*, **48**, 506–12 (1965)
61. Ducommun, P., Vale, W., Sakiz, E., Guillemin, R. *Endocrinology*, **80**, 593–601 (1967)
62. Odell, W. D., Paul, W. E. *J. Biol. Chem.*, **240**, 2043–46 (1965)
63. Bates, R. W., Condliffe, P. G. In *The Pituitary Gland*, **I**, 374 (Harris, G. H., Ed., Butterworth, London, 1966)
64. Jakoby, W. B. *Neurospora Newsletter*, **8**, 17–18 (1965)
65. Lepp, A., Oliner, L. *Endocrinology*, **80**, 369–74 (1967)
66. Meek, J. C., Brown, R. W. *Clin. Res.*, **14**, 431 (1966) Abstr.
67. Arnaud, C. D., Knenbuhler, H. A., Seiling, V. L., Wightman, B. K., Engbring, N. M. *J. Clin. Invest.*, **44**, 1287–94 (1965)
68. Kriss, J. P., Pleshakov, V., Rosenblum, A. L., Holderness, M. Sharp, G., Utiger, R. *J. Clin. Endocrinol.*, **27**, 582–93 (1967)
69. Werner, S. C. *Lancet*, May, 1004–7 (1966)
70. Werner, S. C., Ed. Panel discussion, Hyperthyroidism in Pregnancy and the Neonate, *J. Clin. Endocrinol.* (In press) (November 1967)
71. Elsas, L. J., Whittemore, R., Burrow, G. N. *J. Am. Med. Assoc.*, **200**, 250–52 (1967)
72. Sunshine, P., Kusomoto, H., Kriss, J. P. *Pediatrics*, **36**, 869–76 (1965)
73. Miyai, K., Werner, S. C. *J. Clin. Endocrinol.*, **26**, 504–12 (1966)
74. Meek, J. C. *Clin. Res.*, **15**, 263 (1967) Abstr.
75. Masui, H., Werner, S. C. (Unpublished data)
76. Pinchera, A., Pinchera, M. G., Stanbury, J. B. *J. Clin. Endocrinol.*, **25**, 189–208 (1965)
77. Adams, D. D., Kennedy, T. H. *J. Clin. Endocrinol.*, **27**, 173–77 (1967)
78. Werner, S. C., Feind, C. R., Aida, M. *New Engl. J. Med.*, **276**, 132–38 (1967)
79. McKenzie, J. M. Program, 59th Ann. Meeting Am. Soc. Clin. Invest., 74 (1967)
80. Miyai, K., Fukuchi, M., Kumahara, Y., Abe, H. *J. Clin. Endocrinol.*, **27**, 855–60 (1967)
81. Morishima, K., Grumbach, M., Werner, S. C. (Unpublished data)
82. Burke, G. *J. Lab. Clin. Med.*, **69**, 713–27 (1967)
83. Field, J. B., Remer, A., Bloom, G., Kriss, J. P. Program, 59th Annual Meeting Am. Soc. Clin. Invest., 35 (1967)
84. Fontaine, Y. A., Lopez, E. *Ann. Endocrinol.*, **25**, 719–25 (1965)
85. Winland, R. *Ann. Endocrinol.*, **27**, 247–51 (1966)
86. Horster, F. A., Schleusener, H., Schimmelpfennig, K. *Deut. Med. Wochschr.*, **92**, 661–66 (1967)
87. Kock, H., Kessel, H. V., Stolte, L., Leusden, H. V. *J. Clin. Endocrinol.*, **26**, 1128–34 (1966)
88. Hennen, G. *J. Clin. Endocrinol.*, **27**, 610–14 (1967)
89. Kumahara, Y., Iwatsubo, H., Miyai, K., Masui, H., Fukuchi, M., Abe, H. *J. Clin. Endocrinol.*, **27**, 333–40 (1967)

90. Al Saadi, A. A., Beierwaltes, W. H. *Cancer Res.*, **26**, 676–88 (1966)

91. Lindsay, R. H., Cohen, P. P. *Endocrinology*, **76**, 737–44 (1965)

92. Begg, D. J., McGirr, E. M., Munro, H. N. *Endocrinology*, **76**, 171–77 (1965)

93. Creek, R. O. *Endocrinology*, **76**, 1124–33 (1965)

94. Schneider, A. B., Goldberg, I. H. *Fed. Proc.*, **24**, 383 (1965) Abstr.

95. Tishler, P. V., Ingbar, S. H. *Endocrinology*, **76**, 295–300 (1965)

96. Taurog, A., Thio, D. T. *Endocrinology*, **78**, 103–10 (1966)

97. Schneider, P. B., Wolff, J. *Biochim. Biophys. Acta*, **94**, 114–23 (1965)

98. Larsen, P. R., Wolff, J. Program, Ann. Meeting Am. Thyroid Assoc., 16 (October 1966)

99. Brunberg, J. A., Halmi, N. S. *Endocrinology*, **79**, 801–7 (1966)

100. Wolff, J., Rall, J. E. *Endocrinology*, **76**, 949–57 (1965)

101. Shishiba, Y., Solomon, D. H. Program, 48th Meeting Endocrine Soc., 49 (June 1966)

102. Scranton, J. R., Halmi, N. S. *Endocrinology*, **76**, 441–53 (1965)

103. Schulz, A. R., Fisher, A. G., Oliner, L. Program, Ann. Meeting Am. Thyroid Assoc., 4 (October 1966)

104. Alexander, N. M. *Current Topics in Thyroid Research*, 43 (Academic Press, New York, 1965)

105. Mahoney, C. P., Igo, R. P. *Biochim. Biophys. Acta*, **113**, 507 (1966)

106. Yip, C. C. *Biochim. Biophys. Acta*, **90**, 216–17 (1964)

107. Yip, C. C. *Ibid.*, **96**, 75–81 (1965)

108. Taurog, A. *Mayo Clin. Proc.*, **39**, 569–85 (1964)

109. Schulz, A. R., Oliner, L. Program, 48th Meeting Endocrine Soc., 51 (June 1966)

110. Lupulescu, A., Petrovici, Al. *Current Topics of Thyroid Research*, 85 (Academic Press, New York, 1965)

111. Seed, R. W., Goldberg, I. H. *J. Biol. Chem.*, **240**, 764–73 (1965)

112. Pitt-Rivers, R., Cavalieri, R. R. *Biochem. J.*, **86**, 86–92 (1963)

113. Stein, O., Gross, J. *Endocrinology*, **75**, 787–98 (1964)

114. Tong, W. *Endocrinology*, **76**, 163–65 (1965)

115. Fisher, A. G., Schulz, A. R., Oliner, L. *J. Biol. Chem.*, **240**, 4338–43 (1965)

116. Liunggren, J. G. *Biochim. Biophys. Acta*, **107**, 434–40 (1965)

117. Edelhoch, H., Rall, J. E. *The Thyroid Gland*, 113 (Pitt-Rivers, R., Trotter, W. R., Eds., Butterworth, Washington, 1964)

118. Spiro, R. G. *J. Biol. Chem.*, **240**, 1603–10 (1965)

119. Spiro, R. G., Spiro, M. J. *Current Topics of Thyroid Research* (Academic Press, New York, 1965)

120. Segal, S., Roth, H., Blair, A., Bertoli, D. *Endocrinology*, **79**, 675–80 (1966)

121. Singh, V. N., Raghupathy, E., Chaikoff, I. L. *Biochem. Biophys. Acta*, **103**, 623–34 (1965)

122. Heywood, S. M. *Biochim. Biophys. Acta*, **123**, 188–96 (1966)

123. Simon, C., Droz, B. *Current Topics in Thyroid Research*, 77–84 (Cassano, C., Andreoli, E., Eds., Academic Press, New York, 1965)

124. Nadler, N. J. *Current Topics of Thyroid Research*, 73 (Academic Press, New York, 1965)

125. Nunez, J., Mauchamp, J., Macchia, V., Roche, J. *Biochim. Biophys. Acta*, **107**, 247–56 (1965)

126. Sellin, H. G., Goldberg, I. H. *J. Biol. Chem.*, **240**, 774–81 (1965)

127. Wollman, S. H. *Current Topics of Thyroid Research*, 1 (Academic Press, New York, 1965)

128. Goldberg, I. H., Seed, R. W. *Biochem. Biophys. Res. Commun.*, **19**, 615–22 (1965)

129. Balaslobramaniam, K., Deiss, W. P., Jr. *Biochim. Biophys. Acta*, **110**, 564–75 (1965)

130. Deiss, W. P., Jr., Balaslobramaniam, K., Peake, R. L., Starrett, J. A., Powell, R. C. *Endocrinology*, **79**, 19–27 (1966)

131. Kusakabe, T., Miyake, T. *J. Clin. Endocrinol.*, **26**, 615–18 (1966)

132. Dumont, J. E. *Ann. Soc. Roy. Sci. Med. Nat. Bruxelles*, **18**, 105–241 (1965)

133. DeGroot, L. J. *New Engl. J. Med.*, **272**, 355–62 (1965)

134. DeGroot, L. J., Dunn, A. D., Jaksina, S. *Endocrinology*, **79**, 28–37 (1966)

135. Abraham, S., Kopelovich, L., Chaikoff, I. L. *Endocrinology*, **77**, 863–72 (1965)

136. Abraham, S., Kopelovich, L., Kerkof, P. R., Chaikoff, I. L. *Endocrinology*, **76**, 178–90 (1965)

137. DeGroot, L. J., Dunn, A. D. *Biochim. Biophys. Acta,* **92,** 205–22 (1964)

138. DeGroot, L. J., Dunn, A. D. *Current Topics in Thyroid Research,* 21 (Academic Press, New York, 1965)

139. DeGroot, L. J., Dechene, R., Thompson, J. *Biochim. Biophys. Acta,* **92,** 223–32 (1964)

140. Jarrett, R. J., Field, J. B. *Endocrinology,* **75,** 711–15 (1964)

141. Hall, R., Tubmen, J. *J. Biol. Chem.,* **240,** 3132–35 (1965)

142. Maayan, M. L., Rosenberg, I. N. *Endocrinology,* **78,** 1049–52 (1966)

143. Jarrett, R. J., Epstein, S. M., Remer, A., Field, J. B. *Endocrinology,* **77,** 290–94 (1965)

144. Ohta, M., Field, J. B. *Endocrinology,* **79,** 732–36 (1966)

145. Green, W. L. *Endocrinology,* **79,** 1–9 (1966)

146. DeGroot, L. J., Thompson, J. E., Dunn, A. D. *Endocrinology,* **76,** 632–45 (1965)

147. Lobo, L. C. G., Fridman, J., Rebello, M. A., Hargreaves, F., Figueiredo, J. G. *Metabolism,* **15,** 330–37 (1966)

148 Medeiros-Neto, G. A., Stanbury, J. B. *J. Clin. Endocrinol.,* **26,** 23–32 (1966)

149. Westra, J. P., Polly, R. E., Halmi, N. S. *Endocrinology,* **79,** 197–206 (1966)

150. Tong, W. *Gunma Symp. Endocrinol.,* **3,** 61–70 (1966)

151. Scranton, J. R., Tong, W. *Fed. Proc.,* **26,** 643 (1967) Abstr.

152. Mallette, J. M., Anthony, A. *Exptl. Cell Res.,* **41,** 642–51 (1966)

153. Kerkof, P. R., Chaikoff, I. L. *Endocrinology,* **78,** 1177–88 (1966)

154. Rhaghupathy, E., Stolc, V., Tong, W. Program, 49th Ann. Meeting Endocrine Soc., 96 (1967)

155. Shimada, S., Inoue, K., Greer, M. A. *Endocrinology,* **78,** 1171–76 (1966)

156. Kalderon, A. E., Wittner, M. *Endocrinology,* **80,** 797–807 (1967)

157. Mack, R. E. *Am. J. Physiol.,* **210,** 1048–52 (1966)

158. Flanagan, T. D., Barron, A. L., Beutner, E. H., Witebsky, E. *J. Immunol.,* **97,** 539–45 (1966)

159. Hung, W., Winship, T., Bowen, K., Houck, J. C. *Proc. Soc. Exptl. Biol. Med.,* **122,** 121–26 (1966)

160. Singh, V. N., Chaikoff, I. L. *Endocrinology,* **78,** 339–42 (1966)

161. Sterling, K., Brenner, M. A., Rose, H. G. *Endocrinology,* **77,** 398–400 (1965)

162. Thorson, S. C., Tauxe, W. N., Taswell, H. F. *J. Clin. Endocrinol.,* **26,** 181–88 (1966)

163. Inada, M., Sterling, K. Program, 49th Ann. Meeting Endocrine Soc., 97 (1967)

164. Britton, A., Webster, B. R., Ezrin, C., Volpe, R. *Can. J. Biochem.,* **43,** 1477–87 (1965)

165. Marshall, J. S., Levy, R. P. *J. Clin. Endocrinol.,* **26,** 87–98 (1965)

166. Digiulio, W., Michalak, Z., Weinhold, P. A., Hamilton, J. R., Thoma, G. E. *J. Lab. Clin. Med.,* **64,** 349–354 (1964)

167. Macke-Nauman, A., Chmielewska, I. *Bull. Acad. Polon. Sci.,* **14,** 297–300 (1966)

168. Oppenheimer, J. H., Surks, M. I., Smith, J. C., Squef, R. *J. Biol. Chem.,* **240,** 173–80 (1965)

169. Woeber, K. A., Ingbar, S. H. *Endocrinology,* **75,** 917–22 (1964)

170. Steiner, R. F., Roth, J., Robbins, J. *J. Biol. Chem.,* **241,** 560–67 (1966)

171. Sterling, K. *J. Clin. Invest.,* **43,** 1721–29 (1964)

172. Braverman, L. E., Dawber, N. A., Ingbar, S. H. *J. Clin. Invest.,* **45,** 1273–79 (1966)

173. Braverman, L. E., Foster, A. E., Ingbar, S. H. *J. Clin. Endocrinol.,* **27,** 227–32 (1967)

174. Holvey, D. N., Cutler, R. E., Dowling, J. T. *Metabolism,* **14,** 891–98 (1965)

175. Braverman, L. E., Ingbar, S. H. *J. Clin. Endocrinol.,* **27,** 389–96 (1967)

176. Oppenheimer, J. H., Werner, S. C. *J. Clin. Endocrinol.,* **26,** 715–21 (1966)

177. Hollander, C. S., Roth, J., Scott, R. L. *Clin. Res.,* **14,** 64 (1966) Abstr.

178. Surks, M. I., Oppenheimer, J. H. *J. Clin. Endocrinol.,* **24,** 794–802 (1964)

179. Tritsch, N., Tritsch, G. L. Ann. Meeting Am. Thyroid Assoc., Abstr. No. 18 (Rochester, 1964)

180. Bernstein, G., Oppenheimer, J. H. *J. Clin. Endocrinol.,* **26,** 195–201 (1966)

181. Tritsch, G. L., Tritsch, N. E. *J. Biol. Chem.,* **240,** 3789–92 (1965)

182. Braverman, L. E., Ingbar, S. H. *Endocrinology,* **76,** 547–49 (1965)

183. Nauman, J., Werner, S. C. 48th Meeting Endocrine Soc. (Chicago, June 1966) Abstr.
184. Mitchell, M. L., Bradford, A. H., Collins, S. J. Clin. Endocrinol., 24, 867–74 (1964)
185. Oddie, T. H., Fisher, D. A., Rogers, C. J. Clin. Endocrinol., 24, 628–37 (1964)
186. Oddie, T. H., Meade, J. H., Jr., Fisher, D. A. J. Clin. Endocrinol., 26, 425–36 (1966)
187. Lee, N. D., Henry, R. J., Golub, O. J. J. Clin. Endocrinol., 24, 486–95 (1964)
188. Sterling, K., Brenner, M. A. J. Clin. Invest., 45, 155–63 (1966)
189. Ingbar, S. H., Braverman, L. E., Dawber, N. A., Lee, G. Y. J. Clin. Invest., 44, 1679–89 (1965)
190. Schussler, G. C., Plager, J. E. J. Clin. Endocrinol., 27, 242–50 (1967)
191. Volpert, E. M., Martinez, M., Oppenheimer, J. H. J. Clin. Endocrinol., 27, 421–28 (1967)
192. Nauman, J., Werner, S. C. (Unpublished data)
193. Oppenheimer, J. H., Surks, M. I. J. Clin. Endocrinol., 24, 785–93 (1964)
194. DeGroot, L. J. J. Clin. Endocrinol., 26, 149–73 (1966)
195. Rall, J. E., Robbins, J., Lewallen, C. G. The Thyroid. In The Hormones, 5, 159 (Pincus, G., Thimann, K. V., Astwood, E. B., Eds., Academic Press, New York, 1964)
196. Berman, M., Hoff, E., Barandes, M., Becker, D. V., Sonenberg, M., Besun, R., Koutras, D. A. J. Clin. Endocrinol. (In press) (1967)
197. Blomstedt, B., Plantin, L. O. Acta Endocrinol., 48, 536–46 (1965)
198. Cavalieri, R. R., Searle, G. L. J. Clin. Invest., 45, 939–49 (1966)
199. Oppenheimer, J. H., Bernstein, G., Hasen, J. J. Clin. Invest., 46, 762–77 (1967)
200. Anbar, M., Guttmann, S., Rodan, G., Stein, J. A. J. Clin. Endocrinol., 44, 1986–91 (1965)
201. Woeber, K. A., Hecker, E., Ingbar, S. H. Program, Ann. Meeting Am. Thyroid Assoc. (1966)
202. West, C. D., Kumagai, L. F., Chavre, V. J., Bigler, A. H. J. Clin. Invest., 45, 1085 (1966) Abstr.
203. Ermans, A. M., Dumont, J. E., Bastenie, P. A. J. Clin. Endocrinol., 23, 539–60 (1963)

204. Nagataki, S., Shizume, K., Nakao, K. J. Clin. Endocrinol. (In press)
205. Beckers, C., Malvaux, P., DeVisscher, M. J. Clin. Endocrinol., 26, 202–6 (1966)
206. Weinert, H., Masui, H., Radichevich, I., Werner, S. C. J. Clin. Invest., 46, 1264–74 (1967)
207. Schussler, G. C., Vance, V. K. Clin. Res., 15, 266 (1967) Abstr.
208. Oddie, T. H., Myhill, J., Pirnique, F. G., Fisher, D. A. J. Clin. Endocrinol. (In press)
209. Myhill, J. J. Endocrinol., 33, 429–36 (1965)
210. Stewart, R. D. H., Murray, I. P. C. J. Clin. Endocrinol., 27, 500–8 (1967)
211. Akerman, M., DiPaola, R., Tubiana, M. J. Clin. Endocrinol. (In press)
212. Koutras, D. A., Sfontouris, J. J. Endocrinol., 35, 135–43 (1966)
213. DeNayer, Ph., Malvaux, P., Van den Schrieck, H. G., Beckers, C., DeVisscher, M. J. Clin. Endocrinol., 26, 233–35 (1966)
214. Ponchon, G., Beckers, C., DeVisscher, M. J. Clin. Endocrinol., 26, 1392–94 (1966)
215. Aboul-Khair, S. A., Crooks, J., Turnbull, A. C., Hytten, F. E. Clin. Sci., 27, 195–207 (1964)
216. Oddie, T. H., Meade, J. H., Jr., Fisher, D. A. J. Clin. Endocrinol., 26, 425–36 (1966)
217. Gregerman, R. I., Solomon, N. J. Clin. Endocrinol., 27, 93–105 (1967)
218. Oddie, T. H., Fisher, D. A. J. Clin. Endocrinol., 27, 89–92 (1967)
219. Malvaux, P., DeNayer, Ph., Beckers, C., Van den Schrieck, H. G., DeVisscher, M. J. Clin. Endocrinol., 26, 459–62 (1966)
220. Dowling, J. T., Freinkel, N., Ingbar, S. H. J. Clin. Endocrinol., 16, 280–81 (1956)
221. Braverman, L. E., Ingbar, S. H. J. Clin. Endocrinol., 27, 389–96 (1967)
222. Fisher, D. A., Oddie, T. H., Epperson, D. J. Clin. Endocrinol., 26, 878–84 (1966)
223. Dowling, J. T., Appleton, W. G., Nicoloff, J. T. J. Clin. Endocrinol. (In press)
224. Stolte, L., Kock, H., Van Kessel, H., Kock, L. Acta Endocrinol., 52, 383–90 (1966)
225. Hollander, D., Meek, J. C., Manning,

R. T. *New Engl. J. Med.,* **276,** 900–2 (1967)

226. Inada, M., Sterling, K. (In press) (1967)

227. Gorman, C. A., Flock, E. V., Owen, C. A., Paris, J. *Endocrinology,* **79,** 391–405 (1966)

228. Bernstein, G., Hasen, J., Artz, S. A., Oppenheimer, J. H. Program, 59th Ann. Meeting Am. Soc. Clin. Invest., 17 (1967)

229. Levy, R. P., Marshall, J. S., Sheahan, M. G. *Clin. Res.,* **15,** 262 (1967) Abstr.

230. Hollander, C. S., Scott, R. L., McKerron, C. G., Asper, S. P. *Clin. Res.,* **15,** 259 (1967) Abstr.

231. Siegel, E., Tobias, C. A. *Science,* **153,** 763–65 (1966)

232. Jorgensen, E. C. *Mayo Clin. Proc.,* **39,** 560–68 (1964)

233. Barker, S. B., Shimada, M., Makiuchi, M. *Endocrinology,* **76,** 115–21 (1965)

234. Barker, S. B., Taylor, R. E., Jr., Tu, T., Jorgensen, E. C. 48th Meeting Endocrine Soc., 47 (Chicago, 1966) Abstr.

235. Barker, S. B., Shimada, M. *Mayo Clin. Proc.,* **39,** 609–25 (1964)

236. Campbell, P. L., Deibler, G. E., Gelber, S., Sokoloff, L. *Endocrinology,* **75,** 304–11 (1964)

237. Tata, J. R. *Mechanism of Hormone Action,* 173 (Karlson, P. Ed., Thieme, Studgard, 1965)

238. Tapley, D. F. *Mayo Clin. Proc.,* **39,** 626–36 (1964)

239. Bronk, J. R. *Science,* **153,** 638–39 (1966)

240. Bronk, J. R. *Biochim. Biophys. Acta,* **97,** 9–15 (1965)

241. Glick, L. I., Bronk, J. R. *Biochim. Biophys. Acta,* **92,** 23–28 (1965)

242. Glick, J. L., Bronk, J. R. *Ibid.,* **97,** 16–22 (1965)

243. Hoch, F. L. *J. Biol. Chem.,* **241,** 524–25 (1966)

244. Greif, R. L., Alfano, J. A. *Endocrinology,* **75,** 770–75 (1964)

245. Goldberg, M. L., Atchley, W. A. *Proc. Natl. Acad. Sci.,* **55,** 989–96 (1966)

246. Roodyn, D. B., Freeman, K. B., Tata, J. R. *Biochem. J.,* **94,** 628–41 (1965)

247. Buchanan, J., Tapley, D. F. *Endocrinology,* **79,** 81–89 (1966)

248. Brown, D. M. *Endocrinology,* **78,** 1252–54 (1966)

249. Wolff, E. C., Wolff, J. In *The Thyroid Gland,* 237 (Pitt-Rivers, R., Trotter, W. R., Eds., Butterworth, Washington, 1964)

250. Lee, Y. P., Lardy, H. L. *J. Biol. Chem.,* **240,** 1427–36 (1965)

251. Hoffman, W. W., Reichert, D. A., Westerfeld, W. W. *Endocrinology,* **78,** 1189–97 (1966)

REPRODUCTION[1]

By A. V. Nalbandov and Brian Cook

Department of Animal Science—Genetics
University of Illinois, Urbana, Illinois

INTRODUCTION

There is no doubt that the study of reproduction has become one of the major areas of physiology. In no small measure this is due to the population explosion and the attendant interest in contraceptive techniques (pills and intrauterine devices), as well as in the application of endocrine principles to synchronization of estrus in domestic animals which promises to increase the efficiency of livestock production. As one leafs back through previous reviews on the subject of reproductive physiology in the *Annual Review of Physiology* and elsewhere, one is struck by the fact that ten years ago most of the references included dealt with laboratory mammals, principally the rat. The reviews in the last three volumes, this one included, draw more and more on work done with domestic animals. This is auspicious for the future of reproductive endocrinology because it indicates that more people are beginning to realize that, useful as the laboratory rat has been and will continue to be, it has provided information which pertains only to rats and which frequently has little or no bearing on the method of reproduction and mechanisms of endocrine control evolved by other mammals, especially man. The endocrine mechanism of formation and maintenance of the corpus luteum is a prime example of this and it will be dealt with in this review just as it has been in the two previous volumes. One also begins to get glimmerings that the hypothalamic control system of the pituitary gland, which is being worked on so intensively in the rat, and which was reviewed so masterfully by Guillemin (54), may be found applicable only sketchily to other species of mammals, and perhaps not at all to birds. There are other examples which show that the rat is not a good prototype for other mammals. Hopefully, the trend will continue, of testing basic findings obtained from rats on other species, especially domestic animals, which in most respects resemble man in reproductive endocrinology more closely than does the rat.

The unfortunate tendency to generalize from the rat to other species, especially man, leads to the situation where, in many cases, information contained in textbooks is not labeled as specifically applicable to the rat, and is inappropriately ascribed to man and other animals. One major advantage of introducing comparative aspects of reproduction into reviews, symposia, and textbooks is that it acquaints research workers, especially

---

[1] This survey was concluded in June 1967.

clinicians who need it most, with the unbelievable versatility of reproductive endocrinology and the many diverse means by which the same reproductive problem is solved by different species. This review should be read with the understanding that it will not provide the reader with a final generalization but only with an insight into the sometimes bewildering complexity of the reproductive process. Perhaps organizers of symposia, refresher courses, and postgraduate colloquia will be moved to include among their faculties and speakers, experts who can discuss results obtained not only from laboratory mammals but from domestic animals as well.

The field of reproductive physiology continues to produce a mass of publications in scientific journals. Fortunately for the reviewers, most of them are in the nature of "dotting the i" and are at present only of interest to the dedicated specialist rather than the general reader. Most of these have been ignored in the present review. Instead, we have selected broad areas of interest which form a continuum within themselves and with previous reviews in this series.

Among the big publishing events of the past year was the appearance of the three-volume work entitled *The Pituitary Gland* edited by Harris & Donovan (58). It is an excellent compendium written by experts and it belongs on the bookshelves of every endocrinologist. It also is an example of a major problem confronting editors and writers of textbooks. The lag between submission of the chapters and publication of the three volumes was almost two years, making certain that a good share of the information in the rapidly moving fields covered was obsolete and even totally incorrect by the time the volumes reached the shelves of students and scientists. Also in 1966, the first of two volumes entitled *Neuroendocrinology* (95) has become available. These volumes were also authored by experts. Finally, the first volume of what promises to become a serial publication under the title of *Advances in Reproductive Physiology* (98) has made its appearance. Once the editors and contributors decide whether they should write for the general reader or the expert, and standardize their contributions, this series will become a welcome addition to the libraries of research workers.

ANALYTICAL TECHNIQUES

One of the year's most provocative papers was that of Bush (19). Here the hypothesis was developed that current analytical methods, in clinical practice generally, but in steroid determination particularly, were too slow, not by a moderate factor, but by approximately two orders of magnitude. Using breast cancer as an example, Bush maintained that retrospective studies of such diseases were unlikely to lead to the discovery of significant causal factors. The desirable approach is to examine a presently healthy population large enough so that one can expect to find a significant number of individuals succumbing to the disease over a reasonable period of study, and then to correlate the appearance of the disease with metabolic differences between those who succumb and those who do not. A population of between 5000 and 8000 women has been estimated to be necessary for such a project, and, if urine or blood samples are collected only once a week during two menstrual periods per year, between 40,000 and 64,000 samples would result, in which up to thirty hormones or metabolites might need to be determined. Bush also noted that apart from the large-scale investigation of diseases of multifactorial origin, methods of measuring "complex biochemicals" are the rate-limiting factors in many laboratory investigations, a fact to which many of us can attest.

Automation of the analytical process was proposed as a solution to these problems. Bush described his own machine CASSANDRA which is adequate to cope with the numbers of samples likely to be presented and, although sophisticated, should not be too expensive for most laboratories. Direct scanning of absorbent or fluorescent spots on paper or thin-layer chromatograms is the method of quantitation used in this apparatus. This technique offers several advantages: (a) such chromatograms can be produced in quantity with little investment in equipment; (b) specificity is given to the method by the chromatographic separation of components; (c) it is simpler to automate the chemical processing and scanning of chromatographic strips than eluates and solutions; and (d) processing is fast, once the strips are produced. A disadvantage of such a system is that there is a delay while chromatographic strips are being developed. This is, however, no greater than the delay encountered using gas-liquid chromatography where thin-media separations also have to be used before the extract can be applied to the column. Another problem is that of sensitivity. Bush has shown that a higher degree of sensitivity than was previously thought possible can be obtained from direct scanning of paper strips and it seems that the limit has not yet been reached. At present, the sensitivity of gas-liquid chromatography is greater, but this method is slower because it is limited by the retention times of steroids on the column. Bush thinks that there is at least as good a chance of improving the instrumental sensitivity of thin-media scanners up to the standard required for measuring steroids in blood as there is of improving the specificity of labeling methods, or of gas-liquid chromatography detectors. Bush's approach to the problem of measurement is obviously worthy of serious consideration by reproductive physiologists.

Criticisms of more conventional analytical techniques have recently been published, and the specificity conferred by chromatographic separation of the steroid to be measured has been emphasized (40, 71). Artifacts have been shown to be produced by impure solvents (39) and by silica gel used in thin-layer chromatography (67) as well as in labeled compounds that have been stored (43); this indicates that the advanced chemical technology of 1967 does not absolve the individual investigator from exercising the rigorous care that has always been required in the micromanipulation of steroids.

Two more developments in analytical technique will be of interest to all those engaged in hormone measurement. The first is the development of reliable radioimmunoassays for pituitary and chorionic gonadotropins and the second is the description of assays for steroids using the ability of certain plasma proteins to bind individual steroids specifically. The requirements for assays of this latter type were enumerated by Murphy (112). Essentially the technique is one of isotope dilution. Plasma containing the specific binding protein, but only traces of the steroid to be determined, is treated with radioactive steroid, so that most of the radioactivity is associated with the protein. A sample containing unlabeled steroid is then added to the mixture and this steroid displaces the radioactive steroid on the protein until equilibrium is reached. The protein with the bound steroid is then separated from the unbound steroid, and the radioactivity associated with the protein is inversely related to the amount of steroid in the test sample. Methods using this principle have been described for cortisol (118) and testosterone (41), and its extension to other steroids can be expected once specificity can be assured. These protein-binding assays may well present an alternative approach to that proposed by Bush for the measurement of steroids in large numbers of samples.

Many immunoassays for protein hormones have been described during recent months. Because of their greater sensitivity and specificity, radioimmunoassays are now preferred over the older techniques (hemagglutination, etc.). Human chorionic gonadotropin (HCG) has been shown to produce antibodies which cross-react with human luteinizing hormone (LH), and because HCG is obtained with relative ease, many assays for these two hormones have been described (36, 108, 119, 154, 156). Midgley's technique (108) is typical; the assay is based on competition between ^{131}I-labeled HCG and unlabeled human LH for a limited amount of antibody prepared in rabbits against partially purified HCG. The antibody is subsequently adsorbed exhaustively to remove antibodies to contaminating antigens. Antibody-bound hormone is separated from free hormone by an immunoprecipitation step utilizing sheep anti-rabbit gamma-globulin. Midgley has shown that the antibody reacts specifically with human LH and HCG (103, 105), neutralizes the biological activity of these hormones (103, 105, 107), and, when labeled with fluorescein, reacts with these hormones in the S^1 mucoid cells of the human adenohypophysis (105, 107) and the syncytiotrophoblast of the normal and neoplastic trophoblast (104, 120). He has also used it to measure serum LH during the menstrual cycle (106). More recently similar radioimmunoassays have been described for human follicle-stimulating hormone (37, 109).

The immunoassays for gonadotropins are an advance over methods previously available. The specificity of the ovarian ascorbic acid depletion assay for luteinizing hormone has recently been called into question (38, 45), and it is probable that the radioimmunoassay will alleviate problems of this type. Radioimmunoassays are not rapid, the antibodies and the hormones need to equilibrate for about 24 hours before measurements can be made. The antisera are also troublesome to prepare, but small quantities of good serum are sufficient for numerous determinations. These disadvantages are probably less severe than the problems associated with the more usual bioassays, where considerable time is needed to prepare the animals and quantitate the ultimate response.

Gas-liquid chromatographic techniques for the determination of steroid hormones are the subject of two recently published books (84, 157). Anyone contemplating the use of gas chromatography for steroid separation and measurement should certainly read them. The latter gives a useful introduction to the theory and practice of chromatography whereas the former is of especial value in the critical evaluation of different techniques. Lipsett's volume (84) consists of the proceedings of the workshop on Gas-Liquid Chromatography of Steroids in Biological Fluids held in February 1965, and the discussions of the various sections by the members of the workshop are particularly useful, informative, and entertaining.

Any laboratory in which a spectrophotometer is used should have available on the bench *Practical Hints on Absorption Spectrometry* (33). This wise and witty book offers a wealth of information on the art of spectrometry, and it cannot fail to entertain those who cannot benefit from its counsel (if such beings exist). If you use a spectrometer, read the book; if your staff uses the instrument, make them read the book; if you instruct others in the use of the technique, make sure they read the book too.

THE CORPUS LUTEUM—STUDIES *IN VIVO*

The endocrine mechanism of formation and function of the corpus luteum continues to occupy front and center of the stage of reproductive physiology. The habitual reader of the *Annual Review of Physiology* may wonder why it is necessary to review the corpus luteum story in two consecutive years (128). The reason is twofold: first, additional evidence has become available since Dr. Short's summary appeared in print and, second, what is more important, there are those of us who feel that it is healthy for scientific growth to present the views of both sides of a controversial subject. The mechanism of corpus luteum formation and function in mammals other than rats supremely qualifies as a controversial subject. In addition, the corpus luteum story is an excellent example of what happens when one tries to apply information obtained from rats to other mammals. Thus, this review should be read as a continuation of, and a complement to, last year's summary (128) to which the reader should also go for references which supplement the ones cited here. In this way the reader, we feel, will obtain a more complete overview of the subject matter.

Is There a Luteolysin?

To begin with we are faced with the fact that in many animals hysterectomy leads to the maintenance of the corpus luteum. This in turn leads to the perhaps natural conclusion that, if the corpus is maintained in the absence of the uterus, then the uterus must produce something, a luteolytic substance, that causes the demise of luteal tissue. This concept has inflamed the imagination of many and resulted in a convergence of effort on this problem which, to this day, has not produced any well-documented evidence for the existence of such a luteolytic substance. Evidence for the existence of luteolytic mechanisms has been adduced from the most imaginative mutilations of the Müllerian duct system which has involved amputation of halves, thirds, or fifths of the uterine horns or of the whole uterus, its slashing, its transplantation in whole or in part, and its deflection away from the ovaries as well as combinations of such surgical incursions. In fact, it is doubtful if any imaginable surgical insult to the system remains unperformed as of this writing. It is only on this kind of evidence that the existence of a luteolytic factor rests because, as already mentioned, all attempts to isolate such a substance by chemical extraction have been unsuccessful or unconvincing.

The claim (155) that acetone extracts of two whole bovine uteri contain a substance which causes regression of corpora lutea of some of the pseudopregnant rabbits injected with the extract is not adequately documented and will need to be substantiated by others before it can be discussed in detail. Furthermore, statistical analysis of the published data on the effect of the uterine extracts on acetate incorporation into progesterone by the corpora lutea of treated rabbits showed that the difference between uterine and muscle extracts was not significant. To those who work with *in vitro* incubation systems involving acetate uptake, this is not surprising, since it is commonly known that to establish statistically significant differences a great many more flasks are needed per treatment group than these authors used. In another study, extracts of bovine uterine endometria only, proved to be totally devoid of luteolytic activity in rats (86). Efforts to demonstrate a luteolytic substance in the uteri of sheep injected into hysterectomized sheep with functional corpora lutea, also failed (82). Thus, the bulk of the published evidence is unable to support the single claim (155) that the uterus contains an extractable luteolytic substance which has already been dubbed ULH (for uterine luteolytic hormone).

To complicate the situation still further, let us recall that Duncan et al. (32) found that crude endometrial filtrates obtained from pigs on days twelve to thirteen of the estrous cycle increased the rate of *in vitro* synthesis of progesterone by corpora lutea, whereas filtrates from endometria on days sixteen to eighteen of the cycle caused a significant depression in progesterone synthesis. These data were partially confirmed (23) in that guinea pig "uterine extracts" were found to inhibit *in vitro* progesterone synthesis and, furthermore, the degree of inhibition was found to be proportional to the amount of "uterine extract" added. Neither of these studies unequivocally demonstrates the presence of either luteolytic or luteotropic uterine factors. *In vitro* progesterone synthesis may have been inaccurately measured because of the ability of the uterus to metabolize progesterone and thus reduce the amount of progesterone detectable in the medium (116). Neither of the studies used radioactive progesterone added to the incubation medium to assess progesterone turnover.

In this connection it is important to note that the six-day-old rabbit blastocyst appears to contain enzymes which enable it to convert progesterone, as well as several other steroids, into their respective metabolites (64). This important study, furthermore, shows that blastocysts can also biosynthesize cholesterol and pregnenolone from acetate-^{14}C added to the substrate.

The complexity of the subject is further illustrated by the observation that the plasma progesterone levels in female rats which are allowed to eat their placenta immediately after delivery are significantly higher on day four postpartum than in females in which placentophagy is prevented (53). Nothing is known about the nature of the stimulus involved in this steroidogenic effect, nor about the pathways of this effect. (The same study also shows clearly that the progesterone level in peripheral blood drops significantly prior to parturition which, at least in rats, supports the view of those who feel that parturition is contingent on a drop in progesterone level.)

Finally, there is evidence (136) that the conceptus produces a luteotropic substance which directly or indirectly acts on the corpora lutea of pregnant rabbits and protects them against the luteolytic effects of exogenous luteinizing hormone.

These studies are cited to call attention to the extreme complexity of the whole problem and to emphasize the view that the endometrium, the embryo, and placenta all participate in the metabolism of steroids and in the control of their biosynthesis, a view which, in our opinion, is not commonly recognized. The roles of the endometrium, the embryo, and the placenta in steroid metabolism need to be explored in much greater detail (116).

The Role of the Pituitary

The mechanism of corpus luteum formation in the rat is well known and has been restated many times (51). There is now little doubt that in that species prolactin is usually luteotropic. Equally undisputed is the fact that prolactin is not luteotropic in most mammals in which maintenance of the corpus luteum was attempted with that hormone. Early work from this laboratory (14, 15, 125), using pituitary-blocking doses of progesterone in pigs, showed that the formation of the corpora lutea of the cycle could not be prevented once ovulation had occurred but that the corpus luteum of pregnancy was completely dependent on the pituitary gland for maintenance. This work was subsequently confirmed by hypophysectomizing pigs immediately after ovulation or during pregnancy (100, 101).

Thus, for the pig, the concept was proposed (15, 125) that the short time release of a luteotropic substance at the time of ovulation was sufficient to induce the formation of corpora lutea of the cycle which then would be able to maintain themselves morphologically and functionally, as measured by progesterone synthesis, for the duration of the cycle without additional hypophyseal support. If the pig becomes pregnant, additional and continuous hypophyseal support of an undetermined nature becomes essential. These facts remain undisputed.

Similar evidence was adduced by the French workers for the sheep in that here too hypophysectomy was unable to prevent the formation of the corpus luteum of the cycle (25, 26). For the sake of simplicity, a concept which would apply to most species would have been nice. However, the early work, already showed that guinea pigs were an exception to the rule because, in this species, release of a luteotropic substance was shown to be required for at least three days after ovulation if the corpus of the cycle was to develop normally (2). Subsequent work in this laboratory showed that the sheep was also different from the pig and that in ewes (contrary to the French work), the pituitary gland was essential for corpus luteum formation (76). Thus, if hypophysectomy was complete (every sella turcica in this study was examined histologically), and was performed on day one (day of ovulation), no luteal tissue formed and, if hypophysectomy was done on day five of the cycle, when the corpus was partially formed, it regressed promptly and completely. The results of the French (26) and American (76) workers differ only in that the former maintain that the corpus luteum will form, at least in part, after hypophysectomy on day one whereas the latter contend that hypophysectomy completely inhibits corpus luteum formation.

If a few cells of the adenohypophysis were left behind, results were variable in that formation of the corpus luteum was either normal, or partially, or totally inhibited (76). The ability of residual pituitary tissue to support luteal function in some ewes is probably influenced by the amount, type, and location of the remaining cells, as well as by their degree of encapsulation and vascularization.

Of some interest is the observation that most hypophyseal remnants in incompletely hypophysectomized sheep, regardless of whether they were or were not able to cause formation of the corpus luteum, consisted preponderantly of acidophilic cells which appears to be typical of transplanted or otherwise injured pituitary tissue. Only prolactin and growth hormone are known to be produced by acidophils, and prolactin alone appears not to be luteotropic in sheep (76).

Thus, according to most recent evidence the sheep is different from the pig in that it requires continuous support of a luteotropic hypophyseal substance for normal corpus luteum formation during the cycle. Both the French (26) and the American (76) workers agree that hypophysectomy of pregnant sheep leads to degeneration of the corpus luteum and death of the fetus. For this reason and those stated earlier a search was begun for a luteotropic substance in both hypophysectomized nonpregnant and pregnant sheep.

Having clearly established that the pituitary gland is essential for corpus luteum formation, the question arose whether the search for a luteotropic substance should be conducted in a sheep with an intact uterus or in a hysterectomized animal. If the uterus has the alleged luteolytic effect, then any exogenous hormone has to overcome it—thus, it would have been easier to find a luteotropic hormone had hysterectomized sheep been used. However, normally the hypophyseal luteotropic substance acts in a sheep with its uterus *in situ* and for this reason hypophysectomized sheep with intact uteri were used. All early attempts in which a range of doses of sundry pure of mixed hypophyseal hormones were injected, failed. On a serendipendous hunch, injections were replaced with continuous infusion of the desired hormone via the jugular vein. In order to make the task as difficult and the results as convincing as possible, the sheep were hypophysectomized twelve days after ovulation, the corpora lutea were marked with carbon black, the infusions were begun immediately and continued to day twenty, or well beyond the time when the corpus luteum would have totally regressed in a normal sheep. (The duration of the normal cycle in sheep is sixteen plus or minus one days.)

The following results emerged from this study. Totally ineffective in maintaining the corpora lutea were prolactin and estrogen. Totally able to maintain the corpus luteum morphologically and functionally (as measured by their ability to synthesize progesterone) were crude hypophyseal gonadotropic extracts (Abbott) and a crude luteinizing hormone preparation (Abbott). In contrast, pure luteinizing hormone [NIH-LH-S10 or purified ovine LH (Abbott)] was either unable to maintain corpora lutea or caused only partial maintenance as judged by morphological appearance and progesterone content. It was interesting to note than in all cases in which the infusion system broke down, if only for one hour, the corpora regressed in spite of the fact that the failure was rectified as soon as noted, and infusion of the crude luteinizing hormone continued for the remainder of the experiment.

In all maintained twenty-day-old corpora lutea the progesterone content and concentration were determined chemically and it was found that the progesterone levels fell within the range found in corpora lutea of normal sheep at the peak of their activity during the cycle. These results clearly show that a hypophyseal preparation containing predominantly luteinizing hormone as well as a small amount of a contaminant, which is not follicle-stimulating hormone, is luteotropic, and is steroidogenic in sheep. Furthermore, and most convincingly, it was found that when sheep were hypophysectomized in early pregnancy they aborted. If, however, crude luteinizing hormone was infused after hypophysectomy, the corpora lutea and pregnancy were maintained and the embryos were alive as judged by the presence of a heartbeat seven days after hypophysectomy. Since the sheep belongs to the class of animals in which castration is incompatible with maintenance of early pregnancy, this experiment clearly shows that the infused crude luteinizing hormone was able to cause progesterone synthesis by the corpora lutea, and that the latter were able to release this hormone. Whereas the crude form was effective in maintaining pregnancy for more than seven days, the pure form was effective for only five or six days, which indicates again that a factor in addition to luteinizing hormone is necessary to complete the luteotropic complex.

It will be recalled that luteinizing hormone is also luteotropic in the cow (28) and that a combination of follicle-stimulating hormone and prolactin is required for the maintenance of the corpus luteum in the hamster (51). In the work on cows (28) the hormones with luteinizing activity were homogenized with Freund's adjuvant and only one single injection was made. The estrous cycles of hormone-treated intact cows were 31.0 ± 2.9 days for pituitary extract, 36.4 ± 2.5 for bovine luteinizing hormone as compared to 20.0 ± 0.7 days for uninjected control cows. This study provides no information on the length of time the corpus luteum could have been maintained had the hormone treatments been repeated. As in the case of hypophysectomized ewes (76) where it was found essential to infuse the luteinizing hormone constantly in order to maintain the corpus luteum, the adjuvant added to the luteinizing hormone preparations injected into cows probably caused the hormone to be effective for a longer period than would have been possible without the adjuvant.

The significance of this research lies in the fact that the corpus luteum was maintained in the totally hypophysectomized ewe either during the cycle in the presence of the uterus, or during pregnancy, but this could be accomplished only if the crude luteinizing hormone was infused continuously. The other important fact is that there are at least two categories of animals: those, like the pig, in which the corpus luteum of the cycle develops and functions without sustained hypophyseal support, and those, like the sheep, in which the corpus is in need of constant support throughout the cycle and during pregnancy.

THE ROLE OF ESTROGEN

It has been known for a long time that estrogen is luteotropic in hypophysectomized rabbits (122). More recently it has been shown that luteinizing hormone is luteotropic in hypophysectomized rabbits (80), but luteolytic in intact does (131, 134, 137). Finally, a recent study has shown that normal corpora lutea, in the absence of follicles (destroyed by X irradiation), are incapable of synthesizing progesterone, as shown by the absence of this steroid in the ovarian effluent blood, and that rabbits prepared in this way are unable to maintain pregnancy (79). If the follicular source of estrogen is replaced by the injection of 2–4 µg of estadiol per day, the corpora lutea contain and secrete normal quantities of progesterone and pregnancies are maintained. This study shows that the estrogen effect is direct on the corpus luteum and is not mediated via the adenohypophysis. Neither exogenous luteinizing hormone nor whole crude pituitary preparation was able to cause corpora lutea to secrete progesterone or to maintain pregnancy in the absence of exogenous or endogenous estrogen. In the same study (79), it was found that 20α-hydroxy-4-pregnene-3-one (20α-OH) is secreted in copious quantities in the absence of either endogenous or exogenous estrogen, but is unable to maintain pregnancy.

Striking confirmation of the work by Keyes & Nalbanov (79) was recently provided (132). Pregnant rabbits were injected with anti-NIH-LH (S8 and S10) serum. This treatment greatly reduced the weight of corpora lutea and caused all the embryos to die. If this treatment was combined with the daily injection of 4 μg of estradiol-17β, the size of the corpora lutea was normal and the embryos survived. It is interesting that in this study too, the crucial dose of estrogen was 4 μg daily. The conclusion is reached that the anti-LH serum suppressed endogenous estrogen secretion which in turn resulted in decreased progesterone synthesis and abortion. This study provides evidence for a direct effect of estrogen on the corpus luteum and supports the work of Keyes strongly.

At present it is not known whether the primary role of estrogen is to keep the corpus luteum morphologically alive and capable of synthesizing progesterone or whether it actually plays a role in the biochemical process of progesterone synthesis.

Estrogen is luteotropic in the rat (13), the pig (42), and the ewe (24). However, in the hypophysectomized ewe it has no effect (76) which indicates that its luteotropic action in the intact ewe is mediated via the pituitary gland. Estrogen is not luteotropic in the cow (74), ferret (29), or woman (17).

One is greatly tempted to speculate about the importance of endogenous estrogen as an intraovarian (local) luteotropic factor. Can it be that luteinizing hormone is found to be luteolytic in intact rabbits (134, 135) because when injected into intact females it causes luteinization or ovulation of follicles, thus removing the local sources of estrogen? This possibility is supported by the fact that the luteolytic effect of luteinizing hormone in rabbits can be counteracted by the injection of estrogen (135).

In both papers cited, additional corpora lutea were induced in pseudopregnant or pregnant rabbits with the possibility that ovarian follicles may have been caused to luteinize or to ovulate, thus foreclosing the ovarian sources of estrogen. It was also found that prolactin is luteolytic in hypophysectomized rats (88, 89) and is unable to prolong the life-span of corpora lutea of intact pseudopregnant rats by more than three days (87). The question arises whether prolactin has antigonadotropic action in the rat sufficient to suppress follicular development, thus depriving corpora lutea of the luteotropic effects of estrogen.

The role of 20α-OH, a metabolic product of progesterone synthesized by the ovarian interstitial tissue, in reproduction is obscure. It is unable to support pregnancy in spayed rats (144), mice (153), or rabbits (79). Recently Hilliard et al. (63) have presented evidence that in mated intact rabbit does, 20α-OH may play a role in causing sustained release of luteinizing hormone from the pituitary gland after the initial coitus-induced burst of this hormone which also occurs in spayed-estrogen-primed does. In spayed does, in the absence of ovarian interstitial tissue and hence 20α-OH, only the initial burst of luteinizing hormone release is noted and no sustained release of hypophyseal luteinizing hormone takes place. From this evidence it is argued that 20α-OH may normally feed back on the hypothalamo-hypophyseal system causing it to release luteinizing hormone over a period of several hours after mating, which is essential for maximal efficiency of ovulation.

In the rat more 20α-OH than progesterone is recoverable from the ovarian effluent blood (35, 147). The progesterone peaks occur in proestrus, while 20α-OH is at its highest during estrus. In view of what was just stated concerning the role of 20α-OH in the sustained release of luteinizing hormone in the rabbit (63), the question arises whether a similar role may not be played by this steroid in the rat. The activity of the enzyme 20α-hydroxysteroid dehydrogenase which effects the conversion of progesterone to 20α-OH varies during the estrous cycle (152) and is highest in pro- and diestrus, and is concentrated in the corpora lutea of rats (121).

In the female rat (which, of course, is a spontaneous ovulator), copulation or vaginal stimulation causes a significant increase in the amount of hypophyseal luteinizing hormone released as measured in the peripheral plasma (143). Copulations were allowed for five to ten minutes and a rise in plasma luteinizing hormone occurred almost immediately. Copulation in male rats gave a similar result. In both males and females, plasma luteinizing hormone returned to precopulation levels about 120 minutes later but in all instances the amounts of such hormone released were higher in females than in males. These data contain no clue concerning the mechanisms which are responsible for the sustained hormone release. Concomitantly, hypophyseal luteinizing hormone in both males and females dropped. There were no demonstrable effects of copulation or release of hypophyseal follicle-stimulating hormone.

The question of the ability of corpora lutea to secrete estrogen as well as progesterone *in vivo* has not been adequately investigated. The initial observation of Greep that corpora lutea of hypophysectomized rats can synthesize estrogen has been confirmed recently and expanded, and biological (5, 85) and biochemical (9) evidence has been presented that heavily luteinized ovaries of intact rats can and do produce estrogen as well as progesterone when challenged with luteinizing hormone. From the data of Keyes (79), it appears that in the rabbit neither corpora lutea nor the ovarian interstitial tissue produces estrogen. It is a definite lapse that no information is available concerning species other than the rat with regard to the ability of corpora lutea to producce estrogen *in vivo*.

Intrauterine Devices

No less active than the group engaged in surgical manipulation of the Müllerian duct system, is the group studying the effects of the presence of foreign substances in the uterine lumen on the life-span of the corpus luteum and on its secretory activity. Such foreign substances have included glass or plastic beads, plastic coils, or a variety of viscous liquids. Since the physical nature of the foreign substances does not seem to affect the results to be discussed, they will all be referred to as intrauterine devices, for the sake of simplicity. The entire study has been recently summarized (12, 59) and the present review is intended only as a distillate of these more exhaustive treatments which also contain complete bibliographies. In our summary we intend to concentrate on interpretations different from those placed upon the results by previous evaluators.

It all began when the question was asked whether uterine distention, similar to that which may be caused by an implanting blastocyst, would modify the life-span of the corpus luteum. The original work was done on sheep (110, 113, 114) and showed that small beads anchored in the uterine lumen had no effect on the length of the cycle and that with beads of larger size the cycles were either significantly lengthened or shortened. All subsequent cycles were significantly lengthened if the beads were inserted on day three of the sixteen-day cycle, were shortened if the beads were inserted on day eight, and had no effect whatever if they were introduced into the uterus on day thirteen. Essentially similar results were obtained in cows (158–160) and in guinea pigs (11, 12, 111). However, when this work was repeated on sheep (68), only the short cycles were obtained and the explanation was proposed that in the original work (110, 113) the sheep may have reovulated and formed a new corpus luteum which may have been mistaken for the original one. This explanation is very improbable because in all cases in which prolonged cycles were observed, the corpus luteum was found in the same ovary in which it was observed at the time of the insertion of the bead.

In spite of the fact that intrauterine devices have been found to prolong or to shorten the life-span of the corpus luteum in at least three different species, sheep, guinea pig, and cow, most reviewers usually cite only the fact that these devices shorten the cycle length (99). This fits with the prevalent theory, mentioned earlier, that the uterus produces a luteolysin (12, 128) which they feel is responsible for luteal demise. To assure that the uterine tissue at one stage of the cycle responds to the intrauterine device by producing a luteolysin, at another by producing a luteotropin, and at a third by producing neither, cannot be easily fitted into the popular concept of corpus luteum control mechanisms and is thus ignored by the devotees of the luteolysin theory. It is also important to remember that the modification in the life-span of the corpus luteum occurs only if the intrauterine device is sufficiently large. Thus, for instance, in sheep a 2 mm bead produced no effect at any time while an 8 mm bead which caused uterine distention did modify cycle length. Similarly, no explanation is offered by the proponents of the luteolysin concept for the fact that in sheep the uterine segment containing the intrauterine device must be fully enervated. If it is not, regardless of when in the cycle the device is introduced, the cycles remain normal. It is difficult to conceive of a denervated, but otherwise macro- and microscopically normal uterine segment containing the device, not being able to secrete either a luteolysin or a luteotropin, especially since the denervated portion is so small in relation to the rest of the intact uterine mass. If one considered all of the available evidence, one is forced to conclude that none of the current explanations is satisfactory and that both systemic and local control mechanisms, both neural and humoral, may play a role in controlling the life-span and function of corpora lutea.

To continue in this vein of puzzlement, it must be pointed out that in some species intrauterine devices have no effect on the cycle length. Thus, neither swine (3, 44) nor primates (77, 150) show either a lengthening or a shortening of the cycle. The reasons for the species differences between sheep, cows, and guinea pigs, on the one hand, and swine and primates, on the other, remain totally obscure.

Evidence for a local luteolytic effect is adduced from the observation that in gilts with intrauterine devices the corpora lutea weighed less than in control animals but there was no difference in either the progesterone concentration or content of the corpora lutea between the control and experimental groups (59). Similar indications were obtained in guinea pigs in which one horn contained an intrauterine device, the other did not. Here corpora lutea on the side of the device were smaller than on the opposite side (11, 46, 59). In rabbits no such local effect of these devices was found (65).

In the cases cited, then, the local unilateral effect of the intrauterine devices is significant but not drastic, as compared to hypophysectomy, and the reduced size of the corpora lutea certainly suggests the existence of a luteolytic effect. However, a difficulty arises when it is considered that in sheep the unilateral reduction in corpus luteum weights caused by intrauterine devices can be prevented by the systemic injection of human chorionic gonadotropin (59, 137). The implication is that the endogenous hypophyseal luteotropin cannot overcome the local luteolytic effect produced by the intrauterine device even though it can maintain the size of the corpus luteum on the opposite side from the device. Furthermore, the local luteolytic effect of the device can be easily overcome by the injection of an exogenous luteotropin, human chorionic gonadotropin. This particular paradox will require much study before it can be interpreted.

If we return briefly to the uterine mutilation studies we are faced with the problem that the only way in which a luteotropic or a luteolytic effect of the Müllerian duct system can be demonstrated is by amputation of either the whole uterus or parts of it. This raises the question to what extent surgery itself may cause alterations in the life-span of corpora lutea. Thus, for instance, the mere ligation and the cutting of the oviduct and mesosalpinx of rats causes extension of the duration of pseudopregnancy from 13.5 to 15.2 days and if, in addition to this, the uterus is retracted from the ovary, pseudopregnancy is further lengthened to 16.6 days (10). One wonders whether uterine mutilations or, for that matter, any interference with the duct system has specific effects on the life-span of the corpora lutea or whether the results observed from such surgical interventions are totally nonspecific and therefore to be considered as artifacts. In any event, it appears essential to control future work of this type much more carefully than has been done in the past.

In sum, we are left with a bewildering array of leads, some of which suggest that the uterus may play a role in the control of the corpus luteum via postulated but otherwise elusive local or systemic luteolytic or luteotropic humors.

It appears abvious that different species solve the vital problem of corpus luteum formation and function in different ways. In all species the pituitary appears to be essential for corpus luteum function during pregnancy. In at least one species, the pig, the corpus luteum of the cycle will form in the absence of the pituitary gland, whereas in sheep, the pituitary gland is essential for its formation. In hypophysectomized sheep, either crude anterior pituitary extracts or luteinizing hormone and an unidentified contaminant (which is not follicle-stimulating hormone), is luteotropic, while in cows, luteinizing hormone alone is luteotropic. Equally diverse are the responses of different species to hysterectomy; in some species this operation has no effect on cycle length (monkey, woman, ferret, dog), while in others hysterectomy causes prolongation of the cycle (guinea pig, pig, cow, sheep). Similarly, the presence of intrauterine devices affects the cycle in some (sheep, cows), but not in other species (monkey, woman, pig). Thus, any attempt to formulate a unifying concept concerning the role of the pituitary or of the uterus in the control of corpus luteum function appears premature.

THE CORPUS LUTEUM—STUDIES *IN VITRO*

Studies of factors affecting the synthesis of steroids *in vitro* by corpora lutea are being reported with increasing frequency, and an analysis of the scope and limitations of *in vitro* methods is desirable. The experimental techniques that have been used range from short-term incubation of tissue slices (31, 32, 127) through perfusion of isolated glands (123) and long-term tissue culture (20) to various preparations of disrupted cells, e.g., homogenates (146), isolated mitochondria, (70), and mitochondrial extracts (56, 66). Each of these systems may be of considerable value in the elucidation of the different factors involved in steroid synthesis by the corpus luteum. The overriding question is which techniques can be employed most profitably in attempts to solve the presently outstanding problems of ovarian physiology.

As far as the corpus luteum is concerned, most of the problems studied using *in vitro* techniques were defined in the initial reports of Duncan et al. (31, 32) and Mason, Marsh & Savard (96). Duncan et al. tried: (*a*) to establish relative rates of progesterone synthesis throughout the estrous cycle, and (*b*) to discover substances which would modulate progesterone production *in vitro*. Savard's group went on to examine: (*a*) the primary site at which such modulation took place, and (*b*) the mechanism by which modulation of progesterone synthesis is effected (127). To these four areas of investigation a fifth can be added, the elucidation of biosynthetic pathways in ovarian tissue (124). These five questions are the basis for the following discussion.

It is obvious that slices of tissue suspended in buffer solution cannot operate as efficiently as the intact organ *in situ*. Absolute rates of secretion and metabolism of hormones must thus be determined *in vivo* where hormones, substrates, and sources of metabolic energy are delivered under probably ideal conditions to the cells being considered. The cell *in vivo* not only is endowed with an optimal supply of the factors it needs, but also is equipped with a system to remove secretory products and excess intermediates. These conditions do not hold *in vitro* where intermediates and end-products may accumulate in the cells and the bathing medium, possibly bringing feedback mechanisms into play. On the other hand, experiments *in vivo* are very apt to produce erroneous results. A recent paper (133) has clearly shown that ACTH, administered intravenously, will increase ovarian blood flow in the adrenalectomized dog and cat without affecting systemic blood pressure. The release of growth hormone in unanesthetized monkeys in response to mild stress (pinching), withdrawal of blood, and surgical trauma has recently been demonstrated (102). Stress also appears to cause growth hormone release in man (52). This leads to the possibility that gonadotropins may also be released under stress. Since the ovarian vein cannot be cannulated without subjecting the animal to stress, we may have an extension of Heisenberg's Uncertainty Principle from quantum mechanics to reproductive physiology; we cannot determine the value that we are trying to measure because the act of measurement changes that value. Perhaps catheters placed chronically in ovarian veins from which samples placed chronically in ovarian veins from which samples could be withdrawn after the animal has recovered from surgical trauma would ameliorate this problem. An alternative approach, e.g., that of using isotopic steroids to measure hormone production rates (141), may be equally accurate and technically easier. The secretion of steroid hormones *in vivo* has recently been reviewed (34) and the reader seeking more information on the relative merits of *in vivo* and *in vitro* experiments is referred to this source.

To return to the question of relative rates of progesterone synthesis *in vitro,* Duncan et al. (31) showed that, in tissues obtained from cyclic pigs, progesterone synthesis was highest on day four of the cycle and remained high until day sixteen. Between days sixteen and eighteen there was a dramatic decline. Synthesis in tissues obtained from pregnant animals remained fairly constant almost up to parturition. Armstrong & Black (6) observed fairly constant high rates of progesterone synthesis in corpora lutea obtained surgically from cows during the first half of the estrous cycle; the rate of synthesis showed a gradual decline from mid-cycle to eighteen days after estrus whereas the decline was very steep toward the onset of the next estrus. These facts were interpreted to mean that the size of the corpus luteum is probably the principal factor regulating total progesterone output during the first two weeks of luteal life; beyond this time a loss of synthetic capacity per unit weight of tissue occurs, and the loss becomes dramatic preceding the next ovulation. The results of these studies in the pig and the cow are thus quite similar.

The results of these *in vitro* experiments have been supported by *in vivo* observations of progesterone concentrations in ovarian venous plasma of pigs (97) and cows (47), and by measurement of progesterone concentrations in peripheral plasma of cows (62). The measurements of progesterone concentration in peripheral plasma by Gomes et al. (47) did not correlate well with their measurements in ovarian venous plasma, probably because of the insensitivity of their method. Incubations of bovine corpora lutea have shown that progesterone synthesis is greater on day 28 of pregnancy than on day 14 of the cycle when the tissues for the reproductive states are obtained from the same cow (151). The sensitivity of bovine corpora lutea to luteinizing hormone was shown to be greatest at mid-cycle, and progesterone synthesis did not appear to be different within three dairy breeds examined (69). This latter point is not clearly established because of the small sample sizes.

Factors which modulate progesterone synthesis are necessarily of two types: stimulatory and inhibitory. The first pituitary factor that was shown to stimulate progesterone synthesis *in vitro* was luteinizing hormone (96). Subsequent work by the same group (94) revealed that only compounds with luteinizing hormone activity will stimulate steroidogenesis in corpora lutea. All pituitary hormones were tested except thyrotropin. Subsequently, Armstrong (9) showed that thyrotropin would stimulate progesterone synthesis *in vitro* by bovine corpora lutea to a degree greater than was expected from the luteinizing hormone contamination of the thyrotropin. Several thyrotropin preparations have been shown to stimulate glycolysis in prepubertal rat ovaries and to inhibit cholesterol ester synthesis in rabbit ovarian interstitial tissue. Whether these results arise because the ascorbic acid depletion assay is underestimating the luteinizing hormone content of the thyrotropin, or whether thyrotropin itself is responsible, remains unclear. A steroidogenic action of prolactin has been demonstrated only in the isolated, perfused, bovine ovary (123). The prolactin concentrations used were very high, but the stimulation of progesterone synthesis was not thought by the author to be due to luteinizing hormone contamination. It is difficult to evaluate these data because of the variable results obtained with the perfusion technique.

Species specificity of gonadotropins does not seem to be an important consideration in studies *in vitro*. Bovine corpora lutea have been shown to respond to luteinizing hormone preparations of bovine, equine, ovine, and human origin (127). It was originally stated that human corpora lutea would respond only to luteinizing hormone of human origin (127) but recently the ovine form has also been shown to be steroidogenic in this species (83). Slices of porcine corpora lutea have been shown to respond equally well to ovine, bovine, and porcine luteinizing hormone *in vitro,* but not to follicle-stimulating hormone or prolactin (22). The stimulatory effects of estrogen on progesterone synthesis in the corpus luteum of the rabbit (discussed elsewhere in this article) have not been demonstrated *in vitro* (9).

Luteinizing hormone has been observed to stimulate progesterone synthesis *in vitro* in corpora lutea of cows (127), sheep (75), pigs (22), women (127), rats (4), rabbits (30, 48), and opossums (21). These animals exhibit many types of reproductive cycles and show diverse luteotropic and luteolytic mechanisms (128), yet corpora lutea from all of them show this common response to luteinizing hormone *in vitro*. Even the opossum, an animal in which the life-span of the corpus luteum is not extended by pregnancy or hysterectomy, shows this same response to exogenous luteinizing hormone. It is true that in the rabbit and the pig the responses are small; in the latter case exhaustive testing was needed before the effect could be demonstrated, but there is no reason to suspect that the effects are not real. A search for metabolic differences between corpora lutea showing large and small responses might be profitable in attempting to elucidate the mechanism of action of luteinizing hormone.

The effects of inhibitors of progesterone synthesis have not been extensively studied *in vitro*. The original observations of Duncan et al. (32) that uterine extracts from late in the estrous cycle inhibited progesterone synthesis whereas uterine extracts from early in the cycle were stimulatory must be cautiously evaluated. Striated muscle extracts were shown to be inhibitory, and progesterone metabolism by the uterine extracts themselves was not studied. Thus the "inhibition" could have been due to further catabolism of progesterone that was synthesized by the luteal slices so that the final estimate of the steroid was low. This objection says nothing about the stimulatory effect of uterine extracts from the early part of the cycle. We cannot postulate that uterine extracts can synthesize progesterone.

Those who would look for a chemical luteolysin of uterine origin may have an adequate assay system available in the tissue culture technique of Channing (20). Degeneration of the cells in the culture on the addition of the right extract could prove to be a satisfactory end point. Those of us who remain skeptical can ask that the following criteria be met:

1. Luteolytic activity shall be present in uterine extracts from late in the cycle and absent from extracts from pregnant uteri.

2. Extracts of other smooth muscle shall be devoid of activity.

3. Only luteal cell cultures shall be affected, and control cultures of any other tissue cells shall remain viable.

Criterion 1 might be too rigorous if it is postulated that luteolytic activity is always present, but is negated by a trophic effect from the pituitary. Criterion 2 must always hold. Criterion 3 is essential because the uterus contains bactericidal agents that could conceivably inhibit any cell culture. The need for proven specificity has been emphasized in other connections in the section Analytical Techniques.

The site of action of stimulatory or inhibitory factors is best conceived in biochemical or biophysical terms. Essentially three steps are involved in hormone action. First, there must be an interaction of the hormone with some pre-existing receptor site in or on the cells of the target tissue. Second, the biological function of the receptor molecules must be changed by the interaction. Third, the primary response produced by the interaction must be amplified by modification of other metabolic processes within the target cells. The second step represents the primary response to the hormone and the third step leads to the gross physiological response of the target tissue. In this discussion we will be concerned only with the site of action of luteinizing hormone, as this is the only compound that has been conclusively shown to modulate progesterone synthesis *in vitro*.

In determining the site of action of luteinizing hormone, two factors must be evaluated: the point of action in the cell and the point of action in the metabolic pathway. Studies *in vitro* have thrown some light on both these factors. Luteinizing hormone has been shown to stimulate progesterone synthesis only in intact cells, and not in disrupted cell preparations. Hall & Koritz (56) showed that this hormone could not stimulate the conversion of cholesterol to pregnenolone in aqueous extracts of acetone powder of mitochondria of corpora lutea. A re-examination of this system using intact mitochondria (the integrity of the organelles was demonstrated by electron microscopy) also failed to show a stimulation of side-chain cleavage in cholesterol (70). Current evidence suggests, but does not prove, that the site of luteinizing hormone action is not found in mitochondria.

Savard's group initially claimed, as a result of their studies, that the increased formation of progesterone resulted not only from increased conversion of cholesterol but also involved the added stimulation of the synthesis of cholesterol from earlier precursors (127). Hall & Koritz (57) subsequently concluded that the principal site of action of luteinizing hormone is on the conversion of cholesterol to progesterone, and that "it seems unnecessary to postulate a second site of action before cholesterol." Nevertheless, Hellig & Savard (61) showed that the hormone increased the incorporation of acetate-1-^{14}C into squalene when bovine luteal slices were incubated anaerobically. More recently, Armstrong (8) has shown that the hormone will stimulate cholesterol conversion to progesterone in slices of rabbit interstitial tissue when acetate incorporation into cholesterol is reduced by an inhibitor (AY9944). Acetate-1-^{14}C incorporation into both progesterone and 20α-hydroxy-4-pregnene-3-one was also reduced even though the total mass of steroids produced was unaffected. Similar results have been obtained with bovine luteal tissue (9). Thus, it seems quite clear that luteinizing hormone exerts a major effect on the conversion of cholesterol to progesterone, and the case for a second site of action preceding cholesterol in the metabolic pathway is not totally convincing.

In considering the mechanism of action of luteinizing hormone in the cell we must remember that the change in function of a receptor molecule triggers an amplification process. Thus, many secondary effects may result from an interaction at the primary site. Also, we have no basis for assuming that there is only one primary site, so that many centers might each trigger a cascade of secondary responses. Possibly there is only one primary site of action, but many responses in luteal cells induced by this hormone have been examined. How they intermesh, and how they are ordered remain unclear. Perhaps the simplest approach to a vast array of observations is to take the approach of Savard's group (127), to consider a possible sequence of events and to see how the observed facts fit the hypothesis. Haynes et al. (60) modified an original model for the action of ACTH in the synthesis of corticosteroids. Reinterpreted to account for the action of luteinizing hormone in progesterone synthesis (127), the hypothesis states that the hormone increases the activity of glycogen phosphorylase by increasing the rate of production of the cyclic nucleotide, 3',5'-adenosine monophosphate. The accelerated glycogen breakdown gives increased quantities of glucose-6-phosphate, which, when metabolized by the pentose phosphate pathway, yields increased amounts of NADPH. This cofactor is utilized in many of the steps of steroid biosynthesis, and its increased availability consequently enhances steroidogenesis. Initially, it was demonstrated that both LH and NADPH stimulate progesterone synthesis, LH activated phosphorylase in luteal slices, and 3',5'-AMP enhanced progesterone synthesis *in vitro* (see 127 for references). Savard & Casey (126) showed that the effects of LH and NADPH were additive, which was inconsistent with the model. Armstrong (7) demonstrated that the NADPH may have been acting principally in the medium into which enzymes had leached from the tissue slices, perhaps from damaged cells. Thus, if LH were acting only within the cells, and NADPH were acting principally in the medium, because of the relative impermeability of the cell membrane to NADPH, then some additivity of response would be expected. Eik-Nes & Hall (34) point out that those who speak of "physiological concentrations" may be deceiving themselves (and others) because if concentrations of a compound are high in a medium, it does not necessarily follow that they are high at the point where the compound exerts an effect or is metabolized. The same can be true *in vivo*. The permeability of membranes is often quite an unknown factor in the type of study we are discussing. For the present we can conclude only that the role of NADPH is enigmatic.

Subsequently, luteinizing hormone was shown to activate luteal phosphorylase, and 3',5'-AMP was shown to stimulate progesterone synthesis in incubated luteal slices (127). The facts to this point are compatible with the hypothesis, but when it was shown that 3',5'-AMP did not stimulate luteal phosphorylase when progesterone production was enhanced, the hypothesis encountered difficulties. It followed that 3',5'-AMP had to act through a mechanism that did not involve phosphorylase, and the luteinizing hormone stimulation of phosphorylase must not have been directly involved in the stimulation of progesterone synthesis. The stimulatory effects of 3',5'-AMP on progesterone synthesis have been confirmed in bovine luteal slices (57) and in rabbit ovarian interstitial tissue (81). In the latter work, theophylline, which inhibits phosphodiesterase, the enzyme which normally inactivates 3',5'-AMP by converting it to 5'-AMP, was shown to enhance the effects of both luteinizing hormone and 3',5'-AMP. This hormone has been shown to cause the accumulation of 3',5'-AMP in bovine luteal slices incubated *in vitro,* and the increase in the nucleotide was observed to precede the increased rate of progesterone synthesis.

The enzymes catalyzing the rate-limiting step in the conversion of cholesterol to pregnenolone [20α-hydroxylation of cholesterol (56, 66)] are located in the mitochondria, and are not influenced by LH. The enzymes involved in the synthesis of 3',5'-AMP are believed to be in the cell membrane (138). One would like to conclude that the primary site of LH action is in the cell membrane, and that the amplification of the LH response involves the action of 3',5'-AMP at many points in the cell, including the stimulation of the 20α-hydroxylation of cholesterol. Unfortunately, a stimulation of this process by cyclic AMP has not been described. The stimulation of cyclic-AMP production could itself be a secondary response to a factor resulting from LH interaction with the LH receptor. This factor could also stimulate the phosphorylase system.

Another well-documented response to luteinizing hormone in luteal cells which appears to be well removed from the primary action is stimulation of carbohydrate metabolism. Species differences appear in this effect; in the rat, the response is seen some time after the administration of the hormone *in vivo* and cannot be demonstrated *in vitro*, whereas bovine luteal tissue shows a response *in vitro* (7). Armstrong believes that the first effect of this hormone is to stimulate conversion of a precursor to progesterone, and once the stores of this precursor become low, secondary mechanisms are brought into play to cause replenishment. Increased glycolysis and increased acetate incorporation are thought to be reflections of these secondary processes.

The inhibition of protein synthesis with puromycin (93, 94) or cyclo-heximide (49) abolishes the ability of luteinizing hormone to stimulate progesterone synthesis *in vitro*. On the other hand, the inhibition of RNA synthesis with actinomycin D does not eliminate the response to the hormone (49). These observations suggest that this hormone acts by stimulating the translation of a stable messenger RNA. The protein produced by this process must turn over rapidly. Since puromycin inhibits the stimulation of progesterone synthesis by cyclic AMP, but does not affect the accumulation of cyclic AMP in response to luteinizing hormone, it is suggested that the labile protein influences processes following and not preceding 3′,5′-AMP synthesis.

As far as biosynthetic pathways are concerned, it can be seen from this discussion that the basic outlines are clear (61, 124) but individual reaction steps and mechanisms are obscure. Biochemically, we need to know much more about mixed-function oxidase systems before many of the steps in steroid synthesis can be understood; and understanding of the individual reactions probably needs to precede the knowledge of how the individual steps are integrated and controlled. Studies continue to be reported in which the effect of various steroids in the metabolic pathway on the accumulation of other steroids is described (55). These phenomena could represent a second level of control in which the availablity of metabolites in the biogenic sequence is regulated after the output of the final product has been set by the gonadotropin.

From this discussion it is clear that both *in vivo* and *in vitro* experiments are not without hazards, but taken together they can lead to great insight into many problems. It seems less profitable to study relative rates of synthesis of progesterone *in vitro* with different experimental variables and to examine more species for a response to luteinizing hormone than to examine some of the unsolved problems concerned with the control and expression of such response in luteal tissue. It is probable that a response *in vitro* can be demonstrated in any species even though in many cases the response may be small. Under these circumstances, the power of the *in vitro* technique could be most profitably applied to solving some of the outstanding biochemical problems rather than to producing an accumulation of results of dubious physiological significance.

THE MECHANISM OF ACTION OF ESTROGEN ON THE UTERUS

At the Second International Congress of Endocrinology in 1964, Bush delivered a "Future Advances" lecture entitled "Hormones and Receptors" (18). In this presentation he stressed the need for an integration of biological and physicochemical concepts and developed a general theory of biological catalysis. He drew comparisons between the mechanism of hormone action, drug and antagonist action, and olfaction. He suggested that the path to follow, as far as the study of hormone receptors was concerned, was that which had been mapped out by the enzymologists. Hence, the first step was to "find and isolate receptors. This sounds like a tall order, and, indeed, it is." Within the last year, two groups of workers have independently isolated, by different techniques, a possible receptor molecule, specific for estradiol, from the uterus, and have gone some way towards its characterization.

Initially, Jensen & Jacobson (72) showed that the uterus and the vagina preferentially bound tritiated estradiol, whereas nontarget tissues did not. Noteboom & Gorski (117) extended these studies and demonstrated that the estrogen receptor is stereospecific and probably a protein. Subcellular fractionation of the rat uterus indicated that approximately 50 per cent of the receptor was in a heavy nuclear-myofibrillar fraction and 30 per cent was in the soluble fraction (105,000 $\times$ g supernatant fluid). Toft & Gorski (148) injected estradiol-17β into immature rats and then killed the animals at various time periods up to four hours after the injection. The uteri were homogenized; the soluble fraction was obtained, layered on a sucrose density gradient, and centrifuged. The radioactivity was shown to be associated with a component with a sedimentation coefficient of 9.5S. Maximum binding was found within twenty minutes of injection, the shortest time period studied. When rat intestine was similarly treated, estrogen did not appear to be bound in the gradient. Corticosterone or testosterone did not affect the binding of estradiol-17β whereas diethylstilbestrol greatly reduced the radioactivity in the 9.5S peak. Estradiol-17α also had little effect on estradiol-17β binding capacity. These facts indicate the existence of a macromolecular component present in uterus, but absent from intestine, which binds estrogens but not nonestrogenic steroids very soon after they are administered to the animal. These are the properties one expects of a specific receptor molecule.

In a later paper, Toft, Shyamala & Gorski (149) demonstrated that similar results could be obtained in an *in vitro*, cell-free system. Uteri from immature rats were homogenized and the soluble fraction isolated as before. Steroids dissolved in ethanol were then added to the soluble fraction and incubated at 0 to 4° C for fifteen minutes. Samples from the soluble fraction were layered on a sucrose gradient and centrifuged. The results obtained were similar to those previously described (148). The molecular weight of the component binding the estrogen was shown to be about 200,000 and its binding capacity was destroyed by pronase and trypsin, but not by ribonuclease or deoxyribonuclease. The pH optimum for binding was approximately 7.0, and heat-treatment, sulfhydryl-reacting agents, and detergents destroyed the binding capacity. These facts substantiate the claim that the material is a protein.

The dissociation constant of the estrogen complex was calculated to be 7.1 $\times$ 10^{-10} M (149) which compares with a value of "about 10^{-11}" estimated by Bush (18) from the original results of Jensen & Jacobson (72). Toft et al. (149) consider their value for the dissociation constant to be an overestimate. The concentration of estrogen-binding sites was estimated to be 10.3 × 10⁻¹³ moles per mg of protein or about 8.9 × 10⁻¹³ moles per uterus.

Jensen, de Sombre & Jungblut (73) are not in total agreement with the other workers (145, 149) regarding the distribution of the receptor molecule. Autoradiographs do not reveal any appreciable extranuclear radioactivity (73), and the percentage of the total uterine radioactivity appearing in the supernatant fraction remains fairly constant with different estradiol doses or periods of time after injection. Estrogen antagonists inhibit the uptake of tritiated estradiol to the same degree in both the nuclear and soluble fractions. Homogenates of induced mammary tumors, which are estradiol sensitive, contain much less radioactivity in the soluble fraction than similar uterine preparations, possibly because conditions for homogenization of mammary tumors are much less severe. These observations suggest that there is but one component which normally occurs near the surface of the nucleus, and the appearance of radioactivity in the supernatant fluid results from breakdown of the nuclear envelope during cell fractionation.

Jensen et al. (73) isolated the estradiol-binding substance from calf uterus using a column which was packed with *p*-aminobenzylcellulose which had been diazotized and coupled to estradiol to give a packing containing steroid residues joined by azolinkages to either the two or four position of the estradiol. The steroid content of the material thus prepared was about 1 μeq per gram with 60 per cent of the estradiol linked through position four. When excess uterine extract is passed through the column, the compound possessing the highest affinity for the estrogen should displace all the others. Applying this technique to 1 kg of calf uterus, two preparations were made, one from the supernatant fraction and one from a dialysate of the nuclear fraction. A few milligrams of product were obtained from each of these sources. The former was slightly contaminated, but was antigenically pure, giving rise to the same single antibody as the nuclear fraction. The product isolated was a protein, containing phosphorus, and was soluble in aqueous ethanol. The antibody to the product precipitated the radioactive estradiol-receptor complex obtained from the nuclei of calf endometrium exposed to tritiated estradiol *in vitro*. The techniques of both these groups should lead to a more clear delineation of the nature of the estrogen receptor molecule. Those readers interested in a more general discussion of estrogen effects in the uterus may find reference (50) helpful.

The capacity and structural specificity of the sites for the binding of estradiol in target tissues other than the uterus, namely the hypothalamus and the anterior pituitary, have also been studied (78) but receptor compounds have not yet been isolated.

Finally, studies have been published concerning the presence of histamine receptors in the uterus, and the relationship between estrogen, histamine, and the decidual reaction. Szego and her associates (129, 130, 139, 140) proposed that histamine was the mediator of estrogen action in the uterus. Estrogen was believed to cause local histamine release which result-ed in dilation and expansion of the microcirculatory system within the uterus. The resulting increase in the permeability of the tissue to metabo-lites then permitted increased metabolic activity and growth.

Marcus & Shelesnyak dispute this scheme as they have shown that in the pregnant rat, the histamine release in the uterus which follows the es-trogen surge preceding the start of gestation could not be prevented by the injection of an estrogen antagonist (MER-25) under conditions of dose and timing which prevented nidation. MER-25 did not cause histamine re-lease in the uterus of ovariectomized rats, but prevented histamine release following estrogen injection in the ovariectomized rat. Thus histamine re-lease in the pregnant rat uterus does not appear to be a response to estro-gen action (90).

Evidence for histamine receptors in rat endometrium involved in the decidual reaction was then provided by demonstration of an association be-tween specific retention of histamine-^{14}C and decidual induction (91). The time course of this reaction was such that the greatest retention of radioac-tivity was associated only with decidual induction.

The turnover of receptors in the rat uterus appears to be rapid (92), so that the receptors do not persist from one estrous cycle to the next. The reduction in histamine receptor concentration occurred through the proes-trous-estrous phase of the cycle.

IN VITRO CULTURE OF EGGS AND EMBRYOS

"Result: they're decanted as freemartins—structurally quite normal (ex-cept . . . that they do have the slightest tendency to grow beards), but ster-ile. Guaranteed sterile. Which brings us at last . . . out of the realm of mere slavish imitation of nature into the much more interesting world of human invention."

In the lecture from which this is an excerpt, the Director of the Central London Hatchery and Conditioning Centre also described in vitro fertiliza-tion, the culture of human eggs, and the production of innumerable identi-cal twins in which heredity had been modified, as well as the ultimate hatching of embryos from bottles. From this glimpse into the "Brave New World" of Huxley to scientific reality is a disappointingly big step. Even though the first attempts at in vitro culture of mammalian eggs date back to 1880, we are still at a stage where cultivation of mammalian eggs is a precarious and uncertain affair (16). In preimplantation stages, eggs have been cultured in hanging drops, in small tubes, or in flasks containing liq-uid media. Brinster (16) considers that a general medium for the culture of mammalian eggs might consist of: 1. Krebs-Ringer bicarbonate, 2. a so-dium-bicarbonate buffer, 3. an atmosphere of 5 per cent CO_2 in the gas phase, 4. a pH of about 7.4, 5. a protein concentration of 1 to 10 mg/ml, 6. a glucose concentration of 1 mg/ml, and 7. a pyruvate concentration of about $5 \times 10^{-4} M$.

In general, the greatest successes in culturing ova have been obtained with mouse and rabbit eggs. In these cultures, two-celled eggs frequently go to the morula stage and, if culture begins with advanced cleavage stages, they can be brought to the blastocyst stage which, when transferred to properly prepared host mice, will develop into normal young. In contrast to these two species, rat, guinea pig, and hamster ova are all difficult to culture, and in most cases, development beyond two cells cannot be achieved. Similarly, *in vitro* culture of ova from the larger domestic animals, pigs, sheep, goats, and cattle, and from primates is not nearly as successful as that of mice and rabbits (16). The reasons for these differences are not known and no obvious explanation comes to mind.

Of great interest is the finding that six-day-old rabbit blastocysts can be caused to develop to the primitive groove stage if either luteinizing hormone or ACTH is added to the incubation medium (64). The effect of luteinizing hormone is more pronounced than that of ACTH and the effect of the two hormones together is not additive. The increment in the rate of differentiation of the blastocysts caused by these hormones is not due to the addition of the amount of protein contained in the hormones since the addition of a twofold amount of albumin to the medium had no effect on the rate of development. These blastocysts were cultured successfully for four days and, as mentioned in another section of this review, remained biosynthetically active throughout this period. Apparently, this is the most encouraging published report concerning the potential development of rabbit blastocysts *in vitro*.

The reasons for the difficulties encountered in *in vitro* cultures of eggs and blastocysts are not clear but the fault may lie in factors present in the duct system but not added to the synthetic media. Fertilized tubal eggs can be caused to develop in Millipore filters (1). If the Millipore filters are placed inside the uterus, the eggs inside them will develop into expanding blastocysts, but they have a smaller diameter than the free-living uterine control blastocysts. In contrast, eggs encased in Millipore filters and placed for 48 hours into the abdominal cavity and then moved to the uterus, showed distinctly retarded development. This experiment suggests that there may be a tubal factor which may be missing from the artificial, chemically defined media usual for culture of blastocysts *in vitro*.

More promising than egg culture appears to be the culture of postimplantation rat embryos (115). Here one can start with embryos of the five-to-seventeen-somite stage and grow them in homologous serum to the early limb bud stage (about thirty somites).

During this culture period the embryos synthesize considerable amounts of protein and it is improbable that growth stops at the thirty-somite stage because the medium has become exhausted of nutrients. Death is presumably caused by the inability of the embryo to obtain oxygen and nutrients from the culture medium fast enough. It is at this stage that the embryo *in vivo* grows most rapidly and develops a placenta which in the cultured embryos fails to form.

The paucity of data in this most fascinating field is most disappointing. While the transfer of ova, or even of embryos in various stages of development, into pigs, sheep, or rabbits has become routine, it teaches us little if anything concerning the requirements of eggs and embryos for *in vitro* culture. Quite active is the interest in initial culture of eggs *in vitro* with subsequent transfer into recipient females. The esoteric or pragmatic worth of such studies is not totally clear.

Of some interest are the studies concerned with the influence of the uterine environment on the survival of ova. Thus, for instance, the decreasing litter size in aging mice may be ascribed to some undefined change in the uterine environment in old females. When morulae or blastocysts from young females were transferred to uteri of old hosts, only 14 per cent of them survived, whereas transplants from young donors to young hosts yielded 48 per cent survival (142). When morulae and blastocysts from aged or from young donors were transplanted to young recipients, both groups survived equally well.

In another experiment (27), rats were castrated and injected with progesterone. Blastocysts were transferred into their uteri five days after castration, one day after castration, or on the day of ovariectomy. Implantation was precipitated with a systemic injection of estrone. It was found that the percentage of viable young increased as the interval from castration to blastocyst transfer increased. These data are interpreted to mean that ovarian estrogen is inimical to implantation and that progesterone treatment "neutralized" a uterine factor which caused death of those embryos which were transferred at the time of castration or one day later.

We observed at the outset that the resources being devoted to the study of reproduction are steadily increasing. The reader may infer from this brief review of a few of the facets of reproduction in female mammals that such increased support is enabling progress to be made. The advances we have discussed in our knowledge of reproductive processes could be multiplied many times in female mammals alone, without even considering studies in the male. The next reviewer in this series will not lack raw material.

ACKNOWLEDGMENT

We thank Mrs. Natalie Sutterlin for her editorial assistance in the preparation of this review and Mrs. Alberta McClara for typing the manuscript. The preparation of this paper was partially supported by grant number AM-06976 of the National Institutes of Health.

LITERATURE CITED

1. Ahlgren, M. Development of fertilized tubal rabbit eggs in diffusion chambers *in vivo*. *J. Reprod. Fertility*, **12**, 145–48 (1966)

2. Aldred, J. P., Sammelwitz, P. H., Nalbandov, A. V. Mechanism of formation of corpora lutea in guinea pigs. *J. Reprod. Fertility*, **2**, 394–99 (1961)

3. Anderson, L. L. Effect of intrauterine distention on the estrous cycle of the gilt. *J. Animal Sci.*, **21**, 597–601 (1962)

4. Armstrong, D. T., O'Brien, J., Greep, R. O. Effects of luteinizing hormone on progestin biosynthesis in the luteinized rat ovary. *Endocrinology*, **75**, 488–500 (1964)

5. Armstrong, D. T., Greep, R. O. Failure of deciduomal response to uterine trauma and effects of LH upon estrogen secretion in rats with ovaries luteinized by exogenous gonadotropins. *Endocrinology*, **76**, 246–54 (1965)

6. Armstrong, D. T., Black, D. L. Influence of LH on corpus luteum metabolism and progesterone biosynthesis throughout the bovine estrous cycle. *Endocrinology*, **78**, 937–44 (1966)

7. Armstrong, D. T. Comparative studies of the action of luteinizing hormone upon ovarian steroidogenesis. *J. Reprod. Fertility, Suppl. 1*, 101–12 (1966)

8. Armstrong, D. T. On the site of action of luteinizing hormone. *Nature*, **213**, 633–34 (1967)

9. Armstrong, D. T. *In vitro* synthesis of progesterone. *J. Animal Sci., Suppl. 27* (In press) (1968)

10. Bailey, D. A., Butcher, R. L., Inskeep, E. K. Local nature of utero-ovarian relationships in the pseudopregnant rat. *Endocrinology*, **79**, 119–24 (1966)

11. Bland, K. P., Donovan, B. T. Uterine distension and the function of the corpora lutea in the guinea pig. *J. Physiol. (London)*, **186**, 503–15 (1966)

12. Bland, K. P., Donovan, B. T. The uterus and the control of ovarian function. *Advan. Reprod. Physiol.*, **1**, 179–216 (1966)

13. Bogdanove, E. M. Preservation of functional corpora lutea in the rat by estrogen treatment. *Endocrinology*, **79**, 1011–15 (1966)

14. Brinkley, H. J., Norton, H. W., Nalbandov, A. V. Role of a hypophysial luteotrophic substance in the function of porcine corpora lutea. *Endocrinology*, **74**, 9–13 (1964)

15. Brinkley, H. J., Norton, H. W., Nalbandov, A. V. Is ovulation alone sufficient to cause formation of corpora lutea? *Endocrinology*, **74**, 14–20 (1964)

16. Brinster, R. L. Culture of mammalian embryos. *J. Animal Sci., Suppl. 27* (In press) (1968)

17. Brown, W. E., Bradbury, J. T., Jennings, A. F. Experimental alteration of the human ovarian cycle by estrogen. *J. Clin. Endocrinol. Metab.*, **8**, 453–60 (1948)

18. Bush, I. E. Hormones and Receptors. *Proc. Intern. Congr. Endocrinol., 2nd, Part II*, 1324–35 (*Intern. Congr. Ser. No. 83*, Excerpta Med. Found., London, 1965)

19. Bush, I. E. Automation of steroid analysis. *Science*, **154**, 77–83 (1966)

20. Channing, C. P. Progesterone biosynthesis by equine granulosa cells growing in tissue culture. *Nature*, **210**, 1266 (1966)

21. Cook, B., Nalbandov, A. V. The effect of some pituitary hormones on progesterone synthesis *in vitro* by the luteinized ovary of the common opossum (*Didelphis marsupialis virginia*). *J. Reprod. Fertility* (In press)

22. Cook, B., Kaltenbach, C. C., Norton, H. W., Nalbandov, A. V. The synthesis of progesterone *in vitro* by porcine corpora lutea. *Endocrinology* (In press)

23. Cooper, E., Hess, M. The role of uterine materials upon *in vitro* steroidogenesis. *Anat. Record*, **157**, 230 (1967)

24. Denamur, R., Mauléon, P., Contrôle endocrinien de la persistance du corps jaune chez les ovins. *Compt. Rend. Acad. Sci.*, **257**, 527–30 (1963)

25. Denamur, R., Martinet, J., Short, R. V. Secretion de la progesterone par les corps jaunes de la brebis après hypophysectomie, section de la tige

pituitaire et hysterectomie. *Acta Endocrinol.*, **49**, 72–90 (1966)

26. Denamur, R. Formation and maintenance of corpora lutea in domestic animals. *J. Animal Sci., Suppl. 27* (In press) (1968)

27. Dickmann, Z. Hormonal requirements for the survival of blastocysts in the uterus of the rat. *J. Endocrinol.*, **37**, 455–61 (1967)

28. Donaldson, L. E., Hansel, W. Prolongation of the life span of the bovine corpus luteum by single injections of bovine luteinizing hormone. *J. Dairy Sci.*, **48**, 903–4 (1965)

29. Donovan, B. T. Hormonal control of corpus luteum function in the ferret. *Abstr. Intern. Congr. Physiol. Sci., 23rd, Tokyo*, 284 (1965)

30. Dorrington, J. H., Kilpatrick, R. Effects of pituitary hormones on progestational hormone production by the rabbit ovary *in vivo* and *in vitro*. *J. Endocrinol.*, **35**, 53–63 (1966)

31. Duncan, G. W., Bowerman, A. M., Hearn, W. R., Melampy, R. M. *In vitro* synthesis of progesterone by swine corpora lutea. *Proc. Soc. Exptl. Biol. Med.*, **104**, 17–19 (1960)

32. Duncan, G. W., Bowerman, A. M., Anderson, L. L., Hearn, W. R., Melampy, R. M. Factors influencing *in vitro* synthesis of progesterone. *Endocrinology*, **68**, 199–207 (1961)

33. Edisbury, J. R. *Practical Hints on Absorption Spectrometry* (Hilger and Watts, Ltd., London, 266 pp., 1966)

34. Eik-Nes, K. B., Hall, P. F. Secretion of steroid hormones *in vivo*. *Vitamins Hormones*, **23**, 153–207 (1965)

35. Eto, T. H., Masuda, Y., Hosi, T. Progesterone and pregn-4-ene-20α-ol-3-one in rat ovarian venous blood at different stages in the reproductive cycle. *Japan. J. Animal Reprod.*, **8**, 34–40 (1962)

36. Faiman, C., Ryan, R. J. Radioimmunoassay for human FSH. *J. Lab. Clin. Med.*, **68**, 872–73 (1966)

37. Faiman, C., Ryan, R. J. Radioimmunoassay for human follicle-stimulating hormone. *J. Clin. Endocrinol. Metab.*, **27**, 444–47 (1967)

38. Frankel, A. I., Gibson, W. R., Graber, J. W., Nelson, D. M., Reichert, L. E., Jr., Nalbandov, A. V. An ovarian ascorbic acid depleting factor in the plasma of adenohypophysectomized cockerels. *Endocrinology*, **77**, 651–57 (1965)

39. Frankel, A. I., Nalbandov, A. V. Effect of the evaporation of various solvents upon the stability of corticosterone-1,2-³H and corticosterone-4-¹⁴C. *Steroids*, **8**, 749–64 (1966)

40. Frankel, A. I., Cook, B., Graber, J. W., Nalbandov, A. V. Determination of corticosterone in plasma by fluorometric techniques. *Endocrinology*, **80**, 181–94 (1967)

41. Fritz, G. R., Knobil, E. The measurement of testosterone in plasma by competitive protein binding analysis. *Fed. Proc.*, **26**, 757 (1967)

42. Gardner, M. L., First, N. L., Casida, L. E. Effect of exogenous estrogens on corpus luteum maintenance in gilts. *J. Animal Sci.*, **22**, 132–34 (1963)

43. Geller, L. E., Silberman, N. The effect of chemical impurities on the stability of labelled steroids. *Steroids*, **9**, 157–61 (1967)

44. Gerrits, R. G., Hawk, H. W. Effect of intrauterine devices on fertility in pigs. *J. Animal Sci.*, **25**, 1266 (1966)

45. Gibson, W. R., Frankel, A. I., Graber, J. W., Nalbandov, A. V. An ovarian ascorbic acid depletion factor in starch gel preparations following electrophoresis. *Proc. Soc. Exptl. Biol. Med.*, **120**, 143–46 (1965)

46. Ginther, O. J., Mahajan, J., Casida, L. E. Local ovarian effects of an intrauterine device in intact and unilaterally ovariectomized guinea pigs. *Proc. Soc. Exptl. Biol. Med.*, **123**, 775–78 (1966)

47. Gomes, W. R., Estergreen, V. L., Frost, O. L., Erb, R. E. Progestin levels in jugular and ovarian venous blood, corpora lutea, and ovaries of the nonpregnant bovine. *J. Dairy Sci.*, **46**, 553–58 (1963)

48. Gorski, J., Padnos, D., Nelson, N. J. *In vitro* effects of luteinizing hormone on rabbit ovaries. *Life Sci.*, **4**, 713–19 (1965)

49. Gorski, J., Padnos, D. Translational control of protein synthesis and

control of steroidogenesis in rabbit ovary. *Arch. Biochem. Biophys.*, **113**, 100–6 (1966)

50. Gorski, J., Notides, A., Toft, D., Smith, D. E. Mechanism of sex steroid action. *Clin. Obstet. Gynecol.*, **10**, 17–28 (1967)

51. Greenwald, G. S., Rothchild, I. Formation and maintenance of corporalutea in laboratory animals. *J. Animal Sci., Suppl. 27* (In press) (1968)

52. Greenwood, F. C., Landon, J. Growth hormone secretion in response to stress in man. *Nature,* **210,** 540–41 (1966)

53. Grota, L. J., Eik-Nes, K. B. Plasma progesterone concentrations during pregnancy and lactation in the rat. *J. Reprod. Fertility,* **13,** 83–91 (1967)

54. Guillemin, R. The adenohypophysis and its hypothalamic control. *Ann. Rev. Physiol.,* **29,** 313–48 (1967)

55. Haksar, A., Romanoff, E. B., Hagino, N., Pincus, G. *In vitro* inhibition of cholesterol synthesis by pregnenolone in bovine corpus luteum. *Steroids,* **9,** 405–14 (1967)

56. Hall, P. F., Koritz, S. B. The conversion of cholesterol and 20α-hydroxycholesterol to steroids by acetone powder of particles from bovine corpus luteum. *Biochemistry,* **3,** 129–34 (1964)

57. Hall, P. F., Koritz, S. B. Influence of interstitial cell-stimulating hormone on the conversion of cholesterol to progesterone by bovine corpus luteum. *Biochemistry.,* **4,** 1037–43 (1965)

58. Harris, G. W., Donovan, B. T., Eds. *The Pituitary Gland* (Butterworths, London, 3 vols., 1966)

59. Hawk, H. W. Effect of intrauterine devices on corpus luteum function. *J. Animal Sci., Suppl. 27* (In press) (1968)

60. Haynes, R. C., Sutherland, R. W., Rall, T. W. The role of cyclic AMP in hormone action. *Recent Progr. Hormone Res.,* **16,** 121–38 (1960)

61. Hellig, H., Savard, K. Sterol biosynthesis in the bovine corpus luteum *in vitro. Biochemistry,* **5,** 2944–56 (1966)

62. Hendricks, D. M., Oxenreider, S. L., Anderson, L. L., Guthrie, H. D. Progesterone in systemic and ovarian venous blood and corpora lutea

of cycling, hypophyseal stalk-sectioned, stalk-sectioned hysterectomized, and stalk-sectioned oxytocin treated cows. *Fed. Proc.,* **26,** 366 (1967)

63. Hilliard, J., Penardi, R., Sawyer, C. H. A functional role for 20α-hydroxypregn-4-en-3-one in the rabbit. *Endocrinology,* **80,** 901–9 (1967)

64. Huff, R. L., Eik-Nes, K. B. Metabolism *in vitro* of acetate and certain steroids by 6-day old rabbit blastocysts. *J. Reprod. Fertility,* **11,** 57–63 (1966)

65. Hunter, G. L., Casida, L. E. Absence of local effects of the rabbit uterus on weight of corpus luteum. *J. Reprod. Fertility,* **13,** 179–81 (1967)

66. Ichii, S., Forchielli, E., Dorfman, R. I. *In vitro* effect of gonadotrophins on the soluble side-chain cleaving enzyme system of bovine corpus luteum. *Steroids,* **2,** 631–56 (1963)

67. Idler, D. R., Kimball, N. R., Truscott, B. Destruction of micro quantities of steroids on silica gel as shown by repeated thin layer chromatography. *Steroids,* **8,** 865–76 (1966)

68. Inskeep, E. K., Oloufa, M. M., Howland, B. E., Pope, A. L., Casida, L. E. Effect of experimental uterine distention on estrous cycle lengths in ewes. *J. Animal Sci.,* **21,** 331–32 (1962)

69. Inskeep, E. K., Johnson, C. E., McNary, J. E., Hall, P. F. Variations in biosynthesis of progesterone and response to interstitial cell-stimulating hormone *in vitro* in bovine corpora lutea. *J. Animal Sci.,* **26,** 540–44 (1967)

70. Jackanicz, T. M., Armstrong, D. T. Progesterone biosynthesis in rabbit ovarian interstitial tissue mitochondria. *Fed. Proc.,* **26,** 425 (1967)

71. James, V. H. T., Townsend, J., Fraser, R. Comparison of fluorimetric and isotopic procedures for the determination of plasma cortisol. *J. Endocrinol.,* **37,** xxviii (1967)

72. Jensen, E. V., Jacobson, H. I. Basic guides to the mechanism of estrogen action. *Recent Progr. Hormone Res.,* **18,** 387–414 (1962)

73. Jensen, E. V., de Sombre, E. R., Jungblut, P. W. Interaction of

estrogens with receptor sites *in vivo* and *in vitro*. *Proc. Intern. Congr. Hormonal Steroids, 2nd* (In press, *Intern. Congr. Ser.,* Excerpta Med. Found., London, 1967)

74. Kaltenbach, C. C., Niswender, G. D., Zimmerman, D. R., Wiltbank, J. N. Alteration of ovarian activity in cycling, pregnant, and hysterectomized heifers with exogenous estrogens. *J. Animal Sci.,* **23,** 995–1001 (1964)

75. Kaltenbach, C. C., Cook, B., Niswender, G. D., Nalbandov, A. V. Progesterone synthesis by ovine luteal tissue in vitro. *J. Animal Sci.,* **25,** 926 (1966)

76. Kaltenbach, C. C. Pituitary control of luteal function in the ewe. *J. Animal Sci., Suppl. 27* (In press) (1968)

77. Kar, A. B., Chowdhury, S. R., Kambaj, V. P., Chaudra, H., Chowdhury, A. R. Effect of an intrauterine contraceptive device on the uterus of the Rhesus monkey. *Intern. J. Fertility,* **10,** 321–26 (1965)

78. Kato, J., Villee, C. Factors affecting uptake of estradiol-6,7-^{3}H by the hypophysis and hypothalamus. *Endocrinology,* **80,** 1133–38 (1967)

79. Keyes, P. L., Nalbandov, A. V. Maintenance and function of corpora lutea in rabbits depend on estrogen. *Endocrinology,* **80,** 938–46 (1967)

80. Kilpatrick, R., Armstrong, D. T., Greep, R. O. Maintenance of the corpus luteum by gonadotrophins in the hypophysectomized rabbit. *Endocrinology,* **74,** 453–61 (1964)

81. Kilpatrick, R., Dorrington, J. H. Effect of 3′,5′-AMP and theophylline on progestational steroid synthesis by rabbit ovarian tissue *in vitro. Proc. Intern. Congr. Hormonal Steroids, 2nd,* 191 (*Intern. Congr. Ser. No. 111,* Excerpta Med. Found., London, 1966)

82. Kiracofe, G. H., Spies, H. G. Late luteal hysterectomy and uterine extracts in ewes. *J. Animal Sci.,* **23,** 908 (1964)

83. Le Maire, W. J., Rice, B. F., Savard, K., Further studies of effects of gonadotropins *in vitro* on steroidogenesis in human corpora lutea. *Proc. 48th Meeting Endocrine Soc.,* Chicago, 131 (1966)

84. Lipsett, M. B. *Gas Chromatography of Steroids in Biological Fluids* (Plenum Press, New York, 315 pp., 1965)

85. MacDonald, G. J., Armstrong, D. T., Greep, R. O. Stimulation of estrogen secretion from normal rat corpora lutea by luteinizing hormone. *Endocrinology,* **79,** 289–93 (1966)

86. Malven, P. V., Hansel, W. Effect of bovine endometrial extracts, vasopressin, and oxytocin on duration of pseudopregnancy in hysterectomized and intact rats. *J. Reprod. Fertility,* **9,** 207–15 (1965)

87. Malven, P. V., Sawyer, C. H. Formation of new corpora lutea in mature hypophysectomized rats. *Endocrinology,* **78,** 1259–63 (1966)

88. Malven, P. V., Sawyer, C. H. A luteolytic action of prolactin in hypophysectomized rats. *Endocrinology,* **79,** 268–74 (1966)

89. Malven, P. V., Hansel, W., Sawyer, C. H. A mechanism antagonizing the luteotrophic action of exogenous prolactin in rats. *J. Reprod. Fertility,* **13,** 205–12 (1967)

90. Marcus, G. J., Shelesnyak, M. C. Studies on the mechanism of nidation. XX. Relation of histamine release to estrogen action in the progestational rat. *Endocrinology,* **80,** 1028–31 (1967)

91. Marcus, G. J., Shelesnyak, M. C. Studies on the mechanism of nidation. XXV. A receptor theory for induction of decidualization. *Endocrinology,* **80,** 1032–37 (1967)

92. Marcus, G. J., Shelesnyak, M. C. Studies on the mechanism of nidation. XXVI. Proestrous estrogen as a hormonal parameter of nidation. *Endocrinology,* **80,** 1038–42 (1967)

93. Marsh, J. M., Savard, K. The stimulation of progesterone synthesis in bovine corpora lutea by adenosine-3′5′-monophosphate. *Steroids,* **8,** 133–48 (1966)

94. Marsh, J. M., Savard, K. Mode of action of LH on steroidogenesis in the corpus luteum *in vitro. J. Reprod. Fertility, Suppl. 1,* 113–26 (1966)

95. Martini, L., Ganong, W. F. *Neuroendocrinology,* **I** (Academic Press, New York, 774 pp., 1966)

96. Mason, N. R., Marsh, J. M., Savard, K. An action of gonadotropin *in vitro. J. Biol. Chem.,* **237,** 1801–6 (1962)

97. Masuda, H., Anderson, L. L., Hendricks, D. M., Melampy, R. M. Progesterone in ovarian venous plasma and corpora lutea of the pig. *Endocrinology,* **80,** 240–46 (1967)

98. McLaren, A., Ed. *Advances in Reproductive Physiology,* **I** (Academic Press, New York, 295 pp., 1966)

99. Melampy, R. M. The role of the uterus in corpus luteum function. *J. Animal Sci., Suppl.* 27 (In press) (1968)

100. du Mesnil du Buisson, F., Léglise, P. C. Effet de l'hypophysectomie sur les corps jaunes de la truie. Résultats préliminaires. *Compt. Rend. Acad. Sci.,* **257,** 261–63 (1963)

101. du Mesnil du Buisson, F., Léglise, P. C., Anderson, L. L., Rombauts, P. Maintien des corps jaunes et de la gestation de la truie an cours de la phase préimplantatoire après hypophysectomie. *Proc. Intern. Congr. Animal Reprod., 5th, Trento,* **3,** 571–75 (1964)

102. Meyer, V., Knobil, E. Growth hormone secretion in the unanesthetized Rhesus monkey in response to noxious stimuli. *Endocrinology,* **80,** 163–71 (1967)

103. Midgley, A. R., Jr., Pierce, G. B., Weigle, W. O. Immunobiological identification of human chorionic gonadotropin. *Proc. Soc. Exptl. Biol. Med.,* **108,** 85–89 (1961)

104. Midgley, A. R., Jr., Pierce, G. B. Immunohistochemical localization of human chorionic gonadotropin. *J. Exptl. Med.,* **115,** 289–94 (1962)

105. Midgley, A. R., Jr., Immunofluorescent localization of human pituitary luteinizing hormone. *Exptl. Cell Res.,* **32,** 606–9 (1963)

106. Midgley, A. R., Jr., Jaffe, R. B. Human luteinizing hormone in serum during the menstrual cycle: Determination by radioimmunoassay. *J. Clin. Endocrinol. Metab.,* **26,** 1375–81 (1966)

107. Midgley, A. R., Jr. Human pituitary LH — an immunohistochemical study. *Histochem. Cytochem.,* **14,** 159–66 (1966)

108. Midgley, A. R., Jr. Radioimmunoassay: A method for human chorionic gonadotropin and human luteinizing hormone. *Endocrinology,* **79,** 10–18 (1966)

109. Midgley, A. R., Jr. Radioimmunoassay for human follicle-stimulating hormone. *J. Clin. Endocrinol. Metab.,* **27,** 295–99 (1967)

110. Moore, W. W., Nalbandov, A. V. Neurogenic effects of uterine distention on the estrous cycle of the ewe. *Endocrinology,* **53,** 1–11 (1953)

111. Moore, W. W. Effect of uterine distention on the estrous cycle of the guinea pig. *Physiologist,* **4,** 76 (1961)

112. Murphy, B. E. P. Application of the property of protein-binding to the assay of minute quantities of hormones and other substances. *Nature,* **201,** 679–82 (1964)

113. Nalbandov, A. V., Moore, W. W., Norton, H. W. Further studies on the neurogenic control of the estrous cycle by uterine distention. *Endocrinology,* **56,** 225–31 (1955)

114. Nalbandov, A. V. Comparative physiology and endocrinology of domestic animals. *Recent Progr. Hormone Res.,* **17,** 119–46 (1961)

115. New, D. A. T. Development of rat embryos cultured in blood sera. *J. Reprod. Fertility,* **12,** 509–24 (1966)

116. Niswender, G. D. The influence of the uterus on corpus luteum function. *J. Animal Sci., Suppl.* 27 (In press) (1968)

117. Noteboom, W., Gorski, J. Stereospecific binding of estrogens in the rat uterus. *Arch. Biochem. Biophys.,* **111,** 559–68 (1965)

118. Nugent, C. A., Mayes, D. M. Plasma corticosteroids determined by use of corticosteroid-binding globulin and dextran coated charcoal. *J. Clin. Endocrinol. Metab.,* **26,** 1116–22 (1967)

119. Odell, W. D., Ross, G. T., Rayford, P. L. Radioimmunoassay for human LH. *Metabolism,* **15,** 287–89 (1966)

120. Pierce, G. B., Midgley, A. R. The origin and function of human synctiotrophoblastic giant cells. *Am. J. Pathol.,* **43,** 153–73 (1963)

121. Pupkin, M., Bratt, H., Weisz, J., Lloyd, C. W., Balogh, K. Dehydrogenases in the rat ovary. I. A histochemical study of 5-3β and 20 α-hydroxysteroid dehydrogenases and enzymes of carbohydrate oxidation during estrous cycle. *Endocrinology,* **79,** 316–27 (1966)

122. Robson, J. M. Maintenance by oestrin

of the luteal function in hypophysectomized rabbits. *J. Physiol. (London)*, **90**, 435–39 (1937)

123. Romanoff, E. B. Steroidogenesis in the perfused bovine ovary. *J. Reprod. Fertility, Suppl. 1*, 89–100 (1966)

124. Ryan, K. J., Smith, O. W. Biogenesis of steroid hormones in the human ovary. *Recent Progr. Hormone Res.*, **21**, 367–409 (1965)

125. Sammelwitz, P. H., Aldred, J. P., Nalbandov, A. V. Mechanisms of maintenance of corpora lutea in pigs and rats. *J. Reprod. Fertility*, **2**, 387–93 (1961)

126. Savard, K., Casey, P. J. Effects of pituitary hormones and NADPH on acetate utilization in ovarian and adrenocortical tissue. *Endocrinology*, **74**, 599–610 (1964)

127. Savard, K., Marsh, J. M., Rice, B. F. Gonadotrophins and ovarian steroidogenesis. *Recent Progr. Hormone Res.*, **21**, 285–365 (1965)

128. Short, R. V. Reproduction. *Ann. Rev. Physiol.*, **29**, 373–400 (1967)

129. Spaziani, E., Szego, C. M. The influence of estradiol and cortisol on uterine histamine of the ovariectomized rat. *Endocrinology*, **63**, 669–78 (1958)

130. Spaziani, E., Szego, C. M. Further evidence for mediation by histamine of estrogenic stimulation of the rat uterus. *Endocrinology*, **64**, 713–23 (1959)

131. Spies, H. G., Coon, L. L., Gier, H. T. Luteolytic effect of LH and HCG on the corpora lutea of pseudopregnant rabbits. *Endocrinology*, **78**, 67–74 (1966)

132. Spies, H. G., Quadri, S. K. Regression of corpora lutea and interruption of pregnancy in rabbits following treatment with rabbit serum to ovine LH. *Endocrinology*, **80**, 1127–32 (1967)

133. Stark, E., Varga, B., Acs, Z. An extra-adrenal effect of corticotrophin. *J. Endocrinol.*, **37**, 245–52 (1967)

134. Stormshak, F., Casida, L. E. Effect of gonadotropins on corpora lutea of pseudopregnant rabbits. *Endocrinology*, **75**, 321–25 (1964)

135. Stormshak, F., Casida, L. E. Effects of LH and ovarian hormones on corpora lutea of pseudopregnant and pregnant rabbits. *Endocrinology*, **77**, 337–42 (1965)

136. Stormshak, F., Casida, L. E. Fetal placental inhibition of LH-induced luteal regression in rabbits. *Endocrinology*, **78**, 887–88 (1966)

137. Stormshak, F., Lehmann, R. P., Hawk, H. W. Effect of intrauterine plastic spirals and HCG on the corpus luteum of the ewe. *J. Reprod. Fertility*, **14** (In press) (1967)

138. Sutherland, E. W., Øye, I., Butcher, R. W. The action of epinephrine and the role of the adenyl cyclase system in hormone action. *Recent Progr. Hormone Res.*, **21**, 623–46 (1965)

139. Szego, C. M., Lawson, D. A. Influence of histamine on uterine metabolism: Stimulation of incorporation of radioactivity from amino acids into protein, lipids and purines. *Endocrinology*, **74**, 372–81 (1964)

140. Szego, C. M. Role of histamine in mediation of hormone action. *Fed. Proc.*, **24**, 1343–52 (1965)

141. Tait, J. F. Review: The use of isotopic steroids for the measurement of production rates *in vivo*. *J. Clin. Endocrinol. Metab.*, **23**, 1285–97 (1963)

142. Talbert, G. B., Krohn, P. L. Effect of maternal age on viability of ova and uterine support of pregnancy in mice. *J. Reprod. Fertility*, **11**, 399–406 (1966)

143. Taleisnik, S., Caligaris, L., Astrada, J. J. Effect of copulation on the release of pituitary gonadotropins in male and female rats. *Endocrinology*, **79**, 49–54 (1966)

144. Talwalker, P. K., Krähenbühl, C., Desaulles, P. H. Maintenance of pregnancy in spayed rats with 20 α-hydroxypregn-4-ene-3-one and 20 β-hydroxypregn-4-ene-3-one. *Nature*, **209**, 86–87 (1966)

145. Talwar, G. P., Segal, S. J., Evans, A., Davidson, O. W. The binding of estradiol in the uterus: A mechanism for derepression of RNA synthesis. *Proc. Natl. Acad. Sci.*, **52**, 1059–66 (1964)

146. Tamaoki, B., Pincus, G. Biogenesis of progesterone in ovarian tissues. *Endocrinology*, **69**, 527–33 (1961)

147. Telegdy, G., Endröczi, E. The ovarian secretion of progesterone and 20 α-hydroxypregn-4-ene-3-one in rats during the estrous cycle. *Steroids*, **2**, 119–23 (1963)

148. Toft, D., Gorski, J. A receptor molecule for estrogens: isolation from the rat uterus and preliminary characterization. *Proc. Natl. Acad. Sci.*, **55**, 1574–81 (1966)

149. Toft, D., Shyamala, G., Gorski, J. A receptor molecule for estrogens: studies using a cell-free system. *Proc. Natl. Acad. Sci.* (In press) (1967)

150. Vorys, N., de Neif, J. C., Bontselis, J. G., Dettmann, F. G., Scott, W. P., Stevens, V. C., Besch, P. K. Effect of intrauterine devices on the normal menstrual cycle. *Proc. Intern. Congr. Intra-Uterine Contraception, 2nd*, 147–56 (*Intern. Congr. Ser. No. 86*, Excerpta Med. Found., London, 1965)

151. Wickersham, E. W., Tanabe, T. Y. Functional state of bovine corpora lutea as determined by *de novo* production of progesterone *in vitro*. *J. Animal Sci.*, **26**, 158–62 (1967)

152. Wiest, W. G., Wilcox, R. B., Kirschbaum, T. H. Rat ovarian 20 α-hydroxysteroid dehydrogenase: Effects of estrogens and pituitary gonadotrophins. *Endocrinology*, **73**, 588–95 (1963)

153. Wiest, W. G., Forbes, T. R. Failure of 20 α-hydroxy-Δ⁴-pregnen-3-one and 20 β-hydroxy-Δ⁴-pregnen-3-one to maintain pregnancy in ovariectomized mice. *Endocrinology*, **74**, 149–50 (1964)

154. Wilde, C. E., Orr, A. H., Bagshawe, K. D. Sensitive radioimmunoassay for HCG and LH. *J. Endocrinol.*, **37**, 23–35 (1967)

155. Williams, W. F., Johnston, J. O., Lauterbach, M., Fagan, B. Luteolytic effect of a bovine uterine powder on the corpora lutea, follicular development and progesterone synthesis of the pseudopregnant rabbit ovary. *J. Dairy Sci.*, **50**, 555–57 (1967)

156. Wilson, P. M., Hunter, W. M. Development of a radioimmunoassay for human LH. *J. Endocrinol.*, **35**, i-ii (1966)

157. Wotiz, H. W., Clark, S. J. *Gas Chromatography in the Analysis of Steroid Hormones* (Plenum Press, New York, 288 pp., 1966)

158. Yamauchi, M., Nakahara, T. Effects of uterine distention on the estrous cycle of cattle. *Japan. J. Animal Reprod.*, **3**, 121–23 (1958)

159. Yamauchi, M., Nakahara, T., Kaneda, Y. Effect of intrauterine administration of a viscous gel-like substance on the estrous cycle of cattle. I. The estrous cycle length and the fertility following the treatment. *Japan. J. Animal Reprod.*, **11**, 54–62 (1965)

160. Yamauchi, M., Nakahara, T., Kaneda, Y., Inui, S. Effect of intrauterine administration of a viscous gel-like substance on the estrous cycle in cattle. II. Irritating effects of the treatments on the uterus. *Japan. J. Animal Reprod.*, **12**, 58–65 (1966)

DISTAL MECHANISMS OF VERTEBRATE COLOR VISION[1,2]

By Mathew Alpern

University of Michigan, Ann Arbor, Michigan

INTRODUCTION

The basic mechanism of vision is the catching of light quanta by one or more visual pigments situated in photoreceptors—the retinal rods and cones. The response of any one pigment is univariant. Thus, with only one pigment any two wavelengths affect the response identically if matched for quanta absorption.

The mechanism assumed for color therefore requires the interaction of at least two different kinds of pigment systems. But the presence of two pigments does not guarantee color vision. Cone monochromats have at least two (ordinary rhodopsin in their quite ordinary rods and one cone pigment), but they do not have color vision (120, 176). Ordinarily, however, when more than one cone pigment is present in a normal retina, it is reasonable to expect some kind of color vision.

LOSSES IN THE EYE MEDIA

Comparing *in vivo* action spectra with *in vitro* absorption spectra requires a correction for prereceptor light losses. This correction has the difficulty that the best measurements on ocular media transmittance have

[1] The period covered extends roughly from May 1964 to May 1967, but I have gone outside this period when necessary. The editors asked that the review be highly selective and that no effort should be made to consider all the papers which appeared in the assigned period. These are some of the ground rules of the selection process. First of all, I am strongly persuaded—when evaluating the results of psychophysical (i.e. subjective) experiments—by Brindley's (34) arguments that class A experiments are the most likely to predict and test heuristically physiological hypotheses. A second bias is that the results from psychological, psychophysical, psychophysiological, or physiological experiments are most appropriately used to infer the nature of underlying visual pigments when they are based on an action spectrum. This means one measures the number of quanta at each frequency in the spectrum required to produce some constant effect. The size of the response to a so-called equal energy (or alternatively an equal quantum) spectrum is of less (almost no) use since the relation between response size and quantum absorption is almost never linear. [An exception appears to be the early receptor potential (36, 40, 46, 115); but since, so far, it has told us nothing about mammalian color vision, it falls outside the scope of this review.] A third bias is that the caliber of editorial refereeing an article is likely to have had is a relevant consideration.

[2] Assisted by grant NB 01578-09 from the National Institute of Neurological Diseases and Blindness.

been obtained from enucleated eyes. The recent measurements on living (and intact) human eyes (11) have not attracted much notice, and quite properly so. The measurements require the unproved (perhaps even untestable) assumption that the inside of the living human sclera is a perfectly diffuse reflector. They suggest that the transmittance of ocular media for wavelengths greater than about 500 nm is much higher than that found by Ludvigh and McCarthy in 1938. Since the latter's results are almost always used for this purpose, one must raise minor questions about action spectra corrected in this way. The shape differences are undoubtedly trivial, but at some wavelengths, errors in estimates of quantum loss may not be. If transmittance measurements on enucleated human eyes are to be used for such correction—and because of their much higher precision they probably should be—then it is probably better to use more modern measurements (26) with which the *in vivo* data are in better agreement.

PHOTOSTABLE AND PHOTOLABILE CONE PIGMENTS

HUMAN RED AND GREEN PIGMENTS

In three papers on the green pigment (chlorolabe) (134–136) published before the period covered by this review, Rushton reported studies of the fovea of protanopes. He could find only a single pigment; he worked out its kinetics and its action spectrum—which agree well with the protanope's foveal luminosity curve. Chlorolabe regenerates along a time curve that coincides with the protanope's foveal dark-adaptation curve. It is therefore not surprising that he begins his erythrolabe papers with examination of the deuteranope's fovea. The first paper (137) demonstrates that the deuteranope's fovea contains a single pigment in the red-green range, the change in reflectivity being identical when half bleaching was produced either by deep red or by blue-green. Lights of various wavelengths adjusted in intensity to bleach erythrolabe equally were also judged by the deuteranope as equally bright by flicker photometry (its action spectrum of bleaching is identical to the deuteranope's luminosity curve). This paper also examines the serious artifact from entoptic stray light that can be introduced by measuring reflectivity in terms of the double density difference spectrum. Rushton shows that by using a transmissivity difference spectrum $(T_0 - T)/T_0$ (where T_0 is the transmissivity of the balancing red wedge after full bleach and T its transmissivity under the conditions being studied), this artifact can be obviated. This difficulty apparently accounts for the variety of spectra of erythrolabe that have been reported (127).

The second paper (138) evaluates the kinetics of erythrolabe in the deuteranope's fovea although it permits no estimate of its density in the retina. This general kinetic equation is a first-order differential equation,

$$-dp/dt = pI \cdot (10)^{-6} - (1 - p)/130$$

in which I is the intensity of retinal illuminance in trolands, p is the fraction of total erythrolabe, and t is in seconds. This equation is nearly identical to the general kinetic equation

$$-dp/dt = pI \cdot (10)^{-6.2} - (1 - p)/125$$

found previously (136) for chlorolabe in the protanope's fovea. As was found to be the case for chlorolabe in the protanope, the foveal dark-adaptation curve of the deuteranope has the same shape and time-course as the regeneration of the erythrolabe in this fovea as measured by retinal densitometry.

The third paper (139) examines the problem of stray light in retinal densitometry. Stray light is of two kinds—superficial stray light scattered by the eye media, which is more or less neutral, and fundal stray light, which has the color of the fundus (orange-red). The light scattered from a ring (4.3° outside diameter and 2.8° inside diameter) was examined in a central 2° area. It was found to be 10 per cent of the total reflected light at 650 nm and 2 per cent at 530 nm. The sum of all light amounted to 6 per cent. Of this, not more than 1 per cent can be due to superficial stray light. From this Rushton is able to show quantitatively that the transmissivity difference spectrum gives a good estimate of the absorption difference spectrum.

With this groundwork on protanopes and deuteranopes, Baker & Rushton (17) turn to the normal fovea which can now be analyzed in a straightforward way. The normal fovea has at least two pigments which have the characteristics of erythrolabe (as measured on the deuteranope's fovea) and of chlorolabe (as measured on the protanope's fovea), respectively. Subjects especially rich in erythrolabe were selected. Reflectivity measured with 625 nm measuring light in such eyes has the action spectrum of erythrolabe of the deuteranope and also that of the Stiles (155) red mechanism (II_5) in these same subjects. The time-course of pigment regeneration after full red bleach coincides with that found in the deuteranope as well as with the normal foveal dark-adaptation curve after a full red bleach. In the normal, the transmissivity difference spectrum following full red bleach resembles approximately: (a) that of the deuteranope, (b) the deuteranope's luminosity curve, and (c) Stiles' red mechanism. The changes in the transmissivity difference spectrum following changes from a deep-red equilibrium bleach to a blue-green one (which in a deuteranope produce no spectrum changes) must be due to the green-sensitive pigment alone. This change in transmissivity difference spectrum fits the chlorolabe spectrum of the protanope and the Stiles green mechanism in the normal.

Human Blue Cone Pigment

Retinal densitometry does not reveal a blue cone pigment in the human retina. There are a number of reasons for this. (a) Measurements have to be made on the fovea to avoid the possibility of contamination from rhodopsin. But in the fovea (the blue-absorbing), macular pigment has its greatest density. The most recent measurements of macular pigment (169) show peak density at 455 nm of 0.49 (the average of eight series of measurements on human maculas). (*b*) The media of the eye also absorbs strongly at these wavelengths. The *in vitro* human measurements estimate this to be about 0.4 density at 450 nm (26). (*c*) Reflection densitometry requires the use of very stable light sources. So far this is best achieved by the tungsten filament which emits very little blue light. (*d*) There is a growing body of evidence which suggests that in the center of the fovea—as indeed elsewhere in the retina—the blue cones are much less numerous than the red and green ones [see, however, Brindley (32)].

To summarize current knowledge of human cone pigments from retinal densitometry: The normal fovea contains two pigments, chlorolabe whose action spectrum of bleaching agrees with the foveal luminosity curve of the protanope (λ_{max} about 540 nm) and erythrolabe whose action spectrum of bleaching agrees well with the foveal luminosity curve of the deuteranope (λ_{max} about 570 nm). The kinetics of these two pigments are almost identical; their regeneration goes hand in hand with the recovery of the foveal threshold in the dark following a full bleach. There remain two questions about human visual pigments which reflection densitometry in man is not yet able to answer: (*a*) Is there a third visual pigment, cyanolabe, which has a bleaching action spectrum equivalent to that of Stiles' blue mechanisms? (*b*) Do the visual pigments in man reside individually in separate cones or, alternatively, are they all mixed together in each and every cone? (These, of course, represent only the extreme possibilities. Any combination along a continuum between these extremes is also feasible.)

MICROSPECTROPHOTOMETRY

Fish visual pigments.—The modern measurement of the absorbance characteristics of subcellular chemical constituents *in situ* was introduced over thirty years ago (45). Considering the relative sophistication of visual physiologists on optical matters, it seems surprising that twenty years had to go by before these methods were applied successfully to the measurements of difference spectra of visual pigments in intact retinal cones. In 1957, Hanaoka & Fujimoto (82) succeeded in measuring the difference spectrum of single outer segments of carp cones by focusing a 3 μ spot of monochromatic light on them. The intensity of this spot was compared to that of light of the same wavelength which bypassed the retina. Difference spectra were measured by comparing such measurements made upon a fully dark-adapted cone outer segment to that made on the same specimen following a full bleach. Of the forty-four cone outer segments studied, one cell was found with λ_{max} 420–430 nm, twelve at 490–500 nm, eleven at 520–540 nm, ten at 560–580 nm, seven at 620–640 nm, and three at 670–680 nm. A few cones had difference spectra with two maxima. The technique suffers from the handicap of a relatively insensitive photocathode (S-8) and a test and bypass light beam with considerably different optical components.

Further improvements have now been realized in the very elegant measurements of Marks (103) on the goldfish. The more sensitive S-20 photocathode gives him considerably greater signal/noise ratio and allows the test and comparison spots (1 μ) to pass through exactly the same optics. The test enters the outer segment while the comparison goes through a bit of clear retina outside the cone. The difference spectra are obtained without further bleaching since the process of making the absorption measurements itself induces a considerable bleach. The absorption spectrum obtained after the last of several successive repetitions when subtracted from the first is taken as the difference spectrum. Corrections for loss of visual pigment during the scan rest on three reasonable assumptions. Each cone has only a single photolabile pigment. Measurements on a sample of 113 single goldfish cones have λ_{max} values which cluster in three different groups (625 nm, 530 nm, and 455nm). Marks found five to ten times as many red and green as blue receptors. However, there are difficulties. Electrophysiological evidence in the tench, carp, and bream (109)—as we shall see—provides unequivocal evidence for a fourth visual pigment with a λ_{max} in the deep red, and this pigment has almost exactly the form described by Hanaoka & Fujimoto (82) in three cones (of sample of 44) in the carp retina with λ_{max} at 670–680 nm. The explanation of this discrepancy is probably not species differences since all are very closely related, though the goldfish's loss by mutation of the deep-red pigment cannot be excluded with available evidence. Whether artifacts in the process of dissecting out of the retina in deep-red or blue light, undetected artifacts in what appears to be very careful experimental work, the relative scarcity of this pigment in the goldfish or inadequate search, or some combination of these things is also relevant can only be excluded by further work.

This problem aside, the microspectrophotometry on single goldfish cones provides additional confirmation that the cone visual pigments, like those of the frog rod, are packed into their respective outer segments with considerable density. The concentration in each case is about 2.5 mM. Liebman (100) has proved that in the full length (50 μ) of the frog rod the axial density is 0.9. This agrees well enough with photographic measurements (53) of 0.76, particularly because there is a good deal of uncertainty about the total length of the rod. Similar, if not somewhat higher, values are found in the retinae of deep-sea fish (52).

It seems likely that similar concentrations also apply to human rods and cones. Dowling's (62) most recent measurements show (for monkey) that foveal cone outer segments have a length of 40 μ. For concentrations that Liebman measures for the frog rod, this would give an estimate of 0.72 density from one end of the outer segment to the other at the peak wavelengths. All of these estimates agree with those made on quite different grounds by Enoch & Stiles (68). The latter used the self-screening of erythrolabe and chlorolabe in human cones as an explanation for the hue shift in displacing a monochromatic light beam to the edge of the pupil (Stiles-Crawford effect of the second kind). They estimate that in Enoch's eye the chlorolabe has a density of 1.0 at its peak wavelength while erythrolabe has a density of 0.72. Brindley (33) estimated a value of about 0.98 for erythrolabe as a result of experiments in which he measured mismatches in the anomaloscope immediately after a full bleach with a yellow adapting light. The immediate effect of such a bleach was dichromatism, but within about ten seconds the eye was severely protanomalous (requiring $0.51 \log_{10}$ units more red in a red-green mixture to match a 570 nm spectral yellow) as compared to normal matches. The recovery of the normal matches followed more or less what we now know to be the timecourse of regeneration of erythrolabe (138).

Without apparently being aware of Brindley's paper, Baker (15) has very recently done a very similar experiment and obtained a quite different answer. His bleaches were red rather than yellow and his anomaloscope was designed so that the red and green primaries at the extremes were equated for brightness to the yellow by a protanope and therefore for equal chlorolabe absorption. In this way, settings of the proportion of red and green in the mixture with a single knob reflected changes in concentration of erythrolabe alone (16). Baker's recovery curves were very much quicker than Brindley's and lead him to the opposite conclusion, namely that the knob adjustments after full red bleach could not be tracing the recovery of erythrolabe. None of the obvious (and rather second-order) differences in experimental design seem reasonable explanations for this discrepancy. These results have some implications for the theory of protanomalous color blindness and will be discussed further below.

Among other things, experiments of this sort both in man and animals lead to the inference that Dartnall's (50) nomogram, developed on the basis of extracts of frog's rhodopsin, is much broader than the absorption spectra of extracts—in dilute solution—of cone visual pigments will prove to be when it becomes possible to measure them sufficiently well. As a matter of fact, test-tube extracts of iodopsin, the only cone pigment so far isolated (170), have an extinction spectrum narrower than that predicted from the nomogram.

Insects.—In the insect eye of Diptera, Langer & Thorell (97) used the microspectrophotometer to examine pigments in different rhabdomeres of the same ommatidium. Six of the seven seem to have the same pigment (λ_{max} at 500 and 350 nm), which fits the Dartnall nomogram. In the central rhabdomere, however, the λ_{max} falls at a shorter wavelength (about 470 nm). The relevance of this arrangement for insect color vision remains to be established. [This paper was presented at an international symposium. The proceedings (20), *The Functional Organization of the Compound*

Eye, contain an elegant collection of papers on every aspect of insect visual physiology.]

Oil droplets.—The cones of a variety of birds, reptiles, and amphibians contain color oil droplets through which the light must pass before it reaches the photolabile (visual) pigment in the cone outer segment. Because iodopsin seems to be the only photolabile cone pigment one can isolate from the chicken retina, it is usually assumed that it has no other. Thus, the ability of these animals to discriminate colors is assumed to depend upon the combination of a variety of different oil droplets for different cones (there being one oil droplet per cone) and a single-cone visual pigment—iodopsin. The evidence to support this view, however, is equivocal, and the late Gordon Walls, for one, believed it to be wrong (171). For him, oil droplets had quite different "reasons for survival". The yellow filters reduce the effects of chromatic aberration and minimize glare and dazzle and enhance contrast; they are quite analogous to the macular pigment in our own eyes. The foveal cones of the bird, for example, have only yellow oil droplets. Walls suggested that in birds the red filters act to reduce effects from Rayleigh scattering in the atmosphere, particularly during early morning sunrise when birds do most of their work. Like so many speculations of this kind, it is impossible to imagine an unequivocal experimental way of rejecting them. But the question as to whether the cones in a bird retina all have the identical visual pigment—iodopsin—or whether birds, like fish, have different visual pigments in different cones, one cone–one pigment, is now approaching the limits of experimental examination. So far, no one has yet succeeded in measuring by microspectrophotometry the difference spectrum of visual pigments in a single cone in the bird retina, much less in accumulating a representative sample of such spectra. Fujimoto, Yanase & Hanaoka (72) attempted to do this over ten years ago. They thought it would be possible to improve the apparatus to complete such an experiment, but I have not succeeded in finding a description of further experiments.

The oil droplets are a different matter, however. Their absorption spectra can be measured by microspectrophotometry. Fujimoto et al. looked at hens, ducks, and doves and two species of land turtles. Strother (157) looked at the American bronze turkey, swamp turtle, wood turtle, and the domestic white pigeon. He found that the absorption peak was relatively flat at about 80 per cent for all colors regardless of (oil droplet) size or species (except for the colorless filter which has a peak absorption of 60 per cent). Similarly, all colors show a rather steep slope at cutoff. Cutoff wavelength for the red was 570 nm; for the orange, 540–530 nm; for the yellow, 510 nm; for the green, 440 nm; and 390 nm for the colorless ones. The values of Fujimoto et al. are all consistently (and appreciably) shifted toward the higher frequencies (i.e. shorter wavelengths) in comparison to Strother's values, although they also found that differences among the species are trivial. Thus, the differences appear to be experimental rather than differences due to difference in species; and, as is often the case, it seems difficult to decide who—if either—is right. Strother's results are more recent, and measurements of Fujimoto et al. frequently show a rather higher transmission in the long-wave end and lower transmission in the short-wave end than might be anticipated.

Primate visual pigments.—Previous reviews (12, 23, 56) have already described the excitement generated in the last few years by the application of the technique of microspectrophotometry to cones in primates and in man (41, 42, 104). With one exception (41), this enthusiasm has all been generated by brief preliminary reports (42, 104) or by lectures at conferences and symposia (102, 167, 169). To date, the most important point that seems to have been documented without much doubt is that the chromophore of both erythrolabe and chlorolabe, like that of rhodopsin, is the 11-*cis*-aldehyde of vitamin A. Erythrolabe in a group of retinal cones when bleached away by deep-red light regenerates if 11-*cis*-retinaldehyde is added to the bathing fluid of the retina under the microspectrophotometer (41). The same also is true for chlorolabe (though the dominant wavelength of its bleaching light must be changed). And so all human visual pigments so far examined have the same chromophore, only the opsin—the apoprotein—seems to distinguish erythrolabe from chlorolabe and either of these from rhodopsin.

All the other exciting inferences suggested by the preliminary reports on monkey and man can only be regarded as tentative, pending publication of the definitive article by at least one of the five or six different laboratories now working on this problem. These experiments are sweeping in their generality for human color vision. They include the demonstration: (*a*) that there is a photolabile substance—cyanolabe—a blue pigment whose absorption spectrum agrees with the action spectrum of Stiles' II_1 mechanism; (*b*) that there are three (and only three) different kinds of human cone visual pigments (erythrolabe, chlorolabe, and cyanolabe); and (*c*) that all visual pigments reside in separate cones—one cone, one pigment. Thus, they represent the "resonators" of Thomas Young's color vision theory. For this reason, it is easy to understand the impatience with which those of us not making measurements with retinal microspectrophotometry await the publication of the definitive articles describing the work of those who are. How long are we to wait for them? It may yet be some time. The preliminary reports appeared in the spring of 1964 and are therefore already outside the period covered by this review.

One can gather at least some feeling for the difficulties that this work entails in a fine paper by Wald & Brown (169) and in the discussion of it (67). This paper for the first time presents both the raw data and the difference spectrum computed from them for one (red-sensitive) cone. It is left as an exercise for the student to check the computation. Since the signal/noise ratio of the raw data at λ_{max} of the difference spectrum is only three, it will come as no surprise that my own answer was not in very good agreement with that predicted by: (*a*) Dartnall's nomogram, nor (*b*) the iodopsin absorption spectrum, nor (*c*) any of the action spectra of erythrolabe inferred from retinal densitometry, from the luminosity curve of the deuteranope, or by Stiles' (155) two-color threshold measurements, nor were they even in exact agreement with (*d*) the calculation made by Wald & Brown from the same data. The discrepancy in (*d*) at least can easily be accounted for by slight differences in reading the raw data, but the other discrepancies are real enough (though smaller) even when Wald & Brown's calculated curve is used for the comparison. Make no mistake, these experiments represent an enormous technological achievement, but one must keep in mind the preliminary nature of the results so far available.

In using microspectrophotometric measurements to compute *in vivo* pigment density or to appraise the possibility that a single cone may contain two or more pigments, one prefers results from a system in which the light beam has been prefocused to include only a single cone (101, 104) rather than one in which it illuminates a large area of cells with the cone to be measured being selected by an aperture stop in the viewing plane (169). Contamination from stray light passing through surrounding rods is much easier to evaluate in the former than in the latter case. A dramatic demonstration of this effect has recently been made on the living frog retina by Villermet & Weale (164).

Summary.—On the basis of available data, then, it is probably safe to conclude that in man color vision at the receptor level depends upon three visual pigments—cyanolabe, chlorolabe, and erythrolabe—and that these visual pigments occupy separate blue, green, and red cones, one cone–one pigment. It is less certain from these relatively direct measurements what exact form the absorption spectra of these pigments have either in very dilute solution or *in situ*. There is a growing body of evidence suggesting that insofar as its physiological effects on human color vision are concerned these two are not the same. To infer the effective absorption spectra in the intact organism, we must turn then to indirect experiments which make it possible to estimate action spectra of the red, green, and blue cones.

ELECTROPHYSIOLOGICAL MEASUREMENTS ON SINGLE RETINAL CONES

Of all such estimates, the least certain are obtained from electrical responses of cones themselves. The literature on electrophysiology of the vertebrate retina abounds in examples of slow changes in voltage evoked by light flashes recorded from microelectrodes within or adjacent to small retinal compartments which overeager investigators have designated on the basis of insufficient evidence as cone receptor potentials. Almost invariably, subsequent and more thoughtful experiments have shown the hasty designations to be in error. To date there is still no unequivocally documented example of cone action potentials, much less any action spectra which might help us to identify visual pigments. In the light of this background, the reader will understand the skepticism with which the new suggestions of action potentials from cone receptors must be regarded. These new findings are on salamanders (27–29) and carp (159, 160). These two different investigators both describe photically evoked slow (as distinct from nerve action) potentials, but in detail the phenomena are quite different; and with the available evidence it is not at all certain that the discrepancies are due to species difference. The salamander responses appear to be very much like S potentials—both hyperpolarizations and depolarizations are evoked by light, though wavelength effects have not yet been systematically studied.

The descriptions of the carp experiments in which wavelength is being exhaustively manipulated are still only very preliminary (159, 160). This potential, though very slow sustained hyperpolarization, differs from S potentials in several ways: It is one order of magnitude smaller, it has no area effect (the voltage is independent of the size of the illuminating patch), it is generated in a region 50–70 μ more distal in the retina, and the polarity is independent of wavelength, always being hyperpolarizing. Histology suggests that it is generated in the layer of the cone inner segment (one inner segment is about 10 μ across and 30 μ long), but the latency is quite long (about 10 msec). There are still no action spectra from these recordings. A single "intracellular" record can be held for a few minutes and this permits only a quick traverse of the spectrum of successive wavebands of differing numbers of quanta. We do not know how the voltage varies with the number of absorbed quanta at a fixed wavelength. The "spectra" obtained by plotting volts vs. wavelength show a single peak. A histogram of 142 such peaks as a function of wavelength is trimodal with maxima at 462 ± 15 nm, 529 ± 14 nm, and 611 ± 23 nm (125). These values agree remarkably with Marks' goldfish peaks although the relative distribution is radically different (74 per cent red, 10 per cent green, and 16 per cent blue compared with 21 per cent red, 58 per cent green, and 16 per cent blue found by Marks). The solution to these and countless other questions relating to the form of the absorption spectra of the visual pigments as revealed by intracellular recording in cone inner segments must await a hard analysis of the definitive article describing this work when it appears. It should be emphasized that these spectra have been gleaned from preliminary reports included in lectures at symposia and that the relative frequency was obtained secondhand, appearing in a lecture by Riggs (125). They are described here because, while one must remain skeptical about cone action potentials, the data are obviously of importance if the nature of the voltage can be unequivocally documented.

There are, of course, a variety of other voltages recorded extracellularly and designated as receptor potentials, both early and late. The action spectrum for the early receptor potential of the all-cone ground squirrel retina has been measured by Pak & Ebrey (116). This very broad curve shows a single peak at 535 nm in an eye for which there is good electrophysiological (105) and behavioral (49) evidence for at least two color receptor systems.

OTHER ELECTROPHYSIOLOGICAL EXPERIMENTS

S *potentials in cyprinid fish.*—It will be recalled that Svaetichin & MacNichol (158) classified the compartments from which S potentials can be recorded into two groups: C (color) and L (luminosity). There are two types of C compartments, those which depolarize to green and hyperpolarize to blue (G/B) and those which depolarize to red and hyperpolarize to green (R/G). Naka & Rushton (109) analyzed these responses by superimposing spectral flashes upon a steady monochromatic background. In this way a spectral range can be found in which only a single kind of cone is effective. In this range the relation between the light intensity and the voltage is hyperbolic—the relation that would be found if cone signals increased conductance through a polarized S membrane in proportion to the flux of quanta caught. By obtaining such a curve for each monochromatic stimulus within this range, the action spectra of the pigments in the cones causing the conductance change can be specified. The blue pigment was not analyzed. The green pigment appears to be identical to the 540 nm pigment found by Marks in goldfish. Its action spectrum is the same for a G/B unit as for an R/G unit. The red pigment ($\lambda_{max} = 680$ nm)—confirmed recently by Witkovsky (180) in the carp—has almost exactly the action spectrum needed to fit the red pigment found by microspectrophotometry in three separate red cones in the carp retina (82).

C potentials are frequently cited as exactly the physiological model of what is required for an opponent color theory such as that of Hurvich & Jameson (83, 84). Naka & Rushton's experiments show this analogy to be specious. In the opponents' scheme, wavelengths eliciting pure hues are independent of luminance, but for R/G units the neutral wavelengths (analogous to the "pure" hue) shift further into the red the greater the luminance.

The L units are more complex then the C units. They receive signals from 680, 620, 540, and possibly the 455 nm λ_{max} cones (the last was not analyzed, however). Quantum catch in any of these contributes to hyperpolarization, but the interaction is not just the simple addition of independent cone effects. In contrast to results on *Gerridae* (158), the L units of the tench are remarkably altered by chromatic adaptation. The action of the green cones is enhanced by a steady red background and that of red cones by a steady green background (111).

Action spectra from single neurons.—It is possible to infer the nature of the visual pigments in cones by studying the action potentials of single retinal ganglion cells [carp (179)] and the lateral geniculate nucleus [monkey (54, 55)] to monochromatic lights after intense chromatic adaptation. In the latter case, it has been shown that in R/G opponent cells the green pigment can be isolated by intense red bleaching, and its action spectrum then agrees with that of chlorolabe of the human fovea (55). Green adaptation does not similarly isolate the red pigment alone since the red cones are appreciably influenced by green bleaching. These studies of geniculate neurons shed some light on the processing of color information by the retina and central nervous system and will be discussed below.

Electroretinograms (*ERG*).—Electroretinogram spectral-sensitivity curves are frequently used to infer underlying visual pigment absorption spectra. Crescitelli's recent experiments on the gecko (48) emphasize once more what a tricky business this is. The increased responsiveness in the red end of the spectrum to what is expected from pigment difference spectra does not change even after intense red or blue bleaches. The explanation here—just as it is in the scotopic ERG or the rod pupil light reflex in man (5)—is that light transmitted twice by the choroid, reflected by the sclera, and then exciting the retina is colored by the hemoglobin in the choroid. Burkhardt (43) measured the ERG spectral-sensitivity curve of the intact goldfish. By using the ERG equivalent of the Stiles' two-color threshold experiment with a red test target and different monochromatic backgrounds, he obtained suggestive evidence that the photopic ERG is influenced by at least two spectrally distinct subsystems.

Of the methods of estimating the absorption spectrum of visual pigments by action spectra, the most informative have been psychophysical, and it seems appropriate to discuss these next.

COLOR BLINDNESS

Studies as to the nature of color blindness will be discussed below, but it is appropriate in this section to emphasize that the most insightful way of estimating the absorption spectrum of cone visual pigments is the determination of the foveal luminosity curve in dichromats and in some cone monochromats. Such certainty, of course, is only possible now that we have at hand (17) the demonstration that in the red-green range the normal fovea has two visual pigments—erythrolabe, whose action spectrum agrees with the luminosity curve of the deuteranope, and chlorolabe, whose action spectrum agrees with the luminosity curve of the protanope. But the luminosity curves of protanopes and deuteranopes can be measured with much greater precision and more exactly than the difficult methods of retinal densitometry can yet achieve. Hence, if we wish to know the exact shape of the action spectra of the human fundamental color mechanisms—and no question has been more exhaustively debated since Thomas Young first suggested his component resonators—then Rushton has shown us that by far the best method of doing this is to measure the dichromat luminosity-curves.

By far the best data of this kind to become available during the period of this review are the measurements of Wald (167, 168). These measurements consist of foveal spectral thresholds (1° test flash, 40 msec duration) in the dark and under conditions of bright yellow, purple, and blue-green adaptation. Wald studied five protanopes, thirteen deuteranopes, and three tritanopes. The action spectrum of erythrolabe, revealed by the measurements on the deuteranope in the dark and after intense blue-green and purple adaptation, peaks somewhere between 560 and 578 nm. The position of the peak and the form of action spectrum are the same in all three adaptation conditions, as is to be expected if the absorption of quanta by erythrolabe alone determines the form of the curve. Analogous findings are obtained with chlorolabe on the protanope. Here Wald finds peaks between 550 and 540 nm. Only the role of the blue mechanism in the red-green dichromats remains unclear in such work. Intense yellow adaptation always yields a double-humped curve. In both types of dichromats the long-wavelength hump appears to agree with the remaining red (or green) pigment peak. Tritanopes show no blue mechanism under bright yellow adaptation, but their dark curves sometimes show a mysterious hump near 450 nm.

Among colorblind subjects the blue-mechanism action spectrum appears most unambiguously in a rare form of sex-linked recessive inherited monochromacy in which the retina lacks both red and green cones (8). Because the visual acuity of the blue cones is so poor (32), they are easily confused with the typical total (rod) monochromats. The inheritance is different however (153). Under certain conditions, the region of the retina that such observers use for fixation resembles, in its action spectrum and in the sensitivity of the underlying receptor mechanism, the blue mechanism revealed by Stiles' two-color threshold experiments.

Two-Color Thresholds

Since Rushton's measurements on chlorolabe agree in a general way with Stiles' green (II_4) mechanism and those on erythrolabe with Stiles' red (II_5) mechanism, it might be assumed that Stiles' experiments would be a very good way of determining the absorption spectra of the red, green, and blue cone pigments. A number of experiments using Stiles' two-color methods have recently been described. They were carried out with the colored background held fixed while test wavelength was varied. At any wavelength, test-flash intensity for threshold was the dependent variable. This technqiue, used originally by Stiles & Crawford in 1933, has a number of disadvantages compared to Stiles' later methods. It has the one advantage, with the monochromators ordinarily available, that action spectra can be measured with much more intense backgrounds. Sperling, Tryon & Jolliffe (151, 152), Wald (166, 169), and Stiles (156) have all recently proceeded in this way. Of these, Stiles appears the most reluctant to draw inferences from the results as to the nature of the absorption spectra of the underlying pigments. It therefore seems appropriate here to attempt an evaluation of the justifications for drawing such inferences from the two-color threshold experiment.

In favor are the following considerations:

(*a*) There seems to be a converging body of evidence suggesting that the blue mechanisms (at least for wavelengths shorter than 530 nm) outlined by the two-color threshold experiments must represent an absorption spectrum of the pigment in the blue-sensitive cones. Their action spectra agree with the luminosity curve of the blue (8) cone monochromat and can be expressed quite well as a linear combination of the small-field, color-matching functions.

(*b*) The λ_{max} and the general shapes of the red and green mechanisms agree reasonably well with measurements of erythrolabe and chlorolabe by retinal densitometry, although existing techniques of retinal densitometry are still relatively crude when one is attempting a precise estimate of the shape of the absorption spectrum of a pigment.

(*c*) The Stiles green mechanism (Π_4') agrees fairly well with the protanope's luminosity curve, although the red mechanism (Π_5) does not match the deuteranope's quite so well.

Opposed are the following:

(*a*) Stiles' experiments on the fovea do not define three different mechanisms, but five. Π_1 and Π_3 (and less certainly Π_2) have the same shape for wavelengths shorter than 530 nm. For longer wavelengths, a second maximum in the region of 570 becomes progressively more pronounced as one moves from Π_3 to Π_1 to Π_2. The significance of this second peak is unclear. If it were either chlorolabe or erythrolabe, it should be absent in one or the other varieties of red-green dichromats, but it is not [although in the protanope Wald (168) finds its peak closer to 540 nm].

(*b*) The shapes of the red and green mechanisms Π_4 and Π_5 undergo a quite pronounced change when the background brightness is increased by two orders of magnitude. The changes in the green mechanism to Π_4' can be accounted for by self-screening although the light levels are rather low for this to occur; but the new red mechanism Π_5' changes in the wrong direction for self-screening. Other explanations, including the possibility of contamination from screening by color bleach products and distortions from light which passes through the hemoglobin in the choroid twice, being reflected by the sclera and only thereafter acting upon the cone visual pigments, have so far received no experimental attention. The mechanisms which Wald (166) derives with very bright backgrounds on normal eyes are narrower than Π_4 and Π_5, but they are still too broad compared with the action spectra he obtains on the foveas of the deuteranopes and protanopes (where we have every reason for believing the luminosity function is showing the spectrum of a single visual pigment for wavelengths greater than 450 nm).

(*c*) While Π_1 and Π_4' can be reasonably expressed by linear combinations of the small-field color-matching functions, this is not at all true of the red mechanisms Π_5 or Π_5'. Moreover, in this respect making the background brighter makes matters worse, not better.

(*d*) A fundamental assumption in deriving action spectra by the two-color methods is that at threshold the different color mechanisms are independent of one another. How valid is this assumption? This question has been recently examined by Boynton, Ikeda & Stiles (31) who measured test-flash increment thresholds for red (630 nm) light in combination with flashes of other wavelengths. The background was intense enough to depress the green mechanism, and the two test wavelengths excited the red and blue mechanisms, respectively. Three possibilities were considered: energy integration or cancelation within receptors, physiological summation and inhibition of receptor outputs, and probability summation. Since, in fact, all of these phenomena were found to occur, it is evident that the basic assumption which underlies the inference of visual pigment absorption spectra from two-color threshold experiments is an obvious oversimplification. How much this oversimplification will require us to modify our interpretation of the results from two-color experiments still needs elucidation.

This is probably the place to point out that measurements of the absolute threshold of the fovea for monochromatic lights (166) is not a valid way of measuring the normal photopic luminosity curve. Evidence for this comes from experiments (80, 81) in which the foveal absolute threshold is determined first for single monochromatic lights and then for mixtures of two monochromatic lights. It will come as no surprise to those who are familiar with Stiles' threshold measurements (31, 154) that the results are quite different from those to be expected if the threshold at each wavelength were determined by the Commission Internationale de l'Eclairage (C.I.E.) photopic luminosity curve, or, for that matter, by the absorption spectrum for a single photosensitive pigment, such as can be measured on protanopes and deuteranopes with $\lambda \geqslant$ 450 nm. What is less clear, however, is how to interpret the results. Stiles (154) shows that at absolute threshold one color mechanism occupies quite a different relative position with respect to the other two from one observer to the next. Threshold spectral-sensitivity curves and photopic luminosity curves seem to measure two quite different characteristics of the eye. How the threshold is determined in the special case when the test light is a mixture of two lights—one of which, say, excites the red, the other of which excites the green, mechanism—is not yet understood.

Burkhardt & Whittle (44) measure spectral sensitivity by setting a fixed contrast 32 per cent increment flash which is homochromatic with the background and they vary the radiance of both for threshold. This method yields a narrower spectral-sensitivity function than those found by absolute threshold.

It is also very much an open question how the red, green, and blue cone mechanisms pool their respective responses to yield the photopic luminosity curve as measured in the usual (suprathreshold) way. The individual differences in this respect are not distributed on a continuum but seem to

cluster into different classes (98). Rushton & Baker (144) found evidence
for a relation between the shape of the normal luminosity curve and the
relative proportion of chlorolabe to erythrolabe in the fovea.

In summary, the two-color experiments have been extremely useful in
specifying in a general way the absorption peaks of the three cone visual
pigments and (less certainly) in outlining in some fairly precise quantitative way (for wavelengths smaller than 530 nm) the absorption spectrum
of the cyanolabe in the blue-sensitive cones. The precise estimation of the
absorption spectrum of the red and green pigments in the normal eye
seems less certain by this method. For this, one is probably safer in using
these same (or other) methods on the far simpler foveas of protanopes and
deuteranopes (where in the red-green spectral range only a single cone pigment seems to be involved). In that case, interactions of the kind described by Boynton, Ikeda & Stiles are less apt to lead to erroneous inferences.

OTHER PSYCHOPHYSICAL METHODS

Krauskopf & Srebro (94) used color-naming of small dim monochromatic flashes. They developed a statistical method of differentiating responses
determined by a single neural unit from those activated by more than one
neural unit. From responses activated by single neural units, they derive
curves similar to the difference spectra of erythrolabe and chlorolabe. (Yellow flashes always appear either red or green at or near threshold.) Although this is a class B experiment, the subjects—the two authors—were
highly experienced, and the analysis is such that the implicit (though not
explicit) psychophysical linking hypothesis is plausible.

Bird & Jones (22) attempted to find a linear combination of the C.I.E.
1931 Standard Observer's tristimulus functions that would plausibly relate
to action spectra of organic dyes. This criterion yields an almost unique determination of the "fundamental response functions" of the human cone pigments. The blue and green "pigments" are in reasonable agreement with
those obtained by methods already described. The red "pigment" peaks too
far in the red and has a modest secondary maximum at 443 nm.

Judd (90) gives an analytical proof of Maxwell's method of determining the color mechanism which is lacking in dichromatic eyes by
subtracting the tristimulus values of a dichromat's match from those a normal obtains for a color. In a summary of the fundamental studies of color
vision in the hundred years since Maxwell's measurements of the color-
matching functions of the normal eye (91), he summarizes among other
things the various attempts to infer the spectra of the fundamental color
vision mechanism from the intersection of the dichromat's confusion lines.
This review is an excellent summary of an almost overwhelming literature
and should prove quite useful. Judd emphasizes what is easy to forget, that

color-matching functions are basic to any quantification of color vision theory.

WAVEGUIDES

The diameter of the outer segments of monkey foveal cones has recently been studied by electronmicroscopic methods by Dowling (62). They are (0.9 μ) almost twice the wavelength of visible light. The inner segments are 30 μ long and 2.5 to 3.0 μ at the base, and they taper gradually to a tip diameter of 1.5 μ. The consequence is, of course, that a considerable amount of light funneling is possible even in foveal cones. This is the accepted explanation for cone directional sensitivity, i. e. the greater brightness effect of light entering the eye pupil through its center compared to its margin (or the Stiles-Crawford effect of the first kind) (66). Because the relevant dimensions are of the order of a wavelength of light, one cannot treat the matter as merely a problem of classical geometrical optics, as has been clear for about twenty years. The idea that the organelles of foveal cones have properties analogous to dielectric rod antennae originally suggested by Toraldo di Francia (161) has led to a number of color vision schemes of one sort or another. Such ideas continue uninhibited down to our own day.

To separate sense from nonsense among these ideas, it is especially useful to keep in mind a very simple experiment of Brindley & Rushton (37) who showed that the color of a monochromatic light was not appreciably altered whether it entered the cone in the usual way (through the pupil), at right angles to the usual way (by reflection off the blind spot), or 180° from the usual way (through sclera from behind). Analogously one can compare, by microspectrophotometry, spectra on cones as a function of the angle at which the bleaching light strikes the outer segment. The results so far seem to be nearly independent of such effects. Such experiments seem to rule out the extreme possibility, i.e. that vision results from quantum absorption in a single cone pigment and that color results exclusively from different waveguide modes.

There is little doubt that because of the size of the outer segments waveguide modes are seen in isolated retinas, and Enoch has photographed at least the twelve modes with the lowest cutoff frequencies (66). What is not at all clear is their relevance for normal color vision. The most likely possibility—a role in the Stiles-Crawford effect of the second kind—has yet to receive serious quantitative attention. Quantitative treatments of this phenomenon, the upset of metameric matches when light enters the eye pupil through its edge, so far have been based on macroscopic models using geometrical optics alone. Enoch & Stiles (68) and Walraven (173) are thus led to conclude that chlorolabe in the green cones and erythrolabe in the red cones are in quite high density. The available experimental results are explained reasonably well, although still imperfectly, in this way, and it remains to be shown to what extent a theoretical model based on the idea of wavemodes would do it more successfully.

Ripps & Weale (128) have demonstrated both Stiles-Crawford effects objectively by retinal densitometry on the human fovea.

CONE INTERACTION

At Retinal Levels

In adaptation.—Although dark and light adaptation as such fall outside the scope of this review, the way different color mechanisms interact in the adaptation process does not, and so a word about the recent developments in this field is in order. Rushton (143) proposed a very simple—if still somewhat schematic—way in which the large mass of seemingly confusing facts on dark and light adaptation can be conceptualized. A large number of photoreceptors feed into a common excitation pool. The state of sensitivity of the pool determines the threshold. The pool is imagined as an "automatic gain control" device similar in its characteristics to the model proposed by Fuortes & Hodgkin (74) to explain the change in sensitivity and time characteristics of the generator potential of the limulus photoreceptor during light and dark adaptation. The input to the pool is proportional to the quantum catch, the output very nearly to the logarithm of the light intensity. The output of the pool is fed (a) to the optic nerve to signal the visual stimulus and (b) back into the pool to regulate its sensitivity. Both the effects of an existing stimulus and of the "dark light" of the bleaching —the afterimages (18)—feed into the excitation pool. For the rods, at least, Rushton (141) showed that the "real" light enters the pool through the input stage but that the "dark" light enters the pool through the feedback.

For those curious as to the possible site of the excitation pool in the vertebrate, a recent paper of Dowling's (63) will be of interest. Dowling shows that the a-wave of the ERG saturates at background levels where ΔI is still increasing linearly with I for the b-wave in rat. Naka & Kishida (108) observed that the light intensity necessary to elicit S potentials at the dynamic range of the V log I curve was far stronger than that required for ganglion cell thresholds. This suggests to them that the L-type S potential is concerned with the depression of ganglion cell spike discharge in adaptation to background field. However, Witkovsky (180) found in the carp that the response of the L compartment S potential saturated at backgrounds where ΔI is still increasing linearly with I for the ganglion cell. Electronmicroscopic evidence suggests to Dowling (63) that amacrine bipolar cell complex may prove to be the anatomical correlate of the automatic gain control box.

Increment threshold and afterflash experiments suggest that rods and cones can behave quite independently of each other and therefore feed into different excitation pools. Does the same sort of relation hold among the different cone mechanisms, i.e. do the red cone mechanisms feed into a separate red automatic gain control pool which is insensitive to the signals from blue and green cone mechanisms? Such a relation, in fact, would describe Stiles' two-color (155) experiments which have proven so insightful in defining—at least in an approximate way—the three color mechanisms of the normal retina. Chlorolabe recovery in the protanope (136) and erythrolabe in the deuteranope (138) go hand in hand with the respective foveal dark-adaptation curves following a full bleach just as rhodopsin follows a recovery of rod threshold (log threshold increases linearly with fraction of free opsin). Similar results are obtained on the normal fovea (17). If the equivalent background of bleaching exhibits the mutual independence that Stiles showed for real background, it might be expected that breaks in the dark-adaptation curves between one cone branch and another can be found similar to the breaks Stiles has shown in increment threshold experiments. In fact, the experiments of Auerbach & Wald (14) show such a break in the cone dark-adaptation curve, but they do not establish that the equivalent background of bleachings spreads exclusively from each cone mechanism to its own pool.

Du Croz & Rushton ask: "Is the equivalent background of a bleached cone pigment independent of the bleachings of other pigments?" (64). Bleaching by orange and testing with a blue flash yields a kinked dark-adaptation curve, the upper branch having the same dark-adapted threshold as Stiles' Π_1 and the lower that of Π_4 (although if a white test was used, only the unkinked Π_4 curve was obtained). When the curve was obtained against steady backgrounds and Π_4 alone was involved, the results fit the curves calculated on the assumption that the equivalent and real backgrounds add together in determining threshold [just as in the rods (24)]. The Π_1 mechanism recovers at about the same rate as Π_4 or Π_5 or slightly slower. This is the first clear evidence of the regeneration rate of cyanolabe. Dark-adaptation curves with red (Π_5) and green (Π_4) limbs can be obtained after a deep-red bleach using a red test flash on a green background. The results of these experiments are readily explained by assuming that the three cone systems each have separate excitation pools and the state of excitation of the pool of one cone system is independent of that in the other two (64).

Independence of the different receptor mechanisms in interaction experiments across contiguous (but not overlapping) regions of the retina have been demonstrated in contrast-flash experiments (4, 9, 10). In these experiments a flash applied to one region of the field increases the threshold in an adjacent region. If the test flash excites rods (and rods alone), its threshold is elevated in proportion as the contrast flash excites rods and is independent of the extent that it excites cones (4). Similarly, when the test flash excites blue (Π_1) cones alone, the threshold is elevated by the contrast flash by the extent to which it also excites Π_1 cones, while the extent to which the contrast flash excites the other two cone systems is irrelevant to its ability to elevate Π_1 threshold. Analogous results were obtained for the other two cone systems as well (9). The contrast-flash effects are not due to entopic scatter of light onto the region of the retina excited by the test flash (10). This sort of arrangement can provide an appropriate basis for the phenomenon of simultaneous color contrast according to which a gray square on a red background appears blue-green. The responses of the red cones excited by the gray square are inhibited by the responses of the red cones excited by the red backgrounds by some lateral inhibition mechanism within the retina. Since the blue and green mechanisms excited by the gray square are not inhibited by the red background, the resulting color of the gray square is blue-green (3).

While these experiments show that the state of excitation of one of the three color mechanisms is relatively independent of the state of excitation of the other two (and very much dependent upon the state of excitation of the same mechanism even over separate regions of the retina), it would be wrong to infer that this independence is a unique and universal description of interaction among the various cone mechanisms and with the rod mechanism. Both rods and cones contribute to the brightness of twilight and to the photopupil response evoked by a flash of light presented in the center of visual field to a dark-adapted eye (5). Both red and green cone mechanisms contribute to the brightness of a yellow light. Even at threshold the various cone mechanisms sometimes are not completely independent (30, 31, 80, 81) as we have already seen. The physiological mechanism responsible for these latter (and apparently small) departures from complete independence has not yet been subject to analysis. Thus in their relations one to another, rods and the various types of cones sometimes "add," sometimes "subtract", and sometime remain relatively unresponsive.

S *potentials*.—The way Naka & Rushton (109) analyzed the action spectra of the cone systems contributing to the responses of the S potentials in C units has already been described. Since the 680 nm action spectrum was not comparable to any pigment revealed by Marks (103), they considered the possibility that an action spectrum of this kind might be obtained by the interaction of two cone receptors (such as Marks' 540 nm and 620 nm pigment). This theoretical possibility would follow directly from an interaction function which is a simple linear transform such as that observed in limulus [for the most recent summaries see (96, 123)] or in the frog ganglion cell. But an interaction function which matches a single pigment for all monochromatic lights will not match it for certain mixtures. The interaction function implies, under certain conditions where only the "680" action spectrum is operative, that the *addition* of a small amount of green (500 nm) light to a large amount of deep red (720 nm) acts like the *subtraction* of light at another wavelength (110). This result was never found. Thus, the 680 nm action spectrum was behaving as a true pigment. Similarly, monochromatic lights of all wavelengths were matched by mixtures of monochromatic red and monochromatic green, when the criterion of identical responses is used. From this the action spectrum of the red pigment was obtained without involving neural organization, except as a null detector. Again the 680 nm λ_{max} action spectrum was found. These experiments refute the idea that a 680 nm action spectrum results from a complex neural interaction of 540 nm and 620 nm cones before the R/G compartment. They agree with the simple idea that 540 nm cones hyperpolarize the compartment and the 680 nm cones depolarize it. A simple electrical analog of how this happens is presented (110).

An analogous model for the L compartments is less successful (111). The L compartment has the additional complexity that the action of green cones is enhanced by a steady red background (and vice versa). The full appreciation of the way this comes about requires a better understanding of the role that S potentials play in retinal organization.

Electroretinograms (ERG).—One evidence of progress is that in any previous year a paragraph on human ERG would be quite inappropriate in a review of this sort. The reader should not infer from this that we have recently acquired a reasonable understanding of the origin of the ERG. In this regard, we have only a suggestion (with no additional evidence) by Kuffler & Nicholls (95) that the responses of glial cells may eventually provide a basis for at least part of the electroretinogram. However this may be, what makes possible a paragraph on ERG in a review on color vision is the application of computer methods to obtain responses with gross corneal electrodes following excitation of human cones and cones alone. Two different methods have been employed (1, 89), both of which yield action spectra in good—almost exact—agreement with the psychophysical photopic luminosity curve.

Johnson, Riggs & Schick (89) observed the response obtained by displacement of a square grating of seventeen bars (19° visual angle), the brighter set of bars being 0.6 $\log_{10}$ units more intense than the dimmer. Alternation of one bar width produces an ERG voltage, and when both brighter and dimmer bars are of the same wavelength, one can measure the intensity at each wavelength required for a criterion voltage. Experienced observers succeed in maintaining steady fixation on a point in this field so that movement artifacts apparently do not contaminate the records. The directional sensitivities of the receptors excited by the stimulus in this way, as measured by ERG and psychophysically, are the same and have the characteristics of cones (13). When the alternate bars are of different dominant wavelengths and each bar equated for equal ERG effectivity (according to the curve obtained when the bars were of the same wavelength), then movement through one bar width evokes bigger voltages (for some wavelength differences) than when intensity differences alone define the gratings. Riggs, Johnson & Schick (126) have used the size of the relative amplitudes of responses evoked by different pairs of bars to estimate the relative color responsiveness at each wavelength of the three color mechanisms.

Aiba, Alpern & Maaseidvaag (1) measured the responses to a 2° monochromatic test field against a large (40°), bright (2×10^4 scotopic trolands) blue background. Controls similar to those used by Brindley & Westheimer (38) with white light prove that the responses are recorded from localized retinal regions and the action spectrum for foveal fixation agrees well with the observer's foveal luminosity curve. The evidence suggests that under these conditions one records responses evoked by excitation of cones (and cones alone) principally, if not exclusively, from the fovea. Sinusoidal transition from a red to a green light equated in intensity for ERG effectivity and shifted in time so that the two responses are exactly 180° out of phase shows no signal detectably different from the noise. The reason for this discrepancy with the results of Riggs et al. (126) is unclear. Of course, the stimulus conditions in the two cases are very different, but one might have hoped that if color signals were present in the ERG responses to excitation of cones by one method, they would be just as prominent when evoked by any other. This is apparently not the case. One possible explanation for the discrepancy is that Riggs et al. were looking at phase differences in the responses of the different color mechanisms which Aiba et al. took great care to eliminate before sinusoidally substituting one wavelength for the other. The answers to this question and a host of others opened up by the possibility of color signals in the ERG (the form of the ERG normal color-matching functions to cite only the most obvious example) must await further work.

Ganglion cells.—Interaction of rods and cones at the level of ganglion cells in the monkey has been examined by Gouras & Link (78). Using latency as a criterion and monochromatic stimuli, Gouras (76) examined the independence of the rod and cone contributions to ERG and to the ganglion cell responses. He inferred that the time delays of rod and cone responses were determined before, the interaction of rod and cone signals after, the origin of the *b*-wave. Gouras & Link (78) found both rod and cone signals converging on a single perifoveal ganglion cell. The cone system is less sensitive but faster than that of the rods, and so cones determine latency once they respond. Since the earliest signals leave transitory refractoriness in their wake, the cones tend to predominate. In an as yet unpublished paper, Gouras (77) continues this work by measuring receptive-field size in different states of adaptation. He finds that in dark adaptation, threshold rod and cone signals can be transmitted to the brain by the same or by neighboring ganglion cells but not simultaneously. In the light-adapted state, only the cone signal is transmitted. All of the various ways of documenting that one has in fact isolated responses originating from rods, on the one hand, and from cones, on the other, were not employed, so the arguments are not as compelling as they could have been made.

The spectral characteristics of ganglion cell discharges in animals with color vision are now coming under examination. The best data are from the fish retina. The early work of Motokawa, Yamashita & Ogawa (106) and of Wagner, MacNichol & Wolbarsht (165) is still the point of departure for subsequent work in this field. The latter analyzed responses with threshold action spectra and are hence more insightful. "Color-coded" cells are readily found. Using small spots of light, they analyzed the (rather large) receptive fields of these cells. "On" and "off" center fields were found, but there seems to be an "opponent" process related to spectral sensitivity of the "on" and "off" components in the sense that a cell which has a low threshold for "on" in the red (say) will have a low threshold for "off" in the green (or vice versa). Such cells can be more sensitive to "on" in the center and to "off" in the surround (or vice versa), but the receptive field for red was always smaller than that for green. The opponent processes are invariably red vs. green. "Yellow-blue" antagonism is not seen [although Witkovsky (179) finds a suggestion of such effects in the carp]. The action spectra of these responses, whether "on" or "off," agree with Marks' (103) measurements of the red and green pigments in the goldfish. Some new properties of these cells have now been brought to light by Daw (51), using annular stimuli in addition to small spots. The periphery of the receptive field when mapped with an annulus is very large (5 mm). A cell which gives "on" to 650 nm in the center and "off" to 500 nm in both center and surround when probed by small (and thus relatively high-intensity) spots of light will give "on" to 650 nm and "off" to 500 nm in the center, but "on" to 500 nm and "off" to 650 nm in the surround when the fields are probed by annuli (which evoked responses at relatively weaker light intensities). Opposite relations are, of course, also found. Such cells seem to be by far the most numerous "color-coded" ganglion cells. They are the first unequivocal demonstrations of electrophysiological correlates of simultaneous color contrast at the cellular level. They come about presumably by the excitation of red cones in the center of the field, producing lateral inhibition of the effects of excitation of red cones in the surround, red cones in the surround being uninfluenced by the excitation of green in the center (and vice versa). This is precisely the arrangement which must underlie contrast-flash effects in man (9, 10). It also has been used as a model to account for simultaneous color contrast in man (3). However, we do not yet know if the response of such a cell to a white spot may be made indistinguishable from its response to a red one merely by surrounding the white spot with a green background. But perhaps, after all, this is asking for frosting on the cake!

Annuli as targets in mapping receptive fields need to be applied to other species which show opponent color responses in ganglion cells in order to document the generality of Daw's result. The obvious place to begin is the ground squirrel who behaviorally distinguishes 480 nm from 500 or 520 or 569 or 600 nm or white light of different intensities (49). The retina shows ganglion cells analogous to those found in the goldfish when the receptive fields are mapped with spots of different sizes. The "opponents" are blue and green (105).

Before the retina is left, a word should be said as to our most obvious ignorance. What retinal electrophysiology seems to lack is a John Gunther. Tomita (160), the most promising candidate at the moment, is working on *Inside Carp Cones,* certainly a most needed volume long awaited and eagerly anticipated. But as valuable as it will be, many of the problems of the organization of color information coding will still be unsolved by it. We can only hope that he or other enterprising retinal physiologists will turn to the problems most likely to be solved from the interior of more proximal retinal neurons.

Higher Centers

And so we leave the eye and thus pass a reasonable boundary between "distal" and "proximal" mechanisms of color vision. Nonetheless, I include some of the work on higher centers since at the present time, differences of organization at different levels of the nervous system in color coding are not at all clear. Insightful analysis of the role in processing of the color code of each layer of the visual nervous system at the cellular level analogous to the work on form vision had not yet been achieved.

The responses of the optic tectum of goldfish were studied with spots of monochromatic light (88). The relation of these responses to those of the goldfish ganglion cell just discussed is not clear cut because receptive fields were not mapped. Opponent cell responses were found. The results can be explained by assuming antagonism between two sets of cones, each set containing one of three pigments with λ_{max} at 467, 533, and 620 nm.

The best central nervous system work on color vision is on the primate lateral geniculate nucleus. De Valois and co-workers (57 to 59) studied responses of single cells to 15° homogeneously illuminated fields of monochromatic light. Wiesel & Hubel (178) used small and large spots of light.

With large fields it is convenient to divide the cells into non-opponent and opponent cells (57, 86). The former appear to be related to brightness perception; their action spectrum agrees more or less with C.I.E. luminosity curve which presumably (147) does not differ much from the foveal luminosity curve of the macaque. Such cells are sensitive to change in intensity but much less so to change in dominant wavelength. Opponent cells appear to carry some of the information as to color. They are exquisitely sensitive to changes in dominant wavelength (59) and not at all to changes in intensity. The difference at any wavelength between the logs of the spectral sensitivity of the opponent and non-opponent cells agrees reasonably well with human saturation discrimination data. Wavelength discrimination by opponent cells is relatively good for those parts of the spectrum for which the cells are sensitive (58). However, behavioral wavelength discrimination data for the animal are superior to the best that individual cells succeed in achieving by almost one order of magnitude (even when the preferences for different spectral ranges are assigned to different opponent cells). The maxima and minima occur in the same spectral positions in both types of experiments.

How all this fits with results obtained by stimulation with small spots of light in the visual field has been studied recently by Wiesel & Hubel (178) who have turned their elegant methods for analyzing problems of visual form perception at the cellular level in the central nervous system on the problem of color. Small and large spots of light are used to map the receptive fields. Three types of cells in the lateral geniculate of the monkey are the most prominent: (*a*) those in which the spectral sensitivity in the center and surround differ and the center and surround are antagonistic in sign; (*b*) those in which the field is not divided into a center and surround but in which blue and green (say) are basically antagonistic; and (*c*) those in which the spectral sensitivity includes contributions from all three kinds of cones but in which the center and surround are antagonistic. Conspicuous by their absence are cells, like those described by Daw (51), in the goldfish retina which could serve as a physiological mechanism for color contrast. Perhaps using an annulus as a test target would be as fruitful in the primate as Daw found it to be in the goldfish.

In experiments with small monochromatic test spots, attention needs to be paid to the optics of the eye because, at least in man, chromatic aberration at the extremes of the spectrum can result in a fairly large defocus (2.25 diopters) smearing of the retinal image of a small test spot. The chromatic aberration of the monkey eye has not yet been worked out, but it is unlikely that it is of higher optical quality in this respect.

COLOR BLINDNESS

One consequence of the application of techniques of retinal densitometry is that the various forms of color blindness are rapidly coming to be understood as simple defects of distal (receptor) mechanisms. Thus, given the general scheme of Thomas Young's theory and imagining the simple ways defects could appear, leads to a fairly good picture of current ideas of color blindness.

MONOCHROMATISM

Monochromatism exists in one of several (probably four) different types. Their whole range of color experience can be quantified by a single degree of freedom. Ordinary rod vision in these and all other congenitally colorblind subjects is essentially normal.

Rod monochromatism.—In the retina of the ordinary (rod) totally colorblind subject, histological cones are quite infrequent (70) and one can use this property to study the dark adaptation and increment threshold characteristics of the rod mechanism even at levels where in the normal retina cone vision would dominate (24, 25). [An elegant way of following recovery of rod threshold above cone threshold on the normal retina has recently been described (140), and the agreement with that found on the rod monochromat (24) is very satisfying.] Typical totally colorblind indi-

viduals (so-called rod monochromats) also have high-intensity photoreceptors, but their exact character remains unclear. Histologically they appear
to be cones (70) although many have "ectopic" nuclei. The psychophysical
studies on these high-intensity receptors are confusing. They have been
variously described as having the directional and spectral sensitivities of
cones (73), the directional and spectral sensitivities of rods (24), and the
directional sensitivities of cones and the spectral sensitivity of rods (7). It
is possible, but unlikely, that all three varieties of "rod" monochromats
exist.

   Cone monochromats.—One might expect three categories: blue cone
monochromats, green cone monochromats, and red cone monochromats.
The cones in blue cone monochromats in whatever region they use for fixation have the spectral and intensity sensitivity of the Π_1 (blue) cones of
the normal fovea (8). What they lack apparently are the green and red
cone systems. Since the visual acuity of the blue cone system is poorer than
that of the green and red cones (32), these observers have visual acuity
lower than the normal by a factor of about five. Weale (176) and Pitt
(120), among others, described monochromats with normal acuity and explained them as people with normal receptors but defective postreceptor
structure. In the normal, the visual acuity of either red and green cone systems in isolation is better than 1.0 (32) so that, contrary to the case for the
blue cone and the rod monochromat, patients lacking blue and red cones,
say, would never be easily detected by the usual clinical methods. The argument (176) that because the foveal spectral-sensitivity curve of such observers is narrower than Dartnall's nomogram the defect is "postreceptor"
is also specious. In fact, the agreement of the foveal curve of this observer
with that of the protanope is so good that one finds the argument that such
observers lack red and blue cones quite compelling (since blue cones contribute little to luminosity even in the normal retina). Ikeda & Ripps' (85)
ERG measurements support this view and suggest that the difference spectrum obtained by Weale (177) on this subject after red bleach was that of
chlorolabe and not erythrolabe. Monochromats lacking blue and green
cones with a foveal luminosity curve similar or identical to that of the deuteranope have not yet been described, but one would not be too surprised to
find them. Like the observers of Pitt and Weale, their acuity should be better than 1.0 and therefore just as difficult to ferret out by routine clinical
testing.

   While all of the above is relatively straightforward, some monochromats apparently don't fit this pattern. Siegel et al. (148) describe a case of
"incomplete" monochromacy who becomes "tritanopic" at high intensities
although her clinical acuity is poor. Presumably the few high-intensity receptors are cones deficient in quantity and perhaps also in quality. Their
spectral sensitivity looks like that of none of the known curves for human
visual pigments.

DICHROMATS

The most extensive recent work on spectral sensitivity of dichromats is that of Wald (167, 168) already referred to. Rushton has proved that protanopes lack the red-sensitive erythrolabe, deuteranopes the green-sensitive chlorolabe. If the green-sensitive cones of the deuteranope are filled with the red-sensitive pigment, erythrolabe, then the yellow sensation of the deuteranopic eye in the unilateral deuteranope is explained (79). One might also expect that the deuteranopic fovea would be 0.3 log_{10} units more sensitive for red light than the normal, but this has never been demonstrated. Tritanopes apparently lack the blue-sensitive pigment cyanolabe, yet their color-naming of monochromatic waveband is excellent (168, 172).

ANOMALOUS TRICHROMATISM

Of all the color defectives, anomalous trichromatism is the most difficult to understand. The tritanomalous are extremely rare, and little, if anything, in a quantitative way is known about them. The red-green anomalous (protanomalous and deuteranomalous) are common enough. The former require more red than the normal, the latter more green than the normal, in the red-green match with yellow. In two-color threshold experiments (168), retinal densitometry (142), and luminosity-curve measurements, the protanomalous is virtually indistinguishable from the protanope and the deuteranomalous from the deuteranope. [See, however, de Vries for a different result with a two-color experiment (61).] And yet anomalous trichromats clearly have a third color mechanism. One of Wald's tritanopes was also deuteranomalous. Using two-color thresholds against intense red and blue backgrounds, Wald found a normal red receptor but an abnormal green receptor low in sensitivity and a spectrum displaced toward the red (168). Anomalous trichromatism could not be merely a reduction in the concentration of one of the red-green pigments unless in the normal the anomaloscope match is distorted by self-screening. The self-screening hypothesis leads to a deuteranomalous (imagined having chlorolabe in very dilute solution) requiring more red in the red-green mixture to match yellow than the normal (imagined having chlorolabe in dense solution), i.e. in the wrong direction. The hypothesis works in the correct direction for the protanomalous. The differences between Baker's (15) and Brindley's (33) result in testing this hypothesis for the protanomalous have already been discussed. Deuteranomalous vision is not due to excess of macular pigment, because even 1.0 density at 460 nm of the latter produces no appreciable anomaloscope mismatches in the normal, and the density required for deuteranomalous mismatch is about 10.0 at 460 nm, a completely ridiculous possibility (168). In the protanomalous squirrel monkey, Jacobs & De Valois (87) found the (chromatic) opponent cells in much smaller proportion of the total sample than was the case in the color-normal macaque. The red mechanism also peaks at a shorter wavelength than in the macaque. The reason anomalous trichromats mismatch the anomaloscope remains one of the most important unanswered questions regarding the receptor basis of human color vision.

The color characteristics of the paintings of a deuteranomalous artist (who skillfully avoids color errors and adapts those color choices of his own which please color-normal subjects) were studied by Pickford (118). He has also recently summarized the genetics of color vision defects (117).

COMPLEX PROCESSES

Brindley, Du Croz & Rushton (35) measured the critical flicker frequency of the blue-sensitive color mechanism by using a flickering blue test field on a bright yellow background. Under these conditions, the critical flicker frequency increases with luminance only to about 18 cps after which it remains nearly independent of further luminance increases over a range of about 20. Just as the Π_1 cone system has lower visual acuity and a higher Weber fraction than the green and red cones, its maximum critical flicker frequency is about three times lower than that of the other two mechanisms.

Supersaturated greens, which appear after intense bleaching by red light, depend upon the contrast from the "dark light of bleaching" from the red receptors in the test area (60). Since color mixing, but not color contrast, was observed when the bleach was exposed to one eye and the test to the other, color contrast must be a retinal phenomenon.

The color of the stabilized image of Ishihara test plates desaturates quickly, while the form of the background circles does not disappear (19). Does this mean that the "on" and "off" responses of the color code play key roles in color perception which in normal quasi-steady-state viewing must be evoked by the slight image displacements produced by the physiological nystagmus?

Ratliff (122) describes the green and yellow blotches observed in monochromatic light of about 600 nm which is rapidly changing in wavelength. They appear to be qualitatively similar to those seen by Shurcliff (146) after about five seconds looking through an orange filter which cuts off at about 500 nm. For the Shurcliff effect, the initial stimulus (step 1) must be devoid of, and the afterstimulus (step 2) must be rich in, blue (400–470 nm) light. If the orange light in step 1 can be assumed to depress the sensitivity of the red and green cones, then the blotches seen in step 2 may be revealing the spatial distribution of blue cones.

Nimeroff (112) found that rods make an important contribution to the 10° color-matching functions, and below retinal illuminances of 1000 trolands this effect cannot be neglected. With the 10° field, even when corrections are made for rod responses, failures of additivity persist. They may be the result of rod-cone interactions (113).

Crawford (47) found surprising discrepancies with a 10° field in comparing color-matching functions of spectral lights when measured by the usual "maximum" saturation method with "Maxwell's method" in which the colorimetric field always remains white. Smaller effects still occur with 2° and 1° fields, but they are of little practical significance.

Ruddock has evaluated the effect of age on color-matching functions. Age has no measurable effect on the responses of the receptors (131), but the well-known yellowing of the lens with increased age has the predicted effects on color matching (132). In another experiment, he (133) is led to the conclusion that both Haidinger's brushes and Maxwell's spot are to be attributed to light changes which occur prior to visual excitation. Maxwell's spot is broken up into Haidinger's brush when a monochromatic (10°) blue field is viewed through a rotating plane polarizer. The brushes have the same color as the spot and the intervening field looks just the same as the surround. When the rotation stops, the brushes revert to the circular spot before fading.

Color-mixture functions in the mesopic range have been studied both foveally and parafoveally (124). In the fovea, photometric (but not chromatic) additivity was maintained as the light level was reduced. The changes in the latter were similar to those found parafoveally.

Wavelength discrimination steps are more sensitive to field size than brightness discrimination steps (130). Wider variability exists in wavelength discrimination below 460 nm than in the rest of the spectrum (149).

Different time constants of the red and blue color mechanisms are used to explain the fact that short flashes of red and blue light which match in brightness when seen by the dark-adapted fovea fail to do so after being exposed one after the other in a series of successive alternate exposures (69). The field size was too large (7°) to build a convincing argument. Walraven & Leebeek (174) measured the phase shift required for two alternating colors necessary to eliminate flicker. The phase angles are approximately additive although second-order nonlinearities are present. Verriest & Seki (163) have recently measured the chromaticities of the Fechner-Benham colors.

In an examination of the subjective colors, Munker (107) measured the color of a red flash followed by an uncolored afterflash. When the exposure asynchrony is 25 msec and both the before- and afterflash are 5 msec, the red color disappears. Longer afterflashes produce a very desaturated red appearance at this asynchrony and duration of the beforeflash.

Munker also examined the spatial modulation transfer function for colors by interlacing a grating of two different "monochromatic" bars of constant luminance but of different color modulation depths. No low-frequency cut was found. Van Nes & Bouman (162) measured the spatial modulation transfer function for monochromatic sinusoidal gratings. No differences were found between red, green, and blue when wavelength-dependent diffraction effects were taken into account. The contrast color induced into a central white area by various monochromatic surrounds was studied by a binocular method (39). Good monochromatic components can be found to match colors induced by wavelengths between 400 and 480 and between 564 and 723 nm, but not between 485 and 564 nm. Red induces more saturated greens with longer exposures, but blue induces less saturated yellows (92). Akita & Graham (2) had subjects adjust the wavelength drum of a monochromator for "best" green, yellow, blue, orange, and red with and without an inducing surround. A compensatory shift in wavelength setting for the contrast induced tinge occurs almost always in the direction of the inducing color. Ratio of test to background luminance has an "imprecisely specifiable influence" on the compensatory wavelength shift in the test area. Oyama & Hsia (114) used a similar procedure and obtained analogous results. The effect decreases with increasing separation of the test and inducing fields. The Broca-Sulzer curves for monochromatic flashes (up to 320 msec) were obtained by monocular brightness matches with a constant duration (320 msec) flash 2.25° from the fixation point (175). Most pronounced Broca-Sulzer "overshoots" occurred at 475, 505, and 580 nm. Pronounced differences in such an experiment occur when the pattern is presented precisely to the fovea or just eccentric to the fovea (93).

The old idea that the pathways from the rods somehow converge onto those of the II_1 cones so that rod excitation appears blue received some support from an experiment in which the action spectrum of the background intensity required to raise the threshold for the blue arcs of the retina by a fixed amount was shown to be that of rods and not of blue cones (6).

COLOR THEORIES UNRELATED TO RETINAL PHYSIOLOGY

There is a fairly large class of theories in which the discrimination of color is supposed to depend not simply upon three classes of cone pigments. These include the notions: that the warm (red) system of the cones is parasympathetically involved whereas the cool (blue) system of the rods is orthosympathetically involved (145), that the pure colors of the spectrum are the primary physiological sensations which are as numerous as the number of distinguishable spectral colors (121), and that waveguide modes in the photosensitive regions of the cones produce spatial energy distributions which vary with wavelength and which are converted to time-varying electrical signals (21). They find difficulty in explaining trichromacy, for color information by them would be multidimensional and the observed reduction to only three variables would be unexplained and extremely wasteful processing of visual information. Other theories include allowance for trichromacy in one way or another such as that the photoreceptors are analogous to photoconductive elements or photoresistors with various impurities to give trichromacy (150) or that they are combinations of photovoltaic and photoconductive elements (129) or the possibility that color perception is based on three (or more) waveguide modes in a cone with a single photosensitive material (66) or the idea that there is only one type of cone, one shape of response curve but a continuum of different λ_{max} for different cones all of which would coincide if shifted on the wavelength axis, the tridimensionality being derived from interactions of the receptor responses (75). In one way or another they all fail, either because they do not easily explain how it is that monochromatic light appears the same color when entering the receptors in the normal way or from behind through the sclera or from the side (as reflected from the optic disk) or because they are incompatible with the experimental evidence from micro-spectrophotometry and from retinal densitometry already discussed.

Other once-plausible models for color vision can now also be excluded. These include the idea that each cone contains all three visual pigments (99) (which seems at variance with data coming from single-cone micro-spectrophotometry) and the notion that color coding is transmitted as fre-quency modulation patterns of the optic nerve signals (each nerve fiber carrying the entire color and brightness code) (71)—which does not seem to agree with current electrophysiological data.

SUMMARY

The new technological developments have had considerable impact on the range of plausible hypotheses which still can explain human color vi-sion. We began over one hundred and sixty-five years ago in the thesis of Thomas Young that three broadband "resonators" serve as the receptor basis of color vision. The antithesis of Ewald Hering that six independent unitary colors (red, yellow, green, blue, white, and black) are pooled into three (black-white, red-green, and yellow-blue) opposing pairs (black and white blend to give gray, but equal amounts of yellow and blue or of red and green cancel to zero) came much later. Now it is commonly stated that we have very good evidence at the cellular level for both these views.

Synthesis of these two views is achieved in so-called zone theories. The data from retinal densitometry and the less certain, but more specific, re-sults of microspectrophotometry make it probable that the receptors for color vision, i.e., the cones, contain one of three photopigments—each cell one and only one pigment—whose spectral sensitivities overlap to a consid-erable extent. Thus in this respect, at the receptor level at least, Thomas Young seems to have had it quite right. To the extent that Hering's views directly contradict these ideas at the level of the absorption of light quanta, then, we conclude that Hering had it wrong. But where did he have it right? The conventional wisdom is to point to the "opponent" organization of the C-type S potentials and of the retinal ganglion cells and primate geniculate neuron discharges as revealed by microelectrode studies. But the quantitative inferences about receptors are of a far higher level of sophis-tication than the understanding that we can yet glean from visual electro-physiology. The basic organizational patterns of the S compartments, of ganglion, and of geniculate neurons are only beginning to come to light. As understanding grows on a more and more quantitative level, it is not at all certain that Hering's "opponents" will be able to stand up even when they are presented in their most favorable modern light. In fact, the most recent experiments from which the best quantitative inferences can be drawn are not very encouraging. They include: (*a*) the demonstration (109) that the neutral wavelengths in the R/G S compartment shift further into the red as luminance increases and are not invariant with luminance as the opponent theory requires [similar, if somewhat less dramatic, effects occur for the "opponent" cells of the geniculate body (57)] and (*b*) Daw's (51) analysis of "opponent" color-coded retinal ganglion cells which seem organized largely on the basis of a specificity of cone interaction between the center and the surround (red cones in the center inhibited by red cones in the surround but completely uninfluenced by either green or blue cones in the surround, etc.).

Does all this mean that when we are capable of making the same types of quantitative inferences at the ganglion cell level which we now make for receptors, the Young-Helmholtz theory will stand alone in the elegance of its explanatory power for every aspect of human color vision? This seems quite out of the question. Wherein will we be indebted to Hering's views? At the moment, there are three things which seem likely to become a basic part of color theory, and I am more certain of the first of these than of the other two. It is the idea of lateral inhibition within the retina as a basic organizational feature of retinal information processing (not only of color but of brightness and form as well). No serious physiologist can in 1967 be satisfied with Helmholtz's idea that visual contrast effects are mere errors of judgment! Hering had it right here. He may very well prove to have been right, too, in regarding black as an active stimulus (119) although we know virtually nothing about how it excites.

Finally, and least certainly, we must entertain the possibility that brightness and color are coded into separate channels at a very distal level in the nervous system. However meager our knowledge of the physiology of retinal ganglion cells, everything available suggests that a vast amount of information processing has already occurred at distal levels. Abney's law implies a linearity uncomfortably, infrequently found in the analysis of physiological responses at cellular levels. A compression transformation of the physiological correlates of intensity seems to occur very soon after the absorption of light quanta in the visual pigments (65). For Abney's law to be valid, we assume either that coding of brightness occurs prior to the transformation or that the nervous system performs the transform at several separate levels—a very uneconomical alternative. Of course, this does not necessarily mean that brightness and color are at the same time coded into separate channels, but experiments on the primate lateral geniculate (57) imply that by the time the signals have reached thalamic levels they are, in fact, coded in this way. It is now very popular to discredit Abney's law, justifiably so insofar as the data on which it is based are not from class A experiments. But flicker photometry is a class A experiment and there are good data showing the validity of Abney's law by flicker photometry under certain restricted conditions ($\lambda_1 = 550$, $\lambda_2 = 654$, foveal fixation with suprathreshold intensities equal to, or less than, 50 trolands).

Whatever the uncertainty about the validity of Abney's law, there can be no doubt, at least for normal human foveal color vision, as to the validity of Grassman's laws, and the linearity implied by them imposes no such constraints upon the cite of coding of color and brightness information. For, given—as now seems quite unequivocally to be the case—three different cone visual pigments, one in each kind of cone, if the output is univariant, then Grassman's three laws must necessarily follow.

LITERATURE CITED

1. Aiba, T. S., Alpern, M., Maaseidvaag, F. The electroretinogram evoked by the excitation of human foveal cones. *J. Physiol. (London)*, 189, 43–62 (1967)

2. Akita, M., Graham, C. H. Maintaining an absolute test hue in the presence of different background colors and luminance ratios. *Vision Res.*, 6, 315–23 (1966)

3. Alpern, M. Relation between brightness and color contrast. *J. Opt. Soc. Am.*, 54, 1491–92 (1964)

4. Alpern, M. Rod-cone independence in the after-flash effect. *J. Physiol. (London)*, 176, 462–72 (1965)

5. Alpern, M., Campbell, F. W. The spectral sensitivity of the consensual light reflex. *J. Physiol. (London)*, 164, 478–507 (1962)

6. Alpern, M., Dudley, D. The blue arcs of the retina. *J. Gen. Physiol.*, 49, 405–21 (1966)

7. Alpern, M., Falls, H. F., Lee, G. B. The enigma of typical total monochromacy, *Am. J. Ophthalmol.*, 50, 996–1011 (1960)

8. Alpern, M., Lee, G. B., Spivey, B. E. II_1 cone monochromatism. *Arch. Ophthalmol.*, 74, 334–37 (1965)

9. Alpern, M., Rushton, W. A. H. The specificity of the cone interaction in the after-flash effect. *J. Physiol. (London)*, 176, 473–82 (1965)

10. Alpern, M., Rushton, W. A. H. The nature of rise in threshold produced by contrast-flashes. *Ibid.*, 189, 519–34 (1967)

11. Alpern, M., Thompson, S., Lee, M. S. Spectral transmittance of visible light by the living human eye. *J. Opt. Soc. Am.*, 55, 723–27 (1965)

12. Armington, J. C. Vision. *Ann. Rev. Physiol.*, 27, 163–82 (1965)

13. Armington, J. C. Pupil entry and the human electroretinogram. *J. Opt. Soc. Am.*, 57, 838–39 (1967)

14. Auerbach, E., Wald, G. Identification of a violet receptor in human color vision. *Science*, 120, 401–5 (1954)

15. Baker, H. D. Single variable anomaloscope matches during recovery from artificial red blindness. *J. Opt. Soc. Am.*, 56, 686–89 (1966)

16. Baker, H. D., Rushton, W. A. H. An analytical anomaloscope. *J. Physiol. (London)*, 168, 31–33P (1963)

17. Baker, H. D., Rushton, W. A. H. The red-sensitive pigment in normal cones. *Ibid.*, 176, 56–72 (1965)

18. Barlow, H. B., Sparrock, J. M. B. The role of after-images in dark adaptation. *Science*, 144, 1309–14 (1964)

19. Beeler, G. W., Fender, D. H., Noble, P. S., Evans, C. R. Perception of pattern colour in the stabilized retinal image. *Nature*, 203, 1200 (1964)

20. Bernhard, C. G., Ed. *The Functional Organization of the Compound Eye* (Pergamon, London, 591 pp., 1966)

21. Biernson, G. A feedback-control model of human vision. *Proc. IEEE*, 54, 858–72 (1966)

22. Bird, G. R., Jones, R. C. Estimation of the spectral response functions of the human cone pigments. *J. Opt. Soc. Am.*, 55, 1686–91 (1965)

23. Bishop, P. O. Central nervous system: afferent mechanisms and perception. *Ann. Rev. Physiol.*, 29, 427–84 (1967)

24. Blakemore, C. B., Rushton, W. A. H. Dark adaptation and increment threshold in a rod monochromat. *J. Physiol. (London)*, 181, 612–28 (1965)

25. Blakemore, C. B., Rushton, W. A. H. The rod increment threshold during dark adaptation in normal and rod monochromat. *Ibid.*, 629–40 (1965)

26. Boettner, E. A., Wolter, J. R. Transmission of the ocular media. *Invest. Ophthalmol.*, 1, 776–83 (1962)

27. Bortoff, A. Localization of slow potential responses in the *Necturus* retina. *Vision Res.*, 4, 627–35 (1964)

28. Bortoff, A., Norton, A. L. Positive and negative potential responses associated with vertebrate photoreceptor cells. *Nature*, 206, 626–27 (1965)

29. Bortoff, A., Norton, A. L. An electrical model of the vertebrate photoreceptor cell. *Vision Res.*, 7, 253–63 (1967)

30. Boynton, R. M., Das, S. R., Gardiner, J. Interactions between photopic visual mechanisms revealed by mixing conditioning fields. *J. Opt.*

Soc. Am., **56**, 1775–80 (1966)

31. Boynton, R. M., Ikeda, M., Stiles, W. S. Interactions among chromatic mechanisms as inferred from positive and negative increment thresholds. *Vision Res.*, **4**, 87–117 (1964)

32. Brindley, G. S. The summation areas of human colour-receptive mechanisms at increment threshold. *J. Physiol. (London)*, **124**, 400–8 (1954)

33. Brindley, G. S. A photochemical reaction in the human retina. *Proc. Phys. Soc. B*, **68**, 862–70 (1955)

34. Brindley, G. S. *Physiology of the Retina and the Visual Pathway*, 144–50 (Edward Arnold Ltd., London, 298 pp., 1960)

35. Brindley, G. S., Du Croz, J. J., Rushton, W. A. H. The flicker fusion frequency of the blue-sensitive mechanism of colour vision. *J. Physiol. (London)*, **183**, 497–500 (1966)

36. Brindley, G. S., Gardner-Medwin, A. R. The origin of the early receptor potential of the retina. *J. Physiol. (London)*, **182**, 185–94 (1966)

37. Brindley, G. S., Rushton, W. A. H. The colour of monochromatic light when passed into the human retina from behind. *J. Physiol. (London)*, **147**, 204–8 (1959)

38. Brindley, G. S., Westheimer, G. The spatial properties of the human electroretinogram. *J. Physiol. (London)*, **179**, 518–37 (1965)

39. Brown, J. L., Ranken, H. B. Luminance, purity and wavelength matches of contrast colors. *Vision Res.*, **5**, 443–53 (1965)

40. Brown, K. T., Watanabe, K., Murakami, M. The early and late receptor potentials of monkey cones and rods. *Symp. Quant. Biol.*, **30**, 457–82 (1965)

41. Brown, P. K., Wald, G. Visual pigments in human and monkey retinas. *Nature*, **200**, 37–43 (1963)

42. Brown, P. K., Wald, G. Visual pigments in single rods and cones of the human retina. *Science*, **144**, 45–52 (1964)

43. Burkhardt, D. A. The goldfish electroretinogram : relation between photopic spectral sensitivity functions and cone absorption spectra. *Vision Res.*, **6**, 517–32 (1966)

44. Burkhardt, D. A., Whittle, P. Spectral sensitivity functions for homochromatic-contrast detection. *J. Opt. Soc. Am.*, **57**, 416–20 (1967)

45. Casperson, T. Ueber den Chemischen Aufbau der Strukturen des Zellkernes. *Skand. Arch. Physiol.*, **73**, Suppl. 8, 1–151 (1936)

46. Cone, R. A. The early receptor potential of the vertebrate eye. *Symp. Quant. Biol.*, **30**, 483–90 (1965)

47. Crawford, B. H. Colour matching and adaptation. *Vision Res.*, **5**, 71–78 (1965)

48. Crescitelli, F. The spectral sensitivity of the gecko eye in relation to the state of adaptation. *Vision Res.*, **6**, 129–42 (1966)

49. Crescitelli, F., Pollack, J. D. Color vision in the antelope ground squirrel. *Science*, **150**, 1316–18 (1965)

50. Dartnall, H. J. A. The interpretation of spectral sensitivity curves. *Brit. Med. Bull.*, **9**, 24–30 (1953)

51. Daw, N. W. Color coded units in the goldfish retina (Doctoral thesis, Johns Hopkins Univ., Baltimore, Md., 1967)

52. Denton, E. J. The contributions of the orientated photosensitive and other molecules to the absorption of whole retina. *Proc. Roy. Soc. B*, **150**, 78–94 (1959)

53. Denton, E. J., Wyllie, J. H. Study of the photosensitive pigments in the pink and green rods of the frog. *J. Physiol. (London)*, **127**, 81–89 (1955)

54. De Valois, R. L. Analysis and coding of color vision in the primate visual system. *Symp. Quant. Biol.*, **30**, 567–79 (1965)

55. De Valois, R. L. Behavioral and electrophysiological studies of primate vision. In *Contributions to Sensory Physiology*, **1**, 137–78 (Neff, W. D., Ed., Academic Press, New York and London, 274 pp., 1965)

56. De Valois, R. L., Abramov, I. Color vision. *Ann. Rev. Psychol.*, **17**, 337–62 (1966)

57. De Valois, R. L., Abramov, I., Jacobs, G. H. An analysis of response patterns of LGN cells. *J. Opt. Soc. Am.*, **56**, 966–77 (1966)

58. De Valois, R. L., Abramov, I., Mead, W. R. Single cell analysis of wavelength discrimination at the

lateral geniculate nucleus in the Macaque. *J. Neurophysiol.,* **30,** 415–33 (1967)

59. De Valois, R. L., Jacobs, G. H., Abramov, I. Responses of single cells in visual systems to shifts in the wavelength of light. *Science,* **146,** 1184–86 (1964)

60. De Valois, R. L., Walraven, J. Monocular and binocular aftereffects of chromatic adaptation. *Science,* **155,** 463–65 (1967)

61. de Vries, H. On the basic sensation curves of the three colour theory. *J. Opt. Soc. Am.,* **36,** 121–27 (1946)

62. Dowling, J. E. Foveal receptors of the monkey retina : fine structure. *Science,* **147,** 57–59 (1965)

63. Dowling, J. E. The site of visual adaptation. *Ibid.,* **155,** 273–79 (1967)

64. Du Croz, J. J., Rushton, W. A. H. The separation of cone mechanisms in dark adaptation. *J. Physiol. (London),* **183,** 481–96 (1966)

65. Easter, S. S., Jr. Excitation and adaptation in the goldfish's retina, a microelectrode study (Doctoral thesis, Johns Hopkins Univ., Baltimore, Md., 1967)

66. Enoch, J. M. Optical properties of the retinal receptors. *J. Opt. Soc. Am.,* **53,** 71–85 (1963)

67. Enoch, J. M. Retinal microspectrophotometry. *Ibid.,* **56,** 833–35 (1966)

68. Enoch, J. M., Stiles, W. S. The colour change of monochromatic light with retinal angle of incidence. *Opt. Acta,* **8,** 329–58 (1961)

69. Ercoles, A. M., Sulli, R. Red and blue "time constants" of the central fovea, determined on the basis of suprathreshold sensation of brightness. *Atti Fond. Giorgio Ronchi,* **20,** 550–62 (1965)

70. Falls, H. F., Wolter, J. R., Alpern, M. Typical total monochromacy. *Arch. Ophthalmol.,* **74,** 610–16 (1965)

71. Fry, G. A. Mechanisms subserving color vision. *Am. J. Optom.,* **42,** 271–87 (1965)

72. Fujimoto, K., Yanase, T., Hanaoka, T. Spectral transmittance of retinal colored oil globules re-examined with microspectrophotometer. *Japan. J. Physiol.,* **7,** 339–46 (1957)

73. Fuortes, M. G. F., Gunkel, R. D., Rushton, W. A. H. Increment thresholds in a subject deficient in cone vision. *J. Physiol. (London),* **156,** 179–92 (1961)

74. Fuortes, M. G. F., Hodgkin, A. L. Changes in time scale and sensitivity in the ommatidia of *Limulus. J. Physiol. (London),* **172,** 239–63 (1964)

75. Goguen, J. A., Jr. Color perception using a single cone type with distributed maximum sensitivity. *Bull. Math. Biophys.,* **26,** 121–38 (1964)

76. Gouras, P. Rod and cone independence in the electroretinogram of the dark-adapted monkey's perifovea. *J. Physiol. (London),* **187,** 455–64 (1966)

77. Gouras, P. The effects of light adaptation on rod and cone receptive field organization of monkey ganglion cells. *Ibid.* (In press 1967)

78. Gouras, P., Link, K. Rod and cone interaction in dark-adapted monkey ganglion cells. *J. Physiol. (London),* **184,** 499–510 (1966)

79. Graham, C. H., Hsia, Y. Color defect and color theory. *Science,* **127,** 675–82 (1958)

80. Guth, S. L. Luminance addition : general considerations and some results at foveal threshold. *J. Opt. Soc. Am.,* **55,** 718–22 (1965)

81. Guth, S. L. Nonadditivity and inhibition among chromatic luminances at threshold. *Vision Res.,* **7,** 319–28 (1967)

82. Hanaoka, T., Fujimoto, K. Absorption spectrum of a single cone in carp retina. *Japan. J. Physiol.,* **7,** 276–85 (1957)

83. Hurvich, L. M., Jameson, D. Visual processes in man and animals : introductory lecture. In *Recent Progress in Photobiology,* 91–114 (Blackwell Sci. Publ., Oxford, 400 pp., 1965)

84. Hurvich, L. M., Jameson, D. Theorie der Farbwahrnehmung. In *Handbuch der Psychologie,* **1,** S. 131–60 (Metzger, W., Herausgeber, Verlag Psychol., Göttingen, 1966)

85. Ikeda, H., Ripps, H. The electroretinogram of a cone-monochromat. *Arch. Ophthalmol.,* **75,** 513–17 (1966)

86. Jacobs, G. H. Single cells in squirrel monkey lateral geniculate nucleus with broad spectral sensitivity. *Vision Res.,* **4,** 221–32 (1964)

87. Jacobs, G. H., De Valois, R. L. Chromatic opponent cells in squir-

rel monkey lateral geniculate nucleus. *Nature,* **206,** 487–89 (1965)

88. Jacobson, M. Spectral sensitivity of single units in the optic tectum of the goldfish. *Quart. J. Exptl. Physiol.,* **49,** 384–93 (1964)

89. Johnson, E. P., Riggs, L. A., Schick, A. M. L. Photopic retinal potentials evoked by phase alternation of a barred pattern. In *Clinical Electroretinography,* 75–91 (Burian, H. M., Jacobson, J. H., Eds., Pergamon, London, 376 pp., 1966)

90. Judd, D. B. Relation between normal trichromatic vision and dichromatic vision. *Acta Chromatica,* **1,** 89–92 (1964)

91. Judd, D. B. Fundamental studies of color vision from 1860 to 1960. *Proc. Natl. Acad. Sci.,* **55,** 1313–30 (1966)

92. Kinney, J. A. S. Effect of exposure time on induced color. *J. Opt. Soc. Am.,* **55,** 731–36 (1965)

93. Kinney, J. A. S. Changes in appearance of colored stimuli with exposure duration. *Ibid.,* 738–39

94. Krauskopf, J., Srebro, R. Spectral sensitivity of color mechanisms: derivation from fluctuations of color appearance near threshold. *Science,* **150,** 1477–79 (1965)

95. Kuffler, S. W., Nicholls, J. G. The physiology of neuroglial cells. *Ergeb. Physiol.,* **57,** 1–90 (1966)

96. Lange, D., Hartline, H. K., Ratliff, F. The dynamics of lateral inhibition in the compound eye of Limulus II. In *The Functional Organization of the Compound Eye,* 425–49 (Bernhard, C. G., Ed., Pergamon, London, 591 pp., 1966)

97. Langer, H., Thorell, B. Microspectrophotometric assay of visual pigments in single rhabdomeres of the insect eye. In *The Functional Organization of the Compound Eye,* 145–49 (Bernhard, C. G., Ed., Pergamon, London, 591 pp., 1966)

98. Lee, G. B. Luminosity curve differences among subjects with normal color vision. *J. Opt. Soc. Am.,* **56,** 1451 (1966)

99. Lettvin, J. Y. Observations on color vision. In *Information Processing by Living Organisms and Machines,* 20–31 (Aeron. Systems Div., *ASD TDR 63-946,* 1964)

100. Liebman, P. A. In situ microspectrophotometric studies on the pig-

ments of single retinal rods. *Biophys. J.,* **2,** 161–78 (1962)

101. Liebman, P. A., Entine, G. Sensitive low-light-level microspectrophotometer: detection of photosensitive pigments of retinal cones. *J. Opt. Soc. Am.,* **54,** 1451–59 (1964)

102. MacNichol, E. F., Jr. Retinal processing of visual data. *Proc. Natl. Acad. Sci.,* **55,** 1331–44 (1966)

103. Marks, W. B. Visual pigments of single goldfish cones. *J. Physiol. (London),* **178,** 14–32 (1965)

104. Marks, W. B., Dobelle, W. H., MacNichol, E. F., Jr. Visual pigments of single primate cones. *Science,* **143,** 1181–83 (1964)

105. Michael, C. R. Receptive fields of opponent color units in the optic nerve of the ground squirrel. *Science,* **152,** 1095–97 (1966)

106. Motokawa, K., Yamashita, E., Ogawa, T. Studies on receptive fields of single units with colored lights. *Tohoku J. Exptl. Med.,* **71,** 261–72 (1960)

107. Munker, H. Subjektive Farberscheinungen bei der Wahrnehmung mehrfarbiger Doppelblitze und Rechteckgitter (Doctoral thesis, Univ. of Munich, Germany, 1966)

108. Naka, K. I., Kishida, K. Simultaneous recording of S and spike potentials from the fish retina. *Nature,* **214,** 1117–18 (1967)

109. Naka, K. I., Rushton, W. A. H. S-potentials from colour units in the retina of fish (cyprinidae). *J. Physiol. (London),* **185,** 536–55 (1966)

110. Naka, K. I., Rushton, W. A. H. An attempt to analyse colour reception by electrophysiology. *Ibid.,* 556–86

111. Naka, K. I., Rushton, W. A. H. S-potentials from luminosity units in the retina of fish (cyprinidae). *Ibid.,* 587–99

112. Nimeroff, I. Colorimetry in parafoveal fields—I. color matching functions. *J. Opt. Soc. Am.,* **54,** 824–32 (1964)

113. Nimeroff, I. Colorimetry in parafoveal fields—II. additivity failure. *Ibid.,* 833–38

114. Oyama, T., Hsia, Y. Compensatory hue shift in simultaneous color contrast as a function of separation between inducing and test fields. *J. Exptl. Psychol.,* **71,** 405–13 (1966)

115. Pak, W. L. Some properties of the

early electrical response in the vertebrate retina. *Symp. Quant. Biol.,* **30,** 493–99 (1965)

116. Pak, W. L., Ebrey, T. G. Early receptor potentials of rods and cones in rodents. *J. Gen. Physiol.,* **49,** 1199–1208 (1966)

117. Pickford, R. W. The genetics of colour blindness. *Brit. J. Physiol. Opt.,* **21,** 39–47 (1964)

118. Pickford, R. W. A deuteranomalous artist. *Brit. J. Psychol.,* **55,** 469–74 (1964)

119. Pirenne, M. H. On the problem of black. *J. Physiol. (London),* **185,** 64–65P (1966)

120. Pitt, F. H. G. Monochromatism. *Nature,* **154,** 466–68 (1944)

121. Raman, C. V. Floral colours and the physiology of vision. *Memoirs of the Raman Research Institute,* No. 137, 106 (Bangalore, India, 1963)

122. Ratliff, F. A transient nonuniformity in the appearance of a monochromatic field of illumination produced by a sudden change in wavelength. *J. Opt. Soc. Am.,* **55,** 1553–54 (1965)

123. Ratliff, F., Hartline, H. K., Lange, D. The dynamics of lateral inhibition in the compound eye of Limulus I. In *The Functional Organization of the Compound Eye,* 399–424 (Bernhard, C. G., Ed., Pergamon, London, 591 pp., 1966)

124. Richards, W., Luria, S. M. Color-mixture functions at low luminance levels. *Vision Res.,* **4,** 281–313 (1964)

125. Riggs, L. A. The "looks" of Helmholtz. *Perception and Psychophysics,* **2,** 1–13 (1967)

126. Riggs, L. A., Johnson, E. P., Schick, A. M. L. Electrical responses of the human eye to changes in wavelength of the stimulating light. *J. Opt. Soc. Am.,* **56,** 1621–27 (1966)

127. Ripps, H., Weale, R. A. Cone pigments in the normal human fovea. *Vision Res.,* **3,** 531–43 (1963)

128. Ripps, H., Weale, R. A. Photo-labile changes and the directional sensitivity of the human fovea. *J. Physiol. (London),* **173,** 57–64 (1964)

129. Rosenberg, B. A physical approach to the visual receptor process. *Advan. Radiation Biol.,* **2,** 193–241 (1966)

130. Ruddock, K. H. Integration processes in colour vision. *Tagungsband Luzern,* 215–24 (1965)

131. Ruddock, K. H. The effect of age upon color vision—I. response in the receptoral system of the human eye. *Vision Res.,* **5,** 37–45 (1965)

132. Ruddock, K. H. The effect of age upon colour vision—II. changes with age in light transmission of the ocular media. *Ibid.,* 47–58

133. Ruddock, K. H. Foveal and parafoveal color vision. *J. Opt. Soc. Am.,* **55,** 1180 (1965)

134. Rushton, W. A. H. A cone pigment in the protanope. *J. Physiol. (London),* **168,** 345–59 (1963)

135. Rushton, W. A. H. The density of chlorolabe in the foveal cones of the protanope. *Ibid.,* 360–73

136. Rushton, W. A. H. Cone pigment kinetics in the protanope. *Ibid.,* 374–88

137. Rushton, W. A. H. A foveal pigment in the deuteranope. *Ibid.,* **176,** 24–37 (1965)

138. Rushton, W. A. H. Cone pigment kinetics in the deuteranope. *Ibid.,* 38–45

139. Rushton, W. A. H. Stray light and the measurement of mixed pigments in the retina. *Ibid.,* 46–55

140. Rushton, W. A. H. The rod dark adaptation curve measured above cone threshold. *Ibid.,* **181,** 641–44 (1965)

141. Rushton, W. A. H. Bleached rhodopsin and visual adaptation. *Ibid.,* 645–55

142. Rushton, W. A. H. Discussion on human colour vision. In *Ciba Found. Symp. Colour Vision,* 246–47 (de Reuck, A. V. S., Knight, J., Eds., Little, Brown, Boston, Mass., 382 pp., 1965)

143. Rushton, W. A. H. The Ferrier Lecture: visual adaptation. *Proc. Roy. Soc. B,* **162,** 20–46 (1965)

144. Rushton, W. A. H., Baker, H. D. Red/green sensitivity in normal vision. *Vision Res.,* **4,** 75–85 (1964)

145. Shipley, T. Rod-cone duplexity and the autonomic action of light. *Vision Res.,* **4,** 155–77 (1964)

146. Shurcliff, W. A. New visual phenomenon: the greenish-yellow blotch. *J. Opt. Soc. Am.,* **49,** 1041–48 (1959)

147. Sidley, N. A., Sperling, H. G. Photopic spectral sensitivity in rhesus monkey. *J. Opt. Soc. Am.,* **57,** 816–88 (1967)

148. Siegel, I. M., Graham, C. H., Ripps,

H., Hsia, Y. Analysis of photopic and scotopic function in an incomplete achromat. *J. Opt. Soc. Am.,* **56,** 699–704 (1966)

149. Siegel, M. H. Discrimination of color. IV. sensitivity as a function of spectral wavelength 410 through 500 mμ. *J. Opt. Soc. Am.,* **54,** 821–23 (1964)

150. Smirnov, M. S., Bongard, M. M. Hypothesis concerning the mechanism of photoreception in the retina (an analogy between retinal photoreceptors and semiconducting photoelements). *Biophysics,* **4,** No. 2, 57–63 (1959)

151. Sperling, H. G., Jolliffe, C. L. Chromatic response mechanisms in the human fovea as measured by threshold spectral sensitivity. *Science,* **136,** 317–18 (1962)

152. Sperling, H. G., Tryon, W. G., Jolliffe, C. L. The effects of adaptation to intense metameric yellow lights on the spectral sensitivity of the fovea (Honeywell Mil. Prod. Group Res. Dept., Minneapolis, Minn., *Rept. R-RD 6307,* 8 pp., 1963)

153. Spivey, B. E. The X-linked recessive inheritance of atypical monochromatism. *Arch. Ophthalmol.,* **74,** 327–33 (1965)

154. Stiles, W. S. The determination of the spectral sensitivities of the retinal mechanisms by sensory methods. *Ned. Tijdschr. Natuurk.,* **15,** 125–46 (1949)

155. Stiles, W. S. Color vision: the approach through increment threshold sensitivity. *Proc. Natl. Acad. Sci.,* **45,** 100–14 (1959)

156. Stiles, W. S. Foveal threshold sensitivity on fields of different colors. *Science,* **145,** 1016–17 (1964)

157. Strother, G. K. Absorption spectra of retinal oil globules in turkey, turtle, and pigeon. *Exptl. Cell Res.,* **29,** 349–55 (1963)

158. Svaetichin, G., MacNichol, E. F., Jr. Retinal mechanisms for chromatic and achromatic vision. *Ann. N. Y. Acad. Sci.,* **74,** 385–404 (1958)

159. Tomita, T. Mechanisms subserving color coding in the vertebrate retina (Abstr. II, C III.1, Intern. Biophys. Meeting, Paris-Orsay, 1964)

160. Tomita, T. Electrophysiological study of the mechanisms subserving color coding in the fish retina. *Symp.* *Quant. Biol.,* **30,** 559–66 (1965)

161. Toraldo di Francia, G. Retina cones as dielectric antennas. *J. Opt. Soc. Am.,* **39,** 324 (1949)

162. Van Nes, F. L., Bouman, M. A. Spatial modulation transfer in the human eye. *J. Opt. Soc. Am.,* **57,** 401–6 (1967)

163. Verriest, G., Seki, R. Les chromaticites des couleurs subjectives suscitées par la rotation du disque de Fechner-Benham. *Rev. Opt.,* **43,** 53–63 (1964)

164. Villermet, G. M., Weale, R. A. The biomicroscopy of the living frog retina. *J. Roy. Microscop. Soc.,* **84,** 565–69 (1965)

165. Wagner, H. G., MacNichol, E. F., Jr., Wolbarsht, M. L. Functional basis for "on"-center and "off"-center receptive fields in the retina. *J. Opt. Soc. Am.,* **53,** 66–70 (1963)

166. Wald, G. The receptors of human color vision. *Science,* **145,** 1007–16 (1964)

167. Wald, G. Receptor mechanisms in human vision. *Proc. Intern. Congr. Physiol. Sci., 23rd, Tokyo,* **4,** 69–79 (*Excerpta Med. Found.* 87, 1965)

168. Wald, G. Defective color vision and its inheritance. *Proc. Natl. Acad. Sci.,* **55,** 1347–63 (1966)

169. Wald, G., Brown, P. K. Human color vision and color blindness. *Symp. Quant. Biol.,* **30,** 345–61 (1965)

170. Wald, G., Brown, P. K., Smith, P. H. Iodopsin. *J. Gen. Physiol.,* **38,** 623–81 (1955)

171. Walls, G. L. *The Vertebrate Eye,* 191–205 (Cranbrook Inst. of Sci., Bloomfield Hills, Mich., 785 pp., 1942)

172. Walls, G. L. Notes on four tritanopes. *Vision Res.,* **4,** 3–16 (1964)

173. Walraven, P. L. *On the Mechanisms of Colour Vision* (Inst. for Perception RVO-TNO, Soesterberg, Netherlands, 94 pp., 1962)

174. Walraven, P. L., Leebeek, H. J. Phase shift of sinusoidally alternating colored stimuli. *J. Opt. Soc. Am.,* **54,** 78–82 (1964)

175. Wasserman, G. S. Brightness enhancement and opponent-colors theory. *Vision Res.,* **6,** 689–99 (1966)

176. Weale, R. A. Cone-monochromatism. *J. Physiol. (London),* **121,** 548–69 (1953)

177. Weale, R. A. Photo-sensitive reactions in foveae of normal and cone monochromatic observers. *Opt. Acta,* **6,** 158–74 (1959)

178. Wiesel, T. N., Hubel, D. H. Spatial and chromatic interactions in the lateral geniculate body of the rhesus monkey. *J. Neurophysiol.,* **29,** 1115–56 (1966)

179. Witkovsky, P. The spectral sensitivity of retinal ganglion cells in the carp. *Vision Res.,* **5,** 603–14 (1965)

180. Witkovsky, P. A comparison of ganglion cell and S-potential response properties in carp retina. *J. Neurophysiol.,* **30,** 546–61 (1967)

NERVOUS SYSTEM: AFFERENT MECHANISMS[1]

By Jay M. Goldberg[2] and Robert A. Lavine[3]

Department of Physiology, University of Chicago
Chicago, Illinois

Introduction

The first part of this review surveys the progress made during the last five years in the study of receptor physiology. Emphasis will be placed on the mechanisms of receptor action, on the site of initiation of the nerve impulse, and on the processes governing the discharge of the sensory axon. The physiology of the auditory, visual, and somesthetic pathways will next be considered; Bishop's recent review of these subjects (1) permits us to concentrate on studies published during 1966 and early 1967. Attention will be focused on the ways in which the information contained in sensory signals is coded in first-order neurons and is then modified at successive levels of each sensory system. No survey was made of the literature on the chemical senses; a number of reviews may be recommended (2-6).

Noteworthy among the monographs published in the past two years are the Cold Spring Harbor Symposium on *Sensory Receptors* (7), the Ciba Symposium on *Touch, Heat and Pain* (8), and the volume on *Sensory Mechanisms* (9) edited by Zotterman. Hensel (10) integrates findings from physiology, anatomy, and psychophysics in his comprehensive textbook on somesthesis and the chemical senses. Duncan (11) treats the physiology of sensory receptors within the broader context of the properties of excitable tissue.

Receptor Physiology and the Mechanisms of Repetitive Discharge

Receptor potential.—The dependence of the receptor potential upon the external concentration of sodium ions was first demonstrated by Diamond et al. (12) in the Pacinian corpuscle and confirmed by Edwards et al. (13) in the crustacean stretch receptor and by Ottoson (14) and Calma (15) in the amphibian muscle spindle. The effects of bathing the receptor in a sodium-free medium are reminiscent of those described at the neuromuscular junction (16) in that the receptor potential is not completely abolished but declines to 90 per cent of its original value in the Pacinian corpuscle and 70–80 per cent in the muscle spindle. This observation led Diamond et al. (12) and Ottoson (14) to suggest that a relatively nonspecific increase in

[1] Preparation of the manuscript was aided by grant NB-05237, National Institutes of Health.

[2] Supported by a Career Development Award, National Institutes of Health.

[3] Public Health Services Predoctoral Research Fellow.

ionic permeability, similar to that seen at the endplate (16, 17), underlies the generation of the receptor potential. Calma (15) adds the cautionary note that there may not be a complete equilibration between the test solutions and the fluid surrounding the sensory ending.

If the permeability changes occurring at the sensory ending and the neuromuscular junction are similar in nature, then it might be expected that the receptor potential and the endplate potential would be affected in the same way by pharmacological and other agents. One agent of interest is tetrodotoxin, which abolishes the sodium conductance changes associated with the action potential (18, 19) without affecting endplate potentials (20–23). Loewenstein et al. (24) reported that, in both the crustacean stretch receptor and the Pacinian corpuscle, introduction of tetrodotoxin promptly blocked impulse activity without affecting the receptor potential; the authors concluded that the action potential and the receptor potential were independent events subserved by different mechanisms. Somewhat different observations were made by Nishi & Sato (25), who found that, while tetrodotoxin had little immediate effect on the receptor potential of the Pacinian corpuscle, prolonged exposure caused a reduction in the potential to about 40 per cent of its control value. The concentration used was the minimal needed to block action potentials.

Nishi & Sato (25) point out that the effects of tetrodotoxin on the receptor potential are less striking than its effects on impulse activity. Moreover, the neurotoxin does not reduce the receptor potential as much as does sodium depletion. The reasons for these differences are not clear, but the results are consistent with the possibility that the receptor potential and the action potential share a common mechanism. This possibility must also be given serious consideration in view of the evidence (see below) that the sensory ending not only gives rise to the receptor potential, but may also be the site of initiation of the propagated action potential. A rigorous discussion of mechanisms would require knowledge of the molecular basis of the receptor and action potentials which we do not possess. Nevertheless, a pertinent question may be raised. To what extent and under what circumstances can the nonspecialized portion of an axon be made to behave like a receptor terminal?

Many nonspecialized axons (26–28), as well as some mechanoreceptors (29–32), respond to small temperature changes. Mechanical stimuli can act in an excitatory manner in myelinated nerve fibers (33, 34). The study by Julian & Goldman (34) of the response of lobster giant axons to brief mechanical compressions is of particular interest. Such stimuli resulted in a depolarizing potential which developed immediately and then took several seconds to return to the baseline. The long time-course of the potential was related to the time required for the axon to recover its cylindrical shape. Correlated with the potential change was an increase in transmembrane conductance which could be demonstrated even when the potential variation was minimized. The response of the axon could be greatly diminished, but not abolished in a sodium-free medium, an observation quite analogous to those made in sensory receptors. Finally, the response could be abolished by procaine. Julian & Goldman suggest as a basis of their findings and also as a possible mechanism of receptor action that compression causes a stretching of the membrane and a consequent separation of molecular elements, perhaps in specialized regions. This process would be expected to increase membrane conductance.

Site of impulse initiation.—The generalization that the receptor potential and the propagated action potential originated in different portions of the sensory neuron was mainly based on studies of the Pacinian corpuscle and the crustacean stretch receptor. In the Pacinian corpuscle (35–37) evidence was presented that the graded activity arose from the nonmyelinated terminal, whereas the propagated impulse was initiated at the first node of Ranvier. Hunt & Takeuchi (38) were the first to demonstrate that both orthodromic and antidromic action potentials could propagate in the terminal portion of the corpuscle. Ozeki & Sato (39) confirmed and extended these observations. Microelectrodes were used to penetrate the central core of endings in which the outer lamellae were removed. The potentials elicited by either mechanical or antidromic stimulation were triphasic—positive-negative-positive—which suggests propagation of activity. When the ending was penetrated by two electrodes, antidromic activity appeared first at the proximal and then at the distal electrode. The conduction velocity determined by this means was approximately 1.6 m/sec, a figure consistent with that of unmyelinated nerve fibers (40), but considerably lower than the value obtained by Hunt & Takeuchi (38).

Loewenstein (41, 42) has raised an objection to the conclusions of Hunt & Takeuchi (38) and of Ozeki & Sato (39), basing his reservations on the fact that the space constant of the ending is unknown. More particularly, Loewenstein has suggested that the lamellae of the central core provide a high transverse resistance between the electrode and the terminal, whereas the fluid between lamellae may present a low-resistance pathway to the first node. This notion is difficult to reconcile with the fact that in the study of Ozeki & Sato (39) the negative component of the triphasic potential grew appreciably in amplitude as the electrode was being advanced towards the ending. Sato & Ozeki (43) also made a number of observations on the interactions of the action potential and the receptor potential which support the idea that action potentials are propagated in the nonmyelinated terminal. Only one of these will be cited. An antidromic impulse will normally cause a depression of a receptor potential elicited a few milliseconds later. If the terminal—which has been separated from the first node by a saline-oil interface—is cooled or placed in a sodium-free medium, such a depression is not evident, presumably because of a block of conduction of the antidromic impulse.

The work of Edwards & Ottoson (44) established that, in the crustacean stretch receptor, the action potential is initiated in the axon and only then invades the soma and dendrites. Washizu & Terzuolo (45) and Grampp (46) have studied the antidromic propagation of the impulse and confirm earlier studies that the conducted activity propagates into dendrites, but does not reach their terminal portions. The mode of initiation of impulses in insect chemoreceptors is similar to that in the crustacean stretch receptor (47). Quite a different situation is described by Mellon & Kennedy (48) in bipolar tactile receptors of crayfish. Here it would appear that the action potentials evoked by natural stimulation arise in the dendrite. Two observations lead to this conclusion. Firstly, the impulses recorded from the soma are not preceded by a graded generator potential and, secondly, the impulses elicited by natural stimulation and by electrical stimulation of the dendrite resemble one another and may differ considerably in form from antidromically conducted spikes. Other invertebrate receptors in which propagated activity may be initiated in dendrites have been described by Mendelson (49, 50) and by Larimer & Kennedy (51).

Mechanical events involved in sensory adaptation.—A question of some interest is the extent to which the mechanical properties of a receptor determine the time-course of sensory adaptation. Lippold et al. (52) presented evidence that in the mammalian muscle spindle, mechanical factors were of prime importance. A similar conclusion would seem warranted in the case of the Pacinian corpuscle. In the intact corpuscle, the response to a maintained compression consists of a brief depolarization at the onset of stimulaton and a similar potential—the so-called "off-response"—when the stimulus is removed (53, 54). If the corpuscle is stripped to its central core, however, such a compression leads to a maintained receptor potential similar to that seen in slowly adapting endings (55, 56). Hence, it would appear that the intact corpuscle acts as a high-frequency filter, a conclusion consistent with the observations of Hubbard (57). There is also evidence that the accommodation of the nerve fiber may contribute to adaptive properties of the Pacinian corpuscle. Thus, the nerve responds to a prolonged receptor potential with at most a few spikes (55, 56) and behaves similarly when stimulated by direct currents (55, 58).

Loewenstein & Skalak (59) have developed a linear model of the Pacinian corpuscle which takes into account the compliance of the lamellae and of the interconnections between lamellae as well as the viscosity of the interlamellar fluid. The model satisfactorily accounts for the filter characteristics of the capsule. The off-response is also explained. When compression is removed, the energy stored in the elastic elements is released and results in a pressure wave whose direction is 90° from that of the original compression. Since the ending is not directionally sensitive, a depolarizing potential would result. Somewhat simpler models have been developed by Catton & Petoe (60, 61) to account for the adaptive properties of mechanoreceptors of the frog skin and by Toyama (62) to explain some of the characteristics of the amphibian stretch receptor. Brown & Stein (63) present a descriptive model of the input-output relations in the slowly adapting crustacean stretch receptor.

Eyzaguirre & Kuffler (64) suggested that the differences in the behavior of the slowly and rapidly adapting crustacean stretch receptors were of mechanical origin. Later evidence leads to the conclusion that differences in the electrical properties of the cells are of greater importance. Krnjević & van Gelder (65) found that the two receptors differed only slightly in their mechanical properties. They also reported that the rates of adaptation of individual receptors in response to d.c. stimulation paralleled the time-course of adaptation observed with stretch, an observation confirmed by Nakajima (66). The latter, in addition, found that the rates of decline of the receptor potentials recorded from the two types of cells were similar.

Repetitive discharge.—It is now well established that, in many sensory receptors, there is an approximately linear relation between the magnitude of the receptor potential and the frequency of discharge (67–72). A partial theoretical explanation of this relation is offered by Agin (73) and Stein (74), who studied the behavior of the Hodgkin-Huxley equations under constant current conditions. It was found that discharge rate was logarithmically related to current density. The slope of the relation was quite steep when currents approached threshold. Indeed, Stein (74) states that he was unable to obtain maintained activity at rates less than 50/sec. For rates above this value, a linear relation between discharge frequency and transmembrane potential could be derived, provided that the conductance changes produced by depolarizing currents were taken into account. Another feature of the calculations is that with strong depolarizing currents the action potentials become smaller and eventually repetitive activity is blocked.

The equations would appear to describe the repetitive activity obtained in response to constant currents in giant squid axons (75, 76) and in large crustacean motor fibers (77, 78). However, in some sensory neurons (70, 79, 80) and in Class I crab axons (75, 81), there is no minimal rate of maintained discharge. Moreover, in many preparations (70, 75, 79–85) the relation between impulse frequency and current strength, over a wide range of discharge rates, is linear rather than logarithmic. Whether these discrepancies mean that the equations would have to be extensively modified in order to account for repetitive activity is not clear. It should, nevertheless, be pointed out that the mechanisms governing the timing of repetitive discharges may vary from one neuron to another (67, 75, 81, 86). Given this fact, the development of a general quantitative theory of repetitive activity would appear to be a most challenging undertaking.

The Hodgkin-Huxley equations predict that constant current pulses will result in a repetitive train of impulses showing no decrement in rate as the stimulus is prolonged (74, 87). Again, there is some experimental verification of this prediction in the squid axon (75, 76). Most neurons, however, do adapt in response to constant currents (66, 70, 75, 79, 80, 83, 85, 88). In an attempt to analyze the mechanisms of adaptation, workers have used classical terms such as accommodation and increased refractoriness (75, 79). Such a treatment is of limited usefulness since it gives little insight into the long-term processes responsible for adaptation.

One such long-term process which has been studied in some detail is the accumulation of sodium and potassium ions during prolonged activity (89–91). In both myelinated and unmyelinated axons (92–95), repetitive activity may result in a prolonged hyperpolarizing afterpotential. Ritchie & Straub (93) presented a great deal of evidence that the potential is related to the active transport of potassium ions, sodium ions, or both; it was found that the afterpotential was abolished in potassium-free solutions, when metabolic poisons were introduced, or when external sodium was replaced by lithium. Similar observations were made by Nakajima & Takahashi (95) on the crustacean stretch receptor. In addition, the latter workers observed that the afterpotential was not correlated with any obvious conductance change, nor did it appear to have an equilibrium potential; they interpret their data as indicating that the afterpotential is due to a so-called electrogenic pump.

An observation made by Nakajima & Takahashi (95) clearly points to a relation between the hyperpolarizing afterpotential and sensory adaptation. In spontaneously active neurons, there was a decrease in discharge rate following tetanic stimulation and this decrease was correlated with the time-course of the afterpotential. Such a decrease in discharge rate following stimulation is a prominent manifestation of adaptation in both peripheral and central neurons (64, 67, 96).

AUDITORY SYSTEM

Eighth nerve.—Two recent publications have served to clarify problems related to the physiology of primary auditory neurons. The first is a monograph by Kiang et al. (97), which summarizes their previous work in the cat (98, 99) and also provides much new data. The second is a set of two papers by Rose, Hind and their colleagues (100, 101) dealing with the discharge of eighth nerve fibers in the monkey. Both groups of workers agree that any given fiber responds to only a limited band of frequencies. The tuning curves presented by Kiang et al. (97, 99) are, in most respects, similar to those seen in central auditory neurons.

Kiang et al. (97) devote a good deal of attention to the response of primary auditory neurons to clicks. The poststimulus histogram was used to study discharge patterns. Many of the results can be understood in terms of the mechanical properties of the cochlear partition (102). Thus, the latent period of discharge to clicks is systemically related to the best frequency of the fiber. Units with best frequencies greater than 2000 cps discharge synchronously and with short latent periods, whereas the latent periods of neurons with lower best frequencies are longer and somewhat dispersed (see also 103). The span of discharge times is consistent with the time needed by the traveling wave to run from the basal to the apical turns of the cochlea (102). Kiang et al. (97) also found that the histograms obtained from fibers with best frequencies less than 5000 cps were multimodal, the time between peaks being equal to the period of the best frequency. This finding may be explained in terms of the resonant properties of the cochlear partition. Any point on the partition, when stimulated with a short impulse, should respond with a sequence of damped oscillations at the characteristic frequency of the point. Weiss (104) has described a model which incorporates many of the observations of Kiang et al. (97).

Auditory neurons may preferentially discharge during a limited portion of a low-frequency sinusoid (97, 105–108). Rose et al. (100) have studied this phase-locking or frequency-following in detail. All primary neurons studied were phase-locked for tones up to 5000 cps. The interspike-interval distributions resulting from low-frequency stimulation are polymodal, the peaks occurring at integral multiples of the period of the sine wave. Rose et al. also consider the related discrete distributions which plot the probability of discharge during successive cycles. The histograms obtained are best described as geometric distributions with a dead-time of 1 msec, the latter figure presumably reflecting the fibers' refractory period. Most fibers do not discharge with every cycle, even when tones less than 500 cps are used. Given this fact and also the short refractory period, Rose et al. suggest that the probabilistic mechanisms determining when the neuron will discharge lie peripheral to the parent fiber.

The question arises as to how information concerning the periodicity of tonal stimuli is utilized by higher centers. Two facts may be stated in this context. First, frequency-following provides a means for the coding of information pertaining to phase and such information is a prerequisite for the binaural localization of low-frequency tones (109). Second, there are psychophysical experiments which indicate that the pitch of a complex sound may be determined by its periodicity as well as its spectral content (110).

The possibility that there are inhibitory mechanisms in the cochlea—other than those ascribable to olivocochlear fibers—has been explored in a number of studies. The most common finding (97, 101, 108, 111) is that the presentation of an excitatory stimulus, usually near the edge of the fiber's response area, may cause a reduction in the number of spikes produced by a more effective stimulus near best frequency. Hind et al. (101) state that the number of impulses that result when two tones are presented simultaneously is seldom larger than that in response to the more effective stimulus or less than that in response to the less effective stimulus. Other workers (97, 108, 111), however, have observed that the discharge rate elicited by a two-tone combination may be reduced from that evoked by either tone itself. Whatever be the mechanisms of this effect—the possibility of mechanical interference comes to mind—the suppression does not appear to involve neural inhibition since the suppressing tone is itself excitatory when presented alone. There have been a few descriptions (106, 107) of single tones suppressing spontaneous activity. Such observations would strongly suggest an inhibitory phenomenon. Neither Kiang et al. (97) nor Hind et al. (101) have confirmed these findings.

The results presented in the preceding paragraph are obviously related to the phenomenon of auditory masking. Classically, masking was explained as a "line busy" effect (112). The masked stimulus was assumed less effective because the masking stimulus rendered many fibers refractory. This notion is not supported by recent studies. Thus, a relatively ineffective excitatory stimulus of high intensity may mask a more effective stimulus and the discharge rate may be lower than that produced by the masked stimulus when presented alone (97, 101). Another aspect of masking is the change in the temporal discharge patterns resulting from the introduction of the masking stimulus. Hind et al. (101) found, for example, that when two low-frequency tones were presented simultaneously, the firing of primary neurons could be phase-locked to the first tone, the second tone, or both tones. The discharge pattern and firing rate were both functions of the relative intensities of the component stimuli, a conclusion similar to that of Goldberg & Greenwood (113), who described the response of cochlear nucleus neurons to noise-tone combinations. Kiang et al. (97) have studied the masking of transient stimuli by steady noise in primary neurons. Here adaptation as well as other factors may be involved. Finally, the presence of inhibitory response areas in central auditory neurons also must be considered in any physiological explanation of masking (113, 114).

In anatomical studies of the innervation of the organ of Corti, the inner hair cells are described as being innervated primarily by radial fibers, the outer hair cells by spiral fibers (115, 116). Some workers (105, 106, 108, 117) have, on this basis, looked for two populations of single units within the auditory nerve. Kiang and his co-workers (97) review these studies in the light of their own observations and come to the conclusion that, at present, there are no clear-cut physiological criteria for dividing primary neurons into two groups. They also point out that there are a number of unsolved anatomical problems to be considered. These include the relative numbers of spiral and radial fibers and the possibility of transitional types of innervation. Perhaps the most important and most difficult questions to answer are whether single spiral ganglion cells can innervate both inner and outer hair cells and can give rise to both radial and spiral fibers.

The olivocochlear fibers supply a rich efferent innervation to hair cells and eighth nerve endings (118-122). Stimulation of the olivocochlear fibers in the medulla results in a depression of the response of eighth nerve fibers and an augmentation of the cochlear microphonic (123–128). Both effects are abolished by strychnine (126–129). The augmentation of the microphonic has been ascribed to a postsynaptic inhibition of hair cells, and the decrease in responsiveness of auditory fibers to a similar process occurring in the nerve endings (130). A more recent suggestion is that the diminution in the neural response is a direct consequence of hair cell inhibition (131).

Galambos (123) originally observed that high-frequency stimulation of the olivocochlear bundle was required to produce a significant decrease in the gross neural response. Desmedt and his co-workers (125, 127, 128) quantified the effects of such stimulation. It was found that the greatest effect was obtained by trains of shocks delivered at 400/sec. Stimulation at 50/sec had little, if any, influence. The decrease in the neural response could be expressed as equivalent to a reduction of the intensity of the test stimulus. When so expressed, the maximum change in the neural response —that obtained by high-frequency stimulation of the crossed olivocochlear tract in the cat—was −25 db. These results pose a problem when considered in the light of Fex' microelectrode studies (126, 132). Fex described the response to afferent stimulation of both crossed and uncrossed olivocochlear fibers. The units were characterized by a low and regular discharge rate without a burst of discharges at the onset of afferent stimulation. Discharge rates in excess of 50 spikes/sec were seldom observed. Fex points out that if his observations are representative, then the physiological influence of the olivocochlear fibers, in terms of equivalent sound reduction, must be quite small. The efferent fibers may, nevertheless, exert an important control on primary fibers. Of interest in this regard are the observations that the effects of efferent stimulation are a function of the parameters of the auditory stimulus (133, 134) and may vary from one primary auditory nerve fiber to another (135).

Cochlear nuclei.—Recent studies (97, 100, 101) have emphasized the basic similarity in the discharge characteristics of primary neurons. The behavior of second-order cells is somewhat more complex, and profound transformations of the information transmitted by the auditory nerve take place within the cochlear complex.

One basis of these transformations is the presence of inhibitory response areas in cochlear nucleus neurons (114, 136–138), response areas which are not seen in primary fibers (97, 101). Most second-order neurons are characterized by a central excitatory area flanked by inhibitory areas. One of the supposed functions of these inhibitory areas is to sharpen the excitatory response areas of central neurons (117, 138). The fact that the tuning curves for first- and second-order neurons are quite similar (99) detracts from this notion. There are, nevertheless, many discharge characteristics of cochlear nucleus neurons which depend upon the presence of inhibitory areas. Greenwood & Maruyama (114) found that, while a neuron will respond to a narrow band of noise centered at best frequency, widening of the band so that it encompasses the inhibitory areas may lead to a cessation of discharge. Evans & Nelson (139) point out that the temporal contrast in the response to a frequency-modulated tone may be enhanced as the stimulus moves across the boundary between an inhibitory and an excitatory area. Greenwood & Maruyama (114) and Pfeiffer (140) have described the discharge patterns of cochlear nucleus neurons to tone bursts. Many neurons respond in a relatively simple way, reminiscent of primary neurons. Others exhibit discharge patterns characterized by onset responses or silent pauses in firing. Such cells, located for the most part in the dorsal cochlear nucleus, may also display complicated relations between discharge rate and stimulus intensity. Greenwood & Maruyama (114) view these complications as indicating that the relation between inhibitory and excitatory areas may depend upon time as well as other stimulus parameters.

Another transformation that takes place in the cochlear complex involves the patterns of steady-state discharge. Pfeiffer & Kiang (141) and Goldberg & Greenwood (113) studied the interspike-interval distributions of cochlear nucleus neurons. They found that some neurons were characterized by interval distributions which were exponential in shape and, thus, similar to those seen in primary fibers (97). Many other secondary neurons were characterized by distributions which were markedly nonexponential, the distributions reflecting a more or less regular discharge pattern not seen more peripherally. The functional significance of these variations in steady-state firing patterns is, at present, obscure. One possibility is that neurons exhibiting different discharge patterns handle different aspects of the sensory-coding process. What is required is a study of how various neurons respond to a wide variety of signals, including modulated stimuli as well as pure tones.

The cochlear complex is one of the more complicated nuclear regions in the brain (142–144). Anatomical studies (145, 146) indicate that the various parts of the complex differ in their ascending projections. It might be supposed, on this basis, that neurons in the different regions would possess a variety of discharge characteristics. Kiang, Pfeiffer, Koerber et al. (140, 141, 147, 148) have undertaken a systematic study of this problem. One of their more interesting observations (148) is that section of the eighth nerve abolishes the spontaneous activity seen in the ventral cochlear nuclei, but not that seen in the dorsal cochlear nucleus.

Superior olivary complex.—The superior olivary complex is the lowest level of the auditory system in which ascending fibers related to the two ears converge. Physiological studies have demonstrated that there are cells within the medial superior olive and other nuclei of the complex which are sensitive to the various cues used in binaural sound localization, including differences in the time of arrival and intensity of clicks presented to the two ears (150–153) and also differences in the interaural intensity and phase of continuous stimuli (154, 155). It is not surprising, therefore, that the complex has been thought to play a critical role in the mechanisms of binaural hearing (109). Behavioral studies support this view (156, 157). Masterton et al. (157) investigated the effects of lesions of the complex on the discrimination of the time of arrival of dichotically presented clicks. It was found that normal cats can respond to binaural time separations as low as 50 μsec. After complete section of the trapezoid body, animals can still make the discrimination, but the threshold is elevated to 500 μsec, a value larger than that which can occur under free-field conditions. Masterton et al. point out that the deficit obtained with trapezoid body lesions is less severe than that following removal of auditory cortex (158, 159) and they conclude that, while the superior olive is important for normal sound localization, it is the cortex which is responsible for the integration of sounds into an organized perceptual space.

Anatomical studies have demonstrated that each of the nuclei of the superior olive has a particular pattern of afferent innervation (145, 146, 160, 161). Recent physiological studies bear on this problem. Tsuchitani & Boudreau (162) studied the discharge characteristics of neurons of the lateral superior olivary nucleus. These cells responded in a tonic fashion to ipsilateral ear stimulation; some of the cells were also inhibited by contralateral stimuli (see also 163). In addition, a precise tonotopic organization of the nucleus was demonstrated. Goldberg & Brown (155) described the types of binaural interaction seen in the medial superior olive of the dog. Almost all of the cells encountered were binaural. Of these, three quarters received a convergent excitatory input from the two ears. The remainder were activated by stimulation of one ear—usually the contralateral ear—and inhibited by stimulation of the other ear.

There have been a number of descriptions of medial superior olivary neurons which are sensitive to differences in the time of arrival of clicks presented to the two ears. Such cells receive an excitatory input from one ear and an inhibitory input from the other. Perhaps the most systematic study of these cells was that of Hall (152), who demonstrated that such cells are also sensitive to interaural intensity differences and exhibit time-intensity trading analogous in some respects to that observed in psychophysical experiments. Rupert et al. (153) extended these observations by showing that the latent period could be affected in a systematic way by the interplay of excitatory and inhibitory connections from the two ears. The manner in which cells receiving convergent excitatory inputs respond to clicks was also described. In the latter neurons, stimulation of one ear usually depressed the response to a later stimulus delivered to the other ear, the depression lasting on the order of 10 msec.

Inferior colliculus.—Microelectrode studies of the inferior colliculus (164–168) have demonstrated that the discharge of neurons is governed by a complex interplay of excitatory and inhibitory processes. A similar situation is described by Potter (169) in the midbrain of the bullfrog. Rose et al. (170) emphasize the importance of such interactions in determining the response of collicular neurons to binaural stimuli. Neurons were found to be exquisitely sensitive to changes in the interaural phase relationships of low-frequency tones. The results could best be interpreted by assuming that stimuli delivered to each ear produced periodic excitatory-inhibitory events. Thus, two stimuli—each of which had a net excitatory effect when presented alone—could, when presented binaurally, cause either facilitation or inhibition, the type of response depending upon interaural delay. Direct evidence for the periodic nature of the processes was obtained by showing that, in many of the phase-sensitive cells, the discharge was phase-locked to low-frequency tones presented to either ear. Rose et al. (170) also describe neurons which are sensitive to small interaural intensity differences, such as might arise when a high-frequency sound source was moved in space. These cells, which resemble single units seen in the superior olive (150–153, 155), are usually activated by stimulation of the contralateral ear and inhibited by stimulation of the ipsilateral ear.

Cells which are sensitive to the location of sound sources have similarly been seen in the inferior colliculus of the bat (171, 172). Bats emit a frequency-modulated cry and locate objects by extracting information from the resulting echo. Grinnell & Grinnell (173), on the basis of evoked potential studies in the colliculus, suggest that localization is accomplished by a binaural comparison of the several frequency components contained in the echo.

Nelson et al. (174) studied the response of colliculus neurons to amplitude- and frequency-modulated tones. The temporal discharge pattern was dependent upon the depth and rate of modulation. In many cells there was a direct relation between the modulated stimulus and firing density, independent of the direction of modulation. Other cells were directionally sensitive, an observation recalling those of Suga (168, 175, 176) and of Whitfield & Evans (177). Most of the units observed by Nelson et al. (174) responded to both frequency- and amplitude-modulated signals, but some were activated preferentially by one or the other type of stimulus. An attempt was made to explain the responses to modulated signals in terms of the response to pure tones. Most of the results could be interpreted in this way, provided that the time-courses of both the excitatory and inhibitory processes impinging upon the cell were taken into account. Suga (168, 175, 176) came to a similar conclusion from his studies of frequency modulation in auditory neurons of the bat.

The generalized myoclonic reactions observed in response to a wide variety of stimuli in the chloralose-anesthetized animal present an almost unique opportunity for the study of sensorimotor integration at supraspinal levels. Although the so-called "chloralose-jerks" are not abolished by removal of the cerebral cortex [see (178) for references], they are normally under the control of the appropriate sensory receiving area (179). Ascher et al. (179) suggested that there were one or more subcortical reflex centers which served as zones of convergence for impulses ascending in the sensory pathways and those descending from the cortex. A paper by Buser et al. (178) implicates the lateral part of the inferor colliculus—a region known to receive projections from auditory cortex (149, 178, 180) as well as from the ascending auditory system (181, 182)—as the critical center for sound-induced reactions. Ascher & Gachelin (183) have demonstrated that the superior colliculus plays a similar role for the efferent discharges elicited by photic stimulation. The motor pathways involved, particularly those emanating from the inferior colliculus, are not clearly delimited, but a tectoreticulospinal pathway appears a reasonable possibility.

Geniculocortical auditory system.—Behavioral studies (158, 159) have clearly demonstrated the significance of the geniculocortical auditory system in the mechanisms of sound localization. Thus, the study of Adrian et al. (184) on the response of medial geniculate cells to binaural stimuli is of obvious interest. Approximately 40 per cent of the cells were found to be affected by stimulation of either ear. The types of binaural interaction observed were similar to those seen in lower auditory centers (150–155, 165, 170). Adrian and his co-workers (184) stress the importance of neurons activated by one ear and inhibited by the other since these neurons were shown to be sensitive to interaural time and intensity differences.

The principal division of the medial geniculate is primarily concerned with the transfer of auditory information. Watanabe et al. (185) report that, in a small proportion of the cells of the principal division, the response to acoustic stimuli can be modified by activation of corticofugal fibers emanating from auditory cortex. Stimulation of auditory area AI resulted in a predominant inhibitory effect, whereas the effects elicited from AII were largely facilitatory.

Electrophysiological and anatomical studies have indicated that the magnocellular medial geniculate, in contrast to the principal division, is a center of convergence for the auditory and other sensory systems (181, 182, 186–192). Wepsic (193), in a microelectrode study, confirmed the conclusion of Mickle & Ades (186) that the magnocellular division may serve, among its other functions, as a vestibular relay. A short-latency pathway from the contralateral vestibular nuclei was demonstrated as was a more indirect uncrossed pathway. The convergence onto single cells of fibers related to various modalities was emphasized by the fact that many units responded to somesthetic, auditory, and vestibular inputs.

The apparent unresponsiveness of neurons in auditory cortex remains the most perplexing problem in auditory physiology. Erulkar et al. (194) originally observed that a large number of cells in anesthetized preparations were not affected by auditory stimuli and, of those neurons that were, only a small fraction responded securely. It was also noted that the excitability of neurons was depressed by anesthesia. Studies in unanesthetized preparations have by no means cleared up the problem. Bogdanski & Galambos (195) reported that only about one third of the neurons they encountered responded in a sustained manner. Other types of discharge pattern included sustained inhibition and on-off responses associated with such inhibition. Many cells did not respond to any stimulus and still others responded in an erratic fashion. Other workers have had similar experiences (196, 197).

It is, of course, possible that many neurons in auditory cortex do not

respond in a simple manner to any auditory stimulus. An alternative suggestion is that auditory neurons would adequately respond to stimuli more complex than pure tones. Results to date are disappointing. Suga (176) and
Whitfield & Evans (177) found that, although many neurons respond more
securely to frequency-modulated tones than they do to steady tones, only
a small number of those neurons unaffected by pure tones were activated by
modulated stimuli. A similar conclusion may be drawn from the two-tone
experiments of Oonishi & Katsuki (198). Brugge et al. (199) explored the
possibility that apparently unresponsive neurons could be activated by appropriate binaural stimuli. It was found that the discharge of some low-
frequency cells was quite sensitive to interaural phase differences. Nevertheless, many neurons could not be driven securely by any of the binaural
stimuli employed.

Visual System

Retinal ganglion cells.—The receptive fields of retinal ganglion cells are
typically subdivided into an excitatory or inhibitory center and an antagonistic surround. Such opponent-spatial receptive fields, while first studied in
the cat (200, 201), have been demonstrated in other vertebrate species
(202–206), and their existence in the human retina is strongly suggested
by psychophysical evidence (207–209). Rodieck & Stone (210) observed
that the response amplitude to a discrete photic stimulus is a triphasic
function of stimulus position along any diameter of the receptive field.
They propose a model (210, 211) in which this function is considered as
the sum of two superimposed Gaussian functions of opposite sign, one narrow and steep representing the center mechanism, the other wide and shal-
low representing the surround mechanism.

A similar model was adopted by Enroth-Cugell & Robson (212) in a
study of spatial summation in cat ganglion cells. The stimuli used were
grating patterns having a luminance which varied sinusoidally with distance perpendicular to the direction of the bars. The response of one group
of cells to stationary grating patterns depended in a simple manner on the
phase relation between the sinusoidal stimulus and the receptive field. A luminance maximum focused on the receptive-field center evoked a center-
type response, a luminance minimum elicited a surround-type response,
and, most saliently, a point intermediate between a maximum and a minimum evoked no response. Such characteristics could be accounted for by
assuming that the response of photoreceptors is linearly related to the
intensity of the impinging light and that the signals from the receptors located in the Gaussian-shaped center and surround regions summate separately before affecting the discharge of the ganglion cell. A mathematical
argument allowed the authors to predict the response to moving grating
patterns and to make estimates of the radii of center and surround summating regions consistent with those obtained more directly (210). A re-

duction of the mean luminance appeared to lessen the effectiveness of the surround region (see also 201) and to increase the diameter of both summating regions.

Gouras & Link (213) present electrophysiological evidence for the convergence of rod and cone pathways onto single perifoveal ganglion cells in the primate retina. In the dark-adapted state, the rod-type response has a scotopic action spectrum, low thresholds, and long latent periods, while the cone-type response has a photopic action spectrum, higher thresholds, and shorter latent periods. Flashes of violet and red light were used to stimulate rods and cones, respectively. Ganglion cell discharge evoked by either stimulus was associated with a transient unresponsiveness to excitation through the other pathway. When rods and cones were stimulated simultaneously, the earlier cone response blocked the discharge to rod stimulation. Studies of the electroretinogram led Gouras (214) to suggest that the different response times of the rod and cone systems reflected processes occurring prior to the response of bipolar cells, while the antagonistic interaction between the two systems took place following the bipolar cell response.

There are several features of the receptive fields of mammalian retinal ganglion cells which cannot be accounted for by a simple center-surround type of organization. Some of these involve specializations like those found in the frog optic tectum or cat visual cortex. Thus, throughout the rabbit retina, there are ganglion cells which are directionally sensitive and others which possess large receptive fields and are especially sensitive to fast movements or sudden changes in illumination (215). The rabbit's visual streak region contains orientation-selective units, local-edge detectors, and uniformity detectors (216). Directionally selective cells have been recently described in the cat (217) and squirrel (204, 218). In the squirrel, the response of such units to discrete stimuli presented successively to different parts of the receptive field indicates that a local wave of inhibition is generated to one side of a stimulated region, so that the response to a stimulus moving in that direction is blocked (204). Directional selectivity in the rabbit's retina is thought to involve a similar mechanism (219).

The excitability of cat retinal ganglion cells may be increased by moving stimuli which fall well outside of the classical receptive field (220). McIlwain (221), in a further study of this "periphery effect", has found that it does not simply represent an outward extension of the properties of the receptive-field surround. The effectiveness of a stimulus was related to the presence of moving edges, but not to the direction of movement. A likely mechanism, McIlwain suggests, would involve interactions of spatially separated receptive-field systems. Response characteristics of some cat ganglion cells are reported to be alerted by efferent activity in the optic nerve (217, 222).

Color-sensitive mechanisms may also complicate receptive-field organization. Michael (205) describes cells of the all-cone retina of the ground squirrel which are excited by stimuli in one part of the spectrum and inhibited by stimuli in another part of the spectrum. In some of these cells, the excitatory and inhibitory receptive fields had an identical spatial distribution. Other cells were characterized by receptive fields which were organized into a center and an opponent surround, each possessing different spectral sensitivities. In these latter cells, it was demonstrated—as previously shown in similar cells of the goldfish retina (202) and as assumed in Rodieck & Stone's model (210, 211)—that the surround mechanism extends throughout the receptive field.

Geniculostriate system.—The interaction of excitatory and inhibitory synaptic processes in the lateral geniculate body and visual cortex has been dealt with in several recent studies. These investigations present evidence for the presence of both pre- and postsynaptic inhibition and for the involvement of these inhibitory processes in spatial discrimination, binocular interaction, and the temporal patterning of discharge.

Sefton & Burke (223–227) described two groups of cells in the lateral geniculate body of the rat: P-cells, tentatively identified as principal or geniculocortical relay cells, and I-cells, thought to be interneurons. P-cells typically responded to optic nerve stimulation with a single spike followed by several recurrent bursts of two to five spikes each. The intervals between bursts were approximately 150 msec. Intracellular recordings from P-cells revealed slow, hyperpolarizing IPSP waves (see also 228), which could account for the intervals between bursts and for the depression following a conditioning stimulus. The rippling sometimes superimposed upon these slow waves suggested that they were produced by the repetitive discharge of inhibitory interneurons. The I-cells, which fired in recurrent bursts of about ten spikes each and had longer latent periods than did the P-cells, were believed to be such interneurons.

A recurrent inhibitory circuit, similar to that described by Andersen & Eccles (229) for the ventrobasal thalamus, was proposed to account for the discharge of geniculate neurons to optic nerve stimulation (223–228). The model postulates that optic nerve impulses activate principal cells, that the recurrent collaterals of principal cells excite interneurons, and that these interneurons in turn synapse onto principal cells, producing in them a hyperpolarizing wave composed of summed IPSPs. Recurrent collaterals of relay cells and short axon interneurons have been described in histological studies (230, 231). Aitken et al. (232) suggest a similar model to explain the discharge patterns evoked in medial geniculate neurons by click stimuli.

The dorsal lateral geniculate of the cat includes three cell laminae. The contralateral retina projects to the outer two layers, the ipsilateral retina to the inner layer. Only the interlaminar zones of the geniculate receive a convergent input from the two eyes (233, 234). A very small number of geniculate neurons are activated by stimulation of either eye (235–237). Recent studies indicate, however, that some forms of binocular interaction may be widespread within the lateral geniculate. Suzuki & Kato (238) found that geniculate relay cells typically discharged in response to stimulation of only one optic nerve, but that the response could be inhibited by a prior conditioning stimulus to the other nerve. Intracellular studies revealed that the inhibition was due to delayed and prolonged IPSPs evoked by the conditioning stimulus. Evidence was presented that the IPSPs were produced by interneurons receiving their input, in part, from a feedback circuit involving corticogeniculate fibers. Lindsley et al. (239) observed that, in many geniculate neurons, the response to discrete stimuli presented to the contralateral eye could be modified by a flash delivered to the ipsilateral eye, a result similar to that of Erulkar & Fillenz (235). These binocular cells were not confined to the interlaminar zones.

Although electrical stimulation is an important tool in delineating synaptic mechanisms, studies in which natural stimuli are employed are necessary if the functional significance of such mechanisms is to be understood. McIlwain & Creutzfeldt (240), using discrete photic stimuli, demonstrated that postsynaptic inhibition of lateral geniculate neurons may contribute to the center-surround organization of their receptive fields. Illumination of excitatory areas of the receptive field or darkening of inhibitory areas resulted in compound depolarizations made up of summed EPSPs. IPSPs appeared most commonly during illumination of inhibitory areas, but were sometimes interpolated between phasic and tonic segments of depolarizing responses. In some cases the cessation of spontaneous discharge upon appropriate stimulation occurred without IPSPs. From their observations, the authors conclude that off-type responses may depend upon both the reduction of excitatory input from the retina and synaptic inhibition in the geniculate itself. In an earlier study, Fuster et al. (228) described the postsynaptic potentials evoked by diffuse photic stimulation in cells of the lateral geniculate and visual cortex.

Several papers report that presynaptic inhibition of optic nerve terminals in the lateral geniculate follows stimulation of the visual cortex (241–243) and of various nonvisual pathways (244–246). Presynaptic inhibition may also occur during eye movements, both in paradoxical sleep (247) and in the waking state (248); the suggestion has been made (247) that such a mechanism might account for the elevation of visual thresholds during eye movements in man (249, 250). Marchiafava (251) presents evidence for a reciprocal presynaptic inhibition of terminals of the two optic tracts. The response to discrete retinal stimulation suggested that this effect is spatially specific, involving corresponding areas of the two retinas. A possible anatomical basis for presynaptic inhibition is provided by the observations of axo-axonal contacts in the lateral geniculate (231, 252). However, morphological evidence suggests that the optic terminals are presynaptic to other axons, and also that many axo-axonic contacts are between terminals of short axon cells and corticofugal fibers.

The response of geniculate neurons to monochromatic light has been extensively studied in the rhesus monkey, a primate having color vision similar to that of man (253). Many cells exhibit an opponent-color response, i.e., they are excited by some wavelengths and inhibited by others. DeValois and his co-workers (254) confirm the division of geniculate units into spectrally opponent and non-opponent cells. The spectrally opponent cells are further classified into four types: (a) red excitatory, green inhibitory; (b) yellow excitatory, blue inhibitory; (c) green excitatory, red inhibitory; and (d) blue excitatory, yellow inhibitory. The authors (255) then investigated the spectral sensitivity of these cells by observing changes in firing rate produced by alternation between two monochromatic lights of equal luminance. The sensitivities displayed by the neurons were consistent with those derived from behavioral experiments.

Wiesel & Hubel (256) investigated the relationships between the opponent-color response of lateral geniculate neurons and the organization of their receptive fields. Discrete monochromatic stimuli were used. The most common type of neuron encountered was one which combines opponent-color with opponent-spatial characteristics in a manner similar to that described in the retinal ganglion cells of the goldfish (202) and ground squirrel (205). In the light-adapted state, the receptive fields of these cells are composed of a center and opponent surround with different spectral sensitivities. Less common were cells displaying opponent-color responses without any center-surround organization and cells in which the center and surround mechanisms had nearly parallel spectral-sensitivity curves. Wiesel & Hubel view their observations as indicating a specialization among neurons. Some cells appear to handle information concerned with the spatial characteristics of stimuli, others with color, and still others with both sets of attributes. The most effective stimulus for a given cell is one that stimulates only a limited set of receptors, with that set varying from cell to cell.

Superior colliculus.—The orderly topographic projection of the retina onto the optic tectum or superior colliculus is similar in a wide range of vertebrate species [for references see (257, 258)]. In mammals, the superior colliculus receives a direct visual input from the retina, and an indirect input by way of the visual cortex; corresponding areas of the retina and the superior colliculus may be connected by both direct and indirect projections (259). There is also evidence that visual impulses can be relayed from the superior colliculus to the visual cortex (260). Recent studies of the field potentials evoked in the superior colliculus by electrical stimulation of optic nerve fibers (183, 261, 262) show early and late postsynaptic responses, possibly corresponding to the direct and indirect retinofugal projections. The longer-latency response disappears after the ablation of visual cortex (183, 261).

Most of the superior colliculus neurons studied by Jassik-Gerschenfeld (263) responded to somesthetic as well as to visual stimuli. Horn & Hill (264) demonstrated a significant convergence of visual, auditory, and tactile pathways onto single cells in the superior colliculus and the subjacent tectotegmental region in the rabbit. Receptive fields of light-responsive cells were found to be quite large and variable in shape. They had on centers with off surrounds, on/off centers with no surrounds, or on/off centers with off surrounds. Some units showed directional selectivity and most were excited more by a moving than by a stationary spot, characteristics also found in retinal ganglion cells of the rabbit (215). In addition, the authors emphasized the stimulus-specific decline of the response to repeated stimuli.

Nonvisual cortex.—Evoked potentials can be recorded from association and sensorimotor cortex in response to visual, auditory, and somesthetic stimuli (265–269). A paper by Bignall et al. (270) investigates the pathways involved in the transmission of visual activity to these areas. The evoked potentials recorded from association and sensorimotor cortex were modified, but not abolished, by large thalamic lesions which spared the lateral geniculate or by ablation of visual cortex. Bignall et al. (270) conclude that visual activity reaches the association and sensorimotor cortex by a number of routes, including projections from primary visual cortex (271) and thalamocortical projections not involving the geniculostriate system. Similarly, auditory activity can be transmitted to widespread areas of the cortex by pathways independent of the geniculocortical auditory system (268, 272).

MacLean, Cuénod & Casey (273, 274) found neurons in the posterior limbic cortex which were activated by visual stimuli, possibly via a direct pathway from the lateral geniculate as well as by way of a projection from the striate cortex (275).

Spinelli & Pribram (276) discuss why lesions in circumscribed parts of primate association cortex produce specific sensory agnosias. The authors emphasize that the inputs to these areas do not appear to be modality-specific and they suggest that the deficits resulting from lesions of association cortex may be due to a specificity in the efferent projection from these areas to subcortical nuclei of the primary afferent pathways. This hypothesis is supported by observations of the effects of stimulation or ablation of association cortex on recovery functions in the visual (276) and auditory (277) systems.

SOMATOSENSORY SYSTEM

First-order somatic afferent fibers.—Mechanoreceptors have been classified in terms of the structure and distribution of their endorgans and also on the basis of the discharge behavior and conduction velocity of their afferent fibers. It has sometimes been possible to find correlations among these characteristics. Receptor terminals sensitive to tactile stimuli may be divided into free nerve endings and those associated with accessory structures (278). The latter include tactile hairs, Merkel's disks, Meissner's touch corpuscles, and Pacinian corpuscles in subcutaneous and deeper tissues.

Iggo (279) has made an extensive analysis of the afferent supply to the hairy skin of the cat and rabbit. The great majority of myelinated fibers fell into two basic categories: rapidly adapting units associated with hair follicles and slowly adapting units in the dermis or epidermis. The rapidly adapting hair-follicle units are excited by hair movement, but their discharge quickly disappears if the hair is maintained in a new position. They are divided into three subgroups D, G, and T, according to the kind of hair follicle and the discharge behavior. Type D units are excited by movement of down hairs and have the highest sensitivity. Types G and T innervate larger guard hairs. The slowly adapting units are sensitive to both rate and amount of skin displacement. They are divided into Types I and II. Type I fibers derive from Iggo's "touch corpuscles" (280)—domelike elevations of epidermis having receptor elements at their base which are probably Merkel's disks. These fibers have no resting discharge, but respond to a small indentation of the corpuscle with a high-frequency burst followed by a static response phase. The receptor organs of Type II units are unknown. Type II fibers have a regular resting discharge, and respond to lateral stretching of skin as well as simple indentation. Type D hair-follicle units have small, myelinated fibers conducting in the A-delta range. The other afferent units have more rapidly conducting fibers.

In studies of the myelinated afferent fibers supplying the hairy skin of the rabbit's ear (281, 282), only rapidly adapting units were found. These include Types D and G hair-follicle units, and skin-spot units whose place in Iggo's classification is uncertain (279, 282). In the glabrous skin of the monkey, there are rapidly adapting and slowly adapting units, the latter falling into two categories somewhat similar to those in hairy skin (283).

Of great importance is the question of the existence of specific nociceptors responding only to intense mechanical stimuli. Very few such afferent units were found in the small-myelinated fiber range by Hunt & McIntyre (284) and by Iggo (279). Recently, however, Burgess & Perl (285) have found a significant number of myelinated afferent fibers responding specifically to noxious stimulation of the hairy skin of the cat. Small fibers were sampled from an intact cutaneous nerve with microelectrodes. Fifteen per cent of the fibers conducting at less than 37 m/sec responded only to damaging stimuli, e.g., pinching with forceps or cutting. Their receptive fields were typically large and consisted of small responsive spots separated by unresponsive areas. Other fibers, having higher conduction velocities, were responsive only to relatively intense, but not damaging, mechanical stimuli. The majority of fibers conducting below 37 m/sec were rapidly adapting hair units, probably corresponding to Iggo's Type D. Both the presumed nociceptors and Type D hair units had mean velocities near that of the A-delta peak. Melzack & Wall (286) proposed, as part of their pain theory, that both small myelinated and nonmyelinated afferents provided a constant resting input to the spinal cord. Burgess & Perl (285), however, found no appreciable resting discharge in the small myelinated afferents.

Although most nonmyelinated or C fibers are excited by innocuous stimuli, a significant fraction have been classified as nociceptors (287). These are responsive only to strong mechanical stimuli or extreme temperatures. Muscle nociceptors are found among both the smallest myelinated (288) and the unmyelinated fibers (287).

Quantitative studies of stimulus-response relations have been made for several types of afferent unit. The static displacement sensitivity of Iggo's touch corpuscle units has been extensively analyzed by Werner & Mountcastle (289), the dynamic displacement sensitivity by Tapper (290). The static and dynamic stimulus-response relationships are both described by power functions. A single myelinated fiber may innervate several touch corpuscles (290). Lindblom & Tapper (291) observed that with simultaneous stimulation of two of these corpuscles, no summation is found in the discharge of the parent fiber. This was explained by the combination of antidromic invasion of neighboring terminals with slow recovery of these terminals. The recovery cycles of the terminals are examined in detail in a later publication (292).

The dermal ridges of the glabrous skin of the monkey are innervated by rapidly adapting and slowly adapting afferent units (283, 293, 294). Although the corresponding endorgans are not known with certainty, it has been suggested, partly by analogy with hairy skin, that the slowly adapting units may end in Merkel's disks, and the rapidly adapting units in Meissner's corpuscles (293). Lindblom (293) studied the rapidly adapting units, especially with regard to the critical slope of displacement and the sensitivity to displacement rate. Linear relations between discharge frequency and the logarithm of the displacement rate were found over a wide range. These intracutaneous units have small and well-defined receptive fields. Another type of rapidly adapting unit in this region ends in subcutaneous or deeper tissues, probably in Pacinian corpuscles, and has large and diffuse receptive fields (295).

Both the intracutaneous and the subcutaneous sensory units contribute to the human sense of flutter-vibration in glabrous skin (296). At high frequencies of vibration, the subcutaneous units have the lower thresholds; at lower frequencies, the intracutaneous units are the more sensitive. Mountcastle and co-workers (296) were able to relate this receptor duality, measured in terms of single-unit response in the median nerve of the monkey, to psychophysical data in man. Below 60 cps, sinusoidal displacements applied to the human hand were found to produce a sensation of faint, localized flutter; above 60 cps, the sensations resembled a vibratory hum, moved deep within the hand, and could not be accurately localized. The low- and high-frequency sensations were related to the intracutaneous and subcutaneous receptors, respectively.

The slowly adapting afferent units innervating the dermal ridges of the glabrous skin have been studied by Mountcastle et al. (294). These units have some similarities with Iggo's Type I (279). They respond to a step indentation with a high-frequency burst, from which the discharge rapidly declines to a quasi-steady state. During the steady-state discharge, there is a linear relation between firing rate and indentation amplitude. If the rate of displacement is high enough to saturate the rate-sensitivity function, such a relation is also obtained for the initial part of the discharge.

Several studies of muscle and tendon afferents are worthy of mention. It has been supposed that Golgi tendon organs are only activated by excessive stretch. Houk & Henneman (297) report that this idea may be due in part to the fact that tendon organs are much less sensitive to passive stretch than to stretch produced by active muscle contraction. Active contraction of even a single motor unit lying in series with the tendon organ may excite it. The authors (297) conclude that tendon organs may be involved in a continuously operative negative-feedback system.

Carpenter & Henneman (298) observed that an excitability-size correlation similar to that observed for motoneurons is found in muscle afferents. For most (74 per cent) of the primary spindle afferent pairs compared, the unit with the lower threshold to stretch had the more slowly conducting axon. There was also some tendency for the smaller of two units in a pair to discharge more rapidly than the larger at all levels of stretch.

Primary spindle receptors in the cat are affected by both static and dynamic fusimotor fibers, the two being distinguished by their effect on the sensitivity of the receptor to dynamic stimuli (299). Recent papers (300–302) show that the secondary spindle receptor is only influenced by the static fusimotor fibers, whose effect is facilitatory when the muscle is at a constant length; the response of the secondary spindle receptor to a dynamic stimulus, which in any case is much less than that of the primary spindle receptor, is not significantly altered by fusimotor activity.

Afferent pathways in the spinal cord and medulla.—Cutaneous afferent activity is relayed to the somatosensory cortex by two rapidly conducting ascending pathways: the dorsal column-medial lemniscal system, and the more recently discovered spinocervical system (303–307). Experimental lesions of the spinal cord suggest that some functions classically thought to involve the dorsal columns or spinothalamic tracts may be shared with the spinocervical tract. These functions include two-point tactile sensitivity (308), conditioned reflexes elicited by light tactile stimuli (309), localization of noxious stimuli (310), pain sensitivity (311), limb position sense (312), and possibly certain postural and locomotor reflexes (310).

Some primary afferents send collaterals both through the dorsal columns to the dorsal column nuclei and to cells of origin of the spinocervical tract (307, 313, 314). The cell bodies of the spinocervical tract are located in Rexed's lamina IV of the dorsal horn (315, 316); their axons ascend in the dorsomedial part of the lateral funiculus adjacent to the dorsal spinocerebellar tract (317). The spinocervical tract projects to the lateral cervical nucleus in the first two segments of the cord and the latter relays through the contralateral medial lemniscus to the thalamus and cortex (307, 317–320).

A number of differences between the dorsal column and spinocervical systems have been noted (306, 307, 313, 314). In the dorsal column nuclei, most single units responsive to cutaneous stimuli are thought to receive either hair or touch afferents, but not both, while spinocervical tract units commonly receive a convergent input from both submodalities (313, 314, 321, 322). A significant number of units responding to joint movement or muscle stretching are found in the dorsal column system, but not in the spinocervical system (307, 313).

The input to the dorsal columns appears to be confined to the larger myelinated fibers, and lacks both A-delta and C-fibers (313, 314). Units in the dorsal column nuclei having cutaneous receptive fields typically display a relatively narrow dynamic range with respect to the intensity of natural stimuli (313). The excitatory input to the spinocervical tract includes, in the myelinated fiber group, the smaller A-alpha and the A-delta components (314). In the spinocervical tract, one group of units, having a narrow dynamic range, are adequately excited by light touch from a restricted skin field and receive input only from cutaneous A-fibers (317, 319, 324). A second group of units have a wider dynamic range; they are activated by light tactile stimuli over a restricted receptive field, but can be additionally activated by pressure or pinching over a wider area. These units receive input from both myelinated and nonmyelinated fibers, including high-threshold muscle afferents (314, 317, 322, 323). It is of interest that the smaller myelinated and the nonmyelinated fibers—afferents which presumably do not enter the dorsal columns but do excite spinocervical tract units—include both nociceptors (285, 287) and the most sensitive hair units (279).

Response characteristics of spinocervical tract units have recently been studied by Mendell (324), who found that more than half the cells responding monosynaptically to A-fiber stimulation also responded to C-fiber stimulation. These cells exhibited a wide dynamic range and their discharge patterns consisted of an early discharge and a long-lasting afterdischarge. The wide dynamic range and the afterdischarge were related to C-fiber activation. The duration of the afterdischarge was increased with repetitive stimulation, apparently as a result of a cumulative facilitatory influence exerted by C-fiber input. Volleys in contralateral A-fibers inhibited the discharge in central cells produced by ipsilateral C-fiber stimulation. These response characteristics may be related to the opposite presynaptic effects attributed to A- and C-volleys (325) and incorporated in the pain theory of Melzack & Wall (286). In this theory, small-diameter myelinated and nonmyelinated fibers are supposed to inhibit interneurons in the substantia gelatinosa which in turn exert a presynaptic inhibition on all afferents to second-order relay cells in the dorsal horn. Large myelinated afferent fibers activate such inhibitory interneurons. The balance between the two opposing influences, coupled with descending regulatory influences, modulates the effect of sensory input on the discharge of secondary cells. The augmenting effect of repetitive C-fiber stimulation described by Mendell (324) is of interest in the light of the observation that C-fiber stimulation produces pain in man only after a number of repetitive stimuli (326).

It has often been suggested that the absence of afferent surround inhibition distinguishes the spinocervical system from the dorsal column system (306, 317, 318, 320). In anesthetized preparations, such inhibition is common in cells of the dorsal column nuclei (321, 327) but rare or absent in cells of the spinocervical tract (317) or lateral cervical nucleus (318–320). In unanesthetized decerebrate or spinal preparations, however, inhibitory areas for spinocervical tract units are found outside of, but not concentric to, the excitatory receptive field; the inhibitory effects are abolished by anesthesia (328). The activation of spinocervical units via C-fiber afferents is particularly sensitive to afferent inhibition (324) and to barbiturate anesthesia (322, 324).

Descending systems can affect the behavior of units in both the dorsal column nuclei and the spinocervical tract. Gordon & Jukes (329) observed that, in the gracile nucleus, corticofugal inhibition seemed confined to cells demonstrating afferent inhibition. The possibility has been suggested (329–331) that both types of inhibition may be mediated by inhibitory interneurons within the dorsal column nuclei. Investigation of the descending pathways involved (332) has implicated the pyramidal tract as responsible for excitatory effects in these nuclei, while inhibitory effects are attributed to extrapyramidal fibers.

Spinocervical tract units may be inhibited by stimulation of a number of supraspinal loci, including cerebellar nuclei, midbrain tegmentum, and pyramidal tract (322, 328). In some cases the receptive fields of these units may be constricted and desensitized (328). Wall (322) observed changes in the behavior of cells in lamina IV of the dorsal horn when descending influences were reversibly blocked by cold applied to the cord above the recording level. Both spontaneous and evoked discharge frequently increased. In addition, the dynamic range of many cells was increased. This observation may be related to the earlier report (323) that descending inhibitory influences act specifically upon the high-threshold input to units having a wide dynamic range. Part of the descending influences upon second-order cells in the dorsal horn may be due to presynaptic inhibition of incoming afferent fibers (317). There is evidence for such presynaptic inhibition after stimulation of cortex (333), diencephalon (334), and vestibulospinal pathways (335, 336).

Presynaptic inhibition induced by corticofugal activity has recently been related to the response of second-order neurons in the brainstem trigeminal complex. In previous studies (337) Darian-Smith had concluded that presynaptic inhibition plays a large part in the afferent inhibition of such neurons produced by stimulation of the facial skin. Darian-Smith & Yokota

(338, 339) now report that such presynaptic inhibition may also be produced via corticofugal activity. The inhibition of second-order cells by cortical stimulation is paralleled by primary afferent depolarization both in terms of time-course and of effective cortical fields. The cortical projection of a given group of afferent fibers closely corresponded with the cortical region most effective in depolarizing the central terminals of these fibers. Similar observations are reported by Stewart and co-workers (340, 341).

Afferent fibers of the trigeminal nerve supply a peri-oral region involved in a biting reflex in the cat (342). Stimulation of the hypothalamus which elicits attack also appears to sensitize and expand the sensory fields for this reflex (342).

Thalamocortical system.—Both the lateral cervical and the dorsal column nuclei relay through the lateral part of the thalamic ventrobasal complex to both primary and secondary somatosensory cortex (SI and SII). The thalamic relay of the spinocervical system is located in a border zone lateral to the relay cells of the hindlimb component of the dorsal column projection (343). Andersen, Andersson & Landgren (344) studied the behavior of cells in this region. Many of them are excited by dorsal column as well as spinocervical input, although the effects of the latter have a shorter latent period and are more potent. A number of cells are antidromically activated by stimulation of either SI or SII, which indicates that they project to both areas via a divided axon.

Cutaneous afferent stimuli evoke short-latency, initially positive potentials in somatosensory cortex when either the dorsal column or the spinocervical tracts are severed; when both are severed, the early potentials disappear (303). Oscarsson & Rosén (305) report that the spinocervical tract appears more effective than the dorsal column system in activating SII, while the dorsal column system has a greater projection onto SI. Both activate the primary motor cortex as well. Cutaneous hindlimb stimulation elicits shorter-latency potentials via the spinocervical system, while the dorsal column system is the fastest route for forelimb activation.

There is evidence that activity in Group I afferents from muscle stretch receptors does not result in conscious perception, behavioral discrimination responses, evoked potentials in brainstem reticular formation, or EEG arousal [see (345) for references]. Group I activity does, however, elicit short-latency responses within and adjacent to the motor cortex (305, 345–347) and thus may well be involved in motor control.

Cells in the motor cortex of the monkey have been found to respond to muscle stretching rather than to cutaneous tactile stimulation (348). In the cat, stimulation of Group I afferents evokes short-latency responses in a small region of the cortex around the postcruciate dimple which is transitional between primary motor cortex and SI (305, 346); a smaller area in SII may also be affected (347). The fibers responsible for these potentials ascend in the dorsal columns and not via the spinocervical system (305). Andersson and co-workers (347) found that the thalamic relay involved may be located in a separate subdivision of the ventrobasal thalamus. The cells in this region may be activated by volleys in several muscle nerves and, with a longer latent period, by cutaneous input.

Oscarsson, Rosén & Sulg (349) recorded from neurons in the Group I cortical projection area in the cat. The convergence of excitation, inhibition, or both, was extensive, cells being affected by stimulation of many muscle groups in the forelimb, including antagonistic muscles, and also by stimulation of cutaneous afferents. This convergence, which is also seen at the thalamic level (347), suggests that the Group I projection path carries information primarily concerning changes in muscle tone rather than position of the limbs or the execution of precise movements. Swett & Bourassa (350) found that the cells activated by Group I afferent volleys included pyramidal tract cells.

LITERATURE CITED

1. Bishop, P. O. Central nervous system: Afferent mechanisms and perception. *Ann. Rev. Physiol.*, **29**, 427–84 (1967)
2. Benjamin, R. M., Halpern, B. P., Moulton, D. G., Mozell, M. M. The chemical senses. *Ann. Rev. Psychol.*, **16**, 381–416 (1965)
3. Wenzel, B. M., Sieck, M. H. Olfaction. *Ann. Rev. Physiol.*, **28**, 381–434 (1966)
4. Oakley, B., Benjamin, R. M. Neural mechanisms of taste. *Physiol. Rev.*, **46**, 173–211 (1966)
5. Moulton, D. G., Beidler, L. M. Structure and function in the peripheral olfactory system. *Physiol. Rev.*, **47**, 1–52 (1967)
6. Ottoson, D., Shepherd, G. M. Experiments and concepts in olfactory physiology. In *Sensory Mechanisms* (See Ref. 9), 83–138
7. *Sensory Receptors. Cold Spring Harbor Symp. Quant. Biol.*, **30** (649 pp., 1966)
8. *Touch, Heat and Pain* (de Reuck, A. V. S., Knight, J., Eds., *Ciba Found. Symp.*, Little, Brown, Boston, 389 pp., 1966)
9. *Sensory Mechanisms* (Zotterman, Y., Ed., *Progress in Brain Research*, **23**, Elsevier, Amsterdam, 225 pp., 1967)
10. Hensel, H. *Allgemeine Sinnesphysiologie Hautsinne, Geshmach, Geruch* (Springer-Verlag, Berlin, 343 pp., 1966)
11. Duncan, C. J. *The Molecular Properties and Evolution of Excitable Cells* (Pergamon, Oxford, 253 pp., 1967)
12. Diamond, J., Gray, J. A. B., Inman, D. R. The relation between receptor potentials and the concentration of sodium ions. *J. Physiol. (London)*, **142**, 382–94 (1958)
13. Edwards, C., Terzuolo, C. A., Washizu, Y. The effect of changes of the ionic environment upon an isolated crustacean sensory neuron. *J. Neurophysiol.*, **26**, 948–57 (1963)
14. Ottoson, D. The effect of sodium deficiency on the response of the isolated muscle spindle. *J. Physiol. (London)*, **171**, 109–18 (1964)
15. Calma, I. Ions and the receptor potential in the muscle spindle of the frog. *J. Physiol. (London)*, **177**, 31–41 (1965)
16. Fatt, P., Katz, B. The effect of sodium ions on neuromuscular transmission. *J. Physiol. (London)*, **118**, 73–87 (1951)
17. Takeuchi, A., Takeuchi, N. On the permeability of end-plate membrane during the action of transmitter. *J. Physiol. (London)*, **154**, 52–67 (1960)
18. Narahashi, T., Takehiko, D., Urakawa, N., Ohkubo, Y. Stabilization and rectification of muscle fiber membrane by tetrodotoxin. *Am. J. Physiol.*, **198**, 934–38 (1960)
19. Narahashi, T., Moore, J. W., Scott, W. R. Tetrodotoxin blockage of sodium conductance increase in

lobster giant axons. *J. Gen. Physiol.*, **47,** 965–74 (1964)

20. Furukawa, T., Sasaoka, T., Hosoya, Y. Effects of tetrodotoxin on the neuromuscular junction. *Japan. J. Physiol.*, **9,** 143–52 (1959)

21. Elmqvist, D., Feldman, D. S. Spontaneous activity at a mammalian neuromuscular junction in tetrodotoxin. *Acta Physiol. Scand.*, **64,** 475–76 (1965)

22. Ozeki, M., Freeman, A. R., Grundfest, H. The membrane components of crustacean neuromuscular systems. I. Immunity of different electrogenic components to tetrodotoxin and saxitoxin. *J. Gen. Physiol.*, **49,** 1319–34 (1966)

23. Katz, B., Miledi, R. Tetrodotoxin and neuromuscular transmission. *Proc. Roy. Soc. B,* **167,** 8–22 (1967)

24. Loewenstein, W. R., Terzuolo, C. A., Washizu, Y. Separation of transducer and impulse-generating processes in sensory receptors. *Science,* **142,** 1180–81 (1963)

25. Nishi, K., Sato, M. Blocking of the impulse and depression of the receptor potential by tetrodotoxin in non-myelinated nerve terminals in Pacinian corpuscles. *J. Physiol. (London),* **184,** 376–86 (1966)

26. Bernhard, C. G., Granit, R. Nerve as model temperature end organ. *J. Gen. Physiol.,* **29,** 257–65 (1945)

27. Spyropoulos, C. S. Initiation and abolition of electric response of nerve fiber by thermal and chemical means. *Am. J. Physiol.,* **200,** 203–8 (1961)

28. Dorai Raj, B. S., Murray, R. W. Non-myelinated nerves as a model for thermoreceptors. *Comp. Biochem. Physiol.,* **5,** 311–17 (1962)

29. Witt, I., Hensel, H. Afferente Impulse aus der Extermitätenhaut der Katze bei thermischer und mechanischer Reizung. *Arch. Ges. Physiol.,* **268,** 582–96 (1959)

30. Hensel, H., Boman, K. K. A. Afferent impulses in cutaneous sensory nerves in human subjects. *J. Neurophysiol.,* **23,** 564–78 (1960)

31. Lippold, O. C. J., Nicholls, J. G., Redfearn, J. W. T. A study of the afferent discharge produced by cooling a mammalian muscle spindle. *J. Physiol. (London),* **153,** 218–31 (1960)

32. Ottoson, D. The effects of temperature on the isolated muscle spindle.

J. Physiol. (London), **180,** 636–48 (1965)

33. Rosenblueth, A., Alvarez-Buylla, R., Garcia Ramos, J. The responses of axons to mechanical stimuli. *Acta Physiol. Latinoam.,* **3,** 204–15 (1953)

34. Julian, F. J., Goldman, D. E. The effects of mechanical stimulation on some electrical properties of axons. *J. Gen. Physiol.,* **46,** 297–313 (1962)

35. Diamond, J., Gray, J. A. B., Sato, M. The site of initiation of impulses in Pacinian corpuscles. *J. Physiol. (London),* **133,** 54–67 (1956)

36. Loewenstein, W. R., Rathkamp, R. The sites for mechano-electric conversion in a Pacinian corpuscle. *J. Gen. Physiol.,* **41,** 1245–65 (1958)

37. Loewenstein, W. R. Excitation and inactivation in a receptor membrane. *Ann. N.Y. Acad. Sci.,* **94,** 510–34 (1961)

38. Hunt, C. C., Takeuchi, A. Responses of the nerve terminal of the Pacinian corpuscle. *J. Physiol. (London),* **160,** 1–21 (1962)

39. Ozeki, M., Sato, M. Initiation of impulses at the non-myelinated nerve terminal in Pacinian corpuscles. *J. Physiol. (London),* **170,** 167–85 (1964)

40. Gasser, H. S. Properties of dorsal root unmedullated fibers on the two sides of the ganglion. *J. Gen. Physiol.,* **38,** 709–28 (1955)

41. Loewenstein, W. R. Facets of a transducer process. In *Sensory Receptors* (See Ref. 7), 29–43

42. Loewenstein, W. R. Discussion of paper by M. Sato. In *Touch, Heat and Pain* (See Ref. 8), 226–28

43. Sato, M., Ozeki, M. Response of the non-myelinated nerve terminal in Pacinian corpuscles to mechanical and antidromic stimulation and the effect of procaine, choline and cooling. *Japan. J. Physiol.,* **13,** 564–82 (1963)

44. Edwards, C., Ottoson, D. The site of impulse initiation in a nerve cell of a crustacean stretch receptor. *J. Physiol. (London),* **143,** 138–48 (1958)

45. Washizu, Y., Terzuolo, C. A. Impulse activity in the crayfish stretch receptor neuron. *Arch. Ital. Biol.,* **104,** 181–94 (1966)

46. Grampp, W. The impulse activity in

different parts of the slowly adapting stretch receptor neuron of the lobster. *Acta Physiol. Scand.,* **66,** *Suppl. 262* (36 pp., 1966)

47. Wolbarsht, M. L., Hanson, F. E. Electrical activity in the chemoreceptors of the blowfly. III. Dendritic action potentials. *J. Gen. Physiol.,* **48,** 673–83 (1965)

48. Mellon, D., Kennedy, D. Impulse origin and propagation in a bipolar sensory neuron. *J. Gen. Physiol.,* **47,** 487–99 (1964)

49. Mendelson, M. Some factors in the activation of crab movement receptors. *J. Exptl. Biol.,* **40,** 157–69 (1963)

50. Mendelson, M. The site of impulse initiation in bipolar receptor neurons of *Callinectes sapidus* L. *Ibid.,* **45,** 411–20 (1966)

51. Larimer, J. L., Kennedy, D. Visceral afferent signals in the crayfish stomatogastric ganglion. *J. Exptl. Biol.,* **44,** 345–54 (1966)

52. Lippold, O. C. J., Nicholls, J. G., Redfearn, J. W. T. Electrical and mechanical factors in the adaptation of a mammalian muscle spindle. *J. Physiol. (London),* **153,** 209–17 (1960)

53. Alvarez-Buylla, R., Ramirez de Arellano, J. Local responses in Pacinian corpuscles. *Am. J. Physiol.,* **172,** 237–44 (1953)

54. Gray, J. A. B., Sato, M. Properties of the receptor potential in Pacinian corpuscles. *J. Physiol. (London),* **122,** 610–36 (1953)

55. Loewenstein, W. R., Mendelson, M. Components of receptor adaptation in a Pacinian corpuscle. *J. Physiol. (London),* **177,** 377–97 (1965)

56. Ozeki, M., Sato, M. Changes in the membrane potential and the membrane conductance associated with a sustained compression of the non-myelinated nerve terminal in Pacinian corpuscles. *J. Physiol. (London),* **180,** 186–208 (1965)

57. Hubbard, S. J. A study of rapid mechanical events in a mechanoreceptor. *J. Physiol. (London),* **141,** 198–218 (1958)

58. Gray, J. A. B., Matthews, P. B. C. A comparison of the adaptation of the Pacinian corpuscle with the accommodation of its own axon. *J. Physiol. (London),* **114,** 454–64 (1951)

59. Loewenstein, W. R., Skalak, R. Mechanical transmission in a Pacinian corpuscle. An analysis and a theory. *J. Physiol. (London),* **182,** 346–78 (1966)

60. Catton, W. T. A comparison of the responses of frog skin receptors to mechanical and electrical stimulation. *J. Physiol. (London),* **187,** 23–33 (1966)

61. Catton, W. T., Petoe, N. A viscoelastic theory of mechanoreceptor adaptation. *J. Physiol. (London),* **187,** 35–49 (1966)

62. Toyama, K. An analysis of impulse discharges from the spindle receptor. *Japan. J. Physiol.,* **16,** 113–25 (1966)

63. Brown, M. C., Stein, R. B. Quantitative studies of the slowly adapting stretch receptor of the crayfish. *Kybernetik,* **3,** 175–85 (1966)

64. Eyzaguirre, C., Kuffler, S. W. Processes of excitation in the dendrites and in the soma of single isolated sensory nerve cells of the lobster and crayfish. *J. Gen. Physiol.,* **39,** 87–119 (1955)

65. Krnjević, K., van Gelder, N. M. Tension changes in crayfish stretch receptors. *J. Physiol. (London),* **159,** 310–25 (1961)

66. Nakajima, S. Adaptation in stretch receptor neurons of crayfish. *Science,* **146,** 1168–70 (1964)

67. Katz, B. Depolarization of sensory terminals and the initiation of impulses in the muscle spindle. *J. Physiol. (London),* **111,** 261–82 (1950)

68. MacNichol, E. F., Jr. Visual receptors as biological transducers. In *Molecular Structure and Functional Activity of Nerve Cells,* 34–53 (Grenell, R. G., Mullins, L. J., Eds., Am. Inst. Biol. Sci., Washington, 169 pp., 1956)

69. Fuortes, M. G. F. Electric activity of cells in the eye of Limulus. *Am. J. Opthalmol.,* **46,** 210–23 (1958)

70. Terzuolo, C. A., Washizu, Y. Relation between stimulus strength, general potential and impulse frequency in stretch receptor of crustacea. *J. Neurophysiol.,* **25,** 56–66 (1962)

71. Wolbarsht, M. L. Electrical characteristics of insect mechanoreceptors. *J. Gen. Physiol.,* **44,** 105–22 (1960)

72. Loewenstein, W. R. Mechanisms of nerve impulse initiation in a pres-

sure receptor (Lorenzian ampulla). *Nature,* **188,** 1034–35 (1960)

73. Agin, D. Hodgkin-Huxley equations : Logarithmic relation between membrane current and frequency of repetitive activity. *Nature,* **201,** 625–26 (1964)

74. Stein, R. B. The frequency of nerve action potentials generated by applied currents. *Proc. Roy. Soc. B,* **167,** 64–86 (1967)

75. Chapman, R. A. The repetitive responses of isolated axons from the crab, *Carcinus maenas. J. Exptl. Biol.,* **45,** 475–88 (1966)

76. Spyropoulos, C. S. (Personal communication, 1967)

77. Tomita, T., Wright, E. B. A study of the crustacean axon repetitive response : I. The effect of membrane potential and resistance. *J. Cellular Comp. Physiol.,* **65,** 195–209 (1965)

78. Wright, E. B., Tomita, T. A study of the crustacean axon repetitive response : II. The effect of cations, sodium, calcium (magnesium), potassium and hydrogen (pH) in the external medium. *Ibid.,* 211–28

79. Fuortes, M. G. F., Mantegazzini, F. Interpretation of the repetitive firing of nerve cells. *J. Gen. Physiol.,* **45,** 1163–79 (1962)

80. Fuortes, M. G. F., Poggio, G. F. Transient responses to sudden illumination in cells of the eye of *Limulus. J. Gen. Physiol.,* **46,** 435–52 (1963)

81. Hodgkin, A. L. The local electric changes associated with repetitive action in a non-medullated axon. *J. Physiol. (London),* **107,** 165–81 (1948)

82. Granit, R., Kernell, D., Shortess, G. K. Quantitative aspects of repetitive firing of mammalian motoneurons, caused by injected currents. *J. Physiol. (London),* **168,** 911–31 (1963)

83. Creutzfeldt, O. D., Lux, H. D., Nacimiento, A. C. Intracelluläre Reizung corticaler Nervenzellen. *Arch. Ges. Physiol.,* **281,** 129–51 (1964)

84. Kernell, D. High-frequency repetitive firing of cat lumbosacral motoneurones stimulated by long-lasting injected currents. *Acta Physiol. Scand.,* **65,** 74–86 (1966)

85. Takeda, K., Kennedy, D. The mechanism of discharge pattern formation in crayfish interneurons.

J. Gen. Physiol., **48,** 435–53 (1965)

86. Kernell, D. The limits of firing frequency in cat lumbosacral motoneurones possessing different time course of afterhyperpolarization. *Acta Physiol. Scand.,* **65,** 87–100 (1965)

87. FitzHugh, R. Impulses and physiological states in theoretical models of nerve membrane. *Biophys. J.,* **1,** 445–66 (1961)

88. Kernell, D. The adaptation and the relation between discharge frequency and current strength of cat lumbosacral motoneurones stimulated by long-lasting injected currents. *Acta Physiol. Scand.,* **65,** 65–73 (1965)

89. Frankenhaeuser, B., Hodgkin, A. L. The after-effects of impulses in the giant nerve fibres of *Loligo. J. Physiol. (London),* **131,** 341–76 (1956)

90. Narahashi, T. The properties of insect axons. *Advan. Insect Physiol.,* **1,** 175–256 (1963)

91. Orkand, R. K., Nicholls, J. G., Kuffler, S. W. Effect of nerve impulses on the membrane potential of glial cells in the central nervous system of amphibia. *J. Neurophysiol.,* **29,** 788–806 (1966)

92. Gasser, H. S., Grundfest, H. Action and excitability in mammalian A fibers. *Am. J. Physiol.,* **117,** 113–33 (1936)

93. Ritchie, J. M., Straub, R. W. The hyperpolarization which follows activity in mammalian non-medullated fibres. *J. Physiol. (London),* **136,** 80–97 (1957)

94. Gage, P. W., Hubbard, J. I. Ionic changes responsible for posttetanic hyperpolarization. *Nature,* **203,** 653–54 (1964)

95. Nakajima, S., Takahashi, K. Post-tetanic hyperpolarization and electrogenic Na pump in stretch receptor neurone of crayfish. *J. Physiol. (London),* **187,** 105–27 (1966)

96. Starr, A. Suppression of single unit activity in cochlear nucleus of the cat following sound stimulation. *J. Neurophysiol.,* **28,** 850–62 (1965)

97. Kiang, N. Y.-s., Watanabe, T., Thomas, E. C., Clark, L. F. *Discharge Patterns of Single Fibers in the Cat's Auditory Nerve*

(Mass. Inst. Technol. Press, Cambridge, Mass., 154 pp., 1965)

98. Kiang, N. Y.-s., Watanabe, T., Thomas, E. C., Clark, L. F. Stimulus coding in the cat's auditory nerve. *Ann. Otol. Rhinol. Laryngol.*, **71**, 1009–26 (1962)

99. Kiang, N. Y.-s. Stimulus coding in the auditory nerve and cochlear nucleus. *Acta Oto-Laryngol.*, **59**, 186–200 (1965)

100. Rose, J. E., Brugge, J. F., Anderson, D. J., Hind, J. E. Phaselocked response to low-frequency tones in single auditory nerve fibers of the squirrel monkey. *J. Neurophysiol.*, **30**, 769–93 (1967)

101. Hind, J. E., Anderson, D. J., Brugge, J. F., Rose, J. E. Coding of information pertaining to paired low-frequency tones in single auditory nerve fibers of the squirrel monkey. *Ibid.*, 794–816

102. Békésy, G. von. *Experiments in Hearing* (McGraw-Hill, New York, 745 pp., 1960)

103. Katsuki, Y., Kanno, Y., Suga, N., Mannen, M. Primary auditory neurons of monkey. *Japan. J. Physiol.*, **11**, 678–83 (1961)

104. Weiss, T. F. A model of the peripheral auditory system. *Kybernetik*, **3**, 153–74 (1966)

105. Tasaki, I. Nerve impulses in individual auditory nerve fibers of guinea pig. *J. Neurophysiol.*, **17**, 97–122 (1954)

106. Katsuki, Y., Suga, N., Kanno, Y. Neural mechanism of the peripheral and central auditory system in monkeys. *J. Accoust. Soc. Am.*, **34**, 1396–1410 (1962)

107. Rupert, A., Moushegian, G., Galambos, R. Unit responses to sound from auditory nerve of the cat. *J. Neurophysiol.*, **26**, 449–65 (1963)

108. Nomoto, M., Suga, N., Katsuki, Y. Discharge pattern and inhibition of primary auditory nerve fibers in the monkey. *J. Neurophysiol.*, **27**, 768–87 (1964)

109. Deathrage, B. H. Examination of binaural interaction. *J. Acoust. Soc. Am.*, **39**, 232–49 (1966)

110. Shouten, J. F., Ritsma, R. J., Lopes Cardozo, B. Pitch of the residue. *J. Acoust. Soc. Am.*, **34**, 1418–24 (1962)

111. Frishkopf, L. S. Excitation and inhibition of primary auditory neurons in the little brown bat. *J. Acoust. Soc. Am.*, **36**, 1016 (1964)

112. Stevens, S. S., Davis, H. *Hearing. Its Psychology and Physiology* (Wiley, New York, 489 pp., 1938)

113. Goldberg, J. M., Greenwood, D. D. Response of neurons of the dorsal and posteroventral cochlear nuclei of the cat to acoustic stimuli of long duration. *J. Neurophysiol.*, **29**, 72–93 (1966)

114. Greenwood, D. D., Maruyama, N. Excitatory and inhibitory response areas of auditory neurons in the cochlear nucleus. *J. Neurophysiol.*, **28**, 863–92 (1965)

115. Lorente de Nó, R. The sensory endings in the cochlea. *Laryngoscope*, **47**, 373–77 (1937)

116. Fernandez, C. The innervation of the cochlea (guinea pig). *Laryngoscope*, **61**, 1152–72 (1951)

117. Katsuki, Y. Neural mechanisms of auditory sensation in cats. In *Sensory Communication*, 561–84 (Rosenblith, W. A., Ed., Wiley, New York, 844 pp., 1961)

118. Iurato, S. Efferent fibers to the sensory cells of Corti's organ. *Exptl. Cell Res.*, **27**, 162–64 (1962)

119. Kimura, R., Wersäll, J. Termination of the olivo-cochlear bundle in relation to the outer hair cells of the organ of Corti in guinea pig. *Acta Oto-Laryngol.*, **55**, 11–32 (1962)

120. Smith, C. A., Rasmussen, G. L. Recent observations on the olivo-cochlear bundle. *Ann. Otol. Rhinol. Laryngol.*, **72**, 489–506 (1963)

121. Spoendlin, H. H., Gacek, R. R. Electronmicroscopic study of the efferent and afferent innervation of the organ of Corti in the cat. *Ann. Otol. Rhinol. Laryngol.*, **72**, 660–86 (1963)

122. Smith, C. A., Rasmussen, G. L. Degeneration in the efferent nerve endings in the cochlea after axonal section. *J. Cell Biol.*, **26**, 63–77 (1965)

123. Galambos, R. Suppression of auditory nerve activity by stimulation of efferent fibers to cochlea. *J. Neuro-Physiol.*, **19**, 424–37 (1956)

124. Fex, J. Augmentation of cochlear microphonics by stimulation of efferent fibers to the cochlea. *Acta Oto-Laryngol.*, **50**, 540–41 (1959)

125. Desmedt, J. E. Auditory-evoked potentials from cochlea to cortex as influenced by activation of the

efferent olivo-cochlear bundle. *J. Acoust. Soc. Am.,* **34,** 1478–96 (1962)

126. Fex, J. Auditory activity in centrifugal and centripetal cochlear fibres in cat. *Acta Physiol. Scand.,* **55,** *Suppl. 189* (68 pp., 1962)

127. Desmedt, J. E., LaGrutta, V. Function of the uncrossed efferent olivo-cochlear fibres in the cat. *Nature,* **200,** 472–74 (1963)

128. Desmedt, J. E., Delwaide, P. J. Functional properties of the efferent cochlear bundle of the pigeon revealed by stereotaxic stimulation. *Exptl. Neurol.,* **11,** 1–26 (1965)

129. Desmedt, J. E., Monaco, P. Suppression par la strychnine de l'effet inhibiteur centrifuge exercé par le faisceau olivo-cochléare. *Arch. Intern. Pharmacodyn.,* **129,** 244–48 (1960)

130. Desmedt, J. E., Monaco, P. Mode of action of the efferent olivo-cochlear bundle on the inner ear. *Nature,* **192,** 1263–65 (1961)

131. Fex, J. Efferent inhibition in the cochlea related to hair-cell dc activity: study of postsynaptic activity of the crossed olivo-cochlear fibres in the cat. *J. Acoust. Soc. Am.,* **41,** 666–75 (1967)

132. Fex, J. Auditory activity in uncrossed centrifugal cochlear fibres in cat. *Acta Physiol. Scand.,* **64,** 43–57 (1965)

133. Wiederhold, M. L., Peake, W. T. Efferent inhibition of auditory-nerve responses: dependence on acoustic-stimulus parameters. *J. Acoust. Soc. Am.,* **40,** 1427–30 (1966)

134. Sohmer, H. The effect of contralateral olivo-cochlear bundle stimulation on the cochlear potentials evoked by acoustic stimuli of various frequencies and intensities. *Acta Oto-Laryngol.,* **60,** 59–70 (1965)

135. Wiederhold, M. L., Swift, S. H. Electrical stimulation of the crossed olivo-cochlear bundle—its effect on responses of auditory-nerve fibers to tone bursts. *J. Acoust. Soc. Am.,* **41,** 1584 (1967)

136. Galambos, R. Inhibition of activity in single auditory nerve fibers by acoustic stimulation. *J. Neurophysiol.,* **7,** 287–303 (1944)

137. Rose, J. E., Galambos, R., Hughes,

J. R. Microelectrode studies of the cochlear nuclei of the cat. *Bull. Johns Hopkins Hosp.,* **104,** 211–51 (1959)

138. Katsuki, Y., Sumi, T., Uchiyama, H., Watanabe, T. Electric responses of auditory neurons in cat to sound stimulation. *J. Neurophysiol.,* **21,** 569–88 (1958)

139. Evans, E. F., Nelson, P. G. Responses of neurones in cat cochlear nucleus to modulated tonal stimuli. *J. Acoust. Soc. Am.,* **40,** 1275 (1966)

140. Pfeiffer, R. R. Classification of response patterns of spike discharges for units in the cochlear nucleus: tone-burst stimulation. *Exptl. Brain Res.,* **1,** 220–35 (1966)

141. Pfeiffer, R. R., Kiang, N. Y. -s. Spike discharge patterns of spontaneous and continuously stimulated activity in the cochlear nucleus of anesthetized cats. *Biophys. J.,* **5,** 301–16 (1965)

142. Lorente de Nó, R. Anatomy of the eighth nerve. III. General plan of structure of the primary cochlear nuclei. *Laryngoscope,* **43,** 327–50 (1933)

143. Harrison, J. M., Irving, R. The anterior ventral cochlear nucleus. *J. Comp. Neurol.,* **124,** 15–42 (1965)

144. Harrison, J. M., Irving, R. The organization of the posterior ventral cochlear nucleus in the rat. *Ibid.,* **126,** 391–402 (1966)

145. Harrison, J. M., Irving, R. Ascending connections of the anterior ventral cochlear nucleus in the rat. *Ibid.,* 51–64

146. Warr, W. B. Fiber degeneration following lesions in the anterior ventral cochlear nucleus of the cat. *Exptl. Neurol.,* **14,** 453–74 (1966)

147. Kiang, N. Y.-s, Pfeiffer, R. R., Warr, W. B., Backus, A. S. N. Stimulus coding in the cochlear nucleus. *Ann. Otol. Rhinol. Laryngol.,* **74,** 463–85 (1965)

148. Koerber, K. C., Pfeiffer, R. R., Warr, W. B., Kiang, N. Y.-s. Spontaneous spike discharges from single units in the cochlear nucleus after destruction of the cochlea. *Exptl. Neurol.,* **16,** 119–30 (1966)

149. Rasmussen, G. L. Anatomical relationships of ascending and descending auditory systems. In

Neurological Aspects of Auditory and Vestibular Disorders, 1–15 (Fields, W., Alford, B. R., Eds., Thomas, Springfield, Ill., 383 pp., 1964)

150. Galambos, R., Schwartzkopff, J., Rupert, A. Microelectrode study of superior olivary nuclei. *Am. J. Physiol.*, **197**, 527–36 (1959)

151. Moushegian, G., Rupert, A., Whitcomb, M. A. Medial-superior-olivary-unit response patterns to monaural and binaural clicks. *J. Acoust. Soc. Am.*, **36**, 196–202 (1964)

152. Hall, J. L. Binaural interaction in the accessory superior-olivary nucleus of the cat. *J. Acoust. Soc. Am.*, **37**, 814–23 (1965)

153. Rupert, A., Moushegian, G., Whitcomb, M. A. Superior-olivary response patterns to monaural and binaural clicks. *J. Acoust. Soc. Am.*, **39**, 1069–76 (1966)

154. Moushegian, G., Rupert, A., Whitcomb, M. A. Brain-stem neuronal response patterns to monaural and binaural tones. *J. Neurophysiol.*, **27**, 1174–91 (1964)

155. Goldberg, J. M., Brown, P. B. Response of neurons of the superior olivary complex of the dog to dichotic stimuli. *Physiologist*, **9**, 190 (1966)

156. Neff, W. D. Neural structures concerned in localization of sound in space. *Psychol. Beitr.*, **6**, 492–500 (1962)

157. Masterton, B., Jane, J. A., Diamond, I. T. Role of brainstem auditory structures in sound localization. I. Trapezoid body, superior-olive, and lateral lemniscus. *J. Neurophysiol.*, **30**, 341–59 (1967)

158. Neff, W. D., Fisher, J. F., Diamond, I. T., Yela, M. Role of auditory cortex in discrimination requiring localization of sound in space. *J. Neurophysiol.*, **19**, 500–12 (1956)

159. Masterton, R. B., Diamond, I. T. Effects of auditory cortex ablation on discrimination of small binaural time differences. *J. Neurophysiol.*, **27**, 15–36 (1964)

160. Stotler, W. A. An experimental study of the cells and connections of the superior olivary complex of the cat. *J. Comp. Neurol.*, **98**, 401–32 (1953)

161. Powell, T. P. S., Cowan, W. M. An experimental study of the projection of the cochlea. *J. Anat.*, **96**, 269–84 (1962)

162. Tsuchitani, C., Boudreau, J. C. Single unit analysis of cat superior olive S segment with tonal stimuli. *J. Neurophysiol.*, **29**, 684–97 (1966)

163. Goldberg, J. M., Smith, F. D., Adrian, H. O. Response of single units of the superior olivary complex of the cat to acoustic stimuli: laterality of afferent projections. *Anat. Record*, **145**, 232 (1963)

164. Rose, J. E., Greenwood, D. D., Goldberg, J. M., Hind, J. E. Some discharge characteristics of single neurons in the inferior colliculus of the cat. I. Tonotopical organization, relation of spike-counts to tone intensity and firing patterns of single elements. *J. Neurophysiol.*, **26**, 294–320 (1963)

165. Hind, J. E., Goldberg, J. M., Greenwood, D. D., Rose, J. E. Some discharge characteristics of single neurons in the inferior colliculus of the cat. II. Timing of the discharges and observations on binaural stimulation. *Ibid.*, 321–41

166. Nelson, P. G., Erulkar, S. D. Synaptic mechanisms of excitation and inhibition in the central auditory pathway. *J. Neurophysiol.*, **26**, 908–23 (1963)

167. Grinnell, A. D. The neurophysiology of audition in bats: intensity and frequency parameters. *J. Physiol. (London)*, **167**, 38–66 (1963)

168. Suga, N. Analysis of frequency-modulated sounds by auditory neurones of echo-locating bats. *J. Physiol. (London)*, **179**, 26–53 (1965)

169. Potter, H. D. Patterns of acoustically evoked discharges of neurons in the mesencephalon of the bullfrog. *J. Neurophysiol.*, **28**, 1155–84 (1965)

170. Rose, J. E., Gross, N. B., Geisler, C. D., Hind, J. E. Some neural mechanisms in the inferior colliculus of the cat which may be relevant to localization of a sound source. *J. Neurophysiol.*, **29**, 288–314 (1966)

171. Grinnell, A. D. The neurophysiology of audition in bats: directional localization and binaural interaction. *J. Physiol. (London)*, **167**, 97–113 (1963)

172. Suga, N. Single unit activity in cochlear nucleus and inferior

colliculus of echo-locating bats. *J. Physiol. (London)*, **172**, 449–74 (1964)

173. Grinnell, A. D., Grinnell, V. S. Neural correlates of vertical localization by echo-locating bats. *J. Physiol. (London)*, **181**, 830–51 (1965)

174. Nelson, P. G., Erulkar, S. D., Bryan, J. S. Responses of units of the inferior colliculus to time-varying acoustic stimuli. *J. Neurophysiol.*, **29**, 834–60 (1966)

175. Suga, N. Recovery cycles and responses to frequency modulated tone pulses in auditory neurones of echo-locating bats. *J. Physiol. (London)*, **175**, 50–80 (1964)

176. Suga, N. Functional properties of auditory neurones in the cortex of echo-locating bats. *J. Physiol. (London)*, **181**, 671–700 (1965)

177. Whitfield, I. C., Evans, E. F. Responses of auditory cortical neurons to stimuli of changing frequency. *J. Neurophysiol.*, **28**, 655–72 (1965)

178. Buser, P., St. Laurent, J., Menini, C. Intervention du colliculus inférieur dans l'élaboration et le controle cortical spécifique des décharges cloniques au son chez le chat sous chloralose. *Exptl. Brain Res.*, **1**, 102–26 (1966)

179. Ascher, P., Jassik-Gerschenfeld, D., Buser, P. Participation des aires corticales sensorielles à l'élaboration de réponses motrices extrapyramidales. *Electroencephalog. Clin. Neurophysiol.*, **15**, 246–64 (1963)

180. Nobel, K. W., Dewson, J. H. A corticofugal projection from insular and temporal cortex to the homolateral inferior colliculus in cat. *J. Auditory Res.*, **6**, 67–76 (1966)

181. Moore, R. Y., Goldberg, J. M. Ascending projections of the inferior colliculus in the cat. *J. Comp. Neurol.*, **121**, 109–36 (1963)

182. Goldberg, J. M., Moore, R. Y. Ascending projections of the lateral lemniscus in the cat and monkey. *Ibid.*, **129**, 143–56 (1967)

183. Ascher, P., Gachelin, G. Rôle de colliculus supérieur dans l'élaboration du réponses motrices à des stimulations visuelles. *Brain Res.*, **3**, 327–42 (1967)

184. Adrian, H. O., Lifschitz, W. M., Tavitas, R. J., Galli, F. P. Activity of neural units in medial geniculate body of cat and rabbit. *J. Neurophysiol.*, **29**, 1046–60 (1966)

185. Watanabe, T., Yanagisawa, K., Kanzaki, J., Katsuki, Y. Cortical efferent flow influencing unit responses of medial geniculate body to sound stimulation. *Exptl Brain Res.*, **2**, 302–17 (1966)

186. Mickle, W. A., Ades, H. W. Rostral projection pathway of the vestibular system. *Am. J. Physiol.*, **176**, 243–46 (1954)

187. Altman, J., Carpenter, M. B. Fiber projections of the superior colliculus in the cat. *J. Comp. Neurol.*, **116**, 157–78 (1961)

188. Kruger, L., Albe-Fessard, D. Distribution of responses to somatic afferent stimuli in the diencephalon of the cat under chloralose anesthesia. *Exptl. Neurol.*, **2**, 442–67 (1960)

189. Mehler, W. H., Feferman, M. E., Nauta, W. J. H. Ascending axon degeneration following anterolateral cordotomy: an experimental study in the monkey. *Brain*, **83**, 718–50 (1960)

190. Poggio, G. F., Mountcastle, V. B. A study of the functional contributions of the lemniscal and spinothalamic systems to somatic sensitibility. *Johns Hopkins Hosp. Bull.*, **106**, 266–316 (1960)

191. Whitlock, D. G., Perl, E. R. Thalamic projections of spinothalamic pathways in monkey. *Exptl. Neurol.*, **3**, 240–55 (1961)

192. Darian-Smith, I. Cortical projections of thalamic neurones excited by mechanical stimulation of the face of the cat. *J. Physiol. (London)*, **171**, 339–60 (1964)

193. Wepsic, J. G. Multimodal sensory activation of cells in the magnocellular medial geniculate nucleus. *Exptl. Neurol.*, **15**, 299–318 (1966)

194. Erulkar, S. D., Rose, J. E., Davies, P. W. Single unit activity in the auditory cortex of the cat. *Johns Hopkins Hosp. Bull.*, **99**, 55–86 (1956)

195. Bogdanski, D. F., Galambos, R. Studies of the auditory system with implanted electrodes: Chronic microelectrode studies. In *Neural Mechanisms of the Auditory and Vestibular Systems*, 143–48 (Rasmussen, G. L., Windle, W. F.,

Eds., Thomas, Springfield, Ill., 422 pp., 1960)

196. Gerstein, G. L., Kiang, N. Y.-s. Responses of single units in the auditory cortex. *Exptl. Neurol.,* **10,** 1–18 (1964)

197. Evans, E. F., Whitfield, I. C. Classification of unit responses in the auditory cortex of the unanesthetized and unrestrained cat. *J. Physiol. (London),* **171,** 476–93 (1964)

198. Oonishi, S., Katsuki, Y. Functional organization and integrative mechanism on the auditory cortex of the cat. *Japan. J. Physiol.,* **15,** 342–65 (1965)

199. Brugge, J. F., Dubrovsky, N., Rose, J. E. Some discharge characteristics of single neurons in cat's auditory cortex. *Science,* **146,** 433–34 (1964)

200. Kuffler, S. W. Discharge patterns and functional organization of mammalian retina. *J. Neurophysiol.,* **16,** 37–68 (1953)

201. Barlow, H. B., FitzHugh, R., Kuffler, S. W. Change of organization in the receptive fields of the cat's retina during dark adaptation. *J. Physiol. (London),* **137,** 338–54 (1957)

202. Wagner, H. G., MacNichol, E. F., Jr., Wolbarsht, M. L. Functional basis for "on"-center and "off"-center receptive fields in the retina. *J. Opt. Soc. Am.,* **53,** 66–70 (1963)

203. Brown, J. E., Rojas, J. A. Rat retinal ganglion cells: receptive field organization and maintained activity. *J. Neurophysiol.,* **28,** 1073–90 (1965)

204. Michael, C. R. Receptive fields of directionally selective units in the optic nerve of the ground squirrel. *Science,* **152,** 1092–95 (1966)

205. Michael, C. R. Receptive fields of opponent color units in the optic nerve of the ground squirrel. *Ibid.,* 1095–97

206. Hubel, D. H., Wiesel, T. N. Receptive fields of optic nerve fibers in the spider monkey. *J. Physiol. (London),* **154,** 572–80 (1960)

207. Ratliff, F. *Mach Bands: Quantitative Studies on Neural Networks in the Retina* (Holden-Day, San Francisco, 365 pp., 1965)

208. Westheimer, G. Spatial interaction in the human retina during scotopic vision. *J. Physiol. (London),* **181,** 881–94 (1965)

209. Westheimer, G. Spatial interaction in human cone vision. *Ibid.,* **190,** 139–54 (1967)

210. Rodieck, R. W., Stone, J. Analysis of receptive fields of cat retinal ganglion cells. *J. Neurophysiol.,* **28,** 833–49 (1965)

211. Rodieck, R. W. Quantitative analysis of cat retinal ganglion cell response to visual stimuli. *Vision Res.,* **5,** 583–601 (1965)

212. Enroth-Cugell, C., Robson, J. G. The contrast sensitivity of retinal ganglion cells of the cat. *J. Physiol. (London),* **187,** 517–52 (1966)

213. Gouras, P., Link, K. Rod and cone interaction in dark-adapted monkey ganglion cells. *J. Physiol. (London),* **184,** 499–510 (1966)

214. Gouras, P. Rod and cone independence in the electroretinogram of the dark-adapted monkey's penfovea. *J. Physiol. (London),* **187,** 455–64 (1966)

215. Barlow, H. B., Hill, R. M., Levick, W. R. Retinal ganglion cells responding selectively to direction and speed of image motion in the rabbit. *J. Physiol. (London),* **173,** 377–407 (1964)

216. Levick, W. R. Receptive fields and trigger features of ganglion cells in the visual streak of the rabbit's retina. *J. Physiol. (London),* **188,** 285–307 (1967)

217. Spinelli, D. N., Weingarten, M. Afferent and efferent activity in single units of the cat's optic nerve. *Exptl. Neurol.,* **15,** 347–62 (1966)

218. Cooper, G. F., Robson, J. G. Directionally selective movement detectors in the retina of the grey squirrel. *J. Physiol. (London),* **186,** 116–17P (1966)

219. Barlow, H. B., Levick, W. R. The mechanism of directionally selective units in rabbit's retina. *J. Physiol. (London),* **178,** 477–504 (1965)

220. McIlwain, J. T. Receptive fields of optic tract axons and lateral geniculate cells: peripheral extent and barbiturate sensitivity. *J. Neurophysiol.,* **27,** 1154–73 (1964)

221. McIlwain, J. T. Some evidence concerning the physiological basis of the periphery effect in the cat's retina. *Exptl. Brain Res.,* **1,** 265–71 (1966)

222. Weingarten, M., Spinelli, D. N. Retinal receptive field changes pro-

duced by auditory and somatic stimulation. *Exptl. Neurol.*, **15**, 363–76 (1966)

223. Sefton, A. J., Burke, W. Reverberatory inhibitory circuits in the lateral geniculate nucleus of the rat. *Nature*, **205**, 1325–26 (1965)

224. Sefton, A. J., Burke, W. Mechanism of recurrent inhibition in the lateral geniculate nucleus of the rat. *Ibid.*, **211**, 1276–78 (1966)

225. Burke, W., Sefton, A. J. Discharge patterns of principal cells and interneurones in the lateral geniculate nucleus of rat. *J. Physiol. (London)*, **187**, 201–12 (1966)

226. Burke, W., Sefton, A. J. Recovery of responsiveness of cells of lateral geniculate nucleus of rat. *Ibid.*, 213–29

227. Burke, W., Sefton, A. J. Inhibitory mechanisms in lateral geniculate nucleus of rat. *Ibid.*, 231–46

228. Fuster, J. M., Creutzfeldt, O. D., Straschill, M. Intracellular recording of neuronal activity in the visual system. *Z. Vergleich. Physiol.*, **49**, 605–22 (1965)

229. Andersen, P., Eccles, J. C. Inhibitory phasing of neuronal discharge. *Nature*, **196**, 645–47 (1962)

230. O'Leary, J. L. A structural analysis of the lateral geniculate nucleus of the cat. *J. Comp. Neurol.*, **73**, 405–30 (1940)

231. Szentágothai, J., Hámori, J., Tömböl, T. Degeneration and electron microscope analysis of the synaptic glomeruli in the lateral geniculate body. *Exptl. Brain Res.*, **2**, 283–301 (1966)

232. Aitkin, L. M., Dunlop, C. W., Webster, W. R. Click-evoked response patterns of single units in the medial geniculate body of the cat. *J. Neurophysiol.*, **29**, 109–23 (1966)

233. Hayhow, W. R. The cytoarchitecture of the lateral geniculate body in the cat in relation to the distribution of crossed and uncrossed optic fibers. *J. Comp. Neurol.*, **110**, 1–63 (1958)

234. Moore, R. Y., Karapas, F., Frenkel, M. Lateral geniculate projection from discrete retinal lesions in the cat. *Am. J. Opthalmol.*, **62**, 918–25 (1966)

235. Erulkar, S. D., Fillenz, M. Single-unit activity in the lateral geniculate body of the cat. *J. Physiol. (London)*, **154**, 206–18 (1960)

236. Bishop, P. O., Kozak, W., Levick, W. R., Wakkur, G. J. The determination of the projection of the visual field onto the lateral geniculate nucleus in the cat. *J. Physiol. (London)*, **163**, 503–39 (1962)

237. Hubel, D. H., Wiesel, T. N. Integrative action in the cat's lateral geniculate body. *J. Physiol. (London)*, **155**, 385–98 (1961)

238. Suzuki, H., Kato, E. Binocular interaction at cat's lateral geniculate body. *J. Neurophysiol.*, **29**, 909–20 (1966)

239. Lindsley, D. F., Chow, K. L., Gollender, M. Dichoptic interactions of lateral geniculate neurons of cats to contralateral and ipsilateral eye stimulation. *J. Neurophysiol.*, **30**, 628–44 (1967)

240. McIlwain, J. T., Creutzfeldt, O. D. Microelectrode study of synaptic excitation and inhibition in the lateral geniculate nucleus of the cat. *J. Neurophysiol.*, **30**, 1–21 (1967)

241. Iwama, K., Sakakura, H., Kasamatsu, T. Presynaptic inhibition in the lateral geniculate body induced by stimulation of the cerebral cortex. *Japan. J. Physiol.*, **15**, 310–22 (1965)

242. Suzuki, H., Kato, E. Cortically induced presynaptic inhibition in cat's lateral geniculate body. *Tohoku J. Exptl. Med.*, **86**, 277–89 (1965)

243. Angel, A., Magni, F., Strata, P. Evidence of pre-synaptic inhibition in the lateral geniculate body. *Nature*, **208**, 495–96 (1965)

244. Marchiafava, P. L., Pompeiano, O. Enhanced excitability of intrageniculate optic tract endings produced by vestibular volleys. *Arch. Ital. Biol.*, **104**, 459–79 (1966)

245. Meulders, M., Boisacq-Schepens, N., Godfraind, J. M., Colle, J. Étude macro- et microphysiologique des projections sensorielles somatiques au niveau du corps genouillé latéral du chat anesthesié au chloralose. *Arch. Ital. Biol.*, **104**, 480–502 (1966)

246. Pecci-Saavedra, J., Wilson, P. D., Doty, R. W. Presynaptic inhibition in primate lateral geniculate nucleus. *Nature*, **210**, 740–42 (1966)

247. Bizzi, E. Changes in the orthodromic and antidromic response of optic tract during the eye movements of

sleep. *J. Neurophysiol.*, **29**, 861–70 (1966)

248. Kawamura, H., Marchiafava, P. L. Modulation of transmission of optic nerve impulses in the alert cat: Evidence of presynaptic inhibition of primary optic afferents during ocular movements. *Brain Res.*, **1**, 213–15 (1966)

249. Volkmann, F. C. Vision during voluntary saccadic eye movements. *J. Opt. Soc. Am.*, **52**, 571–78 (1962)

250. Zuber, B. L., Stark, L. Saccadic suppression: Elevation of visual threshold associated with saccadic eye movements. *Exptl. Neurol.*, **16**, 65–79 (1966)

251. Marchiafava, P. L. Binocular reciprocal interaction upon optic fiber endings in the lateral geniculate nucleus of the cat. *Brain Res.*, **2**, 188–91 (1966)

252. Colonnier, M., Guillery, R. W. Synaptic organization in the lateral geniculate nucleus of the monkey. *Z. Zellforsch.*, **62**, 333–55 (1964)

253. DeValois, R. L. Color vision mechanisms in the monkey. *J. Gen. Physiol.*, **43**, Part II, 115–28 (1960)

254. DeValois, R. L., Abramov, I., Jacobs, G. H. An analysis of response patterns of LGN cells. *J. Opt. Soc. Am.* **56**, 966–77 (1966)

255. DeValois, R. L., Abramov, I., Mead, W. R. Single cell analysis of wavelength discrimination at the lateral geniculate nucleus in the macaque. *J. Neurophysiol.*, **30**, 415–33 (1967)

256. Wiesel, T. N., Hubel, D. H. Spatial and chromatic interactions in the lateral geniculate body of the rhesus monkey. *J. Neurophysiol.*, **29**, 1115–56 (1966)

257. Heric, T. M., Kruger, L. Organization of the visual projection upon the optic tectum of a reptile (*Alligator mississippiensis*). *J. Comp. Neurol.*, **124**, 101–11 (1965)

258. Siminoff, R., Schwassmann, H., Kruger, L. An electrophysiological study of the visual projection to the superior colliculus of the rat. *J. Comp. Neurol.* **127**, 435–44 (1966)

259. Garey, L. J. Interrelationships of the visual cortex and superior colliculus in the cat. *Nature*, **207**, 1410–11 (1965)

260. Lyubimov, N. N. Relay of visual information at midbrain level.

Fed. Proc. (Transl. Suppl.), **24**, 1011–14 (1965)

261. Jassik-Gerschenfeld, D., Ascher, P., Guevara, J. A. Influence of the geniculo-cortical system on visual responses of the superior colliculus. *Arch. Ital. Biol.*, **104**, 30–49 (1966)

262. Marchiafava, P. L., Pepeu, G. C. Electrophysiological study of tectal responses to optic nerve volley. *Arch. Ital. Biol.*, **104**, 406–20 (1966)

263. Jassik-Gerschenfeld, D. Somesthetic and visual responses of superior colliculus neurones. *Nature*, **208**, 898–900 (1965)

264. Horn, G., Hill, R. M. Responsiveness to sensory stimulation of units in the superior colliculus and subjacent tectotegmental regions of the rabbit. *Exptl. Neurol.*, **14**, 199–223 (1966)

265. Albe-Fessard, D., Rougeul, A. Activitiés d'origine somesthésique évoquées sur le cortex non-spécifique du chat anesthésié au chloralose: rôle du centre médian du thalamus. *Electroencephalog. Clin. Neurophysiol.*, **10**, 131–52 (1958)

266. Buser, P., Borenstein, P., Bruner, J. Etudes des systèmes "associatifs" visuels et auditifs chez le chat anesthésié au chloralose. *Electroencephalog. Clin. Neurophysiol.*, **11**, 305–24 (1959)

267. Buser, P., Borenstein, P. Réponses somethéstiques, visuelles et auditives, recueillies au niveau du cortex "associatif" suprasylvien chez le chat curarisé non anesthésie. *Electroencephalog. Clin. Neurophysiol.*, **11**, 285–304 (1959)

268. Thompson, R. F., Sindberg, R. M. Auditory response fields in association and motor cortex of cat. *J. Neurophysiol.*, **23**, 87–105 (1960)

269. Thompson, R. F., Johnson, R. H., Hoopes, J. J. Organization of auditory, somatic sensory, and visual projection to association fields of cerebral cortex in the cat. *J. Neurophysiol.*, **26**, 343–64 (1963)

270. Bignall, K. E., Imbert, M., Buser, P. Optic projections to nonvisual cortex of the cat. *J. Neurophysiol.*, **29**, 396–409 (1966)

271. Imbert, M., Bignall, K. E., Buser, P. Neocortical interconnections in the cat. *Ibid.*, 382–95

272. Adrian, H. O., Goldberg, J. M.,

Brugge, J. F. Auditory evoked cortical potentials after lesions of brachium of inferior colliculus. *J. Neurophysiol.*, **29,** 456–66 (1966)

273. MacLean, P. D. The limbic and visual cortex in phylogeny: Further insights from anatomic and microelectrode studies. In *Evolution of the Forebrain*, 443–53 (Hassler, R., Stephan, H., Eds., Georg Thieme, Stuttgart, 1966)

274. Cuénod, M., Casey, K. L., MacLean, P. D. Unit analysis of visual input to posterior limbic cortex. I. Photic stimulation. *J. Neurophysiol.*, **28,** 1101–17 (1965)

275. Casey, K. L., Cuénod, M., MacLean, P. D. Unit analysis of visual input to posterior limbic cortex. II. Intracerebral stimuli. *Ibid.*, 1118–31

276. Spinelli, D. N., Pribram, K. H. Changes in visual recovery functions produced by temporal lobe stimulation in monkeys. *Electroencephalog. Clin. Neurophysiol.*, **20,** 44–49 (1966)

277. Dewson, J. H., Nobel, K. W., Pribram, K. H. Corticofugal influences at cochlear nucleus of the cat: Some effects of ablations of insular-temporal cortex. *Brain Res.*, **2,** 151–59 (1966)

278. Cauna, N. Fine structure of the receptor organs and its probable functional significance. In *Touch, Heat and Pain* (See Ref. 8), 117–27

279. Iggo, A. Cutaneous receptors with a high sensitivity to mechanical displacement. In *Touch, Heat and Pain* (See Ref. 8), 237–56

280. Iggo, A. New specific sensory structures in hairy skin. *Acta Neuroveget.*, **24,** 175–79 (1963)

281. Miller, S., Weddell, G. Mechanoreceptors in rabbit ear skin innervated by melinated nerve fibres. *J. Physiol. (London)*, **187,** 291–305 (1966)

282. Brown, A. G., Iggo, A., Miller, S. Myelinated afferent nerve fibers from the skin of the rabbit ear. *Exptl. Neurol.* **18,** 338–49 (1967)

283. Iggo, A. An electrophysiological analysis of afferent fibres in primate skin. *Acta Neuroveget.*, **24,** 225–40 (1963)

284. Hunt, C. C., McIntyre, A. K. An analysis of fibre diameter and receptor characteristics of myelinated cutaneous afferent fibres in cat. *J. Physiol. (London),* **153,** 99–112 (1960)

285. Burgess, P. R., Perl, E. R. Myelinated afferent fibres responding specifically to noxious stimulation of the skin. *J. Physiol. (London),* **190,** 541–62 (1967)

286. Melzack, R., Wall, P. D. Pain mechanisms: a new theory. *Science,* **150,** 971–79 (1965)

287. Iggo, A. Non-myelinated visceral, muscular, and cutaneous afferent fibres and pain. In *UFAW Symposium on Assessment of Pain in Man and Animals*, 74–87 (Keele, C. A., Smith, R., Eds., Livingstone, Edinburgh, 324 pp. 1962)

288. Paintal, A. S. Functional analysis of Group III afferent fibres of mammalian muscles. *J. Physiol. (London)*, **152,** 250–70 (1960)

289. Werner, G., Mountcastle, V. B. Neural activity in mechanoreceptive cutaneous afferents: stimulus-response relations, Weber functions and information transmission. *J. Neurophysiol.*, **28,** 359–97 (1965)

290. Tapper, D. N. Stimulus-response relationships in the cutaneous slowly-adapting mechanoreceptor in hairy skin of the cat. *Exptl. Neurol.*, **13,** 364–85 (1965)

291. Lindblom, U., Tapper, D. N. Integration of impulse activity in a peripheral sensory unit. *Exptl. Neurol.*, **15,** 63–69 (1966)

292. Lindblom, U., Tapper, D. N. Terminal properties of a vibro-tactile sensor. *Ibid.*, 1–15

293. Lindblom, U. Properties of touch receptors in distal glabrous skin of the monkey. *J. Neurophysiol.*, **28,** 966–85 (1965)

294. Mountcastle, V. B., Talbot, W. H., Kornhuber, H. H. The neural transformation of mechanical stimuli delivered to the monkey's hand. In *Touch, Heat and Pain* (See Ref. 8), 325–45

295. Lindblom, U., Lund, L. The discharge from vibration-sensitive receptors in the monkey foot. *Exptl. Neurol.*, **15,** 401–17 (1966)

296. Mountcastle, V. B., Talbot, W. H., Darian-Smith, I., Kornhuber, H. H. Neural basis of the sense of flutter-vibration. *Science,* **155,** 597–600 (1967)

297. Houk, J., Henneman, E. Responses of Golgi tendon organs to active contractions of the soleus muscle

of the cat. *J. Neurophysiol.*, **30**, 466–81 (1967)

298. Carpenter, D. O., Henneman, E. A relation between the threshold of stretch receptors in skeletal muscle and the diameter of their axons. *J. Neurophysiol.*, **29**, 353–68 (1966)

299. Matthews, P. B. C. The differentiation of two types of fusimotor fibre by their effects on the dynamic response of muscle spindle primary endings. *Quart. J. Exptl. Physiol.*, **47**, 324–33 (1962)

300. Appelberg, B., Bessou, P., Laporte, Y. Action of static and dynamic fusimotor fibres on secondary endings of cat's spindles. *J. Physiol. (London)*, **185**, 160–71 (1966)

301. Brown, M. C., Engberg, I., Matthews, P. B. C. Fusimotor stimulation and the dynamic sensitivity of the secondary ending of the muscle spindle. *J. Physiol. (London)*, **189**, 545–50 (1967)

302. von Euler, C., Peretti, G. Dynamic and static contributions to the rhythmic gamma activation of primary and secondary spindle endings in external intercostal muscles. *J. Physiol. (London)*, **187**, 501–16 (1966)

303. Norrsell, U. An evoked potential study of spinal pathways projecting to the cerebral somatosensory areas in the dog. *Exptl. Brain Res.*, **2**, 261–68 (1966)

304. Norrsell, U., Wolpow, E. R. An evoked potential study of different pathways from the hindlimb to the somatosensory areas in the cat. *Acta Physiol. Scand.*, **66**, 19–33 (1966)

305. Oscarsson, O., Rosén, I. Short-latency projections to the cat's cerebral cortex from skin and muscle afferents in the contralateral forelimb. *J. Physiol. (London)*, **182**, 164–84 (1966)

306. Andersson, S. A. Projection of different spinal pathways to the second somatic sensory area in cat. *Acta Physiol. Scand.*, **56**, *Suppl. 194* (74 pp., 1962)

307. Bowsher, D., Albe-Fessard, D. The anatomophysiological basis of somatosensory discrimination. *Intern. Rev. Neurobiol.*, **8**, 35–75 (1965)

308. Levitt, M., Schwartzman, R. Spinal sensory tracts and two-point tactile

sensitivity. *Anat. Record,* **154**, 377 (1966)

309. Norrsell, U. The spinal afferent pathways of conditioned reflexes to cutaneous stimuli in the dog. *Exptl. Brain Res.*, **2**, 269–82 (1966)

310. Christiansen, J. Neurological observations of macaques with spinal cord lesions. *Anat. Record,* **154**, 330 (1966)

311. Kennard, M. A. The course of ascending fibers in the spinal cord of the cat essential to the recognition of painful stimuli. *J. Comp. Neurol.*, **100**, 511–24 (1954)

312. Vierck, C. J. Spinal pathways mediating limb position sense. *Anat. Record,* **154**, 437 (1966)

313. Wall, P. D. Two transmission systems for skin sensation. In *Sensory Communication,* 475–96 (Rosenblith, W. A., Ed., Wiley, New York, 844 pp., 1961)

314. Taub, A., Bishop, P. O. The spinocervical tract: dorsal column linkage, conduction velocity, primary afferent spectrum. *Exptl. Neurol.*, **13**, 1–21 (1965)

315. Eccles, J. C., Eccles, R. M., Lundberg, A. Types of neurone in and around the intermediate nucleus of the lumbosacral cord. *J. Physiol. (London)*, **154**, 89–114 (1960)

316. Rexed, B. Some aspects of the cyto-architectonics and synaptology of the spinal cord. In *Organization of the Spinal Cord. Progr. Brain Res.*, **11**, 58–90 (1964)

317. Lundberg, A. Ascending spinal hindlimb pathways in the cat. In *Physiology of Spinal Neurons. Progr. Brain Res.*, **12**, 135–63 (1964)

318. Gordon, G., Jukes, M. G. M. An investigation of cells in the lateral cervical nucleus of the cat which respond to stimulation of the skin. *J. Physiol. (London)*, **169**, 28–29P (1963)

319. Oswaldo-Cruz, E., Kidd, C. Functional properties of neurons in the lateral cervical nucleus of the cat. *J. Neurophysiol.*, **27**, 1–14 (1964)

320. Horrobin, D. F. The lateral cervical nucleus of the cat; an electrophysiological study. *Quart. J. Exptl. Physiol.*, **51**, 351–71 (1966)

321. Perl, E. R., Whitlock, D. G., Gentry, J. R. Cutaneous projection to second order neurons of the dorsal

column system. *J. Neurophysiol.,*
25, 337–58 (1962)

322. Wall, P. D. The laminar organization of dorsal horn and effects of descending impulses. *J. Physiol. (London),* **188,** 403–23 (1967)

323. Lundberg, A., Oscarsson, O. Three ascending spinal pathways in the dorsal part of the lateral funiculus. *Acta Physiol. Scand.,* **51,** 1–16 (1961)

324. Mendell, L. M. Physiological properties of unmyelinated fiber projection to the spinal cord. *Exptl. Neurol.,* **16,** 316–32 (1966)

325. Wall, P. D. Presynaptic control of impulses at the first central synapse in the cutaneous pathway. In *Physiology of Spinal Neurons. Progr. Brain Res.,* **12,** 92–115 (1964)

326. Collins, W. F., Nulsen, F. E. Studies on sensation interpreted as pain: central nervous system pathways. *Clin. Neurosurg.,* **8,** 271–81 (1962)

327. Gordon, G., Jukes, M. G. M. Dual organization of the exteroceptive components of the cat's gracile nucleus. *J. Physiol. (London),* **173,** 263–90 (1964)

328. Taub, A. Local, segmental and supraspinal interaction with a dorsolateral spinal cutaneous afferent system. *Exptl. Neurol.,* **10,** 357–74 (1964)

329. Gordon, G., Jukes, M. G. M. Descending influences on the exteroceptive organizations of the cat's gracile nucleus. *J. Physiol. (London),* **173,** 291–319 (1964)

330. Andersen, P., Eccles, J. C., Schmidt, R. F., Yokota, T. Identification of relay cells and interneurons in the cuneate nucleus. *J. Neurophysiol.,* **27,** 1080–95 (1964)

331. Andersen, P., Eccles, J. C., Oshima, T., Schmidt, R. F. Mechanisms of synaptic transmission in the cuneate nucleus. *J. Neurophysiol.,* **27,** 1096–1116 (1964)

332. Levitt, M., Carreras, M., Liu, C. N., Chambers, W. W. Pyramidal and extrapyramidal modulation of somatosensory activity in gracile and cuneate nuclei. *Arch. Ital. Biol.,* **102,** 197–229 (1964)

333. Andersen, P., Eccles, J. C., Sears, T. A. Cortically evoked depolarization of primary afferent fibers in the spinal cord. *J. Neurophysiol.,* **27,** 63–77 (1964)

334. Calma, I. Presynaptic inhibition of the terminals of cutaneous nerve fibres by stimulation of the ventral thalamo-diencephalic region. *J. Physiol. (London),* **185,** 58–60P (1966)

335. Carpenter, D., Engberg, I., Lundberg, A. Primary afferent depolarization evoked from the brain stem and the cerebellum. *Arch. Ital. Biol.* **104,** 73–85 (1966)

336. Erulkar, S. D., Sprague, J. M., Whitsel, B. L., Dogan, S., Jannetta, P. J. Organization of the vestibular projection to the spinal cord of the cat. *J. Neurophysiol.,* **29,** 626–64 (1966)

337. Darian-Smith, I. Neural mechanisms of facial sensation. *Intern. Rev. Neurobiol.,* **9,** 301–85 (1966)

338. Darian-Smith, I., Yokota, T. Cortically evoked depolarization of trigeminal cutaneous afferent fibers in the cat. *J. Neurophysiol.,* **29,** 170–84 (1966)

339. Darian-Smith, I., Yokota, T. Corticofugal effects on different neuron types within the cat's brain stem activated by tactile stimulation of the face. *Ibid.,* 185–206

340. Stewart, D. H., Jr., King, R. B. Effect of conditioning stimuli upon evoked potentials in the trigeminal complex. *J. Neurophysiol.,* **29,** 442–55 (1966)

341. Stewart, D. H., Jr., Scibetta, C. J., King, R. B. Presynaptic inhibition in the trigeminal relay nuclei. *J. Neurophysiol.,* **30,** 135–53 (1967)

342. MacDonnell, M. F., Flynn, J. P. Control of sensory fields by stimulation of hypothalamus. *Science,* **152,** 1406–8 (1966)

343. Landgren, S., Nordwall, A., Wengström, C. The location of the thalamic relay in the spino-cervicolemniscal path. *Acta Physiol. Scand.,* **65,** 164–75 (1965)

344. Andersen, P., Andersson, S. A., Landgren, S. Some properties of the thalamic relay cells in the spino-cervico-lemniscal path. *Acta Physiol. Scand.,* **68,** 72–83 (1966)

345. Swett, J. E., Bourassa, C. M. Comparison of sensory discrimination thresholds with muscle and cutaneous nerve volleys in the cat. *J. Neurophysiol.,* **30,** 530–45 (1967)

346. Oscarsson, O., Rosén, I. Projection to cerebral cortex of large muscle-spindle afferents in forelimb nerves of the cat. *J. Physiol. (London),* **169,** 924–45 (1963)

347. Andersson, S. A., Landgren, S., Wolsk D. The thalamic relay and cortical projection of group I muscle afferents from the forelimb of the cat. *J. Physiol. (London)*, **183**, 576–91 (1966)

348. Albe-Fessard, D., Liebeskind, J. Origine des messages somatosensitifs activant les cellules du cortex moteur chez le singe. *Exptl. Brain Res.*, **1**, 127–46 (1966)

349. Oscarsson, O., Rosén, I., Sulg, I. Organization of neurones in the cat cerebral cortex that are influenced from group I muscle afferents. *J. Physiol. (London)*, **183**, 189–210 (1966)

350. Swett, J. E., Bourassa, C. M. Short latency activation of pyramidal tract cells by group I afferent volleys in the cat. *J. Physiol. (London)*, **189**, 101–17 (1967)

ACTIVITIES OF THE CENTRAL NERVOUS SYSTEM: MOTOR[1]

By Pier Lorenzo Marchiafava[2,3,4]

Department of Psychology, Yale University
New Haven, Connecticut

The papers described in this review have been selected from material published between June 1966 and June 1967. An attempt is made here to integrate these papers within the framework of three main themes: I. Afferent projections to the corticofugal neurons; II. Some aspects of the neural organizations in the motor cortex coordinating the motor outflow, with particular attention to the cortical 'mapping' of the pyramidal tract system; and III. Descending motor pathways other than the pyramidal tract, and the interneuronal mechanisms relaying supraspinal influences to motoneurons. These themes will be taken up in order.

I. Inputs to Corticofugal Neurons

Adaptive motor behaviors are initiated essentially by descending corticospinal volleys culminating in the activation of α- and γ-motoneurons. This corticospinal system, however, does not function as a self-contained source of the patterned motor discharge which impinges on segmental motoneurons. The neurons of the motor cortex, following Sherrington's suggestion (1), should be regarded rather as internuncial, interposed between proprioceptive and cutaneous afferent system and the lower segmental motoneurons. In a more recent formulation of this view, Phillips (2, 3) depicted the corticofugal neurons as recipients of graded excitatory and inhibitory convergence from intracortical neurons, thalamocortical volleys, and callosal afferent pathways, the balance among these synaptic impingements being encoded in the final pattern of impulses discharging from motor cortex.

[1] Supported by grants USPHS 1-F05-TW-1103-01 and NSF G 23584.

[2] On leave of absence from the University of Pisa, Institute of Physiology, Pisa, Italy. Present address: Department of Neurosciences, University of California, San Diego, at La Jolla, California.

[3] I would like to express my deep gratitude to Mr. Steven A. Hillyard who devoted considerable time and effort to improving the English as well as the exposition of the contents of this review.

[4] The kindness of Dr. D. P. Purpura who permitted the author to read some unpublished material from the symposium *Neurophysiological Basis of Normal and Abnormal Motor Activities* is gratefully acknowledged. Miss Paula Thomas' assistance with the bibliography was invaluable.

The afferent input is unquestionably important in regulating cortifugal discharge and is probably essential for the *initiation* of such impulses; according to Gooddy, for example, the ultimate source of all movements is the activation of receptors (4).

There have been many attempts to compile the sources of impulses impinging on the cells of the motor cortex, the distribution of afferents terminals within the various cortical layers, and the pattern of excitatory and inhibitory postsynaptic events influencing these cells. It was first demonstrated by Woolsey et al. in 1947 (5) that action potentials could be evoked from precentral cortex by stimulation of the dorsal roots in *Macaca mulatta*. Subsequently, many other papers appeared showing that these afferent fibers were of cutaneous and muscular origin (6, 7) and projected to the precentral gyrus through the thalamic ventralis posterolateralis (VPL) relay. The directness of this projection was confirmed by the persistence of cortical responses evoked by electrical stimulation of the skin or cutaneous and muscle nerves following ablation of the postcentral sensory cortex (6, 7) the cerebellum (6, 8), or both.

Among the afferents projecting to the motor cortex via thalamic relays, the central role played by the Group I fibers has been known since the work of Kruger (9) in monkeys and of Amassian & Berlin in cats (10, 11). In the former preparation both fore- and hindlimbs send Group I afferents to the motor cortex (9), while in the cat only the forelimbs are represented in this manner. More recently, the majority of contralateral Group I muscle afferents of low threshold in the cat was found by Oscarsson & Rosén (12) to project in a circumscribed fashion to the postcruciate dimple within SI. Cutaneous and Group I fibers of higher threshold terminated in another region of SI, as well as in the secondary somatosensory area, SII. This difference in cortical projection between the low- and higher-threshold afferents is paralleled at the spinal level by distinct distributions of the two fiber systems, those of lower threshold coursing exclusively along the dorsal funiculus and the others along both the dorsal funiculus and the spinocervical tract (13).

Fundamental for the analysis of the inputs of the motor cortex are the results of Andersson, Landgren & Wolsk (14), who recently published a most detailed study of central projections of muscle afferents. The elucidation by Andersson et al. of the electrophysiological properties of these afferent relays at thalamic and thalamocortical levels provides an important contribution toward the delimiting of the relative role of the motor cortex in processing information from Group I muscular afferents. In this study, Group I muscular afferents were found to course within the dorsal column-lemniscal system. Focalized evoked responses in ventralis posterolateralis (VPL) elicited by low-intensity electrical stimulation of the contralateral forelimb's muscular nerve (radial) disappeared after section of the dorsal funiculus. The latency of these responses, 3.8 msec, was at least 1 msec shorter than VPL responses mediated by cutaneous fibers.

Thalamic relay cells activated by Group I fibers were found to project to the perisigmoid dimple (SI) and to a small portion of the anterior suprasylvian gyrus (SII), in agreement with the results of Oscarsson et al. (12), Mallart (15), and Andersen et al. (16). Possible branching of the ascending thalamocortical axons could provide direct connections between VPL and each of these cortical projection areas (14, 16). Axons of VPL relay cells are known to connect mono- and polysynaptically with pyramidal tract cells (17-22). Furthermore, the latency of the perisigmoid gyrus potentials evoked by stimulation of muscle nerves was 4–5 msec (13)—too short to allow time for more than three synapses classically described along the afferent path. Such rapid conduction through this ascending path fits well with the idea that it might provide prompt feedback regulation of corticospinal discharge.

Patterns of convergence of afferents from muscle spindles and skin receptors do not show important changes as investigation proceeds from thalamic to cortical levels (23–25), hence it was not possible to substantiate a more highly integrated brand of information processing in the higher central relays. Even among different layers of the cortex, Oscarsson et al. (24) could not demonstrate ". . . any change in the convergence pattern in the successive tiers of neurons investigated." Therefore, much of the convergence found at the level of cortical neurons may be ascribed to integrations occurring at thalamic level. Albe-Fessard also points out the important role played by the thalamus in the integration of the Group I afferent volleys (26).

The majority of the units investigated in the dorsomedial region of VPL (cat) are activated by both muscular and cutaneous afferents, and about 50 per cent receive converging afferents from two or more separate muscles of the contralateral forelimb (14). Only occasionally was it possible to detect differences in synaptic efficacy between these convergent inputs, revealed by differences in stimulus parameters eliciting gross evoked potentials or unit responses. Stimulation of the contralateral hindlimb was not effective in activating these cells.

Multiple convergence of heterogeneous Group I afferents upon the cells of VPL might well explain the absence of somatotopic organization within this structure. Similarly, skin afferents which converge on the same thalamic cells activated by Group I impulses do not show a well-defined somatotopic pattern of terminal distribution. This feature is in striking contrast to the strict somatotopic organization of the cutaneous afferent system, which also ascends in the medial lemniscus, but terminates on the central core of VPL and projects thence to somatosensory area SI.

Unlike the cutaneous afferents, those from the joint capsule have never been shown to converge on the thalamic neurons activated by Group I afferents; this could be due, however, to the limited number of capsular nerves tested.

The results obtained by Andersson et al. (14) clarify the nature of the processing of afferent volleys within the motor cortex, since they show that Group I cuneatothalamic projections are distributed to cells of VPL in a way quite similar to subsequent thalamomotor cortex terminations (12, 13, 23–25).

Microelectrode recordings reveal that synaptic potentials appear in cortical neurons following activation of the lowest-threshold Group I afferents (25). The majority of these cortical cells are also activated by stimulation of cutaneous fibers, while higher-threshold Group I afferents are relatively ineffective in producing synaptic potentials. Most of these cells are monosynaptically excited by the thalamocortical projection from VPL and are located 1000 μ below the cortical surface (24). Depth measurements were also made upon less numerous cells which were inhibited (intracellular IPSP) by stimulation of Group I afferents in a muscle nerve, and they were found to lie at a deeper level than the activated neurons (EPSP). This evidence was considered as suggestive of an inhibitory action exerted by the more superficial neurons upon the underlying layers, showing similarities with the inhibitory interneurons acting at other cortical sites (27). The latency of these IPSPs (1.5–2 msec), about 1 msec longer than the monosynaptically produced EPSP, is consistent with this hypothesis of an interneuronal inhibitory sequence (24). These considerations will be treated more extensively later on, in the context of possible functional properties of the proprioceptive-cortical feedback mechanisms.

Some cortical neurons exhibited a more complex convergence; EPSPs as well as IPSPs could be elicited, in alternation, by stimulation of different, and occasionally of single muscle nerves. Mixed excitation and inhibition was also observed following stimulation of cutaneous nerves. In another type of convergence, Group I afferents originating from antagonistic muscles, even of the same joint of the contralateral forelimb, excited common cortical neurons with almost equivalent synaptic efficacy.

Hence, in analogy with the thalamic relay, the extensive convergence upon individual cells at the cortical level precludes a well-defined somatotopic organization, even though gross evoked potentials recorded in the perisygmoid gyrus indicate a vaguely somatotopic projection of Group I afferents (23).

Specification of the motor cortex cells which respond to peripheral nerve stimulation has indicated the involvement of pyramidal cells, although we lack a quantitative determination of their relative proportion. Pyramidal tract stimulation failed to activate antidromically any of the cortical cells examined by Oscarsson et al. (24) but succeeded in the experiments of Swett & Bourassa (25, 28). According to the latter report, many of the cortical neurons activated antidromically by bulbar pyramidal tract stimulation were typical in receiving low- and high-threshold Group I plus cutaneous influences. The brief latency of activation of some of these pyramidal neurons by thalamocortical relay cells suggested a monosynaptic linkage (see 22). Gross evoked responses from the pyramidal tract revealed that stimulation of cutaneous afferents activated pyramidal cells much more effectively than did Group I afferents. Group I volleys, although unequivocally effective, produced such limited activation of the pyramidal tract that response averaging (127 sweeps) was necessary for a clear demonstration (25).

Cutaneous and Group I projections to motor cortex have other distinguishing features. At the level of the postcruciate dimple, the Group I evoked response has a latency of 5–7 msec, compared with 6.2–10 msec for the cutaneous response; differences in conduction velocity or an additional neuron at a prethalamic level could account for this longer delay. Furthermore, penetration of a recording electrode through the cortex revealed that reversal of potentials evoked by stimulation of the two kinds of fibers occurred in different cellular layers. These facts, revealing the difference in terminal distribution within the motor cortex, are suggestive of differences in their mechanisms of controlling pyramidal cell excitability.

Some pyramidal cells received convergence from low- and high-threshold Group I muscle afferents as well as cutaneous afferents, and only a few of them (12 out of 57) responded exclusively to Group I volleys, in agreement with what has been shown at other cortical (24) and thalamic regions (14).

In summary, the dominant feature of the peripheral input to motor cortex cells, pyramidal and non-pyramidal, is the extensive convergence of different modalities onto individual cells which are diffusely distributed throughout their regions, with no recognizable patterns of spatial localization based either on modality of input or on the production of excitation versus inhibition. This peculiar fashion in which proprioceptive and skin afferents project to the motor cortex contrasts sharply with the somatotopic cerebellar terminations of the other branch of the proprioceptive system included within the spinocerebellar pathways.

The fundamental differences in the organization of afferent terminals between projections to the motor cortex and those to the somatosensory areas described by Mountcastle (29) suggest different functional roles for the two classes of projections. From a psychophysiological point of view, the evidence that muscular afferents do not play a role in conscious sensation could provide a major clue toward classifying these motor cortex projections on a fundamental plane. Unlike the somesthetic projections to SI and SII, the cortical ramifications of Group I muscle afferents are not involved in perception. That large fibers in the Group I band do not carry perceptual information has been suggested, on a theoretical basis, by Mountcastle et al. (30) and experimentally confirmed by both P. Matthews (31) and Swett et al. (32, 33), who showed that Group I stimulation, in contrast to Group II cutaneous fibers stimulation, was ineffective as a conditioned stimulus in a learning procedure in the cat.

Thus the Group I system, rather than supplying the cortex with a somatotopic representation of muscular sensibility analogous to the somesthetic system's cortical projections, might have the role of directly regulating corticofugal motor discharges. Evidence has already been cited indicating that the muscular afferents reach the motor cortex over the shortest possible route. Considering the reports of Oscarsson et al. (12) and Swett et al. (25), which show that motor cortex cells were activated by low-threshold Group I afferents originating from muscle spindles, the implication of a feedback mechanism for regulation of corticospinal neurons is obvious. The extensive and widespread convergence in the Group I projection path to the motor cortex might suggest that the modality of information carried concerns changes in *muscle tone* (cf. also 24) rather than stages of movements or position. But the fact that the relayed pyramidal tract response to peripheral Group I stimulation disappears at stimulus frequencies about 4/ sec suggests the existence of a recurrent inhibitory circuit located either within the cortex or between VPL and the cortex (25); such a self-limiting mechanism could impede the continuous monitoring of muscle nerve discharges at the motor cortex. However, if this time-dependent inhibition of pyramidal discharge is generated by circuits located postsynaptically to afferent terminations, the information could still be carried continuously to the cortical cells.

Swett et al. (25) showed that Group I and cutaneous afferents, even if converging to the same cell, were *primarily excitatory* and offered further confirmation by recording depolarizing potentials intracellularly from pyramidal cells, after Group Ia fiber stimulation. Different is the interpretation of Oscarsson et al. (24): cortical cells receiving EPSPs are considered inhibitory interneurons transforming Group I volleys in inhibitory PSPs at the level of the pyramidal cells.

An important step toward comprehension of the organization of somatic input to the motor cortex was made by Albe-Fessard and co-workers in the monkey (*Macaca mulatta*) (34). It had already been known that electrical stimulation of either muscular or cutaneous nerves could elicit evoked responses in the motor cortex of the monkey which exhibit a certain degree of convergence from the ipsi- and contralateral limbs (8, 35, 36). Many questions, however, concerning the exact modality of this afferent information and the mechanism of its transmission to the cortex were left unsolved.

The utilization of natural stimulation of the different somatic receptors (34, 37) provided clarification of these points. The advantage of the natural stimulation, which included lightly touching the skin as well as deeper independent stimulation of either single muscles, tendons, or articulations, consisted of the precise determination of the source and, inferentially, of the functional role of the receptors excited. Gross evoked responses were recorded with macroelectrodes placed in pre- and postrolandic gyri and responses of single neurons were also recorded with extracellular microelectrodes. Identification of the cells as pyramidal neurons was indirect, based only upon some of their electrophysiological properties. Microelectrode recording of sensory evoked responses from the postrolandic cortex allowed a direct comparison with those concomitantly recorded in the prerolandic cortex. Consequently, it was found in the motor cortex that both contra- and ipsilateral afferents converge upon the same regions, and in limited areas it was possible to observe convergence from both anterior and posterior limbs. Single-unit recordings confirmed the results obtained with macroelectrodes. The pattern of convergence at the level of the motor cortex was definitely more complex than in the postrolandic gyrus, in that the same unit could receive excitatory and inhibitory influences from both contra- and ipsilateral limbs.

Stimulation of each category of receptor showed that tactile afferents, at variance with those carrying temperature and pain information, do not reach the motor cortex. Receptors situated inside the muscular bulk or within the tendons were capable of activating neurons of the motor cortex. The possibility of differences in the parameters of transmission between Golgi tendon organ and intrafusal receptor afferents, however, was not examined. The pattern of termination of these afferents revealed a great complexity of convergence upon single cortical units from muscles within contra- and ipsilateral limbs and occasionally originating from all four limbs. It was shown that natural stimulation of one or more pairs or antagonistic muscles produced respectively facilitation and depression of the firing rate of the same cortical cells, although for many of them the complex convergence from different muscles could not be assigned any functional meaning. A most distinguishing feature of this cortical input is that the muscle afferent discharge controls the motor cortex units in a tonic fashion, with no sign of accommodation. The authors conclude that such spatial-temporal organization of the inputs to the motor cortex, characterized mainly by a patterned convergence of muscle afferents upon single cortical units combined with a lack of cortical tactile representation, might suggest that a tonic detailed representation of bodily movements is being forwarded to the motor cortex.

The results of Albe-Fessard and colleagues show that in physiological conditions the afferent proprioceptive input, as would be expected from other reports of the Group I projection to the somatomotor cortex of the cat, is indeed capable of driving pyramidal neurons. Furthermore, because afferent input has been proved to be a major instigator of such neuron activity, a quantitative evaluation of its contribution would be essential both in beginning and during movements, in order to define correctly the extent of pyramidal hegemony in the initiation of muscular contraction.

II. Aspects of Neural Organizations in the Motor Cortex Coordinating the Pyramidal Outflow

A study of the primary cortex outflow to segmental motor neurons showing the distinct pattern of facilitation and inhibition inpinging upon groups of motoneurons which innervate different muscles has recently been published by Preston, Shende & Uemura (38). Furthermore, the distinctive functions of early and late components of the corticospinal discharge elicited by single-shock stimulation of the motor cortex in modulating moto-neurons' excitabilities, and the possible involvement of local spinal inter-neural circuits in the transmission of cortical influences to motoneurons have been specified in both cats and baboons (39).

In both species the classical formulation of the pyramidal system as principally facilitatory to flexor motoneuron populations (see 40, 41), re-cently confirmed also by Laursen & Wiesendanger (42), has been recon-sidered through analytical studies which have expanded and clarified its sig-nificance.

Modification of monosynaptic reflexes after test shocks to the motor cortex has revealed, indeed, that pyramidal inhibitory influences do not sys-tematically impinge upon every motoneuron which activates muscles, acting as extensors (with respect to their joint), but instead upon those motoneu-rons which engender a more general antigravity action, as for instance the biceps and the brachialis anterior of the baboon (38). This predominantly inhibitory effect upon antigravity muscular activity has been interpreted by Preston as subserving the arrest of tonic antigravity postural contraction, necessary for simultaneous execution of the most discrete voluntary move-ment.

Furthermore, in both cats and primates a quantitative relationship has been postulated (38) between extent of cortical inhibition of the different motoneuron populations and their relative roles in maintaining antigravity posture. In this respect, for primates, *tonically* active motoneurons are usu-ally subject to the strongest cortical inhibition, but *phasically* discharging motoneurons are equally inhibited if their muscles are essential for antigrav-ity posture. In cat preparations, however, both *tonic* and *phasic* motoneu-rons (extensors of ankle) are equally inhibited by the corticospinal volleys (40, 41).

The dual facilitatory-inhibitory pyramidal control over segmental moto-neurons is not present for those innervating the most distal musculature such as the intrinsic muscle of the cat's paw. These motoneurons, in fact, could only be facilitated by motor cortex stimulation, and the pattern of in-hibition similar to that found in the more proximal muscles is lacking. In primates too, cortical inhibition of motoneurons innervating the forearm and hand was very weak when compared with that of motoneurons control-ling proximal musculature, and was completely absent in the baboon's hand. Using a different approach, Evarts (43) showed that single pyramidal cells were active during volitional flexion and extension of the wrist, which again suggests a facilitatory role for the pyramidal neuron system in both flexors and extensors of distal muscles. Such dissimilarity of the pattern of inhibition over different groups of motoneurons, which suggests an organi-zation of cortical control of distal forelimb musculature, differing from that of the hindlimb and the more proximal forelimb musculature (in the cat) (38), may well be of importance to the behavioral propensities of the intact animal.

Another feature of the connection between pyramidal cells and moto-neurons subserving distal musculature is the prevalence of monosynaptic corticospinal-motoneuron linkage, a well-known characteristic in the monkey (44–46), but almost totally lacking in the cat (47–49). This species difference is reflected in much shorter latencies for the earliest observable PSPs evoked in primate motoneurons (50, 51), via pyramidal tract stimulation. As originally proposed by Kuypers (49) on the basis of anatomical findings, there appears to be a correlation between the degree of monosynaptic connection between pyramidal cells and motoneurons and the discreteness and versatility of movements performed by the activated musculature (cf. also 52). The results of Phillips & Porter (53) and more recently those of Preston et al. (38), showing that the extent of monosynaptic facilitation by stimulating motor cortex in primates is greater in motoneuron populations controlling distal musculature than in those innervating proximal musculature, provide major support for this argument and confirm the original observation of Bernhard et al. (54, 55).

The monosynaptic coupling of pyramidal tract with segmental motoneurons in the monkey contrasts with the polysynaptic interneuronal arrangement in the cat, and there are corresponding differences between these species in the way motoneuron excitability is modified by corticospinal discharge after single-pulse stimulation of the primary motor cortex. The D- and I-waves which characterize the pyramidal discharge after such stimulation (56) were carefully studied in both cats and baboon by Stewart & Preston (39) and were differentiated according to their respective roles in determining changes in excitability of motoneurons. As an index of excitability changes produced by single-shock stimulation of primary motor cortex, variations in the strength of monosynaptic reflex discharge were measured. Accordingly, in the cat a pyramidal tract conditioning volley produced enhancement of the monosynaptic reflex elicited by stimulation of peroneal nerve (flexor) and recorded from L7 ventral root, while inhibition was obtained when the gastrocnemius nerve (extensor) was stimulated.

After ablation of the motor cortex the same stimulus, applied to the underlying white matter and therefore eliciting only the D-wave, failed to produce any change in the monosynaptic reflex. Only by applying short trains of pulses at 500/sec with production of a rapid succession of D-waves could consistent changes in magnitude of the test reflex discharges be obtained; these were simultaneously facilitatory to flexor and inhibitory to extensor motoneurons. It seemed that the short train of D-waves could reproduce, at least partially, the effect of single $D + I$ wave complex elicited from the intact cortex. Temporal summation in the spinal cord thus seems to be required if pyramidal volleys are to change motoneuron responsiveness in the cat.

Based on the inference proposed originally by Adrian & Moruzzi (57) and on other evidence (58, 59), this summation probably occurs in the network of spinal interneurons mediating the pyramidal effect. The necessity for sequential excitation of these interneurons, intermediate between pyramidal cells and motoneurons, might also explain the high threshold for evoking postsynaptic potential in the cat with pyramidal stimulation (59). Possibly they could be identified with the same interneurons associated with the segmental reflexes (60). Facilitation of polysynaptic motoneurons' EPSP produced by repetitive stimulation of medullary pyramids has been observed also in rats by Bannister & Porter (61). In the baboon, unlike the cat, a single D-wave elicited either by stimulation of white matter subsequent to ablation of the gray layer or by submaximal stimulation of intact primary motor cortex always produces considerable alteration of monosynaptic reflexes. In a previous work, in fact, it has been reported that *single cortical* volleys can initiate monosynaptic firing of motoneurons, which shows that the cortex can produce liminal excitation of these neurons without repetitive synaptic impingement (50).

Tight functional coupling between primary motor cortex and the primate motoneuron was shown also by Landgren, Phillips & Porter (62) who discovered similar thresholds for activation of pyramidal fibers and for evoking motoneuronal synaptic potentials by stimulation of the motor cortex.

In the baboon a single cortical volley elicited a rather complex time-course of changes in motoneuron excitability as measured by the amplitude of the monosynaptic reflex. In line with previous observations (50, 51) the initial effect was always a facilitation, for all motoneurons directly activated by pyramidal axons, which was followed by a sequence of inhibition and then late facilitation. In contrast with the cat in which the pattern of pyramidal effects upon segmental motoneurons is well defined as inhibitory to extensor and facilitatory to flexor motoneurons (see p. 366), primate motoneuron populations could be differentiated only on the basis of the degree and duration of the inhibition subsequent to the ordinary initial direct facilitation (41). The early, direct facilitation as well as the early inhibition was strictly dependent upon the D-wave and behaved as a function of peak amplitude. This inhibition, however, was mediated through an interneuron, presumably activated by collateral fibers of the same descending corticospinal neurons which directly connect with motoneurons (38). It is interesting that no summation was required upon this inhibitory interneuron to provoke an output effective for influencing motoneuron excitability (39); it operated with a coupling between input and output similar to that observed for the monosynaptic cortical-motoneuronal pathway. On the other hand, interneuron pools mediating cortically evoked *late* facilitation of motoneurons required summation of repetitive pyramidal input to produce a maximally effective output, in analogy with the cat's polysynaptic system. Accordingly, the late facilitation was greatly enhanced whenever the corticospinal volley included both $D + I$ waves.

These groups of experiments on the pattern of inhibition and excitation of segmental motoneurons directed from motor cortex lead to consideration of the problem of the cortical topographical localization of corticospinal efferents, that is to say, of delimiting the cortical regions projecting axons to different segmental motoneuron pools and the extent of functional or anatomical overlap of these areas. The difficulties to date in obtaining a precise mapping of the motor cortex could result from the gross nature of electrical stimulation techniques utilized up to now, often involving current intensities adequate for producing muscular contractions.

As is known from the report of Phillips (63), the threshold for evoking small movements by punctate stimulation of the motor cortex is higher than that required for excitation of pyramidal units. It would seem that coactivation of large quantities of neighboring cortical cells not necessarily having the same properties must be occurring. The electrode applied superficially, in fact, could have simultaneously excited pools of cortical cells of opposite function, thus resulting in distortion or even in complete failure of "naturally occurring" output. Furthermore, questions like whether corticofugal cells are stimulated directly or indirectly through synapses upstream from them, and the types of cells actually stimulated, remain unsolved.

Progress in surveying the topographical localization of areas in the precentral cortex of the macaque which initiate monosynaptic excitation of forelimb motoneurons has been reported by Landgren, Phillips & Porter (64) and by Phillips (65). A functional unit comprising all those corticopyramidal neurons which monosynaptically connect with a single α-motoneuron was defined as a "colony" (64). Localization of the colonies projecting down to different motoneurons of the baboon's hand and forearm was obtained reportedly "by approaching the real limits of brain surface stimulation as a method of resolving the grain of localization at the headward end of the cortico-motoneuronal projection." The spread of stimulus current was reduced to a minimum by applying brief (0.2 msec) anodal shocks to the cortical surface, weak enough (0.4–3.1 µA) to cause near-minimal monosynaptic effects on motoneurons sampled with intracellular microelectrodes. Even though this minimal current was stimulating a large population of cells (64), including those belonging to overlapping corticomotoneuronal colonies, pyramidal cells responsible for postsynaptic potentials in a single motoneuron were found to be located inside a relatively narrow region, the smallest being 1 mm². These colonies differed, however, in the amount of monosynaptic excitatory action exerted on their respective motoneurons by single shocks, a fact which suggests different densities of monosynaptic impingement from various colonies of pyramidal cells, equated for surface area.

Subsequent experiments in monkeys (53) intended to delimit the surface extent of different colonies by using a stronger cortical shock (up to 8 µA), which also permitted a comparison of monosynaptic efficacy between colonies projecting to motoneurons of proximal muscle groups and those of the forearm and hand. For this purpose, physical spread of the stimulus at the surface and in depth was determined by plotting threshold current intensities for firing of given corticospinal fibers (recorded at the cervical level), as a function of the distance from the lowest threshold point situated either on the cortical surface or "buried" inside. Once the spatial extent of the cell population activated throughout the range of the intensities had been specified, the electrode was fixed and the intensity was incremented until the maximal monosynaptic effect upon the sampled motoneuron was achieved. The largest value of stimulus strength which was capable of producing a further increase in monosynaptic action was used to calculate the surface extent of that particular colony. It was found that motoneurons innervating *proximal* muscles were driven by pyramidal colonies having a wide spatial extent (2.5 × 8 mm), while those going to the *distal* muscles had more focalized colonies. Overlap in cortical loci was observed among colonies having different spinal destinations. Following a cortical shock, changes in motoneuron excitability consisted either of a short-latency (2.4 msec) EPSP (monosynaptic, since the pyramidal reached the C7–8 level within 1.74–2.08 msec after the shock onset), followed at times by an early IPSP after another 1.5 msec, or of this IPSP alone. A similar sequence has been described by Preston & Whitlock (41, 43).

In some cases in which the cortical shock produced only minimal monosynaptic action, repetitive cortical stimulation at 200/sec generated a much larger postsynaptic potential (cf. 62). Hence, application of high-frequency bombardment to pyramidal synapses greatly enhanced their efficacy of transmission, as was similarly shown by Lundberg et al. (60) to occur in cats at the level of pyramidal synapses on lumbar interneurons. These striking potentiations with repetitive stimulation could reflect a special property of the synapses formed by corticofugal pyramidal neurons, involving either an increased transmitter release or a unique disposition of terminals across the somadendritic membrane; a similar phenomenon has been described for the monosynaptic corticofugal connection to reticulospinal neurons of the cat (66). Eccles (67) has pointed out that the capability for such synaptic potentiation might well have a microanatomical correlate in the arrangement of synaptic vesicles and he suggested a comparison with that already observed in Group Ia synapses, which show little potentiation.

The cortical colonies impinging on motor units of distal and proximal muscles differed in their spatial extents, as mentioned before, as well as in the magnitude of monosynaptic excitatory action exerted on their respective motoneurons after equivalent stimulation. *Distal* motoneurons, governed by a very small cortical colony, received a stronger monosynaptic input than do *proximal* motoneurons from their more extended colonies. The degree of neural control would seem to bear close relationship with the dexterity and flexibility of the muscles commanded. The versatility of the hand's volitional movement thus could derive from the discreteness and strength of cortical control of the hand's musculature [a factor postulated long ago by Wood Jones (68) as playing the major role in the evolutionary development of hand movements in primates] through monosynaptic corticospinal connections. Many experiments to be discussed in the following section have confirmed the dominance of the pyramidal system in controlling the more distal musculature (see also 69). In particular, significant motor deficits subsequent to ablation of precentral motor cortex are clearly measurable only at the level of hand movements.

Clear-cut progress toward the definition of the three-dimensional shape of the cortical regions containing cells which engender excitability changes in functionally distinct groups of motoneurons is represented in the recent report of Asanuma & Sakata (70). By means of microstimulation in the depths of the cat's motor cortex, evoking minimal activation of forearm muscles, these authors overcame many of the limitations inherent in surface stimulation. Alteration in monosynaptic spinal reflexes elicited by an optimal stimulus was used as the indicator of effects exerted upon motoneurons by the corticofugal discharge. The possibility that synaptic changes were induced through corticospinal terminals on presynaptic arborizations of the monosynaptic reflex arc was excluded by Anderson et al. (71). Section of the bulbar pyramids resulted in complete disappearance of these segmental effects due to cortical stimulation, strongly suggesting that the pyramidal tract is the major carrier of this corticofugal discharge to spinal levels. Both facilitation and inhibition of motoneurons were obtained, and the respective "effective zones" for each within the cortex, i.e., those which produced opposite changes in reflex amplitude, were found to be distributed according to certain patterns. Localization of *inhibitory* zones in the cortex, in general, was 1.5 mm deeper than that of the *facilitatory* zones which were found at an average depth of 1.0–1.4 mm. Stimulation of single points within the cortex, however, could provoke at the same time both facilitatory and inhibitory effects upon reflexes of different muscles, each with a different threshold. The lowest thresholds were usually the same for facilitatory and inhibitory effects upon monosynaptic reflexes, originating as previously mentioned from cortical points topographically separated by ca. 1–1.5 mm, having a mean value of 9–9.5 μA.

Furthermore, numerous cortical penetrations at different localities showed that the lowest threshold points, facilitatory and inhibitory to the same group of spinal motoneurons, were found gathered together in a confined, narrow zone. These effective zones were composed of cylindrically shaped arrays of cortical motor cells having a common spinal projection and were approximately included within a sector of cortical gray matter extending along the direction of the radial fibers. The average size of such a conical effective zone, as measured on a reconstructed model, was 1 mm in cross-sectioned diameter. As pointed out by Asanuma & Sakata (70), this functional organization of the cortical motor system recalls the columnar distribution of neurons in the somatosensory and visual cortices responding to peripheral stimulation of individual receptive fields, as found by Mountcastle (29) and by Hubel & Wiesel (72) respectively.

The picture of either the organization of the cortical networks governing functionally different groups of motoneurons, or the complex pattern of activity of the cortical efferent system obtained by these experiments, is subject to limitations imposed by the use of electrical currents applied to the brain surface or gray matter. The abnormality of the stimulus as a possible source of erroneous interpretation of the experimental results has been recently discussed by Walshe (73).

Great progress in understanding the pattern of unit activity in the monkey's precentral gyrus during voluntary movement has been made by Evarts (43, 74). Moreover, his simultaneous recording from a pair of pyramidal neurons from the same region has permitted a new interpretation of the localization of function in the cerebral cortex—a subject which has generated so many disparate hypotheses over the past century.

In unanesthetized animals, he showed pyramidal neurons to display characteristic discharge patterns during spontaneous movements of the contralateral arm. After their identification by antidromic activation, these neurons were found to fall into two categories on the basis of their conduction velocities (75): those with high conduction velocity (max. 78 m/sec) were active only during limb movements, and were nearly inactive in the absence of movement, while those with lower conduction velocity (min. 11 m/sec) displayed a tonic discharge whose frequency was altered during motor performance.

Although based merely on a speculative hypothesis, the early writings of Jackson (76) present a similar concept of tonically and phasically active motor cells, these, however, being located in the cerebellum and cerebral cortex respectively. Differences in conduction velocity between the two main groups of pyramidal cells, possibly denoting separate functional roles, were also associated with differences in cell size (77) and other physical and electrophysiological properties, as recently described by several authors (78–81).

Evart's results (75) represent, as far as is known, the first attempt to record from single pyramidal neurons during spontaneous and voluntary movements in the unanesthetized animal and [are] an important breakthrough in the study of the physiology of the motor system. The more recent paper from the same author (43) reports a successful determination of a more specific relationship between pyramidal neurons activity and contraction of forelimb muscles, two of which were usually sampled from a group of functionally opposing ones subserving a simple conditioned movement. The method of using conditioned movements (a sequence of wrist extensoflexion) offered the possibility of an accurate measurement of the latency between the presentation of the conditioned stimulus eliciting the arm movement and the consequent modification both of the pyramidal neuron discharge and of the sampled EMG. The temporal relationship between the two latter events was not an important criterion for distinguishing among pyramidal neurons.

With the minimum latency of about 100 msec after the onset of the conditioned stimulus one group of pyramidal neurons began to discharge, invariably preceding an increase in the EMG of the wrist extensor of the contralateral arm. The interval (about 100 msec) between pyramidal neuron and EMG activation excluded the possibility of feedback from the periphery. A clear-cut linear relationship was found between the latencies of the pyramidal neuron and EMG responses (reaction time) and the pyramidal neuron conduction velocity.

A certain number of pyramidal neurons changed their discharge frequency shortly *after* the beginning of the EMG response. Their activation could be related either to reafference from the periphery or to initiation of the next muscular contraction in the sequential program of the conditioned response. Other pyramidal neurons would anticipate the transient increase in EMG activity by a sudden *decrease* in discharge frequency, but no significant relation was discovered between the direction of change of pyramidal neuron discharge frequency and initiation of extension or flexion at the wrist. Clarification of this point was rendered difficult by the sequential activation of extensor and flexor muscles during conditioned movements, thus preventing ascertainment of whether changes in a single pyramidal neuron should be related to flexor contraction or to the concurrent extensor release or vice versa, or even to an intermediate state of contraction of the two opposing muscles.

An important relationship was observed between the degree of tonic discharge of pyramidal neurons prior to the burst which preceded muscle contraction and their conduction velocity: in line with previous results (75), the slow-conducting neurons displayed a continuous tonic discharge in the absence of movements, whereas the faster-conducting neurons fired intensively only upon the occasion of movements and could be completely quiescent with the arm at rest. The discharge of some pyramidal neurons changed during muscle contractions on either side of the body, and, although we lack more quantitative information, the existence of an ipsilateral projection[5] has been shown for few of them. The majority of these cells, however, was clearly linked more closely to contralateral wrist movements.

Having provided such abundant information about the temporal relationship between pyramidal neuron discharge and their ipsi- or contralateral EMG correlates, Evarts (43) next addressed the question of how the displacement, velocity, and force of movements were represented in their response pattern. The problem, as it motivated the last group of experiments by Evarts (43), was whether the *"primary output variable"* of the motor cortex consisted of the *extent* or rather of the *force* of the voluntary movement. An improvement of the apparatus yielded an instrumental wrist

[5] The appearance of an ipsilateral projection is probably not due to a discrete hidden movement of the contralateral arm, since these pyramidal neurons showed responses timelocked *only* with the ipsilateral EMG.

movement for which independent measurements of its force and extent (displacement) could be made. Specifically, once the range of a given extension or flexion of the hand had been fixed with a mechanical device limiting its excursion (up to 30°), the applied force was varied by means of a wide range of loads alternately opposing flexor, then extensor contraction. Under these conditions a trained monkey could reproduce, at will, movements of the same displacement and speed, while the magnitude and direction of the applied force were changed independently. The result was that both flexion and extension of the wrist could be carried out entirely by contraction and partial decontraction of only that group of muscles working against the load. Dissociation of the direction of "displacement" from the direction of "force" was thereby realized.

The main observation of these experiments was that a given pyramidal neuron discharged only upon activation of those muscles (either flexors or extensors) functionally coupled to it, independently of whether the resulting displacement of the hand amounted to extension or flexion. Thus when a moderately heavy load opposed the flexors, so that both flexion and extension of the hand could be carried out by modulating the degree of contraction of flexor muscles alone, a given pyramidal neuron would discharge with an intensity relative to the strength of the force applied, regardless of the direction of the hand displacement. Later, however, with exactly similar displacement of the hand carried out this time by extensor contraction after shifting the load to the opposite direction, the pyramidal tract unit was virtually completely silent. The reverse pattern could be observed for units correlated with extensor contraction.

It therefore became apparent that firing of pyramidal neurons controlling wrist movement (in 26 out of 33 cases) was related not to displacement of the wrist but rather to the direction and magnitude of the force applied during the contraction. Hence the general conclusion may be drawn that the "major output variable" of the motor cortex represents the force rather than the displacement per se.

Additional recordings of the time derivative of force during the "rising" or the "falling" phases of flexor or extensor contraction showed that pyramidal neuron firing was primarily related to the first and second derivatives of the force instead of its magnitude; a further specification of such neuron activity during movement execution was to define the *relative* extent to which force and its derivative dF/dt were represented in the neuron output. An experimental situation was then created in which a constant force was required to maintain the hand in the steady position, upon which reward was contingent. It was possible to demand exertion of a given force either from flexor or extensor muscles by applying the desired loads with almost complete absence of movement. The maintenance of the steady position, however, required slight, short-lasting fluctuations of the *steady-state force,* in order to compensate for small, spontaneous displacements occurring while the monkey was trying to keep his hand steady. These small increases or decreases of force (which were expressed in terms of dF/dt) could be measured independently of the predominant steady-state force. It was found that the majority of the pyramidal neurons examined under these conditions were more strongly affected by the increment or decrement of the force (dF/dt) rather than by the steady state; furthermore, the magnitude of change in their discharge elicited with these small displacements did not depend very much on the amount of steady force applied prior to their occurrence. This important observation shows that a given pyramidal neuron may operate in controlling movements over a very extensive range of required forces since its discharge seemed to control only the increments in force.

Simultaneous recordings from two adjacent pyramidal neurons during voluntary movements provide insight into the topographical organization of motor patterning mechanisms in cortex since the relationships between neighboring pyramidal neurons which project to motoneurons innervating the same muscles are thereby elucidated. Evarts determined whether activity in each of the two pyramidal neurons was positively or negatively correlated with the other's or with the EMG of the muscle they controlled, or if any fixed relationship was evident. In accordance with the well-known fact that different pyramidal neurons either excite or inhibit [through an interneuron (82)] the motoneurons controlling a given muscle, pairs of adjacent pyramidal neurons always displayed a "fixed" correlation in time (either positive or negative) between their respective activities during hand movements comprised of alternating muscular contractions. In the case of two *positively* correlated neurons, their discharges increased and decreased simultaneously, depending on the phase of muscle contraction. On the other hand, *reciprocally* related pairs of adjacent neurons displayed opposite changes in their firing rates, the contrast between the two being dependent upon the relative activation or quiescence of the muscle.

Samples of two adjacent pyramidal neurons controlling *different* muscles showed a quite unpredictable relationship, which varied as the nature of movement was changed. This was called a "plastic" relationship, as opposed to the aforementioned "fixed" one, because such a pair of neurons could increase their rates of discharge together for a certain type of movement while a few moments later they might be reciprocally or even independently activated as a different movement was executed. It may be inferred that this apparent "independence" in temporal discharge of two such neurons during certain movements actually overlooks a sequential relationship that is fixed and repeatable upon a re-evocation of that movement. Each separate pattern of movement would accordingly entail an associated sequence of discharges among neighboring pyramidal neurons, precisely phaselocked to the sequential contractions of their respective muscles. Plastic relationships were by far the most common among the examined pairs of adjacent pyramidal neurons that governed separate muscles.

Pairs of adjacent pyramidal neurons having such heterogeneous relationships were found, however, to have one feature in common—the *joint* supplied by the different muscles they controlled. The joint, thus, is the "common denominator" of neighboring pyramidal neurons, regardless of the nature of the relationship existing between pairs of them. Furthermore, sequences of pyramidal and nonpyramidal neurons encountered throughout the different cortical layers traversed in a single microelectrode penetration were found to be related to movements of the *same* joint. Sequences of neurons related to the wrist, elbow, and shoulder were found in separate cortical penetrations, and very few units were associated with joints other than the one predominant for that penetration.

The anatomical organization of pyramidal and nonpyramidal neurons in the precentral gyrus with regard to localization of function is thus apparent: those cortical cells having *any* kind of relation with muscles acting upon the same joint are disposed in columnar arrays which are responsible for directing the attached group of muscles, both flexors and extensors, in a specified range of "movements". These correlations between unit activities are in accord with the pioneering cortical stimulation experiments to reveal that neurons of the motor cortex are not grouped into circumscribed clusters to govern either individual muscles or individual movements. The new findings suggest a more valid schema in which contiguous cortical neuronal populations are differentiable into columnar units, each controlling a number of muscles at one particular joint and each possessing the capacity for contracting them in specific combination of distinct, integrated movements.

A more comprehensive examination of previous theories concerning functional localization in the motor cortex provides the background with which to integrate the new concepts outlined above. Ever since electrical stimulation became a common method for studying cortical functions, two contrasting hypotheses have been proposed: [the] one suggesting that single muscles, the other that simple, "abrupt" movements are represented in the motor cortex in a "mosaic" of punctate localizations. The former theory, postulating a fixed topographical representation of structures (muscles), with separate cortical points each controlling an individual muscle, was largely accepted by Fulton, and an extensive account of it is found in his *Physiology of the Nervous System* [(83, p. 406); cf. von Bonin (84)]. Although he did not preclude the evocation of functionally integrated motor patterns from the cortex, Fulton clearly championed the view that stimulation of various cortical points could produce "solitary responses" of single muscles, and the experiments of Chang et al. (85) confirmed this opinion. Giving a different interpretation to Chang's findings, Evarts (43) suggested that a limited activation of motoneurons innervating *only one* muscle could result from threshold stimulation of a set of contiguous cortical neurons which were more strongly associated with that particular muscle. The theory of punctate representation of muscles is contradicted too by the finding of Landgren et al. (64) that a given motoneuron could be influenced by focal stimulation over a cortical area clearly more extensive than that representing a single motor response (8 × 2.5 mm), which indicates an extensive intermingling among pyramidal neurons projecting to motoneurons of different muscles.

The alternative view of "functional" localization in motor cortex maintains that given patterns of movement are represented in discrete foci (cf. 86), which would in modern terms embody a pre-set program for an organized *process* as opposed to a trigger for a simple *structure*. The extreme version of this theory is the ill-defined concept of "cortical equipotentiality", in which Lashley (87) considered that encoded representations of motoric actions could equally inhabit any site in an unspecific and stable structural framework. Jackson's opinion on the nature of cortical representation of both muscles and movements (88) seems to provide grist for a more fruitful discussion in the context of the present results. According to Jackson, a given movement pattern does not arise from one localized cortical generator within a mosaic, specific only for it, but rather derives from a number of "centers" or representations of separate but related movements distributed across the cortex and overlapping to create zones where intermediate movements are elaborated. Most movements, in fact, require the participation of a large set of muscles acting as subordinate components to the predominant group of muscles demanding the coordination of the many separate generators of less complex movements. These complex systems of muscle activation are subserved by correspondingly organized patterns of excitation spread throughout the motor cortex.

In a publication of Walshe (89) the doctrine of Jackson has been very clearly illustrated. In it is implied a distinct, separate representation for each of the countless possible voluntary movements with overlap among them creating common cortical regions having graded, intermediate representations. As a corollary of Jackson's theory, dense intermingling of pyramidal neurons controlling different muscles was assumed with consequent widespread distribution of pyramidal neurons controlling motoneurons of the same muscle. Each of these pyramidal neurons, however, is integrated with various combinations of others to produce different functional outputs responsible for various kinds of movement. Thus, every muscle would be represented many times in the motor cortex, each time as a component of a different movement. Walshe (89, p. 107) supported his view by citing the familiar clinical ". . . case of residual hemiparesis, where we may see the extensor of the wrist 'paralyzed' as prime movers in an attempted voluntary extension of the wrist, but powerfully active as synergist in every forceful grasping movement of the fist." This evidence also agrees with Jackson's notion that there is localization in the motor cortex, not of the parts of the body but rather of the programs for the integrated performances themselves.

The data of Evarts offer the possibility for a more modern formulation of Jackson's theory. The extensive intermingling of cortical neurons projecting to motoneurons innervating different muscles, postulated by Jackson and subsequently demonstrated by Phillips, should be accompanied, as pointed out by Evarts, by a "plasticity in the interrelation of discharge in adjacent PTNs". In accordance with expectations, the activity of two pyramidal neurons projecting to motoneurons of different muscle groups could be either positively or reciprocally related, depending on whether a movement required synchronous or reciprocal co-contraction of the two muscle groups, the former pattern being possible even between a pair of antagonists (90). Evarts' further discovery of the contiguity of pyramidal neurons supplying the same joint, coupled with Jackson's notion of individual movement representations, seems to stabilize the old dispute of muscle versus movement representation at an intermediate stage, wherein both movements and muscles can be localized. Within a column of neurons playing upon the various muscles of a single joint and, hence, anatomically specific, there exist individual pathways selectively primable to produce their specific movements of that joint.

Activity of corticofugal cells has also been analyzed in relation to voluntary eye movements in the monkey by Bizzi et al. (91). Corticobulbar neurons, located in the frontal eye field (area 8) and identified by an antidromic response to stimulation of the cerebral peduncle, displayed a steady-state spiking rate maximal for a specific direction of gaze which changed only *after* the onset of an eye movement. An important observation was that the steady-state discharge of corticobulbar neurons, occurring once a certain position of the eyes had been established, showed little adaptation even during prolonged voluntary fixation. These cells, reflecting a static contractile situation, contrast with the corticospinal cells in the precentral gyrus studied by Evarts which show a stronger relation to the dynamic components of wrist muscle contraction.

A different method for elucidating functions specific to the pyramidal tract consisted of testing the effects of its surgical section upon various motor activities. Even though this approach is inadequate for the resolution of basic issues like the nervous mechanisms disrupted with the pyramidal transection, it may still provide useful information with regard to the range of activities mediated by the pyramidal tract and a better understanding of the etiopathogenesis of some clinical syndromes. Thus a recent study of Bucy, Ladpli & Ehrlich (92) defines the physiological role of the pyramidal tract more accurately by specifying the losses sustained after its destruction. On the basis of these results the classical specification of the pyramidal tract as the only corticospinal pathway responsible for the production of voluntary movements seems no longer tenable. The experiments substantially confirm the original observation made by Tower (93) that extensive recovery supplants the initial motor deficit subsequent to pyramidal transections. Other pathways evidently originating from the primate cerebral cortex and coursing outside the tract are of much importance in performing voluntary motor activity since there is a nearly hopeless impairment of motor function following section of both pyramidal tracts combined with complete hemidecortication (92, 94).

Section of the two cerebral peduncles was performed sequentially by Bucy et al. (92) to assure the complete division of all corticospinal fibers including the pyramidal, corticopontine, and corticobulbar tracts. Complete flaccidity and contralateral paralysis follows immediately upon the first transection and its recovery was slightly impaired by the second operation a few days later, an observation suggesting ipsilateral connections. There ensues, however, a prompt and progressive recovery of motor activities which is almost complete after three to twelve months, the longest time being required for reacquisition of the more skilled, dextrous voluntary movements. Hyperreflexia and hypertonia were not observed routinely, although they were once regarded as parts of the "pyramidal syndrome" (73). The recovery took place in sequential steps: first, walking resumed, followed by climbing and jumping. Once full recovery was attained, the monkeys could again perform individual coordinated movements like picking up small seeds with thumb and index fingers. Recovery began first with the proximal, then with the distal musculature, and in the lower extremities earlier than in the upper ones. In man, however, Bucy, Keplinger & Siqueira (95) have described a different order of recovery.

There appears to be a positive relationship in the monkey between the speed of recovery of skill in different muscles [Bucy et al. (92)] and the density of monosynaptic pyramidal afferents impinging upon their motoneurons. The hypothesis could be advanced that the recovery of function is dependent upon a reafferentation of the deprived motoneurons which would be more extensive for those which had lost the larger pyramidal innervation and hence presented the largest empty surface target for new sprouting. Several authors (52, 96) have proposed that the corticorubrospinal pathway could assume an important role in this recovery, at least for the distal musculature, owing to the predominant facilitatory influence on flexors by the rubrospinal tract (97).

Besides the reafferentation of motoneurons, an alternative hypothesis for the persistence of motor activity after pyramidal section presumes a hierarchical reorganization of the original synaptic arrangement. The dominant role of pyramidal afferents in excitation of the motoneuronal membrane would be taken over after transection by extant synapses on motoneurons from other descending fiber systems. This "reserve" input is functionally less important under normal conditions, but retains the potential capability of driving a patterned, integrated output from motoneurons each having a distinctive intensity of activation resembling that of the intact preparation. In considering this second hypothesis, the paucity of the motor deficit in the hand described by Bucy et al. (92) to result from pyramidal transection confronts the results of Evarts (43) showing a prominent pyramidal neuron discharge timelocked to the voluntary contraction of hand muscles. The teleological significance of the pyramidal discharge for motor control thus remains a puzzle, since its complete abolition does not lead to any esssential impairment. Bucy's description of the minor impairment remaining after complete recovery from a peduncular transection (a deficit the monkey realized, markedly preferring to use his nonaffected side) would indicate that the role of the pyramidal system might consist of adding refinement and dexterity to the execution of movements already initiated by extrapyramidal impulses.

This view is supported by the data of Lawrence & Kuypers (98), who show the only deficit in voluntary motility remaining several weeks after a pyramidal section at the medullary level to be a loss of independent movement of the fingers (which could, however, be utilized usefully together) and a generalized slowness and fatigability more marked than normal. These symptoms were of a lesser degree in those cases of incomplete interruption of the pyramidal tract.

The movements persisting after complete section of pyramidal tracts at the medullary level could be adequately steered, in the opinion of Lawrence & Kuypers (98), by the remaining long descending pathways originating from the brainstem. The respective efficacies of the lateral and ventral bundles of these descending fibers in steering movements of the more distal and proximal musculature were also studied by these authors. Six weeks after bilateral pyramidal section, a selective lesion of the lateral spinal funiculus involving mainly the rubrospinal pathways resulted in the impairment of distal flexor muscles superimposed upon the effects of pyramidotomy, but there was little deficit in the motor activity of either the more proximal or extensor muscles. Proximal motility, on the other hand, was severely disturbed only after a subsequent lesion of the brainstem medial descending pathway, known to originate from the bulbar reticular formation and the vestibular complex (49).

Evidence that these descending extrapyramidal pathways of the brainstem indeed originate from the cortex or can at least be activated from the cerebral cortex was obtained by Lewis & Brindley (99). Movements were induced, this time by electrical stimulation of the motor cortex (prerolandic gyrus), and it was observed that section of both medullary pyramids had "little or no effect on the character of the movements", which implies a cortical control over the extrapyramidal system. Even the somatotopic representation of movement in the motor cortex did not appear to be modified, insofar as the site and the size of the cortical region producing a given movement were concerned. From this evidence an extrapyramidal cortical motor map can be deduced for primates superimposable upon that of the pyramidal system, and Jankowska & Tarnecki (100) report a similar arrangement for cats. Pyramidal transection in cats, however, diminished the number of discernible movements elicitable during the exploration of the motor cortex, raised the electrical thresholds, and, in accordance with what Lawrence et al. (98) found for primate voluntary movements, increased the susceptibility to fatigue. Lewis et al. (99) suggested that a heightened fatigability might depend upon a special property of synaptic relays in the surviving pathways (extrapyramidal). In similar experiments, however, Jankowska et al. (100) stimulated the sensorimotor cortex of normal and pyramidotomized cats and discerned no differences between them in the latencies of potentials evoked in the motor nerve. The inference is that the synaptic and conduction delays are similar for the pyramidal and extrapyramidal systems.

Further results of motor cortex stimulation to cats after total pedunculotomy are reported by Walker & Richter (94), supplemented with observations on the impairment of voluntary motor activity. Such stimulation produced movements only at high intensities, which was explicable by the severance of all low-threshold pyramidal and extrapyramidal systems coursing within the cerebral peduncle (94). The motor deficits persisting several weeks after unilateral pyramidal transection consisted mainly of weakened flexor reflexes in the contralateral hindlimb and increased latencies of contact placing, as reported on cats by Laursen & Wiesendanger (101, 102). By recording electromyographic activity of both flexor and extensors of the affected limbs, they demonstrated a decreased tonus of the flexor musculature, not accompanied by extensor hyperactivity. This evidence would clarify the origin of the apparent extensor hypertonia (extensor rigidity) observed in the affected limbs, and originally ascribed by Liddell & Phillips (103) to unilateral increased tonus in extensors.

III. Activation of Motoneurons by Pathways Other Than the Pyramidal Tract

Descending fiber projections other than the pyramidal system affect the excitability of segmental motoneurons; these may be subdivided into several different cortico-brainstem and brainstem-spinal projections which however are usually lumped together as the *extrapyramidal system* (cf. 49), despite their anatomical and physiological heterogeneity.

The efficacy of the extrapyramidal system for sustaining efficient, useful motor control in pyramidotomized preparations has already been mentioned (see p. 380). To complement the material chosen for the pyramidal system, it seems worthwhile now to review some papers concerning the neuronal organization of the extrapyramidal terminal arborizations at segmental levels, contrasting the operating characteristics of these two basic carriers of motor information to motoneurons in order to stimulate speculation about their respective functional roles.

Fiber tracts in the ventral spinal cord.—An analysis of the mechanisms through which motoneuron excitability is altered by pathways descending along the ventral spinal funiculi [including the reticulospinal (104, 105), vestibulospinal (106, 107), and propriospinal (108) tracts] has been performed in the cat by Willis et al. (109, 110). The previous observation of Lloyd (111) that motoneurons could be activated both monosynaptically and via an interneuronal relay from volleys descending through the ven-

tral funiculi was fully confirmed (110). Changes in monosynaptic reflexes
along with intracellular recordings of membrane potentials were used for
testing the effects of single shocks or repetitive (300/sec) volleys descending upon either flexor or extensor motoneurons. No significant differences
in responsiveness were noted between these latter two groups, sampled at
lumbosacral level. The descending volleys were much more effective upon a
monosynaptic reflex discharge recorded from the ventral roots, if given in
rapid succession (300/sec), and produced a predominant facilitation followed by an inhibition. The facilitation was already present 0.7–0.9 msec
after the presynaptic arrival of a single descending conditioning ventral
cord volley (this was the minimum conditioning-test stimulus interval
used) and persisted for about 12 msec. A repetitive conditioning volley
(four shocks), however, produced a facilitation lasting 25 msec, except in
those cases in which it was overwhelmed by the inhibitory effect occurring
during the last 15–20 msec of its time-course.

     With regard to the mechanisms of the test for monosynaptic reflex fa-
cilitation, intracellular recording from motoneurons showed a monosynaptic EPSP beginning 0.5 msec after a single shock to the ventral cord. This
initial EPSP was then followed after 0.9 msec by a disynaptically mediated
EPSP which, in contrast with the monosynaptic one, was progressively enhanced as the frequency of stimulation of the ventral cord was incremented up to 100/sec. As an explanation for this facilitation of the EPSP, one
can rule out an increase of transmitter release from the ventral terminals,
at stimulation frequency of 100/sec, because there was no facilitation of
the *monosynaptic* EPSP elicited by repetitive stimulation of the ventral
cord. Such potentiation of monosynaptic EPSPs can develop, however,
with similar stimulation frequencies of the Group Ia afferents (112), corticospinal tract (113), and other terminals upon motoneurons (114, 115). In
the opinion of Willis et al. (110) the sizable facilitation of test monosynaptic reflexes observed after repetitive (as compared to single-shock) stimulation of the ventral cord could emanate from recruitment of those segmental
interneurons responsible for transmission of the disynaptic EPSP. After a
repetitive conditioning ventral cord volley the amplitude of the monosynaptic reflex discharge reached values of 200–400 per cent of the control,
which reveals that the interneuronal facilitatory mechanism could be powerful enough to overwhelm the moderate and progressive decline in monosynaptic EPSP which occurred upon increasing the stimulating frequency
from 1 to 100/sec.

     The descending pathways within the ventral funiculus which mediate
the above-mentioned effects on moto- and interneuron excitability have
been identified on the basis of recent anatomical evidence as the vestibulospinal and reticulospinal tracts (104, 107), and physiological studies (116,
137, 146) have concurred that these pathways are capable of producing
synaptic actions upon extensor and flexor motoneurons, respectively. For

further references on descending pathways in the ventral cord which influence ventral cord interneurons see Willis et al. (117, p. 379).

The interneurons involved in the disynaptic excitation of motoneurons via the ventral cord have been tentatively identified (110) with a group of cells localized in Rexed's lamina VIII of the spinal ventral horns (117). These interneurons (called proprioneurons along with all the spinal interneurons except Renshaw cells), together with others located in Rexed's lamina X, displayed an EPSP, often monosynaptically, following stimulation of descending pathways in the ventral cord. Scheibel & Scheibel's (118) anatomical demonstration of ventral horn interneurons located in lamina VIII and distributing axon collaterals to both the ipsi- and contralateral anterior gray matter strongly suggests that these cells could participate in relaying to motoneurons those disynaptic effects generated by ventral cord stimulation (117). Some of these interneurons could also receive, after a polysynaptic delay, strong excitation from stimulation of peripheral nerves, with muscular nerves exclusive of their Group Ia fibers being most effective.

Lundberg, however, cites evidence (119, p. 280) that some interneurons (inhibitory to flexor motoneurons) received convergent excitation from both the vestibulospinal tract and Ia afferents from extensor muscles, but not from either Ib or flexor reflex afferents. The peripheral receptive fields of the ventral cord proprioneurons described by Willis et al. (117) often appeared so wide as to suggest a parallelism with the input to neurons of the brainstem reticular formation (120), perhaps indicative of functional interconnections between the two (brainstem and spinal) systems (cf. 111). Since this group of proprioneurons relays convergent information to motoneurons from the ventral cord descending pathways and from Ib and cutaneous primary afferents, it could considerably function as part of the "flexor system" pathway. If this is so, this system should also contain those neurons involved in transmitting descending corticospinal excitatory impulses to structures such as the terminal arborizations of Group Ib and cutaneous afferents (121–124) and the presynaptic arborizations of ascending spinal pathways (125), and to segmental motoneurons which in the monkey are also under monosynaptic control from pyramidal fibers (39). Furthermore, these interneurons might also relay supraspinal influences to γ-motoneurons as was inferred from the results of different authors (42, 126–128).

The excitatory events in cat's motoneurons, reported by Stewart & Preston (39) to follow pyramidal neuron stimulation, are most likely relayed through spinal proprioneurons, which the authors preferred to identify with those associated with the segmental reflex system. The massive increase of excitability in cat's lumbar motoneurons obtained by high-frequency stimulation of pyramidal neurons (500/sec), as well as the large increase of the *disynaptic* EPSP in motoneurons evoked by repetitive ventral cord stimulation (up to 100/sec) (110), could be consequences of re-cruiting within an interneuronal pool relaying both pyramidal and ventral volleys. The several descending systems probably utilize separate sets of interneurons, however, since their resultant effects on motoneurons are so diverse.

While the activation of some interneurons in the segmental reflex sys-tem clearly demonstrates the monosynaptic convergence of both ventral and peripheral Ib and II fibers upon the same proprioneuron (110), the dis-position of pyramidal neuron volleys into this interneuronal reflex system (39) can also be inferred in the cat from abundant evidence obtained by several authors. Notably, conditioning volleys elicited by stimulation of the motor cortex, even though not producing any effect on the motoneuron membrane potential by itself (122), can instigate a powerful enhancement of the IPSP therein, elicited by a Group Ia volley. Extensor motoneurons were most commonly subject to the Ia inhibition. Although the cortical vol-ley was kept below the threshold for producing synaptic effects in the mo-toneurons, it could still be sufficient for the subliminal excitation of the in-hibitory pathway from Ia afferents to α-motoneurons (60), presumably constituted by an inhibitory interneuron (82). In addition to the facilitatory effects of pyramidal neuron discharge upon the reflex pathways from flexor reflex afferents, which excited flexors and inhibited extensor moto-neurons, there was occasionally a facilitation also of the inhibitory path from flexor reflex afferents to other flexors motoneurons (129), and of the excitatory path from cutaneous afferents to extensor motoneurons (130). Transections of the brainstem, with and without inclusion of the pyramids, have proved that these modifications of reflexes were mediated by the cor-ticospinal tract (60).

The hypothesis that corticofugal volleys eliciting postsynaptic potentials in motoneurons are mediated by facilitation of the segmental reflex path was strengthened (122) by the evidence that stimulation of the sensorimo-tor cortex produced changes in test reflexes consisting of an increased ex-citation of flexors and a prevalent inhibition of extensor motoneurons. Such a pattern of facilitation was believed to arise from the active partici-pation of interneurons of the flexor path because this is the dominant spi-nal reflex (60).

The postulation of segmental interneurons as mediators which assist in determining the pattern of motor response evoked by cortical stimulation would urge reconsideration of a current theory of cortical "representation"; this asserts that activation of the motor cortex produces a pattern of synaptic activity in the motoneurons which mirrors the output already pro-gramed at cortical levels and is not restructured or filtered by neuronal organizations at the level of the reflex interneurons. Such a scheme could be valid in primates, however, in which the monosynaptic connections between pyramidal and motoneurons subserving fine movements (62, 64) bypass the interneuronal reflex system.

Direct evidence of pyramidal activation of an interneuron in the reflex path has been obtained by Lundberg et al. (123) who elicited, by stimulation of the pyramidal tract, an EPSP (probably monosynaptic) from the same interneuron that also received either a monosynaptic excitatory input from Group I muscle afferents or converging excitation of flexor reflex afferents from a very large receptive field. Other interneurons that were inhibited (IPSP) by such cortical volleys were found to be subject to inhibition from flexor reflex afferents. Among the several interneurons sampled, the generalization could be made that the direction of synaptic action (IPSP vs. EPSP) produced by the peripheral volley would determine a similar effect from the cortical discharge. Thus, from the recent experiments of Hongo, Jankowska & Lundberg (131, 132) showing that the majority of interneurons in the spinal cord manifests an IPSP upon stimulation of primary afferents, it would follow that IPSP would also be the prevalent synaptic action exerted on interneurons from a cortical volley. In Lundberg's study, however, the latency of the inhibitory synaptic action from the cortex was long enough to justify the antecedent excitation of another interneuron, upstream and inhibitory to the interneuron from which the IPSP was recorded, which would imply that the direct synaptic action exerted by the corticospinal tract upon interneurons is mainly excitatory. This hypothesis was substantiated by the marked increase in the threshold of the flexion reflex after pyramidal transection (133).

From the evidence reported so far, the conclusion may be drawn that synaptic effects upon motoneurons evoked by stimulation of sensorimotor cortex, pyramidal tract, and ventral cord (excluding the ventral cord-evoked monosynaptic EPSP) are most likely dependent upon activation of interneurons of the segmental reflex path. The operating characteristics of the monosynaptic junctions between the terminals of the ventral pathways and motoneurons are quite different from those of the monosynaptic input to motoneurons from primary afferents or of the corticoreticular synapses described by Magni et al. (115). While repetitive stimulation of the latter two types of junctions leads to an increased efficacy of transmission dependent on an augmented release of transmitter from the presynaptic terminals [three times more at 300/sec than at 100 or 0.4/sec (112), with even more striking increases being obtained at the terminals of the ventral spinocerebellar tract (114)], *no* potentiation of the motoneuron monosynaptic EPSP has ever been found during repetitive ventral cord stimulation. Furthermore, posttetanic depression, instead of potentiation, occasionally appeared after tetanic stimulation of motoneurons through ventral cord synapses (110). Another relevant difference in the frequency-potentiation of synaptic transmission was reported between Group Ia and pyramidal monosynaptic contacts with the same motoneuron in the baboon. These differences in potentiability among different types of synapses on the same neuron might well have specific functional correlates with respect to the integrative action of motoneurons.

Rubrospinal tract.—The interneurons of reflex pathways also receive excitatory impingement from rubrospinal volleys, and some interneurons supplying flexor motoneurons are activated (monosynaptically) only by stimulation of the red nucleus (134). A rubrospinal volley facilitated the disynaptic IPSP induced in extensor motoneutrons via Ia afferents; the time-course of this facilitation combined with intracellular recording indicated that a monosynaptic EPSP was generated in the mediating inhibitory interneuron (134). Rubrospinal efferents also produced monosynaptic excitation of the interneurons relaying Ib inhibition to extensor motoneurons but, unlike the corticospinal tract, did not facilitate interneurons receiving impulses from flexor reflex afferents.

Convergence of impulses from rubrospinal tracts and Group I muscle afferents upon the same elements of the reflex path is consistent with the observed overlapping of the regions within the gray matter from where focal field potentials produced by activation of these two inputs could be recorded (134). The region corresponds, indeed, to the actual locus of termination of the rubrospinal tract within the gray matter (Rexed's lamina VII and VI); a similar anatomical study of the convergence of pyramidal and flexor reflex afferents at the site of pyramidal terminals (48) is now in progress (119, p. 277) and meshes with the precise study of the terminal organization of lateral corticospinal fibers in cats most recently made by Scheibel & Scheibel (135). In contrast with the interneurons relaying pyramidal volleys, those activated by rubrospinal discharge could manifest IPSPs even if the primary afferent volley elicited therein an EPSP: this inhibition, however, could be due to rubrospinal excitation of another interneuron inhibiting the one under study. Somatotopically organized corticorubral projections, originating from the sigmoid and coronal gyri, have been recently described by Mabuchi & Kusama (136).

Vestibulospinal tract.—Vestibulospinal projections, coursing along the ventral spinal cord, have been recently studied by Lund & Pompeiano (137). Monosynaptic excitatory impingement was observed upon 83 per cent of the extensor motoneurons examined after selective stimulation of either the vestibular nucleus or of vestibulospinal fibers, as transection experiments would suggest. Conduction velocity in these pathways, in accordance with the values obtained more recently in the descending tracts of the ventral cord (110), averaged about 100 m/sec. The tight functional relationship between the vestibular nuclei (Deiters') and α-motoneurons, combined with the excitatory effect of vestibular stimulation on muscle spindle discharge (138), prompted Carli et al. (139) to re-examine the relative importance, for a given muscular contraction, of the direct excitation exerted by these supraspinal centers upon motoneurons versus the indirect activation of motoneurons exerted by the same centers through γ-motoneurons and muscle spindles afferents.

This question was originally posed by Merton (140), who concluded that the extrafusal contractions comprising voluntary or postural efforts were brought about reflexively, secondarily to increase excitation of the intrafusal muscle fibers. This supposition was based also upon the evidence given by Hunt (141) that during reflex contractions the motor discharge to intrafusal fibers preceded the excitation of the main extrafusal muscles. Consequently, the supraspinal descending impulses governing voluntary contractions would terminate upon the small γ-motoneurons that give rise to the thin, intrafusal motor nerve fibers. For the execution of very rapid movements, however, a faster and more direct connection was assumed (139, 142) between supraspinal centers and α-motoneurons, as would follow from the abundance and range of voluntary movements persisting after complete deafferentation.

In the experiments of Carli, Diete-Spiff & Pompeiano (139), the descending volleys elicited by stimulation of Deiters' nucleus activated in parallel the segmental α- and γ-motoneurons. Hence, after the γ-loop had been interrupted by cutting the dorsal root, it was not surprising that the rate of rise of tension in the gastrocnemius muscle caused by stimulation of Deiters' nucleus was only slightly reduced because of the abolition of the input from spindle afferents to motoneurons (144–146).

A larger deficit in extrafusal tension was obtained after selective blockage of transmission in γ-motor fibers by cocainization of the motor nerve. Thus, as far as vestibular motor effects are concerned, the γ-loop does not provide to α-motoneurons the input essential for extrafusal contraction. Further evidence, obtained with dorsal roots intact, was the demonstration of an extrafusal motor response to vestibular stimulation while the spindles were deactivated during the brief period preceding the full recovery of intrafusal motor endplates after injection of a curarizing agent (143). That the Deiters' nucleus stimulation can also provoke an independent activation of γ-motoneurons was shown by the persistence of spindle discharge after selective blockage of the extrafusal motor endplates with gallamine triethiodide. As far as the muscular contraction elicited by the Deiters' nucleus stimulation is concerned, the γ-loop seems to function as a "sensitizing" or priming device in concert with the direct monosynaptic vestibulomotoneuron coupling (137) and not as a triggering mechanism, even though this role might apply for muscular contractions induced by different vestibular stimulation procedures. Granit et al. (138) had also suggested that either the α- or γ-motoneurons could alternatively play the decisive role, depending on the nature and origin of contractions.

Reticulospinal facilitatory tract.—Another pathway of supraspinal origin, which can produce increased excitability of either flexor or extensor α-motoneurons, is the reticulospinal pathway, originating from the brainstem facilitatory reticular formation (147) and coursing along the ventral cord (104, 148), thus being identified as one of the fiber tracts activated by Willis et al. (110). A sustained depolarization of the motoneuron's membrane, enabling an otherwise subthreshold monosynaptic EPSP to initiate impulse activity and simultaneously facilitating the monosynaptic reflex discharge (recorded from the ventral lumbar roots), followed the repetitive stimulation of the appropriate region of the reticular formation (147). Only occasionally (in one third of the motoneurons sampled) was it possible to identify an EPSP timelocked to each stimulus in the train applied to the reticular formation. While no data were reported dealing with the pathway which relays these reticular facilitatory effects to motoneurons, monosynaptic EPSPs in flexor motoneurons have been recorded by Grillner & Lund (151) following stimulation of the caudal pontine reticular formation.

Reticulospinal inhibitory tract.—Since the supraspinal synaptic actions mentioned so far have been mainly excitatory (even though the intercalation of an additional interneuron inhibitory to motoneurons occasionally yielded a final outcome of facilitation of an inhibitory segmental reflex), it seems necessary now to briefly survey some recent studies of those pathways having inhibitory effects upon reflex-path interneurons or directly upon motoneurons. This review will not include those experiments concerning supraspinal inhibition at primary afferent level and inhibition of reflex paths to primary afferents which are discussed by Lundberg et al. (119, 152). Likewise, experiments are omitted on the inhibition of transmission of short-latency effects from flexor reflex afferents to motoneurons following injection of DOPA (149, 150).

It has been established that stimulation of the bulbar reticular formation, yielding a tonic inhibition of decerebrate rigidity (153), can produce in the decerebrate cat a tonic suppression of transmission in some paths to motoneurons, by inhibition of the reflex-path interneurons projecting either to extensor α-motoneurons (129, 154), or to the primary afferents (155, 156). Reticular inhibition of γ-motoneurons as an indirect mechanism for suppression of activity of extensor α-motoneurons (157) had already been discredited by showing the persistence of the reticular inhibitory effects on motoneurons after interruption of the γ-loop (158). The newer experiments to be reported have shown that the reticular inhibition is executed by synaptic inhibitory actions causing hyperpolarization of the motoneuron's membrane, although reticular suppression of an excitatory bombardment from interneurons can cooperate as a collateral mechanism for decreasing motoneuron excitability.

This latter mechanism is favored in explaining the new evidence that low-frequency stimulation of the bulbar reticular formation, too weak to elicit primary afferent depolarization or any postsynaptic potentials in the motoneuron sampled, could still effectively inhibit the reflex transmission from flexor reflex afferents to motoneurons (159). The spinal route that mediates this reticular inhibition was localized along the dorsolateral funiculus. The effective locus in the brainstem reticular formation was found to be included within the area of Magoun's inhibitory center (153), but ventral to the region begetting postsynaptic action on motoneurons at the lowest strength of stimulation (160). From the distribution of inhibitory actions elicited by stimulation of the "dorsal reticulospinal tract" to interneurons relaying the influx from flexor reflex afferents, and to primary afferents and some ascending pathways, one can deduce that the reticulospinal pathway is tonically activated during the decerebrate state, in which a similar pattern of inhibitory actions has been observed (119). At present we have no information about the synaptic mechanisms producing such inhibition of interneurons, since an IPSP directly elicited by stimulation of brainstem reticular formation has not been recorded in interneurons, although it could easily be observed with disynaptic delay following a primary afferent volley (131, 132). It is possible that a mechanism of presynaptic inhibition acts upon the terminals from interneurons (159); a similar mechanism has been hypothesized for the inhibition of interneurons mediated through the ventral reticulospinal tract (152).

Postsynaptic inhibitory potentials produced in both extensor and flexor α-motoneurons by stimulation of the brainstem reticular formation have been encountered in a pair of similarly oriented studies (160, 161). Partial transection of the spinal cord showed these inhibitory effects to be mediated through the ventral funiculi, also known to mediate another reticular inhibitory effect which acts upon the reflex path to primary afferents (152). It was suggested that these postsynaptic effects upon motoneurons are involved in the "melting" of decerebrate rigidity caused by stimulation of Magoun's inhibitory center, because the reticular regions from which both effects could be elicited are identical, and the respective stimulus intensities required are the same. The contribution of the tonic inhibitory actions upon reflex-path interneurons mediated through the dorsal reticulospinal tract to the collapse of decerebrate rigidity should not be dismissed, however (162).

Extensor α-motoneurons generated an IPSP following a bulbar reticular formation stimulation that was adequate to suppress decerebrate rigidity (160, 161). This IPSP could be reversed to a depolarizing potential following the passage of hyperpolarizing currents through the recording microelectrodes. The decrease of a test voltage drop across the motoneuron's membrane during reticular formation stimulation was also indicative of an increased conductance during the inhibitory synaptic impingement. The localization of the inhibitory synapses in the proximity of the soma membrane was further confirmed by the disappearance of the somadendritic component in the motoneuron antidromic spike during reticular formation stimulation (161). The reticular inhibition also produced a diminution of the monosynaptically induced EPSP secondary to the reduction of the α-motoneuron excitability, as proved by a concomitant drop in the peak amplitude of the motoneuron EPSP induced by a shock applied through the recording microelectrode.

An alternative hypothesis that reticular inhibition works to abolish an excitatory background of internuncial origin was rendered unlikely by identical reversals of the membrane potential changes after intracellular injection of chloride ions, during both the "direct" and the reticular induced IPSP in motoneurons, which thus has the same equilibrium potential levels. That the IPSP reversals occurred at the same intercellular chloride ion concentration is also indicative of the same ionic mechanism for both postsynaptic inhibitory processes. Inhibition of interneurons, however, could also play a certain role in decreasing both the peak amplitude and the time-course of the monosynaptically induced EPSP.

In flexor α-motoneurons the reticular inhibition also produced sustained membrane hyperpolarization associated with a decrease of excitability. Reticular activation of a presynaptic inhibition of the motoneuron input was ruled out, since injection of picrotoxin did not affect the reticular inhibition of the test monosynaptic EPSP. The reversal of the direct IPSP, however, was never accompanied by a reversal of the reticular IPSP which, in fact, was progressively reduced in amplitude only so long as the electrophoretic injection was continued. Furthermore, the voltage drop caused by a current pulse applied to the motoneuron's soma (where the microelectrode tip was presumably located) was not modified during reticular stimulation.

Once the demonstration had been given that the reticular IPSP depended specifically upon an increase of chloride ion permeability and did not coincide with a change in membrane resistance measured at the soma, Terzuolo (163) concluded that inhibitory synapses on flexor motoneurons activated by the bulbar reticular formation are located so far from the soma that they cannot be influenced by the intracellular ion displacements caused by the chloride injection into the soma. Such a relegation of this inhibitory input to a region too remote for effectively steering the membrane excitability at the site of impulse initiation, could result, nonetheless, because of electrotonic spread of the hyperpolarizing potential from distant dendrites, in a smooth and coordinated tonic control of motoneuron excitability (168).

The notion that a particular distribution of synaptic input across the motoneurons' somadendritic complex might have functional importance in the integration of inputs of different origins has been further developed by these authors (164). In particular, the synaptic terminals have been shown to be nonrandomly distributed, and their localization might provide an index of the extent of their contribution to the integrative process of motoneurons. Other examples of a similar segregation of synaptic inputs have been noted in hippocampal pyramidal cells and Purkinje cells (27, 165). Terzuolo & Llinas discuss (164) the way different inputs reciprocally influence each other's synaptic efficacy, referring to the changes in peak amplitude and time-course of their postsynaptic potentials and related changes in cell membrane characteristics.

Eventually a more general model was proposed for the spatial distribution of the synaptic inputs to motoneurons so far considered: the direct inhibitory input is strictly confined to the soma, while the excitatory input of segmental origin is dispersed throughout the somadendritic complex, but mostly in the dendrites, following a general scheme [K. T. Green & D. C.

Petse, quoted by Terzuolo et al. (164)] placing 50 per cent of the synapses upon the dendrites and only 20 per cent in the somata. Reticular inputs, both excitatory and inhibitory, impinge upon extensor α-motoneuron dendrites close to the soma, while reticular inhibitory influences upon flexor α-motoneurons impinge upon dendrites far from the soma.

The postsynaptic consequences of a given input to the motoneuron might vary, however, if its arrival varies in temporal relation with the sequence of activation of other inputs; a particular pattern of motoneuron discharge might well be characteristic for each different sequence of activation. To support such a possibility, a clear-cut demonstration was made by Rall (quoted in 164) that a group of segregated regional inputs could produce transient postsynaptic effects with different characteristics as their temporal sequence of activation was changed. Thus, the reciprocal interaction between synaptic inputs varying with the integrative actions of the motoneurons would add new degrees of complexity and new properties to the functional characteristics of a given cell. Moreover, the provocative hypothesis was forwarded (164) that such a change in the temporal sequence of activation of different inputs upon given motoneurons might be an adequate synaptic mechanism for the establishment of conditioned responses.

Cerebellar inhibitory mechanisms.—The mechanism of cerebellar inhibition of decerebrate rigidity has been recently explored by Ito and his group (166–169). They showed that electrical stimulation of the anterior lobe engenders monosynaptic IPSPs in the neurons of the lateral portion of vestibular nuclei, to which previous experimenters (see 170) had assigned a critical role in the maintenance of decerebrate rigidity. The direct monosynaptic inhibitory impingement upon Deiters' neurons was assumed to be mediated by the descending axons of Purkinje cells activated by stimulation of the cerebellar surface. Anatomical evidence for such a monosynaptic linkage had already been gathered (171, 172). It is clear that this new information strengthens the view that a bulbar tonogenic center (vestibular nucleus), rather than the segmental neurons, is the recipient of this cerebellar descending inhibition responsible for the decerebrate collapse.

Earlier studies had shown that electrical stimulation to the cerebellar cortex could produce either an increase or depression of firing in Deiters' neurons (173, 174); Moruzzi (175, 176) had also obtained a mixture of effects, which could tend toward excitation or inhibition depending on the frequency of stimulation, indicating that elements other than the purely inhibitory Purkinje cells were also being activated. Intracellular recordings from Deiters' neurons demonstrated an initial IPSP after a cerebellar shock attributed to the volley from directly activated Purkinje cells, which could be distinguished from the subsequent mixture of inhibitory and facilitatory synaptic actions upon these neurons (168). The subsequent polysynaptic potentials were the consequence of excitation of structures other than Purkinje cells, such as cerebellar afferents and relay cells of the cerebellar cortex and nuclei. Extracellular recording of the high-amplitude field potentials generated within Deiters' nucleus by the arrival of the cerebellar corticofugal volley revealed a tight packing of the axons from which the fields emanate. The role of Purkinje cells in the production of IPSPs in Deiters' neurons was later ascertained by the appearance of equivalent inhibitory effects after stimulation of their afferent fibers (169), and by the correspondence of the ipsilaterally evoked IPSP with the ipsilateral anatomical path linking cerebellar cortex to Deiters' nucleus (171, 172). The original paper of Ito et al. (168) presents further evidence substantiating the inhibitory nature of Purkinje cells.

This categorization of Purkinje cells, whose axons reach a length of 10 mm, invalidates the generalization that all inhibitory neurons are necessarily small in size; this assumption was based on studies of inhibitory spinal interneurons (177–179), hippocampal relay cells (180, 181), and interneurons of the cerebral and cerebellar cortices (27, 182). Although the evidence is not conclusive, Ito et al. (168) acknowledge the similarity between Purkinje cells and these latter groups of inhibitory interneurons in their mode of synaptic termination. Among the somata and thick dendrites of Deiters' neurons there are basketlike synapses which have been envisaged as the terminal arborizations of Purkinje cells (183).

LITERATURE CITED

1. Sherrington, C. S. *The Integrative Action of the Nervous System* (Yale Univ. Press, New Haven, Conn., 413 pp., 1947; reprinted 1961)

2. Phillips, C. G. Some properties of pyramidal neurones of the motor cortex. In *The Nature of Sleep,* 4–29 (Wolstenholme, G. E. W., O'Connor, M., Eds., Little, Brown, Boston, 416 pp., 1961)

3. Phillips, C. G. Changing concepts in the precentral motor area. In *Brain and Conscious Experience,* 389–421 (Eccles, J. C., Ed., Springer-Verlag, New York, 591 pp., 1966)

4. Gooddy, W. Sensation and volition. *Brain,* 72, 312–39 (1949) (quoted by Lassek, A. M. *The Pyramidal Tract,* Thomas, 1954)

5. Woolsey, C. N., Chang, H.-T., Bard, P. Distribution of cortical potentials evoked by electrical stimulation of dorsal roots in *Macaca mulatta. Fed. Proc.,* 6, 230 (1947)

6. Malis, L. I., Pribram, K. H., Kruger, L. Action potentials in "motor" cortex evoked by peripheral stimulation. *J. Neurophysiol.,* 16, 161–67 (1953)

7. Gardner, E. D., Morin, F. Spinal pathways for projection of cutaneous and muscular afferents to the sensory and motor cortex of the monkey (*Macaca mulatta*). *Am. J. Physiol.,* 174, 149–54 (1953)

8. Albe-Fessard, D., Liebeskind, J., Lamarre, Y. Projection au niveau du cortex somato-moteur du singe d'afférences provenant des récepteurs musculaires. *Compt. Rend. Acad. Sci.,* 261, 3891–94 (1965)

9. Kruger, L. Characteristics of the somatic afferent projection to the precentral cortex in the monkey. *Am. J. Physiol.,* 186, 475–82 (1956)

10. Amassian, V. E., Berlin, L. Early projection of large muscle afferents from forelimb of cat to somatosensory cortex. *Fed. Proc.,* 17, 3 (1958)

11. Amassian, V. E., Berlin, L. Early cortical projection of Group I afferents in the forelimb muscle nerves of cat. *J. Physiol. (London),* 143, 61P (1958)

12. Oscarsson, O., Rosén, I. Projection to cerebral cortex of large muscle spindle afferents in forelimb nerves of the cat. *J. Physiol. (London),* 169, 924–45 (1963)

13. Oscarsson, O., Rosén, I. Short-latency projections to the cat's cerebral cortex from skin and muscle afferents in the contralateral forelimb. *Ibid.,* 182, 164–84 (1966)

14. Andersson, S. A., Landgren, S., Wolsk, D. The thalamic relay and cortical projection of Group I muscle afferents from the forelimb of the cat. *J. Physiol. (London),* 183, 576–91 (1966)

15. Mallart, A. Projection des afférences musculaires de la patte antérieure au niveau du thalamus chez le chat. *Compt. Rend. Acad. Sci.,* 259, 1215–18 (1964)

16. Andersen, P., Andersson, S. A., Landgren, S. Some properties of the thalamic relay cells in the spino-cervico-lemniscal path. *Acta Physiol. Scand.,* 68, 72–83 (1966)

17. Schlag, J., Balvin, R. Sequence of events following synaptic and electrical excitation of pyramidal neurones of the motor cortex. *J. Neurophysiol.,* 27, 334–65 (1964)

18. Purpura, D. P., Schofer, R. J. Cortical intracellular potentials during augmenting and recruiting responses. I. Effects of injected hyperpolarizing currents on evoked membrane potential changes. *J. Neurophysiol.,* 27, 117–32 (1964)

19. Purpura, D. P., Schofer, R. J., Musgrave, F. S. Cortical intracellular potentials during augmenting and recruiting responses. II. Patterns of synaptic activities in pyramidal and non-pyramidal tract neurons. *J. Neurophysiol.,* 27, 133–51 (1964)

20. Nacimiento, A. C., Lux, H. D., Creutzfeldt, O. D. Postsynaptische Potentiale von Nervenzellen des motorischen Cortex nach elektrischer Reizung spezifischer und unspezifischer Thalamuskerne. *Arch. Ges. Physiol.,* 281, 152–69 (1964)

21. Purpura, D. P., Frigyesi, T. L., McMurtry, J. G., Scarf, T. Synaptic mechanism in thalamic regulation of cerebello-cortical projection activity. In *The Thalamus,* 153–72 (Purpura, D. P., Yahr, M. D., Eds., Columbia Univ. Press, New York and London, 438 pp., 1966)

22. Amassian, V. E., Weiner, H. Monosynaptic and polysynaptic activation of pyramidal tract neurons by thalamic stimulation. In *The Thalamus*, 255–86 (Purpura, D. P., Yahr, M. D., Eds., Columbia Univ. Press, New York and London, 438 pp., 1966)

23. Oscarsson, O. The projection of Group I muscle afferents to the cat cerebral cortex. In *Muscular Afferents and Motor Control*, 307–16 (Granit, R., Ed., Almqvist & Wiksell, Stockholm, 466 pp., 1966)

24. Oscarsson, O., Rosén, I., Sulg, I. Organization of neurones in the cat cerebral cortex that are influenced from Group I muscle afferents. *J. Physiol. (London)*, **183**, 182–210 (1966)

25. Swett, J. E., Bourassa, C. M. Short latency activation of pyramidal tract cells by Group I afferent volleys in the cat. *J. Physiol. (London)*, **189**, 101–17 (1967)

26. Albe-Fessard, D. Activation of thalamocortical projections related to tremorogenic process. In *The Thalamus*, 237–53 (Purpura, D. P., Yahr, M. D., Eds., Columbia Univ. Press, New York and London, 438 pp., 1966)

27. Eccles, J. C. Cerebral synaptic mechanisms. In *Brain and Conscious Experience*, 24–58 (Eccles, J. C., Ed., Springer-Verlag, New York, 591 pp., 1966)

28. Swett, J. E., Bourassa, C. M. Activation of corticospinal tract fibers by Group I afferent volleys. *Physiologist*, **9**, 301 (1966)

29. Mountcastle, V. B. Modality and topographic properties of single neurones of cat's somatic sensory cortex. *J. Neurophysiol.*, **20**, 408–34 (1957)

30. Mountcastle, V. B., Powell, T. P. S. Central nervous mechanisms subserving position sense and kinesthesis. *Bull. Johns Hopkins Hosp.*, **105**, 173–200 (1959)

31. Matthews, P. B. C. Muscle spindles and their motor control. *Physiol. Rev.*, **44**, 219–88 (1964)

32. Swett, J. E., Bourassa, C. M., Inoue, S. Effects of cutaneous and muscle sensory nerve volleys in awake cats: A study in perception. *Science*, **145**, 1071–73 (1964)

33. Swett, J. E., Bourassa, C. M. Comparison of sensory discrimination thresholds with muscles and cutaneous nerve volleys in the cat. *J. Neurophysiol.*, **30**, 530–45 (1967)

34. Albe-Fessard, D., Liebeskind, J. Origine des messages somatosensitifs activant les cellules du cortex moteur chez le singe. *Exptl. Brain Res.*, **1**, 127–46 (1966)

35. Albe-Fessard, D., Liebeskind, J. Comparaison entre les propriétés des cortex prés- et post-rolandiques chez le Macaque. *J. Physiol. (Paris)*, **56**, 271 (1964)

36. Lamarre, Y., Liebeskind, J. C. Projections des afférences d'origine musculaire au niveau de cortex sensori-moteur chez la singe. *J. Physiol. (Paris)*, **57**, 259 (1965)

37. Albe-Fessard, D., Liebeskind, J., Mallart, A. Stimulation naturelles provoquant l'activation des cellules du cortex moteur chez le singe. *J. Physiol. (Paris)*, **56**, 525–26 (1964)

38. Preston, J. B., Shende, M. C., Uemura, K. The motor cortex—pyramidal system: patterns of facilitation and inhibition on motoneurons innervating limb musculature of cat and baboon and their possible adaptive significance. In *Neurophysiological Basis of Normal and Abnormal Motor Activities* (In press)

39. Stewart, D. H., Jr., Preston, J. B. Functional coupling between the pyramidal tract and segmental motoneurons in cat and primate. *J. Neurophysiol.*, **30**, 453–65 (1967)

40. Agnew, R. F., Preston, J. B., Whitlock, D. G. Patterns of motor cortex effects on ankle flexor and extensor motoneurones in the "pyramidal" cat preparation. *Exptl. Neurol.*, **8**, 248–63 (1963)

41. Uemura, K., Preston, J. B. Comparison of motor cortex influences upon various hind-limb motoneurons in pyramidal cats and primates. *J. Neurophysiol.*, **28**, 398–412 (1965)

42. Laursen, A. M., Wiesendanger, M. Pyramidal effect on alpha and gamma motoneurons. *Acta Physiol. Scand.*, **67**, 165–72 (1966)

43. Evarts, E. V. Representation of movements and muscles by pyramidal tract neurons of the precentral motor cortex. In *Neurophysiological Basis of Normal and Abnormal Motor Activities* (In press)

44. Chambers, W. W., Liu, C. N. Cortico-spinal tract in monkey. *Fed. Proc.*, **17**, 24 (1958)

45. Kuypers, H. G. J. M. Central cortical projections to motor and somatosensory cell groups. An experimental study in the Rhesus Monkey. *Brain*, **83**, 161–84 (1960)

46. Liu, C. N., Chambers, W. W. An experimental study of the corticospinal system in the monkey (*Macaca mulatta*). *J. Comp. Neurol.*, **123**, 257–84 (1964)

47. Chambers, W. W., Liu, C. N. Cortico-spinal tract of the cat. An attempt to correlate the pattern of degeneration with deficits in reflex activity following neocortical lesions. *Ibid.*, **108**, 23–56 (1957)

48. Nyberg-Hansen, R., Brodal, A. Sites of termination of corticospinal fibers in the cat. An experimental study with silver impregnation methods. *J. Comp. Neurol.*, **120**, 369–92 (1963)

49. Kuypers, H. G. J. M. The descending pathways to the spinal cord, their anatomy and function. *Progr. Brain Res.*, **11**, 178–202 (1964)

50. Preston, J. B., Whitlock, D. G. Precentral facilitation and inhibition of spinal motoneurons. *J. Neurophysiol.*, **23**, 154–70 (1960)

51. Preston, J. B., Whitlock, D. G. Intracellular potentials recorded from motoneurons following precentral gyrus stimulation in primate. *Ibid.*, **24**, 91–100 (1961)

52. Nyberg-Hansen, R., Rinvik, E. Some comments on the pyramidal tract, with special reference to its individual variations in man. *Acta Neurol. Scand.*, **39**, 1–30 (1963)

53. Phillips, C. G., Porter, R. The pyramidal projection to motoneurones of some muscle groups of the Baboon's forelimb. *Progr. Brain Res.*, **12**, 222–45 (1964)

54. Bernhard, C. G., Bohm, E., Petersén, I. Investigations on the organization of the corticospinal system in monkeys. *Acta Physiol. Scand.*, **29**, Suppl. 106, 79–105 (1953)

55. Bernhard, C. G., Bohm, E. Cortical representation and functional significance of the cortico motoneuronal system. *Arch. Neurol. Psychiat.*, **72**, 473–502 (1954)

56. Patton, H. D., Amassian, V. E. Single- and multiple-unit analysis of cortical stage of pyramidal tract activation. *J. Neurophysiol.*, **17**, 345–63 (1954)

57. Adrian, E. D., Moruzzi, G. Impulses in the pyramidal tract. *J. Physiol. (London)*, **97**, 153–99 (1939)

58. Lloyd, D. P. C. The spinal mechanism of the pyramidal system in cats. *J. Neurophysiol.*, **4**, 525–46 (1941)

59. Hern, J. E., Phillips, C. G., Porter, R. Electrical thresholds of unimpaled corticospinal cells in the cat. *Quart. J. Exptl. Physiol.*, **47**, 134–40 (1962)

60. Lundberg, A. Supraspinal control of transmission in reflex paths to motoneurones and primary afferents. *Progr. Brain Res.*, **12**, 197–221 (1964)

61. Bannister, C. M., Porter, R. Effects of limited direct stimulation of the medullary pyramidal tract on spinal motoneurones in the rat. *Exptl. Neurol.*, **17**, 265–75 (1967)

62. Landgren, S., Phillips, C. G., Porter, R. Minimal synaptic actions of pyramidal impulses on some alpha motoneurones of the baboon's hand and forearm. *J. Physiol. (London)*, **161**, 91–111 (1962)

63. Phillips, C. G. Cortical motor threshold and the thresholds and distribution of excited Betz cells in the cat. *Quart. J. Exptl. Physiol.*, **41**, 70–84 (1956)

64. Landgren, S., Phillips, C. G., Porter, R. Cortical fields of origin of the monosynaptic pyramidal pathways to some alpha motoneurones of the baboon's hand and forearm. *J. Physiol. (London)*, **161**, 112–25 (1962)

65. Phillips, C. G. Afférences pyramidales aux motoneurones de l'avant-bras et de la main. *Actualites Neurophysiol.*, **4**, 91–106 (1962)

66. Magni, F., Willis, W. D. Afferent connections to reticulo-spinal neurons. *Progr. Brain Res.*, **12**, 246–58 (1964)

67. Eccles, J. C. Discussion, 243. In Magni, F., Willis, W. D. *Progr. Brain Res.*, **12**, 246–58 (1964)

68. Wood Jones, F. *The Principles of Anatomy as Seen in the Hand* (Churchill, London, 1920, quoted in Ref. 53)

69. Buxton, D. F. Motor function and the cortico-spinal tracts in the dog and racoon. *J. Comp. Neurol.*, **129**, 341–60 (1967)

70. Asanuma, H., Sakata, H. Functional organization of a cortical efferent

system examined with focal depth stimulation in cats. *J. Neurophysiol.,* **30,** 35–54 (1967)

71. Anderson, P., Eccles, J. C., Sears, T. A. Cortically evoked depolarization of primary afferent fibers in the spinal cord. *J. Neurophysiol.,* **27,** 62–77 (1964)

72. Hubel, D. H., Wiesel, T. N. Shape and arrangement of columns in cat's striate cortex. *J. Physiol. (London),* **165,** 559–68 (1963)

73. Walshe, F. *Further Critical Studies in Neurology and Other Essays and Addresses* (E. & S. Livingstone Ltd., Edinburgh and London, 248 pp., 1965)

74. Evarts, E. V. Pyramidal tract activity associated with a conditioned hand movement in the monkey. *J. Neurophysiol.,* **29,** 1011–27 (1966)

75. Evarts, E. V. Relation of discharge frequency to conduction velocity in pyramidal tract neurons. *Ibid.,* **28,** 216–28 (1965)

76. Jackson, J. H. On post-epileptic states: a contribution to the comparative study of insanities. *The Journal of Mental Science, Oct., 1888* (Reprinted by H. Wolff, Steam Printing Works, First Installment)

77. Towe, A. L., Patton, H. D., Kennedy, T. T. Properties of the pyramidal system in the cat. *Exptl. Neurol.,* **8,** 220–38 (1963)

78. Creutzfeldt, O. D., Lux, H. D., Nacimiento, A. C. Intracelluläre Reizung corticaler Nervenzellen. *Arch. Ges. Physiol.,* **281,** 129–51 (1964)

79. Lux, H. D., Pollen, D. A. Electrical constants of neurons in the motor cortex of the cat. *J. Neurophysiol.,* **29,** 207–20 (1966)

80. Takahashi, K. Slow and fast groups of pyramidal tract cells and their respective membrane properties. *J. Neurophysiol.,* **28,** 908–24 (1965)

81. Yoshida, M., Yajima, K., Uno, M. Different activation of two types of pyramidal tract neurones through the cerebello-thalamocortical pathway. *Experientia,* **22,** 331–32 (1966)

82. Eccles, J. C., Patt, P., Landgren, S. Central pathway for direct inhibitory action of impulses in largest afferent nerve fibres to muscle. *J. Neurophysiol.,* **19,** 75–98 (1956)

83. Fulton, J. F. *Physiology of the Nervous System,* 3d ed., rev. (Oxford Univ. Press, New York, 667 pp., 1949, reprinted 1951)

84. Bonin, G. von. *Essay on the Cerebral Cortex* (Thomas, Springfield, Ill., 150 pp., 1950)

85. Chang, H.-T., Tuch, T. C., Ward, A. A., Jr. Topographical representation of muscles in motor cortex of monkeys. *J. Neurophysiol.,* **10,** 39–56 (1947)

86. Hines, M. Control of movements by the cerebral cortex in primates. *Biol. Rev.,* **18,** 1–31 (1943)

87. Lashley, K. S. *The Neuropsychology of Lashley,* 217–55 (McGraw-Hill, New York, 564 pp., 1960)

88. Jackson, J. H. On some implications of dissolution of the nervous system. In *Selected Writings of John Hughlings Jackson,* **II,** 29–44 (Taylor, J., Ed., Basic Books, New York, 510 pp., 1958)

89. Walshe, F. M. R. On mode of representation of movements in motor cortex, with special reference to "convulsions beginning unilaterally" (Jackson). *Brain,* **66,** 104–39 (1943)

90. Wilson, S. A. K. *Modern Problems in Neurology* (Wood & Co., New York, 364 pp., 1929)

91. Bizzi, E., Evarts, E. V. Discharge of corticobulbar neurons (CNs) during ocular movement. *Fed. Proc.,* **26,** 589 (1967)

92. Bucy, P. C., Ladpli, R., Ehrlich, A. Destruction of the pyramidal tract in the monkey. *J. Neurosurg.,* **25,** 1–23 (1966)

93. Tower, S. S. Pyramidal lesion in the monkey. *Brain,* **63,** 36–90 (1940)

94. Walker, A. E., Richter, H. Section of the cerebral peduncle in the monkey. *Arch. Neurol.,* **14,** 231–40 (1966)

95. Bucy, P. C., Keplinger, J. E., Siqueira, E. I. Destruction of the "pyramidal tract" in man. *J. Neurosurg.,* **21,** 385–98 (1964)

96. Brodal, A. Some anatomical considerations of the cortico-spinal tract and corticofugal fibers to the brainstem. Acute hemiplegia in childhood. *Little Club Clin. Develop. Med.,* **6,** 24–36 (1962) (Quoted by Bucy et al. in Ref. 92).

97. Thulin, C.-A. Effects of electrical stimulation of the red nucleus on the alpha motor system. *Exptl. Neurol.,* **7,** 464–80 (1963)

98. Lawrence, D. G., Kuypers, H. G. J. M. Pyramidal and non-pyramidal pathways in monkeys: anatomical and functional correlation. *Science*, **148**, 973–75 (1965)

99. Lewis, R., Brindley, G. S. The extrapyramidal cortical motor map. *Brain*, **88**, 397–406 (1965)

100. Jankowska, E., Tarnecki, R. Extrapyramidal activation of muscles from the sensori-motor cortex in cats. *Experientia*, **21**, 656–57 (1965)

101. Wiesendanger, M., Laursen, A. M. Effekt der Pyramidenbahndurchtrennung bei der Katze. *Compt. Rend. Soc. Suisse Physiol.*, **65**, C54 (1965)

102. Laursen, A. M., Wiesendanger, M. Motor deficits after transection of a bulbar pyramid in the cat. *Acta Physiol. Scand.*, **68**, 118–26 (1966)

103. Liddell, E. G. T., Phillips, C. G. Pyramidal section in the cat. *Brain*, **67**, 1–9 (1944)

104. Nyberg-Hansen, R. Sites and mode of termination of reticulo-spinal fibers in the cat. An experimental study with silver impregnation methods. *J. Comp. Neurol.*, **124**, 71–100 (1965)

105. Torvik, A., Brodal, A. The origin of reticulospinal fibers in the cat. *Anat. Record*, **128**, 113–35 (1957)

106. Pompeiano, O., Brodal, A. The origin of vestibulospinal fibers in the cat. An experimental-anatomical study, with comments on the descending medial longitudinal fasciculus. *Arch. Ital. Biol.*, **95**, 166–95 (1957)

107. Nyberg-Hansen, R., Mascitti, T. A. Sites and mode of termination of fibers of the vestibulospinal tract in the cat. *J. Comp. Neurol.*, **122**, 369–87 (1964)

108. Szentagothai, J. Propriospinal pathways and their synapses. *Progr. Brain Res.*, 155–74 (1964)

109. Willis, W. D., Willis, J. C., Thompson, W. M., Jones, W. C. A descending pathway which is monosynaptically excitatory to motoneurones. *Nature*, **211**, 1182–83 (1966)

110. Willis, W. D., Willis, J. C., Thompson, W. M. Synaptic actions of fibers in the ventral spinal cord upon lumbosacral motoneurones. *J. Neurophysiol.*, **30**, 382–97 (1967)

111. Lloyd, D. P. C. Activity in neurons of bulbospinal correlation system. *J. Neurophysiol.*, **4**, 115–34 (1941)

112. Curtis, D. R., Eccles, J. C. Synaptic action during and after repetitive stimulation. *J. Physiol. (London)*, **150**, 374–98 (1960)

113. Landgren, S., Phillips, C. G., Porter, R. Minimal synaptic action of pyramidal impulses on some alpha motoneurons of the baboon's hand and forearm. *J. Physiol. (London)*, **161**, 91–111 (1962)

114. Eccles, J. C., Hubbard, J. I., Oscarsson, O. Intracellular recording from cells of the ventral spinocerebellar tract. *J. Physiol. (London)*, **158**, 486–516 (1961)

115. Magni, F., Willis, W. D. Cortical control of brain stem reticular neurons. *Arch. Ital. Biol.*, **102**, 418–33 (1964)

116. Sasaki, K., Tanaka, T., Mori, K. Effects of stimulation of pontine and bulbar reticular formation upon spinal motoneurons of the cat. *Japan. J. Physiol.*, **12**, 45–62 (1962)

117. Willis, W. D., Willis, J. C. Properties of interneurons in the ventral spinal cord. *Arch. Ital. Biol.*, **104**, 354–86 (1966)

118. Scheibel, M. E., Scheibel, A. B. Spinal motoneurons, interneurons and Renshaw cells. A Golgi study. *Arch. Ital. Biol.*, **104**, 328–53 (1966)

119. Lundberg, A. Integration in the reflex pathway. In *Muscular Afferents and Motor Control*, 275–305 (Granit, R., Ed., Almqvist & Wiksell, Stockholm, 466 pp., 1966)

120. Magni, F., Willis, W. D. Subcortical and peripheral control of brain stem reticular neurons. *Arch. Ital. Biol.*, **102**, 434–38 (1964)

121. Andersen, P., Eccles, J. C., Sears, T. A. Presynaptic inhibitory action of cerebral cortex on the spinal cord. *Nature*, **194**, 740–41 (1962)

122. Lundberg, A., Voorhoeve, P. Effects from the pyramidal tract on spinal reflex arcs. *Acta Physiol. Scand.*, **56**, 201–19 (1962)

123. Lundberg, A., Norrsell, U., Voorhoeve, P. Pyramidal effects on lumbosacral interneurones activated by somatic afferents. *Acta Physiol. Scand.*, **56**, 220–29 (1962)

124. Carpenter, D., Lundberg, A., Norrsell, U. Primary afferent depolarization evoked from the sensori-

motor cortex. *Acta Physiol. Scand.*, **59**, 126–42 (1963)

125. Lundberg, A., Norrsell, U., Voorhoeve, P. Effects from the sensorimotor cortex on ascending spinal pathways. *Acta Physiol. Scand.*, **59**, 462–73 (1963)

126. Mortimer, E. M., Akert, K. Cortical control and representation of fusimotor neurons. *Am. J. Phys. Med.*, **40**, 228–48 (1961)

127. Kato, M., Takamura, H., Fujimori, B. Studies on effects of pyramid stimulation upon flexor and extensor motoneurones and gamma motoneurones. *Japan. J. Physiol.*, **14**, 34–44 (1964)

128. Wiesendanger, M., Mosfeldt, L. A. Pyramidal influences on gamma- and alpha-motoneurones in the cat. In *Muscular Afferents and Motor Control*, 465–66 (Granit, R., Ed., Almqvist & Wiksell, Stockholm, 466 pp., 1966)

129. Holmqvist, B., Lundberg, A. Differential supraspinal control of synaptic actions evoked by volleys in the flexion reflex afferents in alpha motoneurones. *Acta Physiol. Scand.*, **54**, *Suppl. 186*, 1–51 (1961)

130. Hagbarth, K.-E., Excitatory and inhibitory skin areas for flexor and extensor motoneurones. *Acta Physiol. Scand.*, **26**, *Suppl. 94*, 1–58 (1952)

131. Hongo, T., Jankowska, E., Lundberg, A. Postsynaptic inhibition evoked from primary afferents in spinal interneurones. *Experientia*, **21**, 465–66 (1965)

132. Hongo, T., Jankowska, E., Lundberg, A. Convergence of excitatory and inhibitory action on interneurones in the lumbosacral cord. *Exptl. Brain Res.*, **1**, 338–58 (1966)

133. Tower, S. S. The dissociation of cortical excitation from cortical inhibition by pyramid section, and the syndrome of that lesion in the cat. *Brain*, **58**, 238–55 (1935)

134. Hongo, T., Jankowska, E., Lundberg, A. Effects evoked from the rubrospinal tract in cats. *Experientia*, **21**, 525–26 (1965)

135. Scheibel, M. E., Scheibel, A. B. Terminal axonal patterns in cat spinal cord. I. The lateral corticospinal tract. *Brain Res.*, **2**, 333–50 (1966)

136. Mabuchi, M., Kusama, T. The cortico-rubral projection in the cat. *Brain Res.*, **2**, 254–73 (1966)

137. Lund, S., Pompeiano, O. Descending pathways with monosynaptic action on motoneurons. *Experientia*, **21**, 602–3 (1965)

138. Granit, R., Pompeiano, O., Waltman, B. Fast supraspinal control of mammalian muscle spindles : extra- and intrafusal co-activation. *J. Physiol. (London)*, **147**, 385–98 (1959)

139. Carli, G., Diete-Spiff, K., Pompeiano, O. Responses of the muscle spindles and of the extrafusal fibres in an extensor muscle to stimulation of the lateral vestibular nucleus in the cat. *Arch. Ital. Biol.*, **105**, 209–42 (1967)

140. Merton, P. A. Speculations on the servo-control of movements. In *The Spinal Cord*, 247–60 (Wolstenholme, G. E. W., Ed., Little, Brown, Boston, 1953)

141. Hunt, C. C. The reflex activity of mammalian small-nerve fibres. *J. Physiol. (London)*, **115**, 456–69 (1951)

142. Hopf, H. C., Handwerker, J., Hausmans, J., Polzien, F. Untersuchungen über den Muskelproprioceptivität auf die Willkürbewegungen. *Klin. Wochschr.*, **14**, 789 (1966)

143. Carli, G., Diete-Spiff, K., Pompeiano, O. Mechanisms of muscle spindle excitation. *Arch. Ital. Biol.*, **105**, 273–89 (1967)

144. Granit, R., Kellerth, J.-O., Szumski, A. J. Intracellular recording from extensor motoneurons activated across the gamma loop. *J. Neurophysiol.*, **29**, 530–44 (1966)

145. Carli, G., Diete-Spiff, K., Pompeiano, O. Persistenza della risposta di recettori fusali alla stimolazione del nucleo di Deiters dopo blocco periferico dei γ-motoneuroni. *Boll. Soc. Ital. Biol. Sper.*, **42**, 1001–3 (1966)

146. Carli, G., Diete-Spiff, K., Pompeiano, O. Skeletomotor and fusimotor control of gastrocnemius muscle from Dieters' nucleus. *Experientia*, **22**, 583–84 (1966)

147. Terzuolo, C. A., Llinás, R., Green, K. T. Mechanisms of supraspinal actions upon spinal cord activities : distribution of reticular and segmental inputs in cat's alpha-motoneurons. *Arch. Ital. Biol.*, **103**, 635–51 (1965)

148. Rossi, G. F., Zanchetti, A. The brain stem reticular formation. Anatomy and physiology. *Arch. Ital. Biol.*, **95**, 199–435 (1957)

149. Andén, N.-E., Jukes, M. G. M., Lundberg, A., Vyklicky, L. The effect of DOPA on the spinal cord. I. Influence on transmission from primary afferents. *Acta Physiol. Scand.*, **67**, 373–86 (1966)

150. Andén, N.-E., Jukes, M. G. M., Lundberg, A. The effect of DOPA on the spinal cord. II. A pharmacological analysis. *Acta Physiol. Scand.*, **67**, 387–97 (1966)

151. Grillner, S., Lund, S. A descending pathway with monosynaptic action on flexor motoneurones. *Experientia*, **22**, 390 (1966)

152. Lundberg, A., Vyklicky, L. Inhibition of transmission to primary afferents by electrical stimulation of the brain stem. *Arch. Ital. Biol.*, **104**, 86–97 (1966)

153. Magoun, H. W., Rhines, R. Inhibitory mechanism in bulbar reticular formation. *J. Neurophysiol.*, **9**, 165–71 (1946)

154. Kuno, M., Perl, E. R. Alteration of spinal reflexes by interaction with suprasegmental and dorsal root activity. *J. Physiol. (London)*, **151**, 103–22 (1960)

155. Carpenter, D., Engberg, I., Lundberg, A. Presynaptic inhibition in the lumbar cord evoked from the brain stem. *Experientia*, **18**, 450–51 (1962)

156. Carpenter, D., Engberg, I., Lundberg, A. Primary afferent depolarization evoked from the brain stem and the cerebellum. *Arch. Ital. Biol.*, **104**, 73–85 (1966)

157. Granit, R., Kaada, B. R. Influence of stimulation of central nervous structures on muscle spindles in cat. *Acta Physiol. Scand.*, **27**, 130–60 (1952)

158. Terzuolo, C., Terzian, H. Cerebellar increase of postural tonus after deafferentation and labyrinthectomy. *J. Neurophysiol.*, **16**, 551–61 (1953)

159. Engberg, I., Lundberg, A., Ryall, R. W. Reticulospinal inhibition of transmission through interneurones of spinal reflex pathways. *Experientia*, **21**, 612–13 (1965)

160. Jankowska, E., Lund, S., Lundberg, A., Pompeiano, O. Postsynaptic inhibition in motoneurones evoked

from the lower reticular formation. *Experientia*, **20**, 701–2 (1964)

161. Llinas, R., Terzuolo, C. A. Mechanisms of supraspinal actions upon spinal cord activities. Reticular inhibitory mechanisms on alpha-extensor motoneurons. *J. Neurophysiol.*, **27**, 579–91 (1964)

162. Holmqvist, B., Lundberg, A. On the organization of the supraspinal inhibitory control of interneurones of various spinal reflex arcs. *Arch. Ital. Biol.*, **97**, 340–56 (1959)

163. Llinas, R., Terzuolo, C. A. Mechanisms of supraspinal actions upon spinal cord activities. Reticular inhibitory mechanisms upon flexor motoneurons. *J. Neurophysiol.*, **28**, 413–22 (1965)

164. Terzuolo, C. A., Llinas, R. Distribution of synaptic inputs in the spinal motoneurone and its functional significance. In *Muscular Afferents and Motor Control*, 373–84 (Granit, R., Ed., Almqvist & Wiksell, Stockholm, 466 pp., 1966)

165. Andersen, P., Holmqvist, B., Voorhoeve, P. E. Entorhinal activation of dentate granule cells. *Acta Physiol. Scand.*, **66**, 448–60 (1966)

166. Ito, M., Yoshida, M. The cerebellar-evoked monosynaptic inhibition of Deiters neurones. *Experientia*, **20**, 515–16 (1964)

167. Ito, M., Kawai, N., Udo, M. The origin of cerebellar-induced inhibition and facilitation in the neurones of Deiters' and intracerebellar nuclei. *Intern. Congr. Physiol. Sci. 23rd, Tokyo, 1965*, 997

168. Ito, M., Yoshida, M. The origin of cerebellar-induced inhibition of Deiters' neurones. I. Monosynaptic initiation of the inhibitory postsynaptic potentials. *Exptl. Brain Res.*, **2**, 330–49 (1966)

169. Ito, M., Obata, K., Ochi, R. The origin of cerebellar-induced inhibition of Deiters' neurones. II. Temporal correlation between the trans-synaptic activation of Purkinje cells and the inhibition of Deiters' neurones. *Exptl. Brain Res.*, **2**, 350–64 (1966)

170. Brodal, A., Pompeiano, O., Walberg, F. *The Vestibular Nuclei and their Connections. Anatomy and Functional Correlations*, 109–12 (Oliver & Boyd, Edinburgh/London, 193 pp., 1962)

171. Walberg, F., Jansen, J. Cerebellar corticovestibular fibres in the cat.

Exptl. Neurol., **3**, 32–52 (1961)

172. Eager, R. P. Efferent cortico-nuclear pathways in the cerebellum of the cat. *J. Comp. Neurol.*, **120**, 81–104 (1963)

173. de Vito, R. V., Brusa, A., Arduini, A. Cerebellar and vestibular influences on Deitersian units. *J. Neurophysiol.*, **19**, 241–53 (1956)

174. Pompeiano, O., Cotti, E. Analisi microelettrodica delle proiezioni cerebello-deitersiane. *Arch. Sci. Biol.*, **43**, 57–101 (1959)

175. Moruzzi, G. *Problems in Cerebellar Physiology* (Thomas, Springfield, Ill., 116 pp., 1950)

176. Moruzzi, G. Effects at different frequencies of cerebellar stimulation upon postural tonus and myotatic reflexes. *Electroencephalog. Clin. Neurophysiol.*, **2**, 463–69 (1950)

177. Eccles, J. C., Fatt, P., Koketsu, K. Cholinergic and inhibitory synapses in a pathway from motor-axon collaterals to motoneurones. *J. Physiol. (London)*, **126**, 524–62 (1954)

178. Szentagothai, J. The anatomical basis of synaptic transmission of excitation and inhibition in motoneurones. *Acta Morphol. Acad. Sci. Hung.*, **8**, 287–309 (1958)

179. Eccles, J. C. *The Physiology of Synapses* (Springer-Verlag, Berlin/Gottingen/Heidelberg, 316 pp., 1964)

180. Andersen, P., Eccles, J. C., Löyning, Y. Location of postsynaptic inhibitory synapses of hippocampal pyramids. *J. Neurophysiol.*, **27**, 592–607 (1964)

181. Andersen, P. O. Structure and function of archicortex. In *Brain and Conscious Experience*, 59–84 (Eccles, J. C., Ed., Springer-Verlag, New York, 591 pp., 1966)

182. Eccles, J. C., Llinas, R., Sasaki, K. The inhibitory interneurones within the cerebellar cortex. *Exptl. Brain Res.*, **1**, 1–16 (1966)

183. Brodal, A., Pompeiano, O., Walberg, F. *The Vestibular Nuclei and their Connections, Anatomy and Functional Correlations*, 64–72 (Oliver, & Boyd, Edinburgh/London, 193 pp., 1962)

MUSCLE[1]

By Lee D. Peachey

Departments of Biochemistry and Biophysics, University of Pennsylvania
Philadelphia, Pennsylvania

Research on muscle at the cellular and subcellular level has reached an interesting stage in each of several areas, including the activation system, the contractile machinery itself, and the relaxation system. In each case, the last decade or so has yielded a single and consistent idea of the basic structural and biochemical aspects of the system. These ideas have been challenged from time to time, and conflicting evidence and ideas have largely been explained away, forgotten for lack of a convincing case, or incorporated into general thinking. The result is reasonably wide acceptance of a single scheme in each case: ionic currents in the T-system[2] and calcium release by the sarcoplasmic reticulum for excitation-contraction (e-c) coupling, the sliding-filament mechanism for contraction, and calcium accumulation by the sarcoplasmic reticulum for relaxation. It seems that each of these schemes as presently formulated can be taken as a first approximation to the real mechanism. However, we must not be too impressed by the success of these schemes so far, and take them as any more than summaries of what we already know. It may well be the deviations from these schemes that will lead us to discovery of the details of the mechanisms underlying the known activities. My goal in this review has not been to defend dogma, but to evaluate the evidence critically.

I have attempted to follow the selective and critical style of the two excellent reviews on muscle by A. F. Huxley in 1964 (1) and Wilkie in 1966 (2). Some of the topics reviewed earlier have been continued and a few topics of particular interest have been expanded or added. Perhaps not unexpectedly, this review has come out with a rather strong morphological emphasis.

COMMUNICATION

The number of different journals in which interesting muscle papers are published is now greater than ever, and it seems impractical if not impossi-

---

[1] The survey of the literature for this chapter was concluded in July 1967.

[2] Abbreviations used in this review: T-system (transverse tubular system); SR (sarcoplasmic reticulum); e-c for excitation-contraction; LMM (light meromyosin); HMM (heavy meromyosin); ATP (adenosine triphosphate); DNFB (2,4-dinitrofluorobenzene); EPP (endplate potential); SJP (small nerve junctional potential).

ble for most of us to check each issue of each likely journal. As mentioned by Wilkie (2), the *Abstracts* provided by the Muscular Dystrophy Association of America offer an efficient solution at no cost to the user. This service continues, and its publishers are anxious for as wide a useful distribution as possible (3). A new service, which I found of some help in preparing this review, is the computer-based MEDLARS Demand Search available from the National Library of Medicine (4); the aim of the system is to have the entire world biomedical literature since 1963 available for search according to any set of topics specified. This would seem to be particularly valuable for selection of references with particularly complex or unusual sets of restrictive classifications.

Wilkie (2) reported the birth of Information Exchange Group No. 4 on the Molecular Basis of Muscle Contraction, better known as IEG 4. Unfortunately I must report its death, at the beginning of this year (5). The convenor of IEG 4, Dr. John Gergely, polled the members for their opinions on the value of such a service, and found that many persons considered it a useful venture, worthy of being continued in some form. Without going into the various plans proposed (an interesting one was the founding of a new journal dealing exclusively with muscle), I will report that Dr. Gergely has set up a system for circulating *Muscle Notes* among persons interested in receiving them, in return for a fee of about $25 per year (6). I have already received several *Notes*. To avoid conflicts with journals that are unwilling to publish manuscripts previously circulated in "substantial numbers" with "essentially identical content" (7), *Muscle Notes* welcomes brief preliminary communications reporting new findings, summaries of papers submitted for publication (whether already accepted or not), and discussions or comments on previously circulated *Muscle Notes* or published journal articles. It is hoped that members will submit such summaries and reports regularly. Authors of *Notes* are expected to be willing to send additional information or complete reports directly to persons who inquire after having seen the *Note*.

I am happy that I, like the previous reviewer (2), can report the formation of a local muscle discussion group. The Philadelphia MYO-BIO Group is now in its third successful year of roughly bimonthly dinner-discussions by its own members and by itinerant muscle men. We welcome to Philadelphia anyone with anything to say about muscle, and will provide a good meal, a projector, and an interested, critical, friendly audience. Our only rule is that the speaker not be allowed to get to his second slide without first having been interrupted.

SYMPOSIA, REVIEWS, BOOKS

Five symposia on muscle have been held or the proceedings published during the review period. One is on e-c coupling (8), a second includes the structural basis for e-c coupling and the mechanical and chemical aspects of the contraction mechanism (9), and a third has papers on the contractile process in muscles and certain nonmuscular biological systems and possibly-related physical chemistry (10). The fourth, a symposium on comparative aspects of muscle (11), should be of great interest because it brings up aspects of those 'way out' muscles we so often neglect in our effort to simplify and unify our ideas. The fifth is on cardiac muscle cells (12), and a Gordon Conference on heart will soon be published (13).

Papers on the structure and electrophysiology of muscle membranes are found in the publications of a conference on the biophysics of excitable membranes (14) and one on biological membranes (15). A symposium on principles of biomolecular organization emphasizes the design and assembly' of myofilaments (16).

Special issues of two journals, dedicated to Hans H. Weber and to Ernest Fischer, contain numerous papers on muscle. The first (17) has over 400 pages of papers on a wide variety of topics in muscle research, and the second (18) contains four papers, covering smooth muscle, slow and fast striated muscle, latency relaxation, and muscle in the 'delta state' after extreme shortening. A commemorative book for H. Kumagai, *Molecular Biology of Muscular Contraction,* also contains a variety of topics about muscle (19).

Many specific topics in muscle research, recently reviewed, include physiology of the heart (20), muscle regeneration (21), calcium in muscle (22–26), membrane structure and e-c coupling (27, 28), muscle proteins (24, 29, 30), the fine structure of skeletal muscle (31), electrophysiology and ion movements (32), and the contractile mechanism of insect muscle (33).

New books on muscle cover it as a food, but with a number of chapters on basic subjects (34), avian myology (35), and the contractile proteins (36). The last one is a translation from the Russian edition of 1965. Individual papers on insect and vertebrate muscles appear in three other books (24, 37, 38). Katz has written an excellent introduction to nerve and muscle physiology (39). This book is intended primarily for students, but obviously it will have even wider value.

CONTRACTION MECHANISM

Gergely has included contraction mechanisms at the end of a recent review on the contractile proteins (29), and Pringle has presented a comprehensive review on the structure and function of the contractile apparatus of insect fibrillar flight muscles (33).

SLIDING-FILAMENT THEORY

As at the time of the two previous reviews (1, 2), the sliding-filament theory maintains a commanding position as the most widely accepted description of the mechanism by which a striated muscle cell changes its length. Although the evidence is much less complete, some form of sliding mechanism is at least compatible with observations on vertebrate smooth muscle (40, 41), some invertebrate nonstriated or irregularly striated muscles (42–46), cilia (47, 48), and bacterial flagellae (43).

Filament arrangement.—Usually it has been found that the arrangement of thick and thin filaments in the region of overlap is precise, almost
crystalline. While the arrangement of thick filaments is rather precisely
hexagonal in all striated muscles, there have been several observations of
irregularly placed thin filaments or an orbit of more than six thin filaments
around one thick filament. It has not been clear if this is a true arrangement or the result of unsatisfactory preservation. Recently thin filaments in
excess of six around each thick filament (usually nine to twelve) have been
found in many invertebrate striated muscles (but not in vertebrate muscles or
insect flight muscles) and in most of these studies preservation appears
generally good (49–59a). In some cases, the possibility of excess thin filaments due to double overlap in highly shortened sarcomeres has
specifically been ruled out, and in these the most likely true number of thin
filaments around each thick filament is twelve. Several years ago, Swan
(60) suggested that in some muscles each thick filament might have its own
orbit of six thin filaments, none of which is shared with another thick filament, which arrangement would give an average of twelve thin filaments
surrounding each thick filament. This idea fits well with the recent electronmicroscopic evidence, but it leaves an uncertainty of how lateral stability
is maintained during contraction in the absence of symmetrical forces on
the thin filaments. As pointed out (56–58) all these invertebrate muscles
with irregular thin-filament arrangements are slow compared to the insect
flight and other fast muscles, which have a precise arrangement, even in
cases where the development of T-system and SR is equivalent. Thus the
precise arrangement may be an adaptation for high speeds of contraction.

Filament structure.—Pepe has presented a model for the myosin filament, based on antibody staining patterns and electronmicroscopic study of
glycerinated chicken breast muscle fibers (61). In this model, myosin molecules are placed tail (LMM end) to tail in the L-region (pseudo-H-zone)
of the A-band, with twelve molecules in a triangular cross section through
this part of the filament. In the region of cross-bridges, eighteen myosin
molecules occupy the cross section, and most or all of the heavy meromyosin (HMM) and possibly even part of the LMM can project outward to
form the cross-bridges. These bridges are arranged approximately in a
double helix with pairs of bridges projecting in opposite directions, in
agreement with the X-ray observations of H. E. Huxley (62). Near their
ends, the thick filaments taper and contain fewer molecules. The M-line
consists of projections, not made of myosin (63), linking together adjacent
thick filaments. The length of synthetic myosin filaments depends on pH
(64), indicating that this form of end-to-end and side-to-side stacking of
molecules can produce stable filaments with lengths other than that found
in striated muscle cells. This possibility may be important in considerations
of the form of myosin aggregates in smooth muscle cells.

In Pepe's model, a single cross-bridge can represent one or more than
one myosin molecule, and it may be that two (65) or three (66) myosin

molecules are present in each cross-bridge, an additional complication for builders of contraction models.

An interesting thought concerning the thick filaments is that they must have a sufficiently labile structure to account for a measured half-life of turnover of myosin of only twenty to thirty days in small mammals (67, 68). Recently, Aronson (69) has suggested that sulfhydryl groups in myosin may contribute to stability of the thick filament, and that oxidation of myosin sulfhydryl groups may accelerate elimination of these molecules from the thick filament. Sulfhydryl groups have also been implicated in regulation of myosin conformation (70) and in actin-myosin interaction (71).

Cross-bridge movement.—According to current ideas on the sliding-filament theory, tension and shortening are generated by cycles of activity of myosin cross-bridges temporarily attaching to the thin filaments and producing transient longitudinal forces or relative motion between the two filaments. Evidence for movement of myosin cross-bridges to a spacing more like that of the thin filaments has been found by X-ray diffraction of frog muscle in rigor (62). During isometric contraction, the X-ray patterns change in a way suggesting that the cross-bridges move asynchronously, but the nature of this movement is not clear (62). Both X-ray diffraction and electronmicroscopy (72) have indicated cross-bridge movement when insect fibrillar flight muscles go from the relaxed state into rigor (see also *Insect muscles*). Cross-bridges on reconstituted myosin filaments are inclined at an angle away from the center of the filament (62, 72a), but apparently become perpendicular to the filament axis when these filaments form compound filaments with actin at low ionic strength and in the presence of ATP (72a). Clearly the cross-bridges can take up various orientations in a rather precise way, but just how and when they do this remains to be found.

Also implicit in the cross-bridge mechanism is an expectation of asynchronous and transient displacements and lengthenings (perhaps minute) of the filaments, as a result of the quantal nature of the force generators. This might be expressed as fluctuations in lengths of individual sarcomeres during isometric contraction. Loss of coherence of laser light has been cited by Carlson as evidence for internal movement [discussion following (63)]. What one really hopes to see is movement or blurring of layer lines as evidence for sarcomere spacing changes, and according to R. E. Davis, M. J. Kushmerick, and R. E. Larson (personal communication), this does occur.

Effects of length changes (vertebrate muscles).—Variation of isometric tension and isometric rate of phosphogen splitting as a linear function of degree of overlap of thin filaments (up to the point where all bridges can form) is expected from the sliding-filament theory. Sandberg & Carlson (73) have now published details of their experiments confirming earlier suggestions that phosphorylcreatine splitting does follow this pattern. ATPase activity decreases with stretch in frog fibers, although not with the expected slope (74). Gordon, Huxley & Julian's length clamp experiments, now reported in full (75), beautifully show the direct relation between number of myosin bridges overlapped by thin filaments and isometric tension. In this paper, they decide that the fall in tension with decrease in sarcomere length begins when the ends of the thin filaments from opposite ends of the sarcomere collide, at the M-line, a point not decided in their preliminary report. Similar results on crayfish fibers point out the effect of the relatively long I-bands in these muscles (76).

Maximum length for contraction.—The question whether a portion of a muscle fiber stretched to the point of no overlap of thick and thin filaments can produce tension was still somewhat unsettled in the two previous reviews (1, 2) because of a small residual tension at lengths where the sliding-filament theory would predict none (77). Subsequently, Carlsen, Fuchs & Knappeis (78) have presented further evidence for unexplained tension development in highly stretched glycerinated psoas muscle fibers with sarcomere lengths up to 4.4 μ. They feel that they have ruled out the possibility that this tension arises from a large number of sarcomeres whose length is sufficiently below the average length to have overlapped filaments. They do not in this paper rule out the possibility of longitudinal slippage of filaments within the A-band such as occurs in glycerinated barnacle muscle (79). In a second paper (80) Carlsen et al. examine this possibility by electronmicroscopy, and conclude that contact between the ends of thick and thin filaments in highly stretched fibrils is maintained by 'gap' filaments, but it is not stated how these authors visualize that tension is produced in these stretched fibrils. It still seems possible that the 'gap' filaments are thick filaments loosened by glycerination and pulled out of the A-band. These projecting thick filaments could interact with thin filaments, producing tension in the ordinary way and pulling the thin filaments toward the residual A-band. Any passively pulled thin filaments not entering the spaces in the thick-filament lattice would fold up against the A-band, explaining the unusual patterns seen in these micrographs (80).

Gordon, Huxley & Julian (81) find residual tension only up to sarcomere lengths about 0.3 μ greater than the expected point of no overlap (living fibers). They suggest three possible sources of this residual tension: atypical filaments extending beyond the usual position in the sarcomere, nonlinear distribution of bridges in the tapered ends of the thick filaments, and length changes in the filaments during activation of contraction. They don't favor any one of these possibilities. Another possibility might be longitudinal vibration of individual filaments occasionally making contact and forming cross-bridges. The origin of this effect remains obscure.

ALTERNATE THEORIES

In an alternate form of the sliding-filament theory, the thin filaments reach past the center of the A-band and attach to the thick filaments in the opposite half of the A-band (82). Contraction consists of a pulling of the ends of thin filaments toward the opposite ends of the thick filaments by a reorganization or migration of myosin in the thick filament, as suggested by fluorescent antibody-staining experiments (83). This immediately implies that the thick filaments are put under compression during contraction rather than under tension, which seems unlikely unless they are very rigid. However, a better argument against this theory is found in the experiments done on glycerinated rabbit psoas fibrils by Stephens (84) in which ultraviolet irradiation of two thirds of an A-band destroyed actin filaments in that region but did not prohibit pulling of thin filaments into the other unirradiated end of the A-band. Thus the thin-thick filament interaction leading to contraction seems to take place in the half-A-band nearer the Z-line to which the thin filaments are attached, as thought in the original sliding-filament theory.

While this seems to dispose of the theory (82) it leaves behind the observations on which the theory was based (83). Since the antimeromyosin method gives results that probably are more qualitative than quantitative (83), the appearance of a shift in LMM to the ends of the A-band during shortening could arise from an increased staining of these regions of the sarcomere for LMM or an inhibition of HMM staining centrally in the A-band, or both, rather than to an actual movement of myosin. This increased LMM staining could arise from an opening up of the thick-filament structure as the fibril widens during shortening (85–86a) or thin filaments could inhibit HMM staining, as Pepe (61, 63) has suggested.

Further ultraviolet irradiation experiments have been done by Stephens (87) on glycerinated fibrils from *Pecten* and three arthropod muscles, with effects on contraction similar to those described above for rabbit psoas (84). Some unexpected and unexplained differences between fibrils contracting unloaded or under tension, and some effects of varying the duration of glycerination are presented and discussed. I won't present these in detail here: it will be sufficient to say that the A-band shortening observed by Stephens (87), and probably also that reported by others (88–91), is an abnormal phenomenon seen only after glycerination and probably not related to normal contraction. In one case (89) this can evidently be explained by longitudinal slippage of thick filaments loosened by the glycerination (79), but in other cases it has not been explained in this way or by any other demonstrated mechanism. The idea that the A-band keeps a constant length during contraction of normal muscle until contraction bands form remains valid, within available accuracy of measurement.

Another proposed mechanism (37) requires a change in longitudinal spacing of cross-bridges during shortening, and has been ruled out by X-ray evidence showing no such change (85, 92).

A mechanism proposed by McNeil & Hoyle (93, 94) depends on the activity of 'very thin T-filaments' thought to be visible in electronmicrographs alongside the thick and thin filaments and extending from Z-line to Z-line. The electronmicroscopic evidence for these filaments is not very convincing, since very few of the densities said to represent 'very thin' filaments are seen in any one field, and many of these can be explained in other ways, e.g. as portions of underlying filaments shaved off in the sectioning process. One would certainly like to see more convincing electron-microscopic evidence before rejecting the large body of evidence that has accumulated for the sliding thick- and thin-filament model.

INSECT MUSCLES

Insect fibrillar flight muscles have been known since 1949 to undergo multiple, oscillatory contractions when connected to a suitable inertial load and stimulated with a single impulse (95). This oscillatory behavior has been shown to arise in living (96) and glycerinated (97) fibers from hysteresis in the relationship between tension and length. Since tension is lower during lengthening than during shortening, external work is done by the muscle during a complete cycle, making sustained oscillations possible. A careful study of glycerol- and detergent-treated fibers shows clearly that these length-tension characteristics are properties of the myofibrils, not of other cellular components (98), and are likely to be due to increase in calcium binding and ATPase activity following stretch (99). It should be noted that the degree of shortening of the sarcomeres during these oscillations is very small, being approximately equivalent to one cross-bridge spacing per half-sarcomere. Damped oscillations of similarly small amplitude have been seen in frog muscle (99a), and so the differences between the contractile apparatus of insect fibrillar flight muscle and that of vertebrate muscles may not be as great as might first appear from these results.

These insect fibrillar flight muscles are different from other muscles, in that they have attachments of the ends of the thick filaments to the Z-line (100, 101). They can be stretched only about 10 per cent above rest length without disruption and probably irreversible damage, presumably because of these connections (102–104). However, these muscles resemble other striated muscles in that their fibrils consists of interdigitating arrays of thick and thin filaments with cross-bridges extending from the thick filaments toward the adjacent thin filaments in the transverse direction (72). In relaxed glycerinated fibrils, these bridges are primarily at right angles to the fiber axis (electronmicroscopy) and spaced at the myosin period of 146 Å (X-ray diffraction, meridional reflection). In rigor, the cross-bridges are spaced by 388 Å (X-ray diffraction, off-meridional layer line), a periodicity characteristic of the thin filaments, and are angled (electronmicroscopy) toward the center of the A-band (72). This implies that the bridges, in rigor at least, are all strongly attached to sites on the thin filaments. This is the first electronmicroscopic evidence for cross-bridge movement presumed to be related to contraction. The second apparent implication of these observations, that the bridges are so angled as to transmit force by pushing rather than pulling on the thin filaments, is somewhat harder to understand. R. E. Davies (personal communication) has suggested that the observation may be an artifact caused during fixation by a flipping over of all previously attached and fixed bridges when the last unfixed and still active bridge forms its link and moves the thin filament a small amount. It doesn't seem as if this possibility can be ruled out, so the conclusions that the bridges push instead of pull must be considered cautiously. Relevant to this are Pepe's arguments that the portion of a cross-bridge that is seen in the electronmicroscope may represent more of the myosin molecule than actually is involved in the movements driving contraction (61, 63). Thus the cross-bridge angle, as we see it, may not be related to whether the active movement of the myosin molecule in contraction is a push or a pull. Pepe's arguments concern vertebrate muscles and are partly based on the need for the cross-bridge to reach a distance that varies as the sarcomere length varies (63). Since this variation is small in these insect muscles, which don't change sarcomere length very much, it must be admitted that this discussion is not on very firm ground. However, it does point out a danger in assuming that the portion of the bridge that we see is necessarily the active element rather than a passive mechanical link.

Pringle, in an extensive review (33), put all the available evidence together into a model, in which the cross-bridges undergo an active stroke during which they change their angle with respect to the fiber axis. The cross-bridges are thought to attach when oriented approximately perpendicular to the fiber axis, and to move during their active stroke to a position where they are inclined about 45° toward the center of the A-band. This incorporates into the model the electronmicroscopic observations on rigor muscle (72), but there seems to be no other reason for this 'push' aspect of the proposed model. The reader is referred to Pringle's review for other details of this model (33).

Physiology.—An interesting new observation relates to the preflight activity of many insects, when the temperature of the thorax increases as much as several °C. The heat produced during this period arises from alternate, damped oscillatory contractions of the two flight muscle antagonists (105). No wing motion is visible during the 'warmup' because the wings are folded and mechanically decoupled from the flight muscles. A mechanical click system apparently operates to provide the sudden releases and stretches needed to operate these muscles in an oscillatory mode without the inertial load provided during flight by the wings. The sound produced during 'warmup' comes from this click system and is thus produced in the same way as the song of certain cicadas (106).

Another interesting paper (107) suggests that the high velocity attained by a jumping locust may partly arise from a situation in which flexors are contracted during preparation for the jump, and are held under tension while activity builds up in the extensors. At the beginning of the actual jump, the flexors begin to relax and now fully activated extensors begin to unfold the leg, whereupon they gain in mechanical advantage over the flexors and quickly overcome their now declining tension. Thus the jump is accomplished from its start by fully activated extensor muscles, and the velocity attained is limited only by the velocity of shortening of a fully activated muscle and not by the rate at which the muscle can become activated. These antagonistic muscles would seem to be interesting to study from a comparative morphological and physiological viewpoint, since the extensors are expected to be strong muscles, with high speeds of shortening, while the flexors ought to relax unusually rapidly. What evidence there is fits with this. The extensors have no 'intracellular' tracheoles, few mitochondria, little SR, and a maximum of fibrils (108). They are thus suited for strong, brief, and anaerobic activity. The flexors have tracheoles, more mitochondria, and loosely packed fibrils surrounded by a more extensive sarcoplasmic reticulum (108, 109), suiting them, morphologically and biochemically, for tonic activity and for more rapid relaxation, according to current ideas on the role of the sarcoplasmic reticulum in relaxation.

MUSCLE PROTEINS

Significant changes have been made in our knowledge of muscle proteins in the last few years. In addition to actin, myosin, and tropomyosin (plus paramyosin in some invertebrate muscles), we now have at least three new proteins to deal with. Some information on possible functions of these new proteins is available but much more will be needed to bring them to the state of actin and myosin in our present knowledge. Ebashi & Endo (26, 110) and Gergely (29) have recently reviewed this area, and Perry has covered myosin (30). I will confine my attention to tropomyosin and the new proteins.

Native tropomyosin (metin) and troponin.—Purified tropomyosin (Bailey's tropomyosin, tropomyosin B) is unable to confer calcium specificity on superprecipitation of purified actomyosin with magnesium and ATP. This difference between purified protein systems and either crude extracts (myosin B) or intact myofibrils, which require calcium, has been an unsatisfying aspect of these model systems for some time. A preparation called 'native tropomyosin' restores the calcium requirement for superprecipitation (111–112a), and has been said to consist of two proteins, tropomyosin, and a new globular protein, troponin (113, 114). Native tropomyosin has higher viscosity and flow birefringence, and a larger sedimentation constant than does tropomyosin. Native tropomyosin can be derived from tropomyosin by an apparent aggregation process promoted by troponin (113) or can be extracted in a native state from muscle if SH groups are protected during isolation (115), although Ebashi & Endo have challenged this last point (26).

Attempts to localize native tropomyosin, troponin (116), and tropomyosin (63, 116) in the fibrils suggest that they are associated with or part of the thin filaments. In this regard, it is interesting that crystalline tropomyosin has a subunit spacing (117) similar to the 388 Å period of the I-band of intact fibrils (62). Thus native tropomyosin may play a structural role in the thin filament as well as control the interaction between actin and myosin so that calcium is required (116). The observation that calcium is not required for superprecipitation of actomyosin in the absence of native tropomyosin has been used as an argument against a direct role of the calcium ion in cross-bridge attachment, suggesting that it acts perhaps through some regulatory protein such as native tropomyosin (112).

Metin, isolated by Szent-Györgyi & Kaminer (118), is now referred to as crude metin (119), and consists of tropomyosin plus a minor component now called metin (119, 120), which apparently corresponds to Ebashi's native tropomyosin, or tropomyosin combined with troponin.

α-*Actinin*.—A protein similar in amino acid composition to actin has been said to promote the superprecipitation of purified synthetic actomyosin and is called α-*actinin* (121, 122). It interacts specifically with F-actin, not with myosin (123, 124), and is possibly a constituent of the Z-line (124).

β-*Actinin*.—F-actin prepared from fibrils without depolymerizing action and avoiding the use of acetone has an apparent particle length (flow-birefringence) of 1–2.5 μ. It is less altered at high shear than is F-actin of the Straub type, which has a longer particle length, and tends to form networks in solution (125). The limitation of F-actin particle length to a range similar to that in the intact fibril has been attributed to another protein, called β-actinin, with an amino acid composition like that of actin (126).

CHEMICAL AND THERMAL ENERGETICS

ATP and phosphorylcreatine.—By 1966 (2), it seemed clear that ATP is the immediate source of free energy driving contraction and that phosphorylcreatine contributes its free energy indirectly through ADP to resynthesize ATP. This was accepted (1, 2) with the reservation that the experiments used to demonstrate it (127, 128) were done on muscles (frog rectus abdominis) treated with DNFB to inhibit ATP: creatine phosphotransferase (creatine kinase), and the inhibition possibly was not complete. Furthermore, one was not sure that these muscles were entirely normal in their contraction parameters. Three laboratories have now provided new and reassuring information on the effects of DNFB on frog sartorius muscles (129–131), where the results are more convincing than are those on the rectus (127, 128).

Conditions of treatment and results are somewhat different among the three most complete papers on the effects of DNFB, but the main conclusions are similar. DNFB-treated muscles contain normal (129) or moderately decreased (130, 131) amounts of ATP and normal (129, 130) or slightly increased (131) phosphorylcreatine. ATP resynthesis through glycolysis and oxidative phosphorylation is not significant, in poisoned muscles, for the duration of the test contractions (129, 130). Studies of extracts of DNFB-treated muscles showed no creatine kinase activity, and a significantly reduced level of myokinase activity (129). However, myokinase and adenosine monophosphate deaminase remain sufficiently active to produce significant amounts of inosine monophosphate (130, 131). Most important, however, is an essentially complete inhibition of creatine kinase in DNFB-poisoned sartorius muscles undergoing short tetani (129, 130), although one paper reports some phosphorylcreatine breakdown in a short series of twitches (131). Thus, the evidence now seems convincing that DNFB treatment does little of biochemical importance to sartorius muscles except to greatly reduce rephosphorylation of ADP through the usual pathways except for myokinase. In spite of this, tension production is approximately normal in poisoned muscles, at least for a few-second-long tetanus (129, 130, 132) or for a few twitches (131), although it declines rapidly thereafter (132). Thus there seems little reason not to accept these experiments as conclusive evidence that ATP is the most immediate metabolically produced source of free energy for contraction.

ATP, HEAT, AND WORK

Several investigations of the quantitative relationships among ATP or phosphorylcreatine used, heat released, shortening, and work done by striated muscle under various conditions of loading and length changes have resulted in information crucial in the important quest for understanding of the molecular mechanism of muscle contraction.

Shortening heat and ATP.—Wilkie (2) reviewed the evidence that the extra heat produced by a tetanized muscle when it shortens is not simply proportional to the distance shortened, but also includes a quantity of heat related either to the size of the load or to the work done by the muscle (133). Also, a muscle that undergoes a complete isometric twitch produces more heat than one whose tension is released near its peak (134), as if there were a third heat "associated with the persistence of tension" (135). The precise status of the heat related to the shortening per se remained somewhat uncertain. Carlson, Hardy & Wilkie (136) could find no evidence for heat production specifically related to shortening when the whole cycle of contraction and relaxation of a twitch was examined.

Nevertheless, a shortening heat can be seen during the early times of single isotonic tetani (133, 137) and twitches (135, 138). The difference between these results could be explained if the heat of shortening appeared early, while the muscle was shortening, and a heat of about the same magnitude appeared later in the nonshortening muscle while tension was being maintained and while it was falling during relaxation (136). Though not explicitly stated by Hill, in his recent papers, it seems implied by his results that the late isometric heat which he postulates to explain the Carlson et al. result (136) and designates as h (135) is at least in part the same as the two heats mentioned above: the one that fails to appear when an isometric muscle is released (134), and the one that appears when a muscle has a heavier load (133). Interestingly enough, Hill said essentially this long ago in a Croonian Lecture (139).

Thus the shortening heat seems to have survived a frontal attack. We now must consider the source of the shortening heat. In a challenge to bio-chemists (140), A. V. Hill has asked for the biochemical equivalent of the shortening heat. Earlier work had shown no dependence of phosphorylcrea-tine breakdown on shortening in complete contractions (141) or early in isotonic twitches (142). Davies and his co-workers (143) have now taken up Hill's challenge and looked for splitting of ATP they could associate with shortening in normal and DNFB-treated frog sartorius muscles. When the experimental design suggested by Hill (140) was adopted and lightly loaded isotonic muscles were compared to isometric ones, the muscles that shortened used less ATP than the ones that did not. Thus, even recognizing that Davies et al. (143) did not measure heat output but calculated it from Hill's values (133), and further that different species of frogs were used by Hill and by Davies et al., there is evidence that there is no extra ATP breakdown underlying the heat of shortening, at least during the time the muscle is shortening.

Professor Hill (personal communication) regards this as an important preliminary step toward finding out what molecular or microstructural changes underlie the shortening heat. He doubts that it is a product of his imagination.

The problem that remains is what is the source of the heat of shorten-ing? Davies et al. (143) suggest that during shortening ATP splitting may be coupled to another reaction with a large negative entropy change. Over-all, the coupled reactions would have the necessary negative free energy change (ΔF) to allow them to proceed, but if the entropy term ($T \cdot \Delta S$) were large and negative, the overall result would be a heat output ($-T \cdot \Delta S$ $-\Delta F$ — work done) much larger than in the absence of the proposed en-tropy decrease (see 144).

Whatever the source of the shortening heat, it must be an effect that is approximately linear with shortening, and yield a heat equivalent to about 10 g-cm per cm of shortening in a toad sartorius weighing about 0.2 g (135). In trying to fit this into the sliding-filament mechanism of muscle contraction, two known phenomena come to mind that seem to have the right characteristics to be considered as possible sources of the shortening heat:

1. The formation of *new* cross-bridge linkages, the number of which is a linear function of shortening in the range of sarcomere lengths from no overlap to full overlap.

2. The transverse expansion of the filament lattice as the sarcomere shortens. Since this lattice remains at constant volume (85–86a), the lateral spacing of filaments increases as the square root of the decrease in sarco-mere length.

According to the first of these, the entropy decrease proposed by Davies et al. (153) could occur when a cross-bridge operates its *first time,* result-ing in a release of heat. When this cross-bridge recycled to its original "in-active" configuration, it would reabsorb that portion of the heat that came from entropy. On the average, as long as this cross-bridge was cycling, it would be somewhere between these states, with part of its entropy released as heat. Accordingly, a quantity of heat is released each time a new cross-bridge is brought into action, and since the number of cross-bridges active increases as the muscle shortens (up to a point), this could account for shortening heat (145). The reverse situation and the concomitant reduction in ATP usage (146) could explain why a muscle that is stretched while active produces less heat, when heat of degraded external work put in is subtracted (147).

The second suggestion above could be treated similarly. As the muscle shortens, the filament lattice expands laterally, and if the myosin filament cross-bridges are to reach to the actin filaments, they must in some way extend across the wider gap. This extension or opening up of the myosin filament might be associated with an entropy change leading to a heat release.

Activation heat.—A new determination of the heat of activation has been made using a new method to extract this quantity of heat from the total heat of a twitch. Gibbs, Ricchiuti & Mommaerts (148), by adjusting the interval between two shocks to an isometric frog sartorius at 0°C, were able (in four fifths of the muscles only) to find an interval where there was apparently a full activation event but only a small (often less than 10 per cent) increase in the mechanical tension as a result of the second shock. This allowed them to measure the extra heat output resulting from the second activation, which they assume to be equal to the normal activation heat of the muscle. Expressed in absolute units, the activation heat per twitch was 1.2 ± 0.3 (sd) mcal per g muscle at 0°C and at L_0 (peak tension length). These workers show quite convincingly that the magnitude of the activation heat as they measure it does not change much with muscle length from approximately $2L_0/3$ (where no tension is developed) to $5L_0/4$, and also does not change systematically with temperature up to 22°C. The results of this new method were checked (with good agreement) against the method used earlier by Hill (138) where the muscle is first shortened to a length where no external tension is produced, and then the activation heat is measured. This agreement implies that if there are errors in these methods, e.g. some internal work is done in Hill's method (138) or the second activation is not a complete one in the double stimulus method (148), then the errors are too small to be detected, since the former error would, I believe, lead to an overestimate of the activation heat while the latter would give an estimate that was too small.

Chemical energetics of activation.—The question arises as to the source of the activation heat. It seems unlikely that it is derived from the free energy of phosphorylcreatine (149) or of ATP. Davies et al. stimulated DNFB-poisoned frog sartorius muscles with five or more shocks at muscle lengths sufficiently short that no external tension was developed [method of Hill (138)], and chemically measured ATP broken down (143). The amount of ATP breakdown was very small (from 0.005 to 0.05 μmoles per g muscle per impulse at various rates of stimulation), and was insufficient to account for an activation heat of 1.2 mcal per g muscle per impulse. This was true even if an enthalpy of ATP hydrolysis as high as 10 kcal/mole and all the free energy were completely degraded to heat, an unlikely situation, since the process then could serve no useful purpose from an energetic standpoint.

A similar conclusion was reached by Jöbsis & Duffield, based on somewhat less direct evidence (150). They estimated the quantity of oxidative phosphorylation in frog and toad sartorii during and after tetani of varying durations from the time integral of reduced nicotinamide adenine dinucleotide (NAD) measured fluorimetrically. A plot of this integral against the time integral of tension for tetani of varying duration extrapolates through the origin, and the authors state that if there is an energy utilization associated with activation, they expect this plot to have a finite intercept on the ordinate. Since it does not, they feel they have eliminated "activation as a significant, fixed contribution to the overall energy utilization." This conclusion is probably justified if it is assumed that a tetanus is associated with a single activation event, but in fact each impulse leads to an additional activation, at least at low stimulation frequencies. Repeated activations would lead to an increase in slope of any plot of energy usage vs. number of stimuli. The abscissa of the relevant plot (Figure 1) is not linear with number of stimuli, except over part of its range, but the fact that it passes through the origin does not seem to rule out activation energy usage as conclusively as the authors state. However, the results are presented in terms unfamiliar to me, and I am on dangerous ground criticizing results I don't quite understand.

Taken all together, the evidence seems to be against an immediate metabolic source for the activation heat in the form of phosphagen breakdown. As has been suggested, activation heat may be related to calcium release from the sarcoplasmic reticulum (145) or to the reaction of myosin to ATP or to calcium (151). Ultimately, of course, this energy must come from metabolism, but apparently it does not do so during the activation itself.

ATP and work.—Kushmerick (152, 153) has reported an extensive study of the relations between ATP used and work performed by DNFB-poisoned frog sartorius muscles contracting at constant velocity. The results show that ATP utilization is proportional to external work done over a wide range of shortening velocities, and extrapolates to a value close to zero at zero work. Over the range of velocities from 0.6 to 2.8 cm/sec about 200 g cm of work per g of muscle was done for each μmole of ATP used. This 'efficiency' decreased at both higher and lower velocities. A small amount of ATP split when no work was done was explained as required for calcium pumping during relaxation. When this ATP usage was subtracted from the total, the 'efficiency' of ATP usage for external work was 70 to 95 per cent in the mid-range of velocities, based on a free energy of ATP splitting of 10 kcal/mole.

SARCOPLASMIC RETICULUM AND TRANSVERSE TUBULES

New evidence on the morphology of the transverse tubules and the sarcoplasmic reticulum (SR) in various types of muscles continues to substantiate the topological pattern now generally accepted, which has developed out of the early electronmicroscope studies (e.g. 154). Other reviews recently have described this in detail (28, 155, 156), and provide many literature references.

Vertebrates.—Kilarski (157) and Nishihara (158) have essentially confirmed Franzini-Armstrong & Porter's (159) earlier studies on fish skeletal muscle, showing well-developed SR in both red and white fibers, with triads adjacent to Z-lines in both. In addition, Kilarski confirms Reger's (160) finding of triads at the A-I junction in fish eye muscles, but only in a group of small-diameter (5–14 μ) fibers containing many mitochondria and thus probably 'red' fibers. Kilarski finds that about 5 per cent of the fibers in these eye muscles are larger in diameter (18–80 μ), have fewer mitochondria, and have triads at the Z-lines, as do the white fibers of the trunk and fin muscles. Thus there is no correspondence between triad location and color for fibers of the eye and the trunk. We still lack any understanding of the meaning of these two different locations of triads.

Several workers (161–163) have reported electronmicroscopic studies of adult frog skeletal muscles including the muscle that is the physiologist's favorite, the frog's sartorius. The results confirm the general features of the SR and T-system of amphibian muscle known earlier, and illustrate them with somewhat greater clarity as a result of better methods of preparation. Two of these papers (162, 163) and one on an insect muscle (164) disagree with an earlier report (165) of holes in the membranes of the SR at the level of the middle of the A-band, and conclude that these structures are fenestrations through the whole SR collar as a result of annular fusions of the two membranes forming the collar. This point may be important in functional considerations of the SR, since according to the former view there would be direct continuity of the interior of the SR and the sarcoplasm. According to the newer interpretation, these fenestrations or pores merely increase the surface area of the SR, providing channels from one side of the SR to the other, and the SR is not open directly to the sarcoplasm. The functional significance of these fenestrations remains a mystery.

Another new interpretation to come from these studies is that the SR is not always interrupted fully at the Z-line, but may extend longitudinally past the Z-line into the next sarcomere. Thus the SR takes on an extensive longitudinal continuity in addition to its well-known transverse continuity (154). In one study (162) such connections were said to be occasional, but in another (163) the author saw them sufficiently often to be convinced that the entire SR of the fiber might be linked together in this way.

Another result of these new studies of frog muscle is the demonstration of a clear separation of the SR of a single sarcomere into a number of interconnected but morphological distinct regions: terminal cisternae, intermediate cisternae, longitudinal tubules, and fenestrated collar, in that order from the Z-line to the center of the A-band (163). There is a strong implication here of corresponding functional differences, and some new physiological evidence discussed below under *Calcium movements during and following activity* begins to suggest this.

Arthropods.—Here we have considerable new information. In a recent review, Smith (28) emphasizes the fairly extensive coverage of insect orders now available. As in other arthropods, the usual form of the contact between the SR and the T-system in insects is the dyad (see also 53, 56, 164, 166–168), and this is almost always located at what has been imprecisely called "near the A-I junction", but which Smith now more accurately describes as midway between the Z-line and the center of the A-band. In muscles with short I-bands, as in the case of insect flight muscles, the latter designation is much more accurate. Exceptions to this location are common in the 'asynchronous' flight muscles, where the dyads are irregularly positioned, and where the SR is not highly developed (28, 167).

Crayfish and crab muscles contain two kind of invaginations of the cell surface (51, 169–171). One consists of large-size clefts containing material like the fibrous extracellular coating of the fiber, and the other is of smaller caliber and appears empty. In the case of crayfish fibers (51, 169) these are interpreted as part of a single, complex transverse tubular sytem, extending transversely and then longitudinally, and forming dyads with the SR midway between the Z-line and the M-line. In the case of crab fibers (170, 171), it is concluded that here are two sets of invaginating tubules extending mostly transversely, in addition to the clefts. One set of tubules, called Z-tubules, associates with Z-lines of the myofibrils, and the other set, called A-tubules, forms dyads with the SR. The latter description seems likely to be correct for crab muscle, because it fits well with experiments localizing sensitivity to depolarization to the ends of the A-bands, where A-tubules connect to the SR (172, 173). These experiments do not agree with the morphological interpretation for crayfish fibers, where many tubules leading to dyads enter the fiber near Z-lines, but it must be admitted that two different species are involved in this negative correlation. What is needed is local activation experiments on crayfish fibers to see if the situation there is really different from that in the crab.

Unusual forms of the SR.—As is often the case, the arthropods provide us with the most unusual forms of a cellular structure, in this case of the SR. Penetration of an extensive network of tubules of SR into the myofibril at the level of the M-line has been reported in some Lepidopteran direct flight muscles (58, 59) but not in leg muscle of the same animal (58) or in some other flight muscles of the same insect order. In those muscles with SR penetrating the A-band, the thick filaments are flat in the M-line and the axis of flattening is related to the direction of orientation of the adjacent SR tubule. The flattened thick filaments, incidentally, are said to consist of two subunits about 60–80 Å in diameter (58). This most certainly is the closest apposition of SR and myofilaments ever observed, the spacing being only about 80–120 Å. Whether this extreme closeness serves for rapid activation, for rapid relaxation, for structural support, or a combination of these cannot be said.

Content of the SR.—Many workers have noticed a dense, apparently granular material inside the SR. In frog (163, 174) and fish (175) body muscle, this dense material has been found to be confined to one part of the SR, the terminal cisternae, possibly held back by a narrow passage between the terminal and intermediate cisternae. In most other muscles, the dense material spreads throughout the SR, or at least no localization has been reported if it exists. It is an interesting possibility that this dense material contains calcium-binding sites, whose presence has recently been suggested (176, 177). Supporting this idea is an observation of staining of the content of the SR in thin sections by thorium dioxide at pH 2, which has been interpreted as cytochemical evidence for binding sites for cations (178).

The evidence presented for membranelike structures within the terminal cisternae of the SR is quite unconvincing (179). The sections appear to be too thick for one to be sure that the membranes seen are not due to overlap of convoluted SR membranes in the thickness of the section.

Junctions between the T-system and the SR.—Several workers have commented on periodic dense structures apparently linking the T-system tubules to the terminal cisternae of the SR in the triads and dyads of vertebrate and arthropod striated muscles (163, 164, 168, 174, 180, 181). The morphological similarity of these specialized contact areas to the septate junctions between epithelial cells (182) has attracted considerable attention because of the very exciting finding in recent years of several examples of ionic coupling between cells via a high conductivity pathway (183). In one case this coupling is thought to take place through septate junctions (182).

To call the T-system-SR junction a 'tight junction' (184) seems to be a misuse of the term as originally employed by Farquhar & Palade (185). I believe that the proper use of 'tight junction' is to refer to unit membranes so closely associated that their adjacent dense lines as seen in the electron-microscope are fused to form a single intermediate line, completely obliterating any space between them. A small space is seen between the adjacent dense lines of the two membranes in *Necturus* kidney (186) and mouse cardiac muscle and capillary endothelial cells (187, 188), and it has been proposed to refer to these less-than-tight junctions as 'gap junctions' (M. J. Karnovsky and J. P. Revel, personal communication). In some epithelia, junctions with gaps have shown a particular structural organization of the material in the gap, in the form of hexagons in the plane of the junction (188) or septae bridging the gap (182). It is certainly clear that the T-system to SR junction is not a tight junction as defined above. According to some descriptions (163, 181) it is similar to the septate junction: in other cases (164, 168) the bridging material reaches only part way across the gap. In any case the general type of this junction is a 'gap' junction. However, it should not be forgotten that the T-system to SR junction is formed between the cytoplasmic side of an intracellular membrane and the intracellular side of the cell surface membrane (T-system). All the other junctions discussed above are between the outer surfaces of two cells. On this basis we should not try too hard to fit the T-system to SR junction into any existing category of cell surface junctions.

Surface continuity of the T-system.—Two years ago there remained a lack of clear electronmicroscopic images of continuity of the T-system with the surface membrane in striated muscle cells of vertebrates other than fish. Three papers (163, 189, 190) have presented micrographs suggesting continuity in adult frog, rat leg, and rat diaphragm, but none is very convincing. Either the micrographs show grey areas that could represent closing membranes cut obliquely (163, 189) or, although the existence of surface-connected tubules is amply clear, it is not certain if these are true transverse tubules since no triads are visible (190). Jasper's image of continuity in lamprey muscle, way down the vertebrate scale, is considerably more convincing (191). This is not to say that such continuity does not exist in higher vertebrates but merely to point out that it has not yet been demonstrated by direct means. Why more convincing images of continuity cannot be obtained in amphibian and mammalian muscles remains unclear, but it could easily be explained if the openings were infrequent, or if the caliber of the openings were approximately the same as or less than the section thickness. Otherwise we can only think that the connections were destroyed during preparation for electronmicroscopy, since there is strong evidence for patent connections from experiments using ferritin (174, 192, 193), a dye (193a), peroxidase (M. J. Karnovsky, unpublished), and lanthanum micelles (188) as tracers. Evidence for a high sodium concentrations in the transverse tubules of frog muscle fibers has been presented (194, 195), based on dense precipitates in the T-system after treatment of living fibers with a fixative containing potassium pyroantimonate. Strictly speaking, these results indicate only a high sodium concentration in the T-system, and don't necessarily mean that the lumen of the T-system is open to the extracellular fluid, unless pyroantimonate cannot penetrate the surface membrane of the fiber and thus gain access to the T-system by an intracellular route. When the sarcolemma is mechanically removed, pyroantimonate does enter the fiber, and precipitates are found in the sarcoplasm, especially associated with the SR (194). The possibility that sodium enters the fiber or moves intracellularly when the sarcolemma is removed, and artifactually attaches to the SR, makes one desire caution in interpreting the intracellular results. However, taking all the evidence together, the continuity of the T-system with the plasma membrane at the surface of the fiber in frog muscle now seems well established.

Of great interest is the recent paper in which a freeze-etch method for electronmicroscopy is used to obtain an image of what certainly looks to be the stumps of broken-off T-system tubules on the inner surface of the sarcolemma of guinea pig papillary muscle. Also shown are dimples in what is interpreted as a view of the outer surface of the sarcolemma (195a). In both views, the structures are arranged in rows both longitudinally and transversely, in excellent agreement with Huxley & Taylor's mapping of sensitive spots on frog skeletal muscle (172).

Development of the T-system and the SR.—In addition to the T-system and SR being separate organelles in the mature muscle fiber, it has recently become clear that they have different origins during development. In a clear demonstration of this, Ezerman & Ishikawa have used ferritin to label the developing T-system in chicken embryo skeletal muscle cells grown *in vitro* (196). The T-system arises from the myoblast surface membrane by a series of pinocytosis-like invaginations that fail to pinch off but remain attached in a chain or network. On the other hand, the SR arises as tubular evaginations from the rough-surfaced endoplasmic reticulum, forming an open lacework around the developing myofibrils. Early in development, dyad and triad associations of various forms appear (196), and later these become triads more regularly positioned near the ends of the A-bands, as in mature chicken muscle (H. Ishikawa, personal communication).

Surface area of the T-system and fiber capacitance.—The surface area of the T-system of frog sartorius muscle fibers has been estimated as five (197) to seven times (163) the outer surface area of the fiber, the latter calculated as the area of a circular cylinder. The internal structure of fibers of different diameters is the same, so the greater the fiber diameter, the larger is the ratio of internal area to outer surface area: the former varies as the cube and the latter as the square of the fiber diameter. The figure of seven times quoted above is for a fiber 100 μ in diameter. Longitudinal extensions of the T-system, while present in both frog and toad sartorius muscles, do not significantly add to the T-system area, although T-system branching may increase these estimates by about 30 per cent (193).

Since the T-system is continuous with the fiber surface, it augments the total surface area of frog sartorius fibers to about eight times the value calculated for a simple cylinder. This has been used to explain the high capacitance (C_e) of frog muscle fibers at low frequency, according to the two time-constant equivalent circuit presented by Falk & Fatt (197) and later confirmed (198). Frog slow fibers have a T-system area only about one times their outer surface area (162), so their total surface area is only about twice that of a cylinder. They have a correspondingly small low-frequency capacitance (199). In the other direction, crayfish and crab fibers have a high capacitance (197, 200) and a very large amount of T-system and other forms of surface invagination (51, 169–171). A two time-constant equivalent circuit has been found in cardiac Purkinje fibers (201), but is not supported by the available morphological information. Dragonfly flight muscles have a well-developed T-system, but their small diameter keeps their surface augmentation ratio down to about the same as that of frog muscle (168). No impedance measurements are available for dragonfly muscle, but electronmicroscopists should be encouraged to make this type of quantitative estimate even in the absence of related physiological data so that the morphological values will be available when the physiology is done.

The series resistance R_e.—The source of the resistance R_e in series with C_e in the equivalent circuit of Falk & Fatt (197) is unknown. It could be the resistance of the mouths of the tubules, if they are narrow or covered with a membrane, it could be within the tubules, or it could be in a current pathway from the T-system through the SR to the sarcoplasm. The failure of R_e to decrease the expected amount when frog sartorius T-system tubules were swollen and the late afterpotential prolonged has been used as evidence against R_e being within the tubules (198). Pugsley has reported that he finds a small R_e and no late afterpotential in toad sartorius fibers. He interprets both of these findings in terms of larger openings of the T-system in toad than in frog, implying that both R_e and a diffusion delay thought to account for the late afterpotential in frog fibers arise at the mouths of the tubules (202). However, no action potential records are shown, and Pugsley (personal communication) says that he looked only after single action potentials, whereas several action potentials are required to show the late afterpotential clearly (203). In fact, Freygang finds a late afterpotential in toad sartorius fibers after ten to twenty action potentials (personal communication). So it seems that R_e may be small in toad fibers, and if it arises at the mouth of the tubule, then the late afterpotential cannot have the same source.

Recent experiments (204) in which the size of the T-system was altered at constant osmotic pressure by changing the ionic strength of the bathing fluid have shown alteration of the time-course of the late afterpotential in a way not predicted by the model developed by Adrian & Freygang (205). This suggests that either the morphological methods are inaccurate, or the model needs modification, so we may look forward to considerable alteration in our ideas of the properties of the T-system during the next few years.

Calcium movements during and following activity.—Several excellent reviews on calcium in muscle have appeared recently (22–26) and therefore this topic will not be covered fully here. The review by Ebashi & Endo (26) is particularly welcome because it includes much work from Japan that either has not been translated or has not been published at all.

Two interesting ideas in recent literature are: different parts of the SR may be specialized for uptake, for storage, and for release of calcium; and some of the calcium stored in the SR may be in a bound form.

Winegrad has used a freeze-dry and vapor-fixation method for preparing muscles for calcium-45 autoradiography (206). No oxalate is needed in this method, and the time resolution achieved is such that he has been able to study calcium movements during recovery from brief tetani. A most interesting result is that at about 20 sec after a 5 sec tetanus, when the muscles are fully relaxed, calcium that moved from the I-band to the A-band during activity is still found in the A-band. It is located between the myofibrils, presumably in the longitudinal elements of the SR. By 3.5 min after the tetanus is over, most of this calcium has returned to the I-band, presumably to the terminal cisternae. The interesting conclusion drawn from these results is that while the terminal cisternae are the site of calcium storage and calcium release, the longitudinal SR, consisting of the longitudinal tubules and fenestrated collar, is the site of rapid calcium uptake during relaxation.

Weber et al. (176) have presented arguments that most of the calcium accumulated by isolated SR vesicles that is not present as calcium oxalate is bound to some other site, an idea that seems to have been favored by Ebashi and co-workers for some time (26). It is not clear if this binding is to sites inside the SR, and follows transport across the membrane (176), or if binding is to the membranes and precedes transport (26). Winegrad's observations are compatible with either of these schemes (206), and it may be that both operate: an initial binding followed by transport into the longitudinal SR, then transfer to internal binding sites in the terminal cisternae.

A very welcome result is that of Jöbsis & O'Connor, who used murexide to obtain spectrophotometric visualization of the transient appearance of free calcium in the sarcoplasm during activation of toad muscles (207). Free calcium begins to appear within 1 to 5 msec after the stimulus, at about 10°C. It peaks at 55 to 75 msec, and is half gone at 110 to 150 msec, slightly before peak tension development. Thus calcium is free during most of the latent period and its disappearance parallels the disappearance of the active state. Relaxation occurs at a very low level of free calcium, as expected if the SR removes calcium from the myofibrils by pumping it out of the sarcoplasmic matrix.

The time when free calcium appears (207) coincides rather well with both the onset of latency relaxation (208) and the early volume increase (209). The presence of free calcium outlasts both these effects, but their decay probably is accelerated by the appearance of active tension development and its associated large volume decrease. Thus there is reason to look for a causative relationship between calcium appearance and the latency relaxation and volume increase. It seems possible that calcium released from bound sites could lead to an increase in osmotic pressure in the sarcoplasm. This increased osmotic pressure could result in a longitudinal force in the relaxation direction, i.e. latency relaxation. The observed decrease in time to the beginning of latency relaxation (208) when the muscle is stretched might be due to a more rapid release of calcium from the terminal cisternae of the SR, which are known to be distorted by stretch (210). These ideas are, however, only supposition.

Incidentally, I recently received from H. Kinosita a reprint of an early and not well-known paper of his with T. Kamada, which describes injection of calcium and other ions into single fibers (211). This was published at about the same time as the first reference to the better-known Heilbruun, Wiercinski & Hamilton experiments (212, 213) and independently reports that calcium, barium, and strontium are the only ions tested that will produce contraction. Many other interesting observations in this paper seem worthy of being followed up.

Mechanism of calcium release from the SR.—Recently there have been reports that ionic currents through the SR can result in release of accumulated calcium. This has been observed using isolated SR vesicles, where the released calcium has been detected spectrophotometrically (214) or radioactively (215), and in 'skinned' fibers, where calcium release is inferred from observations of contraction (216). In the latter system, application of chloride ions is also effective, which implies that changes in polarization of the vesicles may be more important than currents per se. One disturbing aspect of the isolated-vesicle experiments is that monophasic pulses are more effective than diphasic ones (215), which suggests that electrode reactions might be damaging some vesicles and causing them to release their calcium. In agreement with this, Van der Kloot reported failure to get release of calcium from isolated lobster SR with either direct or alternating currents except at high current densities, when vesicles were destroyed (217).

Enzymes located in the SR.—ATPase has been found by many authors in the SR, distributed throughout or localized in the terminal cisternae (e.g. 218, 218a), but there is reason to doubt that either necessarily represents the location of the calcium-accumulating mechanism (219, 219a). The artifactual attachment of reaction product seen in the case of the myofibrils (220) apparently does not occur in the SR (218), so these results probably do have some meaning. The presence of the two glycolytic dehydrogenases in the SR (221) supports the notion that the SR is involved in glycolytic activity as well as in calcium movements. Acetylcholinesterase appears to be present in isolated SR vesicles (217, 221a), and sometimes (221a) but not always (221b) is found in regions of intact fibers where SR should be present. Its function is not known, and there is no reason to think that acetylcholine has any intracellular function.

SLOW MUSCLE

Considerable work has been reported in the last two years on muscles that could be called 'slow'. Limitations on time and space make a complete coverage of this topic here impractical. Two observations provide new and interpretable information as to why these muscles may be inherently slow. Costantin et al. (222) have applied calcium solutions directly to frog slow fibers with the sarcolemma removed, and find that the contraction is characteristically slow. This indicates that the slowness in this case is a property of the myofibrils, not of the e-c coupling system. In agreement with this, there is a relationship between myosin ATPase activity and the speeds of shortening of a variety of vertebrate muscles, so that slower mechanical movement is associated with slower breakdown of ATP (223–225).

Fiber type classification.—While we often speak of fibers or muscles as 'fast' or 'slow', it has not always been clear how one should separate these two categories. Electrical behavior doesn't always work as a criterion, since frog 'slow' fibers don't conduct action potentials (226), but bird 'slow' fibers do (227). While it had been thought that triads are not present in slow fibers of frogs and snakes (228, 229), improved fixation methods show that triads are present, although they may be less accurately aligned with the striations (162, 230). The presence or absence of M-lines seems to fail as a criterion in mammalian extraocular muscles, as apparently does multiplicity of innervation (see next section). For the present we must describe several properties of a particular fiber to classify it.

Other information on fine structure, and especially on histochemical properties of slow and fast fibers, has not yet yielded a clear picture of just how many types of fibers may be present even in a single muscle (e.g. 231–232a). We cannot even rule out the possibility that discrete fiber types don't exist and that there are, in fact, one or more continuous spectra of types. One point that has become clear, however, is that the classification of red and white muscles as slow and fast does not hold in all cases. Red color, due to the presence of myoglobin and mitochondrial cytochromes, is probably related to capability for a high rate of oxidative metabolism. This is usually, but not always, a property of slowly contracting fibers, which are usually employed for sustained activity. Most fast fibers are used for short bursts of intense activity, during which they can operate on glycolysis. A clear exception to this is pigeon breast muscle, which is both fast and red, and which performs sustained work during flight. Partial reversal of enzyme (232b) and myoglobin (232c) content of fast and slow muscles of the cat when they are cross-innervated has been reported, emphasizing that fiber properties are probably not fixed even in fully developed muscles. Some of the complexities of fiber type classification will be clearly illustrated in the section on extraocular muscles.

Action potentials.—The unsettled question whether the slow striated muscle fibers of frogs are capable of propagating action potentials was discussed four years ago by Huxley (1), who cited Shamarina's evidence for slow fibers that give only junctional potentials in response to single nerve impulses but give spikes when stimulated repetitively (233). Huxley also discussed Orkand's conclusion that these are twitch fibers (innervated by large, rapidly conducting nerves) with a low output of transmitter at the endplate, and thus are not a second type of slow fiber (234). Nasledov has distinguished two types of twitch fibers in the frog's iliofibularis tonus bundle by recording intracellular electrical responses to indirect stimulation (235). Nasledov finds a distribution of electrical properties in fibers that are not of the multiply innervated type (detected histochemically). These fibers differ in latency and half-time of decay of single impulse EPPs (2 to 30 msec or more) and have similar resting potentials. There is a greater tendency for the shorter EPP decay half-time fibers to develop spikes when stimulated rhythmically (25–100 per sec). Nasledov (235) designates as *a*-fibers those with rapidly declining synaptic potentials (half-times 2–5 msec), most (45 out of 46) of which will produce spikes, and as *b*-fibers those with more slowly declining synaptic potentials (half-time 5–30 msec) and a lesser but not zero tendency to produce spikes. In fact about 40 per cent of the latter fibers produce spikes when stimulated rhythmically. Nasledov's type-*a* fibers have a shorter latency than his *b* fibers, and thus are presumed to be innervated by larger-diameter nerve fibers, although some of the difference in latency is likely to be due to slower conduction in nonmyelinated terminal ramifications of the smaller-diameter nerves (235a). Orkand (234) didn't report half-times of decline of EPPs for his fibers with low endplate safety factors, but both the latency reported and the half-time of decline of the EPPs estimated from the records in his Figure 1 agree with average values given by Nasledov for type-*a* fibers. Nasledov's type-*b* twitch fibers are electrically different from those studied by Orkand, and it is possible (not certain) that Orkand missed these fibers by partially denervating his muscles. Nasledov feels that his type-*b* fibers are the fibers thought by Shamarina (236) to be spike-producing tonic fibers. However, uncertainties as to whether all the fibers studied were in fact from the tonus bundle, and a lack of information about the degree of stretch of the muscles, which itself can affect the probability of obtaining propagated activity (237), make it difficult to relate these two studies to each other. Whether to call any of these fibers an *intermediate* type of fiber is a matter of personal preference, but it is not entirely clear that they should be called *tonic* fibers. This usage of *tonic* is sometimes based on visual observation of slow contractions during the long-duration EPPs. The relationship between slowness of contraction and *tonus* is not an absolute one, nor does it necessarily follow that the observed contractions do contribute significant tonic tension to the whole muscle. This also brings up the possibility that EPPs beyond a certain size may commonly lead to local contractions even in the absence of a propagated action potential. While this *could* lead to tonus in the muscle, there is no clear physiological evidence that it does so in singly innervated fibers.

Taking all the available evidence together, it still seems as if it is impossible to make a consistent story about the properties of slow striated muscle fibers, and the question of whether they can or do conduct action potentials remains unsettled. What is needed is more work where various physiological and morphological characteristics are studied on one and the same fiber under highly controlled conditions of stimulation, muscle length, etc. This admittedly will be difficult and laborious, but until it is done, we will remain uncertain in this area.

Extraocular Muscles

The interest in these versatile muscles in the last few years warrants a special section. Huxley (1, 2) discussed the important advances made by

Matyushkin and by Hess & Pilar in demonstrating that slow fibers similar to those of the frog are present in extraocular muscles of mammals (rabbit, guinea pig, and cat). More complete presentations of these results and some new physiological studies by these workers subsequently appeared (238–242). The main conclusions are that at least some of the extraocular muscles contain a considerable number of muscle fibers characterized by such properties as small diameter, multiaxonal innervation, multiple nerve endings of a simple type, small junctional potentials, large fibrils incompletely surrounded by sarcoplasmic reticulum, and slow mechanical contractions. These features are also characteristic of the slow, *Felderstruktur* fibers of the frog. Reflex activity following stretch of the inferior rectus muscle of the rabbit is developed largely in these tonic motor units (241).

In addition to these slow fibers, 'ordinary' twitch fibers were found in extraocular muscles (238–242). These were of larger diameter, with single endplate-type nerve endings, endplate potentials, action potentials, and small fibrils surrounded by sarcoplasmic reticulum (*Fibrillenstruktur*). Some of these fibers are remarkably fast (239, 240, 242) in their contraction and in the conduction velocity of the nerves innervating them, and much of this speed develops after birth (240, 242).

This pioneering work on the cat has been followed by several other studies in various mammalian species. While there is general agreement that slow and fast fibers do exist in extraocular muscles of mammals, there is no clear consensus on how many different types of fibers there are or on their physiological and morphological properties.

Physiology.—Bach-y-Rita & Ito (243) have recently studied two cat extraocular muscles. Like Hess & Pilar, they found two fiber types, one mechanically slower than the other. They generally agree with Hess & Pilar on the properties of the faster fibers, but disagree on the properties of the slower type. Bach-y-Rita & Ito conclude that slow fibers in these muscles can produce propagated action potentials, and thus designate these fibers as 'slow, multiply innervated twitch fibers' to distinguish them from 'true' slow fibers as found in frogs. Bach-y-Rita & Ito attribute their failure to record action potentials from all of these fibers to depression of the resting potentials by insertion of the microelectrode and to their cutting of two or three nerve branches innervating the muscle. Clearly the experimental conditions used by Bach-y-Rita & Ito are more 'physiological' (37–38° C, intact circulation and innervation) than those used by Hess & Pilar (20–25°C, muscle *in vitro*). Indeed, Hess & Pilar did obtain action potentials from one out of twenty slow fibers, and they themselves point out that the high magnesium and calcium concentrations they used plus the possibility of membrane damage following impalement keep them from being certain that these slow fibers don't normally produce propagated action potentials.

Thus, while Bach-y-Rita & Ito may be right that cat extraocular slow fibers can conduct action potentials, we should be on the lookout for another explanation for the discrepancy between the results of these two laboratories. Recent morphological studies discussed below suggest one such explanation.

Morphology.—*Felder* and *Fibrillen* fibers have now been described in extraocular muscles from humans (244, 245), rhesus monkeys (246–248), and rabbits (249). Many of Hess & Pilar's findings have been confirmed in these later studies on other species. In addition, the fine structure of the 'en plague' and 'en grappe' endings in cat extraocular muscles has been described (250, 251), and found to be essentially the same as the corresponding endings on frog twitch (252) and slow (162) fibers.

In contrast to these muscles (the recti and obliques), which clearly are mixtures of different fiber types, two other muscles of the extraocular group have been reported to consist entirely of a single presumably fast type of fiber. The human eyelid muscle (levator palpebrae) has only *Fibrillen* fibers with single endplates (244), and the retractor bulbi of the cat has been shown to contain only *Fibrillen* fibers (J. Alvarado and L. D. Peachey, unpublished) with electrical properties of twitch fibers (253).

The morphological situation in the oblique and rectus muscles is now, however, more complex and less clear than is implied above and than seemed to be the case after Hess & Pilar's paper (239). In studies of rhesus monkey muscles, Mayr, Stockinger & Zenker (246) describe two types of singly innervated *Fibrillen* fibers differing in diameter and location in the muscle, and one type of *Felder* fiber with a diameter equivalent to the smaller *Fibrillen* fibers. On the other hand, Cheng & Breinin (247) report finding in the same species two types of *Fibrillen* fibers of equal diameter and smaller, *Felder* fibers. The most complex arrangement suggested for these same muscles is in a recent paper by Miller (248) who reports five types of muscle fibers. Only one of these clearly had *Felderstruktur*.

Layer organization.—Kern (249) has shown very neatly that the superior rectus of the rabbit is organized into two reasonably distinct layers. One layer contains fibers of small diameter (average 18 μ) with *Felderstruktur* appearance in the light microscope, while the larger (average 40 μ) fibers of the other layer are *Fibrillenstruktur* fibers. Actually the observation of layers of fibers with different diameters was made in 1961 by Hess in guinea pig muscles (254) and in 1938 by Kato (255) in a comprehensive study covering several mammalian species. Kato's study showed considerable species differences in the degree of separation of various diameter fibers.

An important contribution of Kern's paper is the demonstration that low concentrations of acetylcholine (0.5 μg per ml) produced a long-lasting contracture of the small-diameter fibers and only a small, brief contraction of the larger fibers, which implies that the small fibers are slow fibers and that the larger fibers are fast. One cannot tell from Kern's paper how these layers in rabbit muscles are oriented *in situ,* but from Miller's paper on rhesus monkey (248) and some recent studies of my own (unpublished) on the cat, it seems as if the smaller-diameter fibers are on the orbital surface and the larger fibers are toward the globe. Here I have oversimplified, because in some species including the cat, the layers do not contain fibers of consistent diameter, and there are sometimes more than two layers. Nevertheless, the region of the muscle containing the largest population of small-diameter fibers seems to be universally orbital. This fact will be important when we now turn to the one available physiological study where this layer organization was kept in mind.

   Possible correlation of morphology and physiology.—Hess & Pilar (239) studied all four recti and both obliques of the cat morphologically, but used only the superior oblique for physiological studies, and all their published histological illustrations are from this one muscle. It is reasonable to say that their results are mostly, if not exclusively, applicable to this muscle. Bach-y-Rita & Ito (243) investigated the superior rectus and the inferior oblique, also of the cat. While they do not distinguish between these muscles in the discussion of their physiological results, they clearly point out differences in physiological layering between the two different muscles.

   In some recent light and electronmicroscopic studies of all three of these muscles, of which only a brief discussion of the results on the inferior oblique has been published (256), I have identified two fiber types that can reasonably be said to be the ones studied by Bach-y-Rita & Ito. Both of these show morphology characteristic of fast fibers, e.g., well-developed SR positioned around discrete fibrils with M-lines. One appears 'morphologically faster', and is located where Bach-y-Rita & Ito find their fast fibers. The other is located only in those layers where Bachy-Rita & Ito find their 'slow, multiply innervated twitch fibers' and the observed morphology, as discussed above, fits this description. In addition, in several inferior obliques, but not in any superior rectus yet examined, a third type of fiber with distinct M-lines clearly has the morphology of *Felderstruktur*. I think the small numbers of these fibers present in the inferior oblique, their apparent absence from the superior rectus, their small size, and their location next to much larger *Fibrillen* fibers make it very reasonable to assume that Bach-y-Rita & Ito missed these fibers with their microelectrode recording technique. Of great interest in this regard is the situation in the superior oblique, which is the muscle used by Hess & Pilar: here the *Felder* fibers are present in much larger numbers than in the inferior oblique, and they tend to be larger relative to the neighboring fast-appearing fibers than in the other muscles. It seems likely that these *Felder* fibers are the slow fibers of Hess & Pilar (239).

   This all makes it seem likely that Hess & Pilar (239) and Bach-y-Rita & Ito (243) were in fact studying different types of slow fibers, and there is no disagreement between their conclusions about the properties of these fibers after all. If this is true, then we can conclude that cat extraocular muscles consist of some very fast twitch fibers, some slower and multiply innervated twitch fibers, and some slow, *Felder* fibers very much like those found in frogs. Whether there are in fact subdivisions of these groups, as Miller's results (248) suggested, will hopefully be settled after more work has been done, but for the present I would be willing only to say that three fiber types have been demonstrated with reasonable certainty.

EAR AND ESOPHAGUS MUSCLES

Another mammalian muscle that may contain some 'true' slow fibers is the tensor tympani of the inner ear, a muscle with a protective function damping the excursion of the ossicles in response to loud sounds. This muscle has been studied electrophysiologically, histochemically, and microscopically by Erulkar et al. (257). They show microscopic evidence of both smooth and striated fibers in this muscle (cat), and further report that both *Felder* and *Fibrillen* fibers are present. The latter point is not entirely convincing as presented, since the one figure (Figure 8) used to substantiate this shows a rather atypical *Felder* pattern and also shows two cases of *Felder* and *Fibrillen* patterns in a single fiber, a situation reported earlier only by Brecht & Feneis in the frog (258), to my knowledge, and not generally accepted. The electrical evidence, however, seems to clearly demonstrate fibers with low resting potentials (20–60 mV) and SJPs, fibers with higher resting potentials (70–100 mV) giving overshoot action potentials, and fibers with typical smooth muscle patterns of spontaneous depolarizations and spikes (257). The electronmicroscopy in this study presents an interesting finding that in a single muscle, triads are at the level of the Z-line in one kind of fiber (said to be a fast fiber) and near the A-I junction in another fiber (said to be slow), a situation like that in fish extraocular muscles (157).

Multiple innervation, suggestive of some form of slow physiology, has been demonstrated in some slow striated muscle fibers of the esophagus of the sheep (259).

ACKNOWLEDGMENTS

Sincere thanks are due to R. E. Davies, A. V. Hill, A. F. Huxley, F. A. Pepe, D. R. Wilkie, and S. Winegrad for reading and criticizing early drafts, and to various persons for valuable discussions and for allowing me to use personal communications.

LITERATURE CITED

1. Huxley, A. F. Muscle. *Ann. Rev. Physiol.*, **26**, 131–52 (1964)
2. Wilkie, D. R. Muscle. *Ann. Rev. Physiol.*, **28**, 17–38 (1966)
3. Muscular Dystrophy Association of America, Inc., 1790 Broadway, New York, N.Y. 10019, USA
4. Assistant to the Director, National Library of Medicine, 8600 Rockville Pike, Bethesda, Md. 20014, USA
5. Confrey, E. A. Information exchange groups to be discontinued. *Science*, **154**, 843 (1966)
6. *Muscle Notes*, Retina Found., 20 Staniford Street, Boston, Mass. 02114, USA
7. Thorpe, W. V. Biological journals and exchange groups. *Nature*, **213**, 547–48 (1967); *Science*, **155**, 1195–96 (1967)
8. *Fed. Proc.*, **24**, No. 5, Part I, 1112–52 (1965)
9. *Proc. Intern. Union Physiol. Sci.*, **4**, *Intern. Congr., 23rd, Tokyo, 1965*, 381–407 (Excerpta Med., Amsterdam, 644 pp., 1965)
10. *Proceedings of a Symposium on the Contractile Process, New York, 1966. J. Gen. Physiol.*, **60**, No. 6, Part 2, 292 pp. (1967); (Little, Brown, Boston, 1967; and J. & A. Churchill Ltd., London, 1967)
11. *Comparative Aspects of Muscle Contraction. Am. Zoologist*, **7**, 433–699 (1967)
12. *The Myocardial Cell. Structure, Function, and Modification by Cardiac Drugs* (Briller, S. A., Conn, H. L., Jr., Eds., Univ. of Pennsylvania Press, Philadelphia, Pa., 374 pp., 1966)
13. *Factors Influencing Myocardial Contractility* (Tanz, R. D., Ed., Academic Press, New York, in press, 1968)
14. Symposium on Physical and Mathematical Approaches to the Study of the Electrical Behavior of Excitable Membrane. Woods Hole, Mass., July 9-11, 1965 (Adelman, W. J., Jr., Ed., *J. Cellular Comp. Physiol.*, **66**, No. 3, Part 2, 170 pp., 1965)
15. *Biological Membranes: Recent Progress* (Weyer, E. M., Hutchins, H., Lowenstein, W. R., Eds., *Ann. N.Y. Acad. Sci.*, **137**, 403–1048 (1966)
16. *Principles of Biomolecular Organization* (Wolstenholme, G. E. W., O'Connor, M., Eds., Little, Brown, Boston, 491 pp., 1966)
17. *Biochem. Z.*, **345**, 1–426 (1966)
18. *Med. Coll. Virginia Quart.*, **2**, 69–99 (1966)
19. *Molecular Biology of Muscular Contraction* (Ebashi, S., Oosawa, F., Sekine, T., Tonomura, Y., Eds., Igaku Shoin, Tokyo, and Elsevier, Amsterdam, 206 pp., 1965)
20. Schaper, W. Heart. *Ann. Rev. Physiol.*, **29**, 259–312 (1967)
21. Betz, E. H., Firket, H., Reznik, M. Same aspects of muscle regeneration. *Intern. Rev. Cytol.*, **19**, 203–27 (1966)
22. Portzehl, H. Die intracelluläre Regulation der Aktivität der contractilen Strukturen des Skeletmuskels. In *Verhandlungen der Deutschen Gesellschaft für innere Medizin, 71 Kongress, 1965*, 125–36 (Verlag J. F. Bergman, München, 1965)
23. Nayler, W. G. Influx and efflux of calcium in the physiology of muscle contraction. *Clinical Orthopaedics*, No. 46, 157–82 (Lippincott, Philadelphia, Pa., 248 pp., 1966)
24. Stracher, A., Dreizen, P. Structure and function of the contractile protein myosin, 154–202; Weber, A. Energized calcium transport and relaxing factors, 203–54. In *Current Topics in Bioenergetics*, **I** (Sanadai, D. R., Ed., Academic Press, New York, 292 pp., 1966)
25. Bianchi, C. P. *Cell Calcium* (Butterworth, Washington, D.C., in press, 1968)
26. Ebashi, S., Endo, M. Calcium ion and muscle contraction. *Progr. Biophys. Mol. Biol.*, **18** (In press) (1968)
27. Sandow, A. Excitation-contraction coupling in skeletal muscle. *Pharmacol. Rev.*, **17**, 265–320 (1965)
28. Smith, D. S. The organization and function of the sarcoplasmic reticulum and T-system of muscle cells. *Progr. Biophys. Mol. Biol.*, **16**, 107–42 (1966)
29. Gergely, J. Contractile proteins. *Ann. Rev. Biochem.*, **35**, Part II, 691–722 (1966)

30. Perry, S. V. The structure and interactions of myosin. *Progr. Biophys. Mol. Biol.*, **17**, 325–81 (1967)

31. Ruska, H. Struktur und Funktion der Skeletmuskelfasern. In *Verhandlungen der Deutschen Gesellschaft für innere Medizin, 71 Kongress, 1965*, 93–104 (Verlag J. F. Bergman, München, 1965)

32. Lüttgau, H. C. Nerven-und Muskel-Elektrophysiologie. *Fortschr. Zool.*, **17**, 272–312 (1965)

33. Pringle, J. W. S. The contractile mechanism of insect fibrillar muscle. *Progr. Biophys. Mol. Biol.*, **17**, 1–60 (1967)

34. *The Physiology and Biochemistry of Muscle as a Food* (Briskey, E. J., Cassens, R. G., Trautman, J. C., Eds., Univ. of Wisconsin Press, Madison, Wis., 437 pp., 1966)

35. George, J. C., Berger, A. J. *Avian Myology* (Academic Press, New York, 500 pp., 1966)

36. Poglazov, B. F. *Structure and Functions of Contractile Proteins* (Academic Press, New York, 321 pp., 1966)

37. Morales, M. On the mechanochemistry of contraction. In *Molecular Biophysics*, 397–410 (Pullman, B., Weissbluth, M., Eds., Academic Press, New York, 452 pp., 1965)

38. Pringle, J. W. S. Locomotion: flight, 283–329 ; Hoyle, G. Neural control of skeletal muscle, 408–49 ; Maruyama, K. The biochemistry of the contractile elements of insect muscle, 451–82 ; Sacktor, B. Energetics and respiratory metabolism of muscular contraction, 484–580. In *The Physiology of Insecta* (Rockstein, M., Ed., Academic Press, New York, 905 pp., 1965)

39. Katz, B. *Nerve, Muscle, and Synapse* (McGraw-Hill, New York, 193 pp., 1966)

40. Lane, B. P. Alterations in the cytologic detail of intestinal smooth muscle cells in various stages of contraction. *J. Cell Biol.*, **27**, 199–213 (1965)

41. Alexander, R. S. Role of calcium in the plasticity of venous smooth muscle. *Am. J. Physiol.*, **213**, 287–94 (1967)

42. Bagby, R. M. The fine structure of myocytes in the sponges *Microciona prolifera* (Ellis and Solander) and *Tedania ignis* (Du-

chassaing and Michelotti). *J. Morphol.*, **118**, 167–81 (1966)

43. Lowy, J., Hanson, J., Elliott, G. F., Millman, B. M., McDonough, M. W. The design of the contractile systems. In *Principles of Biomolecular Organization*, 229–58 (Wolstenholme, G. E. W., O'Connor, M., Eds., Little, Brown, Boston, 491 pp., 1966)

44. Mattisson, A. G. M., Arvidsson, J. A. Some effects of electrical stimulation and exogenous metabolites on the contractile activity and the ultrastructure of the radula-muscle of *Buccinum undatum*. *Z. Zellforsch.*, **73**, 37–55 (1966)

45. Heuman, H.-G., Zebe, E. Über Feinbau und Funktionsweise der Fasern aus dem Hautmuskelschlauch des Regenwurms, *Lumbricus terrestris* L. *Z. Zellforsch.*, **78**, 131–50 (1967)

46. Rosenbluth, J. Obliquely striated muscle. III. Contraction mechanism of *Ascaris* body muscle. *J. Cell Biol.*, **34**, 15–33 (1967)

47. Brokaw, C. J. Non-sinusoidal bending waves of sperm flagella. *J. Exptl. Biol.*, **43**, 155–69 (1965)

48. Satir, P. Morphological aspects of ciliary motility. *J. Gen. Physiol.*, **50**, No. 6, Part 2, 241–58 (1967)

49. Auber, M. Remarques sur l'ultrastructure des myofibrilles chez des scorpions. *J. Microscopie*, **2**, 233–36 (1963)

50. Auber-Thomay, M. Structure et innervation des cellules musculaires de Nématodes. *J. Microscopie*, **3**, 105–9 (1964)

51. Brandt, P. W., Reuben, J. P., Girardier, L., Grundfest, H. Correlated morphological and physiological studies on isolated single muscle fibers. I. Fine structure of crayfish muscle fiber. *J. Cell Biol.*, **25**, No. 3, Part 2, 233–60 (1965)

52. Rosenbluth, J. Ultrastructural organization of obliquely striated muscle fibers of *Ascaris lumbricoides*. *J. Cell Biol.*, **25**, 495–515 (1965)

53. Hagopian, M. The myofilament arrangement in the femoral muscle of the cockroach, *Leucophaea maderae* Fabricus. *J. Cell Biol.*, **28**, 545–62 (1965)

54. Reger, J. F. The fine structure of fibrillar components and plasma membrane contacts in esophageal myoepithelium of *Ascaris lumbri-*

coides (var. *suum*). *J. Ultrastruct. Res.*, **14**, 602–17 (1966)

55. Smith, D. S., Gupta, B. L., Smith, U. The organization and myofilament array of insect visceral muscles. *J. Cell Sci.*, **1**, 49–57 (1966)

56. Smith, D. S. The structure of intersegmental muscle fibers in an insect, *Periplaneta americana* L. *J. Cell Biol.*, **29**, 449–59 (1966)

57. Atwood, H. Crustacean neuromuscular mechanisms. *Am. Zoologist*, **7**, 527–52 (1967)

58. Reger, J. F., Cooper, D. P. A comparative study on the fine structure of the basalar muscle of the wing and the tibial extensor muscle of the leg of the Lepidopteran *Achalarus lyciades*. *J. Cell Biol.*, **33**, 531–42 (1967)

59. Auber, J. Particularités ultrastructurales des myofibrilles des muscles du vol chey des Lépidoptères. *Compt. Rend. Acad. Sci.*, **264**, 621–24 (1967)

59a. Schaefer, C. W., Wanderberg, J. P., Rhodin, J. The fine structure of mosquito midgut muscle. *J. Cell Biol.*, **34**, 905–11 (1967)

60. Swan, R. C. The structure of crayfish sarcomeres. *J. Cell Biol.*, **19**, 68–69A (1963)

61. Pepe, F. A. The myosin filament. I. Structural organization from antibody staining observed in electron microscopy, and II. Interaction between myosin and actin filaments observed using antibody staining in fluorescent and electron microscopy. *J. Mol. Biol.*, **27**, 203–25 and 227–36 (1967)

62. Huxley, H. E. Recent X-ray diffraction and electron microscope studies of striated muscle. *J. Gen. Physiol.*, **50**, No. 6, Part 2, 71–83 (1967)

63. Pepe, F. A. Some aspects of the structural organization of the myofibril as revealed by antibody-staining methods. *J. Cell Biol.*, **28**, 505–25 (1966)

64. Kaminer, B., Bell, A. L. Myosin filamentogenesis: Effects of pH and ionic concentration. *J. Mol. Biol.*, **20**, 391–401 (1966)

65. Huxley, H. E. Muscle cells. In *The Cell*, **IV**, 365–481 (Brachet, J., Mirsky, A. E., Eds., Academic Press, New York, 511 pp., 1960)

66. Chaplain, R. A., Tregear, R. T. The mass of myosin per cross-bridge in insect fibrillar flight muscle. *J. Mol. Biol.*, **21**, 275–80 (1966)

67. Dreyfus, J. C., Kruh, J., Schapira, G. Metabolism of myosin and life time of myofibrils. *Biochem. J.*, **75**, 574–78 (1960)

68. Kruh, J., Dreyfus, J., Schapira, G., Gey, G. O. Abnormalities of muscle protein metabolism in mice with muscular dystrophy. *J. Clin. Invest.*, **39**, 1180–84 (1960)

69. Aronson, J. F. Proposed mechanism for the turnover of myosin and its relation to muscular dystrophy. *Nature*, **210**, 995–96 (1966)

70. McKay, R., Duke, J. A., Boots, J., Morales, M. Conformational changes accompanying modification of myosin ATPase. *Fed. Proc.*, **25**, 224 (1966)

71. Bailin, G., Bárány, M. Role of −SH groups of actin in interaction of actin and myosin. *Fed. Proc.*, **26**, 499 (1967)

72. Reedy, M. K., Holmes, K. C., Tregear, R. T. Induced changes in orientation of the cross-bridges of glycerinated insect flight muscle. *Nature*, **207**, 1276–80 (1966)

72a. Takahashi, K., Yasui, T. Morphological changes of the lateral projections of myosin filament. *J. Biochem. (Tokyo)*, **60**, 231–32 (1966)

73. Sandberg, J. A., Carlson, F. D. The length dependence of phosphorylcreatine hydrolysis during an isometric tetanus. *Biochem. Z.*, **345**, 212–31 (1966)

74. Ward, P. C. J., Edwards, C., Benson, E. S. Relation between adenosinetriphosphate activity and sarcomere length in stretched glycerol-extracted frog skeletal muscle. *Proc. Natl. Acad. Sci.*, **53**, 1377–84 (1965)

75. Gordon, A. M., Huxley, A. F., Julian, F. J. The variation in isometric tension with sarcomere length in vertebrate muscle fibers. *J. Physiol. (London)*, **184**, 170–92 (1966)

76. Zachar, J., Zacharová, D. Potassium contractures in single muscle fibres of the crayfish. *J. Physiol. (London)*, **186**, 596–618 (1966)

77. Carlsen, F., Knappeis, G. G., Buchthal, F. Ultrastructure of resting and contracted striated muscle fiber at different degrees of stretch. *J. Biophys. Biochem. Cytol.*, **11**, 95–117 (1961)

78. Carlsen, F., Fuchs, F., Knappeis, G. G. Contractility and ultrastructure in glycerol-extracted muscle fibers. I. The relationship of contractility to sarcomere length. *J. Cell Biol.,* **27,** 25–34 (1965)

79. Hoyle, G., McAlear, J. H., Selverston, A. Mechanism of supercontraction in a striated muscle. *J. Cell Biol.,* **26,** 621–40 (1965)

80. Carlsen, F., Fuchs, F., Knappeis, G. G. Contractility and ultrastructure in glycerol-extracted muscle fibers. II. Ultrastructure in resting and shortened fibers. *J. Cell Biol.,* **27,** 35–46 (1965)

81. Gordon, A. M., Huxley, A. F., Julian, F. J. Tension development in highly stretched vertebrate muscle fibres. *J. Physiol. (London),* **184,** 143–69 (1966)

82. Szent-Györgyi, A. G., Johnson, W. H. An alternate theory for contraction of striated muscles. In *Biochemistry of Muscle Contraction,* Chap. 46, 485–510 (Gergely, J., Ed., Little, Brown, Boston, 582 pp., 1964)

83. Szent-Györgyi, A., Holtzer, H., Johnson, W. H. Localization of myosin in chick myofibrils determined at various sarcomere lengths with the aid of antibody. In *Biochemistry of Muscle Contraction,* 354–67 (Gergely, J., Ed., Little, Brown, Boston, 582 pp., 1964)

84. Stephens, R. E. Analysis of muscle contraction by ultraviolet microbeam disruption of sarcomere structure. *J. Cell Biol.,* **25,** 129–39 (1965)

85. Elliott, G. F., Lowy, J., Millman, B. M. X-ray diffraction from living striated muscle during contraction. *Nature,* **206,** 1357–58 (1965)

86. Brandt, P. W., Lopez, E., Reuben, J. P., Grundfest, H. The relationship between myofilament packing density and sarcomere length in frog striated muscle. *J. Cell Biol.,* **33,** 255–63 (1967)

86a. Rome, E. Light and x-ray diffraction studies of the filament lattice of glycerol-extracted rabbit psoas muscle. *J. Mol. Biol.,* **27,** 591–602 (1967)

87. Stephens, R. E. Anomalous contraction of invertebrate striated muscle. *J. Cell Biol.,* **27,** 639–49 (1965)

88. DeVillafranca, G. W. The A and I band lengths in a stretched or contracted horseshoe crab skeletal muscle. *J. Ultrastruct. Res.,* **5,** 109–15 (1961)

89. Baskin, R. J., Wiese, G. M. Contraction-band formation in barnacle myofibrils. *Science,* **143,** 134–36 (1964)

90. Gilmour, D., Robinson, P. M. Contraction in glycerinated myofibrils of an insect (Orthoptera, Acrididae). *J. Cell Biol.,* **21,** 385–96 (1964)

91. Sanger, J. W., Szent-Györgyi, A. G. Band pattern changes in the striated adductor muscle of *Pecten irradians. Biol. Bull.,* **127,** 391 (1964)

92. Huxley, H. E., Brown, W., Holmes, K. C. Constancy of axial spacings in frog sartorius muscle during contraction. *Nature,* **206,** 1358 (1965)

93. Hoyle, G. A new formulation of the mechanism of muscular contraction. *Fed. Proc.,* **25,** 465 (1966)

94. McNeill, P. A., Hoyle G. Evidence for superthin filaments. *Am. Zool.,* **7,** 483–98 (1967)

95. Pringle, J. W. S. The excitation and contraction of the flight muscles of insects. *J. Physiol. (London),* **108,** 226–32 (1949)

96. Machin, K. E., Pringle, J. W. S. The physiology of insect fibrillar muscle. II. Mechanical properties of a beetle flight muscle. *Proc. Roy. Soc. B,* **151,** 204–25 (1959)

97. Jewell, B. R., Rüegg, J. C. Oscillatory contraction of insect fibrillar muscle after glycerol extraction. *Proc. Roy. Soc. B,* **164,** 428–59 (1966)

98. Abbott, R. H., Chaplain, R. A. Preparation and properties of the contractile element of insect fibrillar muscle. *J. Cell Sci.,* **1,** 311–30 (1966)

99. Chaplain, R. A. The effect of Ca^{2+} and fibre elongation on the activation of the contractile mechanism of insect fibrillar flight muscle. *Biochim. Biophys. Acta,* **131,** 385–92 (1967)

99a. Armstrong, C. F., Huxley, A. F., Julian, F. J. Oscillatory responses in frog skeletal muscle fibres. *J. Physiol. (London),* **186,** 26–27P (1966)

100. Auber, J., Conteaux, R. Ultrastructure de la strie Z dans les muscles

de Diptères. *J. Microscopie,* **2,** 309–24 (1963)

101. Garamvölgyi, N. The arrangement of the myofilaments in the insect flight muscle I. *J. Ultrastruct. Res.,* **13,** 409–24 (1965)

102. White, D. C. S. (Ph.D. thesis, Oxford, 1966, quoted in Ref. 33)

103. Garamvölgyi, N. Elongation of the primary myofilaments in highly stretched insect flight muscle fibrils. *Acta Biochim. Biophys. Acad. Sci. Hung.,* **1,** 89–100 (1966)

104. Garamvölgyi, N. Structure of the flight muscle fibrils of the bee as seen in the polarizing microscope. *Ibid.,* 293–98

105. Leston, D., Pringle, J. W. S., White, D. C. S. Muscular activity during preparation for flight in a beetle. *J. Exptl. Biol.,* **42,** 409–14 (1965)

106. Pringle, J. W. S. A physiological analysis of cicada song. *J. Exptl. Biol.,* **31,** 525–60 (1964)

107. Hughes, G. M. Locomotion: terrestrial. In *The Physiology of Insecta,* **2,** 227–54 (Rockstein, M. Ed., Academic Press, New York, 905 pp., 1965)

108. Mandelshtam, Y. E. Electron microscopic investigation of muscles in insecta. *Zh. Evol. Biokhim. Fiziol.,* **1,** 391–97 (1965), transl. *Fed. Proc.,* **25,** T475 (1966)

109. Vogell, W., Bishai, F. R., Bücher, T., Klingenberg, M., Pette, D., Zebe, E. Über structurelle und enzymatische Muster in Muskeln von *Locusta migratoria. Biochem. Z.,* **332,** 81–117 (1959)

110. Ebashi, S. Structural proteins controlling the interaction between actin and myosin. In *Symposium über progressive Muskeldystrophie,* 506–13 (Kuhn, E., Ed., Springer-Verlag, Berlin, 1966)

111. Ebashi, S., Ebashi, F. A new protein component participating in the superprecipitation of myosin B. *J. Biochem. (Tokyo),* **55,** 604–13 (1964)

112. Schaub, M. C., Hartshorne, D. J. Perry, S. V. The adenosine-triphosphatase activity of desensitized actomyosin. *Biochem. J.,* **104,** 263–69 (1967)

112a. Katz, A. M. Purification and properties of a tropomyosin-containing protein fraction that sensitizes reconstituted actomyosin to calcium-binding agents. *J. Biol. Chem.,* **241,** 1522–29 (1966)

113. Ebashi, S., Kodama, A. A new protein factor promoting aggregation of tropomyosin. *J. Biochem. (Tokyo),* **58,** 107–8 (1965)

114. Ebashi, S., Kodama, A. Interaction of troponin with F-actin in the presence of tropomyosin. *Ibid.,* **59,** 425–26 (1966)

115. Mueller, H. EGTA-sensitizing activity and molecular properties of tropomyosin prepared in presence of a sulfhydryl protecting agent. *Biochem. Z.,* **345,** 300–21 (1966)

116. Endo, M., Nonomura, Y., Masaki, T., Ohtsuki, I., Ebashi, S. Localization of native tropomyosin in relation to striation patterns. *J. Biochem. (Tokyo),* **60,** 605–8 (1966)

117. Cohen, C., Longley, W. Tropomyosin paracrystals formed by divalent cations. *Science,* **152,** 794–96 (1966)

118. Szent-Györgyi, A., Kaminer, P. Metin and metactomyosin. *Proc. Natl. Acad. Sci.,* **50,** 1033–36 (1963)

119. Azuma, N., Watanabe, S. The major component of metin from rabbit skeletal and bovine cardiac muscle. *J. Biol. Chem.,* **240,** 3847–51 (1965)

120. Azuma, N., Watanabe, S. The minor component of metin from rabbit skeletal muscle. *Ibid.,* 3852–57

121. Ebashi, S., Ebashi, F., Maruyama, K. A new protein factor promoting contraction of actomyosin. *Nature,* **203,** 645–46 (1964)

122. Ebashi, S., Ebashi, F. α-Actinin, a new structural protein from striated muscle. I. Preparation and action on actomyosin-ATP interaction. *J. Biochem. (Tokyo),* **58,** 7–12 (1965)

123. Maruyama, K., Ebashi, S. α-Actinin, a new structural protein from striated muscle, II. Action on actin. *J. Biochem. (Tokyo),* **58,** 13–19 (1965)

124. Goll, D., Mommaerts, W. F. H. M., Seraydarian, K. Is α-actinin a constituent of the Z-band of the muscle fibril? *Fed. Proc.,* **26,** 499 (1967)

125. Hama, H., Maruyama, K., Noda, H. Natural F-actin. I. Direct isolation of F-actin from myofibrils and its physicochemical properties. *Bio-*

chim. Biophys. Acta, **102,** 249–60 (1965)

126. Maruyama, K. Some physico-chemical properties of β-actinin, "actin-factor", isolated from striated muscle. *Biochim. Biophys. Acta,* **102,** 542–48 (1965)

127. Cain, D. F., Davies, R. E. Breakdown of adenosine triphosphate during a single contraction of working muscle. *Biochem. Biophys. Res. Commun.,* **8,** 361–66 (1962)

128. Cain, D. F., Infante, A. A., and Davies, R. E. Chemistry of muscle contraction. Adenosine triphosphate and phosphorylcreatine as energy supplies for single contractions of working muscle. *Nature,* **196,** 214–17 (1962)

129. Infante, A. A., Davies, R. E. The effect of 2,4-dinitroflurobenzene on the activity of striated muscle. *J. Biol. Chem.,* **240,** 3996–4001 (1965)

130. Maréchal, G., Beckers-Bleukx, G. Adenosine triphosphate and phosphorylcreatine breakdown in resting and stimulated muscles after treatment with 1-fluoro-2,4-dinitrobenzene. *Biochem. Z.,* **345,** 286–99 (1966)

131. Dydyńska, M., Wilkie, D. R. The chemical and energetic properties of muscles poisoned with fluorodinitrobenzene. *J. Physiol. (London),* **184,** 751–69 (1966)

132. Medesan, C. La perfusion des muscles striés, moyen d'investigation de la biochimie musculaire. *Rev. Roumaine Biochim.,* **3,** 363–71 (1966)

133. Hill, A. V. The effect of load on the heat of shortening of muscle. *Proc. Roy. Soc. B,* **159,** 297–318 (1964)

134. Hill, A. V. The effect of tension in prolonging the active state in a twitch. *Ibid.,* 589–95

135. Hill, A. V. The variation of total heat production in a twitch with velocity of shortening. *Ibid.,* 595–605

136. Carlson, F. D., Hardy, D., Wilkie, D. R. Total energy production and phosphocreatine hydrolysis in the isotonic twitch. *J. Gen. Physiol.,* **46,** 851–82 (1963)

137. Hill, A. V. The heat of shortening and the dynamic constants of muscle. *Proc. Roy. Soc. B,* **126,** 136–95 (1938)

138. Hill, A. V. The heat of activation and the heat of shortening in a

muscle twitch. *Ibid.,* **136,** 195–211 (1949)

139. Hill, A. V. The laws of muscular motion. *Ibid.,* **100,** 87–108 (1926)

140. Hill, A. F. A further challenge to biochemists. *Biochem. Z.,* **345,** 1–8 (1966)

141. Mommaerts, W. F. H. M., Seraydarian, K., Maréchal, G. Work and chemical change in isotonic muscular contraction. *Biochim. Biophys. Acta,* **57,** 1–12 (1962)

142. Infante, A. A., Klaupiks, D., Davies, R. E. Phosphorylcreatine consumption during single-working contractions of isolated muscle. *Biochim. Biophys. Acta,* **94,** 504–15 (1965)

143. Davies, R. E., Kushmerick, M. J., Larson, R. E. (Professor A. V. Hill's further challenge to biochemists) ATP, activation and the heat of shortening of muscle. *Nature,* **214,** 148–51 (1967)

144. Wilkie, D. R. Thermodynamics and the interpretation of biological heat measurements. *Progr. Biophys. Biophys. Chem.,* **10,** 259–98 (1960)

145. Davies, R. E. A molecular theory of muscle contraction: calcium-dependent contractions with hydrogen bond formation plus ATP dependent extensions of part of the myosin-actin cross-bridges. *Nature,* **199,** 1068–74 (1963)

146. Infante, A. A., Klaupkis, D., Davies, R. E. Adenosine triphosphate: changes in muscles doing negative work. *Science,* **144,** 1577–78 (1964)

147. Hill, A. V., Howarth, J. V. The reversal of chemical reactions in contracting muscle during an applied stretch. *Proc. Roy. Soc. B,* **151,** 169–93 (1959)

148. Gibbs, C. L., Ricchiuti, N. V., Mommaerts, W. F. H. M. Activation heat in frog sartorius muscle. *J. Gen. Physiol.,* **49,** 517–35 (1966)

149. Pool, P. E., Sonnenblick, E. H. The mechanochemistry of cardiac muscle. I. The isometric contraction. *J. Gen. Physiol.,* **50,** 951–65 (1967)

150. Jöbsis, F. F., Duffield, J. C. Force, shortening, and work in muscular contraction: Relative contributions to overall energy utilization. *Science,* **156,** 1388–92 (1967)

151. Mommaerts, W. F. H. M. Energetics

and chemical mechanism of the primary events in muscular contraction. *Proc. Intern. Union Physiol. Sci., 4, Intern. Congr., 23rd, Tokyo, 1965,* 399–404 (Excerpta Med., Amsterdam, 644 pp., 1965)

152. Kushmerick, M. J. *Energetics and efficiency of maximally working muscle* (Ph.D. thesis, Univ. of Pennsylvania, Philadelphia, Pa., 1967)

153. Kushmerick, M. J., Davies, R. E. Energetics and efficiency of maximally working frog sartorius muscles at O°C. *Fed. Proc., 26,* 727 (1967)

154. Porter, K. R., Palade, G. E. Studies on the endoplasmic reticulum. III. Its form and distribution in striated muscle cells, *J. Biophys. Biochem. Cytol., 3,* 269–300 (1957)

155. Peachey, L. D. Transverse tubules in excitation-contraction coupling. *Fed. Proc., 24,* 1124–34 (1965)

156. Peachey, L. D. The role of transverse tubules in excitation contraction coupling in striated muscles. *Ann. N.Y. Acad. Sci., 137,* 1025–37 (1966)

157. Kilarski, W. Organizacja siateczki sarkoplazmatycznej miesni szkieletowych ryb. Czesc II. Okon (Perca fluviatilis L.) —The organization of the sarcoplasmic reticulum in skeletal muscles of fishes Part II. The perch (Perca fluviatilis L). *Acta Biol. Cracov., Ser. Zool., 8,* 51–57 (1965)

158. Nishihara, H. Some observations on the relationship between structure and function in fish red and white muscles. *Sixth International Congress for Electron Microscopy, Kyoto, Japan, 1966, 2,* 693–94 (Ueda, R., Ed., Maruzen & Co., Tokyo, 794 pp., 1966)

159. Franzini-Armstrong, C., Porter, K. R. Sarcolemmal invaginations constituting the T system in fish muscle fibers. *J. Cell Biol., 22,* 675–96 (1964)

160. Reger, J. F. The fine structure of neuromuscular junctions and the sarcoplasmic reticulum of extrinsic eye muscle of *Fundulus heteroclitus. J. Biophys. Biochem. Cytol., 10,* Suppl., 111–21 (1961)

161. Birks, R. I. The sarcoplasmic reticulum of twitch fibres in frog sartorius muscle. In *Muscle,* 199–216 (Paul, W. M., Daniel, E. E.,

Kay, C. M., Monckton, G., Eds., Pergamon, Oxford, 584 pp., 1965)

162. Page, S. G. A comparison of the fine structure of frog slow and twitch muscle fibers. *J. Cell Biol., 26,* 477–97 (1965)

163. Peachey, L. D. The sarcoplasmic reticulum and transverse tubules of the frog's sartorius. *J. Cell Biol., 25,* 209–31 (1965)

164. Hagopian, M., Spiro, D. The sarcoplasmic reticulum and its association with the T-system in an insect. *J. Cell Biol., 32,* 535–45 (1967)

165. Franzini-Armstrong, C. Pores in the sarcoplasmic reticulum. *J. Cell Biol., 19,* 637–41 (1963)

166. O'Connor, A. K., O'Brien, R. D., Salpeter, M. M. Pharmacology and fine structure of peripheral muscle innervation in the cockroach (*Periplaneta americana*). *J. Insect Physiol., 11,* 1351–58 (1965)

167. Smith, D. S. The organization of flight muscle fibers in an aphid, *Megoura viciae* (Homoptera). *J. Cell Biol., 27,* 379–93 (1965)

168. Smith, D. S. The organization of flight muscle fibers in the Odonata. *Ibid., 28,* 109–26 (1966)

169. Girardier, L., Reuben, J. P., Brandt, P. W., Grundfest, H. Evidence for anion-permselective membrane in crayfish muscle fibers and its possible role in excitation-contraction coupling. *J. Gen. Physiol., 47,* 189–214 (1963)

170. Peachey, L. D., Huxley, A. F. Transverse tubules in crab muscle. *J. Cell Biol., 23,* 70–71A (1964)

171. Peachey, L. D. Membrane systems of crab fibers. *Am. Zool., 7,* 505–13 (1967)

172. Huxley, A. F., Taylor, R. E. Local activation of striated muscle fibres. *J. Physiol. (London), 144,* 426–41 (1958)

173. Huxley, A. F., Peachey, L. D. Local activation of crab muscle. *J. Cell Biol., 23,* 107A (1964)

174. Huxley, H. E. Evidence for continuity between the central elements of the triads and extracellular space in frog sartorius muscle. *Nature, 202,* 1067–71 (1964)

175. Peachey, L. D. Structure of the sarcoplasmic reticulum and T-system of striated muscle. *Proc. Intern. Union Physiol. Sci., 4,*

Intern. Congr., 23rd, Tokyo, 1965, 388–98 (Excerpta Med., Amsterdam, 644 pp., 1965)

176. Weber, A., Herz, R., Reiss, I. Study of the kinetics of calcium transport by isolated fragmented sarcoplasmic reticulum. *Biochem. Z.,* **345,** 329–69 (1966)

177. Carvalho, A. P. Binding of cations by microsomes from rabbit skeletal muscle. *J. Cell Physiol.,* **67,** 73–84 (1966)

178. Philpott, C. W., Goldstein, M. A. Sarcoplasmic reticulum of striated muscle: Localization of potential calcium binding sites. *Science,* **155,** 1019–21 (1967)

179. Walker, S. M., Schrodt, G. R. Comparative study of membrane structures within the sarcoplasmic reticulum. *Am. J. Phys. Med.,* **44,** 292–305 (1965)

180. Revel, J. P. The sarcoplasmic reticulum of the bat cricothyroid muscle. *J. Cell Biol.,* **12,** 571–88 (1962)

181. Hoyle, G. Nature of the excitatory sarcoplasmic reticular junction. *Science,* **149,** 70–72 (1965)

182. Wiener, J., Spiro, D., Lowenstein, W. R. Studies on an epithelial (gland) cell junction. II. Surface structure. *J. Cell Biol.,* **22,** 587–98 (1964)

183. Loewenstein, W. R., Socolar, S. J., Higashino, S., Kanno, Y., Davidson, N. Intercellular communication: renal, urinary bladder, sensory, and salivary gland cells. *Science,* **149,** 295–98 (1965)

184. Fahrenbach, W. H. Sarcoplasmic reticulum: ultrastructure of the triadic junction. *Science,* **147,** 1308–10 (1965)

185. Farquhar, M. G., Palade, G. E. Junctional complexes in various epithelia. *J. Cell Biol.,* **17,** 375–421 (1963)

186. Claude, P. Cell junctions in the *Necturus* kidney proximal tubule. *J. Cell Biol.,* **31,** 21A (1966)

187. Karnovsky, M. J. The ultrastructural basis of capillary permeability, studied with peroxidase as a tracer. *J. Cell Biol.* (In press)

188. Revel, J. P., Karnovsky, M. J. Hexagonal array of subunits in intercellular junctions of the mouse heart and liver. *J. Cell Biol.,* **33,** C7–12 (1967)

189. Walker, S. M., Schrodt, G. R. Continuity of the T-system with the sarcolemma in rat skeletal muscle

fibers. *J. Cell Biol.,* **27,** 671–77 (1965)

190. Wolff, H. H. Über den Einfluss der Fixierung auf die Elektronenmikroskopische Darstellung der Muskelfasern des Rattendiaphragmas. *Z. Zellforsch.,* **73,** 192–204 (1966)

191. Jasper, D. Body muscles of the lamprey. Some structural features of the T-system and sarcolemma. *J. Cell Biol.,* **32,** 219–27 (1967)

192. Page, S. The organization of the sarcoplasmic reticulum in frog muscle. *J. Physiol. (London),* **175,** 10–11P (1964)

193. Peachey, L. D., Schild, R. F. The distribution of the T-system along the sarcomeres of frog and toad sartorius muscles. *J. Physiol. (London),* **194,** 249–58 (1968)

193a. Endo, M. Entry of fluorescent dyes into the sarcotubular system of the frog muscle. *J. Physiol. (London),* **185,** 224–38 (1966)

194. Tice, L. W., Engel, A. G. The localization of sodium pyroantimonate in frog muscle fibers. *J. Cell Biol.,* **31,** 118A (1966)

195. Zadunaisky, J. A. The location of sodium in the transverse tubules of skeletal muscle. *J. Cell Biol.,* **31,** C11–16 (1966)

195a. Rayns, D. G., Simpson, F. O., Bertaud, W. S. Transverse tubule apertures in mammalian myocardial cells. *Science,* **156,** 656–57 (1967)

196. Ezerman, E., Ishikawa, H. Differentiation of the sarcoplasmic reticulum and T-system in developing chick skeletal muscle *in vitro. J. Cell Biol.,* **35,** No. 2, Part 1, 405–20 (1967)

197. Falk, G., Fatt, P. Linear electrical properties of striated muscle fibres observed with intracellular electrodes. *Proc. Roy. Soc. B,* **160,** 69–123 (1964)

198. Freygang, W. H., Jr., Rapoport, S. I., Peachey, L. D. Some relations between changes in the linear electrical properties of striated muscle fibers and changes in ultrastructure. *J. Gen. Physiol.,* **50,** 2437–58 (1967)

199. Adrian, R. H., Peachey, L. D. The membrane capacity of frog twitch and slow muscle fibres. *J. Physiol. (London),* **181,** 324–36 (1965)

200. Eisenberg, R. S. The equivalent circuit of single crab muscle fibers as

determined by impedance measurements with intracellular electrodes. *J. Gen. Physiol.*, **50**, 1785–1806 (1967)

201. Fozzard, H. A. Membrane capacity of the cardiac Purkinje fibre. *J. Physiol. (London)*, **182**, 255–67 (1966)

202. Pugsley, I. D. Contribution of the transverse tubular system to the membrane capacitance of striated muscle of the toad (*Bufo marinus*). *Australian J. Biol. Med. Sci.*, **44**, 9–22 (1966)

203. Freygang, W. H., Jr., Goldstein, D. A. Hellam, D. C. The afterpotential that follows trains of impulses in frog muscle fibers. *J. Gen. Physiol.*, **47**, 929–52 (1964)

204. Rapoport, S. I., Freygang, W. H., Jr., Peachey, L. D. Effect of swelling of the transverse tubular system on the impedance of frog sartorius muscle membrane. *Proc. Intern. Biophys. Congr. Intern. Organ. Pure Appl. Biophys., 2nd, Vienna, Sept. 5-9, 1966, Abstr. No. 501*

205. Adrian, R. H., Freygang, W. H. The potassium and chloride conductance of frog muscle membrane. *J. Physiol. (London)*, **163**, 61–103 (1962)

206. Winegrad, S. Intracellular movements of calcium in frog skeletal muscle during recovery from tetanus. *J. Gen. Physiol.* (In press) (1968)

207. Jöbsis, F. F., O'Connor, M. J. Calcium release and reabsorption in the sartorius muscle of the toad. *Biochem. Biophys. Res. Commun.*, **25**, 246–52 (1966)

208. Sandow, A. Latency relaxation: A brief analytical review. *Med. Coll. Virginia Quart.*, **2**, 82–89 (1966)

209. Baskin, R. J., Paolini, P. J. Muscle volume changes. *J. Gen. Physiol.*, **49**, 387–404 (1966)

210. Sopis, J. A., Winegrad, S. Effect of stretch on Ca^{45} efflux and on sarcoplasmic reticulum in frog skeletal muscle. *Fed. Proc.*, **26**, 597 (1967)

211. Kamada, T., Kinosita, H. Disturbances initiated from naked surface of protoplasm. *Japan. J. Zool.*, **10**, 469–93 (1943)

212. Heilbrunn, L. V. *An Outline of General Physiology* (Saunders, Philadelphia, Pa. 748 pp. 2nd ed., 1943)

213. Heilbrunn, L. V., Wiercinski, F. J. The action of various cations on muscle protoplasm. *J. Cellular Comp. Physiol.*, **29**, 15–32 (1947)

214. Ohnishi, T. Der Einfluss eines elektrichen Stroms über die Verbindung des Calciums mit den Muskelvesikeln. *J. Phys. Soc. Japan*, **21**, 2424 (1966)

215. Lee, K. S., Ladinsky, H., Choi, S. J., Kasuya, Y. Studies on the *in vitro* interaction of electrical stimulation and Ca^{++} movement in sacroplasmic reticulum. *J. Gen. Physiol.* **49**, 689–715 (1966)

216. Costantin, L. L., Podolsky, R. J. Depolarization of the internal membrane system in the activation of frog skeletal muscle. *J. Gen. Physiol.*, **50**, 1101–24 (1967)

217. Van der Kloot, W. G. Inhibitors of active Ca^{2+} uptake by fragments of the sarcoplasmic reticulum of lobster muscle. *Comp. Biochem. Physiol.*, **17**, 75–86 (1966)

218. Giacomelli, F., Bibbiani, C., Bergamini, E., Pellegrino, C. Two ATPases in the sarcoplasmic reticulum of skeletal muscle fibres. *Nature*, **213**, 679–82 (1967)

218a. Schulze, W., Wollenberger, A. Zytochemische Lokalisation und Charakterisierung von phosphatabspaltenden Fermenten im sarkotubulären System quergestreifter Muskeln. *Histochemie*, **10**, 140–53 (1967)

219. Tice, L. In situ studies of the sarcotubular system. In *Factors Influencing Myocardial Contractility* (Tanz, R. D., Ed., Academic Press, New York, in press, 1967)

219a. Sommer, J. R., Hasselbach, W. The effect of glutaraldehyde and formaldehyde on the calcium pump of the sarcoplasmic reticulum. *J. Cell Biol.*, **34**, 902–5 (1967)

220. Gillis, J. M., Page, S. G. Localization of ATPase activity in striated muscle and probable sources of artifact. *J. Cell Sci.*, **2**, 113–18 (1967)

221. Fahimi, H. D., Karnovsky, M. J. Cytochemical localization of two glycolytic dehydrogenases in white skeletal muscle. *J. Cell Biol.*, **29**, 113–28 (1966)

221a. Ulbrecht, G., Kruckenberg, P. Acetylcholinesterase in the sarcoplasmic reticulum of skeletal muscle. *Nature*, **206**, 305–6 (1965)

221b. Davis, R., Koelle, G. B. Electron microscopic localization of acetylcholinesterase and nonspecific cholinesterase at the neuromuscular junction by the gold-thiocholine and gold-thiolacetic acid methods. *J. Cell Biol.*, **34**, 157–71 (1967)

222. Costantin, L. L., Podolsky, R. J., Tice, L. W. Calcium activation of frog slow muscle fibres. *J. Physiol. (London)*, **188**, 261–71 (1967)

223. Sreter, F. A., Seidel, J. C., and Gergely, J. Studies on myosin from red and white skeletal muscles of the rabbit. I. Adenosine triphosphatase activity. *J. Biol. Chem.*, **241**, 5772–76 (1966)

224. Bárány, M. AtPase activity of myosin correlated with speed of muscle shortening. *J. Gen. Physiol.*, **50**, 197–218 (1967)

225. Trayer, I. P., Perry, S. V. The myosin of developing skeletal muscle. *Biochem. Z.*, **345**, 87–100 (1966)

226. Kuffler, S. W., Vaughan-Williams, E. M. Small-nerve junctional potentials. The distribution of small motor nerves to frog skeletal muscle, and the membrane characteristics of the fibres they innervate. *J. Physiol. (London)*, **121**, 289–317 (1953)

227. Ginsborg, B. L. Some properties of avian skeletal muscle fibres with multiple neuromuscular junctions. *J. Physiol. (London)*, **154**, 581–98 (1960)

228. Peachey, L. D., Huxley, A. F. Structural identification of twitch and slow striated muscle fibers of the frog. *J. Cell Biol.*, **13**, 177–80 (1962)

229. Hess, A. The sarcoplasmic reticulum, the T system, and the motor terminals of slow and twitch fibers in the garter snake. *J. Cell Biol.*, **26**, 467–76 (1965)

230. Hoyle, G., McNeill, P. A., Walcott, B. Nature of invaginating tubules in *Felderstruktur* muscle fibers of the garter snake. *J. Cell Biol.*, **30**, 197–201 (1966)

231. Beatty, C. H., Basinger, G. M., Dully, C. C., Bocek, R. M. Comparison of red and white voluntary skeletal muscles of several species of primates. *J. Histochem. Cytochem.* **14**, 590–600 (1966)

232. Gauthier, G. F., Padykula, H. A. Cytological studies of fiber types in skeletal muscle. A comparative study of the mammalian dia-phragm. *J. Cell Biol.*, **28**, 333–54 (1966)

232a. Lannergren, J., Smith, R. S. Types of muscle fibres in toad skeletal muscle. *Acta Physiol. Scand.*, **68**, 263–74 (1966)

232b. Romanul, F. C. A., Van Der Meulen, J. P. Reversal of the enzyme profile of muscle fibres of fast and slow muscles by cross-innervation. *Nature*, **212**, 1369–70 (1966)

232c. McPherson, A., Tokunaga, J. The effects of cross-innervation on the myoglobin concentration of tonic and phasic muscles. *J. Physiol. (London)*, **188**, 121–29 (1967)

233. Shamarina, N. M. Electric response of 'tonic' muscle fibres of the frog skeletal musculature. *Nature*, **193**, 783–84 (1962)

234. Orkand, R. K. A further study of electrical responses in slow and twitch muscle fibres of the frog. *J. Physiol. (London)*, **167**, 181–91 (1963)

235. Nasledov, G. A. Correlative study of certain morphological and functional features of muscle fibers. *Fiziol. Zh. SSSR*, **50**, 1342 (1964), transl. *Fed. Proc.*, **24**, T1091–95 (1965)

235a. Gray, E. G. The spindle and extrafusal innervation of a frog muscle. *Proc. Roy. Soc. B*, **146**, 416–30 (1957)

236. Shamarina, N. M. Synaptic transmission in different fibers of tonic frog skeletal muscle. *Fiziol. Zh. SSSR*, **51**, 1080 (1965), transl. *Fed. Proc.*, **25**, T589–94 (1966)

237. Ralston, H. J., Libet, B. Effect of stretch on action potential of voluntary muscle. *Am. J. Physiol.*, **173**, 449–55 (1953)

238. Matyushkin, D. P. Varieties of tonic muscle fibers in the oculomotor apparatus of the rabbit. *Byull. Eksperim. Biol. Med.*, **55**, 3–6 (1963)

239. Hess, A., Pilar, G. Slow fibres in the extraocular muscles of the cat. *J. Physiol. (London)*, **169**, 780–98 (1963)

240. Matyushkin, D. P. Postnatal development of phasic oculomotor units in the rabbit. *Fiziol. Zh. SSSR*, **50**, 1045–51 (1964)

241. Baichenko, P. I., Matyushkin, D. P., Suvorov, V. V. Participation of phasic and tonic oculomotor sys-

tems in extension reflexes and labyrinthine reflexes of extrinsic ocular muscles. *Fiziol. Zh. SSSR,* **53,** 82–90 (1967)

242. Matyushkin, D. P. Contractions and their relationships to action potentials in the phasic fibers of the external eye muscles of adult and newborn animals. *Biofizika,* **12,** 462–69 (1967)

243. Bach-y-Rita, P., Ito, F. *In vivo* studies on fast and slow muscle fibers in cat extraocular muscles. *J. Gen. Physiol.,* **49,** 1177–98 (1966)

244. Dietert, S. E. The demonstration of different types of muscle fibers in human extraocular muscle by electron microscopy and cholinesterase staining. *Invest. Ophthalmol.,* **4,** 51–63 (1965)

245. Brandt, D. E., Leeson, C. R. Structural differences of fast and slow fibers in human extraocular muscle. *Am. J. Ophthalmol.,* **62,** 478–87 (1966)

246. Mayr, R., Stockinger, L., Zenker, W. Elektronenmikroskopische Untersuchungen an unterschiedlich innervierten Muskelfasern der äusserern Augenmuskulatur des Rhesusaffen. *Z. Zellforsch.,* **75,** 434–52 (1966)

247. Cheng, K., Breinin, G. M. A comparison of the fine structure of extraocular and interosseus muscles in the monkey. *Invest. Ophthalmol.,* **5,** 535–59 (1966)

248. Miller, J. E. Cellular organization of rhesus extraocular muscle. *Invest. Ophthalmol.,* **6,** 18–39 (1967)

249. Kern, R. A comparative pharmacologic-histologic study of slow and twitch fibers in the superior rectus muscle of the rabbit. *Invest. Ophthalmol.,* **4,** 901–10 (1965)

250. Cheng, K., Breinin, G. M. Fine structure of nerve endings in ex-

traocular muscles. *Arch. Ophthalmol.,* **74,** 822–34 (1965)

251. Pilar, G., Hess, A. Differences in internal structure and nerve terminals of the slow and twitch muscle fibers in the cat superior oblique. *Anat. Record,* **154,** 243–51 (1966)

252. Birks, R., Huxley, H. E., Katz, B. The fine structure of the neuromuscular junction of the frog. *J. Physiol. (London),* **150,** 134–44 (1960)

253. Bach-y-Rita, P., and Ito, F. In vivo microelectrode studies of the cat retractor bulbi fibers. *Invest. Ophthalmol.,* **4,** 338–42 (1965)

254. Hess, A. The structure of slow and fast extrafusal muscle fibers in the extraocular muscles and their nerve endings in guinea pigs. *J. Cellular Comp. Physiol.,* **58,** 63–79 (1961)

255. Kato, T. Über histologische Untersuchungen der Augenmuskeln von Menschen und Säugetieren. *Okajimas Folia Anat. Japon.,* **16,** 131–45 (1938)

256. Peachey, L. D. Fine structure of two fiber types in cat extraocular muscles. *J. Cell Biol.,* **31,** 84A (1966)

257. Erulkar, S. D., Shelanski, M. L., Whitsel, B. L., Ogle, P. Studies of muscle fibers of the tensor tympani of the cat. *Anat. Record,* **149,** 279–97 (1964)

258. Brecht, K., Feneis, H. Über tonische und phasische Reaktionen einzelner quergestreifter Muskelfasern und des Ganzmuskels. *Z. Biol.,* **103,** 355–80 (1950)

259. Comline, R. S., Message, M. A. The neuromuscular physiology of the ruminant stomach. In *Physiology of Digestion in the Ruminant* (Dougherty, R. W., Allen, R. S., Burroughs, W., Jacobsen, N. L., McGilliard, A. D., Eds., Butterworths, London, 480 pp., 1965)

KIDNEY[1,2] 1012

By Klaus Thurau, Heinz Valtin,[3] and Jürgen Schnermann

Physiologisches Institut der Universität München
München, Germany

The last review of renal physiology in this series was published in 1965. The great number of papers which appeared during the last three years makes it impossible to incorporate all publications pertinent to the field of renal physiology into a review of this size. Accordingly, this chapter permits the reader to trace only major advances in this field of physiology. Naturally, in some paragraphs our own interest and competence gained the upper hand, and this may in part have influenced the selection of the material.

Many worthwhile symposia and reviews on renal physiology and related areas have appeared. The reader may find his topic of interest among the titles listed in the bibliography (1–29). We have not considered the physiology of diuretic agents extensively because this material has been adequately summarized in recent articles (30, 31) and in an excellent symposium (32). The limitation on space has also precluded a detailed description of mathematical models of renal function (33–41).

Renal Blood Flow and Glomerular Filtration Rate

Inulin.—In 1964, Shehadeh et al. (42) and Scott et al. (43) reported that inulin was extensively reabsorbed into the circulation after it had been microinjected into the proximal convolutions of normal rats and *Necturi*. Had this finding been substantiated, it would of course have invalidated numerous classical studies in renal physiology. This sword of Damocles was sheathed by a number of subsequent reports. Gutman, Gottschalk & Lassiter (44) injected ^{14}C- or ^{3}H-inulin into the proximal tubules of rats under conditions of free flow. Essentially all of the injected inulin was recovered in the urine of the same kidney. During mannitol and saline diuresis, inulin

---

[1] The survey of the literature was concluded in June 1967.

[2] Abbreviations used in this chapter include: ADH (antidiuretic hormone); C (clearance); E (extraction ratio); GFR (glomerular filtration rate); PAH para-aminohippuric acid); PD (potential difference); $T^c_{H_2O}$ (tubular reabsorption of solute free water); TF/P (tubular fluid-to-plasma ratio); Tm (tubular maximum); U/P (urine-to-plasma ratio).

[3] On leave of absence from the Department of Physiology, Dartmouth Medical School, Hanover, N.H., from January to June 1967. Recipient of United States Public Health Service Research Career Program Award 6-K3-GM-21, 786.

excretion by the contralateral kidney following proximal microinjection was less than 1.0 per cent (45).

Baumann et al. (46) found that less than 2 per cent of inulin microinjected into proximal tubules of rats was reabsorbed in those trials which they considered to be free of experimental artifact. In some of their other experiments, however, as much as 20–30 per cent appeared to be reabsorbed. The authors suggest that in these studies some of the inulin was not injected into the tubule, and that it was reabsorbed into the capillary blood directly from the surface of the kidney. The most conclusive proof for the conservation of inulin in the tubular lumen of rats was established by Marsh & Frasier (47). They infused a known amount of inulin into a single proximal convolution, and collected virtually all of it (99.3 ± 2.9 per cent) from the distal convolution of the same nephron. Since the rate of recovery was the same whether or not the peritubular plasma was loaded with inulin, the possibility of inulin secretion was also excluded. Tanner & Klose (48) microinjected inulin into proximal tubules of *Necturi,* and recovered only insignificant quantities from the blood or the Ringer's bathing medium.

The results recently published by Sonnenberg (49) are more difficult to interpret. During microperfusion of single proximal tubules of rats with isotonic ³H-mannitol containing ¹⁴C-inulin, the concentrations of both substances decreased exponentially with increasing length of perfused segment; this is expected from the transtubular inflow of NaCl and water. Although the slope of the curve for inulin was not significantly different from that for mannitol, the inulin curve was displaced downward. Sonnenberg interpreted this displacement to reflect reabsorption of inulin, but he does not explain why both curves fail to intercept the y-axis at 100 per cent. When the perfusion fluid consisted of isotonic saline instead of mannitol, no evidence for reabsorption of inulin was found, and in these experiments the regression lines did cross the y-axis at about 100 per cent. One interpretation of these data is that a perfusion fluid which is initially free of sodium renders the tubular epithelium permeable to inulin or its breakdown products, but not to mannitol.

On the basis of subsequent data in rats and *Necturus,* similar to those described above, the group which had originally suggested that tubular reabsorption of inulin might occur, has also retracted this view (50, 51). Because of the possibility that inulin may leak at the puncture site, especially in microperfusion experiments, Scott et al. (51) propose that it would be a wise precaution to monitor inulin in the blood so that micropuncture experiments in which an appreciable amount of transtubular movement has taken place can be excluded. Thus, under normal conditons inulin apparently remains the undisputed champion, not only for standard clearance methods but also for the assessment of water reabsorption from the nephron. This does not mean that inulin is a valid substance to assess GFR under all circumstances. In mercury-poisoned rats with damaged tubular epithelium, inulin loss from the tubular fluid may occur as indicated by the micropuncture work of Bank, Mutz & Aynedjian (52).

In retrospect, it seems curious that a major challenge to a long-cherished view was needed to stimulate the experiments which have provided the direct proof that inulin is neither reabsorbed nor secreted by the intact nephron.

Vurek & Pegram (53) have described a new fluorimetric method for measuring inulin in nanoliter samples. This method, however, is no more sensitive than the microanthrone method, and requires no less volume. With the achievement of high plasma concentrations through the use of the more soluble polyfructosan S, an inulin-like polysaccharide, accurate determinations of proximal tubular fluid concentrations on 5 to 10 nl samples can be made by the microanthrone method which, considering the technical difficulties involved in any fluorimetric method, would seem to be preferable. Two new methods permit the accurate determination of inulin in the presence of dextrans (54, 55).

Other substances.—EDTA clearance in dogs resembled inulin clearance (EDTA/inulin 1.02) under many experimental conditions (56), which suggests excretion by glomerular filtration only. The reliability of the exogenous creatinine clearance as a measure of GFR in man was investigated by Harvey, Malvin & Vander (57). In all subjects the creatinine clearance exceeded the inulin clearance, the average ratio being 1.25 ± 0.14 SD. In contrast to rats and dogs, no sex difference was found. Ratios of 1.32 in adrenalectomized females excluded any significant influence of adrenal testosterone or progesterone on tubular creatinine secretion. Isotope methods for assessing GFR have been further developed (58–60).

Glomerular function.—Nissen (61, 62) estimated filtration fractions for the plasma supplying the superficial cortex and that flowing through the deep cortex in the cat kidney. The anatomical separation of subcapsular from deep cortical venous drainage permits the collection of venous blood from these two areas by inserting catheters into a subcapsular and into a deep renal vein. The fractions, calculated from a formula incorporating the arteriovenous differences for protein and inulin, were 0.34 and 0.29 for the subcapsular and deep areas, respectively. The ratio of the reabsorptive to the filtered rate for plasma water was 0.75 for the subcapsular area and 1.35 for the deep region. This suggests that about 35 per cent of the filtrate formed in subcapsular glomeruli is eventually reabsorbed into the deep venous system. Presumably, this excess reabsorbate is derived from Henle's loops of subcapsular nephrons and from collecting ducts.

Continued glomerular filtration during ureteral stop-flow in rats was shown by Selkurt, Deetjen & Brechtelsbauer (63), through the use of inulin, and recording of pressures simultaneously in the proximal tubules and ureters. Pressures remained higher in the proximal tubules for up to one hour during saline diuresis, and for 13 to 25 min during mannitol diuresis. During 15 min of stop-flow in mannitol diuresis, the C_{IN} averaged 25 per cent of the free-flow value. Even though pressure equilibrium is finally reached, the authors point out that changes in other variables, such as total renal blood flow, preclude the use of maximum ureteral stop-flow pressure for the accurate determination of effective filtration pressure.

A more direct method for calculating glomerular capillary pressure was developed by Gertz et al. (64). They blocked distal flow from the first loop of a single superficial proximal tubule of rats through the microinjection of castor oil, and then observed the increase of intratubular pressure proximal to the oil. After 30 to 40 sec, this pressure reached a plateau at a mean of 63 mm Hg. Since no visible flow could be observed in the occluded tubular segment, it was assumed that filtration ceased when the intratubular pressure reached this value. The plateau was constant with arterial pressures between 100 and 160 mm Hg. Assuming a plasma oncotic pressure of 25 mm Hg, the calculated glomerular capillary pressure would be 88 ± 4 mm Hg. The method is based on the assumption that the rise in the pressure within Bowman's capsule from a normal of 15 to 63 mm Hg does not change the pressure in the glomerular vascular tuft from that in the unobstructed glomerulus. Subtracting the glomerular capillary pressure thus derived from the arterial pressure yields a value for the pressure gradient between aorta and glomerular capillaries. This gradient was zero at arterial pressures below 90 mm Hg and increased linearly with increases in pressure above 90 mm Hg.

Koch et al. (65) and Krause et al. (66) used the same method to determine the influence of hypertonic mannitol, hydrochlorothiazide, and furosemide on GFR and glomerular capillary pressure in rats. Since maximum stop-flow pressure in the proximal tubule remained unchanged, the authors concluded that glomerular capillary pressure is not influenced by mannitol diuresis. The decrease in GFR observed during this diuresis appeared to be related, rather, to an increase in the proximal tubular pressure under free-flow conditions. Maximum stop-flow pressure in the proximal convolution was not influenced by hydrochlorothiazide, but was increased by furosemide. The implication drawn from these results is that the decrease in GFR which is induced by hydrochlorothiazide can be attributed to a rise in free-flow proximal pressure which is unaccompanied by elevated glomerular capillary pressure, whereas a concomitant rise in the latter pressure prevents a fall in GFR after furosemide.

Gekle, Bruchhausen & Fuchs (67) sought to determine pore radius of basement membranes isolated from rat renal cortex by means of density-gradient ultracentrifugation. The preparation included basement membranes besides those from glomeruli (68). The authors concluded that the borderline molecular weight for penetration of the basement membranes lies between 80,000 and 90,000. Assuming spherical shapes for these molecules, they calculated a mean pore radius of 29 Å with a maximum of 42–45 Å. Although electronmicroscopic and chemical studies suggest that glomerular basement membranes are not structurally different from the other renal cortical basement membranes, the inclusion of the latter may partly account for the discrepancy between the present results and those of Pappenheimer, which referred only to the glomerular capillary membrane. Chemical analysis of isolated glomerular basement membranes was performed by several authors (69–71). Although the results may be influenced markedly by the extraction method used (69), most investigators agree on the absence of mucopolysaccharides from the glomerular basement membrane. Collagen, glycoprotein, and lipids account for the major portion of this structure (71). A similar composition was found in a mixture of basement membranes from all cortical structures (72).

Renal blood flow.—Ladefoged (73) has given a detailed description of the ^{133}Xe washout technique for measuring renal blood flow. The method is based on the principle introduced by Thorburn et al. (74), for measuring local renal blood flows with ^{85}Kr. The total renal blood flow measured with ^{133}Xe, and that obtained simultaneously with an electromagnetic flowmeter agreed well (75). In contrast to Thorburn et al. (74), who analyzed four intrarenal compartments with different flow rates, Ladefoged & Pedersen (76) did not analyze the tail of the washout curve because they felt that it was invalidated by recirculation. By measuring only the β-emission of ^{85}Kr, one can selectively determine cortical blood flow in the exposed kidney (77), since the maximum range of β-emission in tissue is ∼ 2.6 mm.

Carriere et al. (512) extended their earlier studies (74) on intrarenal blood flow distribution to examine the changes which occur during hemorrhagic hypotension in anesthetized dogs. Compartmental blood flow rates were determined by the ^{85}Kr washout technique (external counting of γ-emission). For localization of the compartments, the kidneys were removed for autoradiography at the end of the experiment at predetermined intervals after the injection of ^{85}Kr into the renal artery. The data indicate that during arterial hypotension of 50 mm Hg the normal pattern of cortical blood flow becomes disrupted to the extent that areas with normal flow rate alternate with areas in which flow rate is reduced to values normally found in the outer medulla. After 60 min of hypotension the percentage of the injected ^{85}Kr entering cortical areas with normal flow rate was reduced from a control value of 85 to 30 per cent (range 3–72 per cent) and after 90 min of hypotension to 40 per cent (range 0–78 per cent). These numbers may approximate the reduction in cortical tissue mass perfused at normal flow rates. Renal medullary blood flow underwent little or no change during the hypotensive period. The localization of these flow rate compartments depends critically on the assumption that the intrarenal distribution of radioactivity found autoradiographically at the end of the experiment reflects the situation which existed during the period of the experiment when the disappearance curve was recorded.

Reubi, Gossweiler & Gürtler (78) used Evans blue or indocyanine dyes to study total renal blood flow, intrarenal distribution of flow, renal transit times, and intrarenal blood volumes in human beings. Since recirculating dye makes an insignificant contribution to the late part of the dye curve, they utilized the deviation from a single exponential curve for compartmental analysis. Such a deviation, however, was not detected by others (79–81). Blood volume in the fast compartment (presumably cortex) ranged between 52 and 78 per cent of total renal blood volume. Blood flow through this compartment amounted to 80–93 per cent of total blood flow, with a mean transit time of 5 to 10 sec. Transit time through the slow compartment (presumably medulla) was 19 to 25 sec. Pedersen & Baerenholdt (82) and Pedersen et al. (83) gave a single bolus of labeled red cells and labeled albumin, into the renal artery, and determined renal circulation times by means of external counting. Their results are comparable to those of Reubi, Gossweiler & Gürtler (78) and Effros et al. (79).

With the use of indocyanine green, Gómez et al. (80) studied the distribution of specific blood flow in the human kidney. Specific blood flow was defined as blood flow per unit functional blood volume (1/mean transit time), anywhere within the renal vascular system. In contrast to others (78) the authors found the downslope of the dilution-curve to conform to a single exponential function, an observation indicating uniform intrarenal distribution of blood flow. The reasons for the discrepancy were not discussed. Using their multiple indicator-dilution technique, Chinard et al. (84) estimated vascular and extravascular volumes in the canine kidney *in situ*. The intrarenal compartments with long transit times could not be detected because late contributions to the venous dilution-curves were eliminated by correcting for recirculation. The venous outflow patterns for fructose and diatrizoate, and for hippurate, iodopyracet, and chlorothiazide after inhibiting their secretion by probenecid, were nearly identical to the outflow pattern for creatinine. The authors therefore concluded that creatinine is restricted to the renal extracellular volume, its distribution apparently limited by flow, not by diffusion. Renal venous recovery of inulin was larger than that of creatinine, and the transit time for inulin was shorter. The authors ascribe these findings to the polydispersity of inulin, which may result in diffusion limitation for the larger fractions across the capillary walls. Interstitial volume (intratubular volume excluded) was about 20 ml per 100 g kidney and renal intracellular water, as determined by the outflow pattern of labeled water, was 39 g per 100 g kidney.

The hydrogen method of Aukland, Bower & Berliner (85) was used by Haining & Turner (86) to measure the renal cortical blood flow of rats, which was calculated to be 3.84 to 4.9 ml per g kidney per min, similar to the values in dogs and man. Cortical blood flow decreased 30 per cent when the body temperature of the rats was reduced to 32°C.

Grängsjö, Ulfendahl & Wolgast (87) used red cells labeled with ^{32}P to determine blood flows in the renal cortex and medulla of dogs. One detector was inserted into the medulla and another was placed on the cortical surface. After injection of the red cells into the renal artery, the indicator dilution curves revealed mean transit times of 3.2 sec in the cortex, and 24 sec in the medulla. Regional blood volumes were calculated from comparison of radioactivity in renal tissues and peripheral blood in the steady state. This calculation entails the false assumption that regional intravascular hematocrit is identical with that in peripheral blood. Nevertheless, the approach used by these authors should be valuable for detecting relative changes in regional blood flows. To study the distribution of red cells within the intrarenal circulation, Moffat injected fluorescent red cells into the systemic circulation of rats (88). In kidneys which were removed and frozen, he could detect no significant difference between the number of fluorescent red cells in cortical and juxtamedullary glomeruli. He therefore concluded that cell separation in the interlobular arteries, as proposed by Pappenheimer & Kinter, does not occur to any appreciable extent. However, since the renal artery and vein were clamped simultaneously before the kidney was removed, blood from the arteries must have passed to the renal veins until the pressure in all vessels was equalized. The process of equalization might have nullified any cell separation that might have occurred in the intact kidney.

Several laboratories have utilized the extraction ratio for PAH (E_{PAH}) to estimate the distribution of renal blood flows. Hársing & Bartha (89) found E_{PAH} in dogs during mannitol diuresis to be 0.72. Cortical blood flow, as measured simultaneously by the uptake of ^{86}Rb (90), was 74 per cent of the total renal blood flow. The authors believe that the coincidence of these two figures favors the concept that during osmotic diuresis, the proportion of the total blood flow which perfuses the cortex can be determined by E_{PAH}. Essential to this thesis is the assumption that there is complete extraction of PAH from the blood passing through the cortex. Some indirect evidence supports this assumption. Pilkington et al. (91) found that in dogs at plasma concentrations of PAH below Tm levels, E_{PAH} did not change as the plasma concentration was varied. Nor was E_{PAH} increased by Na acetate, a stimulator of PAH transport, or by reducing renal blood flow, which prolonged the contact time between the blood and the excretory tissue. The implication that medullary tissue does not extract PAH is supported by the finding that medullary cells from dogs and sheep did not accumulate PAH *in vitro*, while the cortical cells did (92). Obviously, lack of cellular accumulation does not necessarily mean absence of transtubular transport.

Despite this body of circumstantial evidence, Pilkington et al. (91) warn that E_{PAH} can at best provide only an approximation of renal blood flow distribution. Like others (89), they found E_{PAH} to be decreased during mannitol diuresis, which probably indicates a proportionately greater increase in medullary than in cortical blood flow. If one assumes that RBF in their control studies averaged 4 ml per g of kidney per min (kidney weights were not given), and that outer and inner medulla together account for 30 per cent of total kidney weight, then medullary blood flow would have been about 1.0 ml per g medullary tissue per min during control conditions and 2.4 ml during mannitol diuresis. Decreases in E_{PAH} similar to those seen during mannitol diuresis were obtained during renal vasodilation induced by infusion of acetylcholine (91) and of bradykinin (93) into the renal artery. Harvey (94) doubts the validity of using E_{PAH} to estimate regional renal blood flow. During the infusion of acetylcholine (250 μg per min) into the renal artery of dogs, renal blood flow rose from 5.5 to 11.8 ml per g kidney per min, while E_{PAH} declined from 0.77 to 0.64. If the nonextracted portion of PAH can be used to estimate medullary blood flow, this flow would have risen during acetylcholine infusion to 14 ml per g medullary tissue per min, an unbelievably high value. Thus, it seems clear that if distribution of renal blood flow can be deduced from E_{PAH} under certain conditions, the conditions still need to be defined.

Little is known about the mechanisms which regulate medullary blood flow independently of cortical blood flow. The widely accepted assumption that all blood perfusing medullary vessels is of postglomerular origin probably needs revision. Ljungqvist (95) studied the anatomical arrangement of vascular poles in different zones of the human kidney by combining stereomicroangiographic and histological techniques. In most of the vascular poles of juxtamedullary glomeruli, the afferent and efferent arterioles were connected directly by a vessel bypassing the glomerular capillaries. Such bypasses were not found in the more superficial glomeruli. Wells, Bond & Guest (96) used mesenteric capillaries of dogs as a model for assessing the influence of osmolality on the renal medullary blood flow. With increasing osmolality of the bathing medium, blood flow velocity was reduced. The authors suggest that the medullary osmolality per se may partly regulate the rate of medullary blood flow.

Yoshitoshi et al. (97) found that E_{PAH} in the rabbit remained relatively constant through a wide range of renal vein pressure. They therefore suggested that alterations in flow through intrarenal arteriovenous shunts are not responsible for the hemodynamic changes which occur at elevated venous pressures. Since the origin of nonextracted PAH remains in doubt, and intrarenal shunt vessels have not been demonstrated anatomically, the use of E_{PAH} to answer this type of question seems hazardous.

Gilmore (98) and Bálint & Châtel (99) again showed that carotid baroreceptors may contribute to the control of renal blood flow. In anesthetized dogs, collapse of the carotid arteries led to vasoconstriction in the innervated kidney, and increased pressure within the carotid arteries led to renal vasodilation. The latter results can be demonstrated only in the presence of neurogenic tonus within the renal vessels. Such tonus, normally absent, is likely introduced by the surgical preparation of the animal. In cross-circulation experiments on dogs anesthetized with chloralose, Matsushita (100) observed that stimulation of the afferent carotid sinus nerve increased renal blood flow. The nature of this reflexly induced decrease in renal resistance remains obscure, since a neurogenic vascular tone prior to the stimulation was thought to be excluded by the ineffectiveness of α-adrenergic blocking agents on renal blood flow. No efferent renal vasomotor fibers could be demonstrated in the vagus nerve.

In contrast to earlier work of others, Leichtweiss, Schröder & Weiss (101) found that autoregulation of renal blood flow could be maintained in an isolated rat kidney perfused with mineral oil. They suggest that saturation of their perfusate with oxygen may account for the difference. On the assumption that oxygenation prevented hypoxic damage to vascular smooth muscles, they concluded that changes in tangential wall tension may play a major role in autoregulation. Takeuchi et al. (102) confirmed the finding of others, that papaverine abolishes autoregulatory resistance changes. They also found that diminution of the arteriovenous pressure difference, induced by raising renal venous pressure, led to a decrease in renal resistance to flow. Their data thus support the view that autoregulation is due to a myogenic reaction brought about by changes in the arteriovenous pressure difference.

Further evidence for a preglomerular localization of autoregulatory resistance changes, and against intrarenal tissue pressure as an important component in autoregulation, has been obtained by Haddy & Scott (103). They assumed that pressure within an occluded, hilar lymphatic vessel approximates tissue pressure. This lymphatic pressure was influenced very little by reduction in renal arterial pressure from 140 to 20 mm Hg, but greatly by elevation of venous pressure. Similar conclusions were drawn by Gärtner (104), who found that both renal interstitial and renal blood volumes in rabbits were independent of the arterial pressure in the range of autoregulation. A possible role of afferent renal nerve activity in the control of intrarenal vasomotor tone is suggested by Åström & Crafoord (105). An increase in afferent discharges in rats during elevated renal venous pressure and saline infusion, and to a lesser extent during mannitol diuresis, led the author to postulate the existence of intrarenal mechanoreceptors. The dependency of autoregulatory resistance changes on initial vascular tone was studied by Zerbst & Brechmann (106) in rabbits. Vascular tone was varied by electrical stimulation of the renal artery. Only the curve obtained at intermediate vascular tone levels showed slight autoregulation. However, the low control flow rates of 1.0–1.8 ml per g kidney per min, without electrical stimulation, suggest an unusually high resistance to flow in this preparation. Furthermore, the authors' conclusion rests in part on the assumption that electrical stimulation of the main renal artery induces uniform changes in the tonus of all intrarenal vessels.

Scott et al. (107), searching for a possible chemical agent responsible for autoregulatory resistance changes, diverted a portion of the renal venous outflow to the brachial artery of the same dog. Reducing the perfusion pressure gradient, either by lowering renal arterial pressure or by increasing renal venous pressure, led not only to the anticipated renal vasodilation, but also to vasodilation in the perfused forelimb. These effects did not depend on oxygen tension or electrolyte and osmolar concentrations in renal venous blood. Nor were they due to acetylcholine or histamine, since dilation in the forelimb occurred also after pretreatment with atropine or diphenhydramine. The authors therefore conclude that whenever the arteriovenous pressure gradient is reduced, there is an increased concentration of a dilating agent, which is probably a product of metabolism. The thesis is based on their assumption that the rate of renal metabolism remains constant over a wide range of blood flow. However, the work done by the kidney is a function of blood flow, since at reduced blood flow and consequently reduced GFR, the tubular Na load and hence tubular Na reabsorption, are reduced.

To test the idea that one of the adenyl compounds might be the metabolic dilating agent, Scott and co-workers injected adenosine, AMP, and ATP into the renal artery. Like others (108, 109), they found that the metabolites of ATP are potent renal vasoconstrictors; only ATP is a dilating agent in the kidney. Since ATP does not readily cross cell membranes and therefore is unlikely to reach the forelimb, the authors propose that ATP regulates intrarenal resistance, while its breakdown products caused the observed vasodilation in the forelimb. Another explanation seems equally plausible, namely, that the intrarenal formation of a vasoconstricting principle is inhibited whenever the perfusing pressure is reduced. This view has been proposed by Thurau (110), who suggests that the function of the juxtaglomerular apparatus with its renin-angiotensin system plays a central part in autoregulatory resistance changes. An intrarenal role for ATP breakdown products as potent renal vasoconstrictors may also follow from results of Ono, Inagaki & Hashimoto (109). They were able to increase renal resistance by the administration of Persantin, a substance which affects the metabolism of adenine nucleotides. Since spontaneous failure of autoregulation can be corrected by Persantin, they argue that such failure may be due to disturbed metabolism of the nucleotide.

Disagreement continues in regard to the effect of acute acid-base changes on renal hemodynamics in anesthetized dogs. While Simmons & Olver (111) report that elevation of Pco_2 decreases renal vascular resistance, and that this effect depends on arterial Pco_2 and not on pH, Bersentes & Simmons (112) found renal resistance to be decreased during moderate respiratory acidosis but to be increased during severe acidosis. Both reactions appeared to depend on both pH and Pco_2, but were independent of sympathetic innervation. The increase in renal resistance which occurs during hemorrhagic hypotension was found to depend on the acid-base status in the prehemorrhagic state (113). This increase could be abolished by the organic buffer THAM, if given during hemorrhagic hypotension.

Attempts to differentiate renal vascular reactions into α- and β-receptor type responses have thus far failed. Although dopamine causes renal vasodilation (114), this effect could not be abolished by β-adrenergic blockade. Schirmeister et al. (115) found that C_{PAH} in human subjects remained unchanged during infusion of β-stimulating agents.

Renal oxygen consumption.—The oxygen cost of Na reabsorption under various circumstances was studied in dogs by Knox, Fleming & Rennie (116). They agree with the finding of several authors in the early sixties and the more recent results of Bálint & Forgács (117) that suprabasal O_2 consumption is correlated with tubular net Na reabsorption. The ratio of 29 eq Na per mole O_2 remained constant in water diuresis, in saline diuresis, and during the action of ethacrynic acid, but decreased to 20 during a combination of mannitol diuresis and elevated ureteral pressure. Since presumably selective inhibition of fractional Na reabsorption in the distal nephron by ethacrynic acid did not reduce the ratio below normal, the authors concluded that the oxygen cost for Na reabsorption is identical in the proximal and distal segments, and that, hence, the lower ratio during mannitol diuresis is unlikely to be due to delivery of more Na to the distal nephron. Rather, the authors consider unidirectional inward net diffusion of Na into the proximal tubule and subsequent reabsorption, possibly from thick ascending limbs of Henle's loops, to cause the lowered ratio. Since the Na which entered the tubular lumen by net diffusion was not part of the filtered load, the reabsorption of the diffused fraction will not contribute to the net Na reabsorption in a clearance calculation. For this reason, the lowered ratio during mannitol infusion is considered to be apparent, not real.

Torelli et al. (118) calculated the energy requirement for Na reabsorption in the rabbit kidney by measuring the renal O_2 consumption and tubular Na reabsorption. Assuming the total energy for Na reabsorption to be that expended in transporting Na across the peritubular membranes, and neglecting entropy possibly gained in the transluminal step, they calculated that 3300 calories are required for the reabsorption of 1 eq of Na. This would indicate an efficiency for Na transport of about 75 per cent, a value similar to that derived from calculations based on renal tissue slices (119). Since the production of lactic acid was negligible, the high value for efficiency cannot be explained through a partial contribution from anaerobic metabolism. Rather, the authors admit that it may be due to neglecting the energy gained in transferring Na across the luminal membrane.

Renal function during hypothermia was studied by Boylan & Hong (120) in dogs at a body temperature of 25°C. Fractional Na excretion during isotonic NaCl diuresis increased from 7 to 23 per cent, despite a concomitant reduction of GFR to 45 per cent of normal. Similar results have been reported by others (121). The aerobic cost of Na reabsorption remained unchanged. An inability to form hypertonic urine during hypothermia could be only slightly corrected (to a U/P_{osm} of 1.2) by giving ADH. A reduction in Tm_{PAH} was proportional to the reduction in GFR. As an explanation for this finding, the authors favor the concept of Deetjen & Sonnenberg (122) that the amount of secreted PAH is a function of intratubular perfusion rate rather than of tubular mass.

Medullary vasodepressor substances.—Much effort continues to be devoted to the subject of renal medullary depressor substances. In an extensive study, Lee et al. (123) have shown that medullin and prostaglandin-E_1 are chemically and physiologically similar but not identical. Medullin is about fifty times less potent in stimulating nonvascular smooth muscles than is prostaglandin-E_1. A second, biologically active vasodepressor lipid from the renal medulla has tentatively been identified as prostaglandin-E_1. This compound 2 of Lee et al. (123) may be the same as a vasodepressor substance isolated by Strong et al. (124) from the renal medulla of rabbits, pigs, beef, and men, which appears to be inseparable from prostaglandin-E_1. A nonsteroidal, neutral lipid of low molecular weight, which lowers arterial pressure of renal hypertensive dogs, was prepared from renomedullary extracts by Muirhead and associates (125, 126). Because of scarcity of the material, it has not yet been possible to determine the chemical structure of this substance. In contrast to the short-acting vasodepressor lipid isolated by Lee et al. (123), this antihypertensive lipid appears to act only against renoprival hypertension.

Since the hypotensive action of medullin depends on its action upon peripheral resistance rather than on cardiac output or contractility, and since these types of vasodepressor compounds are widely distributed throughout many tissues, Lee et al. (123) suggest that they may influence vascular resistance through a local hormone-like action. Whether these substances help to control medullary blood flow, and hence possibly the countercurrent concentrating system, has not been determined. An influence on the concentrating mechanism through a different route is suggested by the finding that prostaglandin-E_1 may inhibit the production of cyclic AMP (127). Because prior injection of prostaglandin-E_1 reduces the pressor response to angiotensin II, Strong et al. (124) investigated but found no effect of their extracted vasodepressor lipid on the metabolism of angiotensin *in vitro*.

The Function of the Juxtaglomerular Apparatus

Although the anatomical arrangement of the juxtaglomerular apparatus (JGA) has been known for decades, its possible physiological significance has become evident only recently. The JGA, which is the subject of continuing ultrastructural exploration (128–132, 506–509), consists of the tubular epithelium at the end of Henle's loop, the macula densa cells, and the renin-containing cells in the afferent arterioles. These two types of specialized cells come into intimate contact. The fact that the two apposing parts always belong to the same nephron led several authors to propose that the JGA embodies a feedback system which coordinates tubular with glomerular function.

Tobian's (133) recent critical review of the literature on this subject makes it appear likely that the JGA plays an important role in the Na balance of the organism. Vander (134) reported evidence against the concept that the granular cells in the afferent arterioles may be stretch receptors. The rise in the renal venous concentration of renin, which can be induced in dogs by infusing catecholamines or by stimulating the renal nerves, could be prevented by simultaneous osmotic diuresis, even though renal arterial pressure was kept constant. The increase in renal venous renin concentration, which normally accompanies a reduction in arterial pressure, can also be inhibited by mercurial diuretics (135). He therefore suggests that some change in the composition of tubular fluid, possibly at the macula densa site, may regulate renin secretion.

Thurau & Schnermann (136) altered the volume, or osmotic or electrolyte concentrations in the macula densa segment of a single rat nephron, and observed that when the Na concentration was increased above 75 meq/liter (normal in this segment is about 20 meq/liter) the proximal convoluted tubule of that nephron quickly collapsed, indicating cessation of filtration. The reaction was less marked when the macula densa segment was perfused with solutions of lower Na concentration. In rats which had been maintained on a low-Na diet, and in whom the renin content of the JGA was therefore high, the reaction could be provoked repeatedly in the same nephron. But when the renin content in the JGA was first reduced by keeping the animals on a high-Na diet, the reaction could be elicited only irregularly. These findings strongly suggest that the renin-angiotensin system participates in the reaction. Since similar results were obtained with NaBr, but not with choline chloride, the response appears to be specific for the Na ion. Changes in osmolality did not initiate the reaction. Although it remains unclear whether the intratubular Na concentration at the macula densa cells or the concentration of Na in the local reabsorbate is the critical variable, the authors have proposed that a Na-sensitive feedback system, which operates through the JGA, adjusts the GFR and thereby the tubular Na load, to the reabsorptive capacity of the nephron for this ion.

Subsequent experiments are consistent with this proposal. Cortney, Nagel & Thurau (137) simulated an increase in the GFR of single nephrons by microperfusing single loops of Henle. They found a direct correlation between the rate of perfusion and the Na concentration in the early distal convolution, which is close to the macula densa segment. Schnermann, Nagel & Thurau (138) reduced tubular reabsorptive capacity for Na by inducing renal ischemia. There was an inverse correlation between the resulting increase in early distal Na concentration and the GFR.

The hypothesis entails two assumptions: that angiotensin is formed in the walls of afferent arterioles, and that preglomerular resistance to blood flow depends in part on the concentration of angiotensin at the site of renin secretion. Since the main purpose of the feedback system might be the adjustment of tubular Na load to the tubular reabsorptive capacity for Na, autoregulation of GFR and RBF, so long considered to have its own *rai-*

son d'être, may be merely a byproduct of a system which conserves Na (110).

Navar, Guyton & Langston (139) have challenged the concept proposed by Thurau & Schnermann (136). They recorded a direct correlation in dogs, between the serum osmolality and the renal blood flow. Since this relationship held whether the serum osmolality was raised by infusion of 6.75 per cent NaCl, hypertonic mannitol, or hypertonic glucose, they proposed that osmotic agents, independently of their structure, exert a feedback effect on the afferent arterioles. They believe that an increase in serum osmolality is reflected by increased osmolality of tubular fluid at the macula densa which, in turn, causes dilation of preglomerular vessels. In addition to the micropuncture studies cited above, several other findings argue against this thesis. During mannitol diuresis, the osmolality of the tubular fluid bathing the macula densa is essentially unchanged, and in hypertonic NaCl diuresis it is even lower than in hydropenic animals. Furthermore, the JGA feedback system may not function effectively after loading an animal with NaCl, as this maneuver depletes the granular cells of renin. The depletion of renin may occur very rapidly, for release of renin by norepinephrine is inhibited by acute infusions of isotonic saline in Na-depleted dogs (140), and flattening of macula densa cells in rats can be observed after only 24 hours of Na deprivation (141).

On the basis of clinical observations in renovascular hypertensive patients, Stamey (142) suggests that a decrease of tubular Na concentration at the macula densa cells might stimulate renin release. This is thought to cause an efferent vasoconstriction which leads to an increase in filtration fraction. Eigler (143) points to the possibility that the juxtaglomerular apparatus might be responsive to changes in TF/P Na at the macula densa cells. According to his theory an increase in TF/P Na stimulates angiotensin formation and preglomerular vasoconstriction. A decrease in TF/P Na is believed to block the preglomerular action of angiotensin, an effect leading to a systemic and possibly to an efferent glomerular action of angiotensin. Both theories depend largely on the interpretation of urinary Na concentration as reflecting the sodium concentration in the tubular fluid at the macula densa cells. However, the two are not necessarily correlated under various physiological conditions.

Leyssac (144, 145) has proposed the existence of an intrarenal mechanism which may preserve glomerular-tubular balance for Na by maintaining a constant pressure within the proximal tubules (see section on proximal glomerulotubular balance). In this theory an increase in arterial pressure initially would lead to an increase in renal blood flow and GFR. The consequent elevation of intratubular pressure would inhibit angiotensin formation through an as yet unknown pathway, and this, in turn, presumably returns intratubular pressure to the control value by increasing the proximal reabsorption of salt and water. With continued elevation of arterial pressure, there would then have to result a further rise in GFR and RBF.

Thus, the proposed system fails to account for autoregulation. The inhibitory action of angiotensin upon proximal reabsorption of salt and water, which Leyssac inferred from a prolongation of the tubular occlusion time after interrupting renal blood flow, could not be confirmed in micropuncture studies. By the split-droplet method, Horster et al. (146) found no effect of angiotensin on the half-time reabsorption of isotonic saline from the proximal convolutions of rats, whether the angiotensin was given intratubularly or peritubularly. Coviello & Crabbé (147) also could not demonstrate an influence of angiotensin II on Na transport by toad bladder or skin.

TUBULAR ELECTROPHYSIOLOGY

Windhager & Giebisch have pointed out in their excellent review (148) that transport potentials calculated with Ussing's work equation may give only minimum values. Flux asymmetry resulting from leakage of the "nonpermeant" solute in stationary microperfusions, as well as hypothetical shunt paths, would lead to underestimation of the true potential. Windhager, Boulpaep & Giebisch (149) have found evidence for such Na shunts in proximal tubules of the *Necturus* kidney. Increasing the osmolality on both sides of the tubule, or increasing the osmotic gradients across the tubular wall, reduced the transtubular PD and the effective transtubular resistance without significantly affecting the PD or the effective resistance across the membrane. Furthermore, when the peritubular concentration of K was raised, transepithelial resistance dropped while transmembrane resistance increased greatly. Cable analysis yielded specific resistances across luminal and peritubular cell boundaries which were more than ten times greater than the specific transtubular resistance of 650 Ωcm². Hence, the authors conclude that there probably are low-resistance shunts between lumen and peritubular space.

A comparable study on electrical properties of rat proximal tubules was performed by Hegel, Frömter & Wick (150). By determining the effective resistance of the tubular wall and the length constant of passive voltage attenuation along the tubule, they calculated a specific membrane resistance from cable analysis of 5 Ωcm². The validity of this value, much lower than that reported in (149) for *Necturus,* is supported by the agreement with a calculation of specific membrane resistance per unit of tubular length, which, based on measurements of unidirectional fluxes for K, Na, and Cl at zero net volume flux (151), was 647 Ωcm, whereas cable analysis yielded a value of 602 Ωcm.

In 1957, S. Solomon first described a transtubular PD of about −20 mV (lumen negative) in the proximal tubules of rats. This finding was confirmed by many investigators, and electrical asymmetry was generally accepted as a basic characteristic of proximal tubular epithelium. The recent, systematic reinvestigation of this phenomenon by Frömter & Hegel (152) has cast serious doubt on the existence of a proximal transepithelial PD.

Their conclusion is based mainly on three lines of evidence. First, the distribution of stable PD's showed a peak at zero mV, steadily declining to -80 mV. The authors argue that the true transtubular PD is zero, and that all other values have a transmembrane origin, the highest being the true transmembrane PD. What seems not satisfactorily explained is why histograms in earlier studies displayed a maximum at -15 to -20 mV rather than random distribution. Second, all measured PD's could be abolished by ejecting fluid from the tip of the electrode, a method originally applied by Giebisch (1958) on *Necturus*. The authors propose that such ejection establishes free contact between electrode tip and tubular fluid, whereas prior to ejection, a partial contact between electrode tip and cells presumably gives rise to partial transmembrane PD's. This thesis was supported by the finding that the amplitude of coupling pulses, subsequent to the intratubular introduction of a square wave current, increased four- to fivefold at the moment when fluid was ejected from the electrode (153). Proper functioning of the electrode within the lumen was further supported by recording stable PD's of $+10$ to $+30$ mV when the tubule was perfused with 800 mM choline chloride. Third, even when the electrode was threaded along the proximal tubule for a distance up to 120 μ, the transtubular PD remained zero. Had the absence of a potential been due to a leak at the puncture site, then this experimental artifact should have been diminished by advancing the electrode tip within the lumen. Frömter & Hegel emphasize that the absence of a transtubular PD does not eliminate the concept of active Na transport out of the proximal tubule, for transport of Na against a chemical concentration gradient can be demonstrated under certain experimental conditions. The active transport potential of Na under conditions of zero net flux and a consequent steady-state intraluminal concentration for Na of 107 meq/liter, would be about 7 mV.

Frömter & Hegel (152) confirmed the existence of a transtubular PD in the distal tubule of about -60 mV. The dependency of this electrical gradient on changes in luminal or peritubular ion composition was investigated by Giebisch et al. (154) in the rat. The normal PD of about -48 mV, which they recorded, apparently results from different membrane properties at the luminal and peritubular cell boundaries. The transtubular PD was greatly reduced by application to the peritubular side of a solution with high K concentration, but was unaffected by application of choline chloride. The peritubular membrane thus appears to be selectively permeable for K ions, and shunting of Na apparently has little influence on the PD across this membrane. When Na was replaced by K in the tubular lumen, or when intratubular Na and K concentrations were changed without changing their sum, the transtubular PD did not change. Obviously, Na and K exert a similar effect on luminal membrane PD. Transtubular PD was abolished by replacing intratubular Na and K by choline chloride. Selectively reducing either intratubular Na or K led to hyperpolarization of the luminal membrane, presumably by reduced shunting in the case of Na, and by promotion of more rapid efflux from the cell in the case of K. The consequent reduction of the transtubular PD is interpreted to reflect a similar permeability of the luminal cell membrane for Na and K. Since intraluminal application of poorly reabsorbable anions, such as sulfate or phosphate, increased the electrical asymmetry, it appears that Cl also contributes to the luminal membrane PD.

Tubular Transport of Strong Electrolytes

An important advance in understanding the molecular basis of active Na and K transport has been the discovery that an ATP hydrolyzing enzyme system, activated by Na and K, is directly involved in the active movement of these ions across biological membranes. In a recent review Skou (15), who first described the so-called (Na + K)-activated ATPase in 1957, has defined the requirements for such a transport system. Katz & Epstein (155) have presented a lucid summary of this topic, with particular reference to transport of electrolytes in the kidney.

Isotonic fluid reabsorption.—It is generally accepted that active Na transport is associated with isotonic fluid reabsorption from the proximal tubules as well as from other epithelial structures. The mechanism by which water follows in isotonic amounts is unclear, since no osmotic gradient across the tubular wall has been demonstrated. Ullrich, Rumrich & Fuchs (156) calculated that across the proximal tubular epithelium an osmotic gradient of 23 mOsm/liter would be needed to accomplish the known net flux of water. Therefore, all proposals dealing with isotonic fluid reabsorption have considered the existence of osmotic gradients within the epithelial structure itself.

Two main concepts are concurrently under discussion, both emphasizing a striking role of the intercellular channels as the site where intraepithelial osmotic gradients are generated and maintained. The principles of the double-membrane model proposed by Curran & MacIntosh (1962) were applied by Whitlock and his co-workers (157, 158) to explain isotonic reabsorption from the gall bladder. This topic has recently been summarized by Dietschy (159). According to this model sodium is transported laterally into the intercellular space. The basal membrane is suggested to act as a diffusion barrier, preventing rapid dissipation of the osmotic gradient and thus inducing osmotic water flux into the intercellular space. Hydrostatic pressure developed in the interspace then drives the fluid across the basal membrane. Diamond (160, 161), on the other hand, proposed a process of local osmosis to account for isotonic fluid movement across gall bladder epithelium. Recently, Diamond & Tormey (162, 163) developed a modified mechanism of local osmosis which they termed the standing-gradient osmotic flow model. This model assumes that active Na transport occurs mainly into the closed end of the intercellular channels. Osmotic water influx along the whole length of the narrow channels renders the fluid isotonic at the basal end of the interspace. Thus, in this model the geometry of the long and narrow channels prevents the NaCl from diffusing away before osmotic equilibrium has been attained. It is consistent with the above concepts that both groups found the intercellular spaces in the gall bladder to be distended during solute-induced water transport and collapsed when such transport was inhibited by various experimental means (158, 162).

Physiological and anatomical evidence has recently demonstrated the existence of intercellular channels in proximal convolutions of the kidney. Windhager, Boulpaep & Giebisch (149) found the sum of the luminal and peritubular cell membrane resistances in proximal tubules of *Necturus* to be considerably higher than the transepithelial resistance, and they therefore postulated the existence of an extracellular shunt conductance. Intercellular spaces, with tight junctions at the apex, have also been described by many workers in proximal tubules of kidneys (6). Ullrich, Rumrich & Fuchs (156) have proposed that the spaces serve the same function in the kidney that the intercellular channels serve in gall bladders. Variations in size of the renal intercellular channels in response to varying transtubular fluxes of water have yet to be demonstrated. It is interesting that Ullrich, Rumrich & Fuchs found hypertonic fluid influx into proximal tubules perfused with isotonic mannitol solutions. This is consistent with the possibility of a passive diffusion of Na from the hypertonic apical portions of the intercellular space into the proximal tubular fluid.

Transport of sodium.—Ullrich and co-workers (164) have further analyzed the Na transport system in renal tubules of rats, using a combination of micropuncture techniques. As measured by the split-droplet technique of Gertz, net Na transport appeared to be 5.6 times greater in the proximal than in the distal convolution. The steady-state Na concentrations during zero net flux were 107 and 37 meq/liter in the proximal and distal convolutions, respectively. Influx of Na into a Na-free solution was 2.4 times greater in the proximal than in the distal convolution. These significant differences in proximal and distal Na handling were interpreted by use of Linderholm's (1960) electrical analog of NaCl transport, originally applied to frog skin. Within the context of this model, proximal tubular epithelium can be described as having a low resistance for passive ion flux, which leads to large Na influx and a high equilibrium concentration for this ion. Net Na efflux is relatively large, since low membrane resistance facilitates passive diffusion of Cl. As a result of a higher resistance to passive NaCl flux within the distal tubular membrane, both the influx of NaCl and the Na concentration at zero net flux are lower than in the proximal tubule. Sodium efflux is lower in this segment, because passive movement of Cl has to proceed against a greater membrane resistance.

Ullrich (165) has recently estimated the reflection coefficient σ for NaCl by determining the osmolalities of raffinose and NaCl solutions at which the flux of water becomes zero. This determination was accomplished with the microperfusion technique as designed by Sonnenberg & Deetjen (166). Assuming that σ for raffinose equals 1.0, σ for NaCl was calculated to be 0.68 in the proximal tubule of the rat, and 0.52 in the distal tubule. These values suggest that a portion of the NaCl is passively reabsorbed through solvent drag. An even greater influence of solvent drag on NaCl reabsorption in the proximal tubule was suggested by the lower value for σ of 0.36–0.42, reported in preliminary form by Rector et al. (167).

Some biochemical characteristics of active Na transport in proximal tubules of rats have been studied by the split-droplet method. Chertok, Hulet & Epstein (168) described significant reductions in isotonic volume reabsorption when the metabolic inhibitors, amytal, cyanide, or DNP, were introduced into the tubular lumen. S. Solomon & Vanatta (169) found similar reductions following the intratubular injection of solutions containing phospholipase C or pancreatic lipase. Both enzymes reduced the ability of renal homogenates *in vitro* to bind Na and K, while phospholipase D and ribonuclease enhanced cation binding. One of several possible interpretations of these findings is that interaction between the reabsorbed molecule and membrane phospholipids may play a role in the active transport of these ions.

Using stopped-flow microperfusion in distal tubules of *Necturus,* Maude, Shehadeh & Solomon (170) found a steady-state Na concentration of about 31 mM/liter, independent of the initial Na concentration in the perfusate which ranged from 100 to 20 mM/liter. When the perfusate was made isotonic to plasma by adding sucrose, the steady-state Na concentration was decreased to 9 mM/liter, which suggests that the higher value of 31 mM was not caused by limitation of the Na pump. Furthermore, net Na efflux did not fall to zero until Na concentration in the perfusate was reduced to 20 mM/liter. The authors therefore postulate that lowering the osmolality of tubular fluid may enhance the permeability for Na and hence the back-diffusion of this ion and that this phenomenon, rather than limitation of the Na pump, determines the steady-state concentration. Net efflux of Na against an electrochemical gradient requires a sodium pump, probably at the peritubular surface.

Gottschalk, Morel & Mylle (45) devised a microinjection method, based on the indicator-dilution technique of Chinard, for studying tubular permeabilities for Na and other substances in rats. Total urinary recovery of [22]Na when injected into a proximal tubule was 28 per cent in saline diuresis and 7 per cent in mannitol diuresis; when injected into a distal tubule, total recovery averaged 56 per cent in saline and 64 per cent in mannitol diuresis. The time-course for the urinary excretion of [22]Na was similar to that of simultaneously injected inulin. The data suggest that Na does not exchange rapidly with an extratubular pool in the diuretic state and that the distal tubules and collecting ducts have relatively low diffusion permeabilities for Na. DeRouffignac & Morel (171) used the same method to infer Na permeabilities in loops of Henle and proximal convolutions. When very small volumes containing [22]Na were injected into late proximal segments, a mean of only 6.8 per cent of the radiosodium was recovered in the urine, the excretion of the tracer Na preceding that of inulin. The same fraction of ^{22}Na was recovered when the microinjected volume was immobilized within the loop. These results show a high diffusion permeability of some part of the short loops of Henle in rat kidneys.

Similar conclusions were reached also for the long thin loops of golden hamsters (172). For the proximal convolution, 35 per cent of the total unidirectional Na efflux was calculated to be passive (171, 173). This value is much lower than the 70 to 80 per cent determined with the split-droplet technique and from microperfusions with solutions at equilibrium concentrations of Na (151, 165). The diffusion permeabilities of the proximal and distal epithelia for NaCl have been reported by Ullrich (165) to be 89×10^{-4} and 45.5×10^{-4} mm/sec, respectively. The proximal diffusion permeability of the Na ion was found to be 28×10^{-4} mm/sec and of the Cl ion 39.2×10^{-4} mm/sec. Applying to his data the equations of Kedem & Leaf (174) who have defined the relation between the transport coefficients of a salt and its individual ions, Ullrich concluded that a considerable interaction exists between Na and Cl ion movements in the proximal tubule.

Startling results on the degree of intracellular Na binding have been reported by Cope (175). The nuclear magnetic resonance spectrum of Na in fresh tissues (frog and rat muscle, rabbit kidney and brain) was compared with that in washed samples. The author concluded that in all tissues tested about 60–70 per cent of the intracellular Na is present in a complexed state and, as he puts it, "If a major fraction of intracellular Na exists in a complexed state, then major revisions in most theoretical treatments of equilibria, diffusion, and transport of cellular Na become appropriate."

Whittembury (176) studied the extrusion of Na and the uptake of K in renal cortical slices of guinea pigs. The slices had lost K and gained Na by immersion in chilled solutions (0°–3°C), containing 150 mM Na and 0 mM K. During reimmersion in warmer solutions with varying Na and K concentrations, Na was extruded actively from the cell interior, but only if K was in the medium. K influx was passive at bath concentrations higher than 8 mM. At lower K concentrations, K uptake was active, proceeding against an electrochemical gradient. The ratio of Na outflux to K influx was variable, disproving rigid coupling of Na and K movements. Na and K concentrations in fresh tissues were 35 and 156 meq/liter, respectively. Using the potential measurements of Whittembury (176), Smyth (177) calculated the energy requirement for Na extrusion. The "critical energy barrier" at which no further net Na loss from sodium-rich rat or guinea pig kidney slices could be achieved ranged from 1.4 to 1.78 cal/meq, values in good agreement with those of Whittembury (176).

Burg & Orloff (178) found that active cation transport in suspended rabbit tubules can maintain transcellular electrolyte gradients at 0°C, although at a reduced level. This is consistent with Robinson's (179) finding in rat kidney slices that oxygen consumption at 0°C still amounts to 25 per cent of that at 20°C. An unusually high ability to transport ions at low temperature has been demonstrated by Willis (180) in hibernating mammals. K-depleted kidney slices of hamsters and ground squirrels, in contrast to nonhibernators, accumulated K even at 0°C. At 5°C, the body temperature of hibernating mammals, the cells restituted and maintained normal steady-state electrolyte concentrations. Kleinzeller, Nedvidkova & Knotkova (181) showed that increasing the external osmotic pressure at constant Na and K concentrations reduced the Na-pump activity and enhanced the K-pump rate in rabbit kidney cortex slices.

Bojesen & Leyssac (119) suggest, from evaluation of ^{22}Na efflux kinetics of rat or rabbit kidney slices, that the major part of Na in cortical slices is in diffusion equilibrium with the bathing medium; quantitative analysis (182) revealed that 15–20 per cent of the exchangeable Na is not in equilibrium with the medium. Calculated flux rate was ten to a hundred times greater than in striated muscles. The intracellular Na and K concentrations of the functioning cells were calculated (119) to be 4–15 and 125–135 meq/liter, respectively.

In 1964, Burg, Grollman & Orloff showed that Na and K in suspensions of rabbit tubules are each contained in at least two compartments. Recently, Burg & Orloff (183) studied the effect of changing medium K concentration on tubular Na and K content and on Na and K fluxes in isolated rabbit tubules. Increasing medium K concentration induced an increase in the size of both K compartments without altering the relative magnitudes of the Na compartments. This is further evidence against a rigid coupling between K and Na exchange. On the other hand, reduction of external K concentration reduced the efflux rate constant of Na and increased tissue Na concentration, an effect indicating reduced active Na outward transport. The authors suggest that K may influence the energy source for active transport by affecting an ATP-hydrolyzing enzyme system. It is noteworthy that reducing the temperature from 37 to 15°C had no effect on tissue electrolyte and water content, although both Na and K fluxes were reduced. Burg & Abramov (184) concluded, on the basis of kinetic exchange analysis of different isolated tubular segments, that the two K pools in the renal tissues of rabbits consist of a slow compartment in proximal and collecting tubules, and a fast compartment in the thick ascending limb of Henle's loop. In contrast, the two compartments for Na appeared to reside in single proximal cells. It is not yet clear whether more than one compartment for Na exists in other segments of the nephron also. Wiggins found (185), in cortical kidney slices of rats, that the initial Na efflux from the intracellular compartment proceeded about ten times faster than the initial K efflux from the slower intracellular K compartment. After replenishing the cells with Na and K, both cations were lost at about the rate of initial Na efflux. While Na and K efflux seem to be controlled by the same barrier after replenishment, the initial, slower K loss suggests that K must either have been in a different state or enclosed by a less permeable membrane.

Proximal glomerulotubular balance.—The thesis that fractional fluid reabsorption along the proximal convolution is constant, so-called glomeru-lotubular balance, has been investigated by several laboratories. Gertz et al. (186) found in normally hydrated, nondiuretic rats that the reabsorptive half-time for isotonic saline reabsorption measured by the split-droplet tech-nique remained constant despite spontaneous differences in tubular size. Reabsorptive rate and the square of the tubular radius, i.e. tubular volume, correlated with each other. The consequent concept, that under free-flow conditions glomerulotubular balance might be maintained by changes in tu-bular volume, could not be confirmed experimentally. Rather, as GFR was altered by aortic constriction, there was an inverse correlation between GFR and the fractional reabsorption of Na and water (measured as TF/P inulin). Similar results were obtained by Landwehr et al. (187).

Rector, Brunner & Seldin (188, 189) worked with diuretic rats which had undergone unilateral nephrectomy one to three weeks prior to the ex-periment, to permit accurate determination of inulin clearance. They sub-stantiated the findings of Gertz et al. (186) that the reabsorptive half-time, as measured by the split-droplet technique, was constant, whether tubular radius was decreased by aortic constriction or increased by elevating ure-teral pressure (189). Unlike Gertz et al. (186), however, this group found constant proximal transit times and constant fractional reabsorption when GFR was reduced (188). They concluded that glomerulotubular balance was maintained by a mechanism which changes tubular volume and, thus, reabsorptive capacity in proportion to the change in GFR. This conclusion was supported by Steinhausen, Loreth & Olson (190) who showed that the diameter of proximal tubules in cats varied in proportion to changes in GFR, and that GFR could be reduced by about 50 per cent without altering proximal transit time. Further evidence for proximal glomerulotubular bal-ance in the rat was reported by Glabman, Aynedjian & Bank (191), who found constancy of the TF/P inulin at the end of the proximal tubule when GFR was reduced by partial aortic clamping. Because the control GFR's in this study were unusually low, however, the reductions in GFR averaged only 1 ml per min per kg body weight. In the dog, constancy of proximal TF/P inulin following reduction of GFR was found by Watson (192) and by Dirks, Cirksena & Berliner (193, 194) during hydropenia and saline diuresis.

Leyssac (144) favors a different mechanism for glomerulotubular bal-ance, in which primary changes in proximal tubular reabsorption of Na lead to secondary changes in GFR. By the occlusion technique, he observed that angiotensin inhibited Na reabsorption in the proximal tubule (195). It is proposed that whenever Na transport capacity is reduced by increased angiotensin concentration, the transient rise in proximal intratubular pres-sure secondarily reduces GFR. Thus, the mechanism which balances tubu-lar reabsorption with GFR is a constant intratubular pressure. Two points have been cited in support of this theory: that neither proximal tubular pressure, nor tubular volume as inferred from sections of snap-frozen kidneys, changed significantly when GFR was reduced by partial clamping of the renal artery (195, 196) ; and that reduction of GFR did not significantly alter proximal tubular diameters measured photographically 20 to 30 min after tightening the arterial clamp (197).

A different method for determining tubular diameters consists of intravital fixation by either arterial or tubular perfusion with osmium tetroxide or glutaraldehyde (198–200).

Volume expansion and sodium excretion.—The demonstration by de Wardener and his associates in 1961, that isotonic saline infusion in dogs can lead to increased urinary Na excretion despite falls in GFR, has stimulated a great deal of work which has attempted to dissect the influences of GFR, of expansion of blood volume or extracellular space, and of saline per se on the tubular transport of Na. The original observation that the mechanism by which saline infusion increased Na excretion did not involve endogenous mineralocorticoids or ADH has been confirmed by numerous workers (192, 194, 201–204). Lindheimer, Lalone & Levinsky (205) have shown that the increase in Na excretion which follows infusion of isotonic saline in dogs far exceeds that following comparable increases in GFR, unaccompanied by extracellular volume expansion, which were induced by protein feeding, administration of dopamine or dexamethasone, or cross-circulation. These results and others (201, 206) show that increased urinary Na excretion during infusion of isotonic saline is independent of the filtered load of Na. Hence, the mechanism of saline diuresis must involve decreased reabsorption of Na.

Kessler, Nelson & Rosano (207) induced increases in Na excretion in humans, by administering 500 ml isotonic saline or 5 per cent albumin in saline, but not albumin alone. The authors suggest that a small expansion of plasma volume is sufficient to increase Na excretion, if interstitial volume or plasma Na concentration does not decrease. Consistent with the above are experiments of Gann & Wright (208) who showed in dogs treated with 9-α-fluorocortisol that a decrease in extracellular or intravascular volume by hemorrhage or peritoneal dialysis leads to a decreased urinary Na excretion independent of changes in GFR.

Three groups (203, 204, 209) have shown independently, through micropunctures in rats infused with isotonic saline, that proximal reabsorption of Na does not keep pace with the increase in the filtered load of this ion. In fact, the absolute quantity of reabsorbed Na may decrease by as much as 30 per cent. In contrast, Na reabsorption in the loops of Henle increased, although not sufficiently to compensate for its diminution in the proximal convolutions (203, 209). Essentially similar findings were obtained through micropunctures in dogs (192, 194) : the decrease in fractional reabsorption persisted even when a rise in GFR was prevented by aortic clamping. That the suppression of proximal Na reabsorption was independent of changes in GFR was further proven by Rector et al. (204) and Landwehr, Klose & Giebisch (209) in the rat. By use of the split-droplet technique, they demonstrated that saline infusion reduced the intrinsic reabsorptive capacity by about 30 per cent. Rector et al. (204) also recorded a 26 per cent reduction in tubular volume per unit GFR, which led to increased tubular flow velocity. They suggest that, in addition to the reduction of intrinsic reabsorptive capacity, failure of the tubules to alter their diameter in proportion to GFR partly contributes to decreased fractional reabsorption.

The results are not so clear cut during infusion of hypertonic, rather than isotonic, saline. Cortney et al. (203) confirmed the finding that fractional reabsorption in the proximal tubule of the rat remained constant during hypertonic NaCl infusion. Malnic, Vieira & Enokibara (210), on the other hand, recorded a decrease in fractional reabsorption. In the dog, Dirks, Cirksena & Berliner (194) found the reduction in fractional reabsorption to be even greater after hypertonic than after isotonic saline infusion. Kamm & Levinsky (211) concluded that hypernatremia inhibits tubular Na absorption independently of volume expansion. In their experiments in dogs, the infusion of hypertonic saline into a femoral artery-to-renal arterial shunt led to increased Na excretion from the experimental kidney even though its filtered load of Na was reduced below that of the contralateral control kidney.

The original suggestion of de Wardener and his associates (1961), that a humoral factor might cause the reduced intrinsic reabsorptive capacity during infusion of isotonic saline, has been supported by further cross-circulation and perfusion experiments (212–215). Johnston & Davis (213) showed that the recipient animal excreted more Na even though its filtered load of Na was decreased by aortic constriction. However, an increase in Na excretion also occurred in recipient dogs when the donor animal did not receive saline. Furthermore, McDonald, Schrier & Lauler (216) found no significant increase in Na excretion of recipients, even though such increase was found in the donor animals when they were infused with isotonic Ringer's solution. Efforts to isolate diuretic or natriuretic factor(s) from human urine (217–220) continue.

In order to achieve a pure expansion of blood volume in dogs Bahlmann et al. (221) transfused blood, which had been previously equilibrated in the same dog, by cross-circulation or exchange circulation. Renal blood flow, GFR, and Na excretion increased immediately. Natriuresis also occurred in experiments in which the kidney was surgically denervated five to eight days prior to the experiments, although the response was much less. No data are given on the completeness of renal denervation. The authors point out that the rise in Na excretion never occurred without a rise in either arterial pressure or PAH clearance. They conclude that the increase in sodium excretion is due in part to a change in the concentration of some substance which tends to alter renal blood flow. This would mean that the decrease in systemic peripheral resistance, a well known phenomenon after blood volume expansion, is controlled in the kidney by a specific substance. A similar study in dogs by the same authors (222) indicates that reducing hematocrit without changing the blood volume does not lead to a systematic increase in Na excretion.

Earley (223) and McDonald & de Wardener (215) concluded from their experiments that reduction in the concentration of plasma proteins also cannot fully account for the increase in Na excretion during saline diuresis. On the other hand, Vereerstraeten and co-workers (224, 225) showed in dogs and cocks that increasing the concentration of serum albumin reduced the urinary excretion of Na. Although GFR generally decreased, this result suggests to the authors that a minor fraction of the filtered Na is reabsorbed by a passive mechanism depending on the oncotic gradient across the tubular epithelium.

Cort et al. (226) demonstrated that certain analogs of oxytocin completely and reversibly inhibited the saliuresis, but not the rise in arterial pressure or GFR, which follows short periods of bilateral carotid occlusion in cats. In the belief that the saliuresis after carotid occlusion and that following volume expansion by isotonic saline may be effected through the same mechanism, the authors suggest that the saliuretic hormone which is presumed to be elaborated during these maneuvers is chemically related to, but not identical with, oxytocin. Evidence that a hormone related to the reduction of Na reabsorption during salt loading may be produced intracranially is provided by experiments of Lockett (227) in an isolated cat kidney preparation. The natriuretic response to saline injections, when these kidneys were perfused with blood from intact donor animals, was completely abolished when the blood was taken from functionally decapitated donors. Andersson, Jobin & Olsson (228) reported that injections of 0.1 ml of 0.85 M NaCl into the third ventricle of unanesthetized goats produced a marked increase in urine flow and Na excretion.

Most experiments to date thus seem compatible with the view that the infusion of isotonic saline, by increasing extracellular or blood volume, causes the elaboration of some humoral agent which decreases the intrinsic reabsorptive capacity of proximal tubules. Earley, Martino & Friedler (202, 229, 230) have championed an alternate, or at least additional, mechanism. Following acetylcholine infusion in dogs, they observed an increase in renal plasma flow and in Na excretion without a significant change in GFR. This result, which also had been found by Pinter, O'Morchoe & Sikand (231), and the finding that Na excretion could be further enhanced by an increase in blood pressure during acetylcholine-induced vasodilation suggested to the authors that renal blood flow and perfusion pressure are involved in regulating Na excretion. They have proposed that the increased renal perfusion pressure which accompanies saline infusions is transmitted along the intrarenal circulation. The increased renal interstitial pressure may, in turn, depress proximal tubular reabsorption, possibly by decreasing tubular volume. A diminution of tubular volume per unit GFR was found by Rector et al. (204) to accompany infusion of isotonic saline in rats.

Reinhardt & Behrenbeck (232, 233) studied the dependency of urinary Na excretion upon extracellular volume (ECV) in unanesthetized dogs following a sudden change in dietary Na uptake. The pattern of urinary Na excretion was critically dependent upon the level of ECV prior to the salt load. Na excretion was delayed when the ECV was 16 per cent of body weight whereas saliuresis instantaneously followed dietary Na uptake when ECV was at its maximum of 22 per cent of body weight. A postprandial increase in GFR, renal blood flow, and ECV occurred in both groups of animals.

An action of some undefined substance on tubular Na reabsorption was also described by Levinsky & Lalone (234) in a different experimental protocol. Chronic constriction of the thoracic vena cava of dogs nearly abolished the natriuretic effect of an infusion of isotonic saline. Retention of Na, independent of the action of mineralocorticoids, occurred despite an increase in GFR. Acute thoracic caval constriction or chronic constriction of the abdominal vena cava did not lead to Na retention following saline infusion. The authors suggest that chronic congestion of the liver or of some other organ in the portal circulation either results in the formation of a Na-retaining substance or prevents the release of a natriuretic factor. Similar results were obtained by Cirksena, Dirks & Berliner (235) in micropuncture experiments on dogs. Fractional reabsorption of Na in proximal tubules was increased even during acute constriction of the thoracic vena cava and saline infusion. The effect was also independent of changes in GFR, of renal venous pressure, and of plasma concentrations of aldosterone and ADH. The "normal" Na-rejecting effect of saline infusions could be demonstrated if the abdominal vena cava was ligated. A possible clinical counterpart of these experimental models was reported by Heinemann & Laragh (236). In one patient, neoplastic obstruction of the thoracic vena cava led to progressive renal Na retention and edema which was not due to increased aldosterone secretion, whereas in a second patient a similar clinical picture arising from obstruction of the abdominal vena cava was associated with hypersecretion of aldosterone.

Potassium.—A number of laboratories have contributed to clarification of the renal handling of potassium. Malnic, Klose & Giebisch (237, 238) studied the problem in rats, through stationary microperfusion as well as during free flow under widely varying states of Na and K balance. Fractional urinary K excretion varied from 4 per cent in animals pretreated with a low-Na or low-K diet, to 151 per cent in rats maintained on a high-K diet and loaded with Na_2SO_4. Despite these variations in excretion of K, its fractional reabsorption along the proximal convolutions and loops of Henle stayed between 90 and 95 per cent. Only during mannitol diuresis was the fractional reabsorption of K diminished. Reabsorption from the proximal tubule appears to be an active process, with the pump probably being located at the luminal membrane. Khuri, Flanigan & Oken (239), using K-sensitive glass microelectrodes, reached similar conclusions for the proximal tubules of rats, but not of *Necturus*. Watson (240) also found remarkable constancy of fractional K reabsorption in the proximal tubule of dogs, despite widely varying excretory rates for this ion. In rats and dogs, therefore, changes in the urinary excretion of K appear to be mediated primarily by varying secretory rates in the distal nephron.

In rats, distal tubular secretion of K appears to be a passive process, which always occurs down an electrochemical potential gradient (237, 238). Increasing the negativity within the tubular lumen through infusions of Na_2SO_4 and NaCl raised the excretion of K, while decreasing the transtubular PD by infusing choline chloride during stationary microperfusion lowered the TF/P for K below unity. The finding that normally, and even after Na depletion, net Na reabsorption in the distal tubule greatly exceeded K secretion, speaks against a one-to-one ion exchange mechanism. Neither the delivery of Na to the distal tubule, nor the intratubular Na concentration at this site appeared to limit the rate of K secretion. Since in both free-flow and stationary microperfusion, distal tubular K concentrations were found to be lower than those calculated for passive distribution, it was postulated that active reabsorption of K prevents attainment of electrochemical equilibrium in this segment. Solvent drag seems to have little influence on this reabsorptive component, for distal TF/P's for K were similar during free-flow and stationary microperfusion. Maude, Shehadeh & Solomon (170) reached similar conclusions for the distal tubules of *Necturus*. De Rouffignac & Guinnebault (241) have shown, in rats, that K within distal tubular cells appears to be the source of the secreted K. Urinary excretion patterns for inulin and ^{42}K, following their simultaneous injection into proximal or distal tubules, or into cortical peritubular capillaries, indicate passage of excreted ^{42}K through a cellular compartment and a high permeability of tubular cells for K. The turnover rate of the cellular compartment was estimated to be about 30 per cent per minute.

Transport of K in collecting ducts of rats seems to be similar to that in distal tubules (237, 238). Net K secretion in the ducts, which occurs normally, may also be influenced primarily by the transtubular potential difference. Such influence is indicated by the net K reabsorption which occurs along the collecting ducts in animals maintained on a low-Na or low-K diet, under which conditions the transtubular PD may be reduced.

Univalent anions.—Using the stopped-flow microperfusion technique, Kashgarian, Warren & Levitin (242) studied the movement of Cl in the proximal tubule of rats. On the basis of transtubular PD's and TF/P for Cl at zero net volume flux, they concluded that this anion is not distributed in an electrochemical equilibrium, and they therefore postulated an active pump which secretes Cl into the lumen. However, such a pump would not need to be postulated if the transtubular PD is in fact zero, as has been claimed by Frömter & Hegel (152). In stop-flow studies in dogs, Schafer,

Vander & Brubacher (243) found no significant differences among the maximum transtubular concentration gradients (stop-flow minimum) for SCN, Cl, or Br. Arguing that it is highly unlikely that either a single active pump or three individual pumps would establish the same concentration ratios for all three ions, they concluded that these ions are transported passively in the distal tubule of dogs. With the assumption that the stop-flow minimum represents a true steady-state concentration at zero net flux, application of the Nernst equation permitted an estimate of the distal transtubular PD which was −60.2 mV in control experiments, and −102.5 mV after NaCl depletion and infusion of Na_2SO_4. These values may be compared with those measured directly in rats, which were −50.2 mV in the control state and −81.2 mV during NaCl depletion plus Na_2CO_4 infusion (238).

In an extensive series of experiments in dogs, Walser & Rahill (244–246) have tested the theoretical prediction that if two substances are reabsorbed passively in the same portions of the nephron, there should be a power-function relationship between their excretion fractions (247). Such a relationship could be established between Cl on the one hand, and Br, F, and I on the other, under a wide variety of experimental conditions. At extremely low urinary Cl concentrations, however, U/P for F was rarely less than unity. The authors believe, therefore, that F, unlike the other halides tested, is not actively transported out of the distal nephron.

A power-function relationship between the excretion fractions of chloride and those of nitrate, thiocyanate, and perchlorate (248) is consistent with the possibility that these anions are also passively and coextensively reabsorbed in the same portions of the nephron. Active distal processes may modify the results at low clearances.

Multivalent ions.—Several similarities between the transport characteristics of Ca and Na in the proximal tubule of the rat suggest that these ions may be carried by the same or similar mechanisms. Frick et al. (249) found the equilibrium TF/P for Ca at zero net flux of this ion to be 0.78, compared to a value of 0.76 for Na. The calculated active pump potential for Ca was 3.3 mV when no transtubular PD was assumed. The ratio of the net isotonic effluxes of Na and Ca, and the ratio of Na and Ca influxes into perfusion solutions which were free of the ions, were about the same as the ratios of the concentrations of Na and Ca in tubular fluid and plasma, respectively. Inhibition of Na transport by Ca was suggested by Gutman & Gottschalk (250). Total transtubular efflux of ^{22}Na microinjected into the proximal tubule was 18 per cent less when applied in the presence of 20 meq/liter $CaCl_2$. Efflux of ^{22}Na at elevated Ca concentrations was also reduced following distal microinjections. An interdependence between Na and Ca excretion follows from the clearance studies of Better et al. (251). Calcium and magnesium may also share a common pathway for renal transport (252). However, the finding of Kupfer & Kosovsky (253) that the injection of cardiac glycosides into one renal artery of dogs caused a relatively greater increase in the clearances of Ca and Mg than of Na, suggests the existence of some mechanism of Ca and Mg reabsorption which is not shared by Na. In dogs, U/P ratios for beryllium, barium, and radium less than 0.5 suggested to Rahill & Walser (254) that these alkaline earths may be actively reabsorbed. Correlation of the clearances of Ba and Ra with that of Ca pointed to a common transport mechanism.

Clearance and stop-flow experiments in dogs (255) have shown that arsenate appears to be reabsorbed mainly in the proximal tubule, and that arsenite derived from the intracellular conversion of arsenate diffuses across both luminal and peritubular membranes.

Strickler et al. (256) and Carone (257) showed by micropuncture experiments in rats that 75–80 per cent of filtered phosphate is reabsorbed along the proximal convolution, probably by an active mechanism, and that little additional reabsorption occurs in later segments of the nephron. At elevated plasma P levels only 22 per cent of the filtered P was reabsorbed proximally, which indicates limited reabsorptive capacity for P (256). Hellman, Baird & Bartter (258) demonstrated in dogs that the renal phosphate Tm varied considerably at a given filtered load. Since part of this variation could be ascribed to a relationship between GFR and Tm, the authors suggest that renal phosphate transport cannot be ascribed to a simple Tm mechanism. During high oral P intake, renal phosphate reabsorption was found to be reduced, possibly by action of endogenous parathyroid hormone (259). The effect of this hormone on renal phosphate handling was studied in thyroparathyroidectomized dogs (260–262). Clearance and stop-flow techniques indicated that the phosphaturic effect of parathyroid hormone is due to inhibition of phosphate reabsorption in the proximal tubule. No net secretion of P at any site of the nephron could be found in micropuncture experiments in rats (256, 257). Using a modified stop-flow technique, Lambert and co-workers (260) and Samiy, Hirsch & Ramsay (262) found no evidence for secretion of ^{32}P into the tubular lumen in dogs, while Davis, Kedes & Field (263) demonstrated such a secretory movement of ^{32}P into the distal convolution in six out of eight dogs. In chickens, net secretion of P has been observed following administration of parathyroid extract (264).

TUBULAR TRANSPORT OF ORGANIC COMPOUNDS

Glucose.—Dependency of glucose transport upon intratubular Na concentration has been demonstrated. In stopped-flow microperfusion studies on *Necturus,* Khuri et al. (265) found that the rate constant for glucose transport increased when the intratubular NaCl concentration was raised from 0 to 25 mM or higher. This effect could not be elicited when lithium or choline chloride was substituted for NaCl, or when the tubule was perfused with Na-free mannitol solution. Since the transport of a nonmetabolizable sugar was also influenced by the intratubular Na concentration, the mechanism apparently does not involve the metabolism of the transported sugar. Similar findings were reported in the frog by Vogel et al. in a number of papers (266, 267); they found, furthermore, that the inhibition of Na transport by diuretics or poorly reabsorbable anions also reduced glucose transport. Perfusing the kidney with K-free solutions reduced the transport of both Na and glucose, a fact suggesting to the authors that (Na + K)-activated ATPase may be involved in this phenomenon.

Diedrich (268) attempted to quantify the carrier for glucose in dog kidney by measuring the effect of varying doses of phlorizin-^{14}C on glucose Tm. The amount of phlorizin in the kidney was assayed when Tm for glucose was maximally depressed, and calculations involved the assumptions that one molecule of phlorizin interacted with one molecule of carrier, and that all phlorizin which was measured was bound to carrier. The following values were derived: 0.68 μmoles of carrier per 100 g of dog kidney; a minimum turnover rate of 1390 μmoles glucose per μmole carrier per minute; a diffusion coefficient for glucose-carrier complex across luminal membrane of about 4.2×10^{-12} cm^2/sec. The last value implies that passage through the membrane is about 50,000 times slower than through the rest of the cell.

Bailey & Pentchev (269) examined the possibility that rat intestinal and renal mutarotase may be the hypothetical carrier for sugar transport. Sugars which are actively transported showed strong interaction with the enzyme, as reflected by inhibition of enzyme-catalyzed mutarotation of α-D-glucose. Hexoses which are not actively transported showed only slight interaction. However, L-arabinose, which is not actively transported, also reacted strongly with the enzyme, as did two sugars which cannot undergo mutarotation. Thus, the role of mutarotase in sugar transport remains unclear.

Halver (270) concluded that parathyroid hormone enhances the renal transport of glucose, for he demonstrated an elevated Tm$_G$ in hyperthyroid patients, and the reverse effect in patients with hypoparathyroidism.

Van Liew, Deetjen & Boylan (271) have challenged the classical concept of a Tm for glucose. Over a range of plasma glucose concentrations from about 2 to 29 mg per ml in rats, they found glucose reabsorption to vary directly with spontaneous variations of GFR. No maximal reabsorptive plateau could be detected, even when glucose was spilled in the urine. Only when the reabsorptive rate was factored by GFR could a classical titration-curve be obtained. The authors therefore suggest that a maximal transport for glucose may not exist, and that this concept arose from the habit of expressing the data per unit of GFR or of Tm. The authors concede, however, that at very high GFR's—higher than those found in their rats—a true maximal transport rate probably exists.

Urea.—The idea that urea can be transported actively in the mammalian kidney, long championed by Bodil Schmidt-Nielsen, has now received support from many quarters.

Clapp (272) found, in protein-depleted rats undergoing mannitol diuresis, that the TF/P for urea decreased from 6.5 ± 1.7 in superficial distal convolutions to 5.2 ± 0.9 in the final urine, at the same time that TF/P in-ulin rose. However, this decrease was significant in only two of the four trials. In separate experiments, he found the concentration of urea in medullary tissue water to exceed that in the urine. This confirmed the tis-sue analyses of Truniger & B. Schmidt-Nielsen (273) who found the medullary concentrations in protein-depleted rats to be up to three times the urinary urea concentrations. They presented convincing arguments that the higher tissue value was probably not due to synthesis of urea or to pro-tein binding of this substance in the extratubular structures of the medulla. Dialysis of medullary tissues also failed to uncover any evidence of protein binding (274). Further support was presented by Lassiter, Mylle & Gott-schalk (275). Working with young, protein-depleted rats, they found the urea concentration to be 10 per cent higher in vasa recta blood than in col-lecting duct fluid at the same level of the papilla. Like those of others, their calculations, based on TF/P urea and U/P urea, also suggest that ac-tive reabsorption of urea probably occurred somewhere between the distal tubules at the surface of the kidney, and the end of the collecting ducts.

That the site of active transport in rodents may be the collecting ducts is suggested by the more direct approaches of Ullrich, Rumrich & B. Schmidt-Nielsen (276). Having filled a collecting duct with oil, they split the oil for distances of about 1 mm by instilling a $0.45\ M$ solution of man-nitol. After 3–4 min, when a steady state with zero net water flux had been reached, the stopped-flow perfusion sample was withdrawn, and its urea concentration compared to that in a sample obtained from a de-scending limb of an adjacent vas rectum. Whereas no significant differences between the two concentrations could be found in normal rats, in protein-depleted rats the urea concentration in the collecting-duct sam-ples averaged 84 per cent of that in the vasa recta. This difference is similar to that found by Lassiter, Mylle & Gottschalk (275) under free-flow conditions, although Ullrich, Rumrich & B. Schmidt-Nielsen (276) de-tected the gradient only during stopped flow. Whether, in fact, a concentra-tion gradient exists depends critically on the correct location of the refer-ence point, namely, the site of puncture in the descending vasa recta. Since this location is not known, further evidence for active transport was sought (276) by measuring unidirectional outfluxes of urea from collecting ducts. This outflux was 73 per cent greater in protein-depleted than in normal rats. Although this increase might have resulted from enhanced permeabili-ty for urea, in view of their stopped-flow perfusion experiments cited above the authors think it was due to active transport.

The conclusions based on data obtained in rodents have been supported by the studies of Goldberg, Wojtczak & Ramirez (274) in dogs. By giving ethacrynic acid, these workers obliterated the normal corticomedullary gra-dient for electrolytes, and hence presumably also the reabsorption of free water from the collecting ducts. However, the corticomedullary gradient for urea was maintained under these conditions, and beyond that, the concentration of urea was higher in the papilla than in the urine. The authors' conclusion of active reabsorption of urea must be qualified: the lack of $T^C_{H_2O}$ in these experiments need not mean that net water reabsorption from the collecting ducts was zero. To the extent that isoosmotic or even hypoosmotic (347) reabsorption from the ducts may have continued, the data still seem compatible with continued passive reabsorption of urea and the effects of solvent drag. Furthermore, both the corticomedullary gradient for urea, and the urea gradient between collecting ducts and papilla, were diminished by iodoacetate, an inhibitor of anaerobic glycolysis, and by acetamide, an analog of urea, but not by cyanide. The authors suggested, therefore, that the energy supply for the presumed active transport of urea is derived from anaerobic metabolism.

Rabinowitz (277), however, could find no evidence for active transport of urea in dogs. He based this conclusion on a dependence of urea reabsorption on water reabsorption through a range of U/P inulin from 3 to 300, on the absence of transport maxima at high filtered loads of urea, and on the failure of the structurally related compounds, methylurea and acetamide, to inhibit the reabsorption of urea. Since active transport of urea usually can be demonstrated only in protein-depleted animals, it is important to note that Rabinowitz's dogs had no protein restriction.

The question of urea transport may involve more than just whether the transport is active, as suggested by the studies of Kleinman, Radford & Torelli (278). In 20 per cent of their trials on unanesthetized rats kept on a high-protein, high-salt diet, the urea clearance exceeded the simultaneous inulin clearance. Because the results were variable, the authors were reluctant to draw conclusions regarding possible tubular secretion or intrarenal formation of urea. Nevertheless, their results, and those of others which point to active reabsorption of urea, raise the fascinating possibility of bidirectional net transport of urea.

Capek et al. (279) measured diffusional permeabilities for urea in the rat, by means of microperfusion in the proximal tubules and through stopped-flow microperfusion in the distal tubules. This permeability was twenty times greater in the proximal than in the distal convolution. Passive diffusion could account for all of the urea reabsorbed from the proximal tubule. In micropuncture studies in the dog, Clapp (280) estimated this amount to be about 56 per cent of the filtered load. Solvent drag appears to contribute little to the reabsorption of urea from the proximal tubule, but may have an important influence on the urea reabsorption in the distal nephron (279). A low urea permeability of distal convolution and collecting ducts in rats is also suggested by the tracer microinjection studies of Gottschalk, Morel & Mylle (45). Total urea ^{14}C recovery in urine was up to 100 per cent (mean 80 per cent) following the injection of this tracer into the distal convolution.

Using the elegant method of Burg et al. (281) of perfusing single, isolated segments of collecting ducts of the rabbit, Grantham & Burg (282) measured the effect of cyclic $3',5'$-AMP or vasopressin on urea permeability of cortical and outer medullary collecting duct segments. Whether the substances were applied to the luminal or the peritubular border of the cells, urea permeability did not change despite an increase in water permeability. These results agree with the data of Capek et al. (279) obtained in stopped-flow microperfusion studies of rat distal nephrons *in vivo*. Thus, in contrast to the toad bladder, the urea permeability in distal parts of the mammalian nephron may not be influenced by ADH. However, it is still unclear whether the inner medullary part of the mammalian collecting ducts retains the capacity to alter its permeability for urea selectively. Gardner & Maffly (283) also suggest that an increase of papillary urea, induced by vasopressin, might in part be due to solvent drag and in part to increased urea permeability of the collecting ducts. Foulkes (284) inferred an ADH-induced increase in collecting-duct permeability for urea from experiments in which the time-course of isotopic equilibrium of urea and inulin between urine and plasma was measured after a sudden increase of these tracers in the arterial blood.

There is little doubt that, in contrast to the mammal (273), the bullfrog kidney can synthesize urea from endogenous material. Carlisky, Jard & Morel (285) showed through isotope dilution in *Rana catesbiana* that 7.7 per cent of the urinary urea is formed intrarenally from arginine, and 1.0 per cent from uric acid. Brodsky et al. (286) defined some of the metabolic pathways for renal urea formation in the same species. The intrarenal activity of arginase was greater, and that of uricase and allantoicase similar to the activity in frog liver. The authors postulated at least two pathways for the intrarenal formation of urea in the bullfrog, one terminating in hydrolysis of arginine, the other, in the hydrolysis of allantoic acid.

A colorimetric method, considered to be specific, for determining urea in nanoliter samples was described by Marsh, Frasier & Decter (287). Recovery of urea was 99 ± 4.75 per cent.

Uric acid.—Garrod, McSwiney & Bold (288) adduced evidence against a common reabsorptive mechanism for phosphate and urate in patients with hyperuricemia. Phosphate excretion was not altered by the spontaneously high urate load, nor was urate excretion influenced by phosphate infusions. Secretion of uric acid in mongrel dogs was demonstrated by Davis et al. (289). Injection of labeled uric acid 10–15 sec prior to release of stop-flow yielded an activity peak which preceded the newly formed filtrate. This peak, which corresponded to a distal tubular site, could be abolished by pyrazinamide. Beechwood, Berndt & Mudge (290) were unable to demonstrate distal tubular secretion of uric acid in stop-flow experiments in rabbits. Rather, they found evidence for both reabsorption and secretion in proximal tubules; in 20 per cent of the animals, net secretion occurred even during free flow. The secretory peak during stop-flow could be enhanced by chlorothiazide, lactic acid, creatinine, pyrazinoic acid, or ouabain (291) and depressed by probenecid. Proximal tubular secretion of urate, which could be inhibited by probenecid, was also demonstrated in stop-flow experiments on rabbits by Møller (292). This author, like Beechwood, Berndt & Mudge (290), found the distal tubular epithelium relatively impermeable to uric acid. Berndt & Beechwood (291) found that urate uptake by renal cortical slices of rabbits depended on the K concentration in the medium.

Amino acids.—The common renal transport mechanism for proline, hydroxyproline, and glycine, which exists in the rat, was demonstrated in man (293). Reabsorption of hydroxyproline is Tm-limited, and the common transport mechanism appears to have greater affinity for proline and hydroxyproline than for glycine. From clearance and stop-flow studies in rats, Young & Edwards (294) concluded that histidine is actively reabsorbed in the proximal tubule. Its reabsorption could be inhibited by L-methyldopa, but not by the D isomer of this synthetic amino acid. Schwartzman, Crawhall & Segal (295) tested the hypothesis that phosphatidopeptides, which can be extracted from the renal cortex of rats, may serve as active carriers for amino acids. The time-course of incorporation of radioactive lysine and leucine into the phosphatidopeptides, as well as the failure of transport competitors, such as arginine and ornithine, or high concentrations of leucine itself, to alter the rate of incorporation, all spoke against the hypothesis. In dogs, the intravenous infusion of lysine, glycine, and alanine, but not aspartic acid and leucine, depressed the reabsorption of glucose (296). Since saturating the transport mechanism for glucose does not depress the reabsorption of one of the inhibiting amino acids, and vice versa, the authors consider that the inhibition is noncompetitive. Kleit et al. (297) demonstrated net secretion of ascorbic acid in dogs after alkalinization of the urine and following infusion of hypertonic Na sulfate. Stop-flow analysis pointed to the distal convolution as the site of secretion.

Other organic acids and bases.—With a microspectrophotometer, Kinter (298) studied the influx and efflux kinetics of chlorophenol red in separated renal tubules of the flounder. Influx kinetics were typical of active, uphill transport, but the mechanism of efflux was less clear. Although the latter was not influenced by metabolic inhibitors, it was enhanced by low concentrations of PAH, iodopyracet, probenecid, or bromcresol green in the outside medium, and inhibited by high concentrations. This enhancement apparently was not due to inhibition of simultaneous influx, or to countertransport. Kempton (299) has demonstrated tubular secretion of phenol red in the smooth dogfish *Mustelus canis*. With rising plasma concentrations of phenol red, the proportion of the excreted dye which had been secreted decreased from 96 to 60 per cent.

A diphasic effect of organic acids on the washout of PAH from isolated renal tubules of rabbits was reported by Huang & Lin (300). Low concentrations of probenecid and DNP stimulated such washout, and high concentrations inhibited it. The uptake of PAH by this preparation was inhibited by probenecid, its diethyl and dimethyl analogs, and by DNP. The last appeared to act through competition rather than by its influence on energy production. The degree of inhibition induced by the various organic acids was related directly to their partition coefficients in the membrane. Murthy & Foulkes (301) found much higher efflux rate constants of Na, PAH, and tetraethylammonium from isolated rabbit tubular fragments than from kidney slices. They propose that this difference may reveal the participation of the luminal membrane in the efflux process. Tanner & Kinter (302) have further examined the very interesting bidirectional transport systems for PAH and iodopyracet in the kidney of *Necturus*. Octanoate specifically and reversibly converted net reabsorption to net secretion in both intact and perfused kidneys. Studies of unidirectional movements of PAH suggested that octanoate and other fatty acids inhibited mainly the reabsorptive movement of PAH, whereas iodopyracet inhibited both reabsorptive and secretory movement of PAH. The authors postulate active pumps which move iodopyracet and PAH into proximal tubular cells from both their luminal and peritubular borders. Vogel and co-workers (267) demonstrated that PAH transport in the frog, like glucose transport, was related to the reabsorption of Na.

In a comprehensive study, Despopoulos (303) demonstrated that transported weak acids possess certain intramolecular reactive groups not found in nontransported acids. A carboxyl and a carbonyl group in the general structure of transported acids seems indispensable for interaction with membrane receptors. The author suggests that transport initially consists of a contact between substrate and receptor, involving a reinforced ionic bond at the carboxyl and a supporting hydrogen bond at the carbonyl group. In clearance experiments on dogs, Weiner, Blanchard & Mudge (304) found evidence for active secretory movement of sixteen foreign organic acids, mostly substituted benzoic acids. They could not identify chemical groups essential for active transport. Back-diffusion of these substances depended upon acidic strength, lipid solubility, and urinary pH. Clearance experiments in man (305) showed that about 83 per cent of excreted nitrofurantoin is secreted, and that this process can be inhibited by other weak acids, such as PAH. Clearance of nitrofurantoin decreased at lower urine pH, a change indicating increased nonionic back diffusion.

Healy et al. (306) observed that Tm glucose and Tm PAH in unanesthetized dogs remained essentially unchanged during the infusion of angiotensin at doses of 0.025 to 0.1 μg per kg per minute. Deetjen & Sonnenberg (122) have challenged the classical Tm concept, not only for glucose but also for PAH. During microperfusion of single proximal tubules of rats, they found no relationship between PAH secretion and the length of the perfused segment. This suggests that PAH secretion does not depend on the number of transport sites. Rather, the secretion seemed to be limited by the intratubular concentration of PAH, active transport into the lumen ceasing when the concentration reached about 3.85 mM. More PAH was transported per unit time at higher rates of perfusion, but the limiting intratubular concentration remained the same.

A number of laboratories have concerned themselves with the question of back-diffusion of PAH out of the mammalian nephron. Bahlmann & Ochwadt (307) found no evidence for such back-diffusion in clearance experiments in dogs, not even during systemic acidosis, which would be expected to further nonionic back-diffusion. Nor could Deetjen & Sonnenberg (122) detect any back-diffusion when they perfused single proximal tubules of rats with solutions containing PAH. Recently, Deetjen reported that the short loops of Henle and distal convolutions also do not allow significant re-entry of secreted PAH into the blood (308). However, back-diffusion may occur in medullary structures. Schnermann & Thurau (309) observed the concentration of PAH to be eight times greater in medullary vasa recta of hamsters than in peripheral plasma, and four times lower than in collecting-duct fluid. The PAH concentration increased toward the tip of the papilla, and it was decreased during mannitol diuresis. These results were taken to mean that PAH might diffuse from the loops of Henle, the collecting ducts, or both, into the medullary capillaries, where it is probably trapped by countercurrent diffusion.

Thus, while even net reabsorption of PAH has been described in *Necturus* (302), no major reabsorptive flux of PAH could be demonstrated in the mammalian kidney. In addition, the microperfusion experiments of Deetjen & Sonnenberg (122) show that neither a tubular Na concentration as low as 100 meq/liter nor the rate of net Na transport influences the rate of PAH secretion in the rat, as Vogel (267) found in the frog. Thus, as Deetjen (308) has recently pointed out, the results obtained in one species cannot be extrapolated to the other species.

Sonnenberg, Oelert & Baumann (310) showed that the lack of back-diffusion of PAH in cortical tubules may be related to its low lipoid solubility. During microperfusion of single proximal tubules of rats with acidotic fluid which favors nonionic back-diffusion, they found that the extent of such diffusion by the organic acids sulfamerazine and phenobarbital could be related to their lipoid solubility. In contrast, three organic acids with low lipoid solubilities, PAH, uric acid, and sulfaurea, were not reabsorbed. Despopoulos & Segerfeldt (311), however, showed that the passive efflux rates of twenty organic acids from rabbit kidney cortex slices were within a single order of magnitude of each other and that they were correlated with neither their dissociation constants nor their partition coefficients between organic solvents and water.

Coe & Korty (312) obtained evidence for active tubular secretion and passive reabsorption of the organic base hydrazine in clearance experiments on dogs.

Proteins.—Reabsorption of ^{125}I-labeled albumin in the proximal convolution of the rat was studied by Maunsbach (313) through electronmicroscopic autoradiography. Following microinjection of the labeled protein into the tubular lumen, the absorbed substance appeared within vacuoles which may have been formed from invaginations of the apical cell membrane. A portion of the reabsorbed albumin appeared in lysosomes, where it is believed to be degraded. There was no evidence of intercellular transport, or transfer of the albumin from cytoplasmic bodies into the peritubular space. These observations were confirmed by Maunsbach (314) by the use of ferritin, a protein with a core of iron, which can be precisely located in thin sections. There was no evidence that protein molecules as such could traverse the apical cell membrane; apparently they must be carried in tiny pinocytotic vacuoles. Identical conclusions, based on a similar method, were reached independently by Thoenes, Langer & Wiederholt (315). Electronmicroscopic autoradiography was also used to study the absorption of radioisotope-labeled hemoglobin by proximal tubules of rabbits (316). Two and one-half hours after intravenous injection of the hemoglobin, about 85 per cent of the intracellular grains were found in or near specific cytoplasmic bodies, and a small percentage lay in apical vacuoles.

ACID-BASE REGULATION

Rector, Carter & Seldin (317) have presented convincing evidence for the theory that the reabsorption of HCO_3^- in the proximal and distal tubules is mediated through active secretion of cellular H^+. If the theory is correct, then in the steady state, the rate at which H_2CO_3 is removed from the proximal tubular lumen must equal the rate of H^+ secretion, and hence of HCO_3^- reabsorption. Yet, Walser & Mudge in 1960 estimated that if the uncatalyzed dehydration of H_2CO_3 were to account for the observed rates of HCO_3^- reabsorption, the steady-state luminal $[H_2CO_3]$ must be at least ten times the $[H_2CO_3]$ that would exist if it were in equilibrium with luminal or plasma Pco_2. Thus, to drive the uncatalyzed dehydration of H_2CO_3 at a rate equal to HCO_3^- reabsorption would require luminal acidity approximately 1 pH unit lower than the equilibrium pH.

In the proximal tubule of rats undergoing $NaHCO_3$ diuresis, Rector, Carter & Seldin (317) found an intratubular pH *in vivo* identical to the equilibrium pH calculated from plasma Pco_2 and luminal $[HCO_3^-]$. However, when a carbonic anhydrase inhibitor was given intravenously, intratubular pH was 0.85 unit lower than the calculated equilibrium pH. In the distal tubule a "disequilibrium pH" of the same order of magnitude could be observed without inhibition of carbonic anhydrase. The difference could be obliterated by an intravenous infusion of the enzyme. The authors concluded that, in both proximal and distal tubules, H^+ secretion could account for the reabsorption of HCO_3^-. The steep pH gradients against which H^+ can be secreted suggested that H^+ secretion in the proximal and in the distal convolution is driven by an active transport system. While in the proximal convolution the existence of carbonic anhydrase in the luminal membrane prevented the formation of excess H_2CO_3, lack of the enzyme in the wall of the distal convolution led to marked disequilibrium pH. On the basis of clearance data in rats, Guignard (318) reached conclusions similar to those of Rector et al. (317).

Bank & Aynedjian (319) have shown that HCO_3^- may enter the proximal convolutions of rats distal to the glomerulus. During microperfusion of this segment with fluid which is originally free of HCO_3^-, and in the absence of net fluxes of sodium and water, the HCO_3^- concentration in the collected perfusate was about 3 meq/liter during normal systemic acid-base balance. It rose to a mean of 4.3 meq/liter during metabolic alkalosis, and to 15 meq/liter during alkalosis and inhibition of carbonic anhydrase. The last finding suggests that the HCO_3^- was not generated from CO_2 and OH^- within the tubular lumen, but entered the perfusate from an extratubular source. Furthermore, some portion of the proximal luminal border is apparently permeable to HCO_3^-.

Reid & Hills (320) studied the effects of the rate of urine flow on urinary pH and Pco_2 in humans. Very alkaline urines had highest pH and Pco_2 when urine flow rate was minimal, whereas acid urines had highest values for pH and Pco_2 when flow rate was maximal. The authors propose that dehydration of alkaline urine increases the concentrations of H ion, H_2CO_3, and Pco_2 in the distal nephron, but only CO_2 gas can diffuse out as a consequence of the increased concentration gradients. This results in a rise in pH of distal tubular urine, and yet further formation of H_2CO_3 from bicarbonate at the rising pH results in release of H ions from other urinary buffers. It is suggested that this H_2CO_3 finally dissociates into CO_2 in the gross and impermeable urinary passages; the voided urine is therefore alkaline and has a high Pco_2. The high Pco_2 associated with high flows in acid urines is thought to be due to insufficient contact time in the distal nephron.

Pitts and associates (321–323) explored the metabolic pathways in the formation of urinary ammonia in acidotic dogs. By infusing various amino acids labeled with ^{15}N into one renal artery, they could estimate the sources of urinary ammonia. During metabolic acidosis in dogs, 35–51 per cent of urinary ammonia came from the amide nitrogen of glutamine, 10–26 per cent from the amino nitrogen of this amino acid, and 3–8 per cent, 3–6 per cent, and 1–2 per cent from the amino nitrogens of alanine, glycine, and glutamate, respectively. The contributions of the last two amino acids may be overestimated, as their arterial concentrations had to be significantly increased to add sufficient isotope. Such elevation of the plasma concentration leads to an increased contribution to the urinary ammonia from that particular amino acid (324). The authors emphasize that other amino acids, besides the five studied, no doubt also contribute to the formation of urinary ammonia. Because, following the infusion of ^{15}N-amino-labeled glutamine into one renal artery, aspartate and alanine within renal tissue were more highly labeled than glutamate or urinary ammonia, Pitts concluded that the first step in the metabolism of glutamine involves transamination rather than deamidation. This conclusion suggests that the enzyme glutamine transaminase, rather than glutaminase, may be involved in the control of renal ammonia production. This is not to imply, however, that it is the main or only enzyme controlling this important function.

Fülgraff & Pitts (325) found that more labeled ammonia appeared in the urine 20 sec after injections of amino-^{15}N-labeled glutamine than of amide-^{15}N-labeled glutamine. The disappearance curve of ^{15}N-ammonia in urine appeared to be a single exponential function when the amide nitrogen of glutamine was labeled, and multiexponential when the amino nitrogen was labeled. The authors therefore suggest that deamidation of glutamine is not rate limiting for ammonia production, whereas deamination may be.

Filtration and tubular reabsorption appear to be the major route by which glutamine as a substrate for NH_3 production reaches renal tubular cells. Acute reduction in the renal production of ammonia in dogs could be correlated only with acute reductions in GFR but not in renal blood flow, and not with changes in P_{NH_3} (326).

Two studies, showing that metabolic acidosis can lead to increased renal excretion of ammonia without a concomitant rise in the intrarenal concentration of glutaminase (327), support the view that this enzyme does not primarily control the renal production of ammonia. Goldstein (328) has presented evidence that in the rat, renal glutamate may be one factor which controls the production of ammonia, by inhibiting glutaminase. Glutamate, at concentrations found in rat kidneys, caused significant inhibition of renal glutaminase activity, and the addition of sodium glutamate to acidotic rats reduced their urinary excretion of ammonia. Metabolic acidosis and alkalosis caused, respectively, a decrease and an increase in the renal concentrations of glutamate.

Goodman, Fuisz & Cahill (329) suggest that these changes in levels of glutamate may result from alterations in the rate of gluconeogenesis. They observed that renal cortical slices from rats with metabolic acidosis have an increased capacity to convert glutamine, glutamate, and α-ketoglutarate to glucose. Metabolic alkalosis appeared to have a depressant effect on gluconeogenesis. Balagura (330) reports that acidifying the external medium increased not only the uptake, but also the utilization of α-ketoglutarate by rat renal cortical slices *in vitro*. Possibly related to renal gluconeogenesis is the finding of increased activity of the hexose monophosphate shunt dehydrogenases during acidosis (331). Another possible explanation for this observation is that renal secretion of H is in part effected by a redox pump as well as through the hydration of CO_2.

Sullivan (332) related the total concentrations of ammonium and ammonia in very distal stop-flow samples to urinary pH in acidotic dogs. Urinary pH was varied from 4.5 to 7.3 by infusions of HCl or $NaHCO_3$. With urinary pH from 6.0 and upward, maximal concentrations of ammonium and ammonia described a slope which closely approximated the theoretical relationship predicted by nonionic diffusion. But at urinary pH's below 6.0, the concentrations deviated progressively from this slope, perhaps because of limitation in the rate of ammonia production. The author suggests that such deviation is prevented in the more alkaline range by a countercurrent system which concentrates ammonia in the renal medulla only when collecting-duct fluid is relatively alkaline. Data suggesting the existence of a pH-dependent medullary countercurrent system for ammonia have been presented also by Robinson & Owen (333), although in their proposed system the pH of fluid in the loop of Henle rather than of that in the collecting duct would be the critical variable.

To find out whether some of the ammonia which appears in the proximal tubules might diffuse out of the loops of Henle, Hayes, Owen & Robinson (334) performed micropuncture experiments in rats. During mannitol diuresis and administration of acetazolamide, which presumably elevated pH in the loops and thereby promoted the diffusion of ammonia out of the loops, the ammonia concentration was essentially the same in distal as in proximal tubular fluid. The authors therefore concluded that much of the ammonia which is added to proximal tubules can be reabsorbed at some point between mid-proximal and early distal tubules, presumably in the loops of Henle. The amount of ammonia present in the proximal tubules was sufficient to account for 300 per cent of the absolute quantity of ammonia which appears in the distal tubule, and for 150 per cent of that in the urine.

Like others (335, 336), Hayes, Owen & Robinson (334) calculated, on the basis of pH and P_{NH_3}, that most probably diffusion equilibrium for NH_3 exists between blood and cortical tubular fluid. Consistent with the prevailing concept that ammonia is transported from the tubular cells via a pH-dependent process of nonionic diffusion is their finding that during prolonged ammonium chloride acidosis in dogs, almost identical elevations of urinary ammonia excretion and renal venous ammonia release occur. They point out that it is probably not possible for renal micropunctures to establish the site(s) of ammonia production. Ammonia which is found in proximal tubular fluid (337) may have come from distal tubules and, to a lesser extent, from collecting ducts. Fülgraff & Pitts (325) did, in fact, localize the production of renal ammonia to these structures. This conclusion was based on the time-course of urinary excretion of creatinine and ^{15}N-ammonia, following injections of creatinine and labeled NH_4Cl or glutamine into a renal artery of acidotic dogs.

Hills & Reid (338) have presented a general kinetic equation describing renal ammonia balance, and have compared theoretical predictions with experimental results. In an attempt to explore mechanisms by which augmented renal ammonia excretion occurs during metabolic acidosis, Lotspeich (339) studied growth and enzyme characteristics of rat renal tissue. In metabolic acidosis a true growth of the rat kidney was demonstrated; cell number and cell size increased. It was suggested that in the rat the stimulation of renal growth may be important in the increasing capacity to excrete ammonia during metabolic acidosis.

Factors which govern renal acid excretion during metabolic alkalosis induced by gastric drainage were further explored by Tannen, Bleich & Schwartz in dogs (340). Intravenous administration of HCl, when ample amounts of dietary Na and K were available, was associated with slow correction of the extracellular alkalosis but with a prompt increase in urinary acid excretion in spite of the continuing alkaline pH of extracellular fluid. When the same experiment was conducted with minimal dietary Na and K, extracellular alkalosis was corrected with lesser amounts of administered acid and no increase in renal acid excretion was observed. Administration of HNO_3 (which contains a poorly reabsorbable anion), when adequate Na and K were present in the diet, was accompanied by neither Na or K retention nor complete correction of the extracellular alkalosis. The authors suggested that in the chloride-deficient alkalotic dog the administration of HCl provided the reabsorbable anion with which the animal could retain Na, presumably in lieu of the opportunity to retain H quantitatively. Thus Na was retained and renal acid excretion increased. This hypothesis also accounts, then, for the quantitative retention of HCl when additional dietary cation was not available. Similarly, in the nitric acid experiment the poorly penetrating character of the anion did not facilitate the retention of Na (as chloride did) and obligated the equivalent loss into the urine of H ions as the only cations in the face of Na and K restriction, available to maintain electroneutrality. The authors proposed that the renal excretion of an acid load during metabolic alkalosis is determined primarily by the need for Na conservation and that probably the K^+ and H^+ contents of renal tubular cells are not the determinants of acid excretion under these conditions. Using similar experimental maneuvers the same authors (341) induced metabolic alkalosis in K-deficient dogs by administering K with a poorly reabsorbable anion. Convincing arguments are offered that the state of body K stores is not the critical factor in the genesis of metabolic alkalosis.

Evidence that choline can compete against hydrogen ion in the tubular exchange mechanism has been presented by S. Solomon (342). Using the Chinard technique of simultaneous injection of creatinine and choline into one renal artery of dogs, he showed that choline enters the tubular system by an extraglomerular route. Urinary Na excretion was depressed during the appearance of choline in the urine. The saliuretic effect of acetazolamide was inhibited by infusion of choline. In an experimental model using the cation exchange resin, Amberplex C-I, he demonstrated that choline inhibits hydrogen for Na exchange. Active transport of choline in renal cortical slices of rats was suggested by the experiments of Sung & Johnstone (343). Since DNP inhibited the oxidation of choline to betaine in renal slices but not in homogenates, the authors concluded that active uptake of choline by the intact cells was probably inhibited. The active process appeared to involve Na-dependent ATPase.

CONCENTRATING AND DILUTING MECHANISM

Although it is generally agreed that hypertonic urine is formed by some type of countercurrent system, various details of the mechanism remain obscure. There seems little doubt that reabsorption of NaCl from the thick ascending loops of Henle drives the countercurrent multiplier system, but it is not clear whether this operation is limited to the outer medulla or proceeds through most of the cortex as well. The extension of an appreciable fraction of the thick ascending limbs within the renal pyramids all the way through the cortex suggests the latter possibility, which is further supported by the hypertonicity of cortical homogenates reported from several laboratories. A related question is the exact site of free-water generation. Curiously, the view that this begins in the outer medulla is an assumption based on the recovery of hypotonic fluid from early distal convolutions at the very surface of the cortex. It thus seems premature to restrict to the medullary region the mechanism which creates the renal osmotic gradient, and to assume that interstitial osmolality throughout the cortex is isotonic.

Models of concentrating mechanism.—Using mathematical models several investigators have tried to determine whether active Na transport, if restricted to the thick ascending limbs of Henle's loop in the outer medulla, can contribute to a progressive osmotic gradient in the inner medulla. Loop models of Stephenson (36, 37) and Marsh, Kelman & Howard (34, 35), which incorporate the loops of Henle and the vasa recta, show that under these conditions the maximal interstitial osmolality is achieved at the junction of the outer and inner medulla, and that no further concentration can occur along the axis of the inner medulla. These models, as well as thermodynamic considerations, make it apparent that some energy source within the inner medulla is required to account for its high osmolal content during hydropenia. Several solutions to this problem have been proposed.

Lever (344) has suggested that the energy is supplied by the hydrostatic pressure in the vasa recta. Kuhn rejected this possibility in one of his original papers on this subject, and Berliner & Bennett (345) have reviewed the arguments, based on recent measurements of hydrostatic pressures and albumin concentrations in the vasa recta, why such a system cannot possibly concentrate the urine to the degree observed.

Niesel & Röskenbleck (346) have described a model by which an increase in inner medullary osmolal concentration can be achieved through countercurrent osmosis and countercurrent diffusion. An essential feature of this model is a difference in urea and water permeabilities between collecting ducts on the one hand and loops of Henle and vasa recta on the other. The model, however, fails to explain the increasing NaCl concentration from the outer medulla to the tip of the papilla.

Marsh (347) has proposed that the work is performed by the collecting ducts. Because of his and Solomon's (348) earlier micropuncture observation that neither the descending nor the ascending thin limbs of Henle's loops in hamster papilla transport salt actively, he studied the reabsorptive characteristics of medullary collecting ducts of rats *in vitro*. In the absence of osmotic gradients between the intraductal fluid and the bathing medium, active salt reabsorption from the collecting ducts led to the formation of a hypo-osmolal reabsorbate. Hypo-osmolal reabsorption coupled to active salt transport has been proven to be possible, thermodynamically, if a double-membrane system with certain characteristics is assumed. Repetition of hypo-osmolal reabsorption along the length of the collecting duct would lead to progressive increase in the concentration of collecting-duct fluid, and hence of the reabsorbate, both reaching maxima at the papillary tip. In this context, the term hypo-osmolal is used in respect to the osmolality of the collecting-duct fluid from which the reabsorbate is removed, not to that in peripheral plasma. Marsh has termed this the lineal multiplication mechanism. Although this hypothesis removes a countercurrent multiplier function from the thin limbs of Henle's loops, it incorporates their passive properties and those of the vasa recta as an essential part of the concentrating mechanism. Only through the contiguity of these countercurrent exchangers is it possible to transport Na at any one point against a relatively small concentration gradient, and yet achieve the final high urine osmolalities which are observed.

Jamison, Bennett & Berliner (349) have presented what they view as strong support for Berliner's original proposal that the thin descending and ascending limbs of Henle's loops can transport Na actively and, hence, act as countercurrent multipliers. In contrast to the original hypothesis, they assume that only the ascending limb has restricted permeability to water. The proposal thus assigns a countercurrent function to the thin limbs within the inner medulla, analogous to that generally accepted for the thick limbs in the outer medulla. Their arguments are based on data obtained through the method of Sakai, Jamison & Berliner (350) which renders previously inaccessible portions of the rat renal medulla available for micropuncture: the cortex is partially removed one to three days prior to the experiment, and the papillary tip is pulled out of the renal pelvis toward the cortex. Although the concentrating ability of the operated kidney is only one fourth to one half of normal, the urine remains hypertonic. The transtubular potential in the collecting ducts of the operated kidney was -11 mV, only slightly lower than the -14 mV found in the collecting ducts of hamsters. Using this technique to puncture structures between 2 to 4 mm from the papillary tip of a rat kidney, Jamison, Bennett & Berliner (349) found the osmolality of tubular fluid within ascending limbs to be significantly lower than that within adjacent descending limbs. The mean difference of -117 mOsm/kg was due primarily to the difference in Na concentration. The authors therefore suggest that active Na reabsorption from the thin ascending limbs of Henle's loops creates a hypertonic reabsorbate which, as a single effect, is multiplied by countercurrent flow along the longitudinal axis of the inner medulla.

Jamison, Bennett & Berliner suggested that the higher location of their puncture sites might explain the discrepancy between their results and those of Marsh & Solomon (348). They argue that close to the bend of the loops, the difference in water permeability between the two limbs may be too slight to allow detection of difference in osmolalities. Since water permeability at the bend of the loop is thus presumably still great, and since Jamison et al. assume active Na transport along the entire loop, it seems that Marsh & Solomon, using the split-droplet method, should have been able to demonstrate volume reduction in the descending loop at the papillary tip, and possibly in the ascending loop as well, if active transport were taking place.

One objection frequently raised to assigning active Na transport to the thin limbs of Henle's loops is their anatomical appearance. Jamison, Bennett & Berliner (349) point out that virtually all mammalian cells are capable of active cation transport, and that the paucity of mitochondria and endoplasmic reticulum in cells of the thin limbs may only reflect a predominance of anaerobic over aerobic metabolism in the renal medulla. Possible objections to this point of view are discussed below (351). The validity of assigning different water permeabilities to the two limbs of Henle's loops is supported by ultrastructural differences between these two segments. Osvaldo & Latta (352), as well as Bulger et al. (353), have confirmed earlier findings that the cells of the ascending limbs lack the numerous microvilli and cytoplasmic processes which characterize the descending limbs. Osvaldo & Latta (352), however, found no differences in the basement membranes, which had been reported earlier. Multiple layers of basement membranes increased toward the papillary tip in both descending and ascending limbs. Steinhausen (354) observed that inner diameters of thin descending and ascending limbs of Henle's loops in golden hamsters were 11.9 ± 0.5 and 20.8 ± 1.0 μ, respectively. The lumen widened about 0.25 mm before the bend of the loop. This finding might be related to Osvaldo & Latta's (352) demonstration that the transition from the histologically more complex descending to the simpler ascending limbs occurred in the middle of the descending portion.

Although the anatomical features of the medullary interstitial cells have been studied in considerable detail (355–357), their physiological significance remains in doubt. These cells resemble rungs on a ladder, their long axes lying perpendicular to the tubular and vascular structures of the medulla. The processes of the interstitial cells appear to be more closely related to the capillaries and thin limbs of Henle's loops than to the cells of the collecting ducts (355, 356). The interstitial cells contain many osmiophilic droplets (355), which may contain lipids (356, 357). But because the droplets are not completely surrounded by membranes, and because the cells lack a well developed endoplasmic reticulum (355, 357), Osvaldo & Latta doubt that the interstitial cells have high secretory activity. There is disagreement on the existence of myofibrils in the cytoplasm of these cells

(355, 357) and, therefore, on the possibility of their having a contractile function.

Countercurrent diffusion.—The passive countercurrent exchange properties of the medulla and papilla have been studied by several approaches. Lever & Kriz (358) described a close juxtaposition of ascending vasa recta in the outer medulla of rats to the thin descending limbs of Henle's loops, and pointed out that this spatial arrangement seems ideal for the countercurrent exchange of urea from the former to the latter structure.

Auklund & Berliner (359) inserted platinum electrodes into the renal medulla and papilla of dogs, and measured the local rate of desaturation of hydrogen gas after its inhalation was suddenly stopped. Since the fractional rate of hydrogen removal in the papilla was 0.05 per min at a urine flow of 0.1 ml per kidney per min, and increased to 0.75 per min at a urine flow of 5 ml per kidney per min, the authors suggested that at high urine flows, most of the papillary hydrogen may be removed by the urine. In order to assess the influence of the medullary blood flow on removal of hydrogen, Auklund & Berliner (359) performed stop-flow experiments, assuming that the blood flow remains constant during ureteral occlusion. Under these conditions, fractional removal was about the same as that occurring at a urine flow of 0.2 ml per kidney per min during free flow. Since blood flow in the inner medulla must be assumed to be much higher than 0.2 ml per min, the authors considered the low removal rate as evidence of a highly efficient countercurrent exchange mechanism for hydrogen. This mechanism seems to render desaturation curves in the inner medulla for hydrogen, and probably for other inert gases as well, unsuitable for estimating inner medullary blood flow. Aukland (360) reached a similar conclusion in regard to the applicability of heat clearance from the inner medulla. This clearance was much higher than that for hydrogen gas, and did not vary with alterations in blood flow induced by decreasing renal arterial pressure from 170 to 35 mm Hg. Since the calculated longitudinal heat conduction from papilla toward cortex was in the same range as the observed inner medullary heat clearance, Aukland (360) also considers the method unsuitable for studying countercurrent exchange of heat.

In an extensive study, Perl & Hirsch (361) tested the suitability of heat clearance, which is due exclusively to convection, for measuring total and local rates of blood flow in the kidney. The authors point out that the inaccuracy of the method is reflected in calculated medullary blood flows of dogs, which ranged from 0 to 50 ml per minute per 100 g kidney. Furthermore, cortical blood flow was systematically underestimated by this method, and there was considerable scatter between thermoelectric values and those obtained by PAH clearance.

With the use of ^{131}I-labeled albumin, Carone et al. (362) confirmed the progressive increase in plasma albumin space, from cortex, through medulla, to papilla. Using fluorescein-labeled albumin in tissue slices, they localized the albumin chiefly within the vessels, and not in the surrounding interstitium. They concluded that the 2.5-fold increase in protein concentration along the descending vasa recta results from hydrostatic abstraction of water. In the absence of protein in the medullary interstitium, this process would require a hydrostatic pressure of about 70 mm Hg at the bend of the vasa recta, and pressure of this magnitude has not been found. However, Pomerantz, Slotkoff & Lilienfield (363), using the same method as Carone et al. (362), visualized an extravascular pool of albumin within the renal medulla, a finding consistent with the results of Slotkoff & Lilienfield (364).

Concentrating ability in potassium deficiency.—The urinary concentrating defect in K deficiency seems to be due to reduced osmolality of the medullary and papillary interstitiums, rather than to impaired water permeability of the collecting ducts. Gottschalk et al. (365) found fluid from collecting ducts, from loops of Henle, and from vasa recta at the same level of the papilla of K-deficient hamsters, to have the same osmolal concentration. The reason for the reduced interstitial osmolality is not known. Under free-flow conditions in K-deficient rats, Bank & Aynedjian (366) and Gottschalk et al. (365) recorded an unimpaired ability of the thick ascending limbs of Henle's loops to generate a transtubular concentration gradient for Na. Nevertheless, the finding of Jones, Mylle & Gottschalk (367), that the tubular passage time is prolonged in K-deficient rats, suggests that the absolute amount of Na reabsorbed from the ascending limbs may be decreased in this condition. Consistent with this idea is the finding of Brunner, Rector & Seldin (368), that at any level of C_{Osm}, the reabsorption of solute free water ($T^c_{H_2O}$) is less in K-deficient than in normal rats. Buckalew, Ramirez & Goldberg (369) found that $T^c_{H_2O}$ in K-depleted rats was diminished even when Na delivery to the loops was increased through saline diuresis. They interpreted their data as indicating an intrinsic defect in Na transport in the loop. There is little evidence that increased fractional reabsorption of Na in the proximal tubules curtails the amount of Na delivered to the loops of Henle. Such a mechanism, however, may limit the amount of urea delivered to the loops, for Jones, Mylle & Gottschalk (367) found the urinary recovery of ^{14}C urea to be reduced in K-deficient rats following proximal, but not distal, microinjections of the labeled compound.

Urea and the concentrating mechanism.—The critical role of urea in the urinary concentrating mechanism is becoming increasingly evident. Studies which point to active transport of urea by collecting ducts have been considered in another section. Edelmann, Barnett & Stark (370) increased the urine osmolality of premature infants by supplementing low-protein feedings with urea. The increase, which varied directly with the concentration of urea in plasma, was accounted for entirely by an increase in the urinary concentration of urea. Only at very high rates of urea excretion, above 40 μmoles per min per 1.73 m², could a decrease in the concentration of nonurea solutes be detected. The authors suggested that at the high rates of excretion, urea in the collecting ducts no longer equilibrates with that in the interstitium, and that the water which is therefore retained within the tubular system dilutes the nonurea solutes.

In normal young and adult rats (371) and in rats with diabetes insipidus (372), water deprivation led to a rise in the medullary and papillary contents of urea (mmols per unit of dry solids), whereas the contents of Na varied little or not at all. Analysis of urinary constituents during dehydration of rats with diabetes insipidus also suggested a predominant role of urea (373). During mannitol diuresis in rabbits, the papillary urea concentration decreased to about one fifth of normal, while the Na and Cl concentrations decreased only to one third or one half (374). Urinary concentrating ability during the neonatal period in rats was studied by Yunibhand & Held (375). The concentration of urine that was induced by 24 hours of thirsting increased from 372 mOsm/kg H_2O at one day of age, to about 1400 mOsm/kg H_2O on the thirtieth day. This improvement was associated with a decreased water content of the renal medulla, and an increase in its concentrations of Na and urea. The proportional increase was much greater for urea. These results are highly reminiscent of the gradual increase in urinary osmolality when adult rats with hereditary diabetes insipidus are treated with ADH (376), for this phenomenon is also accompanied by a gradual reduction in tissue water content and rise in medullary and papillary urea (372). It is not known to what extent virgin exposure to ADH—from a slowly maturing hypothalamo-neurohypophyseal system in the neonatal rats (377), or from an exogenous source in the case of the rats with diabetes insipidus—might be responsible for the findings.

Bauman, Guyot-Jeannin & Dobrowolski (378) reported a large reduction in the urine osmolality of rats after 24 hours of fasting. Although the decrease from 2984 to 1604 mOsm/kg H_2O was greater than previously observed after short periods of protein depletion in rats, one must nevertheless suspect this as the cause of the concentrating defect. This report serves as a reminder that the common practice of fasting animals prior to an experiment may exert a deleterious influence on the urinary concentrating process.

Other factors related to medullary function.—Robinson, Owen & B. Schmidt-Nielsen (379) assessed the contribution of free amino acids to renal tissue osmolalities in sheep and goats. Osmolalities in outer and inner medulla, as measured by the method of Appelboom, Brodsky & Scott (380), were always higher than those calculated as urea plus twice the sum of the total electrolyte concentration. The free amino acids could account for the difference in the cortex but not in the inner medulla, which suggests that in antidiuretic sheep and goats, solutes besides electrolytes, urea, and free amino acids contribute to the papillary osmolality.

Scaglione, Dell & Winters (381) measured an increase in medullary, but not in cortical, lactate concentration during mannitol diuresis in rats, with no change during water diuresis. This, they suggest, may reflect a higher rate of medullary glycolysis during mannitol diuresis, possibly paralleling increased reabsorption of Na in the loops of Henle which compensates for decreased reabsorption of Na in the proximal tubules. Washington & Holland (382) draw similar conclusions from the observation in dogs that during mannitol and saline diuresis a decrease in urine Po_2 was associated with an increase in $T^c_{H_2O}$. They inferred that the increase in Na reabsorption from the ascending loop of Henle accounts for diminished medullary Po_2. Ethacrynic acid abolished $T^c_{H_2O}$ and increased urine Po_2.

Goldberg, McCurdy & Ramirez (383) and Mertz (384) have shown that in man, as in the rat, there appears to be no upper limit for the reabsorption of solute-free water ($T^c_{H_2O}$). The apparent upper limit for this variable occurring during mannitol diuresis could be surpassed by the infusion of hypertonic NaCl. During mannitol diuresis, the TF/P for Na presumably falls below a critical value beyond which Na reabsorption in the loops of Henle, and hence generation of free water, is retarded. But this critical limit can be exceeded by offering more NaCl. In the dog, however, Friedler & Earley (385) could not enhance $T^c_{H_2O}$ through infusion of hypertonic NaCl, beyond the maximum obtained during mannitol diuresis. No micropuncture data have thus far been reported in the dog, to indicate whether a maximum for net Na reabsorption along the loops of Henle exists in this species.

Zaborowski et al. (386) determined the urinary stop-flow pattern for Pco_2 and Po_2 in dogs, under the influence of carbonic anhydrase, during inhibition of this enzyme by acetazolamide, and during oxygen breathing. Under all three circumstances, a high Pco_2 and a low Po_2 appeared in the collecting-duct portions. The conclusion followed that these stop-flow patterns were determined by countercurrent diffusion of CO_2 and O_2 within the renal medulla rather than by the distribution of CO_2-producing and O_2-consuming processes along the nephron.

Bernanke & Epstein (351), and others (387), have presented evidence against the generally accepted view that the metabolic pathways within the renal medulla are largely anaerobic rather than aerobic. They incubated slices of inner medulla from hydropenic dogs with glucose and succinate under aerobic and anaerobic conditions, and calculated theoretical maxima of ATP generation from the O_2 uptake and lactate production. Oxidative pathways furnished about twice as much energy as glycolysis, when glucose was the substrate. Hypertonic solutions of NaCl and urea, comparable to the concentrations existing within the inner medulla *in vivo*, depressed O_2 uptake and lactate production equally. Although the reason for this inhibition is not clear, the finding suggests that even during physiological conditions, oxidative metabolism is the predominant source of energy for the inner medulla.

Selkurt, Womack & Dailey (388) explored the mechanism which leads to reduced urinary concentrating ability at high arterial pressures. In the dog, elevation of the renal arterial perfusion pressure resulted in a natriuresis and decreased U/P Osm, while the GFR remained constant. Since under these circumstances the papillary Na concentration (meq per kg wet tissue) was lower than at normal or low perfusion pressures, the authors suggest that the observed changes resulted from washout of papillary Na, most probably by an increase in medullary blood flow. As we have pointed out on page 492, one would need to know the solute content per unit dry solids to substantiate the conclusion, because the observed decrease in concentration might have been due to an increase in the tissue water content.

Studies of various animal species continue to confirm the importance of the loops of Henle in the urinary concentrating mechanism. Poulson (389) has related the remarkable ability of three terrestrial birds to concentrate urine (up to an osmolal U/P of 5.8) to the number of Henle's loops rather than to the length of the loops. In birds, the loops of Henle lie in medullary lobules within each of which a ring of collecting ducts surrounds vasa recta and thin limbs, while the thick segments of the loops are located outside the collecting-duct rings. Poulson suggests that in birds, increasing the number of loops may be a more efficient means of enchancing urinary concentrating ability than increasing the length. Furthermore, this profound concentrating ability by avian kidneys may have been overlooked because previous studies were carried out on birds with functional salt glands.

The distribution of thin segments of Henle's loops in mammals living in desert, semidesert, and wet environments was carefully studied by Munkacsi & Palkovits (390). Like others, they showed a direct correlation between the length, number, and volume of long loops of Henle and the ability to conserve water. Included in this paper are potentially valuable data on Henle's loop of the white laboratory rat.

ANTIDIURETIC HORMONES

Bioassays.—Many modifications for the bioassay of ADH have been reported (392, 393, 395–403). They have been critically reviewed by Share (391) and by Sawyer (394). Chemical extraction of ADH from blood (407–410) permits estimation of plasma concentrations. These usually fall below the limits of detectability in the overhydrated state, are up to 4 μU per ml of plasma during normal hydration, and may rise to 21 μU per ml of plasma during dehydration (392, 396, 401, 410–416). Immunoassays are being developed (404–406).

Distribution volume and metabolism of ADH.—Although there is agreement that ADH is not bound by erythrocytes, estimates of the binding to plasma proteins range all the way from zero (392, 412, 417) to large fractions (410, 418, 419). Calcium appears to interfere with the binding to plasma proteins (418).

The disappearance curve of exogenous ADH from plasma, observed by Czaczkes, Kleeman & Koenig (392, 412), indicated a distribution volume for this hormone in rats, dogs, and man considerably less than the plasma volume. The authors could not explain this low value, and preferred to accept the distribution volumes based on rate of infusion, fractional turnover rate, and plasma concentration of ADH in the steady state; these were approximately equal to plasma volume. This agrees with the findings of most authors, although larger values have been reported. A distribution beyond the vascular space is suggested by the detection of ADH in lymph (415). The distribution volume for exogenous ADH appears to be three to four times greater in hypercalcemic than in normal rats (418).

The peripheral metabolism of ADH was thoroughly and critically reviewed recently by Lauson (420), and by Heller & Ginsburg (421). Working with rats, dogs, and man, Czaczkes & Kleeman (412) confirmed earlier findings that the half-life is related directly to body size. For arginine vasopressin it may range from about 1.0 min in the rat, to 4–24 min in man (421, 392). For lysine vasopressin in man, the half-life appears to be shorter (397).

The kidneys and liver are considered to be by far the major organs which remove ADH from the blood, although the role of the liver appears less important than previously thought. Lauson, Bocanegra & Beuzeville (422) estimated that at physiological doses of ADH in both dogs and rats, the liver removes about one third and the kidneys two thirds of the ADH. The suggestion that earlier reports of 50 per cent extraction by the liver may have been caused by very large concentrations of ADH has been supported by Little et al. (423). The mean extraction ratio in isolated perfused rat livers increased from 0.24 at physiological concentrations of 15–25 μU ADH per ml plasma to 0.63 at 1000–5000 μU ADH per ml.

Disagreement persists as to the proportion of a given dose of ADH which is excreted in the urine. Thorn & Smith (424) reported it to be about 12 per cent in unanesthetized dogs injected with 4–50 mU per kg arginine vasopressin. A somewhat lower figure of 7 per cent was observed in ethanol-inactin-anesthetized rats after the injection of 2 or 5 mU arginine vasopressin. This value increased to 24 per cent in hypercalcemic rats (418). Gauer & Tata (425), using physiological dosages in ethanol-anesthetized rats, recorded 75 per cent recovery in the urine after a single injection of 5 μU. In the same report, they present the hypothesis that 1–1.5 μU of ADH may saturate both kidneys in the rat, and that fluctuations in urine flow in the normally hydrated animal might be due to factors other than changes in the blood concentration of ADH. Harvey, Jones & Lee (419) measured the clearance of ADH in intact dogs, as well as in isolated canine kidneys. The amount of ADH excreted in the urine was always less than that extracted from the blood, and the renal clearance of ADH generally exceeded the inulin clearance. The studies involved artificially high blood concentrations of ADH. The conclusion that ADH, especially at low plasma concentrations, may be secreted by renal tubules as well as filtered, differs from that drawn in other studies on dogs (422, 424).

Mechanism of action of ADH.—Of the three major theories concerning the mode of action of ADH, one has been retracted by its original proponents (431), the second is sustained by further indirect evidence (432), and the third and latest is currently in favor (433).

The theory first proposed by Schwartz & Rasmussen, that an interchange between the disulfide bridge of ADH and sulfhydryl receptor sites leads to dilation of aqueous pores, was withdrawn by these authors and Rudinger (431, 434–436). They showed that analogs of oxytocin which lacked the disulfide bond nevertheless retained the biological activity of the posterior pituitary hormones, including typical antidiuretic activity. Fowl vasodepressor activity persists in a reduced form of oxytocin, lacking the disulfide bond (437).

Dicker & Franklin (432) confirmed the presence of hyaluronic acid in kidneys of pigs, sheep, and dogs. The renal acid mucopolysaccharides from these species could be depolymerized by hyaluronidase extracted from human urine. The authors reviewed the experimental evidence which in their opinion justifies keeping alive the hyaluronidase theory of Ginetzinsky (1958).

The evidence pointing to adenosine-3',5'-phosphate (cyclic AMP) as the intracellular mediator of the action of ADH has been brought up to date by Orloff & Handler, the originators of this theory (433). Cyclic AMP mimics the effect of ADH in perfused collecting tubules of the rabbit and, like ADH, is effective only when applied to the serosal surface (282). Incubation of toad bladder with theophylline, which presumably inhibits the breakdown of cyclic AMP to 5'-AMP, or with arginine vasopressin, led to a significant increase in the tissue concentrations of cyclic AMP; incubation with both substances had a synergistic effect (438). Potassium depletion inhibits osmotic water flow in toad bladder, whether mediated by ADH or by cyclic AMP (439). The inhibition appears to be due specifically to decreased intracellular K concentration, and not to some secondary effect. Since the response to cyclic AMP was also inhibited, Finn, Handler & Orloff (439) suggest that the K-dependent step in hormone-mediated permeability changes must lie beyond the formation of cyclic AMP. Similarities in the effects of a number of metabolic inhibitors on both ADH and cyclic AMP-mediated Na transport and permeability changes in toad bladder, led to a like conclusion (440). In contrast, prostaglandin appears to inhibit the production of cyclic AMP by ADH in toad bladder (127). Orloff & Handler (433) suggest that through this action, prostaglandin may moderate ADH-induced changes in permeability. The absence of ADH leads to a decrease in the urinary excretion of cyclic AMP. Aminophylline caused a perhaps unexpected slight decrease in the urinary excretion of cyclic AMP (441). Jones & Welt (442) showed that the content, and probably also the concentration, of ATP in the renal papilla were lower in rats exposed to endogenous or exogenous ADH than during water diuresis. No significant changes were observed in the cortical content or concentration of ATP. This finding is consistent with the view that ADH accelerates the degradation of ATP to cyclic AMP, although, as the authors point out, it does not prove it.

Effects of ADH on mammalian kidneys.—The influence of ADH on the water permeability of the mammalian nephron has now been tested by fairly direct methods. Gottschalk, Morel & Mylle (45) injected radioactive inulin and other labeled molecules into proximal and distal tubules of rats. During mannitol and saline diuresis, when concentration of endogenous ADH in the blood was assumed to be maximal, recovery of injected tritiated water averaged only 2 per cent for proximal and 5 per cent for distal injections. The considerably lower urinary recovery of tritiated water than of urea and sodium indicates a high water permeability of proximal and distal convolutions and collecting ducts under these conditions. In rats with surgically induced diabetes insipidus, total recovery of tritiated water injected into distal tubules averaged 19 per cent before ADH and 11 per cent after injection of large doses of this hormone (448). The possible influence of tubular flow rates on water reabsorption was presumably eliminated by increasing urine flow during ADH administration by the simultaneous infusion of mannitol. On a theoretical basis, Morel, Mylle & Gottschalk (448) concluded that ADH increases the diffusion permeability for water of the luminal surfaces of the distal convolutions and collecting ducts, but not of the basal surfaces of these structures.

Ullrich and co-workers (156) perfused tubular segments with hyper- or hypotonic mannitol or raffinose solutions with Na concentrations which prevented net flux of NaCl. Osmotic permeability coefficients, calculated from the rates at which osmotic equilibrium with plasma was reached, were expressed as ml cm^{-2} sec^{-1} (cm H$_2$O)$^{-1}$. During antidiuresis, the coefficient was 17.4×10^{-8} in the proximal, and 7.6×10^{-8} in the distal tubule. In rats with electrolytically induced diabetes insipidus, the value in the proximal tubule did not change significantly, but it decreased to 2.6×10^{-8} in the distal convolution. Maude, Shehadeh & Solomon (170) determined a value about 100 times lower in the distal tubule of *Necturus*, 4.1×10^{-10}. Grantham & Burg (282) found that ADH increased the net water absorption along an osmotic gradient, as well as the diffusional permeability to water, of isolated perfused collecting tubules of the rabbit (281). The proportionate increase in both variables, in contrast to amphibian membranes, suggests that in the collecting ducts ADH induces an increase predominantly in the number rather than in the size of aqueous channels. They also demonstrated in the mammalian nephron, as previously shown clearly in amphibian membranes, that ADH acts only when applied to the serosal surface. Skadhauge reached the same conclusion on the basis of experiments using the portal circulation of the avian kidney (449).

Studies on the influence of ADH on the handling of Na, water, and urea in the renal medulla continue to be plagued by methodological difficulties. Several attempts have been made to attack this problem by tissue analysis. Such analyses must be interpreted cautiously in drawing conclusions regarding transport rates because the degree of tissue concentration is obviously not a function solely of the rate of reabsorption. Other variables, such as the effectiveness of countercurrent diffusion or intratubular and intravascular flow rates, contribute to the maintenance of a given tissue concentration. Tissue analyses can furnish fairly accurate information on sequestration of solutes only. Thus far, micropuncture techniques have not solved this problem because of difficulty in puncturing intramedullary structures in intact kidneys which remain fully responsive to ADH.

Appelboom, Brodsky & Scott (380) estimated the proportion of the total papillary "interstitial" osmolality contributed by the collecting ducts in dogs. On the basis of PAH concentration in the urine and in the papillary tip, they concluded that collecting-duct fluid could not have occupied more than 10 per cent of the total fluid in this portion of the kidney. Gardner (450) has pointed out the hazards of using dry weight as a point of reference for expressing renal tissue composition. He showed that during K deficiency in rats, not only the weight but also the density of nonaqueous materials might change enough to obscure differences in absolute water and solute content when dry weight was used as the common denominator. Since the change in density may be due largely to changes in urea, Saikia (451) has proposed the use of urea-free dry solid as a reference point.

Saikia (452) compared the renal tissue composition of rats in acute water diuresis with that after acute administration of ADH. One-half hour after interrupting water diuresis with ADH there was a rise in the inner medullary content of urea, but no significant change in Na content. On the basis of similar findings in rats with hereditary hypothalamic diabetes insipidus, Valtin (453) suggested that ADH influences neither the deposition of Na into the medullary interstitium nor the medullary blood flow. In these animals, which probably have an absolute deficiency of ADH, the medullary and papillary contents of Na did not differ significantly from those in normal rats, nor did these contents increase after treatment with exogenous ADH. In contrast, the contents of urea in both medulla and papilla were very much lower in diabetic than in normal animals, and increased significantly with ADH therapy. Cross & Sherrington, on the other hand (454), agree with an earlier conclusion that ADH promotes the papillary sequestration of Na. White & Rolf (455) studied the time-course of rises in urinary and papillary osmolalities following reversal of acute water diuresis by ADH in dogs. Within 5.5 min after the intravenous injection of 100 mU ADH, urine had become hypertonic, although equilibration with papillary osmolality did not occur until about 10 min after giving ADH. Papillary osmolal and sodium concentrations rose progressively between 5.5 and 13 min after ADH.

Fourman & Kennedy (456) present histological evidence that more of a fluorescent dye appears in the vasa recta in the absence of ADH than in its presence. The authors imply that ADH aids the concentration of urine partly by decreasing medullary blood flow. As Thorn (19) has pointed out, this suggestion involves the assumptions that staining was a function solely of the medullary blood flow and was not influenced by the osmolality of the surrounding medium, and that the intensity of staining could be quantified fairly accurately.

Effects of ADH on amphibian membranes.—As in previous years, more progress has been made in defining the effects of ADH on amphibian than on mammalian membranes. This topic was reviewed recently by Leaf (426) and by Schwartz & Walter (427). The tendency to extrapolate results on amphibian membranes to the mammalian nephron is dangerous. For example, there is still no evidence that ADH influences Na transport or urea permeability in the kidneys of mammals, even though such an effect of the hormone on amphibian membranes has long been known.

Civan, Kedem & Leaf (428) have presented evidence that ADH stimulates Na transport in the toad bladder by reducing a passive permeability barrier to Na, not by enhancing the potential of the Na pump. Under conditions of zero net flux for Na, when the driving force for Na was abolished, the addition of ADH increased the transepithelial electrical potential. Indirect confirmation that the site of the ADH-sensitive permeability barrier is at the mucosal surface followed from the observation that ADH significantly increased the tissue content of THO and ^{14}C-urea, but not of ^{14}C-thiourea, when these were added to the medium bathing the mucosal surface of the toad bladder (11). A similar conclusion for the permeability barrier for water was adduced from swelling of epithelial cells and intercellular spaces of frog bladder under the stimulus of oxytocin (429). Evidence for the existence of at least two permeability barriers in series was presented by Lichtenstein & Leaf (430). The addition of amphotericin B, a polyene antibiotic, to the mucosal bathing medium led to an increase in Na transport and permeability of urea without significantly affecting the net flow of water. The latter could be influenced only by ADH. The authors inferred from these findings that amphotericin B influences the permeability of a dense diffusion barrier for small solutes. A second, porous barrier appears to be acted upon by ADH alone, to induce bulk flow of water.

Factors which modify the effects of ADH.—Analyses to define the number and characteristics of H-dependent steps in ADH-controlled regulation of transepithelial water flow in the isolated toad bladder were advanced by Gulyassy & Edelman (443). Adenyl cyclase, which catalyzes the conversion of ATP to cyclic AMP, has an optimum pH of 7.2–8.2, in contrast to ADH, which is inhibited by acidification in the range of pH 8.4–6.7. The effect of pH on the antidiuretic action of cyclic AMP depends on the concentration of the latter. The results suggest to the authors that different mechanisms operate to inhibit the response above and below the optimum pH of 7.0. The influence of urinary pH on the renal action of ADH in mammals remains unclear, mostly because of the lack of adequate methods. Goodman & Levitin (444) used maximum concentrating ability in the rat together with $T^c_{H_2O}$ measurements in dogs to evaluate the mechanisms underlying the reduced osmolal concentration of alkaline urine. From these measurements they inferred a possible inhibitory effect of increased papillary P_{CO_2} upon ADH-induced water permeability in the collecting ducts.

Ullman, Czaczkes & Menzel (445) induced water diuresis in anesthetized dogs by infusing ethanol and large quantities of hypotonic solutions. The antidiuretic effect of ADH was enhanced during administration of ammonium chloride. Taborsky (446) investigated the possibility that one step in the ADH-mediated reduction of urine flow might be the activation of carbonic anhydrase. He found that acetazolamide inhibited the antidiuretic effect of ADH and, to a lesser extent, of nicotine in the rat. Since the data can be explained by the diuretic action of acetazolamide simply opposing the antidiuretic action of ADH, these experiments do not seem to establish a role for carbonic anhydrase in the action of ADH.

Schwartz & Walter (427) have discussed various factors which modify the permeability response of the toad bladder to arginine vasopressin. The hormone-induced net transfer of water out of the bladder could be inhibited by repeated exposure to large doses of the peptide, by an as yet unidentified factor which was released by the bladder into the bath, by low temperatures, low pH, and low concentrations of Na or K, or by high concentration of Ca in the serosal medium. Repeated exposure to low doses of the peptide enhanced the response. In micropuncture experiments, raising the intratubular concentration of calcium from 0 to 15 meq/liter decreased distal tubular permeability to water in nondiuretic rats (447). Calcium had no effect on the proximal tubular permeability. It could not be determined whether the effect on the distal tubule represented an interaction with ADH.

Diabetes insipidus.—The mechanism by which natrichloriuretic drugs ameliorate diabetes insipidus has not been clarified. Kennedy, Skadhauge & Hague (457) disproved the hypothesis that a decrease in plasma osmolality and a consequent primary reduction in thirst is involved, for in diabetes insipidus rats on a high sodium intake, hydrochlorothiazide reduced urine volume without a reduction in plasma osmolality. In normal rats and rats made obese through hypothalamic lesions, water turnover was increased after hydrochlorothiazide even though their plasma osmolality fell. Skadhauge (458) measured the antidiuretic effect of natriuretic drugs in rats with surgically induced diabetes insipidus. When this effect was expressed as reduction in free-water clearance, the degree of antidiuresis induced by thiazides fluctuated with the extent of NaCl depletion. The antidiuretic effect continued beyond the period of drug administration when depletion of NaCl was maintained by starvation. A rough direct correlation was established between the magnitude of the antidiuretic effect (i.e., decrease in free-water clearance) and the degree of NaCl depletion induced by the nonthiazide natriuretic drugs. The author concluded that the antidiuretic effect of thiazides in diabetes insipidus is a function of NaCl depletion. GFR was not measured.

McDonald & de Wardener (459) showed, in cross-circulation experiments on dogs, that hypotonic urine can be formed in the presence of ADH even when solute output decreases. They suggest that the effect may be due to the presence of a circulating diuretic substance. Dlouhá et al. (460) detected a diuretic factor in water-loaded infant rats, and Mills (461) has found a diuretic hormone in the American cockroach.

The issue of what inhibits acute water diuresis in adrenal insufficiency remains unresolved. Kleeman, Czaczkes & Cutler (464) were unable to detect decreased degradation of, or increased sensitivity to, ADH in adrenal insufficiency. Nor could they detect ADH in the peripheral venous plasma of humans, dogs, and rats with adrenal insufficiency, who had been given large water loads, even though water diuresis was impaired. They therefore concluded that ADH is not responsible for the inhibition. The contrary conclusion was reached by Ahmed et al. (410) who reported sustained, abnormally high plasma concentrations of ADH after acute water loads in patients with adrenal insufficiency. When such patients were treated with glucocorticoids, a normal diuretic response was accompanied by falls in plasma ADH concentrations to undetectable levels. The possibility that adrenal glucocorticoids may, in part, restore acute water diuresis in adrenal insufficiency by decreasing the water permeability of the distal nephron, is supported by the finding that dexamethasone decreases reabsorption of water in the distal tubules of adrenalectomized rats (465).

The search for physiological functions of ADH analogs in nonmammalian vertebrates raises interesting implications for the evolution of renal function. As suggested by Dantzler (462) and Sawyer (463), the predominantly vascular effect of these natural analogs may have been diminished or lost as a more efficient tubular effect developed.

RENAL ACTION OF ALDOSTERONE

Much progress has been made in clarifying the mode of action of aldosterone. Sharp & Leaf (13) recently reviewed this topic comprehensively. Although it is widely accepted that aldosterone stimulates DNA-dependent synthesis of RNA, how this process enhances Na transport is disputed. There are two opposing views: that a permease-like action of the newly synthesized protein facilitates passive entry of Na into an intracellular transport pool (16, 466, 467); or that enzymatic steps involved in the production of high-energy intermediates for the Na pump are stimulated (468–470). Since most of the literature concerning the aldosterone effects on amphibian membranes was reviewed by Sharp & Leaf (13), we will comment only on those papers dealing with the action of aldosterone on the kidney.

Enhancement by aldosterone of Na transport in the distal nephron has been demonstrated by a number of approaches. Yunis et al. (471) reached this conclusion on the basis of clearance studies in hydropenic man. Because injection of hydrocortisone resulted in an increase in $T^c_{H_2O}$, they concluded that the hormone also stimulated Na reabsorption from the ascending loops of Henle. Similar conclusions were drawn by Jick et al. (472) in patients with cirrhosis of the liver. Sigler, Forrest & Elkington

(473) and Kessler et al. (474) found a lower papillary Na concentration in adrenalectomized than in normal rats. Although the cause for the decrease is not known, it may at least in part have resulted from inhibited Na transport out of the ascending loops of Henle or collecting ducts. Using a modified stop-flow technique in rats, McEvoy, Hollmann & Senft (475) observed inhibition of distal tubular Na reabsorption after adrenalectomy.

Hierholzer, Wiederholt & Stolte (476) have shown that aldosterone influences Na transport not only in the distal nephron, but also in the proximal convolution. Using a combination of micropuncture techniques, they have neatly dissected the influence of mineralocorticoids on Na transport from the combined effects of the glucocorticoids on GFR and Na transport. The net transtubular transport of NaCl and water in the proximal and distal tubules was inhibited in adrenalectomized rats maintained on oral saline (476).

Elevation of early distal Na concentration suggests that Na transport in the loops of Henle is also impaired during adrenal insufficiency (477). These abnormalities could be corrected only by steroids with mineralocorticoid action. Surprisingly, the fraction of filtered fluid reabsorbed in the proximal tubule was increased in adrenalectomized rats, probably because of a prolonged tubular passage time. This may explain the failure to detect the depression of proximal intrinsic reabsorptive capacity in stop-flow experiments. Aldosterone further increased fractional reabsorption in the proximal tubule without significantly influencing passage time. The mineralocorticoid action of high dosages of cortisone, which would be expected to increase fractional reabsorption, was nullified by the simultaneous reduction in passage time due to the glucocorticoid effect, so that fractional reabsorption was normal. Dexamethasone given to adrenalectomized rats decreased fractional reabsorption in the proximal tubules by normalizing passage time without restoring reabsorptive capacity (465). It also appears to decrease distal water permeability (478). In view of the demonstrated influence of adrenal steroids on Na transport in the proximal convolution, it is interesting that Schwarz & Wolff (479) observed ultrastructural changes in the brush border of proximal tubular cells of hypophysectomized rats. Because similar findings were noted following adrenalectomy, the authors ascribed the changes to lack of adrenal hormones.

Stimulation of RNA synthesis by aldosterone in rat kidneys was demonstrated by Castles & Williamson (480). The increased RNA synthesis was inhibited by actinomycin D. The results support the view that the stimulation of Na transport by aldosterone is mediated through DNA-dependent synthesis of messenger RNA. A similar conclusion was suggested by two other studies which utilized actinomycin D. Wiederholt (481) showed that the antibiotic reduced isotonic reabsorption, as measured by the split-droplet method, in proximal and distal convolutions of rats which had aldosterone, but not in animals which lacked the hormone. Thus, actinomycin D inhibited only that portion of Na reabsorption influenced by aldosterone.

Ludens, Hook & Williamson (482) found in rats that actinomycin D inhibited aldosterone-induced renal Na retention only when administered one hour prior to administration of the hormone, but not if given after aldosterone.

According to Fanestil & Edelman (483) specific receptors for aldosterone are located in the nuclear fraction of renal cells. Following the subcutaneous injection of ^{3}H-d-aldosterone to adrenalectomized rats, homogenates of the kidneys were separated by differential centrifugation into nuclear, mitochondrial, microsomal, and supernatant fractions. The nuclear fraction had the highest saturation at increasing plasma levels of aldosterone. The uptake of aldosterone by the nuclear fraction, but not by any of the other fractions, could be inhibited competitively by 9-α-fluorocortisol, but not by steroids without mineralocorticoid activity. Since proteolytic enzymes accelerated the release of labeled aldosterone from the nuclear fraction, it is assumed that the specific receptors are proteins. In normal (not adrenalectomized) dogs, Hollander et al. (484) obtained different results. Fifteen minutes after the injection of ^{3}H-d-aldosterone, 60–70 per cent of the renal activity was in the supernatant fraction of kidney homogenates, and only 20–30 per cent in the nuclear fraction. Radioautographs revealed a high concentration of the labeled aldosterone along the wall of convoluted tubular cells.

Tubular Action of Angiotensin

Numerous clearance studies were performed to elucidate the effect of angiotensin on tubular Na reabsorption. Two fundamental difficulties inherent in the clearance method prevent this technique from yielding detailed information about tubular Na transport: clearances can measure only net changes in Na handling without pinpointing the factor(s) which caused the change or localizing the site(s) at which the change occurred; and clearance studies cannot distinguish between an indirect effect of angiotensin on tubular Na reabsorption, brought about by its well known vasoactive influence, and the direct influence of the peptide on the tubular epithelium.

Both diuretic and antidiuretic responses to angiotensin have been reported. Which response is seen may depend on the dose and on the species of experimental animal. Barraclough, Jones & Marsden (485) infused small, subpressor doses of angiotensin (0.5–5 mμg per kg per min) into unanesthetized rats; urinary Na excretion was reduced. Since the plasma concentration of a constantly infused radioactive glomerular filtration marker did not change during the infusion of angiotensin, they concluded that the reduced Na excretion was due to facilitated tubular Na reabsorption rather than to a decrease in GFR. Higher doses of angiotensin (50 mμg per kg per min) had a biphasic response, antinatriuresis followed by natriuresis. An angiotensin-induced reduction in urinary Na excretion was also observed by Eisalo & Räsänen (486). Sodium retention considerably extended the pressor effect of angiotensin. A natriuretic effect of angiotensin in unilaterally nephrectomized rats maintained on 1.0 per cent NaCl as drinking fluid was found by Peters (487) in clearance experiments. When the peptide was infused intravenously at 0.2 μg per min per kg BW, urine flow and Na excretion increased significantly, while GFR remained unchanged.

In the course of an intensive study of renal function in chickens, Cuypers (488) introduced angiotensin into the renal portal circulation. Consistently, he found an equal increase in GFR on both sides, though Na, Cl, and water excretion on the infused side was more pronounced. Langford & Fallis (489) reported similar results, although in their experiments GFR varied considerably on both sides. Both groups suppose that angiotensin directly inhibits tubular reabsorption of Na in the chicken.

Healy et al. (490) and Lameijer, Soghikian & de Graeff (491) found antidiuresis in dogs following the intravenous infusion of low doses (0.003–0.025 μg per kg per min). This could be attributed to the simultaneous decrease in GFR. At higher doses of angiotensin (0.06–0.13 μg per kg per min), an initial decrease in GFR was followed by a return toward normal values at which Na excretion was markedly enhanced. The natriuresis was interpreted to indicate a direct inhibition of tubular Na reabsorption by angiotensin. The inhibitory effect is transient, for the natriuresis declined when administration of high doses of angiotensin was continued for up to 50 min. The conclusion that angiotensin interferes with tubular Na reabsorption must be qualified because, at both dosage levels, there was accompanying systemic hypertension. Such increase in arterial pressure is known to increase Na excretion independently of changes in GFR.

A complex series of changes in renal function in anesthetized dogs following the administration of angiotensin was reported by Louis & Doyle (492). With doses smaller than 0.05 μg per kg per min, Na excretion fell, but as the doses were increased up to 2.5 μg per kg per min, a biphasic response occurred. An initial, transient antidiuretic effect was followed by a marked increase in Na excretion and urine flow. Again, the accompanying rise in arterial pressure observed in this study may partly account for the natriuresis. The dependency of angiotensin-induced fractional Na excretion on the level of arterial pressure may also be inferred from the work of Collignon & Kulbertus (493). They were unable to induce increased Na excretion with angiotensin in isolated, perfused canine kidneys unless the perfusion pressure was high. A dosage-dependent biphasic response to angiotensin was also demonstrated in unanesthetized rabbits by Langford & Pickering (494). During infusion of 0.2 μg per kg per min of synthetic angiotensin, urine volume as well as Na excretion declined in three out of five experiments. GFR and C_{PAH} were not measured at this dosage level. At large doses of angiotensin (1 μg per kg per min), urine flow and Na excretion greatly increased, and urinary Na concentration approached values in systemic plasma. In these experiments, there was no correlation with GFR, but renal blood flow routinely decreased. A partial natriuretic effect of increased arterial pressure might be deduced from the further observation that doses of norepinephrine mimicked the diuretic response to angiotensin.

A natriuretic effect of angiotensin in conscious rabbits was also demonstrated by Akinkugbe, Brown & Cranston (495). Infusion of 1 µg per kg per min of angiotensin into one renal artery led to a fivefold increase in urine volume and a twentyfold increase in Na excretion on the infused side as compared to the contralateral side. Adrenalectomy or saline loading did not affect the natriuretic response to an intravenous infusion of angiotensin in the rabbit. Arterial pressure showed a prompt and sustained rise during the infusion of the peptide (496). The authors deemed it possible that several of the effects observed might have been induced by a change in the intrarenal distribution of blood flow, rather than by a direct effect upon tubular cells.

Cannon, Ames & Laragh (497) support the view that the peptide does not inhibit tubular Na reabsorption directly, but rather as a consequence of its effects on the systemic and renal circulations. The antinatriuresis which follows the intravenous infusion into conscious dogs of up to 4 µg per min of angiotensin, as well as the hypertensive effect, was reversed by pentobarbital anesthesia. Direct renal arterial infusion of angiotensin in subpressor doses resulted in slight Na retention, whereas at pressor doses the electrolyte response was inconstant. When natriuresis did occur, the increment in Na excretion from the infused kidney did not significantly exceed that from the contralateral kidney. The authors suggest that the angiotensin molecule itself does not directly inhibit either tubular Na transport or the metabolic reactions which supply energy for this process. Ames et al. (498) studied the effect of prolonged angiotensin infusion on electrolyte balance in normal man. Angiotensin (0.16–2.6 µg per min) produced a marked renal retention of Na, even though arterial pressure was elevated. After 3.5 days of infusion, "escape" occurred, leading to increased salt excretion. Since angiotensin augmented aldosterone secretion by a mean of 360 per cent, the authors propose that angiotensin participates with aldosterone in the normal regulation of Na balance.

In kidney homogenates Bonting, Canady & Hawkins (499) found no influence of angiotensin on the activity of $(Na + K)$-activated ATPase. Negative findings were also reported by Marc-Aurèle & Bergeron (500) in a study of microsomal fractions of dog kidneys.

An inhibitory effect of angiotensin on tubular reabsorption of Na in rats has been postulated by Leyssac (195). As a measure of Na reabsorption in the proximal convolution, he utilized the time needed for complete tubular occlusion, following abrupt cessation of renal blood flow and GFR. In control experiments with spontaneously varying GFR, the occlusion time was shortened with increasing GFR. This indicated to Leyssac that GFR varies directly with the proximal tubular reabsorptive capacity for

Na. He assessed the effect of single intravenous injections of angiotensin on occlusion time, by beginning the measurement at the moment when the angiotensin-induced vasoconstriction caused visible blanching of the kidney. With increasing doses of angiotensin (5–25 ng), the inverse correlation between occlusion time and GFR diminished and then disappeared. At high doses, the occlusion time had a constant value of 23 sec over the entire range of GFR (0.8–2.0 ml per min per g kidney). The data suggested a regulatory effect of angiotensin on proximal tubular Na reabsorption. Using the same method for measuring tubular occlusion, Thurau et al. (501) could not confirm Leyssac's results. There was no inverse correlation between occlusion time and GFR in control experiments, nor was the occlusion time influenced by angiotensin in doses of 12.5 to 90 ng in single intravenous injections.

The more direct micropuncture methods were used by Horster et al. (146) to evaluate the influence of angiotensin on tubular Na reabsorption. Half-time reabsorption of isotonic saline in the proximal convolution of rats, as determined by the split-droplet method, was constant at GFR's ranging between 0.7 and 1.3 ml per min per g kidney. Furthermore, angiotensin had no effect on half-time reabsorption, whether it was applied at the luminal side in concentrations of $25–250 \times 10^{-6}$ g per 100 ml, or at the peritubular side by intravenous infusion of 0.18×10^{-6} g per min per kg body weight. In addition, angiotensin did not affect Na reabsorption along single perfused loops of Henle when its concentration in the perfusate was 0.5 or 5.0×10^{-6} g per 100 ml. The authors concluded that urinary Na excretion is altered by angiotensin through some intrarenal action(s) other than a direct effect upon intrinsic tubular reabsorptive capacity.

Isolated Kidney Preparations

Efforts to develop satisfactory preparations of isolated, perfused kidneys continue. Rosenfeld, Kraus & McCullen (502) compared the functioning of intact kidneys with that in their preparation of an isolated rabbit kidney perfused with whole blood in an artificial heart-lung system. Subnormal function in the perfused kidney was reflected by a Na excretion of 6.1 per cent of the filtered load, a U/P creatinine of 16, a creatinine clearance of 27 ml per 100 g kidney per min, and a blood flow of 215 ml per 100 g kidney per min. The last two values may have been low because of the relatively low perfusion pressure of about 82 mm Hg. After two to four hours of perfusion, the preparation gradually deteriorated. Schröder, Ochwadt & Bethge (503) succeeded in reducing the period of renal ischemia to 80 sec by cannulating the renal vein and artery of dogs *in situ*. Blood in the cannulas was oxygenated artificially, and an infusion of 20 per cent mannitol was begun prior to isolation. Despite these efforts, renal blood flow and O_2 consumption decreased to 77 and 59 per cent of normal values, respectively; GFR, which was only 42 per cent of normal during the first 15 min of isolation, continued to decline thereafter. Diminished concentrating ability was reflected by an osmolal U/P of about 1.3, and fractional Na reabsorption was only 0.95. Within 12 min after the perfused kidney was reconnected to the systemic circulation, function was restored almost to normal.

Lockett (504) perfused kidneys of cats from a heart-lung circuit. Renal blood flow and O_2 consumption appeared to be normal, and the Na excretion, which was initially increased, became normal after addition of aldosterone to the circulating blood. Time-courses were not given. Bahlmann et al. (505) perfused isolated rat kidneys with recirculating Krebs-Henseleit solution containing 5.5 per cent albumin, and analyzed tubular function by micropuncture. Although the rate of perfusion was three to four times greater than the normal renal blood flow, GFR declined to 0.57 ml per g kidney per min during the first hour, and to 0.34 ml during the second hour. Forty per cent of the filtered fluid was reabsorbed by the end of the proximal convolution, and the half-time reabsorption of isotonic saline in this segment, as measured by the split-droplet method, was prolonged by 50 per cent over normal. Twenty-four per cent of filtered Na appeared in the early distal segment; TF/P for Na was close to unity at this point, and declined toward the end of the distal convolution. Reabsorption of Na along the distal convolution and collecting duct was calculated to be 16 per cent of tubular load, which is slightly greater than that observed in kidneys *in situ*. Eight per cent of the filtered Na appeared in the urine. The data suggest that in the perfused rat kidney, decreased fractional reabsorption of Na in the proximal tubules is not fully compensated by the slight increase of fractional reabsorption in the distal nephron, so that a Na diuresis results.

ACKNOWLEDGMENTS

The authors would like to acknowledge the excellent secretarial assistance of Anneliese Geltinger and Lawrence Morin in preparing the bibliography and the manuscript. We are also indebted to Dr. David Levine for valuable comments on some sections of this review.

LITERATURE CITED

1. *Proc. III Intern. Congr. Nephrol., Washington* (Hans Huber, Basel-New York, 1967): Vol. **I**, *Physiology* (Handler, J. S., Ed., 288 pp.); Vol. **II**, *Morphology, Immunology, Urology* (Heptinstall, R. H., Ed., 363 pp.); Vol. **III**, *Clinical Nephrology* (Becker, E. L., Ed., 382 pp.)

2. *Handbuch der Inneren Medizin,* **VIII**, *Nierenkrankheiten* (Schwiegk, H., Ed., Springer-Verlag, Berlin- Heidelberg-New York, 2920 pp., 1967)

3. *Progress in Pyelonephritis* (Kass, E. H., Ed., F. A. Davis Co., Philadelphia, 766 pp., 1965)

4. *Normale und pathologische Funktionen des Nierentubulus* (Ullrich, K. J., Hierholzer, K., Eds., Hans Huber, Bern-Stuttart, 465 pp., 1965)

5. *Renal Metabolism and Epidemiology of Some Renal Diseases* (Metcoff, J., Ed., Natl. Kidney Found., New York, 344 pp., 1964)

6. *Ultrastructure of the Kidney* (Dalton, A. J., Hagueneau, F., Eds., Academic Press, New York, 240 pp., 1967)

7. *Biological Membranes: Recent Progress. Ann. N.Y. Acad. Sci.,* **137**, Art. 2, 403–1048 (Loewenstein, W. R., Ed., N.Y. Academy of Sciences, New York, 1966)

8. Leaf, A. Transepithelial transport and its hormonal control in toad bladder. *Ergebn. Physiol.,* **56**, 216–63 (1965)

9. Bentley, P. J. The physiology of the urinary bladder of amphibia. *Biol. Rev.,* **41**, 275–316 (1966)

10. Tosteson, D. C. Membrane transport of Na and K. A synopsis of contemporary concepts and experiments. *Physiologist,* **9**, 89–96 (1966)

11. *The State and Movement of Water in Living Organisms* (Fogg, G. E., Ed., Cambridge Univ. Press, New York, 432 pp., 1965)

12. Skou, J. C. Enzymatic basis for active transport of Na^+ and K^+ across cell membrane. *Physiol. Rev.,* **45**, 596–617 (1965)

13. Sharp, G. E., Leaf, A. Mechanism of action of aldosterone. *Physiol. Rev.,* **46**, 593–633 (1966)

14. *Symposium on Antidiuretic Hormones* (Schwartz, I. L., Schwartz, W. B., Eds., *Am. J. Med.,* **42**, 651–827, 1967)

15. *The Pituitary Gland,* **3** (Harris, G. W., Donovan, B. T., Eds., Univ. of California Press, Berkeley and Los Angeles, 678 pp., 1966)

16. Thorn, N. A. The influence of the neurohypophysial hormones and similar polypeptides on the kidney. In *Handb. Exptl. Pharmacol.,* **23**, *Neurohypophysial Hormones and Similar Polypeptides* (Berde, B., Ed., Springer-Verlag, Berlin-Heidelberg-New York, 785 pp., 1967)

17. *Neuroendocrinology,* **I** (Martini, L., Ganong, W. F., Eds., Academic Press, New York, London, 774 pp., 1966)

18. *Aktuelle Probleme der Nephrologie* (Wolff, H. P., Krück, F., Eds., Springer-Verlag, Berlin-Heidelberg-New York, 465 pp., 1966)

19. *Renin Mechanisms and Hypertension. Circ. Res.,* **20/21**, *Suppl. II* (Wood, J. E., Ed., 226 pp., 1967)

20. *Proc. Intern. Symp. Angiotensin, Sodium and Hypertension* (Genest, J., Marc-Aurele, J., de Mignault, J. L., Eds., *Can. Med. Assoc. J.,* **90**, No. 4, 153–341 (1964)

21. Munck, A. The effects of hormones at the cellular level in: *Recent Advances in Endocrinology* (James, V. H. T., deMowbray, R., Eds., Churchill Ltd., London, 1968)

22. Bittar, E. E. *Cell pH* (Butterworths, London, 137 pp., 1964)

23. Dick, D. A. T. *Cell Water* (Butterworths, London, 155 pp., 1966)

24. Kernan, C. P. *Cell K* (Butterworths, London, 159 pp., 1966)

25. *Water and Electrolyte Metabolism,* **II** (DeGraeff, J. Leijnse, B., Eds., Elsevier, Amsterdam-London-New York, 251 pp., 1964)

26. *Sekretion und Exkretion* (Wohlfarth-Bottermann, K. E., Ed., Springer-Verlag, Berlin-Heidelberg-New York, 404 pp., 1965)

27. Baer, J. E., Beyer, K. H. Renal pharmacology, *Ann. Rev. Pharmacol.,* **6**, 261–92 (1966)

28. Welt, L. G., Sachs, J. R., Gitelman, H. J. Electrolyte and mineral metabolism. *Ann. Rev. Pharmacol.,* **6**, 77–88 (1966)

29. *Transport und Funktion intrazellulärer Elektrolyte* (Krück, F., Ed., Urban and Schwarzenberg, München-Berlin-Wien, 299 pp., 1967)

30. DeGraff, A. C., Lyon, A. F. *Diuretic Therapy* (Mosby, St. Louis, 41 pp., 1965)

31. Peters, G. Pharmacology of diuretics, In *Antihypertensive Therapy*, 31–57 (Gross, F., Ed., Springer-Verlag, Berlin-Heidelberg-New York, 632 pp., 1966)

32. *The Physiology of Diuretic Agents. Ann. N.Y. Acad. Sci.*, **139**, Art. 2, 273–539 (Seldin, D. W., Ed., N.Y. Academy of Sciences, New York, 1966)

33. Kelman, R. B. Mathematical analysis of sodium reabsorption in proximal part of nephron in presence of nonreabsorbed solute. *J. Theoret. Biol.*, **8**, 22–26 (1965)

34. Kelman, R. B., Marsh, D. J., Howard, H. C. Nonmonotonicity of solutions of linear differential equations occuring in the theory of urine formation. *STAM Rev.*, **8**, 463–78 (1966)

35. Marsh, D. J., Kelman, R. B., Howard, H. C. The theory of urine formation in water diuresis with implications for antidiuresis. *Bull. Math. Biophys.*, **29**, 67–89 (1967)

36. Stephenson, J. L. Ability of counterflow systems to concentrate. *Nature*, **206**, 1215–1219 (1965)

37. Stephenson, J. L. Concentration in renal counterflow systems. *Biophys. J.*, **6**, 539–51 (1966)

38. Macey, R. I. Hydrodynamics in the renal tubule. *Bull. Math. Biophys.*, **27**, 117–24 (1965)

39. Levine, S. N. A model for renal-electrolyte regulation. *J. Theoret. Biol.*, **11**, 242–56 (1966)

40. Friedlander, S. K., Walser, M. Some aspects of flow and diffusion in the proximal tubule of the kidney. *J. Theoret. Biol.*, **8**, 87–96 (1965)

41. DeHaven, J. C., Shapiro, N. Z. On the control of urine formation. *Nephron, Suppl. 4* (1967)

42. Shehadeh, I., Maude, D. L., Scott, W. N., Solomon, A. K. Absorption of inulin by the renal tubule of the rat. *Physiologist*, **7**, 254 (1964)

43. Scott, W. N., Maude, D. L., Shehadeh, I., Solomon, A. K. Inulin and albumin absorption from the proximal tubule in *Necturus* kidney. *Science*, **146**, 1588–90 (1964)

44. Gutman, Y., Gottschalk, C. W., Lassiter, W. E. Micropuncture study of inulin absorption in the rat kidney. *Science*, **147**, 753–54 (1965)

45. Gottschalk, C. W., Morel, F., Mylle, M. Tracer microinjection studies of renal tubular permeability. *Am. J. Physiol.*, **209**, 173–78 (1965)

46. Baumann, K., Oelert, H., Rumrich, G., Ullrich, K. J. Ist Inulin zur Messung des Glomerulumfiltrates beim Warmblüter geeignet? *Arch. Ges. Physiol.*, **282**, 238–41 (1965)

47. Marsh, D., Frasier, C. Reliability of inulin for determining volume flow in rat renal cortical tubules. *Am. J. Physiol.*, **209**, 283–86 (1965)

48. Tanner, G. A., Klose, R. M. Micropuncture study of inulin reabsorption in *Necturus* kidney. *Am. J. Physiol.*, **211**, 1036–38 (1966)

49. Sonnenberg, H. Inulin loss from rat proximal tubule. *Experientia*, **22**, 683–84 (1966)

50. Maude, D. L., Scott, W. N., Shehadeh, I., Solomon, A. K. Further studies on the behavior of inulin and serum albumin in rat kidney tubule. *Arch. Ges. Physiol.*, **285**, 313–16 (1965)

51. Scott, W. N., Maude, D. L., Shehadeh, I., Solomon, A. K. Transtubular movement of albumin in *Necturus* kidney. *Am. J. Physiol.*, **211**, 1039–42 (1966)

52. Bank, N., Mutz, B. F., Aynedjian, H. S. The role of leakage of tubular fluid in anuria due to mercury poisoning. *J. Clin. Invest.*, **46**, 695–704 (1967)

53. Vurek, G. G., Pegram, S. E. Fluorometric method for the determination of nanogram quantities of inulin. *Anal. Biochem.*, **16**, 409–19 (1966)

54. Liewendahl, K., Tallgren, L. G., Rusk, J. Separation of inulin from chemically interfering dextrans by gel filtration. *Scand. J. Clin. Lab. Invest.*, **18**, 553–56 (1966)

55. Nagel, W., Wolff, G., Gigon, J. P., Enderlin, F. Zur Bestimmung der Inulinclearance in Gegenwart von Dextran. *Klin. Wochschr.*, **45**, 137–40 (1967)

56. Forland, M., Pullman, T. N., Lavender, A. R., Aho, I. The renal excretion of ethylenediaminetetraacetate in the dog. *J. Pharmacol. Exptl. Therap.*, **153**, 142–47 (1966)

57. Harvey, A., Malvin, R. L., Vander, A. J. Comparison of creatinine

secretion in men and women. *Nephron, 3,* 201–5 (1966)

58. Granberg, P. O., Reizenstein, P. Radiovitamin B$_{12}$ as a biological reference substance. III. Glomerular filtration rate. *Acta Med. Scand., 445,* 451–54 (1966)

59. Schmidt, H. A. E. Die Bestimmung des Glomerusfiltrats mit nuklearmedizinischer Technik. *Klin. Wochschr., 44,* 625–28 (1966)

60. Sigman, E. M., Elwood, C. M., Knox, F. The measurement of glomerular filtration rate in man with sodium iothalamate 131 I (Conray). *J. Nucl. Med., 7,* 60-63 (1965)

61. Nissen, O. I. The filtration fractions of plasma supplying the superficial and deep venous drainage area of the cat kidney. *Acta Physiol. Scand., 68,* 275–85 (1966)

62. Nissen, O. I. The relation between reabsorption rate and filtration rate in the superficial and deep venous drainage area of the cat kidney. *Ibid.,* 286–94 (1966)

63. Selkurt, E. E., Deetjen, P., Brechtelsbauer, H. Tubular pressure gradients and filtration dynamics during urinary stop flow in the rat. *Arch. Ges. Physiol., 286,* 19–35 (1965)

64. Gertz, K. H., Mangos, J. A., Braun, G., Pagel, H. D. Pressure in the glomerular capillaries of the rat kidney and its relation to arterial blood pressure. *Arch. Ges. Physiol., 288,* 369–74 (1966)

65. Koch, K. M., Dume, Th., Krause, H. H., Ochwadt, B. Intratubulärer Druck, glomerulärer Capillardruck und Glomerulumfiltrat während Mannit-Diurese. *Arch. Ges. Physiol., 295,* 72–79 (1967)

66. Krause, H. H., Dume, Th., Koch, K. M., Ochwadt, B. Intratubulärer Druck, glomerulärer Capillardruck und Glomerulumfiltrat nach Furosemid und Hydrochlorothiazid. *Ibid.,* 80–89

67. Gekle, D., Bruchhausen, F. v., Fuchs, G. Über die Größe der Porenäquivalente in isolierten Basalmembranen der Rattennierenrinde. *Arch. Ges. Physiol., 289,* 180–90 (1966)

68. Bruchhausen, F. v., Merker, H. J. Gewinnung und morphologische Charakterisierung einer Basalmembranfraktion aus der Nierenrinde der Ratte. *Arch. Exptl. Pathol. Pharmacol., 251,* 1–12 (1965)

69. Lange, C. F. Markowitz, A. S. Chemistry of whole human glomerular basement membranes and of a soluble fraction prepared by trypsinization. *Biochem. Biophys. Acta, 101,* 217–20 (1965)

70. Dische, R. M., Pappas, G. D., Graver, A., Dische, Z. The carbohydrate of basement membranes of human kidney glomeruli. *Biochem. Biophys. Res. Commun., 20,* 63–70 (1965)

71. Misra, R. P., Berman, L. B. Studies on glomerular basement membrane 1. Isolation and chemical analysis of normal glomerular basement membrane. *Proc. Soc. Exptl. Biol. Med., 122,* 705–10 (1966)

72. Bruchhausen, F. v., Merker, H. J. Morphologischer und chemischer Aufbau isolierter Basalmembranen aus der Nierenrinde der Ratte. *Histochemie, 8,* 90–108 (1967)

73. Ladefoged, J. Measurements of the renal blood flow in man with the [133]Xenon washout technique. A description of the method. *Scand. J. Clin. Lab. Invest., 18,* 299–315 (1966)

74. Thorburn, G. D., Kopald, H. H., Herd, J. A. Hollenberg, M., O'Morchoe, C. C. C., Barger, A. C. Intrarenal distribution of nutrient blood flow determined with krypton 85 in the unanesthetized dog. *Circ. Res., 13,* 290–307 (1963)

75. Ladefoged, J., Pedersen, F., Doutheil, U., Deetjen, P., Selkurt, E. E. Renal blood flow measured with Xenon-133 washout technique and with an electromagnetic flowmeter. *Arch. Ges. Physiol., 284,* 195–200 (1965)

76. Ladefoged, J., Pedersen, F. Renal blood flow, circulation times and vascular volume in normal man measured by the intra-arterial injection—external counting technique. *Acta Physiol. Scand., 69,* 220–39 (1967)

77. Bell, G., Harper, A. M. Measurement of local blood flow in the renal cortex from the clearance of krypton 85. *J. Surg. Res., 5,* 382–86 (1965)

78. Reubi, R. C., Gossweiler, N., Gürtler, R. Renal circulation in man studied by means of a dye-dilution

method. *Circulation,* **33,** 426–41 (1966)

79. Effros, R. M., Lowenstein, J., Baldwin, D. S., Chinard, F. P. Vascular and extravascular volumes of the kidney of man. *Circ. Res.,* **20,** 162–73 (1967)

80. Gómez, D. M., Demeester, M., Steinmetz, P. R., Lowenstein, J., Sammons, B. P., Baldwin, D. S., Chasis, H. Functional blood volume and distribution of specific blood flow in the kidney of man. *J. Appl. Physiol.,* **20,** 703–8 (1965)

81. Lowenstein, J., Steinmetz, P. R., Effros, R. M., Demeester, M., Chasis, H., Baldwin, D. S., Gómez, D. M. The distribution of intrarenal blood flow in normal and hypertensive man. *Circulation,* **35,** 250–59 (1967)

82. Pedersen, F., Baerenholdt, O. Mean circulation time and fastest circulation time for red cells and plasma in the human kidney measured by an external counting method. *Scand. J. Clin. Lab. Invest.,* **18,** 245–53 (1966)

83. Pedersen, F., Ladefoged, J., Doutheil, U., Selkurt, E. E. Circulation times in the dog kidney measured by an external counting technique and by a dye dilution method. *Arch. Ges. Physiol.,* **286,** 36–43 (1965)

84. Chinard, F. P., Enns, T., Goresky, C. A., Nolan, M. F. Renal transit times and distribution volumes of T-1824, creatinine, and water. *Am. J. Physiol.,* **209,** 243–52 (1965)

85. Aukland, K., Bower, F. B., Berliner, R. W. Measurement of local blood flow with hydrogen gas. *Circ. Res.,* **14,** 164–87 (1964)

86. Haining, J. L., Turner, M. D. Tissue blood flow in rat kidneys by hydrogen desaturation. *J. Appl. Physiol.,* **21,** 1705–8 (1966)

87. Grängsjö, G., Ulfendahl, H. R., Wolgast, M. Determination of regional blood flow by means of small semiconductor detectors and red cells tagged with phosphorus-32. *Nature,* **211,** 1411–12 (1966)

88. Moffat, D. B. The distribution of red blood cells in the renal cortex. *Clin. Sci.,* **28,** 125–30 (1965)

89. Hársing, L., Bartha, J. Renal blood flow and *p*-amino-hippurate extraction in osmotic diuresis. *Acta Physiol. Acad. Sci. Hung.,* **30,** 225–32 (1966)

90. Hársing, L., Pelley, K. Die Bestimmung der Nierenmarkdurchblutung aus der Ablagerung und Verteilung von ⁸⁶Rb. *Arch. Ges. Physiol.,* **285,** 302–12 (1965)

91. Pilkington, L. A., Binder, R., de Haas, J. C. M., Pitts, R. F. Intrarenal distribution of blood flow. *Am. J. Physiol.,* **208,** 1107–13 (1965)

92. Gans, J. H., Wakefield, D., Kilscheimer, G. In vitro distribution of inulin and PAH in dog and sheep kidney cortex and medullary slices. *Proc. Soc. Exptl. Biol. Med.,* **122,** 624–26 (1966)

93. Murphy, G. P., Homsy, E. G., Scott, W. W. Evaluation of pharmacologically induced renal vasodilation. *J. Surg. Res.,* **5,** 525–37 (1966)

94. Harvey, R. B. Effects of acetylcholine infused into renal artery of dogs. *Am. J. Physiol.,* **211,** 487–97 (1966)

95. Ljungqvist, A. Structure of the arteriole-glomerular units in different zones of the kidney. Microangiographic and histologic evidence of an extraglomerular medullary circulation. *Nephron,* **1,** 329–37 (1965)

96. Wells, C. H., Bond, T. P., Guest, M. M. Changes in capillary blood flow induced by the extravascular application of hypertonic solutions: a possible mechanism for the control of renal medullary blood flow. *Texas Rept. Biol. Med.,* **23,** 128–33 (1965)

97. Yoshitoshi, Y., Honda, N., Morikawa, A., Seki, K. Alterations in the renal hemodynamics induced by increased renal vein pressure in the rabbit kidney. *Japan. Heart J.,* **7,** 289–99 (1966)

98. Gilmore, J. P. Contribution of baroreceptors to the control of renal function. *Circ. Res.,* **14,** 301–17 (1964)

99. Bálint, P., Châtel, R. Renal circulation and baroreceptor reflexes. *Acta Physiol. Hung.,* **28,** 363–71 (1965)

100. Matsushita, S. Absence of vagal control on renal circulation. *Tohoku J. Exptl. Med.,* **91,** 271–81 (1967)

101. Leichtweiss, H. P., Schröder, H., Weiss, Ch. Die Beziehung zwischen Perfusionsdruck und Perfusionsstromstärke an der mit Paraffinöl perfundierten isolierten

Rattenniere. *Arch. Ges. Physiol.,* **293,** 303–9 (1967)

102. Takeuchi, J., Kubo, T., Sawada, T., Funaki, E., Sanada, M., Kitagawa, T., Nakada, Y. Autoregulation of renal circulation. *Japan. Heart J.,* **6,** 243–55 (1965)

103. Haddy, F. J., Scott, J. B. Role of transmural pressure in local regulation of blood flow through kidney. *Am. J. Physiol.,* **208,** 825–31 (1965)

104. Gärtner, K. Das Volumen der interstitiellen Flüssigkeit der Niere bei Änderungen ihres hämodynamischen Widerstandes; Untersuchungen an Kaninchen. *Arch. Ges. Physiol.,* **292,** 1–12 (1966)

105. Åström, A., Crafoord, J. Afferent activity recorded in the kidney nerves of rats. *Acta Physiol. Scand.,* **70,** 10–15 (1967)

106. Zerbst, E., Brechmann, W. Die Abhängigkeit der Autoregulation der Niere von der Durchblutungsgröße. *Arch. Ges. Physiol.,* **285,** 26–34 (1965)

107. Scott, J. B., Daugherty, R. M., Jr., Dabney, J. M., Haddy, F. J. Role of chemical factors in regulation of flow through kidney, hindlimb, and heart. *Am. J. Physiol.,* **208,** 813–24 (1965)

108. Hashimoto, K., Kumakura, S. The pharmacological features of the coronary, renal, mesenteric, and femoral arteries. *Japan. J. Physiol.,* **15,** 540–51 (1965)

109. Ono, H., Inagaki, K., Hashimoto, K. A pharmacological approach to the nature of the autoregulation of the renal blood flow. *Japan. J. Physiol.,* **16,** 625–34 (1966)

110. Thurau, K. The nature of autoregulation of renal blood flow. *Proc. III Intern. Congr. Nephrol., Washington,* **I,** 162–73 (Hans Huber, Basel-New York, 288 pp., 1967)

111. Simmons, D. H., Olver, R. P. Effects of acute acid-base changes on renal hemodynamics in anesthetized dogs. *Am. J. Physiol.,* **209,** 1180–86 (1965)

112. Bersentes, T. J., Simmons, D. H. Effects of acute acidosis on renal hemodynamics. *Am. J. Physiol.,* **212,** 633–40 (1967)

113. Kirchheim, H. Die Wirkung von Tris (Hydroxymethyl) Aminomethan (THAM) auf die Nierendurchblutung im hämorrhagischen

Schock. *Arch. Ges. Physiol.,* **286,** 323–35 (1965)

114. McNay, J. L., Goldberg, L. I. Comparison of the effects of dopamine, isoproterenol, norepinephrine and bradykinin on canine renal and femoral blood flow. *J. Pharmacol. Exptl. Therap.,* **151,** 23–31 (1966)

115. Schirmeister, J., Decot, M., Hallauer, W., Willmann, H. β-Receptoren und renale Hämodynamik des Menschen. *Arzneimittel-Forsch.,* **16,** 847–50 (1966)

116. Knox, F. G., Fleming, J. S., Rennie, D. W. Effects of osmotic diuresis on sodium reabsorption and oxygen consumption of kidney. *Am. J. Physiol.,* **210,** 751–59 (1966)

117. Bálint, P., Forgács, I. Natriumreabsorption und Sauerstoffverbrauch der Niere bei osmotischer Belastung. *Arch. Ges. Physiol.,* **288,** 332–41 (1966)

118. Torelli, G., Milla, E., Faelli, A., Costantini, S. Energy requirement for sodium reabsorption in the in vivo rabbit kidney. *Am. J. Physiol.,* **211,** 576–80 (1966)

119. Bojesen, E., Leyssac, P. P. The kidney cortex slice technique as a model for sodium transport in vivo. A qualitative evaluation. *Acta Physiol. Scand.,* **65,** 20–32 (1965)

120. Boylan, J. W., Hong, S. K. Regulation of renal function in hypothermia. *Am. J. Physiol.,* **211,** 1371–78 (1966)

121. Walker, A. W., Smith, G., Frazer, S. C. Renal responses to hypothermia. *Clin. Chim. Acta,* **14,** 462–74 (1966)

122. Deetjen, P., Sonnenberg, H. Der tubuläre Transport von PAH. Mikroperfusionsversuche am Einzelnephron der Rattenniere in situ. *Arch. Ges. Physiol.,* **285,** 35–44 (1965)

123. Lee, J. B., Covino, B. G., Takman, B. H., Smith, E. R. Renomedullary vasodepressor substance, Medullin: isolation, chemical characterization and physiological properties. *Circ. Res.,* **17,** 57–77 (1965)

124. Strong, C. G., Boucher, R., Nowaczynski, W., Genest, J. Renal vasodepressor lipid. *Mayo Clin. Proc.,* **41,** 433–52 (1966)

125. Muirhead, E. E., Daniels, E. G., Booth, E., Freyburger, W. A., Hinman, J. W. Renomedullary

vasodepression and antihypertensive function. *Arch. Pathol.,* **80,** 43–49 (1965)

126. Muirhead, E. E., Brooks, B., Kosinski, M., Daniels, E. G., Hinman, J. W. Renomedullary antihypertensive principle in renal hypertension. *J. Lab. Clin. Med.,* **67,** 778–91 (1966)

127. Orloff, J., Handler, J. S., Bergstrom, S. Effect of prostaglandin (PGE₁) on the permeability response of toad bladder to vasopressin, theophylline and adenosine 3',5'-monophosphate. *Nature,* **205,** 397–98 (1965)

128. Faarup, P. On the morphology of the juxtaglomerular apparatus. *Acta Anat.,* **60,** 20–38 (1965)

129. Barajas, L. The development and ultrastructure of the juxtaglomerular cell granule. *J. Ultrastruct. Res.,* **15,** 400–13 (1966)

130. Bucher, O., Riedel, B. Der juxtaglomeruläre Apparat der Niere. *Hippokrates,* **36,** 857–65 (1965)

131. Riedel, B., Bucher, O. Die Ultrastruktur des juxtaglomerulären Apparates des Meerschweinchens. *Z. Zellforsch.,* **79,** 244–58 (1967)

132. Hatt, P. Y. L' appareil juxtaglomérulaire. *Presse Med.,* **74,** 2269–71 (1966)

133. Tobian, L. Renin release and its role in renal function and control of salt balance and arterial pressure. *Fed. Proc.,* **26,** 48–54 (1967)

134. Vander, A. J. Effect of catecholamines and the renal nerves on renin secretion in anesthetized dogs. *Am. J. Physiol.* **209,** 659–62 (1965)

135. Vander, A. J., Luciano, J. R. Effects of mercurial diuresis and acute sodium depletion on renin release in dog. *Am. J. Physiol.,* **212,** 651–56 (1967)

136. Thurau, K., Schnermann, J. Die Natriumkonzentration an den Macula densa-Zellen als regulierender Faktor für das Glomerulumfiltrat (Mikropunktionsversuche). *Klin. Wochschr.,* **43,** 410–13 (1965)

137. Cortney, M. A., Nagel, W., Thurau, K. A micropuncture study of the relationship between flow-rate through the loop of Henle and sodium concentration in the distal tubule. *Arch. Ges. Physiol.,* **287,** 286–95 (1966)

138. Schnermann, J., Nagel, W., Thurau, K. Die frühdistale Natriumkonzentration in Rattennieren nach renaler Ischämie und hämorrhagischer Hypotension. *Arch. Ges. Physiol.,* **287,** 296–310 (1966)

139. Navar, L. G., Guyton, A. C., Langston, J. B. Effect of alterations in plasma osmolality on renal blood flow autoregulation. *Am. J. Physiol.,* **211,** 1387–92 (1966)

140. Bunag, R. D., Page, I. H., McCubbin, J. W. Influence of dietary sodium on stimuli causing renin release. *Am. J. Physiol.,* **211,** 1383–86 (1966)

141. Reeves, G., Sommers, S. C. Sensitivity of the renal macula densa to urinary sodium. *Proc. Soc. Exptl. Biol. Med.,* **120,** 324–25 (1965)

142. Stamey, T. A. Some observations on the filtration fraction, on the transport of sodium and water in the ischemic kidney, and on the prognostic importance of RPF to the contralateral kidney in renovascular hypertension. In *Antihypertensive Therapy* (Gross, F., Ed., Springer-Verlag, Berlin-Heidelberg-New York, 632 pp., 1966)

143. Eigler, F. W. Regulierung von Glomerulumfiltrat und arteriellem Blutdruck durch den Natriumgradienten an den Macula densa-Zellen. Eine Hypothese über die Stimulierung des Renin-Angiotensin-Systems. Zugleich ein Beitrag zu verschiedenen Hochdruckformen. *Klin. Wochschr.,* **45,** 23–30 (1967)

144. Leyssac, P. P. The regulation of proximal tubular reabsorption in the mammalian kidney. *Acta Physiol. Scand.,* **70,** Suppl. 291, 152 pp. (1966)

145. Leyssac, P. P. Intrarenal function of angiotensin. *Fed. Proc.,* **26,** 55–59 (1967)

146. Horster, M., Nagel, W., Schnermann, J., Thurau, K. Zur Frage einer direkten Angiotensinwirkung auf die Natriumresorption im proximalen Tubulus und in der Henleschen Schleife der Rattenniere. *Arch. Ges. Physiol.,* **292,** 118–28 (1966)

147. Coviello, A., Crabbé, J. Effect of angiotensin II on active transport of sodium by toad bladder and skin. *Biochem. Pharmacol.,* **14,** 1739–44 (1965)

148. Windhager, E. E., Giebisch, G. Electrophysiology of the nephron. *Physiol. Rev.*, **45**, 214–44 (1965)

149. Windhager, E. E., Boulpaep, E. L., Giebisch, G. Electrophysiological studies on single nephrons. *Proc. III Intern. Congr. Nephrol., Washington*, **I**, 35–47 (Hans Huber, Basel-New York, 288 pp., 1967)

150. Hegel, U., Frömter, E., Wick, T. Der elektrische Wandwiderstand des proximalen Konvolutes der Rattenniere. *Arch. Ges. Physiol.*, **294**, 274–90 (1967)

151. Baumann, K., Holzgreve, H., Kolb, F., Peters R., Rumrich, G., Ullrich, K. J. Unidirektionale Flüsse für ^{24}Na, ^{42}K, ^{45}Ca, ^{38}Cl, ^{82}Br und ^{131}J im proximalen Konvolut der Rattenniere. *Arch. Ges. Physiol.*, **289**, R77 (1966)

152. Frömter, E., Hegel, U. Transtubuläre Potentialdifferenzen an proximalen und distalen Tubuli der Rattenniere. *Arch. Ges. Physiol.*, **291**, 107–20 (1966)

153. Frömter, E., Wick, T., Hegel, U. Untersuchungen über die Ausspritzmethode zur Lokalisation der Mikroelektrodenspitze bei Potentialmessungen am proximalen Konvolut der Rattenniere. *Arch. Ges. Physiol.*, **294**, 265–73 (1967)

154. Giebisch, G., Malnic, G., Klose, R. M., Windhager, E. E. Effect of ionic substitutions on distal potential differences in rat kidney. *Am. J. Physiol.*, **211**, 560–68 (1966)

155. Katz, A. I., Epstein, F. H. The physiological role of sodium-potassium activated adenosine triphosphatase in the active transport of cations across biological membranes. *Israel J. Med. Sci.*, **3**, 155–66 (1967)

156. Ullrich, K. J., Rumrich, G., Fuchs, G. Wasserpermeabilität und transtubulärer Wasserfluß corticaler Nephronabschnitte bei verschiedenen Diuresezuständen. *Arch. Ges. Physiol.*, **280**, 99–119 (1964)

157. Whitlock, R. T., Wheeler, H. O. Coupled transport of solute and water across rabbit gallbladder epithelium. *J. Clin. Invest.*, **43**, 2249–65 (1964)

158. Kaye, G. I., Wheeler, H. O., Whitlock, R. T., Lane, N. Fluid transport in the rabbit gallbladder. A combined physiological and electron microscopic study. *J. Cell Biol.*, **30**, 237–68 (1966)

159. Dietschy, J. M. Recent developments in solute and water transport across the gallbladder epithelium. *Gastroenterology*, **50**, 692–707 (1966)

160. Diamond, J. M. Transport of salt and water in rabbit and guinea pig gallbladder. *J. Gen. Physiol.*, **48**, 1–14 (1964)

161. Diamond, J. M. The mechanism of isotonic water transport. *Ibid.*, 15–42

162. Diamond, J. M., Tormey, J. McD. Role of long extracellular channels in fluid transport across epithelia. *Nature*, **210**, 817–20 (1966)

163. Diamond, J. M., Tormey, J. McD. Studies on the structural basis of water transport across epithelial membranes. *Fed. Proc.*, **25**, 1458–63 (1966)

164. Ullrich, K. J. Analysis of renal function by microtechniques. *Proc. Intern. Congr. Physiol., 23rd, Tokyo*, 53–66 (1965)

165. Ullrich, K. J. Renal transport of sodium. *Proc. III. Intern. Congr. Nephrol., Washington*, **I**, 48–61 (Handler, J. S., Ed., Hans Huber, Basel-New York, 288 pp., 1967)

166. Sonnenberg, H., Deetjen, P. Methode zur Durchströmung einzelner Nephronabschnitte. *Arch. Ges. Physiol.*, **278**, 669–74 (1964)

167. Rector, F. C., Jr., Martinez-Maldonado, M., Brunner, F. P., Seldin, D. W. Evidence for passive reabsorption of NaCl in proximal tubule of rat kidney. *J. Clin. Invest.*, **45**, 1060 (1966)

168. Chertok, R. J., Hulet, W. H., Epstein, B. Effects of cyanide, amytal, and DNP on renal sodium absorption. *Am. J. Physiol.*, **211**, 1379–82 (1966)

169. Solomon, S., Vanatta, J. C. Implication of phospholipids in rat proximal tubule reabsorption. *Proc. Soc. Exptl. Biol. Med.*, **122**, 1040–45 (1966)

170. Maude, D. L., Shehadeh, I., Solomon, A. K. Sodium and water transport in single perfused distal tubules of Necturus kidney. *Am. J. Physiol.*, **211**, 1043–49 (1966)

171. deRouffignac, C., Morel, F. La perméabilité au sodium des différents segments du néphron étudiée chez le rat en diurèse saline à l'aide de microinjections intratubulaires

de ^{22}Na. *Nephron*, **4**, 92–118 (1967)

172. Morel, F., Lechène, C. Microinjections de sodium et d'inuline marqués dans les capillaires du rein de Hamster. II. Permeabilité au sodium des segments tubulaires medullaires. *Nephron*, **2**, 219–29 (1965)

173. Lechène, C., Morel, F. Microinjections de sodium et d'inuline marqués dans les capillaires du rein de Hamster. I. Permeabilité au sodium des segments tubulaires corticaux. *Ibid.*, 207-18

174. Kedem, O., Leaf, A. The relation between salt and ionic transport coefficients. *J. Gen. Physiol.*, **49**, 655–62 (1966)

175. Cope, F. W. NMR evidence for complexing of Na$^+$ in muscle, kidney, and brain, and by actomyosin. The relation of cellular complexing of Na$^+$ to water structure and to transport kinetics. *J. Gen. Physiol.*, **50**, 1353–75 (1967)

176. Whittembury, G. Sodium extrusion and potassium uptake in guinea pig kidney cortex slices. *J. Gen. Physiol.*, **48**, 699–717 (1965)

177. Smyth, H. Energy barriers to sodium extrusion from sodium-rich kidney cortex slices. *J. Physiol. (London)*, **187**, 361–68 (1966)

178. Burg, M. B., Orloff, J. Active cation transport by kidney tubules at 0° C. *Am. J. Physiol.*, **207**, 983–88 (1964)

179. Robinson, J. R. Oxygen consumption and electrolyte composition of kidney slices between 20 and 0°C. *J. Physiol. (London)*, **177**, 112–21 (1965)

180. Willis, J. S. Characteristics of ion transport in kidney cortex of mammalian hibernators. *J. Gen. Physiol.*, **49**, 1221–39 (1966)

181. Kleinzeller, A., Nedvidkova, J., Knotkova, A. Effect of saline osmolarity on the steady-state level of water and electrolytes in kidney cortex cells. *Biochim. Biophys. Acta*, **135**, 286–99 (1967)

182. Bojesen, E., Leyssac, P. P., Nielsen, B. S. Analysis of the efflux kinetics of sodium from small cylinders of rabbit kidney cortex. *Acta Physiol. Scand.*, **65**, 105–19 (1965)

183. Burg, M. B., Orloff, J. Effect of temperature and medium K on Na and K fluxes in separated renal

tubules. *Am. J. Physiol.*, **211**, 1005–10 (1966)

184. Burg, M. B., Abramow, M. Localization of tissue sodium and potassium compartments in rabbit renal cortex. *Am. J. Physiol.*, **211**, 1011–17 (1966)

185. Wiggins, P. M. A kinetic study of the state of potassium in kidney tissue. *Biochim. Biophys. Acta*, **109**, 454–66 (1965)

186. Gertz, K. H., Mangos, J. A., Braun, G., Pagel, H. D. On the glomerular tubular balance in the rat kidney. *Arch. Ges. Physiol.*, **285**, 360–72 (1965)

187. Landwehr, D., Schnermann, J., Klose, R. M., Giebisch, G. The effect of acute reduction in glomerular filtration rate on renal tubular sodium and water reabsorption. *Fed. Proc.*, **26**, 547 (1967)

188. Rector, F. C., Jr., Brunner, F. P., Seldin, D. W. Mechanism of glomerulotubular balance. I. Effect of aortic constriction and elevated ureteropelvic pressure on glomerular filtration rate, fractional reabsorption, transit time, and tubular size in the proximal tubule of the rat. *J. Clin. Invest.*, **45**, 590–602 (1966)

189. Brunner, F. P., Rector, F. C., Jr., Seldin, D. W. Mechanism of glomerulotubular balance. II. Regulation of proximal tubular reabsorption by tubular volume, as studied by stopped-flow microperfusion. *Ibid.*, 603–11

190. Steinhausen, M., Loreth, A., Olson, S. Messungen des tubulaeren Harnstromes, seine Beziehungen zum Blutdruck und zur Inulin-Clearance. *Arch. Ges. Physiol.*, **286**, 118–41 (1965)

191. Glabman, S., Aynedjian, H. S., Bank, N. Micropuncture study of the effect of acute reductions in glomerular filtration rate on sodium and water reabsorption by the proximal tubules of the rat. *J. Clin. Invest.*, **44**, 1410–16 (1965)

192. Watson, J. F. Effect of saline loading on sodium reabsorption in the dog proximal tubule. *Am. J. Physiol.*, **210**, 781–85 (1966)

193. Dirks, J. H., Cirksena, W. J., Berliner, R. W. Micropuncture study of the effect of various diuretics on sodium reabsorption by the proximal tubules of the dog. *J. Clin. Invest.*, **45**, 1875–85 (1966)

194. Dirks, J. H., Cirksena, W. J., Berliner, R. W. The effect of saline infusion on sodium reabsorption by the proximal tubule of the dog. *Ibid.*, **44**, 1160–70 (1965)

195. Leyssac, P. P. The in vivo effect of angiotensin on the proximal tubular reabsorption of salt in rat kidneys. *Acta Physiol. Scand.*, **62**, 436–48 (1964)

196. Leyssac, P. P. The effect of partial clamping of the renal artery on pressures in the proximal and distal tubules and peritubular capillaries in the rat kidney. *Ibid.*, 449–56

197. Baines, A. D., Leyssac, P. P., Gottschalk, C. W. Proximal tubular volume and inulin clearance in nondiuretic rats. *III Intern. Congr. Nephrol., Washington,* Abstr. p. 152 (1967)

198. Maunsbach, A. B. The influence of different fixatives and fixation methods on the ultrastructure of rat kidney proximal tubule cells. I. Comparison of different perfusion fixation methods and of glutaraldehyde, formaldehyde and osmium tetroxide fixatives. *J. Ultrastruct. Res.*, **15**, 242–82 (1966)

199. Sitte, H. Beziehungen zwischen Zellstruktur und Stofftransport in der Niere. In *Sekretion und Exkretion,* 343–77 (Wohlfarth-Bottermann, K. E., Ed., Springer-Verlag, Berlin-Heidelberg-New York, 404 pp., 1965)

200. Thoenes, W., Hierholzer, K., Wiederholt, M. Gezielte Fixierung von Nierentubuli in vivo durch Mikroperfusion zur licht- und elektronenmikroskopischen Untersuchung. *Klin. Wochschr.*, **43**, 794–96 (1965)

201. Levinsky, N. G. Nonaldosterone influences on renal sodium transport. *Ann. N.Y. Acad. Sci.*, **139**, 295–303 (1966)

202. Earley, L. E., Friedler, R. M. Studies of the mechanism of natriuresis accompanying increased renal blood flow and its role in the renal response to extracellular volume expansion. *J. Clin. Invest.*, **44**, 1857–65 (1965)

203. Cortney, M. A., Mylle, M., Lassiter, W. E., Gottschalk, C. W. Renal tubular transport of water, solute, and PAH in rats loaded with isotonic saline. *Am. J. Physiol.*, **209**, 1199–1205 (1965)

204. Rector, F. C., Jr., Sellman, J. C., Martinez-Maldonado, M., Seldin, D. W. The mechanism of suppression of proximal tubular reabsorption by saline infusions. *J. Clin. Invest.*, **46**, 47–56 (1967)

205. Lindheimer, M. D., Lalone, R. C., Levinsky, N. G. Evidence that an acute increase in glomerular filtration has little effect on sodium excretion in the dog unless extracellular volume is expanded. *J. Clin. Invest.*, **46**, 256–65 (1967)

206. Stein, R. M., Bercovitch, D. D., Levitt, M. F. Dual effects of saline loading on renal tubular sodium reabsorption in the dog. *Am. J. Physiol.*, **207**, 826–34 (1964)

207. Kessler, E., Nelson, W. P. III, Rosano, C. L. Urinary electrolytes at low rates of urine flow after expansion of extracellular volume. *J. Lab. Clin. Med.*, **65**, 804–16 (1965)

208. Gann, D. S., Wright, H. K. Increased renal sodium reabsorption after depletion of the extracellular or intravascular fluid volumes. *J. Surg. Res.*, **6**, 196–204 (1966)

209. Landwehr, D. M., Klose, R. M., Giebisch, G. Renal tubular sodium and water reabsorption in the isotonic sodium chloride loaded rat. *Am. J. Physiol.*, **212**, 1327–33 (1967)

210. Malnic, G., Vieira, F. L., Enokibara, H. Effect of Furosemid on chloride and water excretion in single nephrons of the kidney of the rat. *Nature*, **208**, 80–81 (1965)

211. Kamm, D. E., Levinsky, N. G. Inhibition of renal tubular sodium reabsorption by hypernatremia. *J. Clin. Invest.*, **44**, 1144–50 (1965)

212. Lichardus, B., Pearce, J. W. Evidence for a humoral natriuretic factor released by blood volume expansion. *Nature*, **209**, 407–9 (1966)

213. Johnston, C. I., Davis, J. O. Evidence from cross circulation studies for a humoral mechanism in the natriuresis of saline loading. *Proc. Soc. Exptl. Biol. Med.*, **121**, 1058–63 (1966)

214. Davis, J. O., Johnston, C. I., Howards, S. S., Wright, F. S. Humoral factors in the regulation of renal sodium excretion. *Fed. Proc.*, **26**, 60–69 (1967)

215. McDonald, S. J., de Wardener, H. E.

512 THURAU, VALTIN & SCHNERMANN

The relationship between the renal arterial perfusion pressure and the increase in sodium excretion which occurs during an infusion of saline. *Nephron*, **2**, 1–14 (1965)

216. McDonald, M., Schrier, R. W., Lauler, D. P. Effect of acute extracellular volume expansion on cross-circulated dogs. *Nephron*, **4**, 1–12 (1967)

217. Little, J. M. Renal hemodynamic and electrolyte excretion effects of the urinary diuretic factor (UDF). *J. Pharmacol. Exptl. Therap.*, **148**, 363–66 (1965)

218. Krück, F., Krecke, H. J. The renal sodium excretion during oral hydration in man. *Nephron*, **2**, 321–33 (1965)

219. Krück, F. Biologischer Nachweis eines humoralen natriuretischen Prinzips im Urin gesunder Menschen. *Klin. Wochschr.*, **45**, 30–34 (1967)

220. Linkenbach, H. J., Eckert, P., Gauer, O. H. Nachweis eines diuretischen Faktors im menschlichen Serum während der durch Expansion des intrathorakalen Blutvolumens ausgelösten Diurese. *Arch. Ges. Physiol.*, **293**, 107–14 (1967)

221. Bahlmann, J., McDonald, S. J., Ventom, M. G., de Wardener, H. E. The effect on urinary sodium excretion of blood volume expansion without changing the composition of blood in the dog. *Clin. Sci.*, **32**, 403–13 (1967)

222. Bahlmann, J., McDonald, S. J., Dunningham, J. G., de Wardener, H. E. The effect on urinary sodium excretion of altering the packed cell volume with albumin solutions without changing the blood volume in the dog. *Clin. Sci.*, **32**, 395–402 (1967)

223. Earley, L. E. Effect of renal arterial infusion of albumin on saline diuresis in the dog. *Proc. Soc. Exptl. Biol. Med.*, **116**, 262–65 (1964)

224. Vereerstraeten, P., Myttenaere, M., Lambert, P. P. Réduction de la natriurèse par la perfusion de protéines dans l'artère rénale du chien. *Nephron*, **3**, 103–22 (1966)

225. Vereerstraeten, P., Toussaint, C. Réduction de la natriurèse par la perfusion d'albumine dans la veine porte rénale du coq. *Nephron*, **2**, 355–66 (1966)

226. Cort, J. H., Rudinger, J., Lichardus, B., Hagemann, I. Effects of oxyto-cin antagonists on the saluresis accompanying carotid occlusion. *Am. J. Physiol.*, **210**, 162–68 (1966)

227. Lockett, M. F. Effects of saline loading on the perfused cat kidney. *J. Physiol. (London)*, **187**, 489–500 (1966)

228. Andersson, B., Jobin, M., Olsson, K. Stimulation of urinary salt excretion following injections of hypertonic NaCl-Solution into the 3rd brain ventricle. *Acta Physiol. Scand.*, **67**, 127–28 (1966)

229. Earley, L. E., Friedler, R. M. The effects of combined renal vasodilation and pressor agents on renal hemodynamics and the tubular reabsorption of sodium. *J. Clin. Invest.*, **45**, 542–51 (1966)

230. Earley, L. E., Martino, J. A., Friedler, R. M. Factors affecting sodium reabsorption by the proximal tubule as determined during blockade of distal sodium reabsorption. *J. Clin. Invest.*, **45**, 1668–84 (1966)

231. Pinter, G. G., O'Morchoe, C. C. C., Sikand, R. S. Effect of acetylcholine on urinary electrolyte excretion. *Am. J. Physiol.*, **207**, 979–82 (1964)

232. Reinhardt, H. W., Behrenbeck, D. W. Untersuchungen an wachen Hunden über die Einstellung der Natriumbilanz. I. Die Bedeutung des Extracellulärraumes für die Einstellung der Natrium-Tagesbilanz. *Arch. Ges. Physiol.*, **295**, 266–79 (1967)

233. Behrenbeck, D. W., Reinhardt, H. W. Untersuchungen an wachen Hunden über die Einstellung der Natriumbilanz. II. Postprandiale Elektrolyt- und Wasserbilanz bei unterschiedlicher Kochsalzzufuhr. *Arch. Ges. Physiol.*, **295**, 280–92 **(1967)**

234. Levinsky, N. G., Lalone, R. C. Sodium excretion during acute saline loading in dogs with vena caval constriction. *J. Clin. Invest.*, **44**, 565–73 (1965)

235. Cirksena, W. J., Dirks, J. H., Berliner, R. W. Effect of thoracic cava obstruction on response of proximal tubule sodium reabsorption to saline infusion. *J. Clin. Invest.*, **45**, 179–86 (1966)

236. Heinemann, H. O., Laragh, J. H. Inappropriate renal sodium loss reverted by vena cava obstruction.

Ann. Internal Med., **65**, 708–721 (1966)

237. Malnic, G., Klose, R. M., Giebisch, G. Micropuncture study of distal tubular potassium and sodium transport in rat nephron. *Am. J. Physiol.*, **211**, 529–47 (1966)

238. Malnic, G., Klose, R. M., Giebisch, G. Microperfusion study of distal tubular potassium and sodium transfer in rat kidney. *Ibid.*, 548–59

239. Khuri, R. N., Flanigan, W. J., Oken, D. E. Potassium in proximal tubule fluid of rats and Necturus measured with glass electrodes. *J. Appl. Physiol.*, **21**, 1568–72 (1966)

240. Watson, J. F. Potassium reabsorption in the proximal tubule of the dog nephron. *J. Clin. Invest.*, **45**, 1341–48 (1966)

241. Rouffignac, C. de, Guinnebault, M. Etude, à l'aide de microinjections de ⁴²K, de la perméabilité au potassium des segments corticaux du néphron. *Nephron*, **3**, 175–97 (1966)

242. Kashgarian, M., Warren, Y., Levitin, H. Micropuncture study of proximal renal tubular chloride transport during hypercapnea in the rat. *Am. J. Physiol.*, **209**, 655–58 (1965)

243. Schafer, J. A., Vander, A. J., Brubacher, E. S. Anion concentration gradients and electrical potentials in distal tubule of dog. *Am. J. Physiol.*, **210**, 1285–89 (1966)

244. Walser, M., Rahill, W. J. Renal tubular reabsorption of bromide compared with chloride. *Clin. Sci.*, **30**, 191–205 (1966)

245. Walser, M., Rahill, W. J. Renal tubular reabsorption of iodide as compared with chloride. *J. Clin. Invest.*, **44**, 1371–81 (1965)

246. Walser, M., Rahill, W. J. Renal tubular transport of fluoride compared with chloride. *Am. J. Physiol.*, **210**, 1290–92 (1966)

247. Walser, M. Mathematical aspects of renal function : reabsorption of individual solutes as interdependent processes. *J. Theoret. Biol.*, **10**, 327–36 (1966)

248. Walser, M., Rahill, W. J. Nitrate, thiocyanate, and perchlorate clearance in relation to chloride clearance. *Am. J. Physiol.*, **208**, 1158–64 (1965)

249. Frick, A., Rumrich, G., Ullrich, K. J., Lassiter, W. E. Microperfusion study of calcium transport in the proximal tubule of the rat kidney. *Arch. Ges. Physiol.*, **286**, 109–17 (1965)

250. Gutman, Y., Gottschalk, C. W. Microinjection study of the effect of calcium on sodium transport in the rat kidney. *Israel J. Med. Sci.*, **2**, 243–45 (1966)

251. Better, O. S., Gonick, H. C., Chapman, L. C., Varrady, P. D., Kleeman, C. R. Effect of urea-saline diuresis on renal clearance on calcium, magnesium, and inorganic phosphate in man. *Proc. Soc. Exptl. Biol. Med.*, **121**, 592–96 (1966)

252. Knippers, R., Hehl, U. Die renale Ausscheidung von Magnesium, Calcium und Kalium nach Erhöhung der Magnesiumkonzentration im Plasma des Hundes. *Z. Ges. Exptl. Med.*, **139**, 154–65 (1965)

253. Kupfer, S., Kosovsky, J. D. Effects of cardiac glycosides on renal tubular transport of calcium, magnesium, inorganic phosphate, and glucose in the dog. *J. Clin. Invest.*, **44**, 1132–43 (1965)

254. Rahill, W. J., Walser, M. Renal tubular reabsorption of trace alkaline earths compared with calcium. *Am. J. Physiol.*, **208**, 1165–70 (1965)

255. Ginsburg, J. M. Renal mechanism for excretion and transformation of arsenic in the dog. *Am. J. Physiol.*, **208**, 832–40 (1965)

256. Strickler, J. C., Thompson, D. D., Klose, R. M., Giebisch, G. Micropuncture study of inorganic phosphate excretion in the rat. *J. Clin. Invest.*, **43**, 1596–1607 (1964)

257. Carone, F. A. Micropuncture study of renal phosphate excretion and action of parathyroid hormone. *Clin. Res.*, **12**, 249–56 (1964)

258. Hellman, D., Baird, H. R., Bartter, F. C. Relationship of maximal tubular phosphate reabsorption to filtration rate in the dog. *Am. J. Physiol.* **207**, 89–96 (1964)

259. Hellman, D., Baird, H. R., Bartter, F. C. Relationship of maximal tubular phosphate reabsorption to dietary phosphate in the dog. *Ibid.*, 97–103

260. Lambert, P. P., Vanderveiken, F., De Koster, J. P., Kahn, R. J., De Myttenaere, M. Study of phosphate excretion by the stop-flow

technique. Effects of parathyroid hormone. *Nephron*, **1**, 103–17 (1964)

261. Hirsch, P. F., Munson, P. L. The phosphaturic response of thyroparathyroidectomized dogs to the administration of parathyroid hormone by unilateral renal arterial infusion. *Arch. Exptl. Pathol. Pharmacol.*, **248**, 319–30 (1964)

262. Samiy, A. H., Hirsch, P. F., Ramsay, A. G. Localization of phosphaturic effect of parathyroid hormone in nephron of the dog. *Am. J. Physiol.*, **208**, 73–77 (1965)

263. Davis, B. B., Kedes, L. H., Field, J. B. Demonstration of distal tubular flux of phosphorus using modified stop-flow analysis. *Metabolism*, **15**, 482–91 (1966)

264. Ferguson, R. K., Wolbach, R. A. Effects of glucose, phlorizin, and parathyroid extract on renal phosphate transport in chickens. *Am. J. Physiol.*, **212**, 1123–30 (1967)

265. Khuri, R. N., Flanigan, W. J., Oken, D. E., Solomon, A. K. Influence of electrolytes on glucose absorption in *Necturus* kidney proximal tubules. *Fed. Proc.*, **25**, 899–902 (1966)

266. Vogel, G., Tervooren, U., Stoeckert, I. Untersuchungen zur Abhängigkeit des renal tubulären Glucose-Transportes vom Ionen-Angebot sowie des Na⁺-Transportes vom Angebot an Glucose. *Arch. Ges. Physiol.*, **288**, 359–68 (1966)

267. Vogel, G., Stoeckert, I. Die Bedeutung des Anions für den renal tubulären Transport von Na⁺ und die Transporte von Glucose und PAH. *Arch. Ges. Physiol.*, **292**, 309–15 (1966)

268. Diedrich, D. F. Glucose transport carrier in dog kidney: its concentration and turnover number. *Am. J. Physiol.*, **211**, 581–87 (1966)

269. Bailey, J. M., Pentchev, P. G. Inhibition of rat intestinal and rat kidney mutarotase by actively transported sugars. *Am. J. Physiol.*, **208**, 385–90 (1965)

270. Halver, B. The effect of parathyroid hormone on the tubular reabsorption of glucose. *Acta Med. Scand.*, **179**, 427–32 (1966)

271. Liew, J. B. van, Deetjen, P., Boylan, J. W. Glucose reabsorption in the rat kidney. *Arch. Ges. Physiol.*, **295**, 232–44 (1967)

272. Clapp, J. R. Renal tubular reabsorption of urea in normal and protein-depleted rats. *Am. J. Physiol.*, **210**, 1304–8 (1966)

273. Truniger, B., Schmidt-Nielsen, B. Intrarenal distribution of urea and related compounds: effects of nitrogen intake. *Am. J. Physiol.*, **207**, 971–78 (1964)

274. Goldberg, M., Wojtczak, A. M., Ramirez, M. A. Uphill transport of urea in the dog kidney: effects of certain inhibitors. *J. Clin. Invest.*, **46**, 388–99 (1967)

275. Lassiter, W. E., Mylle, M., Gottschalk, C. W. Micropuncture study of urea transport in rat renal medulla. *Am. J. Physiol.*, **210**, 965–70 (1966)

276. Ullrich, K. J., Rumrich, G., Schmidt-Nielsen, B. Urea transport in the collecting duct of rats on normal and low protein diet. *Arch. Ges. Physiol.*, **295**, 147–56 (1967)

277. Rabinowitz, L. Mechanism of renal excretion of methylurea and acetamide in the dog. *Am. J. Physiol.*, **209**, 188–94 (1965)

278. Kleinman, L. I., Radford, E. P., Jr., Torelli, G. Urea and inulin clearances in undisturbed unanesthetized rats. *Am. J. Physiol.*, **208**, 578–84 (1965)

279. Capek, K., Fuchs, G., Rumrich, G., Ullrich, K. J. Harnstoffpermeabilität der corticalen Tubulusabschnitte von Ratten in Antidiurese und Wasserdiurese. *Arch. Ges. Physiol.*, **290**, 237–49 (1966)

280. Clapp, J. R. Urea reabsorption by the proximal tubule of the dog. *Proc. Soc. Exptl. Biol. Med.*, **120**, 521–25 (1965)

281. Burg, M. B., Grantham, J., Abramow, M., Orloff, J. Preparation and study of fragments of single rabbit nephrons. *Am. J. Physiol.*, **210**, 1293–98 (1966)

282. Grantham, J. J., Burg, M. B. Effect of vasopressin and cyclic AMP on permeability of isolated collecting tubules. *Am. J. Physiol.*, **211**, 255–59 (1966)

283. Gardner, K. D., Jr., Maffly, R. H. An in vitro demonstration of increased collecting tubular permeability to urea in the presence of vasopressin. *J. Clin. Invest.*, **43**, 1968–75 (1964)

284. Foulkes, E. C. The action of pitressin on solute permeability of the rabbit nephron in vivo. *J. Gen. Physiol.*, **50**, 1–8 (1966)

285. Carlisky, N. J., Jard, S., Morel, F. In vivo tracer studies of renal urea formation in the bullfrog. *Am. J. Physiol.,* **211,** 593–99 (1966)

286. Brodsky, W. A., Carlisky, N. J., Gonzalez, C. F., Shamoo, Y. E. Metabolic pathways for urea production by the amphibian kidney. *Am. J. Physiol.,* **208,** 546–54 (1965)

287. Marsh, D. J., Frasier, C., Decter, J. Measurement of urea concentrations in nanoliter specimens of renal tubular fluid and capillary blood. *Anal. Biochem.,* **11,** 73–80 (1965)

288. Garrod, P. R., McSwiney, R. R., Bold, A. M. Investigation of renal excretion of phosphate and urate. *Clin Sci.,* **31,** 9–17 (1966)

289. Davis, B. B., Field, J. B., Rodnan, G. P., Kedes, L. H. Localization and pyrazinamide inhibition of distal transtubular movement of uric acid-2-C^{14} with a modified stop-flow technique. *J. Clin. Invest.,* **44,** 716–21 (1965)

290. Beechwood, E. C., Berndt, W. O., Mudge, G. H. Stop-flow analysis of tubular transport of uric acid in rabbits. *Am. J. Physiol.,* **207,** 1265–72 (1964)

291. Berndt, W. O., Beechwood, E. C. Influence of inorganic electrolytes and ouabain on uric acid transport. *Am. J. Physiol.,* **208,** 642–48 (1965)

292. Møller, J. V. The tubular site of urate transport in the rabbit kidney, and the effect of probenecid on urate secretion. *Acta Pharmacol. Toxicol.,* **23,** 329–36 (1966)

293. Scriver, C. R., Goldman, H. Renal tubular transport of proline, hydroxy-proline, and glycine. II. Hydroxy-1-proline as substrate and as inhibitor in vivo. *J. Clin. Invest.,* **45,** 1357–63 (1966)

294. Young, J. A., Edwards, K. D. G. Clearance and stop-flow studies on histidine and methyldopa transport by rat kidney. *Am. J. Physiol.,* **210,** 667–75 (1966)

295. Schwartzman, L., Crawhall, J., Segal, S. Incorporation of amino acids into a lipid fraction of kidney cortex. *Biochim. Biophys. Acta,* **124,** 62–70 (1966)

296. Webber, W. A., Campbell, J. L. Effects of amino acids on renal glucose reabsorption in the dog.

Can. J. Physiol. Pharmacol., **43,** 915–23 (1965)

297. Kleit, S., Levin, D., Perenich, T., Cade, R. Renal excretion of ascorbic acid by dogs. *Am. J. Physiol.,* **209,** 195–98 (1965)

298. Kinter, W. B. Chlorphenol red influx and efflux : microspectrophotometry of flounder kidney tubules. *Am. J. Physiol.,* **211,** 1152–64 (1966)

299. Kempton, R. T. Studies on the elasmobranch kidney. IV. The secretion of phenol red by the smooth dogfish, Mustelus canis. *Biol. Bull.,* **130,** 359–68 (1966)

300. Huang, K. C., Lin, D. S. T. Kinetic studies on transport of PAH and other organic acids in isolated renal tubules. *Am. J. Physiol.,* **208,** 391–96 (1965)

301. Murthy, L., Foulkes, E. C. Movement of solutes across luminal cell membranes in kidney tubules of the rabbit. *Nature,* **213,** 180–81 (1967)

302. Tanner, G. A., Kinter, W. B. Reabsorption and secretion of *p*-aminohippurate and Diodrast in Necturus kidney. *Am. J. Physiol.,* **210,** 221–31 (1966)

303. Despopoulos, A. A definition of substrate specificity in renal transport of organic anions. *J. Theoret. Biol.,* **8,** 163–92 (1965)

304. Weiner, I. M., Blanchard, K. C., Mudge, G. H. Factors influencing renal excretion of foreign organic acids. *Am. J. Physiol.,* **207,** 953–63 (1964)

305. Schirmeister, J., Stefani, F., Willmann, H., Hallauer, W. Der intrarenale Nitrofurantoin-Transport am Menschen. *Klin. Wochschr.,* **44,** 402–7 (1966)

306. Healy, J. K., Barcena, C., Schreiner, G. E. Effect of angiotensin on maximal tubular transport of PAH and glucose in dogs. *Am. J. Physiol.,* **209,** 651–54 (1965)

307. Bahlmann, M., Ochwadt, B. Untersuchungen über die Para-Aminohippursäure-Clearance in Acidose. *Arch. Exptl. Pathol. Pharmakol.,* **250,** 397–404 (1965)

308. Deetjen, P. Zellulärer Transport organischer Säuren. In : *Transport und Funktion intrazellulärer Elektrolyte* (Krück, F., Ed., Urban und Schwarzenberg, München-Berlin-Wien, 299 pp., 1967)

309. Schnermann, J., Thurau, K. Mikropunktionsversuche zum Verhalten

der PAH-Konzentration im Vasa recta-Blut der Goldhamsterniere. *Arch. Ges. Physiol.*, **283**, 171–81 (1965)

310. Sonnenberg, H., Oelert, H., Baumann, K. Proximal tubular reabsorption of some organic acids in the rat kidney in vivo. *Arch. Ges. Physiol.*, **286**, 171–80 (1965)

311. Despopoulos, A., Segerfeldt, A. Efflux of organic acids from rabbit kidney cortex. *Am. J. Physiol.*, **207**, 118–22 (1964)

312. Coe, F. L., Korty, P. R. Mechanism of hydrazine excretion by the mammalian kidney. *Am. J. Physiol.*, **212**, 394–99 (1967)

313. Maunsbach, A. B. Absorption of I^{125} labeled homologous albumin by rat kidney proximal tubule cells. A study of microperfused single proximal tubules by electron microscopic autoradiography and histochemistry. *J. Ultrastruct. Res.*, **15**, 197–241 (1966)

314. Maunsbach, A. B. Absorption of ferritin by rat kidney proximal tubule cells. Electron microscopic observations of the initial uptake phase in cells of microperfused single proximal tubules. *Ibid.*, **16**, 1–12 (1966)

315. Thoenes, W., Langer, K. H., Wiederholt, M. Resorption von Ferritin im proximalen Konvolut der Rattenniere (nach intratubulärer Applikation durch Mikropunktion). *Klin. Wochschr.*, **44**, 1379–81 (1966)

316. Neustein, H. B., Maunsbach, A. B. Hemoglobin absorption by proximal tubule cells of the rabbit kidney. A study by electron microscopic autoradiography. *J. Ultrastruct. Res.*, **16**, 141–57 (1966)

317. Rector, F. C., Jr., Carter, N. W., Seldin, D. W. The mechanism of bicarbonate reabsorption in the proximal and distal tubules of the kidney. *J. Clin. Invest.*, **44**, 278–90 (1965)

318. Guignard, J. P. Mécanisme de la réabsorption rénale des bicarbonates chez le rat. *Helv. Physiol. Pharmacol. Acta*, **24**, 193–218 (1966)

319. Bank, N., Aynedjian, H. S. A microperfusion study of bicarbonate accumulation in the proximal tubule of the rat kidney. *J. Clin. Invest.*, **46**, 95–102 (1967)

320. Reid, E. L., Hills, A. G. Diffusion of carbon dioxide out of the distal

nephron in man during anti-diuresis. *Clin. Sci.*, **28**, 15–28 (1965)

321. Pitts, R. F., Pilkington, L. A., de Haas, J. C. M. N^{15} tracer studies on the origin of urinary ammonia in the acidotic dog, with notes on the enzymatic synthesis of labeled glutamic acid and glutamines. *J. Clin. Invest.*, **44**, 731–45 (1965)

322. Pitts, R. F. The renal metabolism of ammonia. *Physiologist*, **9**, 97–109 (1966)

323. Pitts, R. F. The renal metabolism and excretion of ammonia. *Proc. III Intern. Congr. Nephrol., Washington*, **I**, 123–35 (Handler, J. S., Ed., Hans Huber, Basel-New York, 288 pp., 1967)

324. Pitts, R. F., Pilkington, L. A. The relation between plasma concentrations of glutamine and glycine and utilization of their nitrogens as sources of urinary ammonia. *J. Clin. Invest.*, **45**, 86–93 (1966)

325. Fülgraff, G., Pitts, R. F. Kinetics of ammonia production and excretion in the acidotic dog. *Am. J. Physiol.*, **209**, 1206–12 (1965)

326. Oelert, H., Nagel, W. Die Abhängigkeit der Ammoniakproduktion von der GFR bei Ureterabklemmung und bei Durchblutungsdrosselung in der Hundeniere. *Arch. Ges. Physiol.*, **292**, 129–39 (1966)

327. Pollak, V. E., Mattenheimer, H., de Bruin, H., Weinman, K. J. Experimental metabolic acidosis: the enzymatic basis of ammonia production by the dog kidney. *J. Clin. Invest.*, **44**, 169–81 (1965)

328. Goldstein, L. Relation of glutamate to ammonia production in the rat kidney. *Am. J. Physiol.*, **210**, 661–66 (1966)

329. Goodman, A. D., Fuisz, R. E., Cahill, G. F. Renal gluconeogenesis in acidosis, alkalosis, and potassium deficiency: its possible role in regulation of renal ammonia production. *J. Clin. Invest.*, **45**, 612–19 (1966)

330. Balagura, S. Uptake and utilization of α-ketoglutarate by rat renal cortical slices. *Acta Physiol. Latinoam.*, **16**, 6–12 (1966)

331. Dies, F., Lotspeich, W. D. Hexose monophosphate shunt in the kidney during acid-base and electrolyte imbalance. *Am. J. Physiol.*, **212**, 61–71 (1967)

332. Sullivan, L. P. Ammonium excretion during stopped flow: a hypothetical

ammonium countercurrent system. *Am. J. Physiol.*, **209**, 273–82 (1965)

333. Robinson, R. R., Owen, E. E. Intrarenal distribution of ammonia during diuresis and antidiuresis. *Am. J. Physiol.*, **208**, 1129–34 (1965)

334. Hayes, C. P., Owen, E. E., Robinson, R. R. Renal ammonia excretion during acetazolamide or sodium bicarbonate administration. *Am. J. Physiol.*, **210**, 744–50 (1966)

335. Oelert, H., Hills, A. G., Rumrich, G., Ullrich, K. J. Corticaler Ammoniakdruck und Ammoniakausscheidung in der Rattenerre. In : Aktuelle Probleme der Nephrologie, 537–42 (Wolff, H. P., Krück, F., Eds., Springer-Verlag, Berlin-Heidelberg-New York, 796 pp., 1966)

336. Owen, E. E., Robinson, R. R. Renal ammonia release during ammonium chloride acidosis. *Am. J. Physiol.*, **208**, 58–60 (1965)

337. Clapp, J. R., Owen, E. E., Robinson, R. R. Contribution of the proximal tubule to urinary ammonia excretion by the dog. *Am. J. Physiol.*, **209**, 269–72 (1965)

338. Hills, A. G., Reid, E. L. Renal ammonia balance. A kinetic treatment. *Nephron*, **3**, 221–56 (1966)

339. Lotspeich, W. D. Renal hypertrophy in metabolic acidosis and its relation to ammonia excretion. *Am. J. Physiol.*, **208**, 1135–42 (1965)

340. Tannen, R. L., Bleich, H. L., Schwartz, W. B. The renal response to acid loads in metabolic alkalosis ; an assessment of the mechanisms regulating acid excretion. *J. Clin. Invest.*, **45**, 562–72 (1966)

341. Bleich, H. L., Tannen, R. L., Schwartz, W. B. The induction of metabolic alkalosis by correction of potassium deficiency. *Ibid.*, 573–79

342. Solomon, S. Evidence that choline can exchange for hydrogen across proximal tubules of dogs. *Arch. Intern. Physiol. Biochem.*, **74**, 354–64 (1966)

343. Sung, C. P., Johnstone, R. M. Evidence for active transport of choline in rat kidney cortex slices. *Can. J. Biochem.*, **43**, 1111–18 (1965)

344. Lever, A. F. The vasa recta and countercurrent multiplication. *Acta Med. Scand.*, **178**, *Suppl.* **434**, 1–43 (1965)

345. Berliner, R. W., Bennett, C. M. Concentration of urine in the mammalian kidney. *Am. J. Med.*, **42**, 777–89 (1967)

346. Niesel, W., Röskenbleck, H. Konzentrierung von Lösungen unterschiedlicher Zusammensetzung durch alleinige Gegenstromdiffusion und Gegenstromosmose als möglicher Mechanismus der Harnkonzentrierung. *Arch. Ges. Physiol.*, **283**, 230–41 (1965)

347. Marsh, D. J. Hypo-osmotic reabsorption due to active salt transport in perfused collecting ducts of the rat renal medulla. *Nature*, **210**, 1179–80 (1966)

348. Marsh, D. J., Solomon, S. Analysis of electrolyte movement in thin Henle's loops of hamster papilla. *Am. J. Physiol.*, **208**, 1119–28 (1965)

349. Jamison, R. L., Bennett, C. M., Berliner, R. W. Countercurrent multiplication by the thin loops of Henle. *Am. J. Physiol.*, **212**, 357–66 (1967)

350. Sakai, F., Jamison, R. L., Berliner, R. W. A method for exposing the rat renal medulla in vivo : micropuncture of the collecting duct. *Am. J. Physiol.*, **209**, 663–68 (1965)

351. Bernanke, D., Epstein, F. H. Metabolism of the renal medulla. *Am. J. Physiol.*, **208**, 541–45 (1965)

352. Osvaldo, L., Latta, H. The thin limbs of the loop of Henle. *J. Ultrastruct. Res.*, **15**, 144–68 (1966)

353. Bulger, R. E., Tisher, C. C., Myers, C. H., Trump, B. F. Human renal ultrastructure. II. The thin limb of Henle's loop and the interstitium in healthy individuals. *Lab. Invest.*, **16**, 124–41 (1967)

354. Steinhausen, M. In vivo-Beobachtungen an der Nierenpapille von Goldhamstern nach intravenöser Lissamingrün-Injektion. *Arch. Ges. Physiol.*, **279**, 195–213 (1964)

355. Osvaldo, L., Latta, H. Interstitial cells of the renal medulla. *J. Ultrastruct. Res.*, **15**, 589–613 (1966)

356. Bulger, R. E., Trump, B. F. Fine structure of the rat renal papilla. *Am. J. Anat.*, **118**, 685–722 (1966)

357. Gloor, F., Neiditsch-Halff, L. A. Die interstitiellen Zellen des Nieren-

markes der Ratte. *Z. Zellforsch.,* **66,** 488–95 (1965)

358. Lever, A. F., Kriz, W. Countercurrent exchange between the vasa recta and the loop of Henle. *Lancet,* **I,** 1057–60 (1966)

359. Aukland, K., Berliner, R. W. Renal medullary countercurrent system studied with hydrogen gas. *Circ. Res.,* **15,** 430–42 (1964)

360. Aukland, K. Renal medullary heat clearance in the dog. *Circ. Res.,* **20,** 194–203 (1967)

361. Perl, W., Hirsch, R. L. Local blood flow in kidney tissue by heat clearance measurement. *J. Theoret. Biol.,* **10,** 251–80 (1966)

362. Carone, F. A., Everett, B. A., Blondeel, N. J., Stolarczyk, J. Renal localization of albumin and its function in the concentrating mechanism. *Am. J. Physiol.,* **212,** 387–93 (1967)

363. Pomerantz, R. M., Slotkoff, L. M., Lilienfield, L. S. Histochemical and microanatomical differences between renal cortical and medullary interstitium. In *Progress in Pyelonephritis* (Kass, E. H., Ed., F. A. Davis Co., Philadelphia, 766 pp., 1965)

364. Slotkoff, L. M., Lilienfield, L. S. Extravascular renal albumin. *Am. J. Physiol.,* **212,** 400–6 (1967)

365. Gottschalk, C. W., Mylle, M., Jones, N. F. Winters, R. W., Welt, L. G. Osmolality of renal tubular fluids in potassium-depleted rodents. *Clin. Sci.,* **29,** 249–60 (1965)

366. Bank, N., Aynedjian, H. S. A micropuncture study of the renal concentrating defect of potassium depletion. *Am. J. Physiol.,* **206,** 1347–54 (1964)

367. Jones, N. F., Mylle, M., Gottschalk, C. W. Renal tubular microinjection studies in normal and potassium-depleted rats. *Clin. Sci.,* **29,** 261–75 (1965)

368. Brunner, F. P., Rector, F. C., Jr., Seldin, D. W. The mechanism of the urinary concentrating defect in potassium deficient rats. *Arch. Ges. Physiol.* **290,** 202–10 (1966)

369. Buckalew, V. M., Ramirez, M. A., Goldberg, M. Free water reabsorption during solute diuresis in normal and potassium-depleted rats. *Am. J. Physiol.,* **212,** 381–86 (1967)

370. Edelmann, C. M., Jr., Barnett, H. L., Stark, H. Effect of urea on

concentration of urinary nonurea solute in premature infants. *J. Appl. Physiol,* **21,** 1021–25 (1966)

371. Yunibhand, P., Held, U. Nierenmark und Urinosmolalität nach der Geburt bei der Ratte unter Flüssigkeitsentzug. *Helv. Physiol. Acta,* **23,** 91–96 (1965)

372. Valtin, H. Hereditary hypothalamic diabetes insipidus in rats (Brattleboro Strain). *Am. J. Med.,* **42,** 814–27 (1967)

373. Fusco, M., Malvin, R. L., Churchill, P. Alterations in fluid, electrolyte and energy balance in rats with median eminence lesions. *Endocrinology,* **79,** 301–8 (1966)

374. Urakabe, S., Orita, Y., Furukawa, T., Abe, H. Analysis of urea excretion with special reference to the influence of abrupt change in urine flow. *Japan. Circ. J.,* **29,** 923–30 (1965)

375. Yunibhand, P., Held, U. Der Einfluß der zunehmenden Hydropenie auf Nierenmark, Serum und Urin bei Albinoratten. *Helv. Physiol. Pharmacol. Acta,* **23,** 139–44 (1965)

376. Harrington, A. R., Valtin, H. Vasopressin effect on urinary concentration in rats with hereditary hypothalamic diabetes insipidus (Brattleboro Strain). *Proc. Soc. Exptl. Biol. Med.,* **118,** 448–50 (1965)

377. Dawson, A. B. Early secretory activity in the hypothalamic nuclei and neuro-hypophysis in the rat; determined by selective staining. *J. Morphol.,* **118,** 549–60 (1966)

378. Bauman, J. W., Guyot-Jeannin, C., Dobrowolski, J. Nutritional state and urine concentrating ability in the rat. *J. Endocrinol.,* **30,** 147–48 (1964)

379. Robinson, R. R., Owen, E. E., Schmidt-Nielsen, B. Intrarenal distribution of free amino acids in antidiuretic ruminants. *Comp. Biochem. Physiol.,* **19,** 187–95 (1966)

380. Appelboom, J. W., Brodsky, W. A., Scott, W. N. Effect of osmotic diuresis on intrarenal solutes in diabetes insipidus and hydropenia. *Am. J. Physiol.,* **208,** 38–45 (1965)

381. Scaglione, P. R., Dell, R. B., Winters, R. W. Lactate concentration in the medulla of rat kidney. *Am. J. Physiol.,* **209,** 1193–98 (1965)

382. Washington, J. A., Holland, J. M. Urine oxygen tension: effects of osmotic and saline diuresis and of ethacrynic acid. *Am. J. Physiol.*, **210**, 243–50 (1966)

383. Goldberg, M., McCurdy, D. K., Ramirez, M. A. Differences between saline and mannitol diuresis in hydropenic man. *J. Clin. Invest.*, **44**, 182–92 (1965)

384. Mertz, D. P. Pseudomaximaler Nettoentzug von osmotisch freiem Wasser während der Harnkonzentrierung bei hypertoner Mannitdiurese. *Arch. Ges. Physiol.*, **290**, 1–17 (1966)

385. Friedler, R. M., Earley, L. E. Reduced renal concentrating capacity during isotonic saline loading. *Proc. Soc. Exptl. Biol. Med.*, **121**, 352–57 (1966)

386. Zaborowski, D. T., Koch, B., Bates, D. V., Dossetor, J. B. Studies of the carbon dioxide and oxygen tensions of urine during application of the stop-flow technique. *Can. J. Physiol. Pharmacol.*, **44**, 731–43 (1966)

387. Dzurik, R., Krajci-Lazary, B. Carbohydrate metabolism in renal medullary slices. *Physiol. Bohemoslov.*, **16**, 63–69 (1967)

388. Selkurt, E. E., Womack, I., Dailey, W. N. Mechanism of natriuresis and diuresis during elevated renal arterial pressure. *Am. J. Physiol.*, **209**, 95–99 (1965)

389. Poulson, T. L. Countercurrent multipliers in avian kidneys. *Science*, **148**, 389–91 (1965)

390. Munkacsi, I., Palkovits, M. Study on the renal pyramid, loops of Henle and percentage distribution of their thin segments in mammals living in desert, semidesert and water-rich environment. *Acta Biol.*, **17**, 89–103 (1966)

391. Share, L. Vasopressin, its bioassay and the physiological control of its release. *Am. J. Med.*, **42**, 701–12 (1967)

392. Czaczkes, J. W., Kleeman, C. R., Koenig, M. Physiologic studies of antidiuretic hormone by its direct measurement in human plasma. *J. Clin. Invest.*, **43**, 1625–40 (1964)

393. Tata, P. S., Gauer, O. H. Vasopressin studies in the rat. I. A sensitive bioassay for exogenous vasopressin. *Arch. Ges. Physiol.*, **290**, 279–85 (1966)

394. Sawyer, W. H. Biological assays for neurohypophyseal principles in tissues and in blood. In *The Pituitary Gland*, **3**, 288–306 (Harris, G., W., Donovan, B. T., Eds., Univ. of California Press, Berkeley and Los Angeles, 678 pp., 1966)

395. Jones, J. J., Lee, J. The value of the pre-operated rat in the bioassay of vasopressin. *J. Endocrinol.*, **33**, 329–30 (1965)

396. Vierling, A. F., Little, J. B., Radford, E. P., Jr. Antidiuretic hormone bioassay in rats with hereditary hypothalamic diabetes insipidus (Brattleboro Strain). *Endocrinology*, **80**, 211–14 (1967)

397. Miller, L., Fisch, L., Kleeman, C. R. Relative potency of arginine-8-vasopressin and lysine-8-vasopressin in human. *J. Lab. Clin. Med.*, **69**, 270–91 (1967)

398. Kramár, J., Grinnel, E. H., Duff, W. M. Observations on the diuretic activity of the antidiuretic hormone. *Am. J. Med. Sci.*, **252**, 53–61 (1966)

399. Sawyer, W. H., Valtin, H. Antidiuretic responses of rats with hereditary hypothalamic diabetes insipidus to vasopressin, oxytocin and nicotine. *Endocrinology*, **80**, 207–10 (1967)

400. Jones, J. J., Lee, J. The value of rats with hereditary hypothalamic diabetes insipidus for the bioassay of vasopressin. *J. Endocrinol.*, **37**, 335–44 (1967)

401. Yamane, Y., Kunishige, K. Bioassay of ADH on the experimental diabetes insipidus rats with a study on the ADH level in normal human plasma. *Japan. Circ. J.*, **30**, 1381–86 (1966)

402. Forsling, M. L., Jones, J. J., Lee, J. Intravenous vasopressin infusion to increase the sensitivity of its assay in the water-ethanol loaded rat. *Nature*, **215**, 433–34 (1967)

403. Pliska, V., Krejci, I. The dose-response relation of the antidiuretic and vasopressor activities of 4-asparagine-8-lysine-vasopressin. *Arch. Intern. Pharmacodyn. Therap.*, **161**, 289–97 (1966)

404. Gilliland, P. F., Prout, T. E. Immunologic studies of octapeptides. II. Production and detection of antibodies to oxytocin. *Metabolism*, **14**, 918–23 (1965)

405. Permutt, M. A., Parker, C. W., Utiger, R. D. Immunochemical studies with lysine vasopressin.

Endocrinology, **78,** 809–14 (1966)

406. Roth, J., Glick, S. M., Klein, L. A., Petersen, M. J. Specific antibody to vasopressin in man. *J. Clin. Endocrinol. Metab.,* **26,** 671–75 (1966)

407. Share, L. Effects of carotid occlusion and left atrial distension on plasma vasopressin titer. *Am. J. Physiol.,* **208,** 219–23 (1965)

408. Share, L., Levy, M. N. Effect of carotid chemoreceptor stimulation on plasma antidiuretic hormone titer. *Am. J. Physiol.,* **210,** 157–61 (1966)

409. Moran, W. H., Jr., Miltenberger, F. W., Shuayb, W. A., Zimmerman, B. The relationship of antidiuretic hormone secretion to surgical stress. *Surgery,* **56,** 99 (1954)

410. Ahmed, A. B. J., George, B. C., Gonzalez-Auvert, C., Dingman, J. F. Increased plasma arginine vasopressin in clinical adrenocortical insufficiency and its inhibition by glucosteroids. *J. Clin. Invest.,* **46,** 111–23 (1967)

411. Little, J. B., Radford, E. P., Jr. Circulating antidiuretic hormone in rats: effects of dietary electrolytes and protein. *Am. J. Physiol.,* **207,** 821–25 (1964)

412. Czaczkes, J. W., Kleeman, C. R. The effect of various states of hydration and the plasma concentration on the turnover of anti-diuretic hormone in mammals. *J. Clin. Invest.,* **43,** 1649–58 (1964)

413. Heintz, R., Drews, E. F., Drews, G., Brass, H. Untersuchungen über den Gehalt des menschlichen Plasmas an antidiuretischem Hormon mit einer verbesserten Methode zum Hormonnachweis. *Klin. Wochschr.,* **42,** 771–76 (1964)

414. Irmscher, K., Franken, F. H., Siadatpur, A. Zur Frage der Adiuretinkonzentration im Blutplasma des Menschen. *Klin. Wochschr.,* **42,** 1227–32 (1964)

415. Tata, P., Heller, J., Gauer, O. H. Über die antidiuretische Aktivität in der Lymphe von Katzen. *Arch. Ges. Physiol.,* **283,** 222–29 (1965)

416. Tata, P. S., Buzalkov, R. Vasopressin studies in the rat. III. Inability of ethanol anesthesia to prevent ADH secretion due to pain and hemorrhage. *Arch. Ges. Physiol.,* **290,** 294–97 (1966)

417. Brook, A. H., Share, L. On the question of protein-binding and the

diffusibility of circulating antidiuretic hormone in the dog. *Endocrinology,* **78,** 779–85 (1966)

418. Smith, M. W., Thorn, N. A. The effects of calcium on protein-binding and metabolism of arginine vasopressin in rats. *J. Endocrinol.,* **32,** 141–51 (1965)

419. Harvey, N., Jones, J. J., Lee, J. The renal clearance and plasma binding of vasopressin in the dog. *Endocrinology,* **38,** 1–9 (1967)

420. Lauson, H. D. Metabolism of antidiuretic hormones. *Am. J. Med.,* **42,** 713–44 (1967)

421. Heller, H., Ginsburg, M. Secretion, metabolism and fate of the posterior pituitary hormones. In *The Pituitary Gland,* **3,** 330–73 (Harris, G. W., Donovan, B. T., Eds., Univ. of California Press, Berkeley and Los Angeles, 678 pp., 1966)

422. Lauson, H. D., Bocanegra, M., Beuzeville, C. F. Hepatic and renal clearance of vasopressin from plasma of dogs. *Am. J. Physiol.,* **209,** 199–214 (1965)

423. Little, J. B., Klevay, L. M., Radford, E. P., Jr., McGandy, R. B. Antidiuretic hormone inactivation by isolated perfused rat liver. *Am. J. Physiol.,* **211,** 786–92 (1966)

424. Thorn, N. A., Smith, M. W. Renal excretion of synthetic arginine vasopressin injected into dogs. *Acta Endocrinol.,* **49,** 388–92 (1965)

425. Gauer, O. H., Tata, P. S. Vasopressin studies in the rat II. The amount of water reabsorbed by the rat kidney after a single i.v. injection of vasopressin: The vasopressin water equivalent. *Arch. Ges. Physiol.,* **290,** 286–93 (1966)

426. Leaf, A. Membrane effects of antidiuretic hormone. *Am. J. Med.,* **42,** 745–56 (1967)

427. Schwartz, I. L., Walter, R. Factors influencing the reactivity of the toad bladder to the hydro-osmotic action of vasopressin. *Am. J. Med.,* **42,** 769–76 (1967)

428. Civan, M. M., Kedem, O., Leaf, A. Effect of vasopressin on toad bladder under conditions of zero net sodium transport. *Am. J. Physiol.,* **211,** 569–75 (1966)

429. Carosso, N., Favard, P., Bourguet, J., Jard, S. Rôle du flux net d'eau dans les modifications ultrastructurales de la vessie de grenouille

stimulée par l'ocytocine. *J. Microscopie*, **5**, 519–23 (1966)

430. Lichtenstein, N. S., Leaf, A. Effect of amphotericin B on the permeability of the toad bladder. *J. Clin. Invest.*, **44**, 1328–42 (1965)

431. Schwartz, I. L., Rasmussen, H., Rudinger, J. Activity of neurohypophysial hormone analogues lacking a disulfide bridge. *Proc. Natl. Acad. Sci.* **52**, 1044–45 (1964)

432. Dicker, S. E., Franklin, C. S. The isolation of hyaluronic acid and chondroitin sulphate from kidneys and their reaction with urinary hyaluronidase. *J. Physiol. (London)*, **186**, 110–20 (1966)

433. Orloff, J., Handler, J. The role of adenosine 3′,5′-phosphate in the action of antidiuretic hormone. *Am. J. Med.*, **42**, 757–68 (1967)

434. Rudinger, J., Jost, K. A biologically active analogue of oxytocin not containing a disulfide group. *Experientia*, **20**, 570 (1964)

435. Rudinger, J. *Oxytocin, Vasopressin and their Structural Analogues* (Pergamon, Oxford, 195 pp., 1964)

436. Jost, K., Rudinger, J. Amino acids and peptides. LXIX. Synthesis of two biologically active analogues of deaminooxytocin not containing a disulphide bond. *Coll. Czech. Chem. Commun.* **32**, 1229–41 (1967)

437. Yamashiro, D., Gillessen, D., Du Vigneaud, V. Oxytoceine and deamino-oxytoceine. *Biochemistry*, **5**, 3711–20 (1966)

438. Handler, J. S., Buchter, R. W., Sutherland, E. W., Orloff, J. The effect of vasopressin and of theophylline on the concentration of adenosine 3,5-phosphate in the urinary bladder of the toad. *J. Biol. Chem.*, **240**, 4524–26 (1965)

439. Finn, A. L., Handler, J. S., Orloff, J. Relation between toad bladder potassium content and permeability response to vasopressin. *Am. J. Physiol.*, **210**, 1279–84 (1966)

440. Handler, J., Petersen, M., Orloff, J. Effect of metabolic inhibitors on the response of the toad bladder to vasopressin. *Am. J. Physiol.*, **211**, 1175–80 (1966)

441. Takahashi, K., Kamimura, M., Shinko, T., Tsuji, S. Effects of vasopressin and water-load on urinary adenosine-3,5-cyclic monophosphate. *Lancet*, **II**, 967 (1966)

442. Jones, N. F., Welt, L. G. Adenosinetriphosphate in rat renal papilla: effects of vasopressin and of ischemia. *Am. J. Physiol.*, **212**, 939–44 (1967)

443. Gulyassy, P. F., Edelman, I. S. Hydrogen ion dependence of the antidiuretic action of vasopressin, oxytocin and deaminooxytocin. *Biochim. Biophys. Acta*, **102**, 185–97 (1965)

444. Goodman, A., Levitin, H. Effect of urinary pH on the renal concentrating mechanism. *Am. J. Physiol.*, **208**, 847–51 (1965)

445. Ullmann, T. D., Czaczkes, W. J., Menczel, J. Modification of the antidiuretic effect of vasopressin by acid and alkaline loads. *J. Clin. Invest.*, **44**, 754–64 (1965)

446. Taborsky, J. Über die Hemmung der antidiuretischen Wirkung von Vasopressin und Nikotin mittels Acetazolamid bei wasserbelasteten Ratten. *Med. Pharmacol. Exptl.*, **15**, 427–31 (1966)

447. Lassiter, W. E., Frick, A., Rumrich, G., Ullrich, K. J. Influence of ionic calcium on the water permeability of proximal and distal tubules in the rat kidney. *Arch. Ges. Physiol.*, **285**, 90–95 (1965)

448. Morel, F., Mylle, M., Gottschalk, C. W. Tracer microinjection studies of effect of ADH on renal tubular diffusion of water. *Am. J. Physiol.*, **209**, 179–87 (1965)

449. Skadhauge, E. Effects of unilateral infusion or arginine vasotocin into the portal circulation of the avian kidney. *Acta Endocrinol.*, **47**, 321–30 (1964)

450. Gardner, K. D., Jr. Dry weight as a point of reference in studies of renal papillary composition. *Am. J. Physiol.*, **211**, 1031–35 (1966)

451. Saikia, T. C. Composition of the renal cortex and medulla of rats during water diuresis and antidiuresis. *Quart. J. Exptl. Physiol.*, **50**, 146–157 (1965)

452. Saikia, T. C. The acute effect of vasopressin upon the composition of the rat renal cortex and medulla. *Ibid.*, 158–68

453. Valtin, H. Sequestration of urea and nonurea solutes in renal tissues of rats with hereditary hypothalamic diabetes insipidus: effect of vasopressin and dehydration on the

countercurrent mechanism. *J. Clin. Invest.*, **45**, 337–45 (1966)

454. Cross, R. B., Sherrington, L. A. The effect of vasopressin on water distribution in the rat kidney. *Australian J. Exptl. Biol. Med. Sci.*, **43**, 505–10 (1965)

455. White, H. L., Rolf, D. Urine and papilla concentrations during transition from hypotonic to hypertonic urine. *Am. J. Physiol.*, **208**, 397–400 (1965)

456. Fourman, J., Kennedy, G. C. An effect of antidiuretic hormone on the flow of blood through the vasa recta of the rat kidney. *J. Endocrinol.*, **35**, 173–76 (1966)

457. Kennedy, G. C., Skadhauge, E., Hague, P. The effect of hydrochlorothiazide on water intake and plasma osmolality in diabetes insipidus in the rat. *Quart. J. Exptl. Physiol.*, **49**, 417–23 (1964)

458. Skadhauge, E. Studies of the antidiuresis induced by natrichloriuretic drugs in rats with diabetes insipidus. *Quart. J. Exptl. Physiol.*, **51**, 297–310 (1966)

459. McDonald, S. J., de Wardener, H. E. Some observations on the production of a hypo-osmotic urine during the administration of 0.9% saline and vasopressin in the dog. *Clin. Sci.*, **28**, 445–59 (1965)

460. Dlouhá, H., Křeček, J., Kraus, M., Pliška, V. Sensitivity of rats to vasopressin in the weaning period. *Physiol. Bohemoslov.*, **14**, 217–24 (1965)

461. Mills, R. R. Hormonal control of excretion in the American cockroach. I. Release of a diuretic hormone from the terminal abdominal ganglion. *J. Exptl. Biol.*, **46**, 35–41 (1967)

462. Dantzler, W. H. Glomerular and tubular effects of arginine vasotocin in water snakes (*Natrix sipedon*). *Am. J. Physiol.*, **212**, 83–91 (1967)

463. Sawyer, W. H. Evolution of antidiuretic hormones and their functions. *Am. J. Med.*, **42**, 678–86 (1967)

464. Kleeman, C. R., Czaczkes, J. W., Cutler, R. Mechanisms of impaired water excretion in adrenal and pituitary insufficiency. IV. Antidiuretic hormone in primary and secondary adrenal insufficiency. *J. Clin. Invest.*, **43**, 1641–48 (1964)

465. Wiederholt, M., Stolte, H., Brecht, J. P., Hierholzer, K. Mikropunktionsuntersuchungen über den Einfluß von Aldosteron, Cortison und Dexamethason auf die renale Natriumresorption adrenalektomierter Ratten. *Arch. Ges. Physiol.*, **292**, 316–33 (1966)

466. Sharp, G. W. G., Coggins, C. H., Lichtenstein, N. S., Leaf, A. Evidence for a mucosal effect of aldosterone on sodium transport in the toad bladder. *J. Clin. Invest.*, **45**, 1640–47 (1966)

467. Crabbé, J., de Weer, P. Action of aldosterone and vasopressin on the active transport of sodium by the isolated toad bladder. *J. Physiol. (London)*, **180**, 560–68 (1965)

468. Fanestil, D. D., Edelman, I. S. On the mechanism of action of aldosterone on sodium transport: effects of inhibitors of RNA and of protein synthesis. *Fed. Proc.*, **25**, 912–16 (1966)

469. Fanestil, D. D., Porter, G. A., Edelman, I. S. Aldosterone stimulation of sodium transport. *Biochim. Biophys. Acta*, **135**, 74–88 (1967)

470. Fimognari, G. M., Porter, G. A., Edelman, I. S. The role of the tricarboxylic acid cycle in the action of aldosterone on sodium transport. *Biochim. Biophys. Acta*, **135**, 89–99 (1967)

471. Yunis, S. L., Bercovitch, D. D., Stein, R. M., Levitt, M. F., Goldstein, M. H. Renal tubular effects of hydrocortisone and aldosterone in normal hydropenic man: comments on sites of action. *J. Clin. Invest.*, **43**, 1668–76 (1964)

472. Jick, H., Snyder, J. G., Moore, E. W., Morrison, R. S. The effects of aldosterone and glucocorticoid on free water reabsorption. *Clin. Sci.*, **29**, 25–32 (1965)

473. Sigler, M. H., Forrest, J. N., Jr., Elkington, J. R. Renal concentrating ability in the adrenalectomized rat. *Clin. Sci.*, **28**, 29–37 (1965)

474. Kessler, E., Allen, R. L., Jr., Kirman, D., Strauss, H. Effect of aldosterone and cortisol on sodium and water content of the rat kidney. *Am. J. Physiol.*, **207**, 109–12 (1964)

475. McEvoy, J., Hollmann, G., Senft, G. Einfluß von Mineralocorticoiden auf die tubuläre Rückgewinnung von Natriumionen. *Arch. Exptl. Pathol. Pharamakol.*, **250**, 318–24 (1965)

476. Hierholzer, K., Wiederholt, M., Stolte, H. Hemmung der Natriumresorption im proximalen und distalen Konvolut adrenalektomierter Ratten. *Arch. Ges. Physiol.*, **291**, 43–62 (1966)

477. Hierholzer, K., Wiederholt, M., Holzgreve, H., Giebisch, G., Klose, R. M., Windhager, E. E. Micropuncture study of renal transtubular concentration gradients of sodium and potassium in adrenalectomized rats. *Arch. Ges. Physiol.*, **285**, 193–210 (1965)

478. Wiederholt, M., Wiederholt, B. Wirkung eines synthetischen Corticosteroids (Dexamethason) auf die Wasserpermeabilität des distalen Konvoluts adrenalektomierter Ratten. *Arch. Ges. Physiol.*, **294**, R30 (1967)

479. Schwarz, W., Wolff, J. Veränderungen am Hauptstück und peritubulären Kapillaren der Rattenniere nach Hypophysektomie. Elektronenmikroskopische Beobachtungen. *Z. Zellforsch. Mikroskop. Anat.*, **71**, 441–54 (1966)

480. Castles, T. R., Williamson, H. E. Stimulation in vivo of renal RNA-synthesis by aldosterone. *Proc. Soc. Exptl. Biol. Med.*, **119**, 308–11 (1965)

481. Wiederholt, M. Mikropunktionsuntersuchungen am proximalen und distalen Konvolut der Rattenniere über den Einfluß von Actinomycin D auf den mineralocorticoidabhängigen Na-Transport. *Arch. Ges. Physiol.*, **292**, 334–42 (1966)

482. Ludens, J. H., Hook, J. B., Williamson, H. E. Lack of effect of Actinomycin D on aldosterone induced antinatriuresis when administered after the hormone. *Proc. Soc. Exptl. Biol. Med.*, **124**, 539–41 (1967)

483. Fanestil, D. D., Edelman, I. S. Some characteristics of the renal nuclear receptors for aldosterone. *J. Clin. Invest.*, **45**, 1005–6 (1966)

484. Hollander, W., Kramsch, D. M., Chobanian, A. V., Melby, J. C. Metabolism and distribution of intravenously administered d-aldosterone-1,2-H^3 in the arteries, kidneys, and heart of dog. *Circ. Res.*, **18**, 135–45 (1966)

485. Barraclough, M. A., Jones, N. F., Marsden, C. D. Effect of angiotensin on renal function in the rat. *Am. J. Physiol.*, **212**, 1153–57 (1967)

486. Eisalo, A., Räsänen, V. Effect of equipressor doses of synthetic α- and β-angiotensin II on urinary volume and urinary electrolytes in normotensive subjects. *Acta Med. Scand.*, **177**, 121–26 (1965)

487. Peters, G. Effects of Val$_5$-angiotensin II-amide and of hydrochlorothiazide on the kidneys of renal hypertensive rats. *Nephron*, **2**, 95–106 (1965)

488. Cuypers, Y. Récherches sur les fonctions et propriétés respectives des glomérules et des tubes renaux chez le coq (Thesis, Univ. of Liège, 1966)

489. Langford, H. G., Fallis, N. Diuretic effect of angiotensin in the chicken. *Proc. Soc. Exptl. Biol. Med.*, **123**, 317–320 (1966)

490. Healy, J. K., Barcena, C., O'Connell, J. M. B., Schreiner, G. E. Renal and pressor action of angiotensin in the normal dog. *Am. J. Physiol.*, **208**, 1093–99 (1965)

491. Lameijer, L. D. F. Soghikian, K., de Graeff, J. The effect of angiotensin on renal sodium excretion: studies in normal dogs and in dogs with experimental renal artery stenosis. *Clin. Sci.*, **30**, 529–41 (1966)

492. Louis, W. J., Doyle, A. E. The effects of varying doses of angiotensin on renal function and blood pressure in man and dogs. *Clin. Sci.*, **29**, 489–504 (1965)

493. Collignon, P., Kulbertus, H. Influence de la pression de perfusion sur la réponse à l'angiotensine du rein de chien transplanté au cou. *Arch. Intern. Physiol. Biochim.*, **74**, 565–73 (1966)

494. Langford, H. G., Pickering, G. W. The action of synthetic angiotensin on renal function in the unanesthetized rabbit. *J. Physiol. (London)*, **177**, 161–73 (1965)

495. Akinkugbe, O. O., Brown, W. C. B., Cranston, W. I. The direct renal action of angiotensin in the rabbit. *Clin. Sci.*, **30**, 259–66 (1966)

496. Akinkugbe, O. O., Brown, W. C. B., Cranston, W. I. Response to angiotensin infusion before and after adrenalectomy in the rabbit. *Am. J. Physiol.*, **212**, 1147–52 (1967)

497. Cannon, P. J., Ames, R. P., Laragh, J. H. Indirect action of angiotensin infusion to inhibit renal

tubular sodium reabsorption in dogs. *Am. J. Physiol.*, **211**, 1021–30 (1966)

498. Ames, R. P., Borkowski, A. J., Sicinski, A. M., Laragh, J. H. Prolonged infusions of angiotensin II and norepinephrine and blood pressure, electrolyte balance, and aldosterone and cortisol secretion in normal man and in cirrhosis with ascites. *J. Clin. Invest.*, **44**, 1171–86 (1965)

499. Bonting, S. L., Canady, M. R., Hawkins, N. M. Angiotensin and renal Na-K activated adenosine triphosphatase. *Biochim. Biophys. Acta*, **82**, 427–29 (1964)

500. Marc-Aurèle, J., Bergeron, M. Lack of evidence for an inhibitory effect of angiotensin on Na+-K+ adenosinetriphosphatase. *Rev. Can. Biol.*, **25**, 107–9 (1966)

501. Thurau, K., Schnermann, J., Nagel, W., Horster, M., Wahl, M. Composition of tubular fluid in the macula densa segment as a factor regulating the function of the juxtaglomerular apparatus. *Circ. Res.*, **20/21**, *Suppl. II*, 79 (1967)

502. Rosenfeld, S., Kraus, R., McCullen, A. Effect of renin, ischemia, and plasma protein loading on the isolated perfused kidney. *Am. J. Physiol.*, **209**, 835–43 (1965)

503. Schröder, E., Ochwadt, B., Bethge, H. Herstellung und Funktion eines isolierten Nierenpräparates vom Hund. *Arch. Ges. Physiol.*, **286**, 189–98 (1965)

504. Lockett, M. F. Perfusion of cat kidneys from heart-lung circuits. *Proc. Soc. Exptl. Biol. Med.*, **121**, 937–41 (1966)

505. Bahlmann, J., Giebisch, G., Ochwadt, B., Schoeppe, W. Micropuncture study of isolated perfused rat kidney. *Am. J. Physiol.*, **212**, 77–82 (1967)

506. Lee, J. C., Hurley, S., Hopper, J. Secretory activity of the juxtaglomerular granular cells of the mouse. *Lab. Invest.*, **15**, 1459–76 (1966)

507. Biava, C., West, M. Lipofuscin-like granules in vascular smooth muscle and juxtaglomerular cells of human kidneys. *Am. J. Pathol.*, **47**, 287–313 (1965)

508. Biava, C. G., West, M. Fine structure of normal human juxtaglomerular cells I. General structure and intercellular relationships. *Ibid.*, **49**, 679–721 (1966)

509. Biava, C. G., and West, M. Fine structure of normal human juxtaglomerular cells II. Specific and nonspecific cytoplasmatic granules. *Ibid.*, 955–79

510. Rudinger, J., Krejcí, I. Antagonists of the neurohypophysial hormones. In *Handb. Exptl. Pharmacol.*, **23**, Neurohypophysial Hormones and Similar Polypeptides (Berde, B., Ed., Springer-Verlag, Berlin-Heidelberg-New York, 785 pp., 1967)

511. Clapp, J. R., Robinson, R. R. Osmolality of distal tubular fluid in the dog. *J. Clin. Invest.*, **45**, 1847–53 (1966)

512. Carriere, S., Thorburn, G. D., O'Morchoe, C. C. C., Barger, A. C. Intrarenal distribution of blood flow in dogs during hemorrhagic hypotension. *Circ. Res.*, **19**, 167–79 (1966)

HEMODYNAMICS[1] 1013

By Donald A. McDonald

Department of Physiology and Biophysics
University of Alabama Medical Center, Birmingham, Alabama

While it is gratifying to be given the task of initiating a separate section, this topic also robs me of that great academic prop—a precedent. Therefore I propose first, briefly, to create my own definition, with an attempted justification, and then to write an essay on the "state of the art" rather than confine myself to a detailed coverage of the past twelve months. Rarely, however, will we need to go back before my own monograph of 1960 (1) (while the new version of it will now inevitably appear later than this review), and in general the publication of the symposium *Pulsatile Blood Flow* (2) in 1964 will be taken as summarizing the main trends to that date.

Classically, fluid dynamics is divided into two major compartments. That concerned with compressible fluids is aerodynamics; the study of incompressible fluids, i.e. liquids, is termed hydrodynamics. Although in the nature of things water is by far the commonest liquid studied, physicists and technologists do not feel the urge to invent a new "science" each time they, perforce, study some other liquid. Hence we have so far been spared "oleodynamics", "molassodynamics", etc. While there seemed time to divert the torrent I refused to use the term hemodynamics; a puny attempt in this direction was a review by M. G. Taylor and myself in 1959 (3) which was firmly entitled "The hydrodynamics of arterial circulation". The objection that hydrodynamics was too exact a science to apply to a biological system can easily be countered by a wonderfully apt remark by Sir Cyril Hinshelwood (cited in 5): "In the 19th century fluid dynamicists were divided into hydraulic engineers who observed what could not be explained, and mathematicians who explained things that could not be observed"—to which Birkhoff (4) adds: "It is my impression that many survivors are still with us."

The hydrodynamical background of studies of flowing blood has been exclusively and well reviewed by several authors; Fry (5) in 1959 gave an excellent brief account which is especially valuable for defining the terminology more thoroughly than the diffuse account in (1) did. Skalak's review (6) is highly recommended for re-evaluating the original Womersley contributions in the light of later developments and integrating with the analyses of wall elasticity necessary for a comprehensive coverage; Rudinger (7) has presented a rather shorter but very clear review and others by Attinger (8–10) cover the field well.

[1] This review was completed in June 1967.

While "hemodynamics" has no strong logical case as the hydrodynamics of blood, its survival indicates that it does fill a need. The term might be interpreted as "the physical aspect of the cardiovascular system" or "cardiovascular biophysics". Such a definition breaks any but an etymological connection of "hemodynamics" with "hydrodynamics" for the former, of necessity, considers the solid structures which confine the blood. Thus we are beginning to lean heavily, in pulse-wave propagation and elasticity studies, on colleagues well versed in solid mechanics [e.g. Fung (11, 12), Anliker (13)]. Again I consider that the physical properties of the pump are an essential part of this view; exigencies of space, personal ignorance, and the fact that cardiac and vascular muscle are easier to consider by comparison with the detailed work on skeletal muscle from which it has sprung, will, however, exclude a review of this topic from this chapter. The flow properties of blood, as such, are mainly of importance in studying small vessels and the majority of the contributions to this topic have appeared in relation to the microcirculation, which is now virtually a speciality of its own. The flow of a non-Newtonian liquid can be regarded as in the purview of "rheology"—a term coined by Bingham in the 1920's to cover substances which flowed but had some properties more appropriate to solids (his best-remembered work was on paint). As the analytical apparatus of rheology— the spring-dashpot arrays such as Maxwell and Saint Venant bodies, etc.—is useful in studying the viscoelastic properties of the arterial wall, it will, properly, be included here. It, too, has subdivided, and the species of hemorheology has appeared and held its first International Congress [in Iceland, 1966 (14)]. This produced a number of interesting papers but as they were not confined to blood it is hard to distinguish the title from biorheology which has its own journal, albeit not widely known, and has held an international symposium subordinate to a wider congress in rheology [in Rhode Island, 1963 (15)].

In the array of new classification titles, "biomedical engineering" must clearly be noted. Defining this as distinct from biophysics has proved, for this reviewer, as impossible as obtaining any universal distinction between a physicist and an engineer. In practice, the Biophysical Society (now ten years old) has latterly concentrated on biology at the cellular or subcellular level, and thus many more contributions in our present field have appeared at the Biomedical Engineering meetings. The meetings of the American Congress on Engineering in Medicine and Biology (ACEMB) which I have attended in 1964, 1965, and 1966 (16–18) have had many interesting contributions to which reference will be made. The American Society of Mechanical Engineers has also held valuable meetings and their symposium volumes (19, 20) carry papers more detailed than the ACEMB limit of about 600 words allows. To the naive biologist, like myself, who thinks of engineers as applied physicists there has been a disappointing tendency to avoid important practical matters such as instrumentation. The invaluable contributions from Rushmer's group in Seattle, and its former members, show how vital this is to acquire the necessary data in complicated situations such as the living body presents. Instead there is a strong tendency to present theoretical analyses and analogs, usually electrical, of systems about which we have only very imperfect descriptive data. As this review is in a volume entitled *Physiology* no serious attempt will be made to cover articles which are not primarily based on experimental data in the living organism.

It is also appropriate to pay tribute to Information Exchange Group (IEG) No. 3 (defunct, alas, since early 1967). Though entitled "Computer Simulation of Biological Systems" it, in fact, most valuably covered most of the field discussed in this review. That it, in fact, never lived up to the high hopes expressed, with regard to the Muscle IEG, by Wilkie (21) was mostly, I feel, due to the inertia of us members who used it only as a prepublication medium, and who were discouraged in our attempt to make the slogan "A continuing international congress by mail" a reality of exchanging ideas rather than only confirmed, publishable data. I shared Wilkie's view and am very sorry to see the scheme fail.

Pulsatile Flow. Pressure-Flow Relations

Reference has been made to a symposium held in Philadelphia in April 1963 (2). Understandably uneven as such meetings are, it produced one outstanding contribution that contained a deal of speculation. This was the paper by M. G. Taylor (22) in which he considered the "design" of the arterial tree in terms of optimal work loads under physiologically varying conditions.[2] Part of this considered the effects of rates changes on the length of diastole and adequacy of filling, etc., but the germinative idea (to my mind) concerned the arterial tree. He suggested that the increasing "stiffness" of arteries with increasing distance from the heart had the effect of a "tapered" transmission line which would, in effect, decouple the oscillatory work load of the ventricle from the necessarily high terminal impedance represented by the arterioles and capillaries. Thus the heart would, in essence, be ejecting into a system whose input impedance was almost wholly determined by the physical properties of the proximal arterial tree; the heart could change its rate and output in response to direct physiological demands without having its load suddenly changed by variations in the arteriolar bed, particularly where reflections create "node" and "antinode" frequencies. Caro & McDonald (25) had noted that the "natural" heart rate seemed to place the heart at a nodal position where the output load would be minimal; a change in frequency could therefore cause a marked increase in load—physiologically, a clear disadvantage. This description is necessarily too brief. A more detailed mathematical analysis for

---

[2] Before I arouse the ire of those, like Kleiber in the precedent volume to this (23), or the vigorous debaters at the symposium on gastrointestinal flow in 1966 (24), who regard "design" as a term of teleology, I would say that it is used here as shorthand for "evolutionary modification" or some such concept. As Kleiber correctly points out, teleology was, historically, a branch of theology; his discussion of evolutionary adaptation suggests that this meaning of "design" would be acceptable to him.

a line of progressively increasing elastance filled with an ideal (nonviscous) liquid was published later [Taylor (26)] and a computer-simulated model of a formalized branching arterial tree changing geometry and filled with a "bloodlike" liquid was analyzed in two papers in 1966 [Taylor (27, 28)].

In the meantime, improving precision in flow measurements [deriving from such detailed work on calibration as that of O'Rourke (29) and Gessner & Bergel (30, 31)] had allowed a much clearer appreciation of the amplitude and frequency pattern of the input impedance of the aorta. In particular the phase lag in these meters following the design lines of Kolin (32) is the best of those tested, if only because its phase error is linear with frequency and thus easily corrected. The amplitude recorded did not deviate significantly from 100 per cent until 15 cps or so with the larger probes. Gessner & Bergel's conclusion was that electrical calibration was as good as hydraulic calibration. Hydraulic calibrations using an accurate sine-wave pump [modified from that described by Yanof et al. (33)] were being simultaneously done by myself with Attinger's group in Philadelphia (unpublished) and we essentially concur with their findings; if anything, the hydraulic calibration was better in amplitude response than that reported in (31), and tended to overread rather than the reverse above 15 cps, but the difference was not significant because of signal "noise" (possibly due to disturbances in flow pattern but more probably due to vibration of the tube). It may also be due to the fact that in Baltimore they were using an earlier Medicon model (K-2000) than we usually were (M-4000).

The input arterial impedance as the ratio of the harmonic terms of the pressure at the input to the correspondingly oscillatory flow terms has received continuing attention. Detailed studies have been made in the dog femoral bed by O'Rourke (34) and O'Rourke & Taylor (35) which greatly improve the detail in early, cruder experiments described by McDonald (1) in 1960. The analysis of frequency distribution in terms of interaction with reflected waves remains essentially the same. The main difference is in the estimation of the terminal reflection coefficient. Calculating this from the values of the low-frequency input impedance (as an approximation of the terminal impedance) and an estimated characteristic impedance, McDonald (1) predicted a reflection coefficient of about 35 per cent in normal dogs falling to 20 per cent in vasodilatation and rising to 60 per cent in vasoconstriction. With the computer model the corresponding values of O'Rourke & Taylor (35) were 75, 0, and 95 per cent. McDonald (36) has cast doubt on the meaning of "characteristic" impedance in a nonuniform system but his 1960 values (1) are undoubtedly too low because it was not appreciated how far from the limiting impedance value his fundamental frequencies were, seen in the light of results with a new technique by Taylor (37). The latter figures in (35) may be a little unrealistic in that the reflection coefficient is in "the arterioles" isolated in a computer. Reflection coefficient is here defined as by Womersley (38), and in transmission terminology, as reflection at a point of mismatch in impedances (i.e. $Rf = Z_T - Z_0)/Z_T + Z_0$) where Z_T and Z_0 are the impedances on the distal and proximal sides of the mismatch). The term is also used for the ratio of the centrifugal to the centripetal components of the pressure pulse wave at a given frequency at any point of measurement in an artery. Its phase will clearly vary with its distance from the termination in terms of wavelength. The term reflection coefficient, without emphasis on its quite different character from the usual terminal reflection coefficients, has been used by others for techniques that separate forward and reflected waves, as in the method of Gessner & Bergel (39). Clarity would be gained if a different name, such as reflection ratio, were given to it.

Patel & Austen (40) measured the input impedance in various large arteries in the human at operation. Gabe (41) has measured the impedance in the intact human iliac and femoral arteries, using two pressure measurements to derive the flow [as Bergel et al. (42) had done in the dog]. Further, he used a very elegant routine (43) on an analog computer to obtain a close approximation to the full Womersley equations. This should have received more attention, although, in America, there are now probably more digital computers than good analog computers in use by physiologists.

VENTRICULAR LOAD

The input impedance in the large vessels at the heart is of especial interest, because they represent a major part of the pulsatile work load of the ventricles. The amplitude pattern recorded in 1963 by Patel, de Freitas & Fray (44) in the ascending aorta has been confirmed by Noble et al. (45) in conscious dogs and by Taylor (37), O'Rourke & Taylor (46), and McDonald et al. (47) in anesthetized dogs. A paper by Attinger et al. (48) from the same laboratory, apparently incorporating some of this data, appeared the following year. The analysis of the impedance was not stressed and the data are a little difficult to interpret because results from all twelve dogs are presented as if they had identical heart rates, although no comment is made as to how this unusual synchrony was obtained.

The impedance is characterized by high values at low frequencies which rapidly fall to a low value (ca. 10 per cent of the total peripheral resistance) by 3–4 cps; thereafter it remains remarkably constant with increasing frequency. Taylor's (37) technique provides specially detailed information; in this the heart is paced at a randomly irregular rate and a frequency spectrum analyzed which gives values at much smaller frequency steps than a Fourier analysis, at a regular heart rate, can give. The method further allows exploration at frequencies far below the normal minimal heart frequency (values for frequencies about to 0.1 cps have been calculated). The usual interpretation of such a pattern would involve the effect of reflected waves in the ascending aorta at frequencies above 2 cps, or so, which might be attributed to a very high attenuation of reflected waves which fail to reach the ascending aorta. This, however, is impossible to reconcile with the findings of McDonald et al. (47) of a well-marked "reflection pattern" in the midthoracic aorta and those of O'Rourke (34, 46) that such a pattern can be seen there and in the brachiocephalic artery. This led to the hypothesis that reflected waves arriving at the arch of the aorta from the periphery of the forepart of the arterial tree will almost always be out of phase with those arriving from the hindpart because the heart is eccentrically placed in the body. In its simplest analytical form (in collaboration with Gessner in Baltimore and nicknamed "the eccentric T-tube"), the ascending aorta is represented by a short stub pumping into a single line with a termination of the anterior averaged arteriolar bed at half the distance of the posterior arteriolar bed; this was discussed by McDonald in 1965 (49). Contemporaneously O'Rourke, in an M.D. thesis under Taylor in Australia, was working on the same hypothesis.[3] A more detailed analysis has been made in (46).

The detailed line analysis of this model by Gessner (unpublished) has shown that modifying its parameters such as attenuation [from values of McDonald & Gessner (52)] and nonuniform elastic properties [from McDonald (53)] produced insufficient variation in the pattern of amplitude variation with frequency to allow for any critical experimental test. The phase of the input impedance, however, did vary considerably with these modifications so that accurate assessment of the model concept must await a generally agreed phase pattern, or improved measurement of the impedance phase.

So far, all the workers cited in the past three years agree that the phase at the lowest frequencies is about $-60°$ (i.e. flow leading pressure) but that it decreases as frequency increases to 3–4 cps; thereafter it stays approximately constant until the highest frequencies analyzed (usually ~ 20 cps). The values of Patel et al. (40) could be interpreted as not varying significantly from this, but neither did they vary significantly from a steady progression such as might be shown by a lumped system; it is not clear whether correction was made for phase errors in their meter. The difference in the steady value is that Gabe et al. (45) and McDonald et al. (47) found it to be in the range $+35$ to $45°$ whereas O'Rourke & Taylor

---

[3] For students of priorities, the embryonic idea of the effects of interaction between the two "subsystems" had been formulated in London in 1955 and had been briefly mentioned, and credited to Taylor (unpublished) in my 1960 monograph (1) —but quite forgotten when the idea seemed to be born again in the summer of 1965. Then the book entry was pointed out to me by Dr. Allen Scher in Seattle in September 1965. When in early 1966 O'Rourke's thesis became available, I assumed that Taylor had suggested it to his pupil and so credited Taylor with it in a symposium (24, 50) in September 1966, only to find that Taylor had also forgotten his idea of 1955 and thought that the idea had arisen *de novo* in O'Rourke's mind. The relevant observation would appear to be that of the Preacher (51)—"There is no new thing under the sun.—See, this is new? it hath been already, in the ages that were before us."

(46) find it to be around 0?—often negative and sometimes markedly so. This discrepancy is as yet unexplained. Hydrodyamic theory would predict it to be very close to zero (actually $\varepsilon_{10}/2$ in terms of the standard Womersley parameters). More detailed studies on this have recently been made by O'Rourke & Milnor (54) in the pulmonary artery and are discussed below.

In parallel studies by Bergel & Milnor (55), the pulmonary artery of the dog appeared to show slightly more reflection effects than the aorta—but less than Caro & McDonald (25) had found previously in perfused rabbit lungs (many probably edematous to some degree). They also showed that the assumed quarter-wavelength minimum was shifted by serotonin in a way suggesting that the wave velocity in the larger pulmonary vessels was increased, presumably by the action of 5-HT on the smooth muscle in the wall, as shown by Somlyo & Somlyo (56) in isolated strips.

A subsidiary point is also clearly made, from dogs with surgically induced heart block and then paced, that the system is effectively linear; for example, the value of the impedance for the second harmonic at a heart rate of 1 cps is the same as that for the fundamental harmonic when the heart rate is doubled to 2 cps. Similar observations in the aorta of conscious dogs were made by Gabe et al. (45) and in the aorta of dogs with the heart replaced by a sinusoidal pump by Kendrick (57); in isolated perfused aortas pumped with an accurate sine-wave pressure, Attinger, Anné & McDonald (58) found no significant evidence of nonlinearity (less than 5 per cent of second harmonic created). So for practical purposes [as Womersley (59) calculated], at present the nonlinear terms in wave transmission and impedance analysis may be neglected even though they continue to worry workers concerned only with the mathematical analysis (ref. any biomedical engineering meeting discussion). In terms of analysis of wall-movement, Taylor & Gow (60) find that these terms need to be considered.

CARDIAC OUTPUT

This lengthy discussion of the impedance at the outflow points of the ventricles is necessary to understand fully the approximations which can be tolerated in deriving ventricular output from pressure measurements made in the ascending aorta and pulmonary artery. While approximate methods based originally on the Windkessel hypothesis, and amended in various empirical ways by different authors, have been introduced from time to time, none has won general critical acceptance. Since the hydrodynamic analyses of Womersley (61) and McDonald (62) in 1955 and Fry, Mallos & Casper (63) in 1956, the development of cardiac output based on classic hydrodynamics has been potentially achievable. The starting point, mathematically, is the derivative of pressure in respect of distance along the artery, dP/dz. (Conventionally the axis of the tube is the Z-axis.) The obvious approximation to this is the pressure gradient over a finite distance; this was the first approach of McDonald (62) and Fry et al. (63) and was explored by the latter, and associates, in (64-68). The "finite interval correction" was mentioned briefly by McDonald & Taylor in 1959 (3), was discussed by Fry & Greenfield (67), and has been investigated, with respect to the pulmonary artery, by Milnor & Gessner (personal communication). The error depends on the distance between measuring points and, where Δz is the separation and λ the wavelength of any given frequency component, the error is of the order of $\Delta z/2\lambda$.

This method poses the technical problem of measuring a very small pressure difference to a high degree of accuracy. The restriction of the "finite interval correction" in the living animal is minor compared to the restriction that anatomy imposes. The primary assumption—so obvious that it tends to be forgotten—is that the volume that flows past both pressure points is essentially the same, i.e. that there are no major branches in the interval over which the gradient is measured. As pressure measurement behind a valve-cusp is very subject to artifact, the possible interval is, at limit, from the tip of the opened valve-cusp to the proximal margin of the first branch—and for accurate measurements avoiding big secondary flows it should be shorter by at least one vessel radius. O'Rourke & Milnor (54) found it just possible to attain a separation of 3 cm in the pulmonary artery of a large dog and I doubt if the available distance in the dog aorta is ever much longer. Fry et al. (63), in the original paper of his method [used in various forms by other workers subsequently, e.g. (65, 66)], explicitly states that the interval used was "6 cm in the upper aorta". Later a double-lumen catheter, used with a fixed separation of 5 cm, was introduced by Porjé & Rudewald (69) and employed by Barnett, Greenfield & Fox (65). This catheter has very narrow lumens and these last authors (65) calibrated a "flat" amplitude response to 15 cps with P23 Db manometers. This is tolerable in humans; in dogs it is perilously low for the precision required for the gradient method.

The problem of gradient measurement led to the use by McDonald in 1955 (57) of the relation, pointed out by Womersley (59, 61), of the time derivative of the pressure, dP/dt, and the relation $dP/dz = -1/c \cdot dP/dt$, where c is the complex wave velocity of a wave of simple harmonic form. The problem now is the evaluation of c. Its meaning was reviewed by McDonald (1) and the conclusion reached that the velocity calculated from the phase shift of each harmonic component [the "apparent phase velocity" (1, 3, 70, 71)] will allow for distortions in wave transmission such as those due to reflected waves. This variation of "velocity" with frequency parallels the variation of impedance and, from the discussion above, indicates that a constant value might be tolerable if the heart rate is high enough. Otherwise it involves doing Fourier analyses in both pressure waves recorded and so is not suitable for the analog method of Fry. The usual value taken for c is the "foot-to-foot" velocity or some similar measure such as the "wavefront velocity" (53), which Greenfield and Fry (68) did, essentially, in a comparison of gradient and time-derivatives methods in the thoracic aorta, by measuring transmission time between the peaks of the time-derivatives. Not altogether surprisingly, they found large discrepancies between the two methods. For better accuracy in measuring the gradient, an interval of 10 cm in the thoracic aorta was used.

Since in man, recording dP/dt is attractive in that only one pressure apparently need be recorded, the paper of Jones et al. (72) in 1949 drew attention; it has been followed by others such as that of Jones & Griffin (73), comparing the results directly with the flow recorded with an electromagnetic meter, and later reports (74). Essentially, the radius of the vessel and the velocity c are treated as unknown constants and calibrated, as it were, by comparing the stroke volume recorded by the analog display with that measured by an indicator-dilution method repeated at intervals. The correlation has been around 0.85 or better. The original method has been described again (75) with similar results. The problem with such empirical methods is that they can be adjusted for a standard physiological condition and then become unreliable if the defining conditions vary appreciably, but Jones & Reeves (74) have obtained good correlations in normal and cardiac patients from rest through moderate exercise. It is pertinent, though possibly unkind, to ask what is the intrinsic value of a method that constantly needs to be checked against another. The word calibrated was used above and this, essentially, is what it is. When stroke volumes are measured in each case, a good correlation between the two should be no surprise; only the reverse should cause concern because one calibrates the other. That the correlation is not higher may be related to the fact that variation of the order of ±8 per cent in indicator-dilution output measurements seems to be an irreducible minimum. From an analysis of pressure components in an animal with an extremely (indeed artificially) stable heart rate and mean arterial pressure over some two to three hours [McDonald & Attinger (76)] they found a minimum S.D. of ±5 per cent; this suggests that the heart cannot reproduce successive beats to a greater accuracy than that; normally other physiological variables will also influence it. To be able to watch even an approximation of stroke volume beat-by-beat is, of course, useful but with the manual adjustment of the diastolic "flow" necessary in the Fry analog method it is difficult for a nonexpert to monitor.

It is fair to ask whether this information is much greater than an expert will get from watching a continuous recording of the central aortic pressure. Remington and Hamilton in 1954 [see Hamilton (77)] stated that the central aortic pulse pressure, less 20 mm Hg, correlated better with stroke volume than any contour method tested and recently Osborn (78) has reported correlations of the order of 0.95 between total pulse pressure and stroke volume. The physical explanation of this was discussed in (1,3), where the "water-hammer" formula $P = \rho Vc$ was postulated. This relates the pressure rise of a single flow pulse P with the linear velocity V, where V

$(cm \cdot sec^{-1}) = Q$ $(cm^3 \cdot sec^{-1})$/cross-sectional area (cm^2); ρ, the density of blood, is constant and c, the wave velocity, is determined by the elastic properties of the wall of the proximal segment of the vessel. Here again, an assumed constancy of c, as in the former methods, will be dubious if, for example, the mean arterial pressure varies appreciably. Thus in clinical conditions where following the stroke output is critical, e.g. after myocardial infarctions or cardiac surgery, these methods are most suspect.

With the present availability of digital computers in all main centers, usually with on-line facilities, the attraction of very simple methods involving large and unknown assumptions would seem to be reduced. The application of the full Womersley equations using the time-derivative is now feasible. The available length in the ascending aorta is not so limiting if the second pressure is only used to measure phase velocity, nor is the precise matching of calibrations of the two manometers. The former needs to be explored more critically; the latter allows the use of the very high-frequency intra-arterial manometers (e.g. the Telco or the Statham SF-1) now available or similar manometers which can be used with fine catheters. The steps necessary for such flow estimations were outlined fairly explicitly in 1960 (1, p. 276). If extracorporeal manometers are used, however, it is essential that their performance be accurately known.

The potential accuracy of easily available manometers has been studied critically by Yanof et al. (33) and by McDonald & Navarro (79) who emphasize that the smallest trace of entrapped air will degrade the performance severely. Manometry has also been reviewed by Franke (80) and Piemme (81). Scrupulous care in manometry must be insisted on since it is not always appreciated how large a flow can be generated by very small pressure gradients in a vessel as large as the aorta; this is the basic reason for the controversy over the form of the pressure gradient between the left ventricle and the aorta. The positive "spike" recorded by Spencer & Greiss (82) is almost certainly a manometer artifact, for it would create enormous flows if it were real. Furthermore it is not seen when a high-frequency manometer is used. The discussion on this point by Alexander (83) is interesting from a pupil of Carl Wiggers but neglects the general form of the pressure gradient created by a traveling wave discussed by McDonald (62) in 1955. Taking a derivative of a pressure wave will also greatly magnify small errors.

If the use of the Womersley equations has become feasible for studying ventricular outflow, then it is necessary to look more carefully into its possible inherent errors. Womersley (59) showed how the complex impedance, by analogy with an electrical circuit, could be expressed as a resistance term (the real part) and an inductance term (the imaginary part). In large vessels such as the aorta, i.e. in tubes where α is large, in effect greater than ten [$\alpha = R$ $(\omega/\upsilon)^{1/2}$ where R = radius, ω = the angular frequency in radians/sec, and υ = the kinematic viscosity in stokes], the resistance is close to the sine of ε which is very small. Previous measurements, calculated from aortic impedance, by Fry's group (84, 85) had been a little confusing as the first results showed a resistance that was often smaller than predicted and the latter ones a resistance that was too high. When one considers the technical problem of measuring small phase angles, this is not very surprising.

In a very careful study on the pulmonary artery aimed at this question, O'Rourke & Milnor (54) have found that the resistance term may be fifteen to twenty times larger than it should be. Factors that contribute considerably to this are the "finite interval error" noted above, and a small phase error in their manometers. This last is probably less than 10° even in the higher-frequency components and is normally regarded as negligible; but when one is looking for a predicted angle of 4° or less, such a distortion is proportionately very large. Even so, from Fry's measurements and these, values for the resistive component are still four to five times as large as predicted in the Womersley analysis. Milnor's (personal communication) current view is that this is due to the geometrical tapering of the lumen in either pulmonary artery or aorta. It is certainly true that neither vessel is a perfect cylinder in the analytical sense; but it is highly probable that, with the "sinuses" at the valves and the "flaring" before the origin of the main branches, (a) considerable difference in detail exists among individuals and (b) no exact geometrical form is a precise description. Both these, if true, make mathematical correction virtually impossible. The evidence of vessel casts needs to be treated with caution as control of internal pressure is difficult (and often not recorded) during injection and setting; further, the setting cast is very easily distorted, as personal observations have shown. For example, the original casts on which Attinger (86) reported high degrees of ellipticity in the pulmonary artery show a strong similarity to my own casts of the pulmonary artery or arch of the aorta when slight movement of the cannula has flexed the vessel during setting. Caro & Saffman (87) found some ellipticity in pulmonary vessels using X rays, as did Frasher & Sobin (88) in casts near the division of vessels.

My own feeling is that it were better to pay attention to the initial assumption of laminar flow underlying the Womersley equations. This was necessary, mathematically, but is certainly false, to a high degree, near the heart. Turbulence, especially in highly oscillatory flows, is an indeterminate condition, but fully developed turbulence throughout the cycle could have a resistance one hundred times the Poiseuille resistance. Fivefold increase of this "resistive" component, therefore, could easily occur. A note of caution should be sounded, in that the splitting of impedance into inductive and resistive terms, by analogy with electrical circuits where the two components can be physically separated, may be too simplistically artificial in liquid flow. The pragmatic question is whether the error introduced by the laminar flow assumption and the cylindrical tube assumption causes an intolerable error in calculated flow. The results of O'Rourke & Milnor (54) and check calculations suggest that it does not. The conclusion of Attinger et al. (89) that the energy dissipation due to turbulence in pulsatile flow is small would support this conclusion.

External work of heart.—The question of how accurately the pulsatile flow can be measured may become very important when we wish to monitor the external work of the ventricles, or even to monitor the power output continuously. This latter, with present computing facilities, would seem to be the logical extension of the concept, whose general acceptance was due to Sarnoff, that stroke-work is an excellent measure of the functional condition of cardiac muscle. A paper on this topic, destined to be a landmark, has been published by Milnor, Bergel & Bargainer (90) on the hydraulic power output of the right ventricle (dog). Using flow measured with an electromagnetic flowmeter, they have clarified the computation of total external work and shown that the pulsatile work averages some 40 per cent of the external work calculated from the mean pressure and flow terms alone. This is far from the negligible quantity it is usually assumed to be; the implications with regard to conventional ways of analyzing the relation of right ventricular stroke-work to fiber-length have not been explored, but are clearly important.

The kinetic work of the left ventricle has been estimated from accurate flow measurements by O'Rourke (34) and found to average about 8–10 per cent in normal anesthetized dogs. The small component of kinetic energy in the sum of energy expenditure of the left ventricle has a significance in regard to some current concepts that has been rather overlooked. I refer to the concept of the ventricle as an "impulse generator" [as Rushmer (91, 92) has termed it] which is implicit in some of the discussion in the important papers by Noble et al. (93–95). The thesis is that the very rapid acceleration of flow to a peak velocity very early in systole implies a momentum of the blood such as to carry it forward throughout the rest of systole without further propulsion by cardiac muscle shortening. This "momentum" is expressed by the kinetic energy which is commonly treated as negligible, and even the estimate presented above indicates that it is normally not more than 10 per cent of the work done on the blood. That "momentum" may be dominant when the pressure gradient reverses is possibly a helpful concept but the momentum clearly cannot dominate flow for the greater part of ejection. The integrated flow-velocity curve actually matches very closely the form of shortening in a papillary muscle twitch, although the time relations are different; this is not altogether surprising, considering that ventricular fibers are not all activated synchronously and that the orientation of the fibers in the ventricular wall varies greatly. This variation has been shown by Streeter & Bassett (96) to be organized in a "fanlike" arrangement over an arc of 180° from the internal to the external layer. I think that people not working in the specialized field of muscle also tend to confuse the hypothetical concept of the very brief "active state", introduced by A. V. Hill, with the period of active contraction which must persist all the time tension is developed.

Wave-Propagation Characteristics

Milnor et al. (90) have also discussed the energy dissipation through the various regions of the pulmonary circulation, an aspect of hemodynamics that is clearly of importance in producing total-energy "accounts". This topic has been investigated in two interesting papers by Skalak et al., one theoretical (97) and one experimental (98). An approach to the problem of energy dissipation has also been made by Shepard et al. (99) who have introduced the concept of "energy equivalent pressure". Initially studied in the systemic arteries, it has also been used in the pulmonary circulation (100). The stricter description of what is measured is "potential work energy per unit flow volume" (the "pressure equivalent" name was given because it has the same dimensions, dyne $\cdot$ cm^{-2}, as pressure but this can be confusing; e.g. Young's modulus has the same dimensions also but would not be easier to understand if called a pressure). The computational method (101) (on-line with a digital computer), using a power spectrum of a train of pulses, is elegant and the extension of the technique could be valuable both physiologically and clinically (it comes from a department of surgery). This is an application of the earlier analyses of Evans and colleagues (e.g. 102) attempting to define energy dissipation in terms of viscous drag [which concerned Womersley (59, 61)] and energy dissipation in the wall, which was studied by Lawton (103) and Hardung (see 1, 104, 105) in vessel strips. Later Bergel (105) studied it in intact excised vessels and Peterson et al. (106–108) *in vivo* in the carotid artery.

Wave attenuation.—In spite of these efforts to study energy dissipation in the propagated pressure and flow waves, our knowledge of the attenuation is meager in the extreme. Yet wave velocity and attenuation are the two fundamental parameters of wave motion and are commonly combined in a propagation constant (52, 70, 109). Measurement is a problem because only short segments of artery that can be termed homogenous in terms of geometry and elastic properties are available; and the pressure differences along these short segments are of the order of magnitude of our manometer precision. Also, reflected waves are set up in the arterial tree, and these are a major factor in causing all the lower-frequency components of the pressure pulse to increase in size as it travels (1, 76). The elastic nonuniformity effect (22, 26–28) adds into this, overriding the attenuating factors. As a result, without more precise knowledge of the magnitude of this "elastic taper" effect and the attenuation, estimates of reflection coefficient must be very approximate (28, 35, 76—discussed above).

From his estimates of his dynamic elastic modulus of excised arteries, Bergel (105) calculated attenuations per 10 cm length of artery. They were surprisingly in excess of the attenuation calculated from the viscous drag of blood alone by Womersley (59). *In situ,* with reflected waves present, it is necessary to measure pressure at a minimum of three points along the artery, and this was done by McDonald & Gessner (52) who compared *in vivo* measurements with those made *in vitro* with lengths of the same artery perfused with oxygenated Krebs' solution and driven by a sinusoidal pump. The 'three-point method' was first discussed in a thesis by Taylor (110) and re-explored in part by Gessner & Bergel (39). Malindzak et al. (111) had studied the magnitude of reflected components by a two-point method but had, perforce, to assume zero attenuation. The damping found in (52) was higher than that predicted by Bergel (105) and preliminary reports indicate that Taylor & Gow's (60) results agree with his; these, like (104), are derived from the phase lag, in relation to the pressure, of the radial movement measured with a caliper developed by Gow (112). The scatter in (52) is considerable and the discrepancy may not be significant, or it may be due to a more active state of the muscle in (52).

Reflection, as a complication, may be avoided by using a transient which is complete before reflected waves can return to modify it. This necessitates studying frequency components much higher than the main energy components of the pressure pulse wave (1, Chap. 11). Anliker and colleagues have made very valuable theoretical (113) and experimental (114) analyses using this approach. The results of McDonald and Gessner (39) on the thoracic aorta would extrapolate well to fit the data of Anliker et al. (114); those results also confirm Bergel's findings (105) that the dynamic elastic modulus, and hence wave velocity, does not change significantly with frequency above 2 cps, even in the high-frequency range explored in (114). Wave velocity is, however, markedly changed with activity of the vascular smooth muscle, especially in veins (114, 115), and has presented us with a potent method of studying venomotor tone.

In a viscoelastic wall, the viscous element can be analyzed in terms of a parallel spring-dashpot model (104, 105) or more abstractly, e.g. by Womersley's brief mathematical formulation (59), which was used so penetratingly on a rubber-tube model by Taylor (116). McDonald & Gessner (52) combined these approaches and found, as Bergel (105) had, that far from the assumed coefficient of viscosity η remaining constant with frequency, in fact the term $\eta\omega$ (ω = angular frequency in radians/sec) was approximately constant. One should clearly be cautious in relating the concept of the dissipative element, with its curious properties, to such a precise concept as viscosity coefficient. The same doubt may apply in detailed analysis of "spring" arrays in muscle when it is found that, e.g., the series-elastic element is nonlinear in a comparably bizarre fashion. The behavior of waves, with reflections, in a viscoelastic (rubber) tube has also been studied by Martin (117).

The ultimate attenuation of the pressure wave must show up in a reduced amplitude in the arterioles if commonly accepted standards of the relative steadiness of flow in capillaries are to be met. This poses difficult manometer problems but good records have been made in small mammalian mesenteric arteries by Sugiura & Freis (118) and in frog mesenteric arterioles by Wiederhielm et al. (119).

Transmission in the pulmonary circulation.—Since it was pointed out by

Permutt & Riley (120) that the lower pressures in the pulmonary circulation make the hydrostatic forces due to gravity over the height of the lungs comparable to the pressure generated by the heart, a new field of fruitful exploration has been opened out.

In view of the excellent symposium that was held at the Federation of American Societies for Experimental Biology meeting in 1967 (121) on, and around, this topic, it will only be noted briefly here [and the topic is discussed by Campbell (122) in this volume]. Other interesting contributions exploring, among other things, the "symmetry" of the arterial and venous segments have been made by Caro, Harrison & Mognoni (123), Caro, Bergel & Seed (124), and Bergel et al. (125) [West's contribution in (121) summarizes the main findings of these papers]. Measurements of the wave velocity in the dog pulmonary artery by Bargainer (126) show a velocity of 300–350 cm/sec. This is not much lower than the average of about 440 cm/sec that McDonald (53) found in the proximal thoracic aorta. He used the delay line on a Tektronix RM565 oscilloscope to measure the time of transmission of the fast-rising pressure portion (the "wavefront") of the pulse wave; this easily allows accurate and rapid measurement of "wavefront" velocity (shown to be the same as the "foot-to-foot" velocity and that of the incisura, when present) over short regions of the arterial tree (5 cm in the aorta, 10 cm in the carotid, 15 cm in the leg).

Observations in human arteries.—The determination of the frequency components in the pressure waves in man has been done by Patel et al. (127) in addition to the impedance studies (40) noted earlier. Luchsinger et al. (128) have tracked the harmonic components of the pulse wave down the human aorta in a manner comparable to McDonald's analysis (1, 76) in the dog. No firm conclusion can be drawn on the lack of appearance of "node" or "antinode" formation, for their values are smoothed by their averaging results in terms of the first, second, etc., harmonic; the heart frequency varied considerably among their six subjects. The overall rise in pressure amplitude between the rest of the aorta and the femoral is less, proportionately, than is usually found in the dog. They also discuss the dimensions of parameters that might affect the linearity of the system but the reader should be cautioned that the dimensions of the parameters involving wave velocity are inadvertently wrong: a typographical error makes the wave velocity appear ten times too large (6000 cm/sec for 600 cm/sec in the aorta). Aortic regurgitation has been evaluated by Brawley & Morrow (129) and, by an indirect mathematical approach from pressure measurement, by Thwaites (130). Greenfield et al. (131) have studied pressure-flow relations during the Valsalva maneuver.

THEORY AND ANALOGS

As intimated in the introduction there has been a plethora of contributions of a theoretical nature, so detailed notice cannot be taken of them all. I will excuse myself by being narrow in the sense of the word Physiology in the title of this volume, and quoting my late friend and mentor John

Womersley: "No mathematical analysis of a system can be better than the validity of the assumptions it starts from, or the accuracy of the parameters used in the calculation." From the foregoing text it should be clear that in the circulation we only have dubious information about much elementary but necessary quantitative data. The hope that we will acquire knowledge of the impedances or resistances of small artery segments before even their internal *in vivo* diameters (let alone wall-thickness and elastic properties) are known, by using a device like an electrical analog, seems unlikely to be fulfilled.

In spite of the official blessing, as it were, of the chapters in the *Handbook of Physiology* by Remington (132) and Spencer (133), only one major review of Windkessel theory seems to have appeared [Cope (134)] since then. Applications of the theory (which have been invaluable in the past, provided its basic simplifying assumptions are respected) have been made by Goldwyn & Watt (135) and Olson & Cain (136); the latter used three-dimensional models of the waveform in travel which were attractive.

A useful compilation of the dynamic analogies used in the sort of studies reviewed here has been made by Patel (137). Valuable definitions of the CGS units used in quantitative hemodynamics have been collected by Coulter (138); he adds suggestions for eponymous, and other, names for the units of these parameters (cf. the viscosity unit, the Poise, named for Poiseuille) which time and usage may well make acceptable. At present an insistence by editors on CGS units (at least in parenthesis) would aid in interpretation of much published data. Taylor (139) has reviewed recent work in hemodynamics in a manner more elementary than the rigorous style of some of his powerful contributions. Remington (140) has made a very detailed analysis of wave propagation and reflection at numerous major arterial junctions in the vessels of the forepart of the body. The basic assumption is that a dynamic event like a pressure wave can be treated as the sum of short discreet transients (in this case each of 10 msec duration) which travel independently through the system. This appears rather dubious and is clearly extremely tedious as only one set of records is so analyzed in a long paper. The symmetry principle also seems to be breached, in that the reflection coefficients at any one junction when viewed from opposite sides are not always complementary. The paper by Remington & Meisner (141) from which the data are taken is a valuable contribution to our knowledge of a neglected part of the arterial tree—the pressure waveforms in the systemic arteries anterior to the heart.

In the field of electrical analogs of whole systems it is interesting to compare the very detailed segmentation used by Noordergraaf (142) [who uses some 120 units to represent the systemic arterial tree and who has made a similar model of the pulmonary circulation (143)] with the deliberately simplified approaches of Beneken & De Wit (144) and of Robinson (145, 146). The latter represents the heart in terms of the analysis of cardiac muscle by the Hill formulation used by Sonnenblick (263), and Hef-

ner & Bowen (264). Beneken & De Wit (144) have used the same sources
in more detail. Past discussions over this sort of analog have centered on
such questions as "Is the heart a voltage-source or a current-source?" This
smacks of jargon. My own interpretation is that, if it means anything, flow
(current) is primary because the initial physiological event is the onset of
active contraction in the cardiac muscle; of course, this is simultaneously
accompanied by a change in pressure.

The "source impedance" of the left ventricle is calculated by Robinson
(146) to be about six times the input impedance of the aorta. Whether this
should be regarded as "high" or "low" is an open question. From the point of
view of arterial wave transmission when the aortic values are functional,
the source impedance is in effect very high as Taylor (70) postulated in
1957. During systole the source impedance would appear to be high initially
and to fall rapidly until it is virtually zero just before the valves close
(personal discussion with Noordergraaf). No one has made an electrical analog of such a "source". Beneken's analog is designed to analyze the control
systems of the circulation and this demonstrates a useful application of
such analogs because single variables can be altered in isolation in a way
that is impossible in an intact animal.

Fich, Welkowitz & Hilton (147) have studied a model that has shed interesting light on the extent to which elastic nonuniformity ("taper") can
modify the pulse form and account for "peaking". With too many analogs,
analogy is treated more like identitity—as witness the titles. Few have appreciated the clearly proven demonstration by Taylor (116) in 1959 that,
while it is possible to make a transmission line, with passive elements, that
mimics the motion of liquid in a viscoelastic tube, it is only possible to do
this at a single frequency, i.e., with a change in frequency all the components have to be changed in value. Thus a single transmission-line model of
the pulse wave is not possible because it is compounded of many frequency
components.

A significant early paper of 1950 by Iberall (148) has come to light recently; many ideas of the last ten years were there anticipated. With his
colleagues, Iberall has made interesting contributions to branching arrays
(e.g. 149). Mirsky (150, 151) has presented some sophisticated analyses of
arteries considered as orthotropic elastic tubes, which seems a potentially
valuable approach, distinctly different from that of Womersley; the latter
has limitations when wavemodes, other than the long-wavelength longitudinal wave, are considered. In this field Anliker (113) has analyzed nonaxi-
symmetric waves; Atabek (152) has considered several wavemodes of propagation; and Klip (153) has done a detailed (thesis) analysis of wave
transmission and studied torsional waves (154, 155). As an experimental
physiologist I have no clear idea how these various wavemodes may be distinguished *in vivo*.

Consideration of the motion of fluid in a chamber to be used as an
artificial heart has produced some fascinating hydrodynamic studies by R.

T. Jones (156, 157). Oka has analyzed steady and pulsatile flows in a tapered tube (158–160). The geometrical tapering of the aorta has long interested mathematicians but none seems to have seriously considered the well-known physiological fact that with progressive branching the total cross-sectional area of the bed normally increases (exceptions have been cited at the arch of the aorta and division of the pulmonary artery). In the thoracic aorta the tapering data, carefully collected, of Patel et al. (161) are normally used. I have found (unpublished data in only three dogs), in casts, similar values in the main trunk; the intercostals, regarded individually, appear negligible but when all their cross-sectional areas are added together the total values at the diaphragm are some 25 per cent greater than the cross section between the left subclavian and the first intercostal. Young & Cholvin (162) have applied similitude concepts to pulsatile flow studies. Atabek & Chang (163) have followed their earlier theoretical analyses of the inlet length problem with some elegant experimental studies. Kuchar & Ostrach (164) have also studied this problem. Bassingthwaighte & Ackerman (165) have made an interesting analysis of nonlinearity problems in using indicator-dilution techniques for studying circulation transport.

ARTERIAL ELASTICITY

The fine structure of the arterial wall is clearly very important for the full understanding of the special elastic properties of this tissue. Wolinsky & Glagov (166, 167) have made important contributions, especially in the most recent article, to this subject. Their description of lamellar units merits close attention. Wolinsky (168) has published an account of the comparative anatomy of the aortic vasa vasorum; Sobin, Frasher & Tremer (169) likewise showed the value of polymer-injection techniques in demonstrating the vasa vasorum of the pulmonary artery of the rabbit. These papers remind us that hemodynamics tends to neglect the fact that arterial wall is a living tissue, thus differences from inert elastic substances are to be expected. This applies at the simplest level when it is recalled that about 70 per cent of the wall is water easily removed by desiccation [Harkness et al (170)], yet detailed studies of three-dimensional elastic parameters have been made [e.g. Tickner & Sacks (171), Patel et al. (172)] as if the wall were a homogeneous material. The coherence of the results is surprising, rather than the inconsistencies, especially when it is noted that in (171) the measurements are based on radiographs of air-inflated isolated segments. The strain-gauge caliper measurements of arterial wall movements *in vivo* by Patel et al. (161, 173) have been important in establishing norms and are the most detailed information we have. Slight doubt arises in that the wave velocities calculated from the measured elastances are up to 100 per cent higher than those usually accepted as normal. This suggests that the caliper is restraining the wall a little although, without knowing what the wave velocity actually was in these experiments, it might be due to physiological variation. Peterson et al. (106) predicted a wave velocity of 27 m/sec in the carotid artery where McDonald (53) recorded about 7.5 m/sec.

The finding of extremely small longitudinal movement confirms earlier observational impressions and has been followed by a very detailed study of the "longitudinal tethering" of arteries by Patel & Fry (174). As the postulate of stiff longitudinal restraint was an important part of Womersley's (175) justification for using the equations of his "simple" theory in arteries *in vivo,* it is good to have this careful, and ingenious, test of a parameter which did not seem accessible to experimental study. Hardung's (104) chapter in the *Handbook of Physiology* was an excellent review of the subject and the relation of elasticity to wave velocity; he has later written a more detailed study of the anisotropic properties of the wall (176). Learoyd & Taylor (177) have made a detailed study of arterial viscoelastic properties in humans with a technique similar to that of Bergel (105) which is especially valuable because it follows the changes due to age. As noted, Taylor & Gow (60) have detailed studies in the dog with a new caliper with which they measure dilatation values more consistent with "normal" wave velocity than Patel's (Taylor—personal communcation). The relation between flow and arterial dilatation has been studied in models by Foreman & Durie (178).

Cardiovascular sound.—It is still controversial whether sound production in flowing blood arises primarily in the liquid or through movement of solid structures. Meisner & Rushmer (179) studied the relation of the movement of the wall of thin latex tubes to the sound picked up by a microphone under different flow conditions—one of the first critical attempts to evaluate this problem I know of. The problem of Korotkoff sounds was studied extensively in a model by Sacks, Raman & Burnell (180). Anliker (13), collaborating briefly with this group, then produced a highly sophisticated analysis of the wall movement using the mathematical techniques of solid mechanics. He concluded that when "cuff" pressure reduced the transmitted pressure to a low critical value the wall could vibrate in response to very small disturbances in the fluid. This would, in effect, produce a mechanical amplification; using normally accepted values for the wall-thickness and elasticity of an artery, he showed this "amplification" to be, potentially, of a large magnitude. This conclusion is important because most analyses of vascular sound show the energy dissipated in flow disturbances to be extremely small. Considering the poor transmission properties of most biological tissues, one wonders why the disturbances should ever be heard.

The flow situation has been studied in more detail by McCutcheon & Rushmer (181). In human subjects pulsatile flow was recorded with a transcutaneous Doppler flowmaker which, unfortunately, could not discriminate between forward and back flow, though from other studies of pulsatile flow it is possible to make intelligent guesses where back flow occurs. This is pertinent here because a cuff is likely to alter this normal flow-reversal pattern. McDonald (182) has pointed out that the hydrodynamic evidence suggests that the breakdown of stable flow pattern most likely occurs at inflections of the velocity profile due to reversal of flow. With regard to sounds created close to the heart, Piemme, Barnett & Dexter (183) have shown that sound production coincides with high acceleration of blood flow —a situation that also produces disruption of flow patterns (1, p. 25) This suggests that a greater part of the first sound is created in the aorta than has sometimes been suspected. The constraint due to the valve-cusps would also tend to produce a jet effect and Yellin (184, 185) has made some enlightening studies on the noise production by such jets. The problem of cavitation in the circulation has also been studied by Leith (186).

Flow patterns.—The hydrodynamic studies of blood may be considered under (*a*) velocity profiles and (*b*) anomalous viscosity; the latter is better considered with the microcirculation. Freis & Heath (187), using a heat-transfer technique with a thermistor inserted to varying depths in the aorta, have recorded flat velocity profiles across the vessel. These were similar to those calculated by McDonald (180) who also speculated on whether the inflections in the profile that theory predicts in laminar flow would lead to instability (a rather academic point, considering the disturbances that the pulmonary and aortic valves must create: note that the aberrant points on the profiles in the figures are errors in the block—the calculated curves are smooth). Attinger et al. (188) have ingeniously used the flowing birefringence of bentonite in a model to derive the profiles in oscillatory flow and study energy dissipation. Their profiles are very much of predicted form but are extremely asymmetric. This is undoubtedly due to secondary flows across the tube set up by the 90° bend they had proximal to the region of observation; Attinger et al. attribute the asymmetry to a slight ellipticity of the Tygon tube but there seems no reason why a minor (apparently unmeasurable) departure from a perfectly cylindrical tube should produce such an asymmetry in a straight tube.

Caro [(189)—with the assistance of an eminent expert in fluid dynamics, Prof. Lighthill] has studied secondary flow effects among other flow conditions under steady-flow conditions. Neumaster & Krovetz (190) have described a valuable method for making plastic models of actual blood vessel lumens especially at junctions so that flow patterns as *in situ* can be studied in detail (as one who has tried to mimic such vessel junctions with glass tubing I can applaud the technique highly). Using such models, Krovetz (191) has produced useful data on the critical conditions causing the breakup of laminar flow in such vessels.

A most important paper from Kunz & Coulter (192) has appeared in which, in essence, the Womersley equations are tested in glass tubes with blood as the liquid. Over shear rates where blood has an approximately Newtonian behavior, the fit of experimental data by theory is very good. This is as it should be, for the "theory" is only a generalized form of Poiseuille's equation, and equally based in classic hydrodynamics. It is, however, an exacting experimental exercise as witness the variable fits shown in the data in (48), for I had some part in those experiments. At low shear rates when the apparent viscosity of blood greatly increases there is, as expected, a marked deviation of experimental from the simple Womersley data. This should become a standard reference on the effective viscosity of blood in oscillatory flow, as Coulter & Pappenheimer (193) is for steady flow. It would be interesting to compare Kunz & Coulter's results with those calculated by Taylor (194) in 1959.

The Microcirculation

A review entitled "Rheology and the Microcirculation" by Wayland (195) covers the field concerning flow, anomalous viscosity, and related topics so thoroughly that there seems little to add. There followed discussion by McDonald (196), who is far from expert in this field and who makes a second-thought disclaimer (see p. 42). (see p. 42) Leonard Bayliss (197) has left a fine last paper on the flow properties of red cell suspensions which further clarifies the controversial subject of the cell-free margin in narrow tubes; controversy which largely centered on observational artifact until he cleared it up. The viscosity of blood has been studied intensively both in a specially designed Couette viscometer (198) and in capillary tubes (199, 200) by Merrill and his colleagues at the Massachusetts Institute of Technology. It now seems certain that blood does have a finite but small yield stress—which solves a controversy of long standing—further, that it is in large part due to the fibrinogen component of the plasma (200). A review by Bugliarello (201) of microcirculation hemodynamics gives easier access to his own interesting contributions. In the same symposium Charm et al. (202) report on flow properties of blood suspensions and Rudinger (203) on the settling velocity of particles in an elastic tube. McComis (204) has studied pulsed flow in capillary tubes. Two new flow-measuring techniques for use in minute vessels have been described by Lamport (205) and Wayland & Johnson (206). An excellent symposium chaired by Landis (207) was held by the Microcirculation group in 1966; the paper by Sobin & Tremer (208) on the functional geometry of the microcirculation adds to the valuable contributions of vessel geometry made by these authors [as does also the paper on the pulmonary artery by Frasher & Sobin (209)]. Burton (210), Fung (12), and Wayland (195) discuss the geometry of size and shape with reference to red cell properties.

Pressure between capillary and extracellular space.—A series of papers by Guyton and colleagues (211–214) have stimulated some interesting controversy on "interstitial fluid pressure". This phrase has been in common use since Starling's investigation of the forces moving fluids across the capillary wall in the 1890's, but has never been clearly defined. That there is extracellular fluid outside the vascular tree, and that its volume can be measured fairly accurately is not, I think, questionable. Therefore, it must have a pressure. As it is bounded on the one side by cell membranes and, ultimately, on the other by skin (neither of which is rigid, or normally

under tension), it would seem intuitively obvious that this pressure, averaged over any reasonable length of time, is identical to that of the surrounding atmosphere. Verifying this experimentally has been notoriously
difficult because of the minute size of the spaces between cells. Guyton's approach has been in refreshing contrast; instead of using ever smaller tubes,
he has implanted large perforated capsules into which new tissue is allowed
to grow. The results can only be obtained in capsules of 1.5 cm diameter,
or larger; initially a perforated pingpong ball was among the capsules used.
After a period of four to six weeks, when full growth of normal tissue,
with its blood supply, into the capsule is assumed, the pressure recorded in the
capsule is markedly subatmospheric—the average value is −7 mm Hg. That
this is not due to an artificially trapped space is demonstrated by the fact
that factors which would be expected to increase the exudation of fluid into
the intracellular space, e.g. various occlusions, do raise the intracapsular
pressure; and when the occlusion is freed, the pressure reverts to its original value.

The commonest site for insertion of the capsule is in the subcutaneous
tissue of the dog thigh. This immediately suggests that the outward displacement of the skin, which would then be under tension, and could maintain a transcutaneous difference of pressure, is the cause of the observation
and the negative value would therefore be an artifact. A moment's thought,
however, shows that this cannot be true unless the interstitial fluid in the
segment studied was separated by impermeable partitions from the neighboring regions. Since virtually every tissue of the body is interconnected by
branches of the vascular and lymphatic systems, this subsidiary assumption
is untenable if the interstitial fluid is a true fluid and does not have solid
properties. The interconnecting channels may be exceeding fine, but flow
will occur through them if there is a pressure difference across the ends;
and we are given several weeks for equilibration to occur.

In dismissing this objection, however, we create more fundamental reasons for regarding the values obtained as not representing a physiological
condition. For, by extension of the physical continuity condition, all intracellular spaces in a horizontal body at equilibrium will be at the same pressure, when allowances are made for small hydrostatic differences due to
gravity. Thus if tissue pressure is about −7 mm Hg the intrapleural space
will be bounded by membranes whose intracellular spaces will be at a much
lower pressure than that in the capillary fluid layer between the pleural
membranes. In the abdomen the pressure inside the gut must always be
around atmospheric pressure, for the gut is, in effect, open to the atmosphere at both ends; and, as far as can be observed, the lumen of the gut
and the intracellular spaces of the mucosa are apparently in communication
so another inconsistency occurs in relation to intraperitioneal pressure. The
lymphatics form a more visible set of channels. Their central termination
in the great veins at the root of the neck means that their intraluminal
pressure there is close to atmospheric. Yet lymph flow still takes place in
an anesthetized animal in spite of the postulated uphill gradient. One has

only to think of the pressure difference along the venous system, to realize what a large volume flow 7 mm Hg can create. This emphasizes the difficulties caused by accepting these findings.

If these invocations of physical concepts seem too abstract, and theoretical, for physiological consideration, we may briefly look at the requirements this makes of the Starling hypothesis of fluid exchange at the capillary. The long-accepted figures for "normal" capillary pressure, based on Landis' (215) studies, are about 30 mm Hg at the arterial end, and 15 mm Hg at the venous end, with the colloid osmotic pressure of plasma being 25 mm Hg. Taking the extracapillary hydrostatic pressure as zero and the interstitial colloid pressure as a few mm Hg, this accounts satisfactorily for liquid movements back and forth across the capillary. In Guyton's 1966 textbook (216) where the interstitial fluid pressure is taken as −7 mm Hg the "account" can only be balanced by taking the mean capillary pressure as 17 mm Hg. No reference is given, so that the source of this revision of the accepted value cannot be discussed. This in turn will need drastic revision of the *vis a tergo* venular pressure necessary to maintain venous return in an anesthetized animal with an open chest.

To this reviewer these interrelations with other physiological facts make it impossible to accept the assumption that all the extravascular intercellular spaces are far below atmospheric pressure. Recordings through fine needles or micropipettes consistently give the expected value of zero in respect to atmospheric; Guyton's group themselves record this. In an elegant demonstration of the same phenomenon, by recording pressure in undistended veins, Kjellmer (217) records the same results. Nevertheless, the care with which checks and experimental tests have been carried out points inescapably to the fact that in the Guyton capsule the pressure is subatmospheric. The question is—why? An investigation of this problem might well increase our insight into the nature of the "interstitial fluid".

It is apparent from the experiments that the negative pressures are only recorded in capsules which are too big to ever fill with new tissue outgrowths; the central region remains filled with liquid on subsequent examination. The assumption is naturally made that this is normal "tissue fluid"; it is difficult to see why it should not be, if it is the liquid with a low protein content that has been assumed in the past. The assumption has been tacitly challenged by Fung, Zweifach & Intaglietta (218) and Fung (12) with quite a different objective—an adequate physical description of the mechanical properties of the capillary wall. Starting from experiments of Baez, Lamport & Baez (219) which showed no measurable change in diameter of capillaries even when the mean intracapillary pressure was varied from 0 to 90 mm Hg, Fung et al. noted that this implied an elastic modulus for the capillary wall far higher than had been known for any biological tissue (bone possibly excepted). They then postulated a model where the surround of the capillary was a gel rather than simple liquid. As there is no direct visible evidence for this gel structure, it was given arbitrary, but eminently reasonable, dimensions and mechanical properties; the formulation is impressive. In a brief discussion with Wayland (188) on the rheology of the microcirculation McDonald initially challenged the experimental data on the grounds that in a blocked tube like the capillary that is permeable, the pressure down the line will drop. More mature reflection showed that this could only make the capillary pressure a few per cent below the cannulating pressure and that the objection was trivial; it is here unreservedly withdrawn.

Nevertheless, as with the discussion of intercellular tissue pressure, other implications should be considered. The problem is not merely to postulate a model that keeps the distended capillary functionally rigid; it must also allow the capillary to retain its known permeabilities that were quantitated so carefully in the invaluable papers reviewed by Pappenheimer (220). With a television scanning technique the problem of transcapillary transfer has been studied by Bloch (221, 222). Wiederhielm (223) has extended this by detailed quantitative comparison of diffusion rates in the interstitial regions of the mesentery in comparison to that in a gel and finds that the former is much the slower, though it is difficult to allow for the geometry of the intercellular channels. Zweifach & Intaglietta (224) also suggest that the assumption that the interstitial fluid is more a gel than a liquid is compatible with transport data, and cast doubt on Guyton's conclusions.

The strong evidence of Wiederhielm (223), and the suggestive derivations of Fung et al. (218), that we are dealing with a gel between the cells has implications regarding the anomalous pressure recorded in a large capsule partly filled with fluid. In such a situation we might get liquid extruded from a sol-gel complex. Whether this could produce forces large enough to account for the large pressure difference recorded between the intercellular space and the outside world, I am not competent to say. But the papers noted here deserve close attention with a view to rethinking our concepts of what fills the intercellular spaces.

INSTRUMENTATION

To treat this extremely important topic, in which improvement is vital to the progress of hemodynamics, briefly would seem to dismiss it. But once again the series *Methods in Medical Research* has produced a volume (225) that covers this field excellently in that practical way that makes this series so valuable. Happily, the measurement of flow, which is central to hemodynamics, is in the hands of D. L. Fry who contributes two useful survey articles (226, 227); the important article on the electromagnetic flowmeter and its calibration characteristics by Gessner & Bergel (31) has already been noted. A first detailed account of the pulsed ultrasonic flowmeter is provided by Baker (228), though this version seems to have fallen into disuse. It appeared as if it could have produced a standardized calibration, even with oscillatory flows, though none has been published to my knowledge. Most current usage of ultrasonic meters is centering on the Doppler ultrasonic flowmeter which can be used transcutaneously [Stegall et al. (229), Rushmer et al. (230)] and is promising for qualitative clinical work. Not only has no calibration with it been made but, as the amplitude of the reflected signal will presumably be very sensitive to the angle of application to the vessel, it is difficult to see how it could be calibrated. The ordinate in published curves is usually marked in terms of the frequency shift, of the reflected ultrasonic signal. These flow curves in arbitrary units remind one of the popular days of impedance plethysmography, which has now been critically and penetratingly reviewed by Hill, Jansen & Fling (231).

Galle (232) has reviewed thermal methods and the adaptation of fast-acting thermistors to record pulsatile flow. In one version the fluctuation of temperature is due to the changing temperature of varying flows past a heated coil (233). In the other (234) a thermistor is heated with a varying current with a feedback circuit so as to keep its temperature constant. Rasmussen (235) gives a good review of the technical aspects. Although thermistors are greatly improved in speed of reaction, it is doubtful if any are available which can adequately follow flows in the aorta which will accelerate from rest to 150–200 cm/sec in 50–60 msec. The tendency is for calibration to be done by comparing an *in vivo* flow curve obtained by the instrument in question with an electromagnetic meter record, without any justification of the latter's accuracy—indeed often with palpably abnormal records. On the other hand, some manufacturers still attempt to sell flowmeters with no relevant specifications on the strength of a "nice-looking" flow curve "recorded by Dr. X for us." Are physiologists still so gullible? With established makes described independently by Gessner & Bergel (31) the cry of *caveat emptor,* in the forecast days of increasing financial stringency, again becomes important.

The electromagnetic flowmeter is now well established as the most reliable method of accurate quantitative measurement of pulsatile flow. Since Wetterer's important review (236) in the *Handbook* there have been many special modifications. Thus Khouri & Gregg (237) describe a small version for use on dog coronary arteries; Elliott et al. (238) present a version of the standard Kolin meter for use on the largest vessels in conscious dogs and Ryan (239)—from Kolin's laboratory—describes a meter that can be made from easily available components. The growing interest in methods of calibrating these meters, as in papers by Bond (240) and Abel (241), is encouraging. The problems of accurate zero determination with electromagnetic flowmeters which, with an inevitable tendency to drift, make their use for accurate mean flow determination (as opposed to oscillatory flow amplitude) somewhat hazardous have been studied in detail by Sellers & Dobson (242). It was probably unawareness of this in Attinger et al. (48) which led to the publication of data which appear to indicate that the mean flow velocity in the aorta at the diaphragm is about double that at the root of the aorta; this would mean that the total cross-sectional area of the vascular bed at this level is about half that of the aortic arch cross section (1, p. 28), which is contrary to usual concepts of how the vascular tree branches.

A potentially very valuable new instrument is the intra-arterial version of the electromagnetic flowmeter designed by Mills (243). Its open lumen makes possible the measurement of pressure as well as flow at approximately the same site, which greatly enhances the value of the data. Another type of catheter-tip flowmeter has been built by Pieper (244), although its exquisite workmanship may confine its use to the few who can acquire assistants of the necessary skill. It is the only current intravascular device with vanes, so that it is placed in the middle of the stream—the habit of catheters to hug the wall, where the flow velocity is low, is too often overlooked. This factor is not yet of great importance because the size of present intra-arterial devices is such that they usually form a baffle, which effectively breaks up the velocity profile. A polarographic technique has been reported by Mochizuke et al. (245) (under Higasi's direction).

The necessity of accurate calibration is at least as important for the high-frequency manometers used for measuring pulsatile pressure. Yanof et al. (33) carefully studied the frequency responses obtainable by rigorous gas-free preparation of commercial manometers, with standard cardiac catheters attached. The results were rather better than the manufacturers claimed—and in this tedious type of work the highest frequency obtained is the correct one, as all artifacts tend to reduce it. The volume displacement of a Statham P23 G transducer, about 0.601 mm^3 for an applied pressure of 100 mm Hg (higher for other transducer models), makes apparent the degrading effect of invisibly small bubbles of air; the response obviously needs to be tested each time the system is filled. The pump technique used in (33) is time consuming but an easy and rapid method has been described [McDonald & Navarro (246)] which measures the free vibrations after the transient drop in pressure in a chamber on bursting a rubber-membrane. Yet reviews such as Franke (80) still tend to concentrate on simple manometer theory and the mechanics of construction; practical aspects of behavior are confined, apparently, to quoting from manufacturers' brochures. In this case, although Yanof et al. (33) are referred to, the frequency values tabulated are much lower than they found—in spite of a personal attribution of Franke's Figure 47 to Yanof.[4]

Manometer theory was studied by McDonald [(1, pp. 303–304); (247)] by substituting the resistive component calculated from the longitudinal impedance, the "Womersley oscillatory resistance", in place of the

[4] To set the record straight, the original of Figure 47 was recorded in the Department of Cardiology, St. Bartholomew's Hospital, London with a Statham SF-1 transducer—not a piezoelectric one; the P23 Gb manometer was connected to the lumen of the SF-1 through about three feet of polyethylene tubing and its frequency response was correspondingly low—about 25 cps; the recording was in the ventricle, not the right atrium; and of three cases studied at that time this was the only one that showed the marked oscillation on the SF-1 record in late systole and it was thought to be associated with a loud murmur heard in this very abnormal heart.

Poiseuille resistance used by Hansen (248) in the manometer equation. While the Hansen form predicted a much higher amplitude at resonance than was found experimentally, the Womersley term modification predicted values not significantly different from experiment. The difference between the two forms was only apparent at frequencies in excess of 70 per cent of the resonant frequency. Furthermore, no good fit was found above resonance, as a result of which it is unfortunate that (80) should graph the greater amount of the theoretical phase-shift plot at frequencies above resonance—a region of no practical significance.

Okino (249) has done a useful study of the possibilities and limitations of measuring intra-arterial pressure with extravascular transducers. Numerous other technical reports are to be found in the proceedings of biomedical engineering meetings (16–20). Useful computations of new ideas in instruments of many applications appear in the books edited by Alt (250–252).

In (225) are valuable details of the techniques used by Landis (253), Bloch (254), and Wiederhielm (255) for measuring pressures in the microcirculation; the scanning techniques which have led to such rapid advances in flow and diffusion studies in this field are described by Monro (256), Muller (257), Wiederhielm (258, 259), Johnson & Greatbach (260), and Bloch (261). Sobin (262) describes his vascular injection methods. The results recorded with these methods have been discussed in the previous section.

LITERATURE CITED

1. McDonald, D. A. In *Blood Flow in Arteries* (Edward Arnold, London; Williams & Wilkins, Baltimore, Md., 1960)
2. Attinger, E. O., Ed. *Pulsatile Blood Flow* (McGraw-Hill, New York, 1964)
3. McDonald, D. A., Taylor, M. G. In *Progress in Biophysics*, 107–73 (Pergamon, London, 1959)
4. Birkhoff, G. In *Hydrodynamics. A study in logic, fact and similitude,* xi and 184 (Princeton Univ. Press, Princeton, N.J., 1960)
5. Fry, D. L. *IRE Trans. Med. Electron.*, 6, 252–59 (1959)
6. Skalak, R. *Biomechanics,* 20–46 (1966)
7. Rudinger, G. *Biomed. Fluid Mech. Symp.*, ASME, New York, 1966, 1–33
8. Attinger, E. O. In *Pulsatile Blood Flow*, 15–76 (McGraw-Hill, New York, 1964)
9. Attinger, E. O. In *Advances in Hydroscience*, 3, 111–53 (Ven Te Chow, Ed., Academic Press, New York, 1966)
10. Attinger, E. O. *Advances in Biomedical Engineering and Medical Physics,* 1 (Levine, N., Ed., Wiley-Interscience, New York, 1967)
11. Fung, Y. C. *Foundations of Solid Mechanics* (Prentice-Hall, Englewood Cliffs, N.J., 1965)
12. Fung, Y. C. *Fed. Proc.*, 25, 1761–72 (1966)
13. Anliker, M., Raman, K. R. *Intern. J. Solid Struct.*, 2, 467–91 (1966)
14. Copley, A. L., Ed. *Proc. 1st Intern. Conf. Hemorheology* (Pergamon, Oxford, 1967)
15. Copley, A. L., Ed. *Symposium on Biorheology*, Part 4, Proc. 4th Intern. Congr. Rheology, Providence, R.I. (Interscience, New York, 1965)
16. *Proc. 17th Ann. Conf. Eng. Med. Biol.*, 6 (1964)
17. *Proc. 18th Ann. Conf. Eng. Med. Biol.*, 7 (1965)
18. *Proc. 19th Ann. Conf. Eng. Med. Biol.*, 8 (1966)
19. *Proc. Am. Soc. Mech. Eng.* (1965)
20. *Biomed. Fluid Mech. Symp.*, ASME, New York, 1966

21 Wilkie, D. R. *Ann. Rev. Physiol.,* **28,** 17–38 (1966)

22. Taylor, M. G. In *Pulsatile Blood Flow,* 343–72 (McGraw-Hill, New York, 1964)

23. Kleiber, M. *Ann. Rev. Physiol.,* **29,** 1–20 (1967)

24. Jacobson, E. D., Ed. *Symposium on Gastrointestinal Circulation, Gastroenterology,* **52,** Part 2 (February 1967)

25. Caro, C. G., McDonald, D. A. *J. Physiol. (London),* **157,** 426–53 (1961)

26. Taylor, M. G. *Phys. Med. Biol.,* **10,** 539–50 (1965)

27. Taylor, M. G. *Biophys. J.,* **6,** 29–51 (1966)

28. Taylor, M. G. *Ibid.,* 698–716

29. O'Rourke, M. F. *J. Appl. Physiol.,* **20,** 142–47 (1965)

30. Gessner, U., Bergel, D. H. *J. Appl. Physiol.,* **19,** 1209–11 (1964)

31. Bergel, D. H., Gessner, U. *Methods Med. Res.,* **11,** 70–82 (1966)

32. Kolin, A., Wisshaupt, R. *IEEE Trans. Bio-Med. Electron.,* **BME-10,** 61–67 (1963)

33. Yanof, H. M., Rosen, A. L., McDonald, N. M., McDonald, D. A. *Phys. Med. Biol.,* **8,** 407–22 (1963)

34. O'Rourke, M. F. *Pressure and Flow in Arteries* (M.D. thesis, Univ. of Sydney, 1965)

35. O'Rourke, M. F., Taylor, M. G. *Circ. Res.,* **18,** 126–39 (1966)

36. McDonald, D. A. In *Pulsatile Blood Flow,* 115–34 (McGraw-Hill, New York, 1964)

37. Taylor, M. G. *Circ. Res.,* **18,** 585–95 (1966)

38. Womersley, J. R. *Phys. Med. Biol.,* **2,** 313–23 (1958)

39. Gessner, U., Bergel, D. H. *IEEE Trans. Bio-Med. Eng.,* **BME-13,** 2–10 (1966)

40. Patel, D. J., Austen, W. G. *Ann. N.Y. Acad. Sci.,* **115,** 1129–39 (1964)

41. Gabe, I. T. *Clin. Sci.,* **29,** 45–58 (1965)

42. Bergel, D. H., McDonald, D. A., Taylor, M. G. *J. Physiol. (London),* **141,** 17–18P (1958)

43. Gabe, I. T. *Phys. Med. Biol.,* **10,** 407–16 (1965)

44. Patel, D. J., de Freitas, F. M., Fry, D. L. *J. Appl. Physiol.,* **18,** 134–40 (1963)

45. Noble, M. I. M., Gabe, I. T., Trenchard, D., Guz, A. *Cardiovasc. Res.,* **1,** 9–20 (1967)

46. O'Rourke, M. F., Taylor, M. G. *Circ. Res.,* **20,** 365–80 (1967)

47. McDonald, D. A., Sugawara, H., Engelhardt, W., von Attinger, E. O. *Physiologist,* **8,** 230 (1965)

48. Attinger, E. O., Sugawara, H., Navarro, A., Ricetto, A., Martin, R. *Circ. Res.,* **19,** 230–46 (1966)

49. McDonald, D. A. *Proc. ACEMB,* **7,** 1 (1965)

50. Taylor, M. G. *Gastroenterology,* **52,** 358–64 (1967)

51. The Preacher. Ecclesiastes, Chap. 1, verses 10–11, in *The Bible* (Transl.) (English Revised Version; C.U.P. 1884)

52. McDonald, D. A., Gessner, U. *Proc. 1st Intern. Conf. Hemorheology* (In press, Pergamon, Oxford, 1967)

53. McDonald, D. A., *J. Appl. Physiol.* (In press, 1967)

54. O'Rourke, M. F., Milnor, W. R. *Fed. Proc.,* **26,** 269 (1967)

55. Bergel, D. H., Milnor, W. R. *Circ. Res.,* **16,** 401–16 (1965)

56. Somlyo, A. V., Somlyo, A. P. *Am. J. Physiol.,* **206,** 1196–1200 (1964)

57. Kendrick, J. E. *Physiologist,* **9,** 217 (1966)

58. Attinger, E. O., Anné, A., McDonald, D. A. *Biophys. J.,* **6,** 291–304 (1966)

59. Womersley, J. R. *Tech. Rept. WADC-TR56-614* (Off. Tech. Serv., Dept. of Commerce, #PB151356, 1957)

60. Taylor, M. G., Gow, B. *Am. J. Physiol.* (In press, 1967)

61. Womersley, J. R. *J. Physiol. (London),* **127,** 553–63 (1955)

62. McDonald, D. A. *J. Physiol. (London),* **127,** 533–52 (1955)

63. Fry, D. L., Mallos, A. J., Casper, A. G. T. *Circ. Res.,* **4,** 627–32 (1956)

64. Fry, D. L., Noble, F. W., Mallos, A. *J. Circ. Res.,* **5,** 75–78 (1957)

65. Barnett, G. O., Greenfield, J. C., Jr., Fox, S. M., *Am. Heart J.,* **62,** 359–66 (1961)

66. Snell, R. E., Clements, J. M., Patel, D. J., Fry, D. L., Luchsinger, P. C. *J. Appl. Physiol.* **20,** 651–95 (1965)

67. Greenfield, J. C., Jr., Fry, D. L. *Circ. Res.,* **17,** 340–48 (1965)

68. Greenfield, J. C., Jr., Fry, D. L. *J. Appl. Physiol.,* **20,** 1141–47 (1965)

69. Porjé, I. G., Rudewald, B. *Opuscula Med.,* **6,** 3–11 (1960)

70. Taylor, M. G. *Phys. Med. Biol.,* **1,** 258–69 (1957)

71. Taylor, M. G., *Ibid.*, 321–29
72. Jones, W. B., Hefner, L. L., Bancroft, J. R., Klip, W. *J. Clin. Invest.*, **38**, 2087–90 (1959)
73. Jones, W. B., Griffin, J. B. *J. Appl. Physiol.*, **17**, 482–86 (1962)
74. Jones, W. B., Reeves, T. J. *Circulation*, **34**, 137 (1967)
75. Boyett, J. D., Stowe, D. E., Becker, L. H. *USAF Sch. Aerospace Med. Rept. SAM-TR-66–75*, 1–6 (1966)
76. McDonald, D. A., Attinger, E. O. *Circ. Res.* (Submitted, 1967)
77. Hamilton, W. R. In *Handbook of Physiology, Circulation*, **I**, 551–83 (Am. Physiol. Soc., Washington, 1962)
78. Osborn, J. *Am. J. Physiol.* (Submitted, 1967)
79. McDonald, D. A., Navarro, A. *J. Appl. Physiol.* (Submitted, 1967)
80. Franke, E. K. *Methods Med. Res.*, **11**, 122–36 (1966)
81. Piemme, T. E. *Progr. Cardiovasc. Diseases*, **6**, 574–94 (1963)
82. Spencer, M. P., Greiss, F. C. *Circ. Res.*, **10**, 274–79 (1962)
83. Alexander, R. S. *Ann. Rev. Physiol.*, **25**, 213–34 (1963)
84. Fry, D. L. *IRE Trans. Med. Electron.*, **6**, 259–63 (1959)
85. Fry, D. L., Griggs, D. M., Greenfield, J. C., Jr. In *Pulsatile Blood Flow*, 101–14 (McGraw-Hill, New York, 1964)
86. Attinger, E. O. *Circ. Res.*, **12**, 623–29 (1963)
87. Caro, C. G., Saffman, P. *J. Physiol. (London)*, **178**, 193–210 (1965)
88. Frasher, W. G., Jr., Sobin, S. S. *J. Appl. Physiol.*, **20**, 675–82 (1965)
89. Attinger, E. O., Sugawara, H., Navarro, A., Anné, A. *Circ. Res.*, **18**, 447–56 (1966)
90. Milnor, W. R., Bergel, D. H., Bargainer, J. D. *Circ. Res.*, **19**, 467–80 (1966)
91. Rushmer, R. F. In *Pulsatile Blood Flow*, Chap. 2 (McGraw-Hill, New York, 1964)
92. Rushmer, R. F. *Circulation*, **29**, 268–83 (1964)
93. Noble, M. I. M., Trenchard, D., Guz, A., *Circ. Res.*, **19**, 139–47 (1966)
94. Noble, M. I. M., Trenchard, D., Guz, A. *Circ. Res.*, **19**, 148–52 (1966)
95. Noble, M. I. M., Trenchard, D., Guz, A. *Ibid.*, 206–15
96. Streeter, D. D., Jr., Bassett, L., *Anat. Record*, **155**, 503–12 (1966)
97. Skalak, R., Wiener, F., Morkin, E., Fishman, A. P. *Phys. Med. Biol.*, **11**, 287–99 (1966)
98. Skalak, R., Wiener, F., Morkin, E., Fishman, A. P. *Ibid.*, 437–50
99. Shepard, R. B., Simpson, D. C., Sharp, J. F. *Arch. Surg.*, **93**, 730–40 (1966)
100. Simpson, D. C., Shepard, R. B. *Alabama J. Med. Sci.* (In press, 1967)
101. Shepard, R. B., Fontana, J., Simpson, D. C., Sharp, J., Herman-Giddens, S., Williams, N., Redmond, S., Carpenter, M. *Proc. 5th Ann. Meeting Assoc. Comp. Mech.*, 239–64 (1966)
102. Evans, R. L., Berstein, E. F., Lary, D. L. *Am. J. Physiol.*, **202**, 661–63 (1962)
103. Lawton, R. W. *Circ. Res.*, **3**, 403–8 (1955)
104. Hardung, V. *Handbook of Physiology, Circulation*, **I**, 107–35 (Am. Physiol. Soc., Washington, 1962)
105. Bergel, D. H. *J. Physiol. (London)*, **156**, 458–69 (1961)
106. Peterson, L. H., Jensen, R. E., Parnell, J. *Circ. Res.*, **8**, 622–31 (1960)
107. Peterson, L. H. In *Pulsatile Blood Flow*, 263–74 (McGraw-Hill, New York, 1964)
108. Attinger, F. M., Fischer, G. M., Fronek, A., Jones, A. W., Karreman, G., Llaurado, J. G., Peterson, L. H., Webster, D., Weygandt, C. N., Zabara, J., *Proc. ACEMB*, **7**, 110 (1965)
109. Taylor, M. G. *Phys. Med. Biol.*, **4**, 63–82 (1959)
110. Taylor, M. G. (Ph.D. thesis, Univ. of London, 1959)
111. Malindzak, G., Stacy, R. W. *N.Y. Acad. Sci.* **128**, 921 (1966)
112. Gow, B. S. *J. Appl. Physiol.*, **21**, 1122–26 (1966)
113. Anliker, M., Wolterink, L. *Fed. Proc.*, **25**, 394 (1966)
114. Anliker, M., Histand, M., Ogden, E., Westbrook, R. M. *Proc. ACEMB*, **8**, 17 (1966)
115. Anliker, M., Ogden, E. *Physiologist*, **9**, 131 (1966)
116. Taylor, M. G. *Phys. Med. Biol.*, **4**, 63–82 (1959)
117. Martin, J. D. *Biomed. Fluid Mech. Symp.*, *ASME, New York, 1966* 70–77
118. Sugiura, T., Freis, E. D. *Circ. Res.*, **11**, 838–42 (1962)
119. Wiederhielm, C. A., Woodbury, J. W., Kirk, S., Rushmer, R. F. *Am. J. Physiol.* **207**, 173–73 (1964)

120. Permutt, S., Riley, R. L. *J. Appl. Physiol.*, **18**, 924–32 (1962)
121. Dexter, L. (Chm.) *Fed. Proc.*, **26**, 244 (1967)
122. Campbell, E. M. *Ann. Rev. Physiol.* (In press, 1968)
123. Caro, C. G., Harrison, G. K., Mognoni, P. *Cardiovasc. Res.*, **1**, 91–100 (1967)
124. Caro, C. G., Bergel, D. H., Seed, W. A. *Circ. Res.*, **20**, 185–93 (1967)
125. Bergel, D. H., Glazier, J. B., Hughes, J. M. B., Maloney, J. E., West, J. B. *J. Physiol. (London)*, **189**, 28 (1967)
126. Bargainer, J. D. *Circ. Res.*, **20**, 630–37 (1967)
127. Patel, D. J., Mason, D. T., Ross, J., Jr., Braunwald, E., *Am. Heart J.*, **69**, 785–94 (1965)
128. Luchsinger, P. C., Snell, R. E., Patel, D. J., Fry, D. L. *Circ. Res.*, **15**, 503–10 (1964)
129. Brawley, R. K., Morrow, A. G. *Circulation*, **35**, 32–45 (1967)
130. Thwaites, B. *Proc. Roy. Soc.*, **162**, 171–87 (1965)
131. Greenfield, J. C., Jr., Cox, R. L., Hernandez, R. R., Thomas, C., Shoonmaker, F. W. *Circulation*, **35**, 653 (1967)
132. Remington, J. W. In *Handbook of Physiology, Circulation*, **II**, 799–838 (Am. Physiol. Soc., Washington, 1962)
133. Spencer, M. P. In *Handbook of Physiology, Circulation*, **II**, 839–64 (Am. Physiol. Soc., Washington, 1962)
134. Cope, F. W. *Advan. Biol. Med. Phys.*, **12**, 277–356 (1965)
135. Goldwyn, R. M., Watt, T. B. *IEEE Trans. Bio-Med. Eng.*, **BME-14**, 11–17 (1967)
136. Olson, R. M., Cain, S. M. *Fed. Proc.*, **26**, 440 (1967)
137. Patel, D. J. *Med. Res. Eng.*, **5**, 30–33 (1966)
138. Coulter, N. A., Jr. *IEEE Trans. Bio-Med. Eng.*, **BME-13**, 207–8 (1966)
139. Taylor, M. G. *Australian Ann. Med.*, **15**, 71–86 (1966)
140. Remington, J. W. *Am. J. Physiol.*, **208**, 968–83 (1965)
141. Meisner, J. E., Remington, J. W. *Am. J. Physiol.*, **202**, 527–35 (1962)
142. Jager, G. N., Westerhof, N., Noordergraaf, A. *Circ. Res.*, **16**, 121–33 (1965)
143. Pollack, G. H., Noordergraaf, A. *Proc. ACEMB*, **7**, 33 (1965)
144. Beneken, J. E. W., DeWit, B. In *Physical Basis of Circulatory Transport: Regulation and Exchange* (Reeve, E. B., Guyton, A. C., Eds., Saunders, Philadelphia, 1967)
145. Robinson, D. A. In *Circulatory Analog Computers*, 56–81 (Noordergraaf, A., Jager, G. N., Westerhof, N., Eds., North-Holland, Amsterdam, 1963)
146. Robinson, D. A. *Circ. Res.*, **17**, 207–21 (1965)
147. Fich, S., Welkowitz, W., Hilton, R. *Biomed. Fluid Mech. Symp.*, *ASME, New York, 1966*, 34–44
148. Iberall, A. S. Res. Paper, *Bur. Stand. RP2115*, **45**, 85–108 (1950)
149. Iberall, A. S. *Proc. 7th Intern. Congr. Biomed. Eng.*, 81 (1967)
150. Mirsky, I. *Biophys. J.*, **7**, 165–86 (1967)
151. Mirsky, I. *Bull. Math. Biophys.*, **29**, 11–20 (1967)
152. Atabek, H. B., Lew, H. S. *Biophys. J.*, **6**, 481–503 (1966)
153. Klip, W. *Velocity and Damping of the Pulse Wave* (Thesis; Martinus Nijhof, The Hague, 1962)
154. Klip, W., Klip, D. A. B. In *Pulsatile Blood Flow*, 323–30 (McGraw-Hill, New York, 1964)
155. Klip, W., Klip, D. A. B. (Maris, A. W., Wang, P. S., Eds.) *Proc. ASME* (1965)
156. Jones, R. T., Kantrowitz, A. R. *Proc. ACEMB*, **7**, 79 (1965)
157. Jones, R. T. *Motions of a Liquid in a Pulsating Bulb with Application to Problems of Blood Flow* (Rept. Avco-Everett Res. Lab., Everett, Mass., 1965)
158. Oka, S. *J. Phys. Soc. Japan*, **19**, 1481–84 (1964)
159. Fujiki, T., Oka, S. *Rept. Progr. Polymer Phys., Japan*, **8** (1965)
160. Nishimura, J. Oka. *J. Phys. Soc. Japan*, **20**, 449–53 (1965)
161. Patel, D. J., de Freitas, F. M., Greenfield, J. C., Jr., Fry, D. L. *J. Appl. Physiol.*, **18**, 1111–17 (1963)
162. Young, D. F., Cholvin, N. R. *Biomed. Fluid Mech. Symp.*, *ASME, New York, 1966*, 78–88
163. Atabek, H. B., Chang, C. C. *Phys. Med. Biol.*, **9**, 219–27 (1964)
164. Kuchar, N. R., Ostrach, S. *Biomed.*

Fluid Mech. Symp., ASME, New York, 45–69 (1966)

165. Bassingthwaighte, J. B., Ackerman, F. H. *J. Appl. Physiol.,* **22,** 879–88 (1967)

166. Wolinsky, H., Glagov, S. A. *Circ. Res.,* **14,** 400–13 (1964)

167. Wolinsky, H., Glagov, S. A. *Ibid.,* **20,** 99–111 (1967)

168. Wolinsky, H. *Circ. Res.,* **20,** 409–21 (1967)

169. Sobin, S. S., Frasher, W. G., Jr., Tremer, H. M. *Circ. Res.,* **11,** 257–63 (1962)

170. Harkness, M. L. R., Harkness, R. D., McDonald, D. A. *Proc. Roy. Soc. B,* **146,** 541–51 (1957)

171. Tickner, R., Sacks, A. H. In *Biorheology* (In press, 1967)

172. Patel, D. J. (Personal comunication, 1967)

173. Patel, D. J., Fry, D. L. *J. Appl. Physiol.,* **19,** 413–16 (1964)

174. Patel, D. J., Fry, D. L. *Circ. Res.,* **19,** 1011–21 (1966)

175. Womersley, J. R. *Phys. Med. Biol.,* **2,** 178–87 (1957)

176. Hardung, V. *Angiologica,* **1,** 185–96 (1964)

177. Learoyd, B. M., Taylor, M. G. *Circ. Res.,* **18,** 278–91 (1966)

178. Foreman, J. E. K., Durie, N. D. *Biomed. Fluid Mech. Symp., ASME, New York, 1966,* 148–60

179. Meisner, J. E., Rushmer, R. F. *Circ. Res.,* **12,** 651–58 (1963)

180. Sacks, A. H., Raman, K. R., Burnell, J. A. In *Symposium on Biorheology, Part 4, Proc. 4th Intern. Congr. Rheology, Providence, R.I.* (Interscience, New York, 1965)

181. McCutcheon, E. P., Rushmer, R. F. *Circ. Res.,* **20,** 149–61 (1967)

182. McDonald, D. A. In *Symposium On Biorheology, Part 4, Proc. 4th Intern. Congr. Rheology, Providence, R.I.,* 205–14 (Interscience, New York, 1965)

183. Piemme, T. E., Barnett, G. O., Dexter, L. *Circ. Res.,* **18,** 303–15 (1966)

184. Yellin, E. L. *Biomed. Fluid Mech. Symp., ASME, New York, 1966,* 209–21

185. Yellin, E. L. *Circ. Res.,* **19,** 791–804 (1966)

186. Leith, W. C. *Biomed. Fluid Mech. Symp., ASME, New York, 1966,* 110–21

187. Freis, E. D., Heath, W. C. *Circ. Res.,* **14,** 105–16 (1964)

188. Attinger, E. O., Sugawara, H., Navarro, A., Anné, A. *Circ. Res.,* **18,** 447–56 (1966)

189. Caro, C. G. *J. Physiol. (London),* **185,** 501–19 (1966)

190. Neumaster, T., Krovetz, L. J. *J. Appl. Physiol.,* **19,** 1184–86 (1964)

191. Krovetz, L. J. *Phys. Med. Biol.,* **10,** 261–70 (1965)

192. Kunz, A. L., Coulter, N. A., Jr. *Biophys. J.,* **7,** 25–36 (1967)

193. Coulter, N. A., Jr., Pappenheimer, J. R. *Am. J. Physiol.,* **159,** 401–8 (1949)

194. Taylor, M. G. *Phys. Med. Biol.,* **3,** 273–90 (1959)

195. Wayland, H. *Gastroenterology,* **52,** 342–57 (1967)

196. McDonald, D. A. *Ibid.,* 355–57

197. Bayliss, L. E. *J. Physiol. (London),* **179,** 1–25 (1967)

198. Gilinsen, P. J., Dauwalter, C. R., Merrill, E. W. *Trans. Soc. Rheology,* **7,** 319 (1963)

199. Merrill, E. W., Benis, A. M., Gilliland, E. R., Sherwood, T. K., Saltzman, E. W. *J. Appl. Physiol.,* **20,** 954–67 (1965)

200. Merrill, E. W., Gilliland, E. R., Lee, T. S., Saltzman, E. W. *Circ. Res.,* **18,** 437–66 (1966)

201. Bugliarello, G. *Biomed. Fluid Mech. Symp., ASME, New York, 1966,* 192–208

202. Charm, S. E., Kurland, G. S., Brown, S. L. *Biomed. Fluid Mech. Symp., ASME, New York, 1966,* 89–93

203. Rudinger, G. *Biomed. Fluid Mech., ASME, New York, 1966,* 94–99

204. McComis, W. T. *Am. J. Physiol.,* **212,** 49–52 (1967)

205. Lamport, H. *Nature,* **206,** 132–35 (1965)

206. Wayland, J. H., Johnson, P. C. *J. Appl. Physiol.,* **22,** 333–37 (1967)

207. Landis, E. M. *Fed. Proc.,* **25,** 1742–43 (1966)

208. Sobin, S. S., Tremer, H. M. *Fed. Proc.,* **25,** 1744–52 (1966)

209. Frasher, W. G., Sobin, S. S., *J. Appl. Physiol.,* **20,** 675–82 (1965)

210. Burton, A. C. *Fed. Proc.,* **25,** 1753–60 (1966)

211. Guyton, A. C. *Circ. Res.,* **12,** 399–414 (1963)

212. Guyton, A. C. *Ibid.,* **16,** 452–60 (1965)

213. Guyton, A. C., Scheel, K., Murphree, D. *Circ. Res.,* **19,** 412–19 (1966)

214. Guyton, A. C., Prather, J., Scheel, K., McGehee, J. *Circ. Res.,* 1022–30

215. Landis, E. M. *Physiol. Rev.*, **14**, 404–81 (1934)
216. Guyton, A. C. In *Textbook of Medical Physiology* (W. B. Saunders, Philadelphia, 1966)
217. Kjellmer, I. *Acta Physiol. Scand.*, **62**, 31–40 (1964)
218. Fung, Y. C., Zweifach, B. W., Intaglietta, M. *Circ. Res.*, **19**, 441–61 (1966)
219. Baez, S., Lamport, H., Baez, A. In *Flow Properties of Blood*, 122–36 (Copley, A. L., Stainsby, G., Eds., Pergamon, Oxford, 1960)
220. Pappenheimer, J. R. *Physiol. Rev.*, **33**, 387–423 (1953)
221. Bloch, E. H. *Angiology*, **14**, 97–106 (1963)
222. Bloch, E. H., Coyas, S. I. *Angiology*, **15**, 353–61 (1964)
223. Wiederhielm, C. A. *Fed. Proc.*, **25**, 1789–98 (1966)
224. Zweifach, B. W., Intaglietta, M. *Fed. Proc.*, **25**, 1784–88 (1966)
225. Rushmer, R. F., Ed. *Methods Med. Res.*, **11** (1966)
226. Fry, D. L. *Methods Med. Res.*, **11**, 44–49 (1966)
227. Fry, D. L., Ross, J., Jr. *Methods Med. Res.*, **11**, 50–69 (1966)
228. Baker, D. W. *Methods Med. Res.*, **11**, 107–17 (1966)
229. Stegall, H. F., Rushmer, R. F., Baker, D. W. *J. Appl. Physiol.*, **21**, 707–11 (1966)
230. Rushmer, R. F., Baker, D. W., Johnson, W. L., Strandness, D. E. *J. Am. Med. Assoc.*, **199**, 326–28 (1967)
231. Hill, R. V., Jansen, J. C., Fling, J. L. *J. Appl. Physiol.*, **22**, 161–68 (1967)
232. Galle, K. R. *Methods Med. Res.*, **11**, 94–106 (1966)
233. Richards, A. M., Kuether, F. W., Taylor, H. L. *Fed. Proc.*, **26**, 549 (1967)
234. Wessel, H. U., Grahn, A. R., Paul, M. H., Earle, D. P. *Fed. Proc.*, **26**, 549 (1967)
235. Rasmussen, R. A. *Rev. Sci. Instr.*, **33**, 38–42 (1962)
236. Wetterer, E. In *Handbook of Physiology, Circulation*, **II**, 1294–1324 (Am. Physiol. Soc., Washington, 1962)
237. Khouri, E. M., Gregg, D. F. *J. Appl. Physiol.*, **18**, 224–27 (1965)
238. Elliott, S. E., Hoffman, J. I. E., Guz, A. *Med. Electron. Biol. Eng.*, **I**, 323–31 (1963)
239. Ryan, D. P. *IEEE Trans. Bio-Med. Electron.*, **BME-10** 57–60 (1963)
240. Bond, R. F. *J. Appl. Physiol.*, **22**, 358–61 (1967)
241. Abel, F. L. *Med. Res. Eng.*, **5**, 34–37 (1966)
242. Sellers, A. F., Dobson, A. *Gastroenterology*, **52**, 374–80 (1967)
243. Mills, C. J. *Phys. Med. Biol.*, **11**, 323–24 (1966)
244. Pieper, H. P. *Rev. Sci. Instr.*, **34**, 908–10 (1963)
245. Higasi, B., Ed. *The Platinum Flowmeter*, No. 10 (Res. Inst. Appl. Electron., Japan, 1962)
246. McDonald, D. A., Navarro, A. *J. Appl. Physiol.* (Submitted) (Precirculated through Inform. Exchange Group 3) (1967)
247. McDonald, D. A. Discussion in *Pulsatile Blood Flow*, 433–37 (McGraw-Hill, New York, 1964)
248. Hansen, A. T. *Acta Physiol. Scand.*, **19**, *Suppl. 68* (1949)
249. Okino, H. *J. Appl. Physiol.*, **19**, 546–49 (1964)
250. Alt, F., Ed. *Advances in Bioengineerand Instrumentation* (Instr. Soc. Am.; Plenum Press, New York, 1966)
251. Alt, F., Ed. *Biomedical Sciences Instrumentation*, **I** (Instr. Soc. Am.; Plenum Press, New York, 1963)
252. Murry, W. E., Salisbury, P. F., Eds. *Biomedical Sciences Instrumentation*, **2** (Instr. Soc. Am.; Plenum Press, New York, 1964)
253. Landis, E. M. *Methods Med. Res.*, **11**, 184–89 (1966)
254. Bloch, E. H. *Methods Med. Res.*, **11**, 190–94 (1966)
255. Wiederhielm, C. A. *Methods Med. Res.*, **11**, 199–201 (1966)
256. Monro, P. A. G. *Methods Med. Res.*, 202–6 (1966)
257. Müller, H. *Methods Med. Res.*, **11**, 207–11 (1966)
258. Wiederhielm, C. A. *Methods Med. Res.*, **11**, 212–16 (1966)
259. Wiederhielm, C. A. *Ibid.*, 217–19
260. Johnson, P. C., Greatbach, W. H., Jr. *Methods Med. Res.*, **11**, 220–27 (1966)
261. Bloch, E. H. *Methods Med. Res.*, **11**, 228–32 (1966)
262. Sobin, S. S. *Methods Med. Res.*, **11**, 233–38 (1966)
263. Sonnenblick, E. H. In *The Myocardial Cell*, 173–250 (Briller, S. A., Conn, H. L., Eds., Univ. of Pennsylvania Press, Philadelphia, 1966)
264. Hefner, I. L., Bowen, T. E., Jr. *Am. J. Physiol.*, **212**, 1221–27 (1967)

THE NEUROHYPOPHYSIS[1,2]   1014

By Gordon Farrell, Louis F. Fabre, and Elizabeth W. Rauschkolb[3]

Texas Research Institute of Mental Sciences, Baylor University College of Medicine, and the Veterans Administration Hospital, Houston, Texas

Selected research contributions appearing during the period 1964–67 are discussed in this review.

The authors have the impression that little new of a fundamental nature has appeared on the subject of posterior pituitary physiology in the four years since the comprehensive manuscript of Kleeman & Cutler in this *Review* in 1963 (1). The grand outlines of the field have all been well laid out; the chemical structures have been established and most of the factors in control of secretion have been brought to light. The mechanism of action has received much attention. The evolutionary distribution and variation in structure and function are well studied; good recent reviews will be found (2, 3).

What remains is the backing and filling, smoothing over and straightening out, furbishing and refinement, and not the least important, weeding out of "false facts" needed to bring our understanding of posterior pituitary physiology to a fine state of adequacy. All of these have been going on and we shall try to adjudge their success.

The Secretion of Vasopressin and Oxytocin

The physiological control of an endocrine organ is best studied by correlating the rate of secretion of the hormone with the application of stimuli. This has not been routinely possible in studies of the neurohypophysis because of difficult access and complex blood supply (4). These difficulties have led investigators to employ other procedures as an index of secretion: (*a*) determination of the neurohypophyseal content of hormones; (*b*) the light or electronmicroscopic appearance of the gland; or (*c*) estimation of plasma concentrations of the octapeptides in peripheral blood.

[1] The survey of literature for this review was concluded in May 1967.

[2] Research supported by grant T-399 of the American Cancer Society, Inc. and by grant GB-6625 of the National Science Foundation. The authors wish to acknowledge the help of Miss Gladys Smith, Manuscript Editor of the Section of Neuroendocrinology, Texas Research Institute of Mental Sciences in the preparation of this review. Thanks are also due Miss Janet Burris for assistance with bibliographical material, and to Dr. Jiro Nakano for generously allowing us to see the prepublication copy of his manuscript presented at the Gordon Research Conference.

[3] Recipient of a Clinical Investigatorship of the Veterans Administration Hospital, Houston, Texas.

A number of investigators have related the disappearance of stainable neurosecretory material as seen in the light microscope with secretion of hormones (5, 6). Moses et al. (7), however, report that reduction of stainable material occurs without comcomitant depletion of hormones; the method may give misleading results. The disappearance of electron-dense material in the elementary granules of the neurohypophysis has also been taken as an indication that secretion has occurred (8–10), but Lederis and co-workers (11) have evidence that this phenomenon bears no necessary relationship to hormone content of the gland.

The content of hormone as measured by bioassay procedures has been used as a measure of secretion (11–14). Representing as it does the momentary equilibrium between secretion and biosynthesis (15, 16), the measurement is clearly open to question.

The measurement of their blood levels is the most reliable method of estimating the secretory rates of vasopressin and oxytocin, but even this is not free of equivocation, since it obviously represents the balance between secretion and metabolism. Both the plasma level and the state of hydration affect the rate of metabolism of vasopressin; for example, elevation of vasopressin from normal levels to 10 μU/ml reduces the half-life from seven and a half to five minutes (17). Despite these limitations, changes in plasma levels of pituitary octapeptides remain the best indices of changes in secretion rates. Thus, the elucidation of the physiology of neurohypophyseal secretion is dependent on the ability to accurately measure blood levels of biologically active octapeptides. This is not easily accomplished because of the labile nature of the hormones and the extremely small concentrations present in biological fluids. Chemical and physical methods have not been perfected for this analysis, and quantitation has been dependent on bioassay with all its inherent difficulties. The area has been recently and well reviewed (18, 19).

In brief, the assay of vasopressin requires extraction from plasma, removal of other pressor substances and interfering proteins, concentration and bioassay in a suitably prepared animal. A variety of maneuvers have been employed prior to assay (20, 21). Most require removal of blood cells, precipitation of proteins with trichloroacetic acid, extraction of the precipitate, and chromatography on an ion exchange column or silicic acid-impregnated glass paper. Recoveries as high as 90 per cent have been reported for vasopressin added to plasma and processed in this way (22).

Bioassay is carried out in the rat by using either the pressor or antidiuretic response. The former is more rapid and precise but insensitive; the antidiuretic response is most often employed. Jeffers (23) apparently first described the ethanol-anesthetized fasted and hydrated rat for ADH assay. Many modifications have since been used (see 18, 19). The extracts are administered intravenously (24) and the response is compared with that obtained with USP or international posterior pituitary reference standards. A four- or eight-point statistical design is usually utilized. With this procedure a minimum sensitivity of 2–5 μU can be expected. Since the circulating levels of vasopressin in normal man have been estimated to be below 5 μU/ml of plasma (5 × 10⁻⁵ mg, assuming 400 units per mg) (18), the method is of limited value at physiological levels of hormone. Extreme modifications (25, 26) have produced assays sensitive to less than a microunit of ADH but results are variable even in experienced hands (25, 27).

Immunologic methods for assay of antidiuretic hormone show promise. Permutt (28) couples vasopressin to bovine albumen for the antigen. This method is as yet sensitive only to about 6 μU of arginine vasopressin.

Procedures for the preparation and bioassay of oxytocin are generally inferior to those for vasopressin. Some published methods employ little or no preparatory isolation procedure (18). In others, acetone extraction (24), concentration (29), and paper chromatography (29, 30) have been employed. Sodium thioglycollate inactivates oxytocin. Loss of activity when incubated with thioglycollate has been taken as evidence of specificity (31). Recoveries have been poor from paper chromatography (30), and thioglycollate inactivation is not a reliable criterion of specificity (19).

Numerous and varied bioassay methods have been used: *in vivo* contractile response of the uterus (32), *in vitro* contractile response of the uterus (33), degree of milk ejection, time from exposure to milk ejection (34), *in vitro* contractility of mammary gland tissue strips, and depression of blood pressure in fowls (35).

Acetycholine, 5-OH-tryptamine, epinephrine, and high potassium concentration interfere with the uterine contraction assay (19). The milk-ejection assay seems to be more specific but is less sensitive than the rat uterus assay (19). An immunologic assay for oxytocin has been proposed (36). Gilliland & Prout (37) have shown the production in the rabbit of antibodies to synthetic oxytocin and have attempted the radioiodination of oxytocin by the chloramine T method. The products of oxytocin iodination were separated into several components by chromatography; only one was found to be biologically active. On the basis of this work, these workers propose the assay of oxytocin by the inhibition of the reaction between radio oxytocin and anti-oxytocin antibody by unlabeled oxytocin in serum (36). As with vasopressin, the unstimulated levels of oxytocin in plasma cannot be reliably determined by present methods.

The accurate conceptualization of the behavior of the neurosecretory cells of the hypothalamus was voiced by a neuroendocrinologist of great insight, the late Ernst Scharrer, some years ago, despite methodology which would not now be considered optimal (38). The conclusions were reached that: (a) the hypothalmico-hypophyseal fibers consist of neurons whose cell bodies lie in the anterior hypothalamus and whose axons course down into the hypophysis; (b) the axons end as terminal swellings along capillaries; (c) along the axons are found the neurosecretory material (NSM); (d) movement of the NSM occurs from the hypothalamus to the hypophysis; and (e) stimuli causing antidiuresis are associated with depletion of NSM. With the advent of more sophisticated techniques, these concepts have been reaffirmed and embellished. A number of excellent current reviews handle the material in more detail than will appear here (4, 39–42).

It appears that the parikaryon in the hypothalamic supraoptic nucleus or paraventricular nucleus is required for the synthesis of neurosecretory material. This has been established by morphologic experiments including electronmicroscopy (39), cell fractionation with ultracentrifugation (43), and radioisotopic tracer techniques (44).

Oxytocin and vasopressin have been isolated in pure form from the neurosecretory material, which confirms that transport down the axon occurs in this manner (45, 46). The neurosecretory granules do not per se synthesize the octapeptides (16).

Synthesis of vasopressin in the neuron is associated with the ribosomes and at the onset may be inhibited by puromycin (47). A lag period of approximately one hour has been found in tracer experiments *in vitro* (16) or *in vivo* (48). Sachs (47, 49) has suggested that the ribosomal RNA is necessary only for the formation of a precursor of the active hormone and that the formation of ADH from the precursor occurs later during migration down the axon; conversion of precursor to ADH can occur *in vitro* in a cell-free system (49).

The rate of production of ADH does not seem to be influenced by acute physiological stimuli as are the biosynthetic rates of other organs, notably the adrenal (16). In the case of acute stimuli such as hemorrhage, the secretion of ADH is greatest in the first few minutes and declines with time even though the stimulus remains constant.

Sachs (16) has suggested that the stored pool of vasopressin is heterogenous and comprised of a "quickly releasable component" of about 10–20 per cent of the total hormone, and a slowly releasable component. The concept is analogous to that believed to be operable in the neuronal secretion of neurotransmitter substances (16).

Much time and research energy has been given to the elucidation of the mechanism by which vasopressin is released. One possibility is that the arrival of the action potential at the nerve terminal elicits the release of a transmitter substance and that this transmitter substance then causes the release of vasopressin (50). Acetylcholine has been selected as the logical transmitter (50). This situation is envisioned as similar to that occurring at the adrenal medulla.

In opposition to this view are the observations that acetylcholine, atropine, or physostigmine do not affect the release of vasopressin from the neurohypophysis (51). Additionally, an array of other known neurotransmitter substances (norepinephrine, serotonin, epinephrine, and histamine) are similarly ineffective (16).

Another hypothesis implicates the action potential itself in the release of vasopressin. Vasopressin is released *in vitro* by the passage of an electrical current through the medium (51, 52); the action potential arriving at the terminal membrane causes depolarization with increased permeability of the neuron to Ca⁺⁺. The entry of Ca^{++} into the neuron triggers the release of vasopressin (51).

It may be postulated that the Ca^{++} is responsible for disassociation of the octapeptides (oxytocin and ADH) from a carrier protein called neurophysin (53, 54). Sachs and co-workers (54), however, believe that secretion of vasopressin is accompanied by neurophysin. The exact mechanism of Ca^{++} action, therefore, remains obscure.

The important question as to the differential release of neurohypophyseal hormones has been a point of interest for a number of years; there is recent evidence that such does occur. It has been reported that the supraoptic nucleus is sensitive to changes in the osmotic composition of blood, while the paraventricular nucleus responds to stimuli arising from the nipples, uterus, and vagina (55); presumably, the supraoptic nucleus is the main site of vasopressin secretion, the paraventricular nucleus for oxytocin. In pregnant women, suckling and mammary duct dilatation result in oxytocic activity without antidiuresis (56). Administration of nicotine and hypertonic saline result in marked antidiuresis but negligible oxytocic activity (55). Hemorrhage under ether anesthetic leads to significant increases in the amount of free vasopressin, but not of oxytocin in the incubated neural lobes removed after stimulation (11).

It is still not clear whether a given neuron is able to secrete only one hormone or both hormones but in different proportions (57).

The two "classic" stimuli to ADH secretion are those relating to the control of the osmotic pressure of the extracellular fluid and to the regulation of blood volume, though pain and emotion (and certain pharmacologic agents) may affect the output of the hormone secretion (58–60). More recent studies in which plasma levels of ADH were determined by bioassay technics, in general, support the earlier concepts (21, 22, 26, 61–63). The reports that feeding is a stimulus to increased antidiuretic hormone secretion are probably explainable as due to changes in plasma volume or osmolarity caused either by hypertonic intestinal contents withdrawing plasma water, or by absorbed low molecular weight dietary proteins increasing plasma osmolarity (64, 65).

Weinstein et al. (20) provide additional evidence that the control of extracellular volume invokes antidiuretic hormone by the demonstration that plasma levels of vasopressin are elevated by hemorrhage; lesser reductions of blood have been found to be adequate stimuli for stimulation of ADH secretion as well (66, 67). The receptors in this control mechanism have been a subject of debate. Henry, Gauer & Reeves (68) originated the concept that volume receptors located in the left atrium may be involved; the data of Currie & Ullmann lent support (69). The hypothesis was questioned; exogenous vasopressin did not inhibit the diuresis induced by distention of the left atrium (70) and the diuresis could be shown to be associated with increased GFR, RPF, and solute excretion (71).

The Henry-Gauer hypothesis has been defended by Share (72) and by

Baisset & Montastruc (73). Share demonstrated that the elevation in plasma vasopressin titer which occurs after carotid constriction is inhibited by distention of the left atrium (72), in agreement with the earlier less direct observations of Baisset & Montastruc (73).

The high-pressure receptors are also involved; in vagotomized animals in which the carotid area is isolated and perfused at constant pressure, plasma ADH shows a minimal response to hemorrhage; return of the carotid area into the general circulation results in an eightfold increase in vasopressin titer (18). Changing from pulsatile to nonpulsatile perfusion of the carotid sinus, mean pressure unchanged, leads to significant elevation in plasma ADH (74). The chemoreceptors may also play a part probably of lesser importance: perfusion of the isolated carotid with deoxygenated blood results in an increased ADH plasma titer (75).

Henry & Gauer (76), in re-examining the question of volume receptors, have advanced the theory that small changes in volume are detected by the low-pressure segment of the circulation in the atria, right ventricle, left ventricle in diastole, and the pulmonary circulation; when dramatic changes in arterial pressure occur, the baroreceptors are invoked. In agreement, Share (18) has speculated from his data and that of Gupta (77) that the only receptor important in modest hemorrhage (10–20 per cent of blood volume) is the atrium.

Stimulation of the central end of the vagus (or the ulnar nerve) results in release of vasopressin (78). The vagus represents the afferent pathway for left atrial volume receptors and aortic baroreceptors (77). One would imagine that selective stimulation of the fibers conveying information from these would inhibit ADH secretion. This should hold true also for the carotid sinus vasoreceptors and carotid body chemoreceptors, whose fibers are found in the glossopharnygeal nerve (79). Information funnels to the hypothalamus through the brainstem ultimately via the periventricular system of Schutz (78). Areas in the rhinencephalon associated with emotion and mediating cardiovascular responses also mediate an antidiuretic response (80).

Epinephrine, in some experiments, was found to be nearly as potent as vasopressin in producing antidiuresis (81); both agents together produced an effect greater than either alone. The effect is not associated with changes in glomerular filtration rate; a direct stimulatory effect on the hypothalamo-hypophyseal complex is suggested (81, 82).

Vasopressin circulates unbound to plasma proteins and diffuses across capillary-capillary membranes into the extravascular space; it has been detected in lymph and in fluid collected from the thoracic and peritoneal cavities. Plasma concentrations of vasopressin are usually stated as being less than 5 μU/ml; the volume of distribution appears to be several times the plasma volume (18, 83).

The principal sites of removal of vasopressin from blood are the liver and kidneys; the kidneys remove about twice as much as the liver [hepatic portal extraction ratio is 17 per cent, renal extraction ratio, 25 per cent (84)]. The half-time for the metabolism of vasopressin has been found to be seven and a half minutes in the dog (17). Increased plasma level of vasopressin and dehydration are reported to reduce the turnover time to five minutes (17). The teleologic argument has been advanced that this might serve to protect the organism from adverse cardiovascular effects of vasopressin (17).

Oxytocin has a role in milk ejection (85, 86), parturition (87), sperm transport in male (88) and female (89); an action in regulating gonadotropin secretion has been suggested but is unlikely. The physiologic roles of oxytocin in milk ejection and parturition have been widely discussed and stimuli relating to these functions related to its secretion. Pain and emotion may also affect oxytocin secretion rates.

Suckling initiates a reflex release of oxytocin which effects contraction of the myoepithelial ducts. This reaction results in the expression of milk stores aiding the efficient transfer of milk from mother to young (86); the reflex is more active in some species than others. The receptors for the milk-letdown reflex are located within the nipple. Temperature, pressure, and tactile receptors are presumably involved, but the subject has not been well investigated. The integrity of a pathway from the receptors in the nipple to the paraventricular nucleus is evidenced by the finding that gentle suction on the nipples of postpartum cats produces increased electrical activity of neurons in this area (90). Spinal cord section or denervation of the mammary gland has been shown to inhibit reflex milk ejection in the rat (91), cat (92), and rabbit (93). By an indirect assay, Fuchs & Wagner (94) have shown oxytocin release with milk ejection in rabbits. Some fibers mediating the response lie deep within the lateral funiculus and follow an ipsilateral course. With the probable participation of many receptors, it is likely that other pathways are involved as well.

In the goat and sheep (95–97) lactation persists following denervation. Folley & Knaggs measured the oxytocin activity in the external jugular blood of cows, sows, and goats during milking stimuli. In cows and sows oxytocin release was associated with milk letdown. Goats, on the other hand, carefully hand-milked, release milk in the absence of oxytocin (98). There probably are supplementary mechanisms which assist milk letdown; e.g. myoepithelial contraction evoked by direct mechanical stimulation and intrinsic reflexes within the lactating mammary gland (99).

Mechanical stimulation of the female genital tract in mammals reflexly releases oxytocin (100–103). The receptors and afferent pathways have not been adequately studied. Several investigators have found, however, that mechanical or electrical stimulation of the uterus can cause electrical changes in neurons of the hypothalamus. Bower has detected action-potential discharge in afferent nerves from the rabbit uterus in response to increased uterine pressure. Pressure receptors within the uterus have been suggested. Midspinal cord section has been demonstrated to abolish the uterine response to stretch of the cervix.

The pathway through the brainstem has been studied by Beyer and co-workers (104). Stimulation of the rostral part of the dorsal longitudinal fasciculus was found to evoke short-latency responses in the supraoptic and paraventricular nuclei. The rostral pathway to these nuclei appears to be the bundle of Schutz (cf. ADH)—a rostral diencephalic extension of the dorsal longitudinal fasciculus.

The efficacy of oxytocin in parturition has led to its use and misuse in obstetrics (v.i.). The role of oxytocin in the physiologic phenomenon of birth, however, is not well defined. Most investigators agree that oxytocin has some role in parturition. Whether this role is the initiation of labor or the augmentation and maintenance of labor is the present question. Fuchs (105) measured oxytocin by an indirect method in the rabbit and concluded that oxytocin is responsible for the initiation of labor. In other studies in which plasma oxytocin levels have been measured at parturition (106–111), oxytocin levels have been found to be low prior to labor and in the first stage of labor and to rise rapidly to high levels in the second stage of labor. Following expulsion of the fetus, the oxytocin level falls rapidly to levels prior to parturition. These reports suggest that labor is initiated by another mechanism and dilatation of the birth canal results in reflex release of oxytocin which assists in delivery. Fitzpatrick & Walmsley (108) have provided further evidence for the reflex nature of this mechanism by demonstrating that spinal block in the cow results in arrest of the progress of labor and a fall in plasma oxytocin.

On the other hand, it has been reported that in women cervical dilatation does not result in oxytocin release (112), and that normal birth may occur after destruction of the neurohypophysis. A change in the ratio of progesterone to estrogen is another possible mechanism for initiation of labor. Under the influence of estrogen, the uterus has spontaneous activity and is responsive to oxytocin whereas under the influence of progesterone, the organ shows little spontaneous activity and is refractory to oxytocin (113). In the rat and rabbit, administration of progesterone prolongs labor, while removal of the corpus luteum results in abortion (114, 115). The plasma concentration of progesterone in the rabbit has been reported to fall before delivery (116); this may not be true of other species (117).

Cross & Silver (118) report that the response of hypothalamic neurons to genital stimulation is depressed by progesterone, a possible explanation of failure of cervical dilation to stimulate oxytocin release in pregnant women.

If progesterone inhibits the reflex release of oxytocin at the hypothalamic level, and the response of the uterus to the effects of the hormone, a change in the progesterone to estrogen ratio in the blood might indeed cause an augmentation in uterine contractility; sequential blood determinations of oxytocin, progesterone, and estrogens before and during parturition might resolve the question.

Several authors have reported increased posterior hypophyseal content of oxytocin in response to stress. This has been interpreted as indicating increased release of oxytocin. The concept may be in error; indeed, pain and emotional stimuli may inhibit oxytocin release (119). Taleisnik & Deis (119), using weight gain in a litter as an indication of oxytocin release, found fracture of a femur or craniotomy of the mother to result in marked decrease of weight gain. More direct evidence on the point would be desirable.

Stimulation of scattered points in the limbic system has been reported to be associated with milk-ejection responses. It is unlikely that these areas are directly associated with reflex secretion of oxytocin, but rather they may be associated with mechanisms facilitating or depressing these reflexes: emotions, pain, or conditioned responses.

The biosynthesis and release of oxytocin is believed to be analogous to that for vasopressin. Plasma levels of oxytocin in normal man are below the sensitivity limit of bioassay methods currently employed. During pregnancy in women, levels of 50 μU/ml have been reported, and levels higher than 150 μU/ml have been reported during the second stage of labor (109, 110). By use of tritium-labeled oxytocin, a volume of distribution of 40 per cent body water has been observed (120). In pregnant women, a half-life appears to be 2.7 minutes. Oxytocin appears to be cleared from the circulation mainly via the kidney, liver, and lactating mammary gland; the liver removes the hormone to a lesser extent than the kidneys (24). By the use of tritium-labeled oxytocin, urinary excretion of unchanged peptide and two metabolites has been detected (120). Preferential uptake of oxytocin by the mammary glands has been demonstrated (24). Oxytocin is inactivated by a plasma oxytocinase enzyme in pregnant women. The enzyme is found in very low concentrations in nonpregnant women, but is reported to rise to high values with pregnancy. The enzyme has not been found in pregnant rats, dogs, rabbits, or rhesus monkeys. The degree of inactivation of oxytocin by oxytocinase is probably small and it is thought that this enzyme has little physiologic significance.

ACTIONS OF THE NEUROHYPOPHYSEAL HORMONES

A classification of neuroendocrine mechanisms as first, second, and third-order based on the number of endocrine organs interposed between the central nervous system and the target tissues was suggested a few years ago; the classification is still useful and will be employed here in considering the recent experimental findings relating to the neurohypophyseal hormones.

First-order neuroendocrine actions.—A first-order neuroendocrine mechanism is the simplest of neuroendocrine relationships in which a neuron whose cell body is in the central nervous system secretes a substance which is carried in the blood stream to act directly on target cells. Oxytocin and vasopressin have been considered the classical examples (121). The most obvious and best-documented target tissues are, of course, the renal tubules, the cardiovascular system, and uterine tissue; hence the names of the hormones. Actions on the breast are well known; more recently effects on other tissues have been observed. All are first-order actions and few new contributions on the subject have appeared in the literature in the past few years.

On renal tissues, vasopressin and oxytocin seem to have essentially the same types of effects, differing only in the relative dose required. Both hormones lead to an increase in the production of cyclic 3',5'-AMP by epithelial cells which induces permeability changes in the distal nephron; as a consequence, osmotic flow of water occurs into the surrounding renal interstitium (122).

The formation of cyclic 3',5'-AMP is not a necessary accompaniment of all posterior pituitary hormone actions; inhibition of lipogenesis by vasopressin in vitro is not mediated by cyclic AMP according to Horowitz, Beck & Rubinstein (123).

Antidiuresis is not a necessary accompaniment of the administration of neurohypophyseal hormones, at least in some species. In what appears to be a carefully done study, Kramar, Grinnel & Duff have shown that arginine vasopressin at a dose of 1 mμ unit by single injection (0.1 mμ U/minute by infusion) causes modest but definite diuresis in the hydrated alcohol-treated rat. At 5 mμ U the anticipated water retention occurred (124). Sodium excretion was uniformly enhanced along with the diuresis when induced by infusion: the results after single injection were less consistent. Following brief initial antidiuretic action, oxytocin may induce a prolonged diuresis; the net water loss exceeds the retention occurring during the antidiuretic phase (125).

Both vasopressin and oxytocin in dogs and rats increase excretion of sodium, but oxytocin is more active (124). In the hydropenic sheep elaborating concentrated urine, it induces natriuresis associated with increases in filtration rate and tubular sodium rejection (126). One wonders why the filtration rate increases; a possible explanation is that additional nephronal elements became functionally active. The rejection of the increased sodium load presumably reflects a direct effect of the peptide on the tubule (126).

One is reminded of the effects of angiotensin, which also elicits natriuresis unexplained by increased filtration rate per se.

In the study by Lees & Lockett (127) diuresis, natriuresis, and kaluresis were sometimes observed in the rat after oxytocin, in the absence of a change in inulin clearance, which indicates that electrolyte loss is not necessarily a matter of increased filtration rate. Interestingly enough, the diuretic and natriuretic effects of oxytocin are abolished in adrenalectomized animals and hypophysectomized animals and restored by the administration of DCA or of cortisone and salt. It would appear that, when the animal is retaining sodium in a reasonably normal fashion, oxytocin will cause natriuresis; if the animal is spilling sodium as in the adrenalectomized state, no effect is seen.

Vasopressin, though it increases overall peripheral resistance and in general causes a rise in systemic arterial blood pressure, has been reported to bring about increased renal blood flow at dose levels insufficient to cause a rise in systemic pressure (128). It would appear that the increased renal blood flow is the result of a selective action on the renal vasculature.

In man, vasopressin (either arginine or lysine) over a wide range of dosage, though inducing consistent reduction in free-water clearance, has no meaningful effect on sodium excretion (129, 130).

The role of the neurohypophyseal hormones in cardiovascular phenomena continues to intrigue physiologists. An unusually interesting report has appeared from the University of Toronto (131). These workers found that the removal of the posterior part of the pituitary gland in the rat leads to an elevation in arterial pressure. Complete hypophysectomy has, of course, no such effect; the arterial pressure usually falls. The observation stands as one of potentially great importance, though the *modus operandi* is not at all apparent. Most of the work on the subject of peptides in hypertension would implicate an excess rather than a deficiency.

In a piece of work distinguished by care in experimental design and analysis of hemodynamic variables, Hinke (132) has shown that the vascular hyperresponsiveness to norepinephrine in DCA hypertension is also seen with vasopressin. Hyperresponsiveness is not seen with angiotensin. Gardner & Honore (133) have essentially the same finding in adrenal-regeneration hypertensive rats. Increased sensitivity to vasopressin was found in both male and female rats two weeks after the hypertension was initiated; the increase persisted only in the males. There was no correlation between the arterial pressure at the time of the injection and the reactivity of the animals to vasopressin. The animals also did not demonstrate an increased sensitivity to angiotensin.

Phelan (134) reports that renal hypertensive rats also are hyperreactive to vasopressin, though not to angiotensin. He believes that the higher initial arterial pressure values were associated with smaller pressor responses to the injection of the pressor agents.

The combined effects of pressor agents may be meaningful (135). Pressor responses to the catecholamines are potentiated by the prior administration of nonpressor doses of vasopressin.

It has been demonstrated many times that there is an increased tendency to atherosclerosis in animals subjected to repeated bouts of vasoconstriction induced by catecholamines (136). In the rabbit high cholesterol diets by themselves usually do not result in calcification. However, if the diet is combined with the long-term injection of vasopressin in oil, atherosclerotic lesions are induced which according to Cooper & Gutstein are remarkably close to those seen in man (137). The authors would like to implicate the peptide in human atherosclerosis. Chronic hypothalamic stimulation has also been reported to accelerate the production of atherosclerosis in the cholesterol-fed rabbit (138–140).

Nakano & Fisher (141) studied the effects of synthetic oxytocin on the heart and peripheral vessels in the dog. These investigators also examined the action of oxytocin on myocardial contractility, using the guinea pig atrium and the dog papillary muscle. In their studies oxytocin was found to decrease the mean arterial pressure, the left atrial pressure, and the total peripheral resistance, reactions causing a modest increase in heart rate and in myocardial contractility. The net effect is an increase in cardiac output in the beginning, followed by gradual decrease to levels below controls. In their hands no difference was found in the hemodynamic effects of oxytocin in male dogs, estrous females, or pregnant dogs near term, although the magnitude of the changes was somewhat less in the estrous female and pregnant dog than in the male. Injected interarterially, the peptide resulted in increases in blood flows in the coronary, carotid, brachial, femoral, and superior mesenteric arteries. The absence of change in heart rate, mean arterial pressure, left atrial pressure, or myocardial contractility indicates that the cardiovascular effects following the administration of oxytocin are most likely due to the direct vasodilator action.

In a carefully done series of experiments over the past several years, Lloyd and his collaborators have evaluated the peripheral vascular actions of oxytocin. Oxytocin dilates a number of vascular beds and the effect is lost (actually converted to a constrictor one) after ganglionic blockade, surgical sympathectomy of the part, or administration of reserpine (142–145). In a more recent piece of work (142) these workers report that in the sympathectomized hindlimb the normal dilator response to oxytocin is restored if the peptide is administered either during a period of stimulation of the peripheral end of the divided lumbar chain or during an infusion of the epinephrine. Infusions of norepinephrine did not restore the normal response to oxytocin. It is suggested that the fraction of epinephrine released by sympathetic nerves is of functional significance and is essential for the dilator effect of oxytocin. A sidelight is the observation that the estrogens apparently interfere with the synthesis of epinephrine or its release from the sympathetic nerves (142). Thus, in the animal injected with substantial doses of estrogen, or undergoing spontaneous estrus, oxytocin ceases to be a dilator and becomes a constrictor (142). Progesterone has an action similar to that of estrogen, in that it induces the appearance of a pressor response to oxytocin; throughout pseudopregnancy, oxytocin is a pressor substance (146). These actions on vascular smooth muscle differ from those on the uterus. At least in some species, progesterone prevents coordinated mass contraction to oxytocin, while estrogens seem to have the opposite effect (147).

Synthetic oxytocin injected intravenously during caesarian section causes an immediate transient increase in cardiac output, associated with a drop in peripheral resistance and a fall in arterial pressure. It would appear that the primary effect is on the peripheral vasculature to induce vaso-dilation. A few minutes later the peripheral resistance and arterial pressure increase and the heart rate and cardiac output fall; these are to be antici-pated as compensatory responses to the initial phenomenon. The effect does not appear to be mediated via uterine contraction; the authors state that the same pattern is seen following clamping of the uterine arteries (148). This report confirms an earlier work by Kitchin, Lloyd & Pickford (149).

Oxytocin reduces the arterial pressure in the rhesus monkey whilst va-sopressin increases it in this as in other mammalian species (150).

Interest in the antiarrhythmic properties of oxytocin continues. The hormone acts as an antagonist of experimental cardiac anoxic changes in rabbits; in sufficient doses, it prevents the ECG changes due to hypoxia and terminates the ventricular fibrillation produced by picrotoxin (151). It pro-tects against fibrillation induced by chloroform and epinephrine but not against that induced by ouabain (152). Mortari & Sioli (153) have confirmed the observation that oxytocin antagonizes the influence of epi-nephrine in inducing cardiac arrhythmias in the isolated rabbit and rat heart.

Oxytocin also has been reported to reduce the incidence of ventricular fibrillation in hypothermic dogs (154). Much of the information on the sub-ject is summarized in an excellent little paper by Beaulnes and his co-workers (155). They made the intriguing observation that the lengthening of the refractory period observed after injections of the polypeptide prep-aration was due not to the polypeptide but rather to the vehicle, chlorobuta-nol; nevertheless, the antiarrhythmic phenomenon could be obtained in the absence of chlorobutanol. Somlyo et al. (156) claim that the dilator effect of an oxytocin preparation is in fact due to the presence of chlorobutanol. The dilator effects of chlorobutanol had previously been reported by Katz (157). Somlyo and his co-workers added the further observation that some of the variability in previous reports concerning the effects of the polypep-tides on isolated smooth muscle strips may have been due to variations in the amount of magnesium in the *in vitro* preparation. According to these workers, both oxytocin and vasopressin act to contract arterial vascular smooth muscle of man, rabbit, and dog and this effect is prevented if mag-nesium is lacking from the medium (156). The subject needs clarification.

The effects of synthetic oxytocin on cardiac arrhythmias in man have been examined by Katz (157, 158) who was interested in the possibility of using the peptide in the correction of arrhythmias occurring spontaneously on the operating table. He found oxytocin temporarily effective in re-versing the arrhythmias developing after a variety of operative manipula-tions but was disappointed because of the brief duration of action and the development of tachyphylaxis.

There is continued interest in the classic observation that the neurohyp-ophyseal hormones cause the uterus to contract. The effect is enhanced by the pretreatment of the animal with estrogens (159–161). Progesterone, contrariwise, reduces uterine responsiveness to oxytocin (113). The possible participation of magnesium in the estrogen potentiation of oxytocin has come under study (140, 160). In general, magnesium potentiates the uterine-contracting effects of the less active peptides: arginine vasopressin and arginine vasotocin are significantly more active *in vitro* on uteri from diethylstilbestrol-treated animals in the presence of magnesium; so, too, are some synthetic analogues of oxytocin. However, an effect of the ion is not seen with oxytocin itself; indeed, the activities of oxytocin and deamino-oxytocin *in vitro* may be reduced by the presence of the ion, in the diethylstilbestrol-treated animals. It would appear that the effects of the estrogen on the uterine response to oxytocin are not mediated by way of changes in the magnesium in the cellular environment. Estrogens may alter the ability of the myometrial membrane and myoplasma to capture and release calcium ions though evidence on this point cannot be considered to be complete.

The dilemma as to how sperm can be found in the ampulla of the fallopian tubes within a few minutes after coitus, when their natural velocity of movement is such that it should take at least thirty minutes before they can swim that high (at least in the bovine species), has apparently been cleared up (162). It appears that oxytocin is released during coitus and that it causes the tubes to contract and carry the sperm up into the ampullae.

Researchers in dairy husbandry have been intrigued for some time by the observation that a cow may be brought into heat quickly by the injection of oxytocin (in rather substantial dosages) (163, 164). It seems that oxytocin inhibits the secretion of progesterone by the corpus luteum; the reduced progesterone secretion unleashes the secretion of LH and FSH. The uterus must be present for the effect (165). Uterine stimulating (by balloons placed in the lumen) during the early part of the estrous cycle induces early involution of the corpus luteum of heifers. It is presumed, therefore, that oxytocin has its effects here by uterine stimulation, though the mechanism is still unclear (166).

The well-known laboratory phenomenon of milk ejection by oxytocin and vasopressin has not been observed in lactating women, as determined by the use of a cleverly designed microbougie which permits catheterization of the milk duct (167).

Nursing is generally unsatisfactory under stress because of the failure of "milk-letdown". Those who have had the good fortune of growing up on the farm recall that this applies to cows as well as women. In part, the phenomenon is due to the inhibition of oxytocin release. In addition, stress-released catecholamines directly inhibit the action of oxytocin on the myoepithelial cells of the breast (168).

It was supposed by some (169) that the effect resulted from the contraction of the vasculature to the organ preventing oxytocin from reaching the cells. However, Chan (170), using isolated mammary strips, has found that the catecholamines inhibit the action of oxytocin at the level of the myoepithelial cell itself. The inhibitory action is associated with the catechol nucleus per se since other sympathomimetic amines, i.e. ephedrine and amphetamines, lack the property.

The milk-ejection assay of oxytocin in the rabbit is complicated by the fact that vasopressin interferes with oxytocin even when present in a ratio as low as 1:4 (169). Vasopressin by itself has milk-ejecting activity, of course. This appears to be an instance of competitive inhibition, which has been a perennial headache to those in hormone bioassay.

There are other things that the peptides do, presumably as first-order neuroendocrine actions. Whether these are physiological or pharmacological has not been settled.

Vasopressin is claimed to have a direct action on the submaxillary salivary gland (171). A prompt increase in the glycogen content of the gland follows injection of lysine vasopressin, followed by depletion an hour later. At three hours the glycogen content returns to normal. The glandular content at PAS-positive material is reduced ten minutes after injection.

Vasopressin decreases gastric secretion (172) in dogs with gastric pouches. The action presumably reflects a direct decrease of mucosal capillary and arterial flow (173).

It would seem that oxytocin (in large doses) consistently induces hyperglycemia (174, 175). The glucose utilization rate as measured by the disappearance rate of an intravenous load is increased by oxytocin; an action of oxytocin to liberate insulin is invoked (176, 177). The simplest interpretation is that insulin release occurs secondary to the hyperglycemia (discounted by Balasse and co-workers) but remaining is the question (178): "Why the hyperglycemia in the first place?"

According to Vaughan (179) vasopressin increases the hydrolysis of fat tissue with the release of free fatty acids and glycerol in vitro. In the intact animal, this ought to result in an increase in free fatty acids in the plasma. However, according to Goldman (180) quite the opposite occurs in man; the plasma free fatty acids fall.

Rudman (181, 182) comments that the endocrine stimuli responsible for the release of fatty acids from adipose tissue differ from one species to another; release of free fatty acids in a given environmental situation probably represents a part of the stress response, but different animals use different hormones to accomplish it.

A potentially important observation has recently been made by deWied & Bohus (183) concerning long- and short-term effects on retention of a conditioned avoidance response in rats by treatment with long-acting vasopressin and α-MSH. Rats were trained in a conditioned avoidance response situation; the condition stimulus was a buzzer, the unconditioned stimulus, a shock administered via the cage floor. The rats learned to avoid the electric shock when the buzzer sounded by jumping to the other half of the two-compartment cage. After a period of training, extinction was evaluated by presenting the buzzer without shock; extinction was measured by the number of trials subsequently necessary for the animal to learn that he did not have to jump when the buzzer sounded. Animals given a placebo or α-MSH had lost the conditioned response within two weeks; but if vasopressin tannate had been injected during the learning period, the animals continued to respond to the buzzer by leaping the barrier for as long as tested, over a month. The findings indicate that vasopressin can influence formation and retention of memory. It is apparent that the effect is not specific for vasopressin; ACTH has a similar action as Miller and his collaborators (184, 185) previously noted. α-MSH injected during the period of testing for extinction prevented the extinction as well as vasopressin. Nonetheless, there seems little doubt that the peptides influence the learning process.

Second-order neuroendocrine actions.—If a posterior pituitary hormone acts to stimulate an endocrine tissue to release its hormones which in turn act on somatic cells, then it participates as the first component of a second-order neuroendocrine mechanism (121, 186). Possibly the first suggestion that vasopressin might participate in such a second-order mechanism was that by Hilton and his co-workers. In the dog adrenal perfused by an isolated organ technique, the introduction of synthetic arginine vasopressin results in a significant increase in hydrocortisone output (187). The finding was confirmed by other investigators (188–191).

Telegdy & Fendler (192) claimed that both oxytocin and vasopressin increase adrenal progesterone and corticosteroid secretion; the "increase" amounted to a maintenance of initial secretory levels of the steroids which in their hands tended to fall progressively during the experiment. [The reviewers are surprised at this phenomenon, never having seen it; contrarily, bleeding usually causes an increase in the output of adrenal steroids (193).] Telegdy & Fendler's experiments differed from Hilton's in that the polypeptides were injected intravenously into the intact animal rather than an adrenal pouch. Nevertheless, it seems reasonably clear that if one gives enough vasopressin, at least in the dog, there is an increased output of adrenocortical steroids. This phenomenon appears to be, at least in part, direct action of the peptide on the adrenal. A similar corticotropin-like action has been reported for angiotensin (194).

Hilton injected oxytocin into the circulation in the adrenal pouch preparation in hypophysectomized dogs and observed no increase in hydrocortisone output in response to this polypeptide (195). Kovach, Monos & Koltay (196) gave oxytocin intravenously and also observed no effect on steroidogenesis even in large doses, though an increase in adrenal blood flow was noted.

In the rat vasopressin has no effect on steroidogenesis either *in vivo* or *in vitro* (197).

In those species where the polypeptides have been shown to act on the adrenals, the question whether they have a physiologic role as ACTH-like agents remains moot. Certainly, available information on circulating blood levels, by reliable technics, indicates that such is not the case, since the concentrations of vasopressin or oxytocin required to stimulate the adrenal are probably seldom achieved under ordinary circumstances. On the other hand, the surge of vasopressin release seen during hemorrhage (66, 67) might bring the plasma levels to the adrenal-stimulating threshold. ACTH secretion would also be markedly increased at the same time, and one wonders if the additional increment of adrenal stimulation owing to the posterior pituitary hormones would be important. During hemorrhage, as Henry once said, "the red lights all go on" and the organism marshals all of its defenses, not necessarily in a logical or systematic way.

Third-order neuroendocrine actions.—The possibility that the posterior pituitary factors might serve as releasing substances for anterior pituitary hormones was apparently first suggested by McCann & Brobeck (198) some years ago. They claim that antidiuretic hormone could serve as a corticotropin-releasing factor (CRF). If true, this would implicate vasopressin in a third-order neuroendocrine mechanism, one in which a neuroendocrine factor stimulates an endocrine tissue to release its hormone(s), which acts on still another endocrine tissue which releases the hormones which act on somatic cells (121, 199). Third-order neuroendocrine mechanisms permit fine gradations of control as well as amplification of signal: a typical example is the release of CRF by the hypothalamus to act on the anterior pituitary to release ACTH, which in turn, of course, stimulates the adrenals to secrete the corticoids to bring about the action on peripheral tissues for which the original signal was initiated. The concept that vasopressin is CRF was debated for a number of years, with the balance of opinion now firmly against it (200–210).

Antidiuresis and increased ACTH release are seen concurrently in stress; recent evidence indicates the simultaneous release of CRF and ADH rather than implying that ADH per se is CRF (211). The last author, regrettably, has succumbed to the temptation to rename CRF (ACTH-RH). The needless complication of endocrinology by giving one substance several names is to be deplored.

In man, as in other species, the injection of vasopressin can lead to increased levels of circulating corticoids; the effect can be blocked by the prior administration of steroid (212, 213).

The controversy—and it was, at times, not without vituperation—has clearly been resolved in favor of Guillemin's point of view that "natural" CRF is a separate factor, though the chemical structure is still undetermined. As if in re-enactment of this saga in neuroendocrinology, reports have appeared from time to time that either vasopressin, oxytocin, or both could stimulate the release of other anterior pituitary hormones.

Prolactin, growth hormone, and TSH are currently under discussion. Prolactin is a special case in point, and the question—what maintains the secretion of this hormone during lactation—has never been adequately answered. That both oxytocin and prolactin are involved in milk production might suggest an interrelationship, and a not inconsiderable amount of work has supported this view. Injection of oxytocin prevents the involution of mammary gland tissue after removal of the litters, which indicates that oxytocin acts via the adenohypophysis to maintain the secretion of prolactin (214, 215). The notion is attractive; suckling is a known stimulus to oxytocin release, and if oxytocin stimulated prolactin secretion to support milk synthesis, a gratifying lucid neuroendocrine interplay is indicated. There was support for the idea (216, 217).

However, in connection with any discussion of prolactin-secretion regulation, it should be recalled that prolactin release is apparently controlled by an inhibitor mechanism. Specifically, certain hypothalamic lesions result in initiation of lactation, which suggests that an inhibitor of prolactin secretion is abolished (218). If oxytocin stimulated prolactin secretion, it could do so either by direct action on the adenohypophysis to release prolactin or by inhibition of the hypothalamic inhibitor.

In time, it became apparent that there was to be no general agreement whether oxytocin was mainly responsible for prolactin secretion by either mechanism (219–222).

In the work of Ota, Shinde & Yokoyama (223), prolactin injection suppressed the recurrence of vaginal estrous and increase in ovarian weight after removal of litters, an effect presumably reflecting the inhibition of the pituitary secretion of FSH and LH alias ICSH. Though oxytocin maintained lactation after removal of the litter in this work, it did not prevent the recurrence of vaginal estrous and increase in ovarian weight; the authors concluded that the effect of oxytocin was not mediated through increased secretion of prolactin.

Gala & Reece (224) review the evidence that oxytocin may act on the anterior pituitary to increase the secretion of prolactin. Using an *in vitro* preparation of anterior pituitary, they found that neither oxytocin nor vasopressin stimulated the release of prolactin, at least in amounts of the polypeptides which were considered physiological (224).

A good review of the subject is to be found in a chapter by Meites, Nicoll & Talwalker (219) to which the reader is referred. The upshot of the matter seems to be that nothing as simple as the suckling-oxytocin-prolactin scheme can explain the control of LTH secretion, though the participation of the reflex cannot be entirely disregarded.

It has also been claimed that oxytocin stimulates TSH secretion (225). Garcia, Harris & Schindler (226) reported that vasopressin (either natural or synthetic) induces an increase in plasma PBI[131] in the rabbit pretreated with I[131] thyroxine. According to Arimura, Koseki & Itoh (227), the phenomenon has been reproduced in their laboratories. Kovacs, Vertes & Imhof (228) reported that synthetic oxytocin stimulates thyroid I[131] uptake and I[131] content of the plasma. In this work, anterior hypothalamic lesions decreased I[131] uptake by the thyroid and plasma I[131] levels; if the animals were treated with synthetic oxytocin this did not occur. The same group

(229) found that hypothalamic and posterior pituitary extracts as well as synthetic oxytocin increased TSH release from anterior pituitary slices *in vitro*.

LaBella (230) also reported that both oxytocin and synthetic lysine-vasopressin stimulate the release of TSH from slices of bovine anterior pituitary gland. These workers noted that the release phenomenon did not occur at high concentrations of the peptides. LaBella also claims that I^{131} discharge from the thyroids of propylthiouracil-treated chicks could be brought about by the intraperitoneal injection of minute amounts of either vasopressin or oxytocin. At higher dose levels there was less enhancement of the I^{131} discharge, and with further increases, inhibition.

Horster (231) reports that the activity of the exopthalmic factor of the pituitary can be duplicated by vasopressin or oxytocin or a combination of the two.

Finally, Schreiber and his collaborators (232) claim to have isolated a peptide fraction with TRF activity which is different from either vasopressin or oxytocin. The cycle seen with the CRF story may be occurring with TRF.

Reports have appeared that vasopressin increases the secretion of growth hormone (233, 234). At least two groups of workers disagree. Bernardis & Skelton (235) investigated the effects of vasopressin on several parameters of growth in rats with lesions in the supraoptic nuclei. There was no evidence for altered growth hormone secretion in these preparations. Muller, Pecile & Smirne (236) observed that an acid extract of median eminence tissue injected into the carotid artery led to a reduction in pituitary content of growth hormone, presumably reflecting release of the hormone. In the same experimental animal, vasopressin and oxytocin were inactive, which convinced Muller and his co-workers that neither was the factor responsible for the apparent release of growth hormone.

SOME ABNORMALITIES OF NEUROHYPOPHYSEAL FUNCTION IN MAN

The syndrome of inappropriate secretion of antidiuretic hormone has attracted considerable interest since first described in 1957 by Schwartz et al. (237). In addition to the original reports associating inappropriate ADH secretion with bronchogenic carcinoma, this syndrome has been related to other pulmonary abnormalities (pneumonia, tuberculosis, and cavitation), other malignant tumors (carcinoma of the duodenum, pancreas, and thyroid), and a variety of central nervous system disorders (brain abscess, meningitis, head injuries, brain tumors, encephalitis, and subarachnoid hemorrhage). The syndrome was recently reviewed extensively by Bartter & Schwartz (238).

Inappropriate secretion of antidiuretic hormone may be diagnosed from its clinical manifestations: hyponatremia and serum hypotonicity, paradoxical renal salt excretion with urinary hypertonicity, normal or increased extracellular volume, normal adrenal and renal function, poor response of hyponatremia to hypertonic saline, and improvement of salt and water imbalance with restriction of fluid intake (238–242).

The classical clinical and laboratory findings are not always present. The syndrome may be asymptomatic as long as the serum sodium remains above 120 meq/liter. Bernard-Weil et al. (243) have described certain cases in which hyponatremia was not observed. Vague symptoms such as loss of appetite, nausea and vomiting, progressive irritability, personality changes, and confusion precede the cardinal signs of water intoxication, continuous fall in serum sodium, muscular weakness, stupor, or convulsions. The clinical picture of water intoxication can be reliably produced by administering vasopressin tannate and by water loading normal volunteers (244), which supports the concept that increased ADH secretion can account for the syndrome. Direct evidence comes from finding increased plasma ADH levels in cases in which this parameter was measured.

As the extracellular fluid volume (ECF) increases, it is expected that the known regulatory mechanisms will compensate for the hyponatremia. In this circumstance, however, aldosterone-controlling mechanisms operate in opposition. An increase in ECF volume successfully inhibits the secretion of aldosterone to effect decreased renal resorption of sodium and contributing to hyponatremia. Several factors may be involved in the hyponatremia: dilution per se, decreased aldosterone secretory rate in response to increased ECF (241), decreased proximal tubule resorption in response to expansion of the ECF (238), increased glomerular filtration rate with increased filtered load of sodium (242), reduction in medullary hypertonicity resulting from a decrease in resorption of sodium in the loop of Henle (243), and reduction in the permeability of the distal portion of the nephron from prolonged hypotonicity of the body fluids to the end that osmotic equilibrium is not established between luminal fluid and interstitium. The last two factors need further study. Decreased proximal tubule resorption and increased glomerular filtration rate appear to be the most important factor in the production of hyponatremia.

The involvement of the syndrome of inappropriate ADH secretion in a number of disease states raises the question as to the manner in which ADH secretory levels are raised. Several mechanisms might be acting: mechanical stimulation of the hypothalamic nuclei by expanding lesions in the central nervous system, stimulation of volume receptors in the mediastinum whose signal is transmitted via the vagi, change in the responsiveness of the osmoreceptors, production of a substance capable of stimulating the hypothalamus, or finally, production of a polypeptide similar to ADH by tumor cells (242). Of these, only the last has been well established. Oat cell carcinoma of the lung produces a substance very similar to ADH in chemical and biological properties (245). The mechanism by which other disease states produce this syndrome awaits further investigation.

During acute surgical procedures, the pituitary gland may secrete increased amounts of vasopressin (246, 247) as a homeostatic defense mechanism; the magnitude and duration of the response, as anticipated, are in proportion to the severity of the surgery.

Synthetic Analogue

The synthetic analogue, phenylalanine-lysine-vasopressin (PLV-2, "octapressin"), has received considerable attention in the hope of finding clinical usefulness. This agent increases the survival rate of rats in hemorrhagic shock (248) and maintains arteriolar and venular tone in the rat mesoappendix (249).

Cerletti and co-workers (250) studied the actions of PLV-2 and angiotensin on the terminal vascular bed. They report that the synthetic analogue of vasopressin induces sustained constriction of venous vessels with only moderate activity on the arterial side, in contrast to the action of angiotensin and the catecholamines. The claim is made that PLV-2 exhibits microvascular effects which are out of the normal profile of reactivity of the microvessels to usual physiological stimuli; i.e. that the gradient of reactivity for PLV-2 progresses from the venular toward the arteriolar side. A report that a rise in arterial pressure and cardiac output can be induced (in dogs in shock) with increased peripheral resistance suggests that constriction on the venous side was the significant response to the agent (251). The experimental design in this work leaves something to be desired: during the early phases of experimental hemorrhagic shock the sympathetic system is operating to near full capacity, and arteriolar vasoconstriction was probably near maximum prior to administration of the pressor agent. Further, Zweifach and co-workers have data indicating that PLV-2 can induce either potentiation or inhibition of catecholamine action on vascular smooth muscle, depending on the level of vessel reactivity at the time (252).

Thus far, clinical trials of PLV-2 during surgery under general anesthesia suggest a degree of usefulness (253–255). There have been no serious sequelae, only minor bradycardia, nodal rhythm, and hypertension.

LITERATURE CITED

1. Kleeman, C. R., Cutler, R. E. The neurohypophysis. *Ann. Rev. Physiol.*, **25**, 385–432 (1963)
2. Sawyer, W. H. Evolution of neurohypophysial principles. *Arch. Anat. Microscop. Morphol. Exptl.*, **54**, 295–312 (1965)
3. Ferguson, D. R., Heller, H. Distribution of neurohypophysial hormones in mammals. *J. Physiol. (London)*, **180**, 846–63 (1965)
4. Christ, J. F. Nerve supply, blood supply, and cytology of the neurohypophysis. In *The Pituitary Gland*, **3**, 62–130 (Harris, G. W., Donovan, B. T. Eds., Univ. of California Press, Berkeley, 1966)
5. Rothballer, A. B. Changes in the rat neurohypophysis induced with powerful stimuli with particular reference to neurosecretory material. *Anat. Record*, **115**, 21–41 (1953)
6. Leveque, T. F., Scharrer, E. Pituicytes and the origin of the antidiuretic hormone. *Endocrinology*, **65**, 909–19 (1953)
7. Moses, A. M., Leveque, T. F., Giambatista, M., Lloyd, C. W. Disassociation between the content of vasopressin and neurosecretory material in the rat neurohypophysis. *J. Endocrinol.*, **26**, 273–78 (1963)
8. Palay, S. L. An electron microscopic study of the neurohypophysis in normal, hydrated, and dehydrated rats. *Anat. Record*, **121**, 348 (1955)
9. Hartmann, J. F. Electron microscopy of the neurohypophysis in normal and histamine treated rats. *Z. Zellforsh. Mikroskop. Anat.*, **48**, 291–98 (1958)
10. Bodian, D. Cytological aspects of neurosecretion in opposum neurohypophysis. *Bull. Johns Hopkins Hosp.*, **113**, 57–93 (1963)
11. Daniel, A. R., Lederis, K. Effects of ether anesthesia and haemorrhage on hormone storage and ultrastructure of the rat neurohypophysis. *J. Endocrinol.*, **34**, 91–104 (1966)
12. Moses, A. M. Adrenal-neurohypophysial relationships in the dehydrated rat. *Endocrinology*, **73**, 230–36 (1963)
13. Fendler, K. The effect of endocrine factors on the oxytocic activity of the pituitary. *Acta Physiol. Acad. Sci. Hung.*, **20**, 89–92 (1961)
14. Fendler, K., Endröczi, E., Lissak, K. The effect of cervical sympathectomy on posterior pituitary oxytocic activity in rats under chronic stress. *Acta Physiol. Acad. Sci. Hung.*, **27**, 275–78 (1965)
15. Sawyer, W. H., Mills, E. Control of vasopressin secretion. In *Neuroendocrinology*, **1**, 187–211 (Martini, L., Ganong, W. F., Eds., Academic Press, New York, 1966)
16. Takabatake, Y., Sachs, H. Vasopressin biosynthesis. III. *In vitro* studies. *Endocrinology*, **75**, 934–42 (1964)
17. Czaczkes, J. W., Kleeman, C. R. The effect of various states of hydration and the plasma concentration on the turnover of antidiuretic hormone in mammals. *J. Clin. Invest.*, **43**, 1644–58 (1964)
18. Share, L. Vasopressin, its bioassay and physiological control of its release. *Am. J. Med.*, **42**, 701–12 (1967)
19. Sawyer, W. H. Biological assays for neurohypophyseal principles in tissues and in blood. In *The Pituitary Gland* (See Ref. 4), 288–306
20. Weinstein, H., Berne, R. M., Sachs, H. Vasopressin in blood, effect of hemorrhage. *Endocrinology*, **66**, 712–18 (1960)
21. Yoshida, S., Motohashi, K., Ibayashi, H., Okinaka, S. Method for the assay of antidiuretic hormone in plasma with a note on the antidiuretic titer of human plasma. *J. Lab. Clin. Med.*, **62**, 279–85 (1963)
22. Ahmed, A. B. J., George, B. C., Gonzalez-Auvert, C., Dingman, J. F. Increased plasma arginine vasopressin in clinical adrenocortical insufficiency and its inhibition by glucosteroids. *J. Clin. Invest.*, **46**, 111–23 (1967)
23. Jeffers, W. A., Livezey, M. M., Austin, J. H. A method for demonstrating an antidiuretic action of minute amounts of pitressin: statistical analyses of results. *Proc. Soc. Exptl. Biol. Med.*, **50**, 184–88 (1942)
24. Ginsburg, M., Smith, M. W. The fate of oxytocin in male and

female rats. *Brit. J. Pharmacol.*, **14**, 327–33 (1959)

25. Tata, P. S., Gauer, O. H. Vasopressin studies in the rat I. A sensitive bioassay for exogenous vasopressin. *Arch. Ges. Physiol.*, **290**, 279–85 (1966)

26. Czaczkes, J. W., Kleeman, C. R., Koenig, M. Physiologic studies of antidiuretic hormone by its direct measurement in human plasma. *J. Clin. Invest.*, **43**, 1625–40 (1964)

27. James, J. J., Lee, J. The value of the ª pre-operated rat in the bioassay of vasopressin. *J. Endocrinol.*, **33**, 329–30 (1965)

28. Permutt, M. A., Parker, C. W., Utiger, R. D. Immunochemical studies with lysine vasopressin. *Endocrinology*, **78**, 809–19 (1966)

29. Fitzpatrick, R. J. The estimation of small amounts of oxytocin in blood. In *Oxytocin*, 358–77 (Caldeyro-Barcia, R., Heller, H., Eds., Pergamon, London, 1961)

30. Lederis, K. Vasopressin and oxytocin in the mammalian hypothalamus. *Gen. Comp. Endocrinol.*, **1**, 80–9 (1961)

31. Baisset, G. W. The assay of oxytocin and vasopressin in blood and the mechanism of inactivation of these hormones by sodium thioglycollate. In *Oxytocin*, 380–98 (Caldeyro-Barcia, R., Heller, H., Eds., Pergamon, London, 1961)

32. Saameli, K. An indirect method for the estimation of oxytocin blood concentration and half-life in pregnant women near term. *Am. J. Obstet. Gynecol.*, **85**, 186–92 (1963)

33. Coutinho, E. M., Csapo, A. The effect of oxytocics on the "Ca-deficient" uterus. *J. Gen. Physiol.*, **43**, 13–27 (1959)

34. Van Dongen, C. G., Hays, R. L. A sensitive *in vitro* assay for oxytocin. *Endocrinology*, **78**, 1–6 (1966)

35. Chan, W. Y., DuVigneaud, V. Comparison of the pharmacologic properties of oxytocin and its highly potent analogue, deaminooxytocin. *Endocrinology*, **71**, 977–82 (1962)

36. Gilliland, P. F., Prout, T. E. Immunologic studies of octapeptides II. Production and detection of antibodies to oxytocin. *Metabolism*, **14**, 918–23 (1965)

37. Gilliland, P. F., Prout, T. E. Immunologic studies of octapeptides I. Radioiodination of oxytocin. *Ibid.*, 912–17

38. Scharrer, E., Scharrer, B. Hormones produced by neurosecretory cells. *Recent Progr. Hormone Res.*, **10**, 183–240 (1954)

39. Bern, H. A., Knowles, F. G. W. Neurosecretion. In *Neuroendocrinology* (See Ref. 15), 139–86

40. Sloper, J. C. The experimental and cytopathologic investigation of neurosecretion in the hypothalamus and pituitary. *Ann. Rev. Physiol.*, **25**, 131–239 (1963)

41. Green, J. D. Microanatomical aspects of the formation of neurohypophyseal hormones and neurosecretion. In *The Pituitary Gland* (See Ref. 4), 240–68

42. Sachs, H. Biosynthesis and release of vasopressin. *Am. J. Med.*, **42**, 687–700 (1967)

43. Sachs, H. Studies on the intracellular distribution of vasopressin. *J. Neurochem.*, **10**, 289–97 (1963)

44. Sachs, H. Vasopressin biosynthesis II: Incorporation of (^{35}S) cystine into vasopressin and protein associated with cell fractions. *Ibid.*, 299–311

45. Weinstein, H., Malamed, S., Sachs, H. Isolation of vasopressin-containing granules from the neurohypophysis of the dog. *Biochem. Biophys. Acta*, **50**, 386–89 (1961)

46. Barer, R., Heller, H., Lederis, K. The isolation, identification and properties of the hormone granules of the neurohypophysis. *Proc. Royal Soc. B*, **158**, 388–416 (1963)

47. Sachs, H. Neurosecretion in the mammalian hypothalamo-neurohypophyseal complex. In *Protides of the Biological Fluids*, 181 (Peeters, H., Ed., Elsevier, New York, 1966)

48. Sachs, H., Takabatake, Y. Evidence for a precursor in vasopressin biosynthesis. *Endocrinology*, **75**, 943–48 (1964)

49. Porlanova, R., Bissel, E. C., Sachs, H. *In vitro* studies on the formation of vasopressin from a precursor. *Fed. Proc.*, **25**, 795 (1966)

50. Gerschenfeld, H., Trameyzoni, J., DiRoberts, E. Ultrastructure and function in the neurohypophysis of the toad. *Endocrinology*, **66**, 741–62 (1960)

51. Douglas, W., Poissner, A. Stimulus-secretion coupling in a neuro-

secretory organ. The role of calcium in the release of vasopressin from the neurohypophysis. *J. Physiol. (London)*, **172**, 1–18 (1964)

52. Haller, E. W., Sachs, H., Sperelakis, N., Share, L. Release of vasopressin from isolated guinea pig posterior pituitones. *Am. J. Physiol.*, **209**, 79–83 (1965)

53. Ginsburg, M., Ireland, M. The role of neurophysin in the transport and release of neurohypophysial hormones. *J. Endocrinol.*, **35**, 289–98 (1966)

54. Sachs, H., Fawcett, C. P., Haller, E. W. Biosynthesis and release of neurophysin and hormonal peptides. *Proc. 49th Meeting Endocrine Soc., 1967, Bal Harbour, Florida*

55. Brooks, C. McC., Ishikawa, T., Koizumi, K., Lu, H.-H. Activity of neurons in the paraventricular nucleus of the hypothalamus and its control. *J. Physiol. (London)*, **182**, 217–31 (1966)

56. Gaiton, E., Cobo, E., Mizrach, M. Evidence for the differential secretion of oxytocin and vasopressin in man. *J. Clin. Invest.*, **43**, 2310–22 (1964)

57. Heller, H. The hormone content of the vertebrate hypothalamo-neurohypophysial system. *Brit. Med. Bull.*, **22**, 227–31 (1966)

58. Jewell, P. A., Verney, E. B. An experimental attempt to determine the site of the neurohypophyseal osmoreceptors in the dog. *Phil. Trans. Roy. Soc.*, **240**, 197–324 (1957)

59. Heller, H., Ginsburg, M. Secretion, metabolism and fate of the posterior pituitary hormones. In *The Pituitary Gland* (See Ref. 4), 330–73

60. Verney, E. G. The antidiuretic hormone and the factors which determine its release. *Proc. Royal Soc. B*, **135**, 25 (1947)

61. Share, L., Levy, M. N. Cardiovascular receptors and blood titer of antidiuretic hormone. *Am. J. Physiol.*, **203**, 425–28 (1962)

62. Aubry, R. H., Nankin, H. R., Moses, A. M., Streeten, D. H. P. Measurement of the osmotic threshold for vasopressin release in human subjects, and its modification by

cortisol. *J. Clin. Endocrinol. Metab.*, **25**, 1481–92 (1965)

63. Little, J. B., Radford, E. P., Jr., Bioassay for antidiuretic activity in blood of undisturbed rats. *J. Appl. Physiol.*, **19**, 179–86 (1964)

64. Stacy, B. D., Brook, A. H. Antidiuretic hormone activity in sheep after feeding. *Quart. J. Exptl. Physiol.*, **30**, 65–78 (1965)

65. Little, J. B., Radford, E. R., Jr. Circulating antidiuretic hormone in rats: effect of dietary electrolytes and protein. *Am. J. Physiol.*, **207**, 821–25 (1964)

66. Share, L. Acute reduction in extracellular fluid volume and the concentration of antidiuretic hormone in blood. *Endocrinology*, **69**, 925–33 (1961)

67. Share, L. Vascular volume and the blood level of antidiuretic hormone. *Am. J. Physiol.*, **202**, 791–94 (1962)

68. Henry, J. P., Gauer, O. H., Reeves, J. L. Evidence of the atrial location of receptors influencing urine flow. *Circ. Res.*, **4**, 85–90 (1956)

69. Currie, J. C. M., Ullmann, E. Polyuria during experimental modification of breathing. *J. Physiol. (London)*, **155**, 438–55 (1961)

70. Ledsome, J. R., Linden, R. J., O'Connor, W. J. The mechanisms by which distension of the left atrium produces diuresis in anesthetized dogs. *J. Physiol. (London)*, **159**, 87–100 (1961)

71. Lydtin, H., Hamilton, W. F. Effect of acute changes in left atrial pressure on urine flow in unanesthetized dogs. *Am. J. Physiol.*, **707**, 530–6 (1964)

72. Share, L. Effects of carotid occlusion and left atrial distension on plasma vasopressin titer. *Am. J. Physiol.*, **208**(2), 219–23 (1965)

73. Baisset, A., Montastruc, P. Polyurie par distension auriculaire chez le chien; rôle de l'hormone antidiuretique. *J. Physiol. (Paris)*, **49**, 33–36 (1957)

74. Share, L., Levy, M. N. Carotid sinus pulse pressure, a determinant of plasma antidiuretic hormone concentration. *Am. J. Physiol.*, **211**, 721–24 (1966)

75. Share, L., Levy, M. N. Effect of carotid chemoreceptor stimulation on plasma antidiuretic hormone titer. *Ibid.*, **210**, 157–61

76. Gauer, O. H., Henry, J. P. Circula-

tory basis of fluid volume control. *Physiol. Rev.*, **43**, 423–81 (1963)

77. Gupta, P. D., Henry, J. P., Sinclair, R., van Baumgarten, R. Responses of atrial and aortic baroreceptors to nonhypotensive hemorrhage and to transfusion. *Am. J. Physiol.*, **211**, 1429–37 (1966)

78. Mills, E., Wang, S. C. Liberation of antidiuretic hormone: location of ascending pathways. *Am. J. Physiol.*, **207**, 1399–404 (1964)

79. Keele, C. A., Neil, E. *Samson Wright's Applied Physiology*, 10th ed., 196 (Oxford Univ. Press, London, 1961)

80. Yoshida, S., Ibayoshi, H., Murakawa, S., Nakao, K. Cerebral control of secretion of antidiuretic hormone: effect of electrical stimulation of the prepyriform area on the neurohypophysis in the dog. *Endocrinology*, **77**, 597–601 (1965)

81. Mazer, A., Massat, S. Effet renforcateur de l'adrénaline sur l'antidiurèse provaquée por la vasopressine. *J. Physiol. (Paris)*, **56**, 404 (1964)

82. Dearborn, E. H., Lasagna, L. The antidiuretic action of epinephrine and norepinephrine. *J. Pharmacol. Exptl. Therap.*, **106**, 122–28 (1952)

83. Brook, A. H., Share, L. On the question of protein binding and the diffusibility of circulating antidiuretic hormone in the dog. *Endocrinology*, **78**, 779–85 (1966)

84. Lauson, H. D., Bocanegra, M., Beuzeville, C. F. Hepatic and renal clearance of vasopressin from plasma of dogs. *Am. J. Physiol.*, **209**, 199–214 (1965)

85. Benson, G. K., Fitzpatrick, R. J. The neurohypophysis and the mammary gland. In *The Pituitary Gland*, **3**, 414–52 (Harris, G. W., Donovan, B. T., Eds., Univ. of California Press, Berkeley, 1966)

86. Harris, G. W. The central nervous system, neurohypophysis and milk ejection. *Proc. Royal Soc. B*, **149**, 336–53 (1958)

87. Fitzpatrick, R. J. The posterior pituitary gland and the female reproductive tract. In *The Pituitary Gland* (See Ref. 4), 453–504

88. Fitzpatrick, R. J. The neurohypophysis and the male reproductive tract. *Ibid.*, 505–16

89. Hays, R. L., Vandemark, N. L. Effect of stimulation of the reproductive organs of the cow on the release of an oxytocin-like substance. *Endocrinology*, **52**, 634–37 (1953)

90. Cross, B. A. Neural control of lactation. In *Milk: The Mammary Gland and its Secretion*, **1**, 229–327 (Kon, S. K., Ed., Academic Press, New York, 1961)

91. Inglebrecht, P. Influence du systeme nerveux central sur la mamelle lactante chez le rat blanc. *Compt. Rend. Soc. Biol.*, **120**, 1369–71 (1935)

92. Beyer, C., Mena, F., Pacheco, P., Alcoroz, M. Blockage of lactation by brain stem lesions in the cat. *Am. J. Physiol.*, **202**, 465–68 (1962)

93. Mena, F., Beyer, C. Effect of high spinal section on established lactation in the rabbit. *Am. J. Physiol.*, **205**, 313–16 (1963)

94. Fuchs, A. R., Wagner, G. Quantitative aspects of release of oxytocin by suckling in unanesthetized rabbits. *Acta Endocrinol.*, **44**, *Suppl. 83–88*, 581–92 (1963)

95. Denamur, R., Martinet, J. Enervation de la mammelle et lactation chez la brebis et la chèvre. *Compt. Rend. Soc. Biol.*, **148**, 833–36 (1954)

96. Denamur, R., Martinet, J. Les stimulus nerveux mammaires sont-ils nècessaires à l'entretien de la lactation chez la chèvre. *Compt. Rend. Acad. Sci.*, **248**, 743–46 (1959)

97. Linzell, J. L. Some effects of denervating and transplanting mammary glands. *Quart. J. Exptl. Physiol.*, **48**, 34–60 (1963)

98. Folley, S. J., Knaggs, G. S. Milk ejection activity (oxytocin) in the external jugular vein blood of the cow, goat and sow in relation to the stimulus of milking or suckling. *J. Endocrinol.*, **34**, 197–214 (1966)

99. Zaks, M. G. *The Motor Apparatus of the Mammary Gland* (Thomas, Springfield, Ill.; Engl. ed., Fry, D. G., transl.; Cowie, A. T., Ed., Oliver & Boyd, Edinburgh and London, 1962)

100. Ferguson, J. K. W. A study of the motility of the intact uterus at term. *Surg. Gynecol. Obstet.*, **73**, 359–66 (1941)

101. Anderson, L. L., Bowerman, A. M., Melampy, R. M. Neuro-utero-ovarian relationship. In *Advances in Neuroendocrinology*, 345–76 (Nal-

bandov, A. V., Ed., Univ. of Illinois Press, Urbana, Ill., 1963)

102. Anderson, B. Some observations on the neuro-hormonal regulation of milk ejection. *Acta Physiol. Scand.*, **23**, 1–7 (1951)

103. Debackere, M., Peeters, G. The influence of vaginal distension on milk ejection and diuresis in the lactating cow. *Arch. Intern. Pharmacodyn.*, **123**, 462–71 (1960)

104. Beyer, C., Mena, F. Blockage of milk removal in the cat by periventricular diencephalic lesions. *Am. J. Physiol.*, **208**, 585–88 (1965)

105. Fuchs, A. R. Oxytocin and the onset of labor in rabbits. *J. Endocrinol.*, **30**, 217–24 (1964)

106. Van Dongen, C. F., Hays, R. L. Oxytocic activity in unextracted blood plasma during calving. *J. Reprod. Fert.*, **11**, 317–23 (1966)

107. Knaggs, G. S. Blood oxytocin levels in the cow during milking and in the parturient goat. *J. Endocrinol.*, **26**, 24–25 (1963)

108. Fitzpatrick, R. J., Walmsley, C. F. The concentration of oxytocin in bovine blood during parturition. *J. Physiol. (London)*, **163**, 13P–14P (1962)

109. Fitzpatrick, R. J. Blood concentrations of oxytocin in labor. *J. Endocrinol.*, **22**, 19–20 (1961)

110. Coch, J. A., Brovetto, J., Cabot, H. M., Frelity, C. A., Caldeyro-Barcia, R. Oxytocin-equivalent activity in the plasma of women in labor and during the puerperium. *Am. J. Obstet. Gynecol.*, **91**, 10–17 (1965)

111. Folley, S. J., Knaggs, G. S. Levels of oxytocin in the jugular vein blood of goats during parturition. *J. Endocrinol.*, **33**, 301–15 (1965)

112. Sala, N. L., Fisch, L., Schwarcz, R. L. Effect of clinical dilatation upon milk ejection in humans and its relation to oxytocin secretion. *Am. J. Obstet. Gynecol.*, **91**, 1090–94 (1965)

113. Marshall, J. M. Regulation of activity in uterine smooth muscle. *Physiol. Rev.*, **42**, 213–27 (1962)

114. Csapo, A. Progesterone block. *Am. J. Anat.*, **98**, 273–91 (1956)

115. Csapo, A. Function and regulation of the myometrium. *Ann. N.Y. Acad. Sci.*, **75**, 790–808 (1959)

116. Mikhail, G., Noall, M. W., Allen, W. M. Progesterone levels in the rabbit ovarian vein blood through-out pregnancy. *Endocrinology*, **69**, 504–9 (1961)

117. Short, R. V. Blood progesterone levels in relation to parturition. *J. Reprod. Fert.*, **1**, 61–70 (1960)

118. Cross, B. A., Silver, F. A. Effect of luteal hormone on the behavior of hypothalamic neurons in pseudopregnant rats. *J. Endocrinol.*, **31**, 251–63 (1965)

119. Taleisnik, S., Deis, R. P. Influence of cerebral cortex in inhibition of oxytocin release induced by stressful stimuli. *Am. J. Physiol.*, **207**, 1394–98 (1964)

120. Aroskar, J. P., Chan, W. Y., Stouffer, J. E., Schneider, C. H., Murti, V. V. S., DuVigneaud, V. Renal secretion and tissue distribution of radioactivity after administration of tritium labeled oxytocin to rats. *Endocrinology*, **74**, 226–32 (1964)

121. Farrell, G., Rauschkolb, E. W. Neural control of endocrine function. *Ann. Rev. Med.*, **12**, 323–34 (1961)

122. Orloff, J., Handler, J. S. Cellular mode of action of antidiuretic hormone. *J. Clin. Pathol.*, **18**, 533–42 (1965)

123. Horowitz, I., Beck, J. C., Rubinstein, D. The effect of vasopressin in lipogenesis *in vitro. J. Biol. Chem.*, **241**(5), 1031–35 (1966)

124. Kramar, J., Grinnel, E. H., Duff, W. M. Observations on the diuretic activity of antidiuretic hormone. *Am. J. Med. Sci.*, **252**, 53–61 (1966)

125. Chan, W. Y. Effects of neurohypophysial hormones and their deamino analogues on renal excretion of Na, K and water in rats. *Endocrinology*, **77**, 1097–1104 (1965)

126. Gans, J. H. Vasopressin-induced saluresis in sheep. *Am. J. Vet. Res.*, **25**, 918–23 (1964)

127. Lees, P., Lockett, M. F. The influence of hypophysectomy and of adrenalectomy on the urinary changes induced by oxytocin in rats. *J. Physiol. (London)*, **171**, 403–10 (1964)

128. Barer, G. R. The action of vasopressin, a vasopressin analogue (PLV₂), oxytocin, angiotensin, bradykinin and theophylline ethylene diamine on renal blood flow in the anesthetized cat. *J. Physiol. (London)*, **169**, 62–72 (1963)

129. Fisch, L., Miller, L. H., Kleeman, C. R. Effect of vasopressin on calcium and sodium excretion in hydrated normal subjects. *Proc. Soc. Exptl. Biol. Med.*, **119**, 719–22 (1965)

130. Krück, F., Krecke, H.-J. The renal sodium excretion during oral hydration in man. *Nephron*, **2**, 321–33 (1965)

131. Hunter, J., Haist, R. E. Hormonal hypertension resulting from pituitary imbalance. *Can. J. Physiol. Pharmacol.*, **43**, 269–78 (1965)

132. Hinke, J. A. M. *In vitro* demonstration of vascular hyperresponsiveness to norepinephrine in experimental hypertension. *Circ. Res.*, **17**, 359–71 (1965)

133. Gardner, D. L., Honore, L. H. Vascular response to polypeptides in adrenal-regeneration hypertension. *Arch. Intern. Pharmacodyn.*, **150**, 492–503 (1964)

134. Phelan, E. L. Cardiovascular activity in rats with spontaneous inherited hypertension and constricted renal artery hypertension. *Am. Heart J.*, **71**, 50–57 (1966)

135. Bartlestone, H. J., Nasmyth, P. A. Vasopressin potentiation of catecholamine actions in dogs, rats, cat, and rat aortic strip. *Am. J. Physiol.*, **208**, 754–62 (1965)

136. Gutstein, W. H., LaTaillade, J. N., Lewis, L. Role of vasoconstriction in experimental arteriosclerosis. *Circ. Res.*, **10**, 925–32 (1962)

137. Cooper, J., Gutstein, W. H. Calcific aortic atherosclerosis of the rabbit after cholesterol and pitressin treatment. *J. Atheroscler. Res.*, **6**, 75–86 (1966)

138. Gunn, C. G., Friedman, M., Byers, S. Effect of chronic hypothalamic stimulation upon cholesterol-induced atherosclerosis in the rabbit. *J. Clin. Invest.*, **39**, 1963–72 (1960)

139. Munsick, R. A. Effect of magnesium ion on the response of the rat uterus to neurohypophysial hormones and analogues. *Endocrinology*, **66**, 451–57 (1960)

140. Bentley, P. J. The potentiating action of magnesium and manganese on the oxytocic effect of some oxytocin analogues. *J. Endocrinol.*, **32**, 215–22 (1965)

141. Nakano, J., Fisher, R. D. Studies on the cardiovascular effects of synthetic oxytocin. *J. Pharmacol.*

142. Haigh, A. L., Lloyd, S., Pickford, M. A relationship between adrenaline and the mode of action of oxytocin and oestrogen on vascular smooth muscle. *J. Physiol. (London)*, **178**, 563–76 (1965)

143. Lloyd, S. The vascular responses of the rat during the reproductive cycle. *J. Physiol. (London)*, **148**, 625–732 (1959)

144. Lloyd, S. Changes in the vascular responses of the rat during pregnancy. *Ibid.*, **149**, 586–92

145. Lloyd, S., Pickford, M. The action of posterior pituitary hormones and oestrogens on the vascular system of the rat. *J. Physiol. (London)*, **155**, 161–74 (1961)

146. Fullerton, A., Morrison, J. F. B. A comparison of certain responses of the vascular system of rats after the administration of progesterone and oestrogen. *J. Endocrinol.*, **33**, 75–81 (1965)

147. Nakano, J. Effects of synthetic vasopressin and oxytocin on the cardiovascular dynamics. In *Factors Influencing Myocardial Contractility*, Chap. 9, Sect. 7 (Academic Press, New York, in press)

148. Andersen, T. W., DePadua, C. B., Stenger, V., Prystowsky, H. Cardiovascular effects of rapid intravenous injection of synthetic oxytocin during elective cesearian section. *Clin. Pharmacol. Therap.* **6**, 345–49 (1965)

149. Kitchin, A. H., Lloyd, S. M., Pickford, M. Some actions of oxytocin on the cardiovascular system in man. *Clin. Sci.*, **18**, 399–406 (1959)

150. Chaudhury, R. R., Tarak, T. K. Action of the neurohypophysial hormones on the vascular system of the male monkey and the rooster. *J. Pharm. Pharmacol.*, **17**, 316–17 (1965)

151. Melville, K. I., Varma, D. R. Synthetic oxytocin as an antagonist of experimental cardiac anoxic changes in rabbits. *Brit. J. Pharmacol.*, **17**, 218–23 (1961)

152. Varma, D. R., Melville, K. I., Silver, M. D. Influence of synthetic oxytocin on cardiac arrhythmias and on cardiotoxic effects of epinephrine. *Arch. Intern. Pharmacodyn.*, **145**, 440–49 (1963)

153. Mortari, A., Sioli, G. Recherches sur

l'effet de l'ocytocine dans les arythmies cardiaques. *Cor Vasa,* **7**(2), 110–16 (1965)

154. Covino, B. G. Cardiac effects of synthetic oxytocin (Syntocinon). *Am. Heart J.,* **66**, 627–31 (1963)

155. Beaulnes, A., Panisset, J., Brodeur, J., Beltrami, E., Gariepy, G. Arrhythmias in isolated atria and ventricles and in the intact. animal. *Circ. Res., Suppl. 2,* 14, 15, 210–14 (1964)

156. Somlyo, A. V., Woo, C., Somlyo, A. P. Effect of magnesium on posterior pituitary hormone action on vascular smooth muscle. *Am. J. Physiol.* 210, 705–14 (1966)

157. Katz, R. L. Antiarrhythmic and cardiovascular effects of synthetic oxytocin. *Anesthesiology,* **25**, 653–61 (1964)

158. Katz, R. L. Antiarrhythmic action of synthetic oxytocin in anesthetized man. *Experientia,* **19**, 160–61 (1963)

159. Follet, B. K., Bentley, P. J. The bioassay of oxytocin: increased sensitivity of the rat uterus in response to serial injections of stilboestrol. *J. Endocrinol.,* **29**, 277–82 (1964)

160. Munsick, R. A., Jeronimus, S. C. Effects of diethylstilbestrol and magnesium on the rat oxytocic potencies of some neurohypophysial hormones and analogues. *Endocrinology,* **76**, 90–96 (1965)

161. Chan, W. Y., O'Connell, M., Pomeroy, S. R. Effects of the estrous cycle on the sensitivity of rat uterus to oxytocin and desamino oxytocin. *Endocrinology,* **72**, 279–82 (1963)

162. Garm, O. Oxytocinets betydning for spermietransporten I de hunlige genitalia. *Tiel. Norsk. Laegeforen,* **85**, 307–8 (1965)

163. Labhsetwar, A. P., Collins, W. E., Tyler, W. J., Casida, L. E. Effect of progesterone and oxytocin on the pituitary-ovarian relationship in heifers. *J. Reprod. Fert.,* **8**, 77–83 (1964)

164. Armstrong, D. T., Hansel, W. Alteration of the bovine estrous cycle with oxytocin. *J. Dairy Sci.,* **42**, 533–42 (1959)

165. Armstrong, D. T., Hansel, W. Effect of hormone treatment on testis development and pituitary function. *Intern. J. Fert.,* **3**, 296–306 (1958)

166. Hansel, W., Wagner, W. C. Luteal inhibition in the bovine as a result of oxytocin injections, uterine dilation and intra-uterine infusions of seminal and preputial fluids. *J. Dairy Sci.,* **43**, 796–805 (1960)

167. Sala, N. L. Milk ejecting effect induced by various octapeptides in human beings. Comparison between the milk ejecting potency of synthetic oxytocin, natural purified oxytocin, natural purified vasopressin and synthetic lysine-8-vasopressin. *Acta Physiol. Latinoam.,* **15**, 191–99 (1965)

168. Cross, B. A. The hypothalamus and the mechanism of sympatheticoadrenal inhibition of milk ejection. *J. Endocrinol.,* **12**, 15–28 (1955)

169. Kullander, S. Studies on the hormonal control of the milk-ejection activity in lactating rabbits. *Acta Endocrinol.,* **44**, 313–24 (1963)

170. Chan, W. Y. Mechanism of epinephrine inhibition of the milk ejecting response to oxytocin. *J. Pharmacol. Exptl. Therap.,* **147**, 48–53 (1965)

171. Planel, H., Soleilhavoup, J. P., Tixador, R., Étude histophysiologique de l'action de l'hormone antidiurétique sur la glande sous-marillaire et la glande retrolinguale. *Compt. Rend. Soc. Biol.,* **19**, 2177–78 (1964)

172. Lawson, L. J., Dragstedt, L. R. Vasopressin and gastric secretion. *Surg. Forum,* **15**, 118–20 (1964)

173. Peter, E. T., Nicoloff, D. M., Sosin, H., Berstein, E. F., Wangensteen, O. H. Observations upon portal hemodynamics during vasopressin (pitressin) administration in dogs. *J. Surg. Res.,* **2**, 370–72 (1962)

174. Baisset, A., Dang-Tran, L., Montastruc, P. Comparaison des effets de la vaso-pressine et de l'ocytocine sur la glycémie du chien. *J. Physiol. (Paris),* **57**, 544 (1965)

175. Baisset, A., Dang-Tran, L., Montastruc, P. Action hypoglycémiante de la vasopressine chez la chien privé d'hypophyse et de pancreas (Chien de Houssay). *Compt. Rend. Soc. Biol.,* **158**, 1602–4 (1964)

176. Balasse, E., Rasio, E., Conard, V. Action insulinolibératrice de l'ocytocine chez le chien. *Arch. Intern. Physiol. Biochem.,* **73**, 27–32 (1965)

177. Balasse, E. Effets de l'ocytocine sur

la glycémie, la concentration plasmatique des acides gras libres et l'activité insulinique du sérum chez le chien normal. *Compt. Rend. Soc. Biol.*, **158**, 1165–68 (1964)

178. Balasse, E., Conard, V. Action de l'ocytocine sur l'assimilation glucidique du chien normal. *Arch. Intern. Pharmacodyn.*, **153**, 451–56 (1965)

179. Vaughan, M. Effect of pitressin on lipolysis and on phosphorylase activity in rat adipose tissue. *Am. J. Physiol.*, **207**, 1166–68 (1964)

180. Goldman, J. K. Effect of pitressin infusion on plasma free fatty acid levels in man. *Proc. Soc. Exptl. Biol. Med.*, **117**, 164–66 (1964)

181. Rudman, D. The mobilization of fatty acids from adipose tissue by pituitary peptides and catechol amines. *Ann. N. Y. Acad. Sci.*, **131**, 102–12 (1965)

182. Rudman, D., Malkin, M. F., Garcia, L. A., Girolamo, M., Abell, L. L. Inactivation of the adipokinetic property of adrenocorticotropin, β-melanocyte-stimulating hormone, vasopressin and pituitary fraction 1+ by tissues of the rat and rabbit. *Endocrinology,* **75**, 867–76 (1964)

183. deWied, D., Bohus, B. Long term and short term effects on retention of a conditioned avoidance response in rats by treatment with long acting pitressin and α-MSH. *Nature*, **212**, 1484–86 (1966)

184. Murphy, J. V., Miller, R. E. The effect of adrenocorticotrophic hormone (ACTH) on avoidance conditioning in the rat. *J. Comp. Physiol. Psychol.*, **48**, 47–49 (1955)

185. Miller, R. E., Ogawa, N. The effect of adrenocorticotrophic hormone (ACTH) on avoidance conditioning in the adrenalectomized rat. *J. Comp. Physiol. Psychol.*, **55**, 211–13 (1962)

186. Rothballer, A. B. Some endocrine manifestations of central nervous system disease. *Bull. N. Y. Acad. Med.*, **82**, 257–82 (1966)

187. Hilton, J. G., Scian, L. F., Westerman, C. D., Kruesi, O. R. Direct stimulation of adrenocortical secretion by synthetic vasopressin in dogs (24683). *Proc. Soc. Exptl. Biol. Med.*, **100**, 523–24 (1959)

188. Hume, D. M. The method of hypothalamic regulation of pituitary and adrenal secretion in response to trauma. In *Pathophysiologia Diencephalica*, 217–28 (Curri, S. B. Ed., Springer, Vienna, 1958)

189. Royce, P. C., Sayers, G. Extrapituitary interaction between pitressin and ACTH. *Proc. Soc. Exptl. Biol. Med.*, **98**, 70–74 (1958)

190. Giroud, C. J. P., Stachenko, J., Piletta, P. *In vitro* studies of the functional zonation of the adrenal cortex and of the production of aldosterone. In *Ciba Symposium on Aldosterone*, 56–72 (Muller, A. F., O'Connor, M., Eds., London, 1958)

191. Bohus, B., Endröczi, E. Analysis of the direct adrenal action of neurohypophyseal hormones. *Acta Physiol. Acad. Sci. Hung.*, **20**, 285–97 (1961)

192. Telegdy, G., Fendler, K. The effect of posterior pituitary hormones on adrenocortical and ovarian progesterone secretion in dogs. *Acta Physiol. Acad. Sci. Hung.*, **25**, 359–64 (1964)

193. Farrell, G., Rosnagle, R. S., Rauschkolb, E. W. Increased aldosterone secretion in response to blood loss. *Circ. Res.*, **4**(5), 606–11 (1956)

194. Kaplan, N. M., Bartter, F. C. The effect of ACTH, renin, angiotensin II, and various precursors on biosynthesis of aldosterone by adrenal slices. *J. Clin. Invest.*, **41**, 715–24 (1962)

195. Hilton, J. G. Adrenocorticotropic action of antidiuretic hormone. *Circulation*, **21**, 1038–46 (1960)

196. Kovach, A. G. G., Monos, E., Koltay, E. Adrenal blood flow and corticosteroid secretion: II The effect of oxytocin on adrenal blood flow and corticoid secretion before and after acute hypophysectomy in the dog. *Acta Physiol. Acad. Sci. Hung.* **28**, 155–61 (1965)

197. Mialhe-Voloss, C., Koch, B., Ducommun, P., Fortier, C. Actions de l'ACTH et de la lysine-vasopressine sur la synthèse et la libération de la corticosterone chez le rat—étude in vitro. *Rev. Can. Biol.*, **23**(4), 469–72 (1964)

198. McCann, S. M., Brobeck, J. R. Evidence for a role of the supraoptico hypophyseal system in regulation of adrenocorticotrophin secretion.

Proc. Soc. Exptl. Biol. Med., **87**, 318–24 (1954)

199. Rothballer, A. B. Neuroendocrinology. *Excerpta Med.*, **11** (Sect. 3), iii–xii (1957)

200. Sobel, H., Levy, R. S., Marmorston, J., Schapiro, S., Rosenfeld, S. Increased excretion of urinary corticoids by guinea pigs following administration of pitressin. *Proc. Soc. Exptl. Biol. Med.*, **89**, 10–13 (1955)

201. MacDonald, R. K., Weise, V. K. Effect of arginine-vasopressin and lysine-vasopressin on plasma 17-hydroxy-corticosteroid levels in man. *Proc. Soc. Exptl. Biol. Med.*, **92**, 481–83 (1956)

202. Patrick, R. W. Effect of synthetic lysine-vasopressin on plasma hydrocortisone level in man. *Proc. Soc. Exptl. Biol. Med.*, **93**, 348–49 (1956)

203. Mirsky, I. A., Stein, M., Paulisch, G. The secretion of an antidiuretic substance into the circulation of adrenalectomized and hypophysectomized rats exposed to noxious stimuli. *Endocrinology*, **55**, 28–39 (1954)

204. Sayers, G., Burks, R. Pitressin and blood ACTH in adrenalectomized rats. *J. Clin. Endocrinol. Metab.*, **15**, 840–41 (1955)

205. Saffran, M., Schally, A. V., Benfey, G. B. Stimulation of the release of corticotropin from the adenohypophysis by a neurohypophysial factor. *Endocrinology*, **57**, 439–44 (1955)

206. Guillemin, R., Hearn, W. R., Cheek, W. R., Householder, D. E. Control of corticotrophin release : Further studies with *in vitro* methods. *Endocrinology*, **60**, 488–506 (1957)

207. Schally, A. V., Saffran, M., Zimmermann, B. U. A corticotrophin releasing factor : Partial purification and amino acid composition. *Biochem. J.*, **70**, 97–103 (1958)

208. Schally, A. V., Bowers, C. Y., Kuroshima, A., Ishida, Y., Carter, W. H., Redding, T. W. Effect of lysine vasopressin dimers on blood pressure and some endocrine functions. *Am. J. Physiol.*, **207**, 378–84 (1964)

209. Guillemin, R., Dear, W. E., Nichols, B., Jr., Lipscomb, H. S. ACTH releasing activity *in vivo* of a CRF preparation and lysine vasopressin.

Proc. Soc. Exptl. Biol. Med., **101**, 107–11 (1959)

210. Guillemin, R., Schally, A. V. Recent advances in the chemistry of endocrine mediators originating in the central nervous system. In *Advances in Neuroendocrinology* (See Ref. 101), 314–42

211. Anderson, E. Adrenocorticotrophin-releasing hormone in peripheral blood : Increase during stress. *Science*, **152**, 379–80 (1966)

212. Clayton, G. W., Librik, L., Horan, A., Sussman, L. Effect of corticosteroid administration on vasopressin induced adrenocorticotropin release in man. *J. Clin. Endocrinol.*, **25**, 1156–62 (1965)

213. Gwinup, G. Studies on the mechanism of vasopressin-induced steroid secretion in man. *Metabolism*, **14**, 1282–86 (1965)

214. Benson, G. K., Folley, S. J. Oxytocin as stimulator for the release of prolactin from the anterior pituitary. *Nature*, **177**, 700 (1956)

215. Benson, G. K., Folley, S. J. The effect of oxytocin on mammary gland involution in the rat. *J. Endocrinol.*, **16**, 189–201 (1957)

216. Desclin, L. L'Ocytocine peut-elle déclencher la libération de luteotrophine hypophysaire chez le rat? *Compt. Rend. Soc. Biol.*, **150**, 1489–91 (1956)

217. McCann, S. M., Mack, R., Gale, C. C. The possible role of oxytocin in stimulating the release of prolactin. *Endocrinology*, **64**, 870–89 (1959)

218. Haun, C. K., Sawyer, C. H. Initiation of lactation in rabbits following placement of hypothalamic lesions. *Endocrinology*, **67**, 270–72 (1960)

219. Meites, J., Nicoll, C. S., Talwalker, P. K. The central nervous system and the secretion and release of prolactin. In *Advances in Neuroendocrinology* (See Ref. 101), 238–77

220. Meites, J., Nicoll, C. S. Hormonal prolongation of lactation for 75 days after litter withdrawal in postpartum rats. *Endocrinology*, **65**, 572–79 (1959)

221. Meites, J., Hopkins, T. F. Mechanism of action of oxytocin in retarding mammary involution : Study in hypophysectomized rats. *J. Endocrinol.*, **22**, 207–13 (1961)

222. Rothchild, I. The corpus luteum-

pituitary relationship: On the reports that oxytocin stimulates the secretion of luteotrophin. *Endocrinology*, **67**, 122–24 (1960)

223. Ota, K., Shinde, Y., Yokoyama, A. Relationship between oxytocin and prolactin secretion in maintenance of lactation in rats. *Endocrinology*, **76**, 1–8 (1965)

224. Gala, R. R., Reece, R. P. Influence of neurohumors on anterior pituitary lactogen production *in vitro* (30491). *Proc. Soc. Exptl. Biol. Med.*, **120**, 220–22 (1965)

225. Kovacs, S., Vertes, M. The effect of posterior pituitary hormones on the function of the anterior pituitary-thyroid system in vitro. *Acta Physiol. Acad. Sci. Hung.*, **21**, 69–72 (1962)

226. Garcia, J., Harris, G. W., Schindler, W. J. Vasopressin and thyroid function in the rabbit. *J. Physiol. (London)*, **162**, 64–65 (1962)

227. Arimura, A., Koseki, T., Itoh, S. Dual effects of the neurohypophysial hormone on the thyroid activities of mice. *Japan. J. Physiol.*, **14**, 236–44 (1964)

228. Kovacs, S., Vertes, M., Imhof, S. A further study of the effect of oxytocin on pituitary-thyroid function *in vivo*. *Acta Physiol. Acad. Sci. Hung.*, **25**, 39–45 (1964)

229. Vertes, M., Kovacs, S. Mechanism of the hypothalamic control of TSH secretion: Experiments *in vitro*. *Acta Physiol.*, **26**, 329–35 (1965)

230. LaBella, F. S. Release of thyrotrophin *in vivo* and *in vitro* by synthetic neurohypophysial hormones. *Can. J. Physiol. Pharmacol.*, **42**, 75–83 (1964)

231. Horster, F. A. Die Beeinflussung des experimentellen Exophthalmus durch synthetisches Oxytocin. *Klin. Wochschr.*, **42**, 50–55 (1964)

232. Schreiber, V., Kmentova, V., Rybak, M., Eckertova, A. Anti-thyrotrophin releasing factor (TRF) activity of synthetic 3-valine-oxytocin. *Physiol. Bohemoslov.*, **14**, 53–63 (1965)

233. Del Vecchio, A., Genovese, E., Martini, L. Hypothalamus and somatotrophic hormone release. *Proc. Soc. Exptl. Biol. Med.*, **98**, 641–44 (1958)

234. Hiroshige, T., Itoh, S. Nucleic acid content in liver of rats treated with posterior pituitary hormone. *Japan. J. Physiol.*, **10**, 659–65 (1960)

235. Bernardis, L. L., Skelton, F. R. Contribution to the problem of growth hormone-releasing effect of antidiuretic hormone. *Growth*, **28**, 263–72 (1964)

236. Muller, E., Pecile, A., Smirne, S. Substances present at the hypothalamic level and growth hormone releasing activity. *Endocrinology*, **77**, 390–92 (1965)

237. Schwartz, W. B., Bennett, W., Curelop, S., Bartter, F. C. A syndrome of renal sodium loss and hyponatremia probably resulting from the inappropriate secretion of antidiuretic hormone. *Am. J. Med.*, **23**, 529–42 (1957)

238. Bartter, F. C., Schwartz, W. B. A syndrome of inappropriate secretion of antidiuretic hormone. *Am. J. Med.*, **42**, 790–806 (1967)

239. Haden, H. T., Knox, G. W. Cerebral hyponatremia with inappropriate antidiuretic hormone syndrome. *Am. J. Med. Sci.*, **249**, 381–90 (1965)

240. Katz, S. The syndrome of inappropriate secretion of antidiuretic hormone. *Diseases Chest*, **49**, 447–48 (1966)

241. Afifi, A., Joynt, R., Harbison, J. Inappropriate antidiuretic hormone secretion in subarachnoid hemorrhage. *Am. Neurol. Assoc. (Transl.)*, **90**, 217–18 (1965)

242. Delaere, J., DeSousa, R. C., Rudler, J.-C., Mach, R.-S. A propos d'un cas de carcinome bronchique et syndrome de Schwartz-Bartter. *Presse Med.*, **73**, 109–14 (1965)

243. Bernard-Weil, E., David, M., Pertuiset, B. "Inappropriate" secretion of antidiuretic hormone without corresponding hyponatraemia in cerebral pathology. *J. Neurol. Sci.*, **3**, 300–12 (1966)

244. Weston, R. E., Hanenson, I. B., Grossman, J., Berdasco, G. A., Wolfman, M. Natriuresis and chloruresis following pitressin-induced water retention in nonedematous patients: Evidence of a homeostatic mechanism regulating body fluid volume. *J. Clin. Invest.*, **32**, 611 (1953)

245. Thorn, N. A., Transbøl, I. B. Hyponatremia and bronchogenic carcinoma associated with renal excretion of large amounts of

antidiuretic material. *Am. J. Med.,* **35,** 257–68 (1963)

246. Aldrete, J. S., Sheps, S. G., Bernatz, P. E., Didier, E. P. Vasoactive polypeptides of surgical significance. *Proc. Staff Meetings Mayo Clinic,* **41,** 399–417 (1966)

247. Moran, W. H., Jr., Miltenberger, F. W., Shuayb, W. A., Zimmerman, B. The relationship of antidiuretic hormone secretion to surgical stress. *Surgery,* **56,** 99–108 (1964)

248. Hershey, S. G., Mazzia, V. D. B., Gyure, L., Singer, K. Influence of a synthetic analogue of vasopressin on survival after hemorrhagic shock in rats. *Proc. Soc. Exptl. Biol. Med.,* **115,** 325–28 (1964)

249. Hershey, S. G., Mazzia, V. D. B., Altura, B. M., Gyure, L. Effects of vasopressors on the microcirculation and on survival in hemorrhagic shock. *Anesthesiology,* **26,** 179–89 (1965)

250. Cerletti, A., Weber, H., Weidmann, H. Zur Wirkung von Phenylalanin-lysin-Vasopressin (Octapressin) auf den arteriellen und venosen Anteil eines peripheren Gefässgebietes. *Helv. Physiol. Pharmacol. Acta,* **21,** 394–401 (1963)

251. Cort, J. H., Hammer, J., Ulrych, M., Pisa, Z., Dousa, T., Rudinger, J. Synthetic extended-chain analogues of vasopressin and oxytocin in the treatment of experimental haemorrhagic shock. *Lancet,* **2,** 840–41 (1964)

252. Altura, B. M., Hershey, S. G., Zweifach, B. W. Effects of a synthetic analogue of vasopressin on vascular smooth muscle. *Proc. Soc. Exptl. Biol. Med.,* **119,** 258–61 (1965)

253. Bosomworth, P. P. The use of 2-phenylalanine-8-lysine vasopressin in anesthetized patients. *J. New Drugs,* **5,** 308–17 (1965)

254. Crawford, R. A. D. Preliminary trial of a new hemostatic. *Brit. J. Ophthalmol.,* **49,** 49–51 (1965)

255. Kullander, S., Wide, E. A synthetic vasopressin (octapressin, Sandoz) for haemostasis during cone biopsy of the cervix. *Acta Obstet. Gynaecol. Scand.,* **45,** 102–10 (1966)

REGULATION OF THE ADENOHYPOPHYSIS[1,2]   1015

BY SAMUEL MCDONALD MCCANN,[3] ANAND P. S. DHARIWAL,
AND JOHN C. PORTER[4]

*Department of Physiology, University of Texas Southwestern Medical School at
Dallas, Texas*

INTRODUCTION

The purpose of this article is to provide a review of the very recent literature on the regulation of the anterior pituitary gland. We shall begin with a consideration of pituitary blood flow since this is an area which has been relatively neglected but plays a key role in the responsiveness of the gland to stimuli. Then, the various factors that modulate the secretion of the various anterior lobe hormones will be systematically considered. The role of the hypothalamus in regulating the secretion of the gland will be given particular attention, and major emphasis will be placed on the final common pathway between the hypothalamus and pituitary gland which is provided by the recently discovered hypothalamic hypophyseal stimulating and inhibiting hormones. We have made a conscious effort to avoid bias in the presentation, but make no claim for completeness of coverage. Particular attention has been paid to articles which have appeared in the last two years, but older articles have been referred to when it seemed appropriate to provide essential background information.

The primary justification for a review of this field at this time is the very rapid progress which has been made in our understanding of the regulation of this gland in the past few years. A number of important recent

[1] The survey of the literature for this review was concluded in June 1967. The kind assistance of Mrs. Joanna Waters and Mrs. June Gottwald in reviewing the literature and in preparing the manuscript is gratefully acknowledged.

[2] Among the abbreviations used are those for the hypothalamic releasing and inhibiting factors: CRF (corticotropin-releasing factor); FRF (FSH-releasing factor); GRF (growth hormone-releasing factor); LRF (luteinizing hormone-releasing factor); MRF (MSH-releasing factor); TRF (thyrotropin-releasing factor); GIF (growth hormone-inhibiting factor); MIF (MSH-inhibiting factor); PIF (prolactin-inhibiting factor); and those for the following hormones: FSH (follicle-stimulating hormone); GH (growth hormone); HCG (human chorionic gonadotropin); LH (luteinizing hormone); MSH (melanocyte-stimulating hormone); TSH (thyrotropin).

[3] Assisted in part by support from the National Institute of Arthritis and Metabolic Diseases research grant AM 10073-02 and by the Ford Foundation.

[4] Assisted in part by support from the National Institute of Arthritis and Metabolic Diseases research grant AM 01237.

reviews of the subject have been published. These include the reviews by Guillemin (1) and by Meites & Nicoll (2) which have appeared in recent volumes of the *Annual Review of Physiology*. Several important books in this area have also been published in the past year. Of these, *Neuroendocrinology* (Volume I), edited by Martini & Ganong (3), *The Pituitary Gland* (Volumes I-III), edited by Harris & Donovan (4), and *The Brain and Gonadal Function,* edited by Gorski & Whalen (5), are extremely valuable compilations and interpretations of recent advances.

BLOOD SUPPLY OF THE PARS DISTALIS

Introduction.—In 1933 Hinsey & Markee (6) speculated that an excitatory stimulus via pathways from the hypothalamus might activate the posterior lobe of the hypophysis and that the posterior lobe might affect the anterior lobe by hormonal transmission. In view of the limited knowledge at that time about the affluent blood supply of the pars distalis, it seems unlikely that Hinsey & Markee appreciated fully the ramifications of their hypothesis. Nevertheless, if the term neurohypophysis were exchanged for posterior lobe, this attenuated proposal could serve as a forerunner of the modern view of the control of the anterior lobe of the pituitary. It should be noted that the neurohypophysis is that part of the hypothalamus containing the capillaries draining into the vessels supplying the affluent blood of the pars distalis and this deserves special comment.

Long portal vessels.—In many mammals two discrete primary capillary beds supply the portal vessels. The upper part of the pituitary stalk and the floor of the third ventricle, i.e., the median eminence of the tuber cinereum, contain one of these beds. The volume of the region containing these capillaries is small relative to that of the pars distalis. [In rats the volume of the stalk and median eminence is one-fifteenth to one-fourteenth that of the pars distalis (7).] The veins draining these capillaries lie mostly on the surface of the pituitary stalk and are called the long portal vessels. Flow in these vessels was first observed in the toad in 1935 by Houssay, Biasotti & Sammartino (8). In noting that blood flowed from the hypothalamus toward the pituitary, they wrote, "Au microscope on observe qu'à la face ventrale, toute la circulation va depuis la partie antérieure du *lobus infundibularis* jusqu'à la limite postérieure de l'hypophyse. En avant de l'hypophyse, existe une circulation portale qui va toujours du *lobus infundibularis* à l'hypophyse." Fourteen years later Green & Harris reported a similar observation in the rat (9). Still later, Worthington (10) and Török (11) reported confirmatory results for the mouse and dog, respectively. The long portal vessels empty into sinusoids of the pars distalis and undoubtedly provide this gland with most of its blood.

Short portal vessels.—It is now clear, however, that the pars distalis also receives blood from a second set of portal vessels (12, 13). The primary capillary bed of this set of vessels lies in the region of the lower pituitary stalk and neural lobe of the neurohypophysis. The vessels carrying blood from these capillaries to sinusoids in the anterior lobe are called the short portal vessels (12, 13).

Distribution of blood.—The long and the short portal vessels are the sole sources of blood of the pars distalis in the rat (12), sheep (14), goat (15), man (16, 17), and monkey (18). The sinusoids receiving blood from the short vessels seem to be restricted to the more dorsal and peripheral zones of the pars distalis, whereas the more ventral and central part of the gland receives blood from the long vessels (12, 14–19). When the stalk is transected, the ventromedial portion of the anterior lobe becomes necrotic whereas the dorsolateral part of the gland remains viable, which shows that this part receives blood by way of the vessels other than those in the stalk, viz., through the short portal vessels. In man the long vessels supply 78 to 90 per cent of the pars distalis with blood (20, 21) ; in the goat, 76 to 90 per cent (22, 23) ; in the rat, about 70 per cent (7). The remainder of the anterior lobe in each case receives blood from the short portal vessels. Indeed, the affluent blood of a single portal vessel seems to enter the sinusoids of a rather restricted zone of the pars distalis (24), and it is interesting to speculate that a given tropic hormone is secreted preferentially by cells receiving blood from a specific portal vessel. Should this situation prove true, it would lend credence to the notion that a given portion of the hypothalamus may be selectively involved in the control of the secretion of a particular tropic hormone from the pars distalis.

Measurement of blood flow.—The interest of investigators in the blood flow of the pituitary and in the possible relationship that flow may have to the secretion of tropic hormones has led to the development of methods to determine quantitatively blood flow of the pars distalis. One method makes use of the fact that the quantity of rubidium entering the anterior lobe under certain conditions is proportional to the perfusion of the gland (25). This method has the advantage that it permits the determination of mean blood flow of the pars distalis in the unanesthetized animal which may be highly desirable sometimes, but it has the disadvantage of requiring that the animal be sacrificed in order to achieve the measurement. Thus, only one measurement of anterior lobe flow in an animal is possible.

Yates, Kirschman & Olshen (26) injected radioactive iodide into the pars distalis of anesthetized rats, and, by counting the radioactivity in the vicinity of the head of the animal, obtained a disappearance curve for iodide. Flow was computed from a parameter of this curve. Unfortunately, the clearance of iodide was determined by measuring the radioactivity from a region in excess of the anterior lobe. Consequently, the iodide in the sinuses and veins receiving hypophyseal blood was indistinguishable from the tracer in the pars distalis. This situation would be expected to prolong the iodide-disappearance curve, resulting in values that would be less than the true value. Two assumptions of questionable validity were introduced by Yates, Kirschman & Olshen : first, that iodide injected into one lobe of the pars distalis became homogeneously distributed in the ipsilateral lobe and did not enter the contralateral lobe; and second, that only the fastest component of a multicomponent washout curve was related to the clearance of iodide from the anterior lobe by way of its venous drainage.

Porter et al. (7) investigated local blood flow of the pars distalis of the rat by means of the hydrogen desaturation technic. It is possible by this procedure not only to determine flow at different sites in the pars distalis but also to make repeated measurements in the same animal. An analysis of the desaturation curves that were obtained when the electrode was located at various sites in the pars distalis suggested to these workers that blood flow through the ventromedial region resembled that of a single homogeneous compartment, whereas blood flow in the lateral lobes resembled that of a two-compartment model. After the posterior lobe of the pituitary was removed in a manner such that flow from the long portal vessels was not interrupted, blood flow through the lateral lobes resembled that of a single homogeneous compartment. These findings support the view that in the living animal the ventromedial region of the pars distalis receives blood solely from the long portal vessels and the lateral lobes receive blood not only from the long but also from the short portal vessels.

The elucidation of the significance of zonation in the pars distalis as a result of the distribution of blood from the long and the short portal vessels should help in answering several questions. For example, are the tropic hormones secreted by that part of the gland receiving blood from the short vessels qualitatively different from those secreted by tissue receiving blood from the long vessels? Do the secretory elements lying within diffusion distances of the primary capillaries of each portal system respond to different stimuli? If so, there may be a difference in the importance of the neural lobe and of the median eminence in influencing the pars distalis in various circumstances. Adams et al. (20) speculated that certain portal vessels may carry blood from a particular group of cells in one of the hypothalamic nuclei to specific areas of the pars distalis. Such an arrangement, if true, would impart a higher efficiency to the entire hypothalamico-adenohypophyseal system than has been supposed heretofore.

Resistance to flow of the hypothalamico-hypophyseal vasculature.—The effects of a gross reduction in blood flow on the function of the pars distalis have been investigated in several mammalian species, and it has been shown that stalk transection interrupts much of the flow to the pars distalis (27), resulting in necrosis of most of the gland (12, 14–23). Recently, the more subtle effects of changes in flow have also been examined. Goldman (29–31) has recently measured the overall vascular resistance of the hypothalamico-adenohypophyseal blood flow, computed as the ratio of the pressure drop divided by the flow (cf. 28). The results are presented in Table I, together with the pressure and flow values from which resistances were calculated. Vasopressin and norepinephrine both evoke an increased local resistance proportional to the dose. Epinephrine reduces resistance in low doses, increases it in high doses.

Group	Treatment	Cardiac output (ml min⁻¹ g⁻¹ body wt.)	Mean arterial blood pressure (mm Hg)	Blood flow of the pars distalis (ml min⁻¹ g⁻¹ tissue wt.)	Resistance of the pars distalis to blood flow (dyn sec cm⁻⁶ g⁻¹ tissue wt.) ×10⁶	Total body resistance to blood flow (dyn sec cm⁻⁶ g⁻¹ body wt.) ×10⁶
I[c]	Saline	0.272[b]	116	0.59	15.6	33.9
	30 mμ min⁻¹ kg⁻¹ vasopressin	0.235	138	0.65	16.9	46.6
	90 mμ min⁻¹ kg⁻¹ vasopressin	0.142	158	0.39	32.2	88.3
II[c]	Saline	0.272	118	0.67	14.0	34.4
	0.5 μg min⁻¹ kg⁻¹ epinephrine	0.388	118	0.87	10.8	24.1
	5.0 μg min⁻¹ kg⁻¹ epinephrine	0.291	164	0.90	14.5	44.7
	0.5 μg min⁻¹ kg⁻¹ norepinephrine	0.244	129	0.70	14.6	42.0
	5.0 μg min⁻¹ kg⁻¹ norepinephrine	0.188	175	0.69	20.1	73.9
III[d]	Anesthesia plus surgical stress	—	140	0.71	15.6	—
	Anesthesia plus surgical stress	—	70	0.80	6.9	—
	Anesthesia plus surgical stress	—	35	0.97	2.9	—

[a] The authors gratefully acknowledge the kind assistance of Dr. Harold Goldman for providing us with the unpublished values for central arterial pressure in rats in Group I (31). The addition of these data enabled us to compute the values for resistance. Dr. Goldman's kindness is greatly appreciated.

[b] Each value represents the mean of a larger group of measurements.

[c] The experimental values in Groups I and II were obtained by Dr. Harold Goldman (29–31) using unanesthetized, adult female rats in such a way that they may be considered as minimally stressed animals.

[d] The values in Group III were obtained by Porter et al. (7) using adult, male rats anesthetized with a solution of chloralose and urethane; and the values were obtained under conditions such that the animals were stressed maximally.

The effects of lowering arterial pressure on adenohypophyseal flow, as determined by Porter et al. (7), are also shown in Table I. A pressure fall from 140 to 35 mm Hg led to such a marked fall in resistance that the flow increased slightly. This suggests that a compensatory vasodilator mechanism exists tending to maintain constant adenohypophyseal blood flow.

Worthington (10, 32) has suggested that flow in a specific portal vessel may vary independently in consequence of various experimental manipulations. His method of flow measurement by observation of the linear velocity of blood flow in a single vessel is subject to serious error as a consequence of changes in vessel radius. However, his observation that norepinephrine caused such extreme vasoconstriction that an arteriole or a group of capillaries disappeared temporarily from view would seem to be unequivocal evidence of flow diminution in these vessels.

However, there has been no clear-cut demonstration that blood flow of the pars distalis can affect the secretory rate of a tropic hormone, providing flow is adequate to meet the metabolic demands of the tissue. It was shown in rats by Porter, Dhariwal & McCann (33) that two days after bilateral electrolytic lesions—which did not sever the stalk—were placed in the median eminence near its junction with the pituitary stalk, the mean blood flow of the pars distalis was equal to that of rats without lesions. The rats with lesions did not respond to stressful stimulation by increasing the rate of ACTH secretion. Yet, the same rats responded to exogenous corticotropin-releasing factor (CRF) by releasing ACTH. Porter has observed (unpublished data) that ACTH secretion is drastically reduced when the blood supply of the anterior lobe is impaired. It seems that ACTH secretion can be (a) elevated when CRF secretion and blood flow are high (7, 33); (b) low when CRF secretion is depressed and flow is high (33); and (c) low when flow is greatly reduced. Consequently, it is reasonable to conclude that either blood flow or a hypothalamic releasing substance(s) can limit the rate of secretion of ACTH and perhaps other adenohypophyseal hormones, but blood flow of the pars distalis probably has only a permissive role in the function of the gland.

CRF (34-37), luteinizing hormone-releasing factor (LRF) (38) and thyrotropin-releasing factor (TRF) (39) have been found in the effluent blood of the stalk vessels; other releasing factors have not been reported in this blood. One can presume that the combined difficulty of obtaining portal vessel blood and of detecting a releasing factor or an inhibiting factor in small amounts of portal blood has slowed investigators. Hopefully, this situation will be rectified in the future. Recently, two procedures have been described for collecting the effluent blood from the transected stalk of the rat (40, 41). The method of Porter & Smith (41) enables one to collect all of the effluent blood from the stalk without contamination with extraneous blood. By means of this procedure, it should be possible not only to determine the hormonal content of the blood but also to determine the secretion rate of a given hypothalamic hormone.

REGULATION OF ACTH SECRETION

Hypothalamic mediator.—A substance(s) which increases the secretory rate of ACTH is frequently called corticotropin-releasing factor (CRF). Despite the implication of uniqueness, CRF is today a generic term and can be aptly applied to substances in hypophyseal portal vessel blood, in peripheral blood of hypophysectomized rats, in peripheral blood of intact rats, in extracts of hypothalamic tissue, in extracts of posterior pituitary tissue containing vasopressin, and perhaps others. It is not known if each substance would be active in every assay system, but until it has been proven contrary, there is little reason to suppose otherwise. However, it seems fair to say that CRF from stalk-median eminence tissue is probably the CRF having physiologic significance.

Hypothalamic lesions and CRF.—Support in favor of this statement was presented recently by Porter, Dhariwal & McCann (33) using rats in which an electrolytic lesion had been placed in the median eminence on each side of its junction with the pituitary stalk. Two days later, these animals were found to secrete corticosterone at very low rates despite their exposure to such stressful stimuli as anesthesia; cannulation of the trachea; cannulation of both femoral veins, femoral artery, and adrenal vein; laparotomy; and collection of the venous effluent from an adrenal vein— treatment that causes maximal corticosterone secretion in intact rats. When CRF purified from hypothalamic tissue and free of vasopressin (42) was infused into the lesioned rat, sufficient ACTH was secreted by the pituitary to increase the secretory rate of corticosterone fourfold. The blood flow of the anterior lobe in the lesioned animals receiving CRF was not significantly different from that of intact animals, which shows that the limiting factor was CRF and not blood flow through the pars distalis. Because of the ease with which the stalk portal vessels can be inadvertently damaged (43) or severed by means of electrolytic lesions (44) resulting in necrosis of most of the anterior lobe (12), it is important to know that flow has not been impaired.

CRF and vasopressin.—It is worth noting, however, that median eminence lesions produce deficits in hypothalamic function other than those in the CRF-secreting elements. For example, there is the well-known impairment in the mechanism for secreting the antidiuretic hormone. However, rats with hereditary hypothalamic diabetes insipidus, which lack vasopressin, were found by McCann et al. (45) and later by Arimura et al. (46) to respond to stressful stimulation sufficiently well to indicate that these animals could still secrete CRF, a finding which supports the notion that vasopressin and CRF are physiologically distinct substances. In addition, CRF and vasopressin may cause the secretion of ACTH by different means. Hedge et al. (47) suggest that vasopressin causes ACTH release by directly affecting the hypothalamus which subsequently secretes CRF. This suggestion deserves further investigation.

Electrically induced stimulation and inhibition of ACTH secretion.—
Eleftheriou, Zolovick & Pearse (48) reported that twelve hours after lesions were placed in the amygdaloid complex in the deermouse, the concentrations of ACTH and of corticosterone in plasma increased to levels
significantly greater than those of the controls. These authors concluded
that cellular elements of the medial amygdaloid group may exert an inhibitory effect on the secretion of ACTH in the deermouse. However,
McHugh & Smith (49) found that electrical stimulation of the amygdaloid
complex resulted in an increase in the 17-OH-corticosteroid concentration in
plasma of the monkey, providing the stimuli evoked afterdischarges. Slusher & Hyde (50) observed that the concentration of ACTH in the effluent
blood of the jugular vein of cats increased noticeably within one to two
minutes after electrical stimulation of sites in the dorsal midbrain and in
the diencephalon. The facilitative effect of the diencephalon could be inhibited by simultaneously stimulating certain sites in the midbrain or in the
preoptic region. Elevation of the preoptic temperature in dogs by Chowers
et al. (51) and electrical stimulation of the anterior hypothalamus of rats
by D'Angelo & Young (52) caused an increase in the secretory rate of
ACTH. The latter effect was abolished by lesions in the median eminence
(52). Similarly, lesions in the ventromedial and dorsomedial nuclei suppressed the secretion of adrenal steroids in guinea pigs (53). These observations support the view that that part of the median eminence forming the
junction with the pituitary stalk must be functionally intact for certain
stimuli to cause increases in ACTH secretion, presumably through the
mediation of CRF of hypothalamic origin. These results indicate or at least
imply that the level of activity of the median eminence is determined by
afferent impulses from the brain. This view, however, may overly simplify
the true situation.

ACTH secretion by surgically isolated pituitaries.—Halász & Pupp
(54) used a specially constructed knife to isolate the basal hypothalamus,
median eminence, and pituitary from the remainder of the brain. Three to
five weeks after the transection, the level of function of the thyroid, adrenals, and ovaries was such as to suggest that the medial basal hypothalamus with its intact hypophyseal portal circulation could function to some
degree independently of neural afferent impulses from the brain. In a later
study, Halász, Slusher & Gorski (55) concluded that ACTH secretion was
maintained in rats with isolated medial basal hypothalami although such
subtleties as the circadian rhythm were abolished. Egdahl (56) reports that
the administration of pentobarbital to dogs with isolated pituitaries does
not suppress adrenal cortical hypersecretion exhibited by these animals.
Zukoski & Ney (57) found that stalk transection in dogs, in which alu-
minum foil was inserted across the site of the transection to prevent regeneration of the portal vessels, causes the secretion of 17-OH-corticosteroids at
rates similar to those of intact dogs. In this respect, the stalk-sectioned dog
of Zukoski & Ney differs from the animal with an isolated pituitary which,

according to Egdahl (56), supposedly has hypersecretion of corticoids. Zukoski & Ney also state that the dogs with transected stalks were able to increase the output of 17-OH-corticosteroids after traction on the sciatic nerve. In view of the necrosis caused by stalk transection in several mammals, it would be of interest if these investigators would determine the source of the affluent blood of the pars distalis in these dogs. It would also be worthwhile if an alternate method for assessment of ACTH secretion would be used.

CRF in extracellular fluid.—ACTH-releasing substance(s) in extracellular fluid has regrettably received little attention. Anderson (58) claims to have detected ACTH-releasing activity in peripheral blood of rats. If true, her finding would confirm the earlier report by Brodish & Long (59) and the still earlier findings of Porter & associates (34–37). However, Anderson reported that ACTH-releasing activity was not present in the blood of rats one month after hypophysectomy or twenty-four hours, fifteen days, and eighteen days after adenohypophysectomy. To explain this finding, the author proposed ". . . that the access into the peripheral circulation of ACTH-RH [ACTH-releasing hormone] is via an intact portal system of blood vessels." In the absence of evidence that a venous drainage of the median eminence is not formed anew within a few days after hypophysectomy or adenohypophysectomy, it is difficult to accept the suggestion. Anderson's results may reflect a peculiarity of the responsiveness of the ACTH-secreting tumor used in the assay of ACTH-RH. If so, the pertinence of these results to the secretion of CRF by the median eminence is not known.

Pituitary transplants.—Heterotopically transplanted pituitaries in hypophysectomized rats can still secrete small quantities of ACTH as judged from adrenal weights (60–63) and from the secretory rate of corticosterone (60, 61, 63). The secretory rate of ACTH not only varies with the number of heterotopic pituitaries in the recipient animal (61) but also increases when the hypophysectomized animal is subjected to stressful stimulation (63). Removal of the forebrain reduces the secretory rate of ACTH from heterotopic pituitaries to levels observed in hypophysectomized animals (60). In addition, the secretion of ACTH can be suppressed with dexamethasone (62, 63). These results indicate that the secretory rate of ACTH from heterotopic pituitaries is influenced by an ACTH-releasing substance from the brain of hypophysectomized rats and that the stimulator reaches the heterotopic pituitaries through the peripheral circulation.

Hormonal and drug-induced inhibition of ACTH secretion.—The effects on ACTH secretion of several substances implanted in the median eminence have been noted. Thyroxine (64) stimulated, whereas estradiol or testosterone in female rats (65) had no effect on ACTH secretion. Dexamethasone and cortisol (66) implanted in the hypothalamus suppressed the secretory rate of ACTH. Vernikos-Danellis & Twigg (67) report that the concentration of ACTH in blood may inhibit synthesis and secretion of

ACTH. Lorenzen & Ganong (68) suggest that the inhibition by α-ethyl-tryptamine of ACTH secretion in stressed dogs may be related to the pressor activity of the drug. When arterial pressure was held constant, no inhibition of ACTH secretion by α-ethyltryptamine was observed (69).

REGULATION OF THYROTROPIN (TSH) SECRETION

TSH in plasma.—Ducommun, Sakiz & Guillemin (70) observed that the concentration of TSH in plasma of rats was a highly labile entity. When rats were subjected to mild stimulation such as handling or intraperitoneal injection, the concentration of TSH in the plasma fell to undetectable levels within fifteen minutes. Since there was no reason to suspect that the rate of removal of the tropic hormone from the plasma was affected by these treatments, it was presumed that its secretory rate had been reduced. These workers also noted that the TSH concentration in plasma varied throughout the day, which suggests the existence of a circadian rhythm. However, the plasma concentration of TSH tended to be highest when the ACTH level was lowest and vice versa. This inverse correlation was shown later by the same workers to be coincidental rather than causal (71). When rats were subjected to conditioning treatment consisting of periodic exposure to stressful stimuli, it was found that the TSH concentration in plasma eventually assumed a constant value regardless of exposure to the stressful stimulant (72).

Hypothalamic mediator.—The secretory rate of TSH by the adenohypophysis is regulated by a substance called thyrotropin-releasing factor (TRF) (73) which is believed to be secreted by certain hypothalamic secretory elements lying within diffusion distances of the primary capillaries of the portal vessels. TRF has been purified from hypothalamic tissue from such sources as the pig (74, 75), sheep (76), ox (77), and man (78). In addition to the demonstration of TRF in hypothalamic tissue, it is of special interest that it has been reported in the affluent blood of the pituitary of the rat (39). The latter finding is important in the establishment of the notion that a substance of hypothalamic origin is indeed transported to the pars distalis by way of the portal vessels in the pituitary stalk.

Hypothalamic lesions.—Anterior hypothalamic lesions interfere with the secretion of TSH, presumably by suppressing TRF secretion. The lesions that seem most effective in this respect are those that damage the paraventricular nuclei (79). On the basis of the results they obtained by means of a technic that allowed partial or total deafferentation of the medial basal hypothalamus, Halász et al. (80) concluded that the hypothalamic region between the suprachiasmatic nuclei and the anterior border of the ventromedial nuclei is essential in the control of TSH secretion by the hypothalamus.

Hormonally induced stimulation and inhibition.—In addition to TRF, the thyroid hormones are recognized as a major influence in the regulation of the secretory rate of TSH. One of the more direct experiments in this field was reported by Sinha & Meites (81), who found that the TSH-releasing activity was considerably greater in hypothalamic tissue from thyroidectomized rats than in tissue from intact rats. The TSH content of the anterior pituitary also increased after thyroidectomy. Thyroxine administration reduced the TSH content of the anterior pituitary without affecting the TRF level in the hypothalamus. This finding led Sinha & Meites to propose that in the absence of thyroxine, synthesis and secretion of TRF is promoted whereas in the presence of thyroxine, it is inhibited. Thyroxine and triiodothyronine in high doses were observed also by van Rees (82) to lower the TSH content of the anterior pituitary. MacLeod et al. (83) made the interesting observation that the TSH content of the anterior lobe was suppressed in rats bearing a transplantable pituitary tumor which secreted prolactin and growth hormone, but not TSH or ACTH. Panda & Turner (84) examined the effects of thyroidectomy and of cold on the concentration of TSH in the pituitary and in plasma of rats. After thyroidectomy, the plasma TSH concentration increased while the concentration in the pituitary decreased; conversely, when thyroxine was given to thyroidectomized rats, the plasma concentration was lowered and the level in the pituitary rose. When intact rats were exposed to prolonged cold, the concentration in the plasma as well as in the pituitary increased.

Thyrotropin-releasing factor causes the secretion of TSH from pituitaries under *in vitro* conditions. When a hypothalamic extract was added to pituitaries after one hour of incubation (85) or to a three-day-old organ culture of pituitaries (86), TSH was released into the surrounding media. These results support the view that the concentration of TRF in the fluid surrounding the pituitary determines the secretory rate of TSH. This view is also supported by the observations of Greer, Matsuda & Stott (87). They found that a pituitary transplant was most effective in maintaining thyroid function of the hypophysectomized rat when the pituitary was placed directly below the median eminance. Purves, Sirett & Griesbach (88) found that neonatal pituitaries transplanted to the renal capsule were able to maintain normal thyroid size and histological appearance in hypophysectomized rats given the goitrogen, methylthiouracil. It would appear that TRF can enter the peripheral circulation after hypophysectomy.

REGULATION OF GONADOTROPIN AND PROLACTIN SECRETION

In the early forties, Fevold (89) and Greep, Van Dyke & Chow (90) reported that purified preparations of follicle-stimulating hormone produced only follicular growth when administered to hypophysectomized rats. Two recent studies with highly purified FSH preparations (91, 92) have confirmed these early claims and leave little doubt that FSH alone has no effect on estrogen secretion in mouse or rat but stimulates estrogen secretion when mixed with luteinizing hormone (91). Ovulation can be evoked in hypophysectomized rats by either FSH or LH (91, 93) which emphasizes once again that the occurrence of ovulation cannot be equated a priori with LH secretion, although physiologically there appears to be little doubt that the two bear a cause-and-effect relationship. The luteotropic effect of prolactin in the rat has been reconfirmed (93, 94) ; whether it has similar effects in nonrodent species remains controversial. Since this subject has been critically reviewed by Short in the last volume of *Annual Review of Physiology* (95), we will not attempt to unravel the complex roles of LH and prolactin in the maintenance of functional corpora lutea.

REGULATION OF LUTENIZING HORMONE SECRETION

Assay of LH.—Our knowledge of the control of secretion of this hormone has been based on several types of bioassays in rats, such as the ventral prostate assay originated by Greep, Van Dyke & Chow (96) and the ovarian ascorbic acid depletion (OAAD) assay originally perfected by Parlow (97). There have been some differences in the potency estimates obtained by these two widely used tests. Since the test solutions are administered subcutaneously in the ventral prostate assay, whereas intravenous administration has been the preferred route for the OAAD test, Parlow (98) attributed these discrepancies to differences in biological half-life of LH from various species. Reichert (99) has shown that these discrepancies are still apparent when the OAAD method is compared with the ovarian hyperemia method with intravenous administration in both cases. Thus, factors other than biological half-life must contribute to these different potency estimates.

The OAAD method is still the bioassay procedure of choice for estimation of LH in body fluids because of its specificity, sensitivity, and precision; however, certain precautions in its use should be observed. First, there are important strain differences in the precision, sensitivity, and specificity of the assay. Rats of the Holtzman strain appear to give the best results (97). Care must be taken to avoid diurnal fluctuations in ovarian ascorbic acid (100). The two ovary–one hour version of the test (101, 102) is the most sensitive, but is less precise, so that when sufficient LH is available the one ovary—four hour test is preferable (97). Parlow (97) described the use of the second ovary two days after the first, but reported lower precision with this gland. Hershberger, Hansen & Thompson (103) have observed that maximal doses of LH in the first assay impaired the responsiveness of the second gland to the hormone which may explain in part the increased variability seen with assays using the second gland. In general, this is a rather risky assay best used only for screening. The elaborate statistical treatment of the data in the OAAD assay recommended by Sakiz & Guillemin (104) appears to be unnecessary, at least when a satisfactory strain of rat is used. This assay is eminently suited for the estimation of pituitary LH (102, 105, 106–109). It can also be used for the assay of this hormone in rat plasma (102, 105, 109–112), although too insensitive to detect circulating LH except during its preovulatory discharge (110) or in the castrated animal (102, 109, 113). Pelletier (114) has recently claimed that rat plasma evokes a nonspecific discharge of LH from the pituitaries of Wistar rats prepared for the OAAD assay. If this is true, it must be a phenomenon peculiar to his particular strain of rat, for a number of investigators have shown no such nonspecific discharge with assay of rat plasma (102, 105, 109–112). It also appears that plasma LH can be estimated in unfractionated plasma from rabbits (115), and chickens (116). On the other hand, it is clear that plasma from some species causes a nonspecific OAAD, perhaps caused by release of LH from the hypophysis of the test rat as postulated by Pelletier. Plasma from sheep (117), pig (118), and dog (McCann, unpublished observations) appears to produce this nonspecific effect. When assaying plasma from species other than rodents for LH by the OAAD method, it would appear mandatory to concentrate the LH. The ovarian cholesterol depletion assay for this hormone has not yet advanced enough to be applicable to routine bioassay [(119); see also Bell & Lunn (120)].

Recently, several laboratories have developed radioimmunoassays for human chorionic gonadotropin and LH (121–123). Satisfactory agreement has been found between immunoassay and bioassay by the OAAD method. These immunoassays are sufficiently sensitive to measure LH in small amounts of serum during the menstrual cycle: such an immunoassay in the rat has even been reported in brief (124). It would appear that the time is upon us when immunoassay will supplant bioassay of the tropin because of greater sensitivity and precision. Midgley (125) has recently used his antiserum to HCG to localize the LH-secreting cells of the human adenohypophysis: they were aldehyde fuchsin and periodic acid-Schiff positive and were found both in the pars distalis and pars tuberalis. This may be the explanation for the LH found in rat, sheep, and human hypothalamic extracts by McCann, Taleisnik & Friedman (126), by Johnson & Nelson (127), and by Croxatto, Arrau & Croxatto (128).

Factors affecting secretion of LH.—It has been clearly shown in the rat that removal of negative feedback by gonadal steroids in either male or female results in enhanced rates of synthesis and release of LH as evidenced by rises in plasma and pituitary levels of LH (102, 105, 109, 112). Earlier work has also demonstrated that administration of gonadal steroids to the castrate rat will inhibit release and synthesis of LH (102, 109, 129). A recent study (130) demonstrated a fivefold increase in pituitary LH in castrate male rats and showed that estrone, testosterone, Δ⁴-androstenedione, and dehydroepiandrosterone inhibited this postcastration rise. Dose-response relationships were demonstrated. Dehydroepiandrosterone has been found to cause a regression of pituitary LH-secreting cells similar to, but less marked than, that produced by equivalent doses of testosterone (131). In the ewe (132) as in the rat (133, 134), progesterone alone appears to have little ability to inhibit LH release. The plant estrogen coumestrol also appears to inhibit gonadotropin secretion when given in high doses (135).

A nonsteroidal estrogen antagonist has been observed to augment LH secretion in intact but not in ovariectomized rats as predicted by theory (136). Similarly, Neumann, Hahn & Kramer (137, 138) have shown that administration of cyproterone, an androgen antagonist, leads to development of castration cells in the pituitary and may interfere with the masculinization of the hypothalamus which normally is produced by testicular androgens.

Nelson, Norton & Nalbandov (116) have shown that plasma LH increases after castration in the cockerel which indicates that the mechanism of regulation of this hormone in the bird bears some relationship to that already worked out in mammals.

Wakabayashi & Tamaoki (139) have prepared antiovine LH antiserum and have used it to isolate the hormone by immunochemical means from the pituitaries of rats, rabbits, and sheep. With this technique they have been able to demonstrate in short-term incubation experiments the incorporation of ^{14}C-leucine into hypophyseal LH. This is taken to mean that *in vitro* biosynthesis of the hormone has occurred. Castration produced an increase in such biosynthesis which could be reduced by administration of testosterone *in vivo* to either castrates or to normals (140). Testosterone added directly *in vitro* was without effect on the biosynthesis. Furthermore, active immunization of rats with ovine LH (141) counteracted the action of the endogenously produced and exogenous LH, so that changes similar to those with castration were produced. Others have also shown that antisera to gonadotropins will block the biological activity of both exogenous and endogenous gonadotropins (142–145).

In addition to repressing LH secretion, it is clear that ovarian steroids can stimulate this secretion under certain conditions in the normal cycle as indicated by advancement of ovulation [see Everett (146)]. Using the OAAD assay, Nallar, Antunes-Rodrigues & McCann (147) have now shown that 1.5 mg of progesterone given subcutaneously can elevate plasma LH throughout the preovulatory phase of the estrous cycle of the rat: such a rise was observed within six hours and reached particularly high levels at proestrus. At estrus, after ovulation, and during early diestrus there was no effect. This was also the case in spayed rats. There appears to be a fairly wide interval, presumably related to estrogen-priming from the maturing follicles, when progesterone can trigger LH secretion. Since progesterone is present at this stage of the cycle in both man (148) and rat (149), it may play a physiological role in triggering the ovulatory burst of LH secretion.

The effectiveness of progesterone in triggering ovulation in proestrus has also recently been noted by Zeilmaker (150) and by Redmond & Everett (151). Similarly, Zarrow & Hurlbut (152) have defined conditions for both inhibitory and stimulatory effects of progesterone on pregnant mares' serum (PMS)-induced ovulation in immature rats, and Döcke & Dörner (153) have observed that progesterone can facilitate estrogen-induced ovulation in immature rats.

Hilliard, Penardi & Sawyer (154) have recently demonstrated that LH stimulates synthesis and release of 20α-hydroxypregn-4-en-3-one (20α-OH) from rabbit ovarian interstitial tissue. Similar findings have been obtained by Dorrington & Kilpatrick (155). Following coitus, a sustained high output of this steroid during the preovulatory period is correlated with high plasma levels of LH (154). Furthermore, this steroid can maintain high plasma LH in mated-spayed rabbits. It would appear that 20α-OH may be a positive feedback agent which helps trigger the postcoital ovulatory discharge of LH in the rabbit.

Callantine, Humphrey & Nesset (156) have recently demonstrated that daily injections into intact rats of a small dose (0.06 μg/100 g) of 17β-estradiol can elevate plasma and lower pituitary LH on measurement seven days later. Ratner & McCann (unpublished data) have observed that a single injection of estradiol benzoate given on the first day of diestrus can elevate plasma LH on measurement twenty-four hours later. These results substantiate the early work on advancement of ovulation [see Everett (146)] and indicate that estrogens also can play a role in producing the ovulatory surge of LH secretion. The relative importance of estrogenic and progestational steroids in the normal animal remains to be determined.

Rennels & O'Steen (157) found a decrease in pituitary LH on the third day after injection of ovulatory doses of PMS into immature rats which was correlated with an increase in pituitary weight (an effect of estrogen). They postulate that ovarian estrogen produced as a result of PMS triggers ovulation by a positive feedback mechanism. Thus, these positive feedbacks are not limited to the adult, but may also be operative in immature animals.

The antifertility steroids appear to act primarily by inhibiting secretion of gonadotropins (FSH and LH) as indicated by further studies in the rat (158), rabbit (159), and man (160–162). In the latter, reduction in urinary LH has been observed (161) and absence of a preovulatory peak in urinary (160) and plasma LH (162) has also been noted. In view of the variety of steroids and dosages now in use, care must be exercised before generalizing in any particular instance.

As in the case of most other pituitary hormones, evidence is accumulating to indicate that LH may feedback negatively to inhibit its own secretion. In order to be meaningful, such experiments must be carried out in castrates to eliminate effects of gonadal steroids secreted secondarily as the result of LH. The results of two studies have been published (163, 164) in which LH has been implanted into the median eminence of spayed rats. In each study a rather modest fall in pituitary LH was demonstrated. In one (163) plasma LH was reported to be lowered in a single experiment, whereas in the other study no such effect was observed (164).

In our own work on this problem (McCann et al., unpublished data), a small decline in pituitary LH was observed which was of borderline significance. No consistent significant effect of these implants on plasma LH was observed in twelve separate experiments. Large doses of LH were also administered intravenously to ovariectomized and hypophysectomized rats and assays were performed after sufficient time had elapsed to allow for disappearance of the exogenous LH. A borderline lowering of plasma LH was observed in nine experiments, and the circulating LRF found in plasma of the chronically hypophysectomized rats disappeared. Ramirez et al. (165) have just reported that LH injections can alter hypothalamic unit activity in the basal tuberal region, an observation which suggests a feedback action on this portion of the brain.

Taken altogether, the data indicate that this autofeedback of LH does exist, but since the observed effects were small, it would appear to be inoperative except at upper physiological levels of LH secretion. Perhaps this is one factor which causes plasma LH to plateau at a high level in the chronically ovariectomized rat and which serves to shut off LH secretion at the end of the ovulatory burst. From a functional standpoint it seems self-defeating for such a feedback to be operative at lower plasma levels of hormone necessary for the hormone to exercise its effect on the target organs. Whether or not this feedback operates via sensing in the hypothalamus of peripheral circulating levels of LH or via delivery of high levels of LH to the hypothalamus either by retrograde flow in portal vessels or by diffusion from the pars tuberalis remains to be seen.

Overwhelming evidence is now available to indicate that a preovulatory discharge of LH occurs in a wide variety of vertebrate species. Recent observations based on assay of plasma LH indicate this to be the case in woman (121, 122) and in rat (110, 111, 166), cow (166), pig (166, 167), and chicken (168), although in the latter instance three peaks apparently precede ovulation. Pituitary LH also appears to show a relatively constant pattern in rats, with highest levels just prior to ovulation in proestrus and a drop in estrus (107). This has now been observed also in the hamster (169), sheep (170), and chicken (168, 171).

Quinn (172) has added diphenylhydantoin to the list of drugs which block ovulation in the rat. The blockade can be overcome by stimulation of the medial preoptic area. Alleva & Umberger (173) have shown that a variety of drugs block ovulation in hamsters, including phenylisopropylhydrazine, tranylcypromine, iproniazid, and pargyline; however, surprisingly, pentobarbital, chlorpromazine, and reserpine which are effective in rats were without effect in doses which evoked marked behavioral depression. Deanesly (174) has, however, found that reserpine will block ovulation in the guinea pig, but, whereas reserpine evokes pseudopregnancy in the rat, it appears to have an inhibitory effect on development and function of the corpus luteum in the guinea pig. Hiroi, Sugita & Suzuki (175) have used the technique of implantation to localize the action of copper ions in inducing ovulation in rabbits to the posterior median eminence region.

Interestingly enough, Albert & Mendoza (176) have reported a twofold fluctuation in day-to-day urinary gonadotropin secretion in a postmenopausal woman.

Changes in pituitary LH during pregnancy and a fall during lactation have been described in hamster (177), rat (178), and pig (179); however, in the absence of plasma levels of the hormone, conclusions as to the secretion rate of LH remain inferential. In one study (180), lactation was shown to prevent the postspaying elevation in plasma LH. This coupled with decreased pituitary levels indicates decreased synthesis and release.

Puberty has been thought to be caused by a decreased sensitivity to the negative feedback of gonadal steroids since gonadotropin secretion is inhibited by lower doses of gonadal steroids in immature rats than are effective in adult rats (113, 181). Strong support for this hypothesis is provided by the findings of Smith & Davidson (182) that hypothalamic implants of testosterone are much more effective in inhibiting gonadotropin secretion in immature than in adult rats. Small amounts of estrogen from the infantile gonad may bring about this resetting since Ramirez & Sawyer (183) have observed advancement of puberty by injection of minute doses of estradiol.

Taleisnik, Caligaris & Astrada (184) have reported that copulation in rats of either sex causes an acute release of LH as indicated by an increase in plasma and fall in pituitary LH. If spayed rats are pretreated with estrogen-progesterone, copulation can still elevate plasma LH which indicates that this effect occurs independently of alterations in steroid output. Apparently the rat is more like the rabbit than previously suspected. A rise in pituitary FSH was observed four hours after copulation in males, but no other detectable effects on FSH were noted.

Hysterectomy, which is known to be less effective in altering luteal function in the rat than in the guinea pig, failed to alter hypophyseal FSH or LH in pseudopregnant rats (185).

Hypothalamic control of LH secretion.—Hypothalamic control over LH secretion is now well established. It appears that the basal tuberal region mediates basal LH secretion and that in females a more rostral region which includes the suprachiasmatic area is responsible for the ovulatory burst of LH.

Pituitary LH has been studied in rats with constant vaginal estrus as a result of exposure to light, neonatal administration of androgen, or rostral hypothalamic lesions. Although pituitary LH tends to be low in these situations (186–190), this is not always the case, and elevations have even been reported (187, 188). It is still possible that all three of these types of constant estrus act by inhibiting the ovulatory surge of LH, but complications arise depending on the severity and duration of the defect. The constant secretion of estrogen by the ovaries in these animals exerts another complicating influence since estrogen feeds back to alter LH secretion. Antunes-Rodrigues & McCann (191) obviated this difficulty by studying pituitary and plasma LH in ovariectomized rats with rostral hypothalamic lesions of the type known to induce constant estrus. The postcastration rise in plasma and pituitary LH was not altered by the lesions. This led to the conclusion that the negative feedback action of estrogen is intact in such animals and resides more caudally in the hypothalamus as shown by studies with estrogen implants (115, 192–194).

Constant estrus as a result of a neonatal androgen treatment probably is brought about by an inductive action of the steroid on the suprachiasmatic region which eliminates the ovulatory discharge of gonadotropins (195). Wagner, Erwin & Critchlow (196) have provided additional evidence for this point of view. They demonstrated that testosterone implants in the suprachiasmatic region of newborn females could produce the syndrome.

Smith & Davidson (197) have just found that testosterone implants in the median eminence will inhibit gonadotropin secretion even in hypophysectomized rats with pituitary grafts to the kidney capsule. In this situation the implants could hardly have influenced the pituitary directly. This, taken together with other evidence, clearly establishes the existence of negative feedback at the level of the median eminence region.

The positive feedback of both estrogen and progesterone is presumably mediated by steroid-sensitive neurons in the suprachiasmatic region as indicated by the implantation studies of Döcke & Dörner (198), who were able to induce ovulation in immature rats by implantation of estrogen into this area. Palka, Ramirez & Sawyer (199) observed stimulation of LH secretion with more caudally placed implants of radioactive estrogen, but radioactivity was detectable 2 mm from the site of implantation, so that we would conclude that these data are also consistent with a rostral site for the positive feedback. Indeed the receptors which react to gonadal steroids and stimulate LH secretion may be the same detectors which evoke mating behavior following implantation of these steroids into the suprachiasmatic region (200, 201).

Consistent with these postulated loci of estrogen feedback are the recent demonstrations of selective uptake of labeled estradiol by the anterior hypothalamus, median eminence, and anterior pituitary (202–205). A similar hypothalamic uptake of labeled progesterone has also been observed (206).

Changes in activity of single hypothalamic neurons can also be correlated with altered estrogen levels (207, 208). Ovulation-blocking doses of antifertility norsteroids and progesterone derivatives elevated the threshold of the EEG afterreaction, but failed to alter the EEG arousal response (209).

Alterations in hypothalamic catecholamines and cholinesterase with the stages of the estrous cycle or following altered titers of gonadal steroids have recently been observed, which suggest that both cholinergic and adrenergic synapses may be involved in mediating hypothalamic control of gonadotropin secretion (210–212). Furthermore, Coppola, Leonardi & Lippman (213) observed that drugs which deplete brain stores of catecholamines would prevent PMS-induced ovulation in the rat.

The primary controller of gonadotropin secretion lies in the basal, tuberal region. Earlier work with hypothalamic lesions clearly indicated this (105); Halász & Gorski (112) have provided further evidence for this concept by use of an ingenious knife with which it is possible to isolate the medial, basal hypothalamic region from the rest of the brain. Such animals do not ovulate because of loss of the input from the rostral "ovulatory center" just described, but react normally to castration with an increase in plasma and pituitary LH which indicates that the negative feedback mechanism is still operative. Partial cuts block ovulation only if so placed as to interrupt the pathway running from the rostral ovulatory center to the basal tuberal region.

Seven years after its discovery (126), there can be little doubt that the luteinizing hormone-releasing factor constitutes the final common pathway from brain to pituitary gland. This factor has been shown to elevate plasma LH in a variety of test systems (102, 214–216), to be effective even if median eminence lesions have eliminated neural control of the pituitary (215), and to act if injected directly into the pituitary *in vivo* (217, 218) or if added directly to the gland in short-term incubation experiments *in vitro* (219–221). Lastly, it will evoke ovulation (217, 218, 222, 223).

The pituitary responds to LRF at all stages of the estrous cycle with an outpouring of LH (224), which suggests that the ovulatory surge of LH secretion is brought about by increased release of LRF rather than by altered sensitivity of the gland to constant levels of the factor. A variety of situations are associated with altered stores of LRF in the hypothalamus. For example, Piacsek & Meites (220) reported that castration elevated the content of stored LRF in males, whereas in females a fall occurred. Alterations were also reported to occur following injections of steroids. Earlier, Chowers & McCann (225) had noted that testosterone injections could lower the content of stored LRF and that implants of either estrogen or testosterone into the median eminence could lower the content of LRF. These observations, coupled with the sensitivity of the steroid-blocked pituitary to LRF (214, 216), indicate that the hypothalamus is the principal site of the negative feedback of gonadal steroids, although some action at the pituitary level is well documented (193, 226).

In addition, a fall in stored LRF occurs at proestrus (225, 227) and at puberty (228), i.e., times when LH release is accelerated. Campbell & Gallardo (229) have shown that LRF first appears in the hypothalamus of fetal rabbits at the time of development of the hypophyseal portal system.

Studies of the content of LRF stored in the hypothalamus are difficult to interpret in the absence of information on the release of the factor, although it is probably safe to conclude that an acute fall in stored releasing factor is associated with its release. To obtain data on the release of LRF, attempts to measure the plasma level of the factor have been made. Nallar & McCann (230) reported that plasma from long-term but not short-term hypophysectomized rats depleted ovarian ascorbic acid. The activity vanished after destruction of the median eminence and was thus thought to be caused by a circulating LRF. Further studies (Nallar & McCann, unpublished data) showed that exogenous LH injections could lower the activity as could combined treatment with estrogen and progesterone (Antunes-

Rodrigues & McCann, unpublished data). Unfortunately, variable and frequently undetectable levels of the circulating LRF have hampered our study of this problem. A similar activity has been found in plasma of chronically hypophysectomized chickens by Frankel & colleagues (231).

Considerable gonadotropin secretion occurs when multiple pituitary grafts are placed in hypophysectomized hosts. Testicular and accessory sex organ maintenance is frequently pronounced. The degree of maintenance is proportional to the number of such grafts (68). Recent studies by Beddow & McCann (232) indicate that the residual function of the grafted gland is at least in part caused by circulating gonadotropin-releasing factors, for median eminence lesions in grafted animals led to regression of testicular and accessory organ weight.

Studies of the content of LRF in hypophyseal portal vessel blood which are in progress in two laboratories [(38); Porter, Crighton & McCann, unpublished data] should throw new light on the factors influencing its secretion and are eagerly awaited.

The neurosecretory elements which synthesize the LRF are probably located in the basal tuberal region, perhaps in the arcuate nuclei as indicated by early studies of the localization of the factor in hypothalamic extracts (215) and the studies with the isolated basal tuberal region mentioned above (112). In addition, if the pituitary is grafted to the hypothalamus, gonadotrophs differentiate when it is placed in this region (233, 234). Therefore, it is hard to interpret the recent report of LH-releasing activity in a variety of brain loci (235). The extracts were injected directly into the pituitary *in vivo* and one wonders if sufficient material may have reached the hypothalamus by backflow up portal vessels to produce a stimulation of the hypothalamic mechanism evoking LH release.

Evans & Nikitovitch-Winer (236) have observed that chronic infusion of hypothalamic extract into grafted pituitaries will lead to differentiation of gonadotrophs and reinitiation of gonadotropin secretion; this observation is supported by Ducommun & Guillemin (237) who found that topical application of hypothalamic extracts to a pouch containing pituitaries led to maintenance of the staining characteristics of the pituitary cells. The gonadotropin-releasing factors may promote synthesis of hormone as well as release.

An understanding of the mechanism of action of the antifertility steroids in blocking LH release has been the objective of several studies. Norethindrone has been reported (238) to block the LH release to infusion of hypothalamic extract which suggests a pituitary site for the blockade. On the other hand, Gellert & Exley (239) found that chlormadinone failed to block ovulation induced by hypothalamic stimulation which suggests a hypothalamic site. Perhaps, as in the case of other steroids, an action at both sites will eventually be demonstrated.

Clomiphene evokes ovulation by stimulating gonadotropin secretion and elevates plasma LH when implanted directly into the median eminence of rats (240). Apparently the drug acts as an antiestrogen to remove the negative feedback of gonadal steroids which results in a surge of LRF followed by LH.

With reference to other brain areas and gonadotropin secretion, Bar-Sela, Elwers & Critchlow (241) observed that electrical stimulation of the corticomedial division of the amygdaloid complex resulted in delayed puberty in female rats. Stimulation of control areas was ineffective. They suggested a role for the amygdala in the control of the onset of puberty. On the other hand, no effect on the estrous cycle of removal of the olfactory bulbs (242) or of midbrain-hypothalamic afferents (243) was noted in other studies.

Regulation of Follicle-Stimulating Hormone (FSH) Secretion

Assay of FSH.—By comparison with LH, our knowledge of the regulation of FSH secretion has been even more limited by the inadequacies of bioassay. The ovarian weight augmentation assay in rat (244) or mouse (245) is generally accepted to be specific for FSH, but both of these methods are relatively insensitive to the hormone. Igarashi & McCann (246) reported a much more sensitive assay in which uterine weight augmentation in mice was used. This method requires careful control of strain and weight of mice and suffers from a relatively narrow dose-response curve and mediocre precision. Large doses of LH were reported to interfere with the method. Because of its great sensitivity, it made possible multiple assays of plasma FSH which resulted in the discovery and purification of the hypothalamic FSH-releasing factor (FRF) (247–249). Recently, de Reviers & Mauleon (250) have claimed that even low doses of LH interfere with the assay of FSH by this method. These results could not be confirmed by Igarashi & Ehara (251). They may be attributed either to a strain difference or to the use of too low a dose of human chorionic gonadotropin (HCG) to eliminate an augmenting effect of LH on uterine weight. Lamond & Bindon (252) have recently modified the assay of Igarashi & McCann by the use of hypophysectomized mice. They report improved specificity and precision by this change.

Even in the case of the Steelman-Pohley assay, changing the number of daily injections of certain FSH preparations can alter the slope of the dose-response curve (253). Again, the ultimate answer appears to lie in the development of satisfactory immunoassays for FSH (254, 255).

Factors affecting secretion of FSH.—As in the case of LH, castration results in increased plasma (109, 247, 257) and pituitary levels (256–258) of the hormone which indicates that gonadal steroids exert a negative feedback on secretion of FSH. The rise in pituitary levels of the hormone following castration is much more delayed for FSH than for LH (256). Cryptorchidism has recently been reported to cause a rise in both FSH and LH in the pituitary (256). The cause of this interesting effect remains to be elucidated.

As in the case of LH, gonadal steroids can inhibit the postcastration rise in plasma (109, 257) and pituitary FSH (109, 130); however, androgens increase pituitary FSH in the castrate, whereas pituitary LH falls (129, 130). This is one of the prime examples of a difference in the regulation of the two hormones. Perhaps androgens may have a direct effect on the pituitary to stimulate FSH synthesis. Callantine & Humphrey (259) have reported that PMS induces a decrease in pituitary FSH and LH. The decrease in the former but not in the latter is blocked by a large dose of progesterone.

It now appears that a preovulatory discharge of FSH may also take place in both sheep (170) and man (260, 261). Further study of this important point is awaited with interest. As in the case of LH, FSH may act on the hypothalamus to inhibit its own secretion, for Corbin & Story (262) have reported declines in hypothalamic FRF and pituitary FSH in intact rats with implants of FSH into the median eminence. Control implants were ineffective.

Hypothalamic control of FSH secretion.—Since the discovery of FRF in 1963 (247–249), considerable effort has been devoted to the study of this hypothalamic factor. Kuroshima et al. (263) have confirmed the observation that hypothalamic extracts can elevate plasma FSH in the ovariectomized, steroid-blocked rat. Since the factor is active *in vivo* in rats with median eminence lesions which block FSH release (247) and is also active in releasing pituitary FSH *in vitro* in either long-term (264) or short-term incubation studies (263, 265), FRF appears to act directly on the gland to evoke FSH release. Consistent with this concept are the reports that hypothalamic extract can deplete pituitary FSH acutely *in vivo* in normal male rats (266), castrated males treated with testosterone (267), and ovariectomized females treated with estrogen and progesterone (268). Rather surprisingly, Saito et al. (267) found that histamine, spermidine (but not spermine), and vasopressin were also active, although less so than purified FRF, in depleting FSH in the castrate male pretreated with testosterone. This assay may not be sufficiently specific for use in characterization of the FRF.

In a six-hour incubation of adult male rat anterior pituitary halves, Mittler & Meites (265) reported a dose-response relationship between the quantity of hypothalamic extract added and the release of FSH, a result which was confirmed by Watanabe & McCann (269). The former workers reported that castration elevated and testosterone propionate injections reduced the content of stored FRF in the hypothalamus, whereas the latter found a fall in level of stored factor after castration and no change with testosterone (Watanabe & McCann, unpublished data). The explanation for this discrepancy is not at hand.

Watanabe, Dhariwal & McCann (270, 271) and Jutisz & de la Llosa (272) have reported that puromycin and actinomycin will block the FSH-releasing action of hypothalamic extracts *in vitro*. This suggests that protein synthesis may be required for the FRF to evoke release of FSH from the pituitary cell. Similarly, Jutisz (273) has reported that puromycin will block the action of the LRF, a result which has not been confirmed since both Crighton, Watanabe & McCann (274) and Samli & Geschwind (275) failed to find an inhibition in LH release with either puromycin or actinomycin. Since the former workers used the same conditions as in their studies of the effects of the antibiotics on FSH release, it would appear that the mechanism of action of these two factors may be dissimilar. Further studies on the mechanism of action of the gonadotropin-releasing factors may clarify the situation.

REGULATION OF PROLACTIN SECRETION

Assay of prolactin.—The pigeon crop sac assay has remained the major bioassay for this hormone; but here again the advent of immunoassay is eagerly anticipated. Nicoll (276) has developed a further modification of this assay which appears to improve the precision of the method. Additional histological evidence that erythrosinophilic cells constitute the cellular source of prolactin has been presented in rabbit (277) and dog (278).

Factors affecting secretion of prolactin.—Gonadal steroids influence prolactin secretion (146), and it has recently been shown that ovariectomy reduced the pituitary content of prolactin as estimated by the width of the "prolactin band" obtained by means of disk electrophoresis. On the other hand, treatment of ovariectomized rats with norethynodrel intensified the band (279). This effect is probably attributable to the estrogenic action of the norethynodrel. The growth hormone (GH) band was accentuated by ovariectomy and depleted by norethynodrel. It is unfortunate that these interesting results were not confirmed by direct bioassay. Androgen-sterilized rats have been reported to have diminished levels of prolactin in their pituitaries without evidence in terms of mammary changes of enhanced release (280).

It now appears that prolactin can be included among the pituitary hormones which have autofeedback control since MacLeod, Smith & DeWitt (281) have demonstrated that pituitary tumors which secrete both growth hormone (GH) and prolactin have decreased prolactin and GH bands as determined by polyacrylamide gel electrophoresis. On the other hand, tumors which secrete GH but not prolactin show only the reduction in the GH band.

An interesting recent study by Dominic (282) suggests that the olfactory block to pregnancy in mice is caused by an inhibition in prolactin release. The block could be overcome by administration of exogenous prolactin, by reserpine which evokes endogenous prolactin release, or by an ectopic pituitary homograft which again would serve as a source for endogenous prolactin.

A variety of exteroceptive stimuli, such as sound, intermittent bright light, and the odor of oil of peppermint, which were effective in inhibiting oxytocin release, failed to block the nursing-induced depletion of pituitary prolactin in lactating female rats (283). This again would indicate that oxytocin is not the predominant factor which releases prolactin.

Hypothalamic control of prolactin secretion.—Everett & Quinn (284) have shown by electrical stimulation of the rat hypothalamus that the areas which produce ovulation indicative of luteinizing hormone release and those which produce pseudopregnancy indicative of prolactin release are separable. Consequently, it would appear that different hypothalamic regions are involved in the regulation of each of these tropins. They (285) have been able to evoke delayed pseudopregnancy by suitable stimulation of the area controlling prolactin release.

It has previously been shown that implantation of estrogen into the basal tuberal hypothalamus will evoke prolactin secretion in both rat (286) and rabbit (287). Tindal, Knaggs & Turvey (288) have now reported that estrogen implanted in the amygdala or stria terminalis will evoke prolactin release in the rabbit. These results are hard to integrate with current thinking. Perhaps the cells of these extrahypothalamic areas are only minimally sensitive to estrogen so that effects can be obtained with pharmacologically high doses of estrogen adjacent to an implant of the steroid.

Certain mice with gold-thioglucose obesity appear to secrete abnormally large amounts of prolactin (289), probably because of injury to the hypothalamic mechanism which normally inhibits secretion of the hormone. The sterility of genetically dwarf mice (290) can be corrected by treatment with exogenous prolactin or endogenous hormone from pituitary grafts, which suggests that they may have a genetic defect in the central regulation of prolactin secretion.

Some years ago, Gale et al. (291) demonstrated that animals with median eminence lesions which interrupted the inhibitory hypothalamic control over prolactin release secreted large amounts of prolactin sufficient to maintain lactation in female rats. Similar findings have been reported by Ahmad & Lyons (292) in hypophysectomized rats with pituitaries transplanted under the kidney capsule. These animals appeared to secrete prolactin equivalent to at least 75 IU/day of the purified ovine hormone. Further evidence of persistent prolactin secretion after pituitary stalk section has been provided recently in both rat (293) and pig (294).

Removal of inhibitory hypothalamic control of prolactin release is also manifest *in vitro* since pituitaries in tissue culture or in short-term incubation were shown to release and synthesize large amounts of prolactin (295), observations confirmed by Robboy & Kahn (296) and by Gala & Reece (297) for several mammalian species.

Pasteels (298) and Talwalker, Ratner & Meites (299) showed that hypothalamic extracts would inhibit the *in vitro* release of prolactin. This provided the first evidence for a prolactin-inhibiting factor which presumably mediates the inhibitory hypothalamic influence over prolactin secretion. A dose-response relationship has been reported (300) for this effect. Cerebral cortical extracts and a variety of other pharmacologically active agents were without effect on the *in vitro* release of prolactin in these experiments. That the prolactin-inhibiting factor was active *in vivo* was demonstrated by Grosvenor, McCann & Nallar (301), who showed that hypothalamic but not cerebral cortical extracts could block the nursing-induced decline in pituitary prolactin. Kuroshima et al. (302) then showed that pig hypothalamic extracts could block the depletion of pituitary prolactin which follows cervical stimulation (303) in the rat. Thus, both *in vivo* and *in vitro* results point to the existence of a prolactin-inhibiting factor.

The recent report by Gala & Reece (304) is disturbing in that they find a stimulation of prolactin release in three-day cultures of anterior pituitary by epinephrine and commercial oxytocin (Pitocin). Could oxytocin play a role in prolactin release after all? This question needs re-examination.

The content of prolactin-inhibiting factor in the hypothalamus has been reported to vary in situations which alter prolactin release. It falls during lactation (305), although it is not altered detectably following acute suckling (306), and is also depleted by estrogen (305) and reserpine (307).

The inhibitory hypothalamic control of prolactin release also is operative in males since hypothalamic lesions can evoke lactation in male rats (308). The male pituitary incubated *in vitro* also releases considerable quantities of prolactin and this release can be blocked by hypothalamic extract (300). The function of prolactin in the male is not clear, and it is perhaps fortunate that hypothalamic inhibition is present in the male of the species.

As originally shown by Kragt & Meites (309), control of prolactin release in the bird seems to differ fundamentally from the pattern observed in mammals. Pituitary autotransplants in the pigeon fail to stimulate the crop sac (310) and the pigeon pituitary does not release appreciable prolactin when cultured *in vitro* (297). There appears to be a stimulatory hypothalamic influence on prolactin secretion in the bird which is mediated by a prolactin-stimulating factor (309).

Interestingly enough, Sinha & Meites (311) have shown that hypothalamic extract will stimulate growth hormone and inhibit prolactin release from a mammosomatotropic tumor incubated *in vitro*. This indicates that these tumors can still be affected by hypothalamic neurohumors, although not so affected when located *in situ*.

REGULATION OF GROWTH HORMONE (GH) SECRETION

Assay of GH.—In this case, in contrast to the other pituitary hormones, we have been fortunate to have workable radioimmunoassays already available. Application of these assays has already revolutionized our knowledge of the regulation of GH in primates (312, 313). In the rat information has been gleaned by the application of the "tibia assay" in hypophysectomized rats (314). This assay is not completely specific for GH and large amounts of prolactin and TSH interfere (314). A recent paper by Schooley, Friedkin & Evans (315) showed a discrepancy following thyroidectomy between the acidophil numbers and GH concentration as estimated by the tibia test. The discrepancy vanished if the hypophysectomized assay rats were also thyroidectomized. This procedure also resulted in lower estimates of GH in the pituitaries by a factor of four. They concluded that TSH in the pituitary extracts was sufficient to augment the response to GH and thereby lead to erroneous values. It is clear that care must be exercised in the interpretation of results based on the tibia test, and a valid immunoassay for rat GH is eagerly awaited. Such an assay has recently been reported by Schalch & Reichlin (316). It still remains to be determined if it is sufficiently specific for assay of the hormone in rat plasma.

Factors affecting secretion of GH.—A relationship between thyroid hormone levels and GH secretion has long been known. In further studies on this problem it has been shown (315) that thyroidectomy in the rat is associated with a rapid decrease in acidophil numbers and pituitary GH content which correlated well with the cessation of growth. Replacement therapy with 0.25 μg/day of L-thyroxine returned pituitary GH to normal (317).

The important observation that insulin-induced hypoglycemia causes an increase in plasma GH in man first made by Roth et al. (312, 313) has been repeatedly confirmed (318, 319). Similar results are obtained when intracellular glucose metabolism is blocked by α-2-deoxyglucose injection (312, 313, 318). Fasting may not be associated with altered levels of plasma GH (320), and the rise in GH associated with hypoglycemia is usually associated with other symptoms of hypoglycemia (321). This led Marks et al. (321) to conclude that "hypoglycemia is not per se a physiological stimulus to HGH (human growth hormone) secretion and owes its stimulatory effect largely to the neurogenic stress it produces." Regardless of its physiologic significance, hypoglycemia-induced GH secretion has become a valuable tool for study of GH secretion. The response is blunted for unknown reasons in obesity (312, 313, 318) and is reduced in thyrotoxicosis (322) and by treatment with adrenal corticoids (323). Several groups of investigators have demonstrated GH release in hypoglycemic monkeys (324–326).

Even in the rat insulin-induced hypoglycemia (327–330) or α-2-deoxyglucose injection (327) has been shown to result in an acute decrease in pituitary GH concentration indicative of a release of the hormone. Pituitary GH rebounded to normal levels even while blood sugar remained low, an observation suggesting rapid resynthesis of the hormone (327). Tolbutamide-treated weanling rats grew faster than controls, and it was suggested that hyperinsulinism induced by the drug stimulated pituitary GH discharge (331).

Pecile et al. (328, 329) have studied the effect of various drugs on the insulin-induced decline in pituitary GH in the rat. A large dose of cortisol

(5 mg/100 g), given for ten days, suppressed the response, a change in agreement with the findings in humans. Acute treatment with chlorpromazine, reserpine, or α-ethyltryptamine also was effective in blocking the response, whereas pentobarital, morphine, demethylimipramine, d-amphetamine, and iproniazid were ineffective (329). From a variety of other pharmacologic studies Müller et al. (330) concluded that reduction in stores of brain norepinephrine impairs GH release and that brain amines may play a role in the release of hypothalamic neurohumoral transmitters. Confirmation of these interesting results, which in some cases rested on single experiments, will be awaited with interest.

Several amino acids, of which arginine has been most extensively employed, will also trigger GH release in man (332–334). This mechanism is separable from the hypoglycemic trigger since hyperglycemia fails to affect the response to arginine (334). There appears to be a sex difference in the response to arginine, females responding more than males. Males can be made to mimic the female pattern by treatment with diethylstilbestrol. A similar sex difference in the response to exercise has been noted (335).

A variety of other stimuli, such as muscular exercise (312), surgical trauma (313), pain, histamine, epinephrine, chlorpromazine, and even anesthetization with pentobarbital (336), have been shown to elevate plasma GH in man or monkey. Similarly in the rat, surgical trauma, epinephrine, and cold have been found to deplete pituitary GH which suggests a release of the hormone from the gland (327, 329, 337). The pituitary concentration usually rebounded quickly to normal or even elevated levels and for several stimuli (327, 337) the initial decline either failed to occur or was not observed. On the basis of all these observations, it would seem reasonable to conclude that GH secretion is very labile in primates and in the rat and responds to a variety of nonspecific stimuli or stresses with an increase in GH release. The regulation of GH release is thus very reminiscent of that for ACTH, and the effect of insulin-induced hypoglycemia is even blocked by corticoids (323, 328). One discordant note has been struck, however, for Schalch & Reichlin (316) report that ether anesthesia for two minutes lowers GH levels in males and fails to alter them in female rats as determined by radioimmunoassay. The stress of anesthesia would be expected to elevate the levels, unless the rats were prestressed. This is a possibility since initial values were very high on comparison to resting levels in primates. They did not find elevated levels of GH in lactating rats, although Grosvenor et al. (338) have observed that the nursing stimulus causes an acute decline in pituitary GH as determined by bioassay.

As in the case of other anterior lobe hormones, evidence for a feedback of GH to inhibit its own secretion is now quite convincing. Pituitary tumors which secrete GH in the rat are associated with a decrease in anterior lobe size, acidophils, and GH concentration (281, 339). Koneff et al. (340) first showed as far back as 1949 that exogenous GH could produce a decrease in the acidophils in the pituitary. Krulich & McCann (341) recently showed that large doses of exogenous GH led first to an accumulation and later to a fall in GH in the pituitary. Shortly thereafter, Müller & Pecile (342) found that acute administration of GH would prevent the hypoglycemia-induced decline in pituitary GH stores. That this feedback is mediated centrally and not by some peripherally formed metabolite has been demonstrated by Katz, Molitch & McCann (343), who have found that GH implants in the median eminence and adjacent hypothalamic areas caused a reduction in anterior pituitary weight and GH concentration. Presumably, this effect is mediated at the hypothalamic level; however, an effect directly on the pituitary cannot be excluded. Since GH does not have a target gland which produces hormones that in turn feedback to inhibit release of GH, it is reasonable to postulate that GH autofeedback may play a relatively more important role in regulating GH release than is the case for the autofeedback of other anterior pituitary hormones.

No age-related changes in plasma GH have been well documented except for an elevation in premature and newborn infants (313). Plasma levels are not lowered after body growth has been completed.

Hypothalamic control of GH secretion.—Abrams et al. (324) have reported that median eminence or pituitary stalk lesions blocked the GH release in monkeys which follows insulin-induced hypoglycemia, although "basal" levels of plasma GH were normal. Krulich, Dhariwal & McCann (344) found that lesions which included the pituitary stalk and posterior median eminence caused a reduction in pituitary GH content in chronic experiments and blocked the insulin-induced decline in pituitary GH when tested a few days after lesions, at a time when it was still normal. Lesions in the anterior median eminence which block ACTH release from stress were ineffective which suggests a separation of the hypothalamic areas regulating GH and ACTH. Similarly, Han and colleagues (345, 346) have demonstrated an impairment in growth of weanling rats which became obese after lesions involving the ventromedial nuclei and median eminence.

Studies from several laboratories have left little doubt that stalk-median eminence extracts from a variety of species, including man (347, 348), can evoke release of GH when added to pituitaries incubated *in vitro* (349–353) and can produce an acute depletion of pituitary GH when given parenterally to rats (351, 354–356). The *in vitro* results are more impressive than the *in vivo* findings in view of the recent evidence for lability of pituitary GH stores in the living rat. An ideal *in vivo* assay for growth hormone-releasing factor (GRF) will probably require the use of animals with hypothalamic lesions or intrapituitary injection of the GRF. It should be pointed out, however, that cerebral cortical extracts, and a variety of pharmacologically active agents, including vasopressin, were inactive in releasing GH in the rat either *in vitro* or *in vivo* in the above studies. Furthermore, the *in vivo* assay has been used to follow the purification of GRF and its separation from other releasing factors (357, 358), which appears to indicate considerable specificity.

Growth hormone-releasing activity of stalk-median eminence extract has been demonstrated in the sheep where it produced an elevation in immunoreactive plasma GH (359). Cerebral cortical extract was inactive. Rises in plasma glucose and insulin were also noted which were not thought to be primary effects of the extract (359).

Stalk-median eminence extract also produces an elevation in plasma GH when infused into rhesus monkeys (325, 326, 360); cortical extract has little or no effect (325, 326). In the monkey the situation is complicated by the fact that large doses of vasopressin are also effective (361, 362). When the pressor activity of stalk-median eminence extract is destroyed by incubation with thioglycollate, an increase in plasma GH is still observed after injection of the extract, but the response is markedly reduced (362). By contrast, this treatment does not influence the LH-releasing or ACTH-releasing activities of hypothalamic extract (363). Could there be a relative species specificity of growth hormone-releasing factor? Obviously further experimentation is required to clarify the situation.

The beef or rat pituitary incubated *in vitro* can synthesize GH in either short- (353, 364, 365) or long-term incubations (351). Stalk-median eminence extract enhances this biosynthesis as indicated by increases in GH content determined by bioassay (351, 353, 364). Thus, the GRF exerts effects on synthesis as well as on release of GH. Whether the effects on synthesis are primary or secondary to a primary effect on release remains to be determined. The fact that depletion of hormone occurs quickly *in vivo* after administration of extracts indicates a primary effect on release of hormone from the gland.

Alterations in hypothalamic content of GH-releasing factor (GRF) in conditions associated with altered GH release would support the contention that variable rates of release of GRF result in varied output of hypophyseal GH in the intact animal. In this regard, Pecile et al. (366) report diminished GRF in the hypothalami of old rats. Meites & Fiel (367) reported a fall in both GRF and GH in the pituitary of fasting rats. A decline in pituitary GH in the fasted rat has also been noted by others (337, 368).

Convincing evidence for the physiological role of GRF would be provided if it were shown to increase in plasma in situations where GH release is enhanced. Krulich & McCann (369) were able to demonstrate just this when they showed that hypoglycemia led to the appearance of circulating GH-releasing activity in plasma of hypophysectomized rats. The activity vanished after coagulation of the median eminence, so the plasma activity was thought to represent circulating GRF. Katz, Krulich & McCann (370) and Katz, Dhariwal & McCann (371) showed that hypoglycemia in intact rats led to a fall in stored GRF, a result recently confirmed by Müller et al. (329). Thus, the evidence is excellent that hypoglycemia triggers GH secretion by releasing GRF.

Plasma GRF activity has also recently been observed in chronically hypophysectomized rats by Müller et al. (372). The activity was absent in short-term hypophysectomized rats (seven days) as in the study of Krulich & McCann (369). The appearance of LRF in plasma of chronically hypophysectomized rats had previously been observed by Nallar & McCann (230). This phenomenon may prove the rule for all releasing factors. The absence of the pituitary gland causes an atrophy of target glands and a removal of their negative feedback as well as the autofeedback from pituitary hormones. This would provide a maximal stimulus for secretion of releasing factor which finally reaches sufficient levels to be detectable in peripheral blood. It presumably acts via the blood stream to stimulate function of pituitaries grafted to a distant site. This provides an explanation for the residual function of these grafts.

Krulich and his collaborators (353, 373) have recently discovered in the course of screening Sephadex columns for GRF that certain fractions eluted from the column strongly inhibited the release of GH from pituitaries incubated *in vitro*. The active factor was named GH-inhibiting factor (GIF). This GIF was found in tubes which were free of most other releasing factors, such as the gonadotropin-releasers, PIF and CRF. Apparently, it is a distinct entity and appears to block primarily the release of GH. It will antagonize the GH-releasing action of GRF *in vitro*. *In vivo,* it produces no apparent affect on pituitary GH when administered alone, but appears capable of preventing the GRF-induced decline in GH. Does this mean that GH is under dual hypothalamic control by both inhibiting and stimulating factors as already postulated for MSH? (See section on melanocyte-stimulating hormone.) Further study of this intriguing possibility is eagerly awaited. It is of interest that this is an example of a biological effect which was unmasked by chemical fractionation since in crude stalk-median eminence extract the GRF predominates and prevents the GIF from finding expression.

Regulation of Melanocyte-Stimulating Hormone (MSH) Secretion

The regulation of this hormone has received only scant attention in the past. It is generally recognized as a result of the pioneer studies of Etkin (374) that the hypothalamus exercises an inhibitory control over MSH release in amphibians. Kastin & Ross (375) have provided further evidence for this assertion by showing that hypothalamic lesions in frogs led to a fall in pituitary MSH stores and an increase in plasma MSH as determined by parabiosis. Similar results for pituitary MSH were recorded in hypophysectomized rats with pituitary grafts (376).

The function of MSH in mammals remains an enigma. A transplantable pituitary tumor in mice has been shown to secrete MSH (probably α-MSH) (377). Darkening of coat color was produced by the tumor or by exogenous administration of α-MSH (378). Taleisnik & Orías (379) observed that the nursing stimulus would deplete pituitary MSH (but not ACTH) from the pituitary. Thus, MSH must be added to the list of hormones discharged as a result of the suckling stimulus, which included prolactin, ACTH, GH, oxytocin, and vasopressin. The physiological significance of the released MSH is anyone's guess.

Taleisnik & Orías (380) have also reported that rat stalk-median eminence extracts will deplete pituitary MSH. Other substances such as vasopressin and oxytocin, and cerebral cortical extract were inactive, and the active substance has been purified and separated from most other hypothalamic releasing factors (381). This MSH-releasing factor (MRF) has been localized to the paraventricular nucleus and median eminence with lesser amounts found in the neural lobe (382).

In another study Taleisnik & Tomatis (383) reported that rat stalk-median eminence extract also depleted pituitary MSH in the toad. On the other hand, toad hypothalamic extracts had no such effect and in fact blocked the response to rat extract. A dose-response relationship was demonstrated and the MSH-inhibiting factor (MIF) was thermostable and inactivated by trypsin, as was MRF. The toad hypothalamic extract also inhibited the nursing-induced decline in MSH but did not affect release of ACTH or LH. By contrast, toad neural lobe extracts caused a depletion of pituitary MSH, which led to the conclusion that MRF was present in this tissue. Thus, in the toad a dual control of MSH by MRF and an MIF was postulated. More recently, Taleisnik (384) has also produced evidence of a similar kind for MIF in the rat hypothalamus, but the MIF was localized to the supraoptic region. The net MSH-releasing activity in rat median eminence extract and net MIF activity in toad median eminence are attributed to a greater abundance of the predominant one of the two factors in these extracts. In the toad MIF predominates; in the rat MRF has the upper hand.

Bercu & Brinkley (385) have also obtained evidence for a MIF in brain extracts from frog. They used *in vitro* incubation of frog pars intermedia. This tissue released large amounts of MSH spontaneously, which could be decreased by MIF. MIF was found in both hypothalamus and cerebral cortex.

Kastin & Schally (386, 387) have found that rat or beef stalk-median eminence extracts produce an elevation of pituitary MSH concentration, instead of the decrease observed by Taleisnik and collaborators with either rat or sheep hypothalamic extracts. Other substances known to be present in hypothalamus were without effect. They postulated an MIF in such extracts and have purified it by gel filtration, where it was found in the small molecular weight fraction, outside the usual zone containing the releasing factors. Is this MIF the same as that found by Bercu & Brinkley (385) and also observed by Taleisnik & Tomatis (383)? One puzzling feature of Kastin & Schally's results is the marked fluctuations in control pituitary MSH concentrations, which varied as much as fourfold from one experiment to another. Kastin & Schally (387) report that extraction of rat hypothalamic extracts at room temperature as performed by Taleisnik & Orías led to a fall in pituitary MSH, whereas extraction in the cold, according to their own procedure, led to a rise. This may explain the divergent results reported by these two groups. Obviously more work needs to be done to reconcile the divergent findings completely, but it would appear that both an MSH-releasing and an MSH-inhibiting factor may exist. Kastin & Schally (388) have observed that several tranquilizers will produce an acute depletion of pituitary melanocyte-stimulating hormone.

Kastin and associates (389, 390) have implicated the pineal gland in the regulation of MSH release. They observed that melatonin would decrease pituitary MSH stores (389), whereas pinealectomy increased them (390). Further work on this interesting subject is awaited. Many results in the literature suggest the possibility of a relationship between the pineal and the secretion of other anterior lobe hormones as well.

ADVANCES IN THE CHEMISTRY OF THE HYPOTHALAMIC RELEASING FACTORS[2] (p. 589)

The importance of the stalk and median eminence of the tuber cinereum as a source of hypothalamic hormones was demonstrated in 1959 and 1960 when an ACTH-releasing substance was extracted and purified from hypothalamic tissue (391–393). Prior to this time, the posterior lobe had been regarded as the chief source of ACTH-releasing substances, viz., corticotropin-releasing factor [for review, see (394, 395)]. Rumsfeld & Porter (391) used ion exchange chromatography to obtain a purified fraction that possessed ACTH-releasing activity. This fraction contained two ninhydrin-positive substances whose Rf values in five paper chromatographic systems and whose partition-coefficients as determined by countercurrent distribution indicated that the physical and chemical properties of these two substances were similar to, but different from, those of oxytocin and vasopressin. Royce & Sayers (393) purified CRF from hypothalamic tissue which they found by bioassay to be free of pressor activity (392, 393). The preparations of Rumsfeld & Porter and of Royce & Sayers (391–393) were inactive in hypophysectomized rats which indicated that ACTH was not a significant contaminant.

Subsequently, the technic of gel filtration [which was introduced by Porath & Flodin (396) and used later to separate the posterior lobe hormones (397)] has been useful in separating hypothalamic hormones, i.e., the releasing and inhibiting factors. Indeed, nearly all of the factors have been separated one from the other; and the purification of LRF, TRF, FRF, GRF, CRF, MRF, MIF, PIF, and GIF has been successfully achieved by this technic. This feat alone seems sufficient to justify the postulate that the secretory rate of each anterior lobe hormone is under the control of at least one hypothalamic inhibiting or releasing factor. An excellent review of the chemistry of the releasing factors has appeared recently (398).

When crude hypothalamic extracts are filtered through Sephadex G-25, they are eluted in the following order: GRF, CRF, TRF, MRF, FRF, PIF, and LRF as determined from the published work of Krulich, Dhariwal & McCann (353); McCann & Dhariwal (395); Dhariwal et al. (249), 381); Schally et al. (77, 358, 399, 400); and Guillemin (401). LRF is followed by vasopressin and MIF reportedly is most strongly retained on the gel (386). There is some overlap of the zones which contain adjacent factors, but gel filtration alone is sufficient to separate all the factors from vasopressin. A partial separation of FRF from LRF has been achieved (249, 400) and these activities are clearly separated from those of CRF and GRF. A separation of these latter two activities is also possible with sufficiently long columns of Sephadex (353). The newly discovered GH-inhibiting factor emerges from columns of Sephadex immediately after GRF but before CRF (353). We have encountered difficulty in separating PIF from LRF by gel filtration; however, there has been a tendency for PIF to emerge from the column just prior to LRF (402). Furthermore, Arimura et al. (403) reported that highly purified LRF is devoid of PIF activity. MRF (381) and TRF (77) are found near the FRF zone.

All of the factors with the exception of MIF and MRF have been further purified by ion exchange chromatography on carboxymethyl cellulose. [It should be noted that Dhariwal et al. (42, 404) and Schally et al. (399, 400) demonstrated that all solutions ought to be desalted prior to chromatography on CMC.] For example, Guillemin, Jutisz & Sakiz (405) were the first to carry LRF to this stage of purification, a result confirmed by Schally & Bowers (399) and by Dhariwal, Antunes-Rodrigues & McCann (404). Ramirez, Nallar & McCann (406); Fawcett, Harris & Reed (407); and Nikitovitch-Winer, Pribble & Winer (408) have also purified LRF. Ion exchange chromatography separates residual contaminating LRF from FRF (400, 409) and can be used to complete the separation of CRF from GRF as shown by Dhariwal et al. (357). The use of similar techniques enabled McCann, Dhariwal and associates to report the first purification of GRF (410), FRF (248, 249), MRF (381), GIF (353), and PIF (402). TRF is also freed of contaminants by this procedure (77, 411), but LRF and PIF were not clearly separated by carboxymethyl cellulose chromatography (402). Some of the factors have been carried through several additional purification steps. The preparation of highly purified TRF has recently been reported by two laboratories (74, 76).

Although CRF was the first of the factors to be discovered and partial structures of several CRF's (α-2-CRF, β-CRF) have been published (412, 413), its complete structure is still unknown. It is thought that CRF is a peptide since it is inactivated by pepsin (414) and that it is dissimilar from vasopressin and oxytocin since it is not inactivated by thioglycollate (363), an agent which destroys the biological activity of oxytocin and vasopressin by reducing the disulfide bond in each molecule. A similar statement holds for LRF (363). Furthermore, gel filtration on Sephadex is sufficient to separate hypothalamic CRF from vasopressin (42).

The factors LRF (215, 415), GRF (362), MRF (380), MIF (383), TRF

(415), and FRF (409) have also been inactivated by proteolytic enzymes. Techniques of purification designed to separate peptides have been employed to prepare the purified releasing factors, and the amino acid compositions of hypothalamic CRF (357), LRF (399, 401), TRF (77, 411), and GRF (357) have been reported. The assumption has been that the releasing factors constituted a new family of relatively small polypeptides; however, in recent reports Schally et al. (74) and Guillemin et al. (76) have questioned the peptidic nature of TRF since their highly purified fraction contained 30 and 5 per cent, respectively, of amino acids. Furthermore, Guillemin et al. (76) reported that his highly purified TRF was not inactivated by proteolytic enzymes, a result at variance with earlier studies from his laboratory (415). Progress has been hindered by the relatively small amounts of these materials which are found in the hypothalamus. Obviously, much more must be done to elucidate the chemical nature of these new hormones.

LITERATURE CITED

1. Guillemin, R. The adenohypophysis and its hypothalamic control. *Ann. Rev. Physiol.*, **29**, 313–48 (1967)
2. Meites, J., Nicoll, C. S. Adenohypophysis: prolactin. *Ann. Rev. Physiol.*, **28**, 57–88 (1966)
3. *Neuroendocrinology*, 1 (Martini, L., Ganong, W. F., Eds., Academic Press, New York and London, 774 pp., 1966)
4. *The Pituitary Gland*, 1-3 (Harris, G. W., Donovan, B. T., Eds., Univ. of California Press, Berkeley and Los Angeles, 1966)
5. *Brain and Behavior*, 3: *The Brain and Gonadal Function* (Gorski, R. A., Whalen, R. E., Eds., Univ. of California Press, Berkeley and Los Angeles, 289 pp., 1966)
6. Hinsey, J. C., Markee, J. E. Pregnancy following bilateral section of the cervical sympathetic trunks in the rabbit. *Proc. Soc. Exptl. Biol. Med.*, **31**, 270–71 (1933)
7. Porter, J. C., Hines, M. F. M., Smith, K. R., Repass, R. L., Smith, A. J. K. Quantitative evaluation of local blood flow of the adenohypophysis in rats. *Endocrinology*, **80**, 583–98 (1967)
8. Houssay, B.-A., Biasotti, A., Sammartino, R. Modifications fonctionnelles de l'hypophyse après les lésions infundibulo-tubériennes chez le crapaud. *Compt. Rend. Soc. Biol.*, **120**, 725–27 (1935)
9. Green, J. D., Harris, G. W. Observation of the hypophysio-portal vessels of the living rat. *J. Physiol. (London)*, **108**, 359–61 (1949)
10. Worthington, W. C., Jr. Some observations on the hypophyseal portal system in the living mouse. *Bull. Johns Hopkins Hosp.*, **97**, 343–57 (1955)
11. Török, B. Lebendbeobachtung des hypophysenkreislaufes an hunden. *Acta Morphol. Acad. Sci. Hung.*, **4**, 83–89 (1954)
12. Daniel, P. M., Prichard, M. M. L. Anterior pituitary necrosis. Infarction of the pars distalis produced experimentally in the rat. *Quart. J. Exptl. Physiol.*, **41**, 215–29 (1956)
13. Duvernoy, H. *Contribution a l'étude de la vascularisation de l'hypophyse* (Doctoral thesis, École Natl. Med. de Besançon, Paris, 1958)
14. Daniel, P. M., Prichard, M. M. L. The vascular arrangements of the pituitary gland of the sheep. *Quart. J. Exptl. Physiol.*, **42**, 237–48 (1957)
15. Daniel, P. M., Prichard, M. M. L. The effects of pituitary stalk section in the goat. *Am. J. Pathol.*, **34**, 433–69 (1958)
16. Xuereb, G. P., Prichard, M. M. L., Daniel, P. M. The arterial supply and venous drainage of the human hypophysis cerebri. *Quart. J.*

Exptl. Physiol., **39**, 199–217 (1954)

17. Xuereb, G. P., Prichard, M. M. L., Daniel, P. M. The hypophysial portal system of vessels in man. *Ibid.*, 219–30

18. Adams, J. H., Daniel, P. M., Prichard, M. M. L. Volume of the infarct in the anterior lobe of the monkey's pituitary gland shortly after stalk section. *Nature*, **198**, 1205–6 (1963)

19. Szentágothai, J., Flerkó, B., Mess, B., Halász, B. *Hypothalamic Control of the Anterior Pituitary*, 92 (Akad. Kiado, Budapest, 330 pp., 1962)

20. Adams, J. H., Daniel, P. M., Prichard, M. M. L., Schurr, P. H. The volume of the infarct in pars distalis of a human pituitary gland, 30 hr after transection of the pituitary stalk. *J. Physiol. (London)*, **166**, 39P–41P (1963)

21. Adams, J. H., Daniel, P. M., Prichard, M. M. L. Observations on the portal circulation of the pituitary gland. *Neuroendocrinology*, **1**, 193–213 (1965/66)

22. Adams, J. H., Daniel, P. M., Prichard, M. M. L. The long-term effect of transection of the pituitary stalk on the volume of the pituitary gland of the adult goat. *Acta Endocrinol.*, **51**, 377–90 (1966)

23. Adams, J. H., Daniel, P. M., Prichard, M. M. L. Transection of the pituitary stalk in the goat and its effect on the volume of the pituitary gland. *J. Pathol. Bacteriol.*, **87**, 1–14 (1964)

24. Adams, J. H., Daniel, P. M., Prichard, M. M. L. Distribution of hypophysial portal blood in the anterior lobe of the pituitary gland. *Endocrinology*, **75**, 120–26 (1964)

25. Goldman, H. Endocrine gland blood flow in the unanesthetized, unrestrained rat. *J. Appl. Physiol.*, **16**, 762–64 (1961)

26. Yates, F. E., Kirschman, R., Olshen, B. Analysis of adenohypophysial blood flow in the rat by radioisotope washout: estimate of the vasomotor activity of vasopressin in the anterior pituitary. *Endocrinology*, **79**, 341–51 (1966)

27. Dávid, M. A., Csernay, L., Lászlo, F. A., Kovács, K. Hypophysial blood flow in rats after destruc-

tion of the pituitary stalk. *Endocrinology*, **77**, 183–87 (1965)

28. Spencer, M. P., Denison, A. B., Jr. Pulsatile blood flow in the vascular system. In *Handbook of Physiology, Section 2: Circulation*, **2**, 839–64 (Hamilton, W. F., Dow, P., Eds., Am. Physiol. Soc., Washington, D. C., 1786 pp., 1963)

29. Goldman, H. Catecholamine-induced redistribution of blood flow in the unanesthetized rat. *Am. J. Physiol.*, **210**, 1419–23 (1966)

30. Goldman, H. Vasopressin modulation of the distribution of blood flow in the unanesthetized rat. *Neuroendocrinology*, **1**, 23–30 (1965/66)

31. Goldman, H. (Personal communication)

32. Worthington, W. C., Jr. Vascular responses in the pituitary stalk. *Endocrinology*, **66**, 19–31 (1960)

33. Porter, J. C., Dhariwal, A. P. S., McCann, S. M. Response of the anterior pituitary-adrenocortical axis to purified CRF. *Endocrinology*, **80**, 679–88 (1967)

34. Porter, J. C., Jones, J. C. Effect of plasma from hypophyseal-portal vessel blood on adrenal ascorbic acid. *Endocrinology*, **58**, 62–67 (1956)

35. Porter, J. C., Rumsfeld, H. W., Jr. Effect of lyophilized plasma and plasma fractions from hypophyseal-portal vessel blood on adrenal ascorbic acid. *Endocrinology*, **58**, 359–64 (1956)

36. Rumsfeld, H. W., Jr., Porter, J. C. Investigation of the release of ACTH. *Ibid.*, **64**, 942–47 (1959)

37. Porter, J. C., Rumsfeld, H. W., Jr. Further study of an ACTH-releasing protein from hypophyseal portal vessel plasma. *Ibid.*, 948–54

38. Fink, G., Nallar, R., Worthington, W. C., Jr. Determination of luteinizing hormone releasing factor (L.R.F.) in hypophysial portal blood. *J. Physiol. (London)*, **183**, 20P–21P (1966)

39. Averill, R. L. W., Salaman, D. F., Worthington, W. C., Jr. Thyrotrophin releasing factor in hypophyseal portal blood. *Nature*, **211**, 144–45 (1966)

40. Worthington, W. C., Jr. Blood samples from the pituitary stalk of the rat: Method of collection and factors determining volume. *Nature*, **210**, 710–12 (1966)

41. Porter, J. C., and Smith, K. R. Collection of hypophysial stalk blood in rats. *Endocrinology* (In press)

42. Dhariwal, A. P. S., Antunes-Rodrigues, J., Reeser, F., Chowers, I., McCann, S. M. Purification of hypothalamic corticotrophin-releasing factor (CRF) of ovine origin. *Proc. Soc. Exptl. Biol. Med.*, 121, 8–12 (1966)

43. László, F. A., de Wied, D. Pituitary-adrenal system in rats bearing lesions in the pituitary stalk. *Endocrinology*, 79, 547–53 (1966)

44. Dávid, M. A., Csernay, L., László, F. A., Kovács, K. The importance of the hypothalamo-hypophyseal connections in the function of the pituitary-adrenocortical axis. Hypophyseal blood flow after destruction of the pituitary stalk. *Proc. Intern. Congr. Endocrinol., 2nd, London*, 1, 530–37 (1964)

45. McCann, S. M., Antunes-Rodrigues, J., Nallar, R., Valtin, H. Pituitary-adrenal function in the absence of vasopressin. *Endocrinology*, 79, 1058–64 (1966)

46. Arimura, A., Saito, T., Bowers, C. Y., Schally, A. V. Pituitary-adrenal activation in rats with hereditary hypothalamic diabetes insipidus. *Acta Endocrinol.*, 54, 155–65 (1967)

47. Hedge, G. A., Yates, M. B., Marcus, R., Yates, F. E. Site of action of vasopressin in causing corticotropin release. *Endocrinology*, 79, 328–40 (1966)

48. Eleftheriou, B. E., Zolovick, A. J., Pearse, R. Effect of amygdaloid lesions on pituitary-adrenal axis in the deermouse. *Proc. Soc. Exptl. Biol. Med.*, 122, 1259–62 (1966)

49. McHugh, P. R., Smith, G. P. Plasma 17-OHCS response to amygdaloid stimulation with and without after-discharges. *Am. J. Physiol.*, 212, 619–22 (1967)

50. Slusher, M. A., Hyde, J. E. Effect of diencephalic and midbrain stimulation on ACTH levels in unrestrained cats. *Am. J. Physiol.*, 210, 103–8 (1966)

51. Chowers, I., Hammel, H. T., Eisenman, J., Abrams, R. M., McCann, S. M. Comparison of effect of environmental and preoptic heating and pyrogen on plasma cortisol. *Am. J. Physiol.*, 210, 606–10 (1966)

52. D'Angelo, S. A., Young, R. Chronic lesions and ACTH: Effects of thyroid hormones and electrical stimulation. *Am. J. Physiol*, 210, 795–800 (1966)

53. Benson, B. Urinary 17-hydroxycorticosteroid excretion in guinea-pigs with hypothalamic lesions. *Acta Endocrinol.*, 53, 369–81 (1966)

54. Halász, B., Pupp, L. Hormone secretion of the anterior pituitary gland after physical interruption of all nervous pathways to the hypophysiotrophic area. *Endocrinology*, 77, 553–62 (1965)

55. Halász, B., Slusher, M. A., Gorski, R. A. Adrenocorticotrophic hormone secretion in rats after partial or total deafferentation of the medial basal hypothalamus. *Neuroendocrinology*, 2, 43–55 (1967)

56. Egdahl, R. H. Studies on the effect of ether and pentobarbital anesthesia on pituitary adrenal function in the dog. *Neuroendocrinology*, 1, 184–91 (1965/66)

57. Zukoski, C. F., Ney, R. L. ACTH secretion after pituitary stalk section in the dog. *Am. J. Physiol.*, 211, 851–54 (1966)

58. Anderson, E. Adrenocorticotrophin-releasing hormone in peripheral blood: increase during stress. *Science*, 152, 379–80 (1966)

59. Brodish, A., Long, C. N. H. ACTH-releasing hypothalamic neurohumor in peripheral blood. *Endocrinology*, 71, 298–306 (1962)

60. Kendall, J. W., Allen, C. Brain-dependent ACTH secretion from multiple heterotopic pituitaries. *Proc. Soc. Exptl. Biol. Med.*, 122, 335–37 (1966)

61. Kendall, J. W., Stott, A. K., Allen, C., Greer, M. A. Evidence for ACTH secretion and ACTH suppressibility in hypophysectomized rats with multiple heterotopic pituitaries. *Endocrinology*, 78, 533–37 (1966)

62. Gittes, R. F., Kastin, A. J. Effects of increasing numbers of pituitary transplants in hypophysectomized rats. *Endocrinology*, 78, 1023–31 (1966)

63. Purves, H. D., Sirett, N. E. Corticotrophin secretion by ectopic pituitary glands. *Endocrinology*, 80, 962–68 (1967)

64. Bohus, B., Lissák, K., Mezei, B. The effect of thyroxine implantation in the hypothalamus and the anterior pituitary on pituitary-

adrenal function in rats. *Neuro-endocrinology*, **1**, 15–22 (1965/66)

65. Chowers, I., McCann, S. M. Comparison of the effect of hypothalamic and pituitary implants of estrogen and testosterone on reproductive system and adrenal of female rats. *Proc. Soc. Exptl. Biol. Med.*, **124**, 260–66 (1967)

66. Feldman, S., Conforti, N., Davidson, J. M. Adrenocortical responses in rats with corticosteroid and reserpine implants. *Neuroendocrinology*, **1**, 228–39 (1965/66)

67. Vernikos-Danellis, J., Trigg, L. N. Feedback mechanisms regulating pituitary ACTH secretion in rats bearing transplantable pituitary tumors. *Endocrinology*, **80**, 345–50 (1967)

68. Lorenzen, L. C., Ganong, W. F. Effect of drugs related to α-ethyltryptamine on stress-induced ACTH secretion in the dog. *Endocrinology*, **80**, 889–92 (1967)

69. Ganong, W. F., Boryczka, A. T., Lorenzen, L. C., Egge, A. S. Lack of effect of α-ethyltryptamine on ACTH secretion when blood pressure is held constant. *Proc. Soc. Exptl. Biol. Med.*, **124**, 558–59 (1967)

70. Ducommun, P., Sakiz, E., Guillemin, R. Lability of plasma TSH levels in the rat in response to nonspecific exteroceptive stimuli. *Proc. Soc. Exptl. Biol. Med.*, **121**, 921–23 (1966)

71. Ducommun, P., Sakiz, E., Guillemin, R. Dissociation of the acute secretions of thyrotropin and adrenocorticotropin. *Am. J. Physiol.*, **210**, 1257–59 (1966)

72. Ducommun, P., Vale, W., Sakiz, E., Guillemin, R. Reversal of the inhibition of TSH secretion due to acute stress. *Endocrinology*, **80**, 953–56 (1967)

73. Guillemin, R., Yamazaki, E., Jutisz, M., Sakiz, E. Présence dans un extrait de tissus hypothalamiques d'une substance stimulant la sécrétion de l'hormone hypophysaire thyréotrope (TSH). Première purification par filtration sur gel Sephadex. *Compt. Rend. Acad. Sci.*, **255**, 1018–20 (1962)

74. Schally, A. V., Bowers, C. Y., Redding, T. W., Barrett, J. F. Isolation of thyrotropin releasing factor (TRF) from porcine hypothalamus. *Biochem. Biophys. Res. Commun.*, **25**, 165–69 (1966)

75. Schally, A. V., Bowers, C. Y., Redding, T. W. Presence of thyrotropic hormone-releasing factor (TRF) in porcine hypothalamus. *Proc. Soc. Exptl. Biol. Med.*, **121**, 718–22 (1966)

76. Guillemin, R., Burgus, R., Sakiz, E., Ward, D. N. Nouvelles données sur la purification de l'hormone hypothalamique TSH-hypophysiotrope, TRF. *Compt. Rend. Acad. Sci.*, **262**, 2278–80 (1966)

77. Schally, A. V., Bowers, C. Y., Redding, T. W. Purification of thyrotropic hormone-releasing factor from bovine hypothalamus. *Endocrinology*, **78**, 726–32 (1966)

78. Bowers, C. Y., Redding, T. W., Schally, A. V. Effect of thyrotropin releasing factor (TRF) of ovine, bovine, porcine and human origin on thyrotropin release *in vitro* and *in vivo*. *Ibid.*, **77**, 609–16 (1965)

79. Vertes, M., Varga, F., Lelkes, J., Kovács, S. Further study on the mechanism of the hypothalamic control of the pituitary-thyroid system. *Neuroendocrinology*, **1**, 158–65 (1965/66)

80. Halász, B., Florsheim, W. H., Corcorran, N. L., Gorski, R. A. Thyrotrophic hormone secretion in rats after partial or total interruption of neural afferents to the medial basal hypothalamus. *Endocrinology*, **80**, 1075–82 (1967)

81. Sinha, D., Meites, J. Effects of thyroidectomy and thyroxine on hypothalamic concentration of "Thyrotropin Releasing Factor" and pituitary content of thyrotropin in rats. *Neuroendocrinology*, **1**, 4–14 (1965/66)

82. van Rees, G. P. The effect of triiodothyronine and thyroxine on thyrotrophin levels in the anterior pituitary gland and blood serum of thyroidectomized rats. *Acta Endocrinol.*, **51**, 619–24 (1966)

83. MacLeod, R. M., Bass, M. B., Buxton, E. P., Dent, J. N., Benson, D. G., Jr. Suppression of thyroid function by pituitary tumor MtTW5. *Endocrinology*, **78**, 267–76 (1966)

84. Panda, J. N., Turner, C. W. Effect of thyroidectomy and low environmental temperature (4.4° C) upon

plasma and pituitary thyrotrophin in the rat. *Acta Endocrinol.*, **54**, 485–93 (1967)

85. Solomon, S. H., McKenzie, J. M. Release of thyrotropin by the rat pituitary gland in vitro. *Endocrinology*, **78**, 699–706 (1966)

86. Sinha, D. K., Meites, J. Stimulation of pituitary thyrotropin synthesis and release by hypothalamic extract. *Endocrinology*, **78**, 1002–6 (1966)

87. Greer, M. A., Matsuda, K., Stott, A. K. Maintenance of the ability of rat pituitary homotransplants to secrete TSH by transplantation under the hypothalamic median eminence. *Endocrinology*, **78**, 389–95 (1966)

88. Purves, H. D., Sirett, N. E., Griesbach, W. E. Thyrotrophic hormone secretion from pituitary transplants in hypophysectomized rats. *Neuroendocrinology*, **1**, 276–92 (1965/66)

89. Fevold, H. Synergism of the follicle stimulating and luteinizing hormones in producing estrogen secretion. *Endocrinology*, **28**, 33–36 (1941)

90. Greep, R. O., Van Dyke, H. B., Chow, B. F. Gonadotropins of the swine pituitary. *Endocrinology*, **30**, 635–49 (1942)

91. Lostroh, A. J., Johnson, R. E. Amounts of interstitial cell-stimulating hormone and follicle stimulating hormone required for follicular development, uterine growth and ovulation in the hypophysectomized rat. *Endocrinology*, **79**, 991–96 (1966)

92. Eshkol, A., Lunenfeld, B. Purification and separation of follicle stimulating hormone (FSH) and luteinizing hormone (LH) from human menopausal gonadotrophin (HMG). III. Effects of a biologically apparently pure FSH preparation on ovaries and uteri of intact, immature mice. *Acta Endocrinol.*, **54**, 91–95 (1967)

93. Malven, P. V., Sawyer, C. H. Formation of new corpora lutea in mature hypophysectomized rats. *Endocrinology*, **78**, 1259–63 (1966)

94. Grota, L. J., Eik-Nes, K. B. Plasma progesterone concentrations during pregnancy and lactation in the rat. *J. Reprod. Fertility*, **13**, 83–91 (1967)

95. Short, R. V. Reproduction. *Ann. Rev. Physiol.*, **29**, 373–400 (1967)

96. Greep, R. O., Van Dyke, H. B., Chow, B. F. Use of anterior lobe of prostate gland in the assay of metakentrin. *Proc. Soc. Exptl. Biol. Med.*, **46**, 644–49 (1941)

97. Parlow, A. F. Bioassay of pituitary luteinizing hormone by depletion of ovarian ascorbic acid. In *Human Pituitary Gonadotrophins*, 300–10 (Albert, A., Ed., Thomas, Springfield, Ill., 434 pp., 1961)

98. Parlow, A. F. Species differences in luteinizing hormone (LH, ICSH) as revealed by the slope in the prostate assay. *Endocrinology*, **73**, 509–12 (1964)

99. Reichert, L. E., Jr. Measurement of luteinizing hormone by the hyperemia and ovarian ascorbic acid depletion assays. *Endocrinology*, **78**, 815–18 (1966)

100. Stevens, V. C., Owen, L., Fukushima, M., Vorys, N. Diurnal variation in ascorbic acid content of the ovary of the pseudopregnant rat. *Endocrinology*, **74**, 493–94 (1964)

101. McCann, S. M., Taleisnik, S. Effect of luteinizing hormone and vasopressin on ovarian ascorbic acid. *Am. J. Physiol.*, **199**, 847–50 (1960)

102. McCann, S. M., Ramirez, V. D. The neuroendocrine regulation of hypophyseal luteinizing hormone secretion. *Recent Progr. Hormone Res.*, **20**, 131–81 (1964)

103. Hershberger, L. G., Hansen, L. M., Thompson, C. R. Observations on the ovarian ascorbic acid depletion test for luteinizing hormone activity. *Endocrinology*, **77**, 1143–46 (1965)

104. Sakiz, E., Guillemin, R. On the method of ovarian ascorbic acid depletion as a test for luteinizing hormone. *Endocrinology*, **72**, 813–16 (1963)

105. Taleisnik, S., McCann, S. M. Effects of hypothalamic lesions on the secretion and storage of hypophysial luteinizing hormone. *Endocrinology*, **68**, 263–72 (1961)

106. Parlow, A. F., Anderson, L. L., Melampy, R. M. Pituitary follicle-stimulating hormone and luteinizing hormone concentrations in relation to reproductive stages of the pig. *Endocrinology*, **75**, 365–76 (1964)

107. Schwartz, N. B., Bartosik, D. Changes in pituitary LH content

during the rat estrous cycle. *Endocrinology,* **71,** 756–62 (1962)

108. Gorski, R. A., Barraclough, C. A. Adenohypophyseal LH content in normal, androgen-sterilized and progesterone-primed sterile female rats. *Acta Endocrinol.,* **39,** 13–21 (1962)

109. Parlow, A. F. Differential action of small doses of estradiol on gonadotrophins in the rat. *Endocrinology,* **75,** 1–8 (1964)

110. Ramirez, V. D., McCann, S. M. Fluctuations in plasma luteinizing hormone concentrations during the estrous cycle of the rat. *Endocrinology,* **74,** 814–16 (1964)

111. Schwartz, N. B., Caldarelli, D. Plasma LH in cyclic female rats. *Proc. Soc. Exptl. Biol. Med.,* **119,** 16–20 (1965)

112. Halász, B., Gorski, R. A. Gonadotrophic hormone secretion in female rats after partial or total interruption of neural afferents to the medial basal hypothalamus. *Endocrinology,* **80,** 608–22 (1967)

113. Ramirez, V. D., McCann, S. M. Comparison of the regulation of luteinizing hormone (LH) secretion in immature and adult rats. *Endocrinology,* **72,** 452–64 (1963)

114. Pelletier, J. Dosage de l'hormone stimulant l'interstitielle (ICSH) dans le sang par la méthode de l'acide ascorbique ovarien. *Compt. Rend. Acad. Sci.,* **258,** 5979–81 (1964)

115. Kanematsu, S., Sawyer, C. H. Effects of hypothalamic and hypophysial estrogen implants on pituitary and plasma LH in ovariectomized rabbits. *Endocrinology,* **75,** 579–85 (1964)

116. Nelson, D. M., Norton, H. W., Nalbandov, A. V. Hypophysial and plasma LH levels in intact and castrate cockerels. *Endocrinology,* **77,** 731–34 (1965)

117. Pelletier, J. Effet du plasma de brebis sur la décharge de LH chez la ratte. *Compt. Rend. Acad. Sci.,* **260,** 5624–26 (1965)

118. Crighton, D. B. Effects of lactation on the pituitary gonadotrophins of the sow. *Proc. 13th Easter Symp., 1966* ("Reproduction in the Female Mammal", Univ. of Nottingham School of Agriculture, Butterworth, London) (In press)

119. Skosey, J. L., Goldstein, D. P. Observations on ovarian cholesterol depletion (OCD) as a test for luteinizing hormone activity. *Endocrinology,* **78,** 218–19 (1966)

120. Bell, E. T., Lunn, S. F. The pretreatment of animals in the ovarian cholesterol depletion test for luteinizing hormone. *J. Endocrinol.,* **35,** 327–28 (1966)

121. Midgley, A. R., Jr. Radioimmunoassay: A method for human chorionic gonadotropin and human luteinizing hormone. *Endocrinology,* **79,** 10–18 (1966)

122. Odell, W. D., Ross, G. T., Rayford, P. L. Radioimmunoassay for human luteinizing hormone. *Metabolism,* **15,** 287–89 (1966)

123. Wilde, C. E., Orr, A. H., Bagshawe, K. D. A sensitive radioimmunoassay for human chorionic gonadotrophin and luteinizing hormone. *J. Endocrinol.,* **37,** 23–35 (1967)

124. Parlow, A. F., Monroe, S. E., Midgley, A. R., Jr. Radioimmunoassay for rat luteinizing hormone. *Fed. Proc.,* **26,** 533 (1967)

125. Midgley, A. R., Jr. Human pituitary luteinizing hormone: an immunohistochemical study. *J. Histochem. Cytochem.,* **14,** 159–66 (1966)

126. McCann, S. M., Taleisnik, S., Friedman, H. M. LH-releasing activity in hypothalamic extracts. *Proc. Soc. Exptl. Biol. Med.,* **104,** 432–34 (1960)

127. Johnson, D. C., Nelson, D. M. Amount of luteinizing hormone activity in extracts of sheep hypothalamus. *Endocrinology,* **78,** 901–3 (1966)

128. Croxatto, H., Arrau, J., Croxatto, H. Luteinizing hormone-like activity in human median eminence extracts. *Nature,* **204,** 584–85 (1964)

129. Ramirez, V. D., McCann, S. M. Inhibitory effect of testosterone on luteinizing hormone secretion in immature and adult rats. *Endocrinology,* **78,** 412–17 (1965)

130. Ryan, R. J., Philpott, J. E. Effects of androgens on concentrations of LH and FSH in the male rat pituitary. *Proc. Soc. Exptl. Biol. Med.,* **124,** 240–43 (1967)

131. Peillon, F., Racadot, J. Actions comparées de la testostérone, de la déhydroépiandrostérone (DHA) et du sulfate de déhydroépiandrostérone sur la fonction gonadotrope hypophysaire de la ratte prépubère.

Ann. Endocrinol., **26**, 419–28 (1965)

132. McDonald, P. G., Clegg, M. T. The effect of progesterone on serum luteinizing hormone concentrations in the ewe. *J. Reprod. Fertility*, **13**, 75–82 (1967)

133. McCann, S. M. Effect of progesterone on plasma luteinizing hormone activity. *Am. J. Physiol.*, **202**, 601–4 (1962)

134. Kaufman, A. B., Rothchild, I. The corpus luteum-hypophysis relationship: the effect of progesterone treatment on the release of gonadotrophins in the rat. *Acta Endocrinol.*, **51**, 231–44 (1966)

135. Leavitt, W. W. Relative effectiveness of estradiol and coumestrol on the reversal of castration changes in the anterior pituitary of mice. *Endocrinology*, **77**, 247–54 (1965)

136. Callantine, M. R., Humphrey, R. R., Lee, S. L., Windsor, B. L., Schottin, N. H., O'Brien, O. P. Action of an estrogen antagonist on reproductive mechanisms in the rat. *Endocrinology*, **79**, 153–67 (1966)

137. Neumann, F. Auftreten von Kastrationszellen im Hypophysenvorderlappen männlicher Ratten nach behandlung mit einem Antiandrogen. *Acta Endocrinol.*, **53**, 53–60 (1966)

138. Neumann, F., Hahn, J. D., Kramer, M. Hemmung von testosteronabhängigen Differenzierungsvorgängen der männlichen Ratte nach der Geburt, *Acta Endocrinol.*, **54**, 227–40 (1967)

139. Wakabayashi, K., Tamaoki, B.-I. *In vitro* biosynthesis of luteinizing hormone in the anterior pituitary gland. *Endocrinology*, **77**, 264–72 (1965)

140. Wakabayashi, K., Tamaoki, B.-I. *In vivo* and *in vitro* effects of androgens on the biosynthesis of luteinizing hormone (LH) in the anterior pituitary glands of male rats. *Ibid.*, **80**, 409–16 (1967)

141. Wakabayashi, K., Tamaoki, B.-I. Influence of immunization with luteinizing hormone upon the anterior pituitary-gonad system of rats and rabbits, with special reference to histological changes and biosynthesis of luteinizing hormone and steroids. *Ibid.*, **79**, 477–85 (1966)

142. Ely, C. A., Tuercke, R., Chen, B. Comparison of antisera to various gonadotropins as they effect the mouse vaginal cycle. *Proc. Soc. Exptl. Biol. Med.*, **122**, 601–5 (1966)

143. Lunenfeld, B., Eshkol, A., Baldratti, G., Suchowsky, G. K. Preparation and characterization of antiserum to purified gonadotropins from rat pituitary glands. *Acta Endocrinol.*, **54**, 311–27 (1967)

144. Spies, H. G., Quadri, S. K. Regression of corpora lutea and interruption of pregnancy in rabbits following treatment with rabbit serum to ovine LH. *Endocrinology*, **80**, 1127–32 (1967)

145. Quadri, S. K., Harbers, L. H., Spies, H. G. Inhibition of spermatogenesis and ovulation in rabbits with antiovine LH rabbit serum. *Proc. Soc. Exptl. Biol. Med.*, **123**, 809–14 (1966)

146. Everett, J. W. Central neural control of reproductive functions of the adenohypophysis. *Physiol. Rev.*, **44**, 373–431 (1964)

147. Nallar, R., Antunes-Rodrigues, J., McCann, S. M. Effect of progesterone on the level of plasma luteinizing hormone (LH) in normal female rats. *Endocrinology*, **79**, 907–11 (1966)

148. Runnebaum, B., Zander, J. Progesterone in the human peripheral blood in the preovulatory period of the menstrual cycle. *Acta Endocrinol.*, **55**, 91–96 (1967)

149. Porter, J. C., Siiteri, P. K., Yates, C. W., Jr. Secretion of progesterone by the ovary of the rat. *Fed. Proc.*, **26**, 533 (1967)

150. Zeilmaker, G. H. The biphasic effect of progesterone on ovulation in the rat. *Acta Endocrinol.*, **51**, 461–68 (1966)

151. Redmond, W. C., Everett, J. W. LH release facilitated in rats by progesterone injection in early proestrus. *Proc. 49th Meeting Endocrine Soc., June 15–17, 1967, Bal Harbour, Florida*, 58

152. Zarrow, M. X., Hurlbut, E. C. Inhibition and facilitation of PMS-induced ovulation in the immature rat following treatment with progesterone. *Endocrinology*, **80**, 735–40 (1967)

153. Döcke, F., Dörner, G. Facilitative action of progesterone in the induction of ovulation by oestrogen. *J. Endocrinol.*, **36**, 209–10 (1966)

154. Hilliard, J., Penardi, R., Sawyer, C.

H. A functional role for 20α-hydroxypregn-4-en-3-one in the rabbit. *Endocrinology*, **80**, 901–9 (1967)

155. Dorrington, J. H., Kilpatrick, R. Effects of pituitary Hormones on progestational hormone production by the rabbit ovary *in vivo* and *in vitro*. *J. Endocrinol.*, **35**, 53–63 (1966)

156. Callantine, M. R., Humphrey, R. R., Nesset, B. L. LH release by 17β-estradiol in the rat. *Endocrinology*, **79**, 455–56 (1966)

157. Rennels, E. G., O'Steen, W. K. Alterations in LH and FSH content and weight of the anterior pituitary gland of immature female rats treated with PMS. *Endocrinology*, **80**, 82–88 (1967)

158. Dhom, G., Krull, P., Maüsle, E., Strube, R. Der Einfluss eines Ovulationshemmers (17αAethinyl-19-nortestosteron) auf die gonadotropen Zellen der Rattenhypophyse *Beitr. Pathol. Anat. Allgem. Pathol.*, **132**, 1–24 (1965)

159. Hilliard, J., Hayward, J. N., Croxatto, H. B., Sawyer, C. H. Norethindrone blockade of pituitary gonadotropin release; counteraction by estrogen. *Endocrinology*, **78**, 151–57 (1966)

160. Brown, P. S., Wells, M., Warnock, D. G. The effect of an oral contraceptive on urinary gonadotrophin in women at mid-cycle. *J. Reprod. Fertility*, **11**, 481–83 (1966)

161. Bell, E. T., Herbst, A. L., Krishnamurti, M., Loraine, J. A., Mears, E., Jackson, M. C. N., Garcia, C.-R. The effect of the long term administration of oral contraceptives on excretion values for follicle-stimulating hormone and luteinising hormone. *Acta Endocrinol.*, **54**, 96–104 (1967)

162. Midgley, A. R., Jr. Immunoassay of human gonadotropins: Current status. *Clin. Obstet. Gynecol.*, **10**, 119–31 (1967)

163. Dávid, M. A., Fraschini, F., Martini, L. Control of LH secretion: role of a "short" feedback mechanism. *Endocrinology*, **78**, 55–60 (1966)

164. Corbin, A. Pituitary and plasma LH of ovariectomized rats with median eminence implants of LH. *Endocrinology*, **78**, 893–96 (1966)

165. Ramirez, V. D., Komisaruk, B. R., Whitmoyer, D. I., Sawyer, C. H. Effects of hormones and vaginal stimulation on the EEG and hypothalamic units in rats. *Am. J. Physiol.*, **212**, 1376–84 (1967)

166. Anderson, R. R., McShan, W. H. Luteinizing hormone levels in pig, cow and rat blood plasma during the estrous cycle. *Endocrinology*, **78**, 976–82 (1966)

167. Liptrap, R. M., Raeside, J. I. Luteinizing hormone activity in blood and urinary oestrogen excretion by the sow at oestrus and ovulation. *J. Reprod. Fertility*, **11**, 439–46 (1966)

168. Nelson, D. M., Norton, H. W., Nalbandov, A. V. Changes in hypophysial and plasma LH levels during the laying cycle of the hen. *Endocrinology*, **77**, 889–96 (1965)

169. Orsini, M. W., Schwartz, N. B. Pituitary LH content during the estrous cycle in female hamsters: comparisons with males and acyclic females. *Endocrinology*, **78**, 34–40 (1966)

170. Robertson, H. A., Rakha, A. M. The sequence, time, and duration, of the release of follicle-stimulating hormone and luteinizing hormone in relation to oestrus and to ovulation in the sheep. *J. Endocrinol.*, **35**, 177–84 (1966)

171. Heald, P. J., Furnival, B. E., Rookledge, K. A. Changes in the levels of luteinizing hormone in the pituitary of the domestic fowl during an ovulatory cycle. *J. Endocrinol.*, **37**, 73–81 (1967)

172. Quinn, D. L. Influence of diphenylhydantoin on spontaneous release of ovulating hormone in the adult rat. *Proc. Soc. Exptl. Biol. Med.*, **119**, 982–85 (1965)

173. Alleva, J. J., Umberger, E. J. Evidence for neural control of the release of pituitary ovulating hormone in the golden Syrian hamster. *Endocrinology*, **78**, 1125–29 (1966)

174. Deanesly, R. The effects of reserpine on ovulation and on the corpus luteum of the guinea-pig. *J. Reprod. Fertility*, **11**, 429–38 (1966)

175. Hiroi, M., Sugita, S., Suzuki, M. Ovulation induced by implantation of cupric sulfate into the brain of the rabbit. *Endocrinology*, **77**, 963–67 (1965)

176. Albert, A., Mendoza, D. Daily fluctuation in excretion of follicle stimulating and luteinizing hor-

mones by a postmenopausal woman. *J. Clin. Endocrinol. Metab.*, **26**, 371–73 (1966)

177. Greenwald, G. S., Keever, J. E., Grady, K. L. Ovarian morphology and pituitary FSH and LH concentration in the pregnant and lactating hamster. *Endocrinology*, **80**, 851–56 (1967)

178. Greenwald, G. S. Ovarian follicular development and pituitary FSH and LH content in the pregnant rat. *Endocrinology*, **79**, 572–78 (1966)

179. Melampy, R. M., Henricks, D. M., Anderson, L. L., Chen, C. L., Schultz, J. R. Pituitary follicle-stimulating hormone and luteinizing hormone concentrations in pregnant and lactating pigs. *Endocrinology*, **78**, 801–4 (1966)

180. McCann, S. M., Graves, T., Taleisnik, S. The effect of lactation on plasma LH. *Endocrinology*, **68**, 873–74 (1961)

181. Ramirez, V. D., McCann, S. M. Inhibitory effect of testosterone on luteinizing hormone secretion in immature and adult rats. *Endocrinology*, **76**, 412–17 (1965)

182. Smith, E. R., Davidson, J. M. Differential responses to hypothalamic testosterone in relation to male puberty. *Am. J. Physiol.*, **212**, 1385–90 (1967)

183. Ramirez, V. D., Sawyer, C. H. Changes in hypothalamic luteinizing hormone releasing factor (LHRF) in the female rat during puberty. *Endocrinology*, **78**, 958–64 (1966)

184. Taleisnik, S., Caligaris, L., Astrada, J. J. Effect of copulation on the release of pituitary gonadotropins in male and female rats. *Endocrinology*, **79**, 49–54 (1966)

185. Labhsetwar, A. P. Hysterectomy and hypophysial FSH and LH levels in the rat. *J. Reprod. Fertility*, **13**, 169–71 (1967)

186. Barraclough, C. A. Influence of age, prepubertal androgen treatment and hypothalamic stimulation on adenohypophysial LH content in female rats. *Endocrinology*, **78**, 1053–60 (1966)

187. Lawton, I. E., Schwartz, N. B. Pituitary LH content in rats exposed to continuous illumination. *Endocrinology*, **77**, 1140–42 (1965)

188. Bradshaw, M., Critchlow, V. Pituitary concentration of luteinizing hormone in three types of "constant estrous" rats. *Endocrinology*, **78**, 1007–14 (1966)

189. Matsuyama, E., Weisz, J., Lloyd, C. W. Gonadotrophin content of pituitary glands of testosterone-sterilized rats. *Endocrinology*, **79**, 261–67 (1966)

190. Maric, D. K., Matsuyama, E., Lloyd, C. W. Gonadotrophin content of pituitaries of rats in constant estrus induced by continuous illumination. *Endocrinology*, **77**, 529–36 (1965)

191. Antunes-Rodrigues, J., McCann, S. M. The effect of suprachiasmatic lesions on the regulation of LH secretion in the female rat. *Endocrinology*, **81**, 666–70 (1967)

192. Lisk, R. D. Neurosecretion in the rat: changes occurring following neural implant of estrogen. *Neuroendocrinology*, **1**, 83–92 (1965/66)

193. Ramirez, V. D., Abrams, R. M., McCann, S. M. Effect of estradiol implants in the hypothalamo-hypophysial region of the rat on the secretion of luteinizing hormone. *Endocrinology*, **75**, 243–48 (1964)

194. Fendler, K., Endröczi, E. Effects of hypothalamic steroid implants on compensatory ovarian hypertrophy of the rats. *Neuroendocrinology*, **1**, 129–37 (1965/66)

195. Barraclough, C. A. Modifications in the CNS regulation of reproduction after exposure of prepubertal rats to steroid hormone. *Recent Progr. Hormone Res.*, **22**, 503–39 (1966)

196. Wagner, J. W., Erwin, W., Critchlow, V. Androgen sterilization produced by intracerebral implants of testosterone in neonatal female rats. *Endocrinology*, **79**, 1135–42 (1966)

197. Smith, E. R., Davidson, J. M. Testicular maintenance and its inhibition in pituitary-transplanted rats. *Endocrinology*, **80**, 725–34 (1967)

198. Döcke, F., Dörner, G. The mechanism of the induction of ovulation by oestrogens. *J. Endocrinol.*, **33**, 491–99 (1965)

199. Palka, Y. S., Ramirez, V. D., Sawyer, C. H. Distribution and biological effects of tritiated estradiol implanted in the hypothalamo-hypophysial region of female rats. *Endocrinology*, **78**, 487–99 (1966)

200. Lisk, R. D. Reproductive capacity and behavioural oestrus in the rat bearing hypothalamic implants of sex steroids. *Acta Endocrinol.,* **48,** 209–19 (1965)

201. Davidson, J. M. Activation of the male rat's sexual behavior by intracerebral implantation of androgen. *Endocrinology,* **79,** 783–94 (1966)

202. Eisenfeld, A. J., Axelrod, J. Selectivity of estrogen distribution in tissues. *J. Pharmacol. Exptl. Therap.,* **150,** 469–75 (1965)

203. Eisenfeld, A. J., Axelrod, J. Effect of steroid hormones, ovariectomy, estrogen pretreatment, sex and immaturity on the distribution of ^{3}H-estradiol. *Endocrinology,* **79,** 38–48 (1966)

204. Kato, J., Villee, C. A. Preferential uptake of estradiol by the anterior hypothalamus of the rat. *Endocrinology,* **80,** 567–75 (1967)

205. Kato, J., Villee, C. A. Factors affecting uptake of estradiol-6, 7-^{3}H by the hypophysis and hypothalamus. *Ibid.,* 1133–38

206. Laumas, K. R., Farooq, A. The uptake *in vivo* of [1,2-^{3}H]progesterone by the brain and genital tract of the rat. *J. Endocrinol.,* **36,** 95–96 (1966)

207. Lincoln, D. W. Unit activity in the hypothalamus, septum and preoptic area of the rat: characteristics of spontaneous activity and the effect of oestrogen. *J. Endocrinol.,* **37,** 177–89 (1967)

208. Lincoln, D. W., Cross, B. A. Effect of oestrogen on the responsiveness of neurones in the hypothalamus, septum and preoptic area of rats with light-induced persistent oestrus. *J. Endocrinol.,* **37,** 191–203 (1967)

209. Kawakami, M., Sawyer, C. H. Effects of sex hormones and antifertility steroids on brain thresholds in the rabbit. *Endocrinology,* **80,** 857–71 (1967)

210. Donoso, A. O., Stefano, F. J. E., Biscardi, A. M., Cukier, J. Effects of castration on hypothalamic catecholamines. *Am. J. Physiol.,* **212,** 737–39 (1967)

211. Barry, J., Léonardelli, J. Variations de l'activité acétylcholinestérasique de l'hypothalamus chez le Cobaye mâle, castré ou soumis à l'action d'androgènes. *Compt. Rend. Soc. Biol.,* 8–9, 1608–10 (1967)

212. Léonardelli, J. Étude histoenzymologique de l'hypothalamus du Cobaye. I. Recherches sur les variations de l'acétycholinestérase au cours du cycle oestral. *Compt. Rend. Soc. Biol.,* **4,** 757–59 (1966)

213. Coppola, J. A., Leonardi, R. G., Lippman W. Ovulatory failure in rats after treatment with brain norepinephrine depletors. *Endocrinology,* **78,** 225–28 (1966)

214. McCann, S. M., Taleisnik, S. The effect of a hypothalamic extract on the plasma luteinizing hormone (LH) activity of the estrogenized, ovariectomized rats. *Endocrinology,* **68,** 1071–73 (1961)

215. McCann, S. M. A hypothalamic luteinizing-hormone-releasing factor (LH-RF). *Am. J. Physiol.,* **202,** 395–400 (1962)

216. Ramirez, V. D., McCann, S. M. A new sensitive test for LH-releasing activity: the ovariectomized, estrogen progesterone-blocked rat. *Endocrinology,* **73,** 193–98 (1963)

217. Nikitovitch-Winer, M. B. Induction of ovulation in rats by direct intrapituitary infusion of median eminence extracts. *Endocrinology,* **70,** 350–58 (1962)

218. Campbell, H. J., Feuer, G., Harris, G. W. The effect of intrapituitary infusion of median eminence and other brain extracts on anterior pituitary gonadotrophic secretion. *J. Physiol. (London),* **170,** 474–86 (1964)

219. Schally, A. V., Bowers, C. Y. *In vitro* and *in vivo* stimulation of the release of luteinizing hormone. *Endocrinology,* **75,** 312–20 (1964)

220. Piacsek, B. E., Meites, J. Effects of castration and gonadal hormones on hypothalamic content of luteinizing hormone releasing factor (LRF). *Endocrinology,* **79,** 432–39 (1966)

221. Minaguchi, H., Meites, J. Effects of suckling on hypothalamic LH-releasing factor and prolactin inhibiting factor, and on pituitary LH and prolactin. *Endocrinology,* **80,** 603–7 (1967)

222. Sciavi, R., Jutisz, M., Sakiz, E., Guillemin, R. Stimulation of ovulation by purified LH-releasing factor (LRF) in animals rendered anovulatory by hypothalamic lesion. *Proc. Soc. Exptl. Biol. Med.,* **114,** 426–29 (1963)

223. Arimura, A., Schally, A. V., Saito,

T., Müller, E. E., Bowers, C. Y. Induction of ovulation in rats by highly purified pig LH-releasing factor (LRF). *Endocrinology, 80,* 515–20 (1967)

224. Antunes-Rodrigues, J., Dhariwal, A. P. S., McCann, S. M. Effect of purified luteinizing hormone-releasing factor (LH-RF) on plasma LH activity at various stages of the estrous cycle of the rat. *Proc. Soc. Exptl. Biol. Med.,* 122, 1001–4 (1966)

225. Chowers, I., McCann, S. M. Content of luteinizing hormone-releasing factor and luteinizing hormone during the estrous cycle and after changes in gonadal steroid titers. *Endocrinology,* 76, 700–8 (1965)

226. Bogdanove, E. M. Direct gonad-pituitary feedback: an analysis of effects of cranial estrogenic depots on gonadotrophin secretion. *Endocrinology,* 73, 696–712 (1963)

227. Ramirez, V. D., Sawyer, C. H. Fluctuations in hypothalamic LH-RF (luteinizing hormone-releasing factor) during the rat estrous cycle. *Endocrinology,* 76, 282–89 (1965)

228. Ramirez, V. D., Sawyer, C. H. Changes in hypothalamic luteinizing hormone releasing factor (LHRF) in the female rat during puberty. *Ibid.,* 78, 958–64 (1966)

229. Campbell, H. J., Gallardo, E. Gonadotrophin-releasing activity of the median eminence at different ages. *J. Physiol. (London),* 186, 689–97 (1966)

230. Nallar, R., McCann, S. M. Luteinizing hormone-releasing activity in plasma of hypophysectomized rats. *Endocrinology,* 76, 272–75 (1965)

231. Frankel, A. I., Gibson, W. R., Graber, J. W., Nelson, D. M., Reichert, L. E., Jr., Nalbandov, A. V. An ovarian ascorbic acid depleting factor in the plasma of adenohypophysectomized cockerels. *Endocrinology,* 77, 651–57 (1965)

232. Beddow, D., McCann, S. M. (In preparation)

233. Halász, B., Pupp, L., Uhlarik, S., Tima, L. Further studies on the hormone secretion of the anterior pituitary transplanted into the hypophysiotrophic area of the rat hypothalamus. *Endocrinology,* 77, 343–55 (1965)

234. Flament-Durand, J. Observations on pituitary transplants into the hypo-thalamus of the rat. *Endocrinology,* 77, 446–54 (1965)

235. Endröczi, E., Hilliard, J. Luteinizing hormone releasing activity in different parts of rabbit and dog brain. *Endocrinology,* 77, 667–73 (1965)

236. Evans, J. S., Nikitovitch-Winer, M. B. Reactivation of hypophyseal grafts by continuous perfusion with median eminence extracts (MEE). *Fed. Proc.,* 24, 190 (1965)

237. Ducommun, S., Guillemin, R. Maintenance of normal morphology in adenohypophysial transplants by topical administration of hypothalamic extracts. A simple method for transplantation in a pneumoderma pouch. *Proc. Soc. Exptl. Biol. Med.,* 122, 1251–55 (1966)

238. Hilliard, J., Croxatto, H. B., Hayward, J. N., Sawyer, C. H. Norethindrone blockade of LH release to intrapituitary infusion of hypothalamic extract. *Endocrinology,* 79, 411–19 (1966)

239. Gellert, R. J., Exley, D. Site of action of chlormadinone (6-chloroΔ⁶-dehydro-17α-acetoxyprogesterone) in blocking ovulation in the mated rabbit. *Proc. 48th Meeting Endocrine Soc., June 20–22, 1966, Chicago,* 33

240. Igarashi, M., Ibuki, Y., Kubo, H., Kamioka, J., Yokota, N., Ehara, Y., Matsumoto, S. Mode and site of action of clomiphene. *Am. J. Obstet. Gynecol.,* 97, 120–23 (1967)

241. Bar-Sela, M. E., Elwers, M., Critchlow, V. Delayed puberty following electrical stimulation of amygdala in female rats. *Am. J. Physiol.,* 211, 1103–7 (1966)

242. Donovan, B. T., Kopriva, P. C. Effect of removal or stimulation of the olfactory bulbs on the estrous cycle of the guinea pig. *Endocrinology,* 77, 213–17 (1965)

243. Pekary, A. E., Davidson, J. M., Zondek, B. Failure to demonstrate a role of midbrain-hypothalamic afferents in reproductive processes. *Endocrinology,* 80, 365–68 (1967)

244. Steelman, S. L., Pohley, F. M. Assay of the follicle stimulating hormone based on the augmentation with human chorionic gonadotropin. *Endocrinology,* 53, 604–16 (1953)

245. Brown, P. S., Wells, M. Observations

on the assay of human urinary follicle-stimulating hormone by the augmentation test in mice. *J. Endocrinol.*, **35**, 199–206 (1966)

246. Igarashi, M., McCann, S. M. A new sensitive bioassay for follicle stimulating hormone (FSH). *Endocrinology*, **74**, 440–45 (1964)

247. Igarashi, M., McCann, S. M. A hypothalamic follicle stimulating hormone-releasing factor. *Ibid.*, 446–52

248. Igarashi, M., Nallar, R., McCann, S. M. Further studies on the follicle-stimulating hormone-releasing action of hypothalamic extracts. *Endocrinology*, **75**, 901–7 (1964)

249. Dhariwal, A. P. S., Nallar, R., Batt, M., McCann, S. M. Separation of follicle-stimulating hormone-releasing factor from luteinizing hormone-releasing factor. *Endocrinology*, **76**, 290–94 (1965)

250. de Reviers, M. M., Mauleon, P. Étude critique du dosage de l'hormone folliculo-stimulante par la methode d'Igarashi et McCann. *Compt. Rend. Acad. Sci.*, **261**, 540–43 (1965)

251. Igarashi, M., Ehara, Y. (Personal communication)

252. Lamond, D. R., Bindon, B. M. The biological assay of follicle-stimulating hormone in hypophysectomized immature mice. *J. Endocrinol.*, **34**, 365–76 (1966)

253. Reichert, L. E., Jr. Further studies on species differences in follicle stimulating hormone as revealed by the slope in the Steelman-Pohley assay. *Endocrinology*, **80**, 1180–81 (1967)

254. Tamada, T., Soper, M., Taymor, M. L. Immunologic studies with urinary follicle stimulating hormone. *J. Clin. Endocrinol.*, **27**, 379–84 (1967)

255. Faiman, C., Ryan, R. J. Radioimmunoassay for human follicle stimulating hormone. *J. Clin. Endocrinol. Metab.*, **27**, 444–47 (1967)

256. Steinberger, E., Duckett, G. E. Pituitary "total" gonadotropins, FSH and LH in orchiectomized or cryptorchid rats. *Endocrinology*, **79**, 912–20 (1966)

257. McDonald, P. G., Clegg, M. T. Some factors affecting gonadotropin levels in sheep. *Proc. Soc. Exptl. Biol. Med.*, **121**, 482–85 (1966)

258. D'Angelo, S. A. A comparative study of TSH and FSH secretion in rat and guinea pig: effects of gonadectomy and goitrogens. *Endocrinology*, **78**, 1230–37 (1966)

259. Callantine, M. R., Humphrey, R. R. Effect of progesterone on pituitary and ovarian responsiveness to placental gonadotrophins. *Endocrinology*, **77**, 921–31 (1965)

260. Faiman, C., Ryan, R. J. Radioimmunoassay of serum FSH during the menstrual cycle. *Proc. 49th Meeting Endocrine Soc., June 15–17, 1967, Bal Harbour, Florida*, 59

261. Odell, W. D., Parlow, A. F. Some physiological studies of human FSH using radioimmunoassay, *Proc. 49th Meeting Endocrine Soc., June 15–17, 1967, Bal Harbour, Florida*, 61

262. Corbin, A., Story, J. C. "Internal" feedback mechanism: response of pituitary FSH and of stalk-median eminence follicle stimulating hormone-releasing factor to median eminence implants of FSH. *Endocrinology*, **80**, 1006–12 (1967)

263. Kuroshima, A., Ishida, Y., Bowers, C. Y., Schally, A. V. Stimulation of release of follicle-stimulating hormone by hypothalamic extracts *in vitro* and *in vivo*. *Endocrinology*, **76**, 614–19 (1965)

264. Mittler, J. C., Meites, J. *In vitro* stimulation of pituitary follicle-stimulating-hormone release by hypothalamic extract. *Proc. Soc. Exptl. Biol. Med.*, **117**, 309–13 (1964)

265. Mittler, J. C., Meites, J. Effects of hypothalamic extract and androgen on pituitary FSH release *in vitro*. *Endocrinology*, **78**, 500–4 (1966)

266. Dávid, M. A., Fraschini, F., Martini, L. Parallélisme entre le contenu hypophysaire en FSH et le contenu hypothalamique en FSH-RF (FSH-releasing factor). *Compt. Rend. Acad. Sci.*, **261**, 2249–51 (1965)

267. Saito, T., Arimura, A., Müller, E. E., Bowers, C. Y., Schally, A. V. *In vivo* release of follicle-stimulating hormone following administration of hypothalamic extracts in normal, castrated, and castrated testosterone-treated rats. *Endocrinology*, **80**, 313–18 (1967)

268. Kuroshima, A., Arimura, A., Saito, T., Ishida, Y., Bowers, C. Y., Schally, A. V. Depletion of pitu-

itary follicle-stimulating hormone by beef and pig hypothalamic extracts. *Endocrinology,* **78,** 1105–14 (1966)

269. Watanabe, S., McCann, S. M. Localization of FSH-RF in the hypothalamus and neurohypophysis as determined by *in vitro* assay. *Endocrinology* (Submitted for publication)

270. Watanabe, S., Dhariwal, A. P. S., McCann, S. M. Effect of inhibitors of protein synthesis on the FSH-releasing action of hypothalamic extracts *in vitro*. *Endocrinology* (Submitted for publication)

271. Watanabe, S., McCann, S. M. Localization and mechanism of action of follicle stimulating hormone-releasing factor as determined by *in vitro* assay. *Fed. Proc.,* **26,** 365 (1967)

272. Jutisz, M., de la Llosa, P. Effet de la puromycine et de l'actinomycine D sur l'action stimulatrice du FRF (FSH-releasing factor) sur l'hypophyse *in vitro*. *Compt. Rend. Acad. Sci.,* **264,** 118–21 (1967)

273. Jutisz, M., Bérault, A., Novella, M.-A., Chapeville, F. Sur le mécanisme d'action du facteur hypothalamique LRF *in vitro*. *Compt. Rend. Acad. Sci.,* **263,** 664–67 (1966)

274. Crighton, D. B., Watanabe, S., Mc-Cann, S. M. Effect of puromycin and actinomycin on response to LH-RF *in vitro*. (Unpublished observation)

275. Samli, M. H., Geschwind, I. I. Effects of the hypothalamic luteinizing hormone releasing factor (LRF) on the secretion and biosynthesis of luteinizing hormone (LH). *Proc. 49th Meeting Endocrine Soc., June 15–17, 1967, Bal Harbour, Florida,* 58

276. Nicoll, C. S. Bio-assay of prolactin. Analysis of the pigeon crop-sac response to local prolactin injection by an objective and quantitative method. *Endocrinology,* **80,** 641–55 (1967)

277. Allanson, M., Cameron, E., Foster, C. L. Observations on the acidophil cells of the adenohypophysis in pregnant and lactating rabbits. *J. Reprod. Fertility,* **12,** 319–26 (1966)

278. Carlon, N., Stahl, A. Étude expérimentale de la cytologie du lobe antérieur de l'hypophyse chez le chien. *Compt. Rend. Soc. Biol.,* **3,** 578–81 (1966)

279. Baker, B. L., Zanotti, D. B. Electrophoresis of pituitary proteins after treatment of rats with norethynodrel. *Endocrinology,* **78,** 1037–40 (1966)

280. Kurcz, M., Kovács, K., Tiboldi, T., Orosz, A. Effect of androgenisation on adenohypophysial prolactin content in rats. *Acta Endocrinol.,* **54,** 663–67 (1967)

281. MacLeod, R. M., Smith, M. C., DeWitt, G. W. Hormonal properties of transplanted pituitary tumors and their relation to the pituitary gland. *Endocrinology,* **79,** 1149–56 (1966)

282. Dominic, C. J. Observations on the reproductive pheromones of mice. II. Neuro-endocrine mechanisms involved in the olfactory block to pregnancy. *J. Reprod. Fertility,* **11,** 415–21 (1966)

283. Grosvenor, C. E., Mena, F. Effect of auditory, olfactory and optic stimuli upon milk ejection and suckling-induced release of prolactin in lactating rats. *Endocrinology,* **80,** 840–46 (1967)

284. Everett, J. W., Quinn, D. L. Differential hypothalamic mechanisms inciting ovulation and pseudopregnancy in the rat. *Endocrinology,* **78,** 141–50 (1966)

285. Quinn, D. L., Everett, J. W. Delayed pseudopregnancy induced by selective hypothalamic stimulation. *Ibid.,* **80,** 155–62 (1967)

286. Ramirez, V. D., McCann, S. M. Induction of prolactin secretion by implants of estrogen into the hypothalamo-hypophysial region of female rats. *Endocrinology,* **75,** 206–14 (1964)

287. Kanematsu, S., Sawyer, C. H. Effects of intrahypothalamic and intrahypophysial estrogen implants on pituitary prolactin and lactation in the rabbit. *Endocrinology,* **72,** 243–51 (1963)

288. Tindal, J. S., Knaggs, G. S., Turvey, A. Central nervous control of prolactin secretion in the rabbit: effect of local oestrogen implants in the amygdaloid complex. *J. Endocrinol.,* **37,** 279–87 (1967)

289. Browning, H. C., Larke, G. A., Gibbs, W. E. Dependence of mammary stimulation upon ovarian tissue in gold thioglucose-treated

mice. *Neuroendocrinology,* 1, 93–104 (1965/66)

290. Bartke, A. Reproduction of female dwarf mice treated with prolactin. *J. Reprod. Fertility,* 11, 203–6 (1966)

291. Gale, C. C., Taleisnik, S., Friedman, H. M., McCann, S. M. Hormonal basis for impairments in milk synthesis and milk ejection following hypothalamic lesions. *J. Endocrinol.,* 23, 303–16 (1961)

292. Ahmad, N., Lyons, W. R. Lactation in pituitary-autografted rats. *Endocrinology,* 78, 837–44 (1966)

293. Nikitovitch-Winer, M. B. Effect of hypophysial stalk transection on luteotropic hormone secretion in the rat. *Endocrinology,* 77, 658–73 (1965)

294. Anderson, L. L., Dyck, G. W., Mori, H., Henricks, D. M., Melampy, R. M. Ovarian function in pigs after hypophysial stalk transection or hypophysectomy. *Am. J. Physiol.,* 212, 1188–94 (1967)

295. Meites, J., Kahn, R. H., Nicoll, C. S. Prolactin production by rat pituitary *in vitro. Proc. Soc. Exptl. Biol. Med.,* 108, 440–43 (1961)

296. Robboy, S. J., Kahn, R. H. Zone electrophoresis and prolactin activity of rat adenohypophysis cultivated *in vitro. Endocrinology,* 78, 440–44 (1966)

297. Gala, R. R., Reece, R. P. *In vitro* lactogen production by anterior pituitaries from various species. *Proc. Soc. Exptl. Biol. Med.,* 120, 263–64 (1965)

298. Pasteels, J. L. Premiers résultats de culture combinée *in vitro* d'hypophyse et d'hypothalamus dans le but d'en apprécier la sécrétion de prolactine. *Compt. Rend. Acad. Sci.,* 253, 3074–75 (1961)

299. Talwalker, P. K., Ratner, A., Meites, J. *In vitro* inhibition of pituitary prolactin synthesis and release by hypothalamic extract. *Am. J. Physiol.,* 205, 213–18 (1963)

300. Kragt, C. L., Meites, J. Dose-response relationships between hypothalamic PIF and prolactin release by rat pituitary tissue *in vitro. Endocrinology,* 80, 1170–73 (1967)

301. Grosvenor, C. E., McCann, S. M., Nallar, R. Inhibition of nursing-induced and stress-induced fall in pituitary prolactin concentration in lactating rats by injection of acid extracts of bovine hypothalamus. *Endocrinology,* 76, 883–89 (1965)

302. Kuroshima, A., Arimura, A., Bowers, C. Y., Schally, A. V. Inhibition by pig hypothalamic extracts of depletion of pituitary prolactin in rats following cervical stimulation. *Endocrinology,* 78, 216–17 (1966)

303. Herlyn, U., Geeler, H. F., Berswordt-Wallrabe, I. V., Berswordt-Wallrabe, R. V. Pituitary lactogenic hormone release during onset of pseudopregnancy in intact rats. *Acta Endocrinol.,* 48, 220–24 (1965)

304. Gala, R. R., Reece, R. P. Influence of neurohumors on anterior pituitary lactogen production *in vitro. Proc. Soc. Exptl. Biol. Med.,* 120, 220–22 (1965)

305. Ratner, A., Meites, J. Depletion of prolactin-inhibiting activity of rat hypothalamus by estradiol or suckling stimulus. *Endocrinology,* 75, 377–82 (1964)

306. Grosvenor, C. E. Effect of nursing and stress upon prolactin-inhibiting activity of the rat hypothalamus. *Endocrinology,* 77, 1037–42 (1965)

307. Ratner, A., Talwalker, P. K., Meites, J. Effect of reserpine on prolactin-inhibiting activity of rat hypothalamus. *Endocrinology,* 77, 315–19 (1965)

308. de Voe, W. F., Ramirez, V. D., McCann, S. M. Induction of mammary secretion by hypothalamic lesions in male rats. *Endocrinology,* 78, 158–64 (1966)

309. Kragt, C. L., Meites, J. Stimulation of pigeon pituitary prolactin release by pigeon hypothalamic extract *in vitro. Endocrinology,* 76, 1169–76 (1965)

310. Baylé, J. D., Assenmacher, I. Absence de stimulation du jabot du pigeon après autogreffe hypophysaire. *Compt. Rend. Acad. Sci.,* 261, 5667–70 (1965)

311. Sinha, D. K., Meites, J. Direct effects of a hypothalamic extract on hormone secretion by a pituitary mammo-somatotropic tumor. *Endocrinology,* 80, 131–40 (1967)

312. Roth, J., Glick, S. M., Yalow, R. S., Berson, S. A. The influence of blood glucose on the plasma concentration of growth hormone. *Diabetes,* 13, 355–61 (1964)

313. Glick, S. M., Roth, J., Yalow,

R. S., Berson, S. A. The regulation of growth hormone secretion. *Recent Progr. Hormone Res.*, **21**, 241–83 (1965)

314. Geschwind, I. I., Li, C. H. The tibia test for growth hormone. In *International Symposium: The Hypophyseal Growth Hormone, Nature and Actions*, 28–104 (Smith, R. W., Jr., Gaebler, O. H., Long, C. N. H., Eds., McGraw-Hill, New York, 576 pp., 1955)

315. Schooley, R. A., Friedkin, S., Evans, E. S. Re-examination of the discrepancy between acidophil numbers and growth hormone concentration in the anterior pituitary gland following thyroidectomy. *Endocrinology*, **79**, 1053–57 (1966)

316. Schalch, D. S., Reichlin, S. Plasma growth hormone concentration in the rat determined by radioimmunoassay: influence of sex, pregnancy, lactation, anesthesia, hypophysectomy and extrasellar pituitary transplants. *Endocrinology*, **79**, 275–80 (1966)

317. Riekstniece, E., Asling, C. W. Thyroxine augmentation of GH-induced endochondral osteogenesis. *Proc. Soc. Exptl. Biol. Med.*, **123**, 258–63 (1966)

318. Wegienka, L. C., Grodsky, G. M., Karam, J. H., Grasso, S. G., Forsham, P. H. Comparison of insulin and 2-deoxy-D-glucose-induced glucopenia as stimulators of growth hormone secretion. *Metabolism*, **16**, 245–56 (1967)

319. Cerasi, E., Della Casa, L., Luft, R., Roovete, A. Determination of human growth hormone (HGH) in plasma by a double antibody radioimmunoassay. *Acta Endocrinol.*, **53**, 101–20 (1966)

320. Hunter, W. M., Clarke, B. F., Duncan, L. J. P. Plasma growth hormone after an overnight fast and following glucose loading in healthy and diabetic subjects. *Metabolism*, **15**, 596–607 (1966)

321. Marks, V., Greenwood, F. C., Howorth, P. J. N., Samols, E. Plasma growth hormone levels in spontaneous hypoglycemia. *J. Clin. Endocrinol.*, **27**, 523–28 (1967)

322. Burgess, J. A., Smith, B. R., Merimee, T. J. Growth hormone in thyrotoxicosis: effect of insulin-induced hypoglycemia. *J. Clin. Endocrinol.*, **26**, 1257–60 (1966)

323. Frantz, A. G., Rabkin, M. T. Human growth hormone. Clinical measurement, response to hypoglycemia and suppression by corticosteroids. *New Engl. J. Med.*, **271**, 1375–81 (1964)

324. Abrams, R. L., Parker, M. L., Blanco, S., Reichlin, S., Daughaday, W. H. Hypothalamic regulation of growth hormone secretion. *Endocrinology*, **78**, 605–13 (1966)

325. Knobil, E. Tenth Bowditch Lecture. The pituitary growth hormone: an adventure in physiology. *Physiologist*, **9**, 25–44 (1966)

326. Smith, G., Katz, S., Root, A., Dhariwal, A. P. S., Bongiovanni, A., Eberlein, W., McCann, S. M. Effect of crude ovine stalk median eminence extract on plasma growth hormone in Rhesus monkeys. *Proc. 48th Meeting Endocrine Soc., June 20–22, 1966, Chicago*, 35

327. Krulich, L., McCann, S. M. Effect of alterations in blood sugar on pituitary growth hormone content in the rat. *Endocrinology*, **78**, 759–64 (1966)

328. Pecile, A., and Müller, E. Suppressive action of corticosteroids on the secretion of growth hormone. *J. Endocrinol.*, **36**, 401–8 (1966)

329. Müller, E. E., Saito, T., Arimura, A., Schally, A. V. Hypoglycemia, stress and growth hormone release: blockade of growth hormone release by drugs acting on the central nervous system. *Endocrinology*, **80**, 109–17 (1967)

330. Müller, E. E., Sawano, S., Arimura, A., Schally, A. V. Blockade of release of growth hormone by brain norepinephrine depletors. *Ibid.*, 471–76

331. Scherz, D., Lawrence, A. M. Effect of chronic tolbutamide administration on growth and carbohydrate metabolism in weanling rats. *Acta Endocrinol.*, **53**, 499–504 (1966)

332. Floyd, S. C., Fajans, S. S., Knopf, R. F., Rull, J., Conn, J. W. Stimulation of insulin secretion by amino acids. *Clin. Res.*, **13**, 322 (1965)

333. Rabinowitz, D., Merimee, T. J., Burgess, J. A., Riggs, L. Growth hormone and insulin release after arginine: indifference to hyperglycemia and epinephrine. *J. Clin. Endocrinol. Metab.*, **26**, 1170–72 (1966)

334. Merimee, T. J., Burgess, J. A.,

Rabinowitz, D. Sex-determined variation in serum insulin and growth hormone response to amino acid stimulation. *J. Clin. Endocrinol. Metab.*, **26**, 791–93 (1966)

335. Frantz, A. G., Rabkin, M. T. Estrogen stimulation of growth hormone release. *J. Clin. Invest.*, **44**, 1048–49 (1965)

336. Meyer, V., Knobil, E. Growth hormone secretion in the unanesthetized Rhesus monkey in response to noxious stimuli. *Endocrinology*, **80**, 163–71 (1967)

337. Krulich, L., McCann, S. M. Influence of stress on the growth hormone (GH) content in the pituitary of the rat. *Proc. Soc. Exptl. Biol. Med.*, **122**, 612–16 (1966)

338. Grosvenor, C., Krulich, L., McCann, S. M. Depletion of pituitary concentration of growth hormone as a result of suckling in the lactating rat (Submitted for publication)

339. MacLeod, R. M. Suppression of pituitary function by pituitary tumor hormones. *Fed. Proc.*, **26**, 586 (1967)

340. Koneff, A. A., Scow, R. O., Simpson, M. E., Li, C. H., Evans, H. M. Response by the rat thyro-parathyroidectomized at birth to growth hormone and to thyroxine given separately or in combination. II. Histological changes in the pituitary. *Anat. Record*, **104**, 465–73 (1949)

341. Krulich, L., McCann, S. M. Influence of growth hormone (GH) on content of GH in the pituitaries of normal rats. *Proc. Soc. Exptl. Biol. Med.*, **121**, 1114–17 (1966)

342. Müller, E., Pecile, A. Influence of exogenous GH on endogenous GH release. *Proc. Soc. Exptl. Biol. Med.*, **122**, 1289–91 (1966)

343. Katz, S. H., Molitch, M., McCann, S. M. Feedback of hypothalamic growth hormone (GH) implants upon the anterior pituitary (AP). *Proc. 49th Meeting Endocrine Soc., June 15–17, 1967, Bal Harbour, Florida*, 86

344. Krulich, L., Dhariwal, A. P. S., McCann, S. M. Hypothalamic control of growth hormone (GH) secretion. *Proc. 47th Meeting Endocrine Soc., June 17–19, 1965, New York*, 21

345. Han, P. W., Liu, A.-C. Obesity and impaired growth of rats force fed 40 days after hypothalamic lesions.

Am. J. Physiol., **211**, 229–31 (1966)

346. Han, P. W., Lin, C.-H., Chu, K.-C., Mu, J.-Y., Liu, A.-C. Hypothalamic obesity in weanling rats. *Am. J. Physiol.*, **209**, 627–31 (1965)

347. Müller, E. E., Pecile, A. Growth hormone-releasing activity in the hypothalamus of primates. *Endocrinology*, **79**, 448–50 (1966)

348. Schally, A. V., Müller, E. E., Arimura, A., Bowers, C. Y., Saito, T., Redding, T. W., Sawano, S., Pizzolato, P. Releasing factors in human hypothalamic and neurohypophysial extracts. *J. Clin. Endocrinol.*, **27**, 755–62 (1967)

349. Franz, J., Haselbach, C. H., Libert, O. Studies of the effect of hypothalamic extracts on somatotrophic pituitary function. *Acta Endocrinol.*, **41**, 336–50 (1962)

350. Deuben, R. R., Meites, J. Stimulation of pituitary growth hormone release by a hypothalamic extract in vitro. *Endocrinology*, **74**, 408–14 (1964)

351. Deuben, R. R., Meites, J. *In vitro* reinitiation of pituitary somatotropin release by an acid extract of the hypothalamus. *Proc. Soc. Exptl. Biol. Med.*, **118**, 409–12 (1965)

352. Schally, A. V., Steelman, S. L., Bowers, C. Y. Effect of hypothalamic extracts on release of growth hormone *in vitro*. *Proc. Soc. Exptl. Biol. Med.*, **119**, 208–12 (1965)

353. Krulich, L., Dhariwal, A. P. S., McCann, S. M. Stimulatory and inhibitory hypothalamic factors regulating secretion of growth hormone. *Proc. 49th Meeting Endocrine Soc., June 15–17, 1967, Bal Harbour, Florida*, 87

354. Müller, E. E., Pecile, A. Growth hormone releasing factor of a guinea-pig hypothalamic extract: its activity in guinea-pig and rat. *Proc. Soc. Exptl. Biol. Med.*, **119**, 1191–94 (1965)

355. Krulich, L., Dhariwal, A. P. S., McCann, S. M. Growth hormone-releasing activity of crude ovine hypothalamic extracts. *Proc. Soc. Exptl. Biol. Med.*, **120**, 180–84 (1965)

356. Müller, E., Pecile, A., Smirne, S. Substances present at the hypothalamic level and growth hor-

mone releasing activity. *Endocrinology*, **77**, 390–92 (1965)

357. Dhariwal, A. P. S., Krulich, L., Antunes-Rodrigues, J., McCann, S. M. Separation of growth hormone-releasing factor (GH-RF) from corticotrophin-releasing factor (CRF). *Neuroendocrinology*, **1**, 341–49 (1966)

358. Schally, A. V., Kuroshima, A., Ishida, Y., Arimura, A., Saito, T., Bowers, C. Y., Steelman, S. L. Purification of GH-RF from beef hypothalamus. *Proc. Soc. Exptl. Biol. Med.*, **122**, 821–23 (1966)

359. Machlin, L. J., Horino, M., Kipnis, D. M., Phillips, S. L., Gordon, R. S. Stimulation of growth hormone secretion by median eminence extracts in the sheep. *Endocrinology*, **80**, 205–7 (1967)

360. Garcia, J. F., Geschwind, I. I. Increase in plasma growth hormone level in the monkey following the administration of sheep hypothalamic extracts. *Nature*, **211**, 372 (1966)

361. Meyer, V., Knobil, E. Stimulation of growth hormone secretion by vasopressin in the Rhesus monkey. *Endocrinology*, **79**, 1016–18 (1966)

362. Smith, G., Katz, S., Dhariwal, A. P. S., Bongiovanni, A., Eberlein, W., McCann, S. M. Effect of thioglycollate or trypsin on GH-RF activity of ovine SME in Rhesus monkeys. *Fed. Proc.*, **26**, 316 (1967)

363. Ramirez, V. D., McCann, S. M. Thioglycollate stable luteinizing hormone- and corticotrophin-releasing factors in beef hypothalamus. *Am. J. Physiol.*, **207**, 441–45 (1964)

364. Symchowicz, S., Peckham, W. D., Oneri, R., Korduba, C. A., Perlman, P. L. The effect *in vitro* of purified hypothalamic extract on the growth hormone content of the rat pituitary. *J. Endocrinol.*, **35**, 379–83 (1966)

365. Rao, P. M., Robertson, M. C., Winnick, M., Winnick, T. Biosynthesis of prolactin and growth hormone in slices of bovine anterior pituitary tissue. *Endocrinology*, **80**, 1111–17 (1967)

366. Pecile, A., Müller, E., Falconi, G., Martini, L. Growth hormone-releasing activity of hypothalamic extracts at different ages. *Endocrinology*, **77**, 241–46 (1965)

367. Meites, J., Fiel, N. J. Effect of starvation on hypothalamic content of "Somatotropin Releasing Factor" and pituitary growth hormone content. *Endocrinology*, **77**, 455–60 (1965)

368. Friedman, R. C., Reichlin, S. Growth hormone content of the pituitary gland of starved rats. *Endocrinology*, **76**, 787–88 (1965)

369. Krulich, L., McCann, S. M. Evidence for the presence of growth hormone-releasing factor in blood of hypoglycemic, hypophysectomized rats. *Proc. Soc. Exptl. Biol. Med.*, **122**, 668–71 (1966)

370. Katz, S., Krulich, L., McCann, S. M. Effect of insulin-induced hypoglycemia on the concentration of growth hormone (GH)-releasing factor in plasma and hypothalamus of the rat. *Fed. Proc.*, **25**, 191 (1966)

371. Katz, S. H., Dhariwal, A. P. S., McCann, S. M. Effect of hypoglycemia on the content of pituitary GH and hypothalamic GH-RF in the rat. *Endocrinology*, **81**, 333–39 (1967)

372. Müller, E. E., Arimura, A., Saito, T., Schally, A. V. Growth hormone-releasing activity in plasma of normal and hypophysectomized rats. *Endocrinology*, **80**, 77–81 (1967)

373. Krulich, L., Lackey, R. W., Dhariwal, A. P. S. Inhibition of growth hormone (GH) release from the pituitary gland *in vitro* by hypothalamic extracts. *Fed. Proc.*, **26**, 316 (1967)

374. Etkin, W. Hypothalamic inhibition of pars intermedia activity in the frog. *Gen. Comp. Endocrinol. Suppl. 1*, 148–59 (1962)

375. Kastin, A. J., Ross, G. T. Melanocyte-stimulating hormone activity in pituitaries of frogs with hypothalamic lesions. *Endocrinology*, **77**, 45–48 (1965)

376. Kastin, A. J., Ross, G. T. Melanocyte-stimulating hormone (MSH) and ACTH activities of pituitary homografts in albino rats. *Ibid.*, **75**, 187–91 (1964)

377. Geschwind, I. I., Huseby, R. A. Melanocyte-stimulating activity in a transplantable mouse pituitary tumor. *Endocrinology*, **79**, 97–105 (1966)

378. Geschwind, I. I. Change in hair color in mice induced by injection of

α-MSH. *Endocrinology*, **79**, 1165–67 (1966)

379. Taleisnik, S., Orías, R. Pituitary melanocyte-stimulating hormone (MSH) after suckling stimulus. *Endocrinology*, **78**, 522–26 (1966)

380. Taleisnik, S., Orías, R. A melanocyte stimulating hormone-releasing factor in hypothalamic extracts. *Am. J. Physiol.*, **208**, 293–96 (1965)

381. Dhariwal, A. P. S., McCann, S. M., Taleisnik, S., Tomatis, M. E. Purification of hypothalamic melanocyte-stimulating hormone (MSH)-releasing factor with Sephadex. *Proc. Soc. Exptl. Biol. Med.*, **121**, 996–98 (1966)

382. Taleisnik, S., Orías, R., DeOlmos, J. Topographic distribution of the MSH-RF in rat hypothalamus. *Proc. Soc. Exptl. Biol. Med.*, **122**, 325–28 (1966)

383. Taleisnik, S., Tomatis, M. E. Antagonistic effect on melanocyte-stimulating hormone release of two neural tissue extracts. *Am. J. Physiol.*, **212**, 157–63 (1967)

384. Taleisnik, S. (Personal communication, 1967)

385. Bercu, B. B., Brinkley, H. J. Hypothalamic and cerebral cortical inhibition of melanocyte-stimulating hormone secretion in the frog, *Rana pipiens*. *Endocrinology*, **80**, 399–403 (1967)

386. Schally, A. V., Kastin, A. J. Purification of a bovine hypothalamic factor which elevates pituitary MSH levels in rats. *Endocrinology*, **79**, 768–72 (1966)

387. Kastin, A. J., Schally, A. V. MSH activity in pituitaries of rats treated with hypothalamic extracts from various animals. *Gen. Comp. Endocrinol.*, **8**, 344–47 (1967)

388. Kastin, A. J., Schally, A. V. MSH activity in pituitary glands of rats treated with tranquilizing drugs. *Endocrinology*, **79**, 1018–20 (1966)

389. Kastin, A. J., Schally, A. V. *In vivo* assay for melanocyte lightening substances. *Experientia*, **22**, 389 (1966)

390. Kastin, A. J., Redding, T. W., Schally, A. V. MSH activity in rat pituitaries after pinealectomy. *Proc. Soc. Exptl. Biol. Med.*, **124**, 1275–79 (1967)

391. Rumsfeld, H. W., Jr., Porter, J. C. ACTH-releasing activity in an acetone extract of beef hypo-thalamus. *Arch. Biochem. Biophys.*, **82**, 474–76 (1959)

392. McCann, S. M., Haberland, P. Relative abundance of vasopressin and corticotrophin-releasing factor in neurohypophysial extracts. *Proc. Soc. Exptl. Biol. Med.*, **102**, 319–25 (1959)

393. Royce, P. C., Sayers, G. Purification of hypothalamic corticotropin releasing factor. *Proc. Soc. Exptl. Biol. Med.*, **103**, 447–52 (1960)

394. Guillemin, R. Hypothalamic factors releasing pituitary hormones. *Recent Progr. Hormone Res.*, **20**, 89–130 (1964)

395. McCann, S. M., Dhariwal, A. P. S. Hypothalamic releasing factors and the neurovascular link between brain and anterior pituitary. In *Neuroendocrinology*, **1**, 261–96 (Martini, L., Ganong, W. F., Eds., Academic Press, New York and London, 774 pp., 1966)

396. Porath, J., Flodin, P. Gel filtration: a method for desalting and group separation. *Nature*, **183**, 1657–59 (1959)

397. Porath, J., Schally, A. V. Gel filtration of posterior pituitary hormones. *Endocrinology*, **70**, 738–42 (1962)

398. Harris, G. W., Reed, M., Fawcett, C. P. Hypothalamic releasing factors and the control of anterior pituitary function. *Brit. Med. Bull.*, **22**, 266–72 (1966)

399. Schally, A. V., Bowers, C. Y. Purification of luteinizing hormone-releasing factor from bovine hypothalamus. *Endocrinology*, **75**, 608–14 (1964)

400. Schally, A. V., Saito, T., Arimura, A., Müller, E. E., Bowers, C. Y. Purification of follicle stimulating hormone-releasing factor (FSH-RF). *Endocrinology*, **79**, 1087–94 (1966)

401. Guillemin, R. Hypothalamic polypeptides releasing pituitary hormones. *Metabolism*, **13**, 1206–10 (1964)

402. Dhariwal, A. P. S., Grosvenor, C., Antunes-Rodrigues, J., McCann, S. M. Purification of ovine prolactin inhibiting factor (PIF) (Submitted for publication)

403. Arimura, A., Saito, T., Müller, E. E., Bowers, C. Y., Sawano, S., Schally, A. V. Absence of prolactin-release inhibiting activity in highly purified LH-releasing fac-

tor. *Endocrinology,* **80,** 972–74 (1967)

404. Dhariwal, A. P. S., Antunes-Rodrigues, J., McCann, S. M. Purification of ovine luteinizing hormone-releasing factor by gel filtration and ion exchange chromatography. *Proc. Soc. Exptl. Biol. Med.,* **118,** 999–1003 (1965)

405. Guillemin, R., Jutisz, M., Sakiz, E. Purification partielle d'un facteur hypothalamique (LRF) stimulant la sécrétion de l'hormone hypophysaire de lutéinisation (LH). *Compt. Rend. Acad. Sci.,* **256,** 504–7 (1963)

406. Ramirez, V. D., Nallar, R., McCann, S. M. Purification of luteinizing hormone-releasing factor from beef hypothalamus. *Proc. Soc. Exptl. Biol. Med.,* **115,** 1072–76 (1964)

407. Fawcett, C. P., Harris, G. W., Reed, M. The purification of the luteinizing hormone releasing factor (LRF). *Proc. Intern. Congr. Physiol. Sci., 23rd, Tokyo, September 1–9, 1965,* 300

408. Nikitovitch-Winer, M. B., Pribble, A. H., Winer, A. D. Luteinizing hormone-releasing factor: partial purification. *Am. J. Physiol.,* **208,** 1286–90 (1965)

409. Dhariwal, A. P. S., Watanabe, S., Antunes-Rodrigues, J., McCann, S. M. Chromatographic behavior of follicle stimulating hormone-releasing factor on Sephadex and carboxymethylcellulose. *Neuroendocrinology* (In press)

410. Dhariwal, A. P. S., Krulich, L., Katz, S., McCann, S. M. Purification of growth hormone-releasing factor (GH-RF). *Endocrinology,* **77,** 932–36 (1965)

411. Guillemin, R., Yamazaki, E., Jutisz, M. Présence dans un extrait de tissues hypothalamiques d'une substance stimulant la sécrétion de l'hormone hypophysaire thyréotrope (TSH). Première purification par filtration sur gel Sephadex. *Compt. Rend., Acad. Sci.,* **255,** 1018–20 (1962)

412. Schally, A. V., Guillemin, R. Isolation and chemical characterization of a β-CRF from pig posterior pituitary gland. *Proc. Soc. Exptl. Biol. Med.,* **112,** 1014–17 (1963)

413. Schally, A. V., Lipscomb, H. S., Guillemin, R. Isolation and amino acid sequence of α 2-CRF from hog pituitary glands. *Endocrinology,* **71,** 164–73 (1962)

414. Royce, P. C., Sayers, G. Corticotropin-releasing activity of a pepsin-labile factor in the hypothalamus. *Proc. Soc. Exptl. Biol. Med.,* **98,** 677–80 (1958)

415. Jutisz, M., de la Llosa, P., Sakiz, E., Yamazaki, E., Guillemin, R. L'action des enzymes proteolytiques sur les facteurs hypothalamiques LRF et TRF stimulant la sécrétion des hormones hypophysaires de lutéinisation (LH) et thyréotrope (TSH). *Compt. Rend. Soc. Biol.,* **157,** 235–37 (1963)

REGULATION OF INTERNAL BODY TEMPERATURE[1,2]

1016

By H. T. Hammel[3]

John B. Pierce Foundation Laboratory
New Haven, Connecticut

Internal body temperature appears to be regulated in most vertebrates, at least some of the time. This means that internal temperature is compared in some way with a reference, and when a difference occurs an appropriate response is made tending to reduce but not eliminate that difference. I shall attempt to review the recent literature that seems, in my opinion, to be relevant to this physiological process. Most sought after have been reports of quantitative relationships upon which an analysis of the controlling system can be based. Also reviewed are reports describing the many kinds of thermoregulatory responses, the sensory inputs that are implicated in activating them, and the hypotheses that suggest how the response is linked to the input.

Students of regulatory biology are materially aided by the terminology and the concepts of the control systems engineer, although their objectives are markedly different. The former desires to describe an already existing, regulatory process whereas the latter designs a system to regulate or control some quantity. An increasing number of excellent source books assists the physiologist to learn the language and to understand the ideas of the systems engineer. The American Society of Mechanical Engineers has sponsored the development of a standard terminology for automatic control (10) which can and should serve as a basis for developing a language for physiological control systems. Two recent textbooks, one on *Control Theory and Biological Systems* by Grodins (163) and the other on *The Application of Control Theory to Physiological Systems* by Milhorn (286), were written especially to aid the physiologist. Another textbook on *Physiological Controls and Regulations* edited by Yamamoto & Brobeck (402) was written by physiologists who at least recognize the value of trying to analyze certain biological processes in the manner of the control-systems engineer. Ashby has reviewed mathematical models and computer analysis of the function of the central nervous system (25).

[1] The survey of literature for this review was concluded August 1, 1967.

[2] This review was supported in part by Contract DA-49-193-MD-2676 with the U. S. Army Medical Research and Development Command and by Contract AF-33 (615)-2825 with the Aerospace Medical Research Laboratories, Wright-Patterson A.F.B.

[3] Present address: Physiological Research Laboratory, Scripps Institution of Oceanography, University of California, La Jolla, Calif.

Figure 1 is an outline of what I shall attempt to review. Its organization is unusual in that it illustrates a format often used by systems engineers for a feedback control system. Such a block diagram indicates the direction of flow of information and the transformations occurring along the way. Since this system has at least one feedback loop as well as a constant command, it is said to be a closed-loop feedback regulator, where core tem-

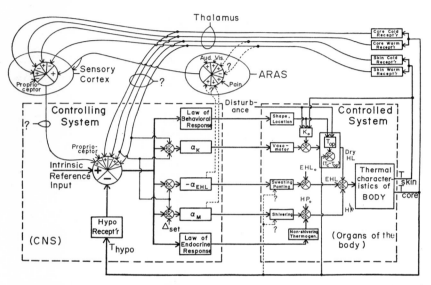

FIG. 1. A schema for the controlling and controlled systems for the regulation of internal body temperature. ARAS = ascending reticular activating system.

perature is probably the directly controlled variable. Each block in the diagram represents a transformation, and the law of the transformation, i.e., the input-output relationship, determines the output for any given input. Each circle represents a mixing point where quantities of the same quality and same dimension are combined. The mixing points in the controlling system probably combine nerve impulses and therefore are shown to be adders or subtractors depicting facilitation or inhibition of nervous activity. The outputs of the controllers are said to be the output forcing functions which, along with the disturbances, become the inputs to the controlled system. With further transformation within the controlled system by organs of the body, each of the forcing functions becomes a rate of heat production or heat loss. The outputs of the controlled system are the body temperatures which are transduced and fed back in some way to the controlling system as nervous activity.

No two reviewers of the thermoregulatory process would draw the same diagram of the controlling and the controlled system, and the differences might be major. There is no agreement as to the site of the regulated temperature in all species or whether there is, in fact, a single regulated temperature. There is agreement that several parts of the body possess receptors which transduce temperature to nervous activity which, in turn, affect a regulatory response, but how these feedback loops are combined remains controversial. Therefore a diagram such as this can serve only as an outline for an evolving point of view. It can render disservice if its user becomes committed to it and its evolution ceases.

Reviews by Hardy (175) and von Euler (131) examine the whole of the literature on regulation of body temperature up to 1961, the beginning of the period covered by this review. Bligh's excellent review covers the period up to 1966 (50). Hemingway (193) and Thauer (379) have reviewed shivering, one of the important thermoregulatory responses in endotherms, and its activation. A source book of great value has been *Temperature: Its Measurement and Control in Science and Industry* (176), especially Section IV on physiological responses to heat, Section V on physiological response to cold, and Section VII on temperature regulation. Another source book revealing the tremendous variety of thermoregulatory responses is the *Handbook of Physiology,* Section IV, on Adaptation to the Environment (115). Of special interest are Gelineo's Chapter 15 on the temperature regulation of organ systems in adaptation, Chapters 17 and 20–27 on terrestrial animals in cold, Chapters 28–35 on terrestrial animals in dry heat, and Chapters 36–39 on terrestrial animals in humid heat. Other papers or monographs, of the nature of reviews and revealing their authors' considered views, should be noted by students of thermal regulation (45, 92, 126, 135, 168, 177, 240, 250, 290, 299, 303, 323, 336, 378, 385). The reader may share my doubt that another review can contribute substantially to the insight already provided by these distinguished thermal physiologists. At best, another review may reflect a different point of view which, at worst, may turn out to be another unsubstantiated opinion.

The Regulated Temperature—A Partial Answer

Specialized temperature transducers are located at many sites within the body and on its surface. Such a transducer is of neural origin, its activity changes with a change in its temperature, and it must have connections with the sensorium where thermal effects are perceived, connections with the temperature regulator, or both, in order that it may influence a thermoregulatory response. Some temperature transducers primarily subserve other than thermoregulatory functions, but these will not be reviewed here. None of the many temperature transducers that have been studied fulfill all three of the above criteria. The usual lack of evidence as to their connections has not led to any controversy over their existence. Body temperatures are perceived and thermoregulatory respones are activated in accordance with appropriate changes in some body temperatures. Controversy arises over which body temperatures are being transduced, which are acted upon to generate a thermoregulatory response, and the combination in which they are acted upon.

Every element linking the temperature detectors with the outputs of the controllers consists of excitable tissue—axons, cell bodies, internuncial neurons, muscle fibers, and secretory cells. Therefore, some or all of the activities (membrane potential, spontaneous firing rate, conduction velocity, metabolism) of each element may be temperature dependent in accordance with the Arrhenius equation (183a). In a sense, then, each of these elements may be temperature sensitive. It is surprising, not that temperature is transduced by excitable tissue, but that the process appears to be achieved principally by specialized thermal detectors or receptors. The existence of these receptors has been inferred from temperature-induced changes in firing rate in (a) a fiber presumed to serve an unseen terminal receptor (195–197, 215, 217–219, 226) and (b) an unseen cell body in the central nervous system (72a, 73, 104–106, 128–129, 159, 178, 269, 270, 291, 293, 294, 393).

There is some doubt that the thermoreceptive nerves of the hairy and glabrous skin are differentiated except as to the tissue in which they terminate. The nerves, with unencapsulated bare endings, terminate either in collagenous tissue throughout the dermis or in smooth muscle associated with the hair follicles and the cutaneous vessels. The differentiated cutaneous sensations of warmth and cold may be attributable to different "nerve ending-tissue associations" (254, 256), but which of these generates which sensation is uncertain. Single myelinated fibers (conduction velocities of 3.6–15 m sec^{-1}) and nonmyelinated fibers (conduction velocities less than 1.5 m sec^{-1}) have been described as cold receptors in the hairy and glabrous skin of the monkey (218). With cooling of the skin from 40 to 20° C, discharge frequency reached a peak of about 150 impulses sec^{-1}. The frequency of the discharge at constant temperature was maximum at some skin temperature between 20 and 35° C and went to zero between 35 and 40° C, although fibers silent at higer temperatures would discharge briefly when cooled to a temperature for which the constant temperature discharge was zero. All fibers could be excited by temperature changes less than 0.5° C and each fiber served a single skin spot of from 0.25 to 0.6 mm^2. No single fiber from a warm receptor was observed; however, in a multifiber preparation some fibers were excited by an increasing skin temperature.

Cutaneous thermal sensitivity, served by single nonmyelinated fibers, was previously described in the hairy skin of the cat, rat, and dog (197, 215, 226). One cold fiber has been found in the hairy skin of man (196). Behavioral studies of cutaneous temperature sensitivity of cats indicate that the furred skin of the back and inner surface of the thigh and the foot pad have no sensitivity to mild increase in temperature and respond only to noxious stimuli (49–52° C) (252, 253). Sensitivity to a mild decrease in temperature is present in the back skin of the cat, but the threshold is about 3.5° C greater than the same skin area of man (252). The inner thigh skin and foot pad also have a sensitivity to cooling below the level for noxious stimulation (253). The face of the cat is comparable in sensitivity to the forehead skin of man (253).

Whether the depolarization of the membrane of the nerve ending leading to a propagated action potential results from thermochemical activity in the associated tissue, in the nerve ending, or in both, or from a thermomechanical process in the tissue (113, 255, 257) is unclear. Less favored is the possibility that the depolarizing potential results from a thermally induced gradient or changing gradient in the membrane potential along the nerve terminus (383). The thermal transducers in the skin have not been identified with any specialized anatomical structures, whereas the rapidly adapting mechanoreceptors of the hairy skin are associated with the hair follicle and some of the slowly adapting mechanoreceptors, with a receptive field of less than 250 μ^2, have a complex structure within the epidermis (216, 217, 219).

Equally unclear is the process by which central nervous detectors, conceivably combinations of neurons, transform temperature into neural activity. A neuron whose spontaneous firing rate is temperature dependent with a Q_{10} of 2 to 3, and which is facilitated by one or more similar neurons, is potentially a "warm-sensitive unit". Its firing rate would increase with a high Q_{10}, the magnitude of which depends upon the number of facilitating units and the facilitation of each. The facilitating units in this pool of neurons, which conceivably becomes a "warm-sensitive unit", may be joined in series as in a cascade or in parallel such that each facilitates a common or focal neuron directly. On the other hand, a focal neuron, having a spontaneous firing rate with a typical temperature dependence ($Q_{10} = 2$ to 3), is potentially a "cold-sensitive unit" if it is inhibited by two or more neurons with spontaneous firing rate and Q_{10} similar to those of the focal neuron, and if each of the inhibitory neurons has a constant level of suppression imposed upon it. For such a pool of neurons at a low temperature, the inhibitory neurons will be suppressed and the focal neuron will fire at a rate determined by its temperature. As the temperature increases, the inhibitory neurons remain suppressed and the focal neuron increases its firing rate. Above some temperature determined by the level of suppression, the inhibitory neurons will no longer remain suppressed and will increase their firing rate with increasing temperature. Over this latter range of increasing temperature, the focal neuron will be increasingly inhibited, thereby showing the temperature dependence presumed to be characteristic of a so-called "cold-sensitive unit". Units with these "bell-shaped" temperature characteristics have been described (73).

Regardless of how "warm" or "cold" sensitivity of neurons is achieved, these neurons or combinations of them must have a spontaneous firing rate at all temperatures over the physiological range. In addition, the warm-sensitive neuron or neuron complex must increase its spontaneous firing rate with increase in temperature over the useful range of temperatures. The cold-sensitive neuron need not necessarily exhibit any temperature effect upon its spontaneous firing rate (168). Presumably, the great majority of neurons within the central nervous system, including the hypothalamus, exhibit no spontaneous firing rate. These must be interneurons for communication with all kinds of responders, including thermoregulatory ones (128, 129, 291). Those neurons which exhibit a spontaneous firing with respect to physical and chemical parameters of the internal environment other than temperature presumably show little or no temperature dependence.

This review will proceed on the assumption that the hypothalamic temperature, when transduced, becomes the regulated temperature and I will indicate how the other body temperatures, as well as other factors, influence the thermoregulatory responses. The logic of this procedure, as illustrated in Figure 1, does not exclude the possibility that any one of the other body temperatures, when transduced, may become the regulated temperature. How, then, are we to decide which is the regulated temperature? Is the view that there is a single regulated temperature only an illusion? If the connections from the thermal receptors of the body to the hypothalamus and its preoptic tissue were known and if the connections within the hypothalamus to the effector neurons—which become the final common pathways for the thermoregulatory responses—were known, then no controversy as to the regulated temperature should exist. No one doubts that these connections occur, but since the circuitry of this region of the brainstem remains completely undescribed, authors differ in their views on the regulated temperature and the role of the other body temperatures.

Whatever the regulated temperature, it is not its magnitude that determines the thermoregulatory response; rather, it is the sign and magnitude of the difference between the regulated temperature and some "virtual set" or "reference" temperature that determines both the type and the magnitude of response. The response must always be appropriate to reduce the magnitude of the difference. The reference activity may be presumed to have a neural basis and may be thought of as transduced from a virtual but not real temperature called the "set" temperature.

A search for the regulated temperature, its transducer, and the neural reference might be based on the premise that these are essential and sufficient to activate the controller and to force the controlled system appropriately. In other words, one might deafferent the generator of the activating signal, thereby allowing only a single feedback loop, and then demonstrate that it alone, among all candidates for the regulated temperature, can regulate. The nervous system, however, is not organized so as to allow one to isolate, one at a time, each of the possible feedback loops and to explore how it performs by itself.

Most authors agree that the most likely part of the nervous system to transduce a relevant body temperature—compare the result with a reference in order to yield an error signal consisting of neural activity of appropriate sign and magnitude—is the hypothalamus and the preoptic region lying rostral to it. While somewhat controversial, the statement can be made plausible. As a first step, the preoptic-hypothalamic region can be at least partially deafferented as, presumably, in dogs said to be "high-thalamic preparations", which had a narrow transverse strip of brain aspirated just rostral to the anterior commissure and preoptic area leaving these parts, the hypothalamus, and the thalamus grossly intact (251). The aspirated strip extended across both cerebral hemispheres and transected the parietal lobes, the corpus callosum, and the fornices, and included the septal area. A week postoperatively, this preparation responded to a moderate heat stress (38° C), with colonic temperature no higher than 39.5° C (about 0.5° C higher than an unoperated dog), by panting and presumably increasing its evaporative heat loss to 50 to 75 per cent of the resting heat production. Exposed to a cold stress (3° C) requiring a two- to threefold increase in heat production, this preparation was able to maintain its colonic temperature at the same level as the unoperated animal.

If the high thalamic preparation were not fully deafferented, then possibly the "low thalamic" or "high hypothalamic" preparations were. In the former, the thalamus rostral to the intermediate mass, the rostral portions of the fornices, all septal tissue, the anterior commissure and its environs, and the preoptic area were removed. When these animals were exposed to the 38° C environment, colonic temperature rose to 40–41° C before heat loss from panting was sufficient to balance heat production; evaporative heat loss may be inferred to be approximately one-half the resting heat production. A similar so-called "raised threshold" was noted in the "high hypothalamic preparation" in which all thalamic tissue was removed with no appreciable damage to the dorsal or anterior hypothalamus, although the anterior commissure and possibly some of the preoptic tissue was gone. The "high hypothalamic" dog responded to 38° C environment by panting at a colonic temperature about 1.5° C higher than the unoperated dog, and responded to the 3° C environment by shivering at a colonic temperature about 1° C below that of the unoperated dog (251).

A normal dog, resting in a neutral environment, may be presumed to have insufficient afferent input to its preoptic-hypothalamic area to activate either panting or shivering and, in this sense, it is like a deafferented preparation. For this animal, a 1 to 2 C increase in hypothalamic temperature is sufficient to exceed the threshold for panting; a 1 to 2° C decrease in hypothalamic temperature will activate shivering (192). These statements may be generalized to any normal endotherm, resting and awake in a neutral environment. Inputs into its thermal regulator (preoptic-hypothalamic area), from thermal receptors located throughout the body, are presumably insufficient to activate either sensible evaporative heat loss or shivering and nonshivering heat production. For this animal, a 1 to 2° C increase above normal in the temperature of the thermal regulator (hypothalamic tem-

perature) will exceed the threshold for evaporative heat loss, while a 1 to 2°
C decrease in regulator temperature (hypothalamic temperature) will activate threshold shivering, nonshivering thermogenesis or both. Endotherms
for which these statements apply include: dog (69, 152, 173, 192), cat (4),
rabbit (127), rat (329), ox (221–223), goat (12, 15, 16, 22), and baboon
(156, 157).

No other part of the central nervous system may be substituted in the
parentheses of the above two general statements in place of the preoptic-
hypothalamic area and its temperature. The evidence that this area is essential for the regulation of body temperature seems overwhelming. Without its ability to transduce its own temperature into neural impulses, and
then to activate either increased rates of heat loss or decreased rates of
heat loss and increased rates of heat production, depending upon the sign
and magnitude of its temperature displacement, there is no regulation of
body temperature. Other parts of the nervous system can transduce their
own temperature and thereby affect a thermoregulatory response, but they
cannot regulate the internal body temperature as does the hypothalamus.

Destruction of the entire preoptic region of the unanesthetized goat by
proton irradiation reduced the animal's responses to external exposure to
heat and cold (21). Put at 45° C for one hour, the lesioned goat began to
pant when rectal temperature increased to 41° C and the panting rate increased to about 200 resp/min at 41.2–41.5° C. The same goats, when normal and similarly exposed, began to pant at less than 40° C and the panting
rate increased to 300–370 resp/min at a rectal temperature of 40.3–40.7°
C. No open-mouth panting occurred in the lesioned goats. When the goats
without preoptic tissue were placed in a moderately cold environment (+5°
C) for four hours, rectal and caval vein temperatures dropped continuously
to between 36 and 37° C whereupon moderate shivering appeared and prevented further drop in temperature. When placed in severe cold (−10° C)
for two hours, the animal responded sooner with more intense shivering
and with only a 1° C drop in caval vein temperature. Thus, most, but not
all, of the neurons involved in generating the activating signal for both
evaporative heat loss and heat production are located in the preoptic tissue.
A response could be activated if the combined external and internal temperature displacements were great enough. A pyrogen, administered intravenously in nine times the normal amount, produced shivering and a 1° C
fever after a forty-minute latency (21). This response also suggests that not
all thermoregulatory neurons reside in the preoptic tissue.

Small electrolytic lesions extending 0.5 mm to either side of the mid-
sagittal plane of the preoptic region in cats led to chronic reductions of
2–3° C in colonic temperature and of 17–20 per cent in oxygen consumption, at air temperatures between 19 and 27° C (235, 237, 238, 359). Vasodilatation inappropriate to the low body temperature sometimes occurred as
did vasoconstriction inappropriate to the rarely occurring high body temperature. During exposure to 40° C, the colonic temperature of the experi-

mental cats rose higher than did that of unoperated control cats, while panting occurred in both (359). With exposure to cold, shivering was induced and the usual hypothermic temperature was increased (237, 238). Thus, also in cats, the medial preoptic tissue contains a high concentration of neurons essential for normal activation of thermoregulatory response, but some such neurons may also reside outside this region. Even decerebrate cats exposed to rapid body cooling (and rapid body warming) were capable of muscle movement including a tremulous activity of 4 to 7 cps but without an appreciable increase in oxygen consumption. This response was not interpreted to be the tremor of shivering, whose frequency is 9 to 11 cps; the neural control of shivering was thought to lie rostral to the midbrain (369). The control of heat production may also be more than a thermoregulatory response, and this other controlled metabolic response may also depend on body temperature (120). By selective destruction of parts of the brain, an intact hypothalamus was found to be important for a febrile response to an intravenous endotoxin (27).

These results on the goat and cat indicate that afferent inputs from cold receptors in the skin and possibly the core (outside the hypothalamus) do not exclusively and directly facilitate those neurons in the hypothalamus (posterior and possibly also anterior) which are in the pathway for activating shivering. If these interneurons were so facilitated, a normal shivering response would be expected in a cold environment in animals without preoptic tissue. The interneurons do appear to be hypersensitive, perhaps because of reduced suppression by removal of the preoptic neurons. The cat shivered in a neutral environment when disturbed by handling, restraint, or unfamiliar surroundings (359), and shivering was dramatically intensified when the goat was led from the cold back to the warm room, apparently facilitated by the forced muscular exercise (21). Dogs with a massive coagulation in the posterior hypothalamus or with a brainstem transection as low as the cerebral peduncle could shiver vigorously, albeit erratically, when exposed to extreme cold ($-15°$ C) (376).

If the preoptic-anterior hypothalamic tissue is essential for normal activation of thermoregulatory responses, if no other central nervous area can regulate internal body temperature, and if the preoptic-hypothalamic area can sense its own temperature, does it always regulate body temperature? If so, how? Before the answers to these questions can be reviewed, other aspects of the regulatory process should be examined. How are thermoregulatory responses related to body temperatures? How do internal body temperatures respond to thermal loads imposed upon the body? Do internal body temperatures respond to any other influences? Many thermal physiological studies have been designed to lump these three questions into one, namely, what are the thermoregulatory responses and the resultant body temperatures caused by thermal stress and other influences? The trend now is to dissociate, where possible, each response, each body temperature, each thermal load and influence and examine it separately.

Thermoregulatory Responses

The regulation of internal body temperature is achieved in vertebrates by activation of two classes of responses in varying proportions. The more advanced thermoregulatory responses have been termed physiological and are the secondary functions of organ systems which can modify rates of heat transfer from the core to body surface or from surface to environment, or modify the level of heat generation. Vasomotor responses, panting, and shivering are obvious examples of this class. An older, but no less important, class of thermoregulatory responses has been termed behavioral. These responses are the coordinated activity of the whole animal in selecting or creating a microenvironment in which the optimal internal temperature may be achieved without assistance from physiological responses. The animal may also behaviorally modify one or more of the physical parameters affecting heat exchange, such as body shape or orientation, when choice of environment is not possible.

A generalization which seems to apply to most, if not all, thermoregulatory responses is that they developed from an evolving innervation to pre-existing organs or organ systems, enabling those organs to subserve a thermal function in addition to their primary function (81). Personal observations of the lizard *Tiliqua scincoides* are suggestive in this connection. When they are startled by sudden handling, a tremor of a few seconds duration is clearly seen and felt over the body of some animals, especially when they are on a low-calcium diet. This ectotherm apparently can increase the rate of heat production, although this was not utilized at all as a defense against hypothermia during cold exposure in a calorimeter. Nor would increased heat production be expected in a poorly insulated animal in which any endothermic heat would be readily lost to the environment and wasted. Chattonet has proposed that the regulation of body temperature was a latecomer to the class of regulated physical properties of the internal environment, awaiting in all cases the development of a process which could subsequently and secondarily serve as a thermoregulatory response (81). To this we might add that the development of these potential thermoregulatory responses must have been sequential, with long gaps in time between each. From this we infer that although the perfected thermoregulatory capability of modern mammals and birds is a recent occurrence, the basic thermoregulatory mechanism involving thermal detectors, a CNS activator, and a response is an ancient talent found in all ectothermic vertebrates and widespread among the invertebrates.

Most of the studies that describe thermoregulatory responses in a variety of species were designed to identify and measure the magnitude of the response as a function of the thermal exposure and, as a correlate, to include measures of the body temperatures. Although such data do not enlighten the central question of body temperature regulation, they reveal the variety and, at the same time, the similarity of responses that have been utilized toward a thermoregulatory end. Measurements of oxygen consumption and heart rate as functions of body temperature and size in several species of lizards (33–35, 110, 209) were made in search of physiological responses that may be thermoregulatory. For some of these animals, the rate of body heating in a hot environment was greater than the rate of cooling at the same body temperature in a cold environment, presumably because of the greater rate of heat production induced by a higher heart rate (31, 33–35). This response was thought to show the presence of some capacity for physiological control of body temperature. Observations on the marine iguana in water suggest that lowering of the body conductance during cooling is a means for slowing loss of stored heat (28). More certain evidences of physiological regulation of body temperature in reptiles are (*a*) the severalfold increase in oxygen consumption at ambient temperatures below 30° C in the brooding, compared with the nonbrooding, female python (214); and (*b*) the large increase in the ratio of evaporative water loss to oxygen consumption in the collared lizard at temperatures above 40° C (110).

Quantitative observations of the responses manifested over the full range of thermal exposure from above to below the thermoneutral temperature have been made on a variety of birds (30, 100, 101, 112, 180, 210, 263–265, 278, 382, 390) and mammals (29, 32, 171, 198, 199, 204, 206, 207, 228, 245, 283, 324, 331–333, 337, 338).

Next, specific types of responses will be reviewed. The order of their listing is intended to reflect the probable phylogenetic order in which they came to be utilized as thermoregulatory responses.

Environmental selection.—No vertebrate has been shown to lack the capability of making this important thermoregulatory response. Goldfish have been trained to bar-press for a coolant to decrease ambient temperature from 41° C to 33.5–36.5° C, or to prevent a rise in temperature above 36.5° C (325). These temperatures are 8–10° C higher than in goldfish given a choice of environments (151). Amphibian larvae show a temperature preference which increases from a mean of about 23° C in May to about 30° C in June (276).

The classical study of Cowles & Bogert (98) and an extensive review by Saint-Girons & Saint-Girons (364) indicate that behavior in lizards can be thermoregulatory. Schmidt-Nielsen & Dawson have reviewed behavioral and other regulatory responses of lizards to thermal stress (334). More recent studies have been designed to show important details of this process. Shade seeking, burrowing, emergence, eye bulging, cloacal discharge, and changes in body contour and orientation have been examined in the horned lizard (186, 189). Variability of body temperatures of nine species of lizards from Baja California measured in the field was attributed to endogenous factors such as sex and size, but the major cause of variability was environmental thermal diversity, as expected (355, 356). However, Heath has cautioned that thermal data on reptiles must be collected and interpreted with the care exercised by Cowles & Bogert (98), since inanimate objects may exhibit thermal characteristics similar to those of reptiles in the field (188, 190).

A survey of preferred body temperatures in Australian lizards revealed pronounced interspecific differences (267, 268). In an environmental thermal gradient, the mean preferred body temperatures of all agamids (35.7–38.2° C) were significantly higher than those of all skinks (26.7–34.7° C), whereas those of several genera of geckos ranged from below those of the skinks to intermediate between the skinks and the agamids. Interspecific differences were found in the mean body temperatures at which these lizards were active in nature. However, the preferred temperatures obtained in the laboratory thermal gradient did not correspond in every case with the field values nor with the macroclimates where each species was represented. The authors concluded that the field values indicated the range of body temperatures acceptable for activity, but not necessarily the temperature of an inanimate object in the same macroenvironment (268). The preferred temperature during inactivity of some American lizards may be less at night than during the day (315). An analysis of the thermal behavior of five tropical species of the lizard genus *Anolis* with respect to their thermal habitats indicates one of the fruitful approaches to the details and evolution of this important regulatory response in ectotherms (326). The regulation of body temperature is fairly precise in the desert iguana—50, 68, and 95 per cent of the body temperatures were between 37.0–39.5, 36.1–40.1, and 33.2–41.8° C respectively (114). The preferred temperature increased to 42° C or higher in August, and the body temperature might rise well above the preferred level in defense of territory but not during feeding or courtship. The preferred temperature of an agamid lizard lies between 30 and 40° C and occurs during 94 per cent of all activity observed (267).

Behavioral responses to thermal stress are no less important in endotherms, although much less studied. Rats bar-press for radiant heat in a cold environment at a rate related to the body temperatures (76, 292, 329, 389). Dogs do the same (318), and both rely on other responses—shivering, curling up, or even escape—before starting to bar-press for heat. Environmental selection is a more natural behavioral response and has been used with dogs (70, 72), but it is difficult to present the results graphically. No quantitative reports since 1961 have come to attention concerning such important behavioral thermoregulatory responses as nest building, adjustment of body shape, or orientation and migration in endotherms. The action of climate upon the proportion of time the walrus spends in and out of Arctic water was explained partly by thermoregulatory demand and partly by the requirement for cutaneous blood flow for nourishing and repairing the skin (134).

In man, thermal discomfort is a stimulus for behavioral activity, and modification of thermal sensation by internal temperature may contribute to behavioral thermoregulation (82, 153, 155). Any thermal environment over a wide range may be perceived as comfortable or uncomfortable depending upon the internal temperature (82). Any cutaneous thermal stimulation tending to restore internal temperature toward normal may be perceived as comfortable, provided that it is not so great as to cause pain (82). This is true even if the cutaneous thermal stimulation is transient (155). Perception of thermal comfort and discomfort appears to result from an integration of thermal inputs from all parts of the body and is distinct from cutaneous perception of cold, cool, tepid, warm, and hot (82, 153, 155). It is not clear whether discomfort is to be attributed directly to an integration of body temperatures, or to activation of physiological thermoregulatory responses and thereby indirectly to an integration of body temperatures.

Vasomotor response.—An increase in blood flow through the cutaneous vessels increases the rate of heat transfer between the skin and the core, the direction of transfer depending on which is at the greater temperature. Since the ability to change the distribution of blood flow from one organ system to another is characteristic of all vertebrates, this may have been one of the first physiological functions to be utilized in thermoregulation. An attractive suggestion is that both heliothermic and thigmothermic lizards increase the cutaneous blood flow at a time when the body temperature is below the preferred temperature, and the animal is exposed to the sun or a warm surface or hot air (97). The recent evidence is based on a heart rate and a rate of body warming when the animal is moved from a cold to a hot environment that are greater than the heart rate and the rate of cooling under reverse conditions (28, 31, 33–35). However, in species from two genera, the differences in the rates of heating and cooling need not be attributed to a greater conductance factor during heating (34, 35). More direct evidence may be necessary to establish that core to surface blood flow is greater in the warming than in the cooling lizard. One species was shown to have a greater cutaneous blood flow when at or above its preferred temperature, but it was not possible to show that this was a thermoregulatory response (169).

Thermoregulatory vasomotor activity is commonplace in endotherms in which the core temperature is usually greater than the ambient temperature. Control of the blood flow to the periphery can readily regulate the flow of heat from core to the skin, and is the only controllable way to distribute internal heat to the skin. However, it is difficult to measure the flow of heat transported by blood flow from the core to the skin because of the complex configuration of the animal and because most arteries serve other tissue, principally muscle, in addition to skin. Therefore, the integrated vasomotor activity is not as attractive to study in relation to its activation by the thermoregulatory controller as are shivering, sweating, panting, or local cutaneous blood or heat flow which can be readily expressed as calories per unit time. Nevertheless, an index of vasomotor variability, termed "tissue conductance" or "body conductance", has been measured as a thermoregulatory response. Tissue conductance equals the rate of heat loss from the body surface per unit area divided by the difference between core and average skin surface temperatures. The heat loss from the body surface is a mixture of heat conducted to the surface and heat transported to the surface by blood flow so that tissue conductance is not a purely vasomotor term. Despite this, tissue conductance has been widely employed as an indicator of an important thermoregulatory circulatory response, especially in man (321). After two hours exposure to environmental temperatures ranging from 12 to 48° C, the near steady-state tissue conductance in man increases linearly from about 6–7 to about 15 kcal m^{-2} hr^{-1} $°C^{-1}$ between 12° and 33° C. Above 33° C ambient temperature, the tissue conductance again increases about linearly, but with three times the slope, reaching 46 kcal m^{-2} hr^{-1} $°C^{-1}$ at 48° C (179, 365). These maximal and minimal values in resting man may be more than doubled during steady-state exercise: during exercise at a metabolic rate of 190 kcal m^{-2} hr^{-1} in an effective temperature of 9.5° C, the tissue conductance was 20 whereas it was 130 kcal m^{-2} hr^{-1} $°C^{-1}$ at 35° C (320).

Regional cutaneous blood flow is equally important to monitor as a thermoregulatory response. The intricacies, innervation, and control of regional blood flow in man in the hot environment are discussed by Robinson (321) and Hertzman (202).

The thermoregulatory function of the peripheral vasculature of endotherms other than man has been less studied. Irving has emphasized the heterothermic condition and the importance of thinly furred appendages and other body surfaces as ports through which heat may be dissipated to the environment under conditions of internal or external heat stress (227). The vascularity of these parts is important in controlling the flow of heat from the core of the animal. Vessels in the horn of a goat dilate in response to external heat stress, to exercise, and to nerve block; and they constrict in the cold, resting goat. Three per cent of the goat's standing heat production may be lost through the horns in a 30° C windy environment. Four per cent of its running heat production may be lost at 0° C; this increases up to 12 per cent after running stops and before vasoconstriction sets in at 0° C (377). The naked tail of the muskrat is important for heat dissipation in a hot environment. For air temperature between 0 and 20° C, the tail temperature was near that of air, but above 25° C or after exercise it increased to 35 to 37° C concomitantly with a 100–180-fold increase in tail blood flow (244). A detailed study of some rodent tails shows many shunts and anastomoses between different arteries and between different veins, forming a complex interconnected vascular system. Arteries and veins are found juxtaposed either as an artery with venae comitantes or in complex vascular bundles (381). Where heat is exchanged between the arterial and venous flow, direct measurement of the rate of heat loss from the extremity is a better indicator of the range of this thermoregulatory response than is blood flow alone.

The uninsulated legs of the wood stork are important in dissipating body heat (248). Gulls and herons lose less than 10 per cent of their metabolic heat at low ambient temperatures, but may lose their entire heat production at 35° C through their legs which are immersed in water at 35° C (363). At all temperatures, heat loss from the legs to water was three to four times higher than to air at the same temperature, and the rate of heat loss reacted within seconds to changes in the ambient temperature (363). Heat loss through the beaver's tail is also essential for preventing hyperthermia at a 25° C ambient temperature. With the tail immersed in 6–10° C water, the body temperature was normal at 37° C, but with the tail in air the body temperature increased to 39° C (362). The swimming flippers of the fur seal in subarctic water may be as cold as the water (228), but may increase nearly to body temperature during exertion on land. Acquisition of unwettable adult body fur and development of effective regulation of circulation of heat to the flippers are essential before the young seal can enter the aquatic environment (228). The ears of rats lack arteriovenous anastomoses, and the vessels of the ear do not dilate in response to body warming or to sympathetic nerve section (161).

The large and highly vascular ears of the jackrabbit also serve to dissipate body heat under heat stress. As the animal rests in the shade during the heat of the day, the ear vessels remain dilated and the ears elevated for operative temperatures (including radiation temperature) up to 40° C. Above this level, the ear vessels constrict and the ears are flattened against the body. The response may be as rapid as the shading of the sun by a passing cloud (333). The ostrich has a similar capacity to dilate cutaneous vessels up to an ambient temperature near body temperature and then constrict these same vessels at still higher air temperatures (100, 101).

Evaporative water loss.—Since survival depends upon keeping nearly all tissue temperatures below 45–50° C, one should expect that vaporizing water from some body surface would be one of the early thermoregulatory responses attained by terrestial vertebrates. No one has suggested when, in what species, or in what form this response first appeared, but it must have been in terrestial species living in a macroenvironment whose operative temperature exceeded 40–50° C for several hours each day. At least one desert lizard can dissipate several times its resting heat production by evaporating water from its mouth and respiratory airways (110), but it does so only under near-lethal thermal exposure. Probably many lizard species can dissipate the resting heat production at temperatures less than maximum voluntary tolerance levels (111). Secretion of water from the external body surface has not been described in lizards, although the skin is not impermeable to water (43, 85). Unpublished observations on the blue tongued lizard *Tiliqua* indicate that it voids bladder and cloacal content in response to severe heat exposure. Although this response may sometimes be activated by handling without thermal stress, it always occurs under heat stress alone and may, perhaps, be considered as thermoregulatory. Ex-

cretion of water by lizards in any form is probably a response limited to
extreme emergencies and is activated only when all behavioral responses
are failing to limit further rise of body temperature above the lethal level,
since water is not freely available to these species.

Many endotherms readily resort to evaporating water in a controlled
manner in response to heat stress. Perhaps the most primitive form of this
response in mammals is wetting of fur with saliva. Unpublished observations of the red kangaroo indicate that it proceeds in a systematic way to
wet and keep wet increasingly larger areas of thinly furred body surface,
starting with the wrists and then the arms, the ankles, and the lower limbs.
No quantitative observations of this thermoregulatory response have been
noted to indicate its relationship to other possible avenues of evaporative
water loss, its efficiency as a dissipator of body heat, or how it is activated.
Wood storks exposed to thermal stress were observed to deposit fluid ex-
crement on their legs, thereby increasing evaporative cooling (248).

It is only a guess that evaporative water loss from the respiratory airways in response to heat stress, i.e., panting, preceded sweating in mammals and was acquired first in furred mammals living in hot environments
or in well-furred mammals of the chase. Sweating is unimportant or undescribed in birds, the other great class of vertebrates with insulated skin surface.

There is an attractive suggestion that the earliest birds and mammals
acquired insulation in order to limit the flux of heat from the environment
to the body (96). Presumably the ambient temperature during the late Jurassic period exceeded the optimal temperature for body tissue for several
hours of the day. Lacking the great size and capacity to store heat possessed by the dominant giant reptiles, these small active precursors to the
flying birds and the free-running mammals could best adapt to the thermal
environment by insulating against the external heat load or dissipating the
internal heat of activity through vaporization of water from the airways.
Panting in the dog costs little energy because it proceeds at a rate determined by the natural frequency of the thoracic basket (99). The energy
cost of panting increases approximately linearly with rate up to a third
of the resting metabolism at 300 breaths/min (380). Similarly, the evaporative water loss increases linearly with the panting rate up to two thirds
of the resting heat loss at 300 breaths/min (380).

The displacement volume of the thoracic cavity per breath also matches
elegantly the respiratory dead space (7), so that no significant changes in
the arterial blood gases occur in thermal panting up to 275 breaths/min
(7) and the increase in alveolar ventilation is just sufficient to match the
increased cost of breathing (7, 8). To what extent these characteristics of
the breathing apparatus are fortuitous in the dog or generalized characteristics for all panting mammals, possibly including those of the late Jurassic,
has not been explored. In the first stage of panting in the sheep, when the
respiratory minute volume rose through an increase in respiratory frequen-

cy and a decrease in tidal volume, the balance between the thermoregulatory demands and the regulation of blood gases was maintained as well in the sheep (165) as in the dog (9), so that blood gases changed only slightly. At a later stage of prolonged heat exposure in the sheep, the minute volume rose through an increase in tidal volume with a lower respiratory rate; the consequent fivefold increase of alveolar ventilation over the control level produced severe alkalosis (165). Respiratory water loss in the ostrich increases elevenfold, going from 0.4 g H_2O min^{-1} at 20–25° C to 4.5 g H_2O min^{-1} at 45° C (101). Throughout this temperature range the respiratory rate stayed at 45/min, so that the tidal volume apparently increased.

Panting in the furred mammal or feathered bird is the most efficient and direct route for dissipating body heat by evaporating water. At an operative environmental temperature in excess of body temperature, the heat of vaporization of every gram of water evaporated from the airways represents nearly the same amount of heat removed from the body core (neglecting only the heat removed from the ventilating air), while heat entering the core from the external environment is limited by the insulated exterior surface. On the other hand, the heat of vaporization of water evaporated from an external surface is derived in part from the environment and not the core; this is especially true of water on the cool wetted surface of fur. Even neglecting the wastage of sweat dripping off the body surface, sweating is less efficient in removing core heat from the body. From this argument, one might presume that sweating evolved in a hot environment in which water was always abundant. By this same argument, the kangaroo's method of evaporating water in the hot arid interior of Australia is a paradox.

Cutaneous evaporation was the major means of heat loss in calves exposed to a heat stress up to 40° C. Between 15 and 20° C, cutaneous and respiratory evaporization were of similar magnitude. From 25 to 40° C, cutaneous evaporation was controlled to balance heat production minus other forms of heat loss or gain (282). In cattle, thermal sweating is controlled by an adrenergic mechanism requiring an intact sympathetic innervation but not adrenomedullary secretion (144). Sheep rely mainly upon panting to dissipate heat in a hot environment by evaporative heat loss (58). Apocrine sweating also occurs in sheep although it is less important than respiratory evaporation (58). Since the sweat glands of sheep serve little or no thermoregulatory function, and since they sometimes discharge synchronously, unlike the characteristic apocrine sweat gland, they may represent a primitive type of apocrine gland (46). As in cattle, activation of the sweat glands of the ram scrotum (388) and of the goat (258) is by sympathetic innervation and does not require adrenomedullary secretion; it may have thermoregulatory importance by cooling the skin of the scrotum. Activation of sweating in the horse at rest and in exercise does depend upon the presence of epinephrine in the blood from the adrenal medulla rather than upon sympathetic innervation of the glands (133). No evidence of

thermal sweating was obtained from the apocrine-like glands in the pig
(220). Most evaporative cooling in the camel is percutaneous; epinephrine
injected intravenously, with the animal in a cool environment, induced
sweating up to 320 g m^{-2} hr^{-1}, a rate greater than that induced in the sun at
42° C (277).

In a review of the recent literature on the temporal and spatial patterns
of sweat discharge of several domestic mammals, Bligh (51) suggests that
the range in activity of the apocrine sweat glands associated with the hair
follicles can be attributed to the quantitative differences in the eccrine component of the secretory process. The fluid is secreted only slowly into the
lumen of the gland and is only rarely discharged, but then simultaneously,
over a wide area of skin. The secretion, supposed to arise from a necro-
biotic process, is discharged by contraction of the myoepithelium investing
the gland or its duct. Such secretions occur in too small quantity to have
thermoregulatory value. Histologically similar apocrine glands do achieve a
rate of sweat formation that is significant for heat dissipation for some
species; these glands are thought to possess an eccrine process of sweat
formation which may be discharged by lumen pressure and, less importantly, by myoepithelial contractions. The eccrine glands in the glabrous skin
of man produce much more fluid than do the most productive sweat glands
of nonprimates in response to heat stress. The evolution of nonprimate
sweat glands into an effective organ for heat dissipation was thought to depend on the development of an eccrine secretory process, while any apocrine secretion was considered vestigial and a remnant of some other function in the primitive skin of mammals (51). Bligh does not attempt to account for the greater output of the sweat glands of man, but he notes that
the eccrine glands on the glabrous skin of man are not associated with hair
follicles and suggests that in primates the hair structures have disappeared
while the sweat glands have remained. He argues that the secretory and
discharge activities of the glands associated with the hair follicles in cattle
are not greatly different from the sweat glands of man.

Thermogenesis.—Two important characteristics of endotherms are the
five to ten times greater unstressed rate of their heat production compared
with ectotherms of comparable size, and their ability to increase the rate of
heat production by shivering and nonshivering thermogenesis. Both these
processes for producing greater heat must have followed in time the evolution of an insulative barrier at the skin surface, between the body core and
a cooling paleoclimate. Without fur or feathers, any trend toward higher
rates of heat production could hardly lead to a useful elevation of body
temperature above a cool environment, from which a selective advantage
could be realized for the premammalian or preavian reptile, especially
when small in size. If a small furry reptile were to evolve in size and, in so
doing, retain the high metabolic rate per gram of tissue of its progenitor, it
would become an endotherm. Once it was a fur-covered endotherm with a
high metabolic rate and a body temperature well above the cool environ-

ment, it would have to decrease its metabolic rate per gram of tissue as it evolved toward greater size, presumably to avoid overheating within the great mass of metabolizing tissue, especially when the internal heat from high activity was added. I suppose the combination of metabolic rate per gram of tissue, body size and shape, amount of extra cutaneous insulation, level of metabolic rate during peak activity, and level of shivering and non-shivering thermogenesis is an evolved solution for each endothermic species in its thermal habitat (107, 182, 240). No doubt, other and variable factors also combine towards a solution compatible with a mean body temperature of 30 to 40° C—at the upper level of this interval for most species.

The shivering tremor in response to body cooling seems to require an intact posterior hypothalamus, activated in turn by preoptic-anterior hypothalamic tissue (81, 193, 367, 368, 370). The elaboration of the shivering tremor was also shown to depend partly on a segmental sensory inflow to the spinal cord for normal rhythmicity (81, 372). Unilateral segmental deafferentation in the cat led to deterioration of the regularity and vigor of tremor, and bilateral deafferentation led to greater loss of rhythmicity, although a residue of shivering activity remained. Important in the segmental sensory inflow was the proprioceptor discharge induced by position and movement of muscle and joint, as indicated by selective deafferentation of muscle and skin (373). The effects of loading the shivering limb further reveal the influence of proprioceptors (373). Thus, the shivering tremor was shown to depend on segmental sensory inflow, proprioceptive input, mechanical factors, and supraspinal influences in an essential way (374). The cerebellum is not required to initiate or maintain shivering, and it has little influence on the rhythmicity of the tremor (371).

The increased consumption of oxygen and production of heat by shivering are described for many endothermic species in reports listed earlier in this section, and the activation of the shivering response is reviewed in Section III. A specialized form of heat production by muscular fasciculation was described in the brooding female python (214).

One of the principal sources of nonshivering thermogenesis in mammals was found to be the thermogenic role of brown fat (349, 350). This activity has been shown to be important in hibernators (78, 79, 122, 185, 242, 243, 347, 352), in unacclimatized (121, 122) and cold-acclimatized (242, 316, 351, 353) rats, in newborn and adult guinea pigs (63, 64, 122), in newborn rabbits (108, 122, 211, 212, 213), in newborn human infants (109, 342), and in monkeys (77, 78a). Skeletal muscle and visceral organs may also participate in nonshivering thermogenesis in cold-acclimatized rats (181, 241).

ACTIVATION OF THERMOREGULATORY RESPONSES

The answer to the central question "What body temperature is regulated?" appears to lie deeply buried in the answers to another question, "What thermal and nonthermal inputs to the regulator activate thermoregulatory responses?" It is easy to recognize in broad terms what these inputs are. Disturbances such as external heat and cold exposure, internal heat loading and heat debt, exercise, emotions, and sleep, when transformed to body temperatures or transduced to neural activity, become inputs to the controlling system. The physiological literature describes profusely and in detail the steady-state and transient effects of these inputs upon the thermoregulatory responses. Yet there is no unanimous acceptance of the hypothalamic temperature as the regulated temperature for all thermoregulatory responses in all vertebrate species and under all conditions for which regulation is occurring.

There are several other views. The hypothalamic temperature may be the regulated temperature for only some species but not for all, or it may be only one of several regulated temperatures, or it may be the regulated temperature for some stresses activating some responses but not for all. In line with the last view, the preoptic-anterior hypothalamic region is said to be the "heat-loss center", meaning that heat loss is activated when the temperature of this center increases above normal. According to this view, the heat-loss center does not activate heat production, but only decreases its inhibition of the "heat-production center" when the hypothalamic temperature falls below normal. The heat-production center is presumed to depend on external stimuli for activation. With equal vigor, one might propose instead that the preoptic-anterior hypothalamic region is the heat-production center and activates shivering, etc. when its temperature falls below normal. By this view, the heat-loss center depends on external stimuli for activation, but can be inhibited more or less by the preoptic heat-production center.

No one has proposed that the hypothalamic temperature is never the regulated temperature, although a commonly held view implies that under most ordinary circumstances the hypothalamic temperature is not involved in the activating signal for a thermoregulatory response. According to this view, the preoptic hypothalamic tissue can sense its own temperature and, thereby, become involved in regulating body temperature; but it does so only under severe thermal stress, not under low or moderate heat or cold stress. From a review of the observations of hypothalamic temperature of some animals in a variety of thermal states, and of the effects of artificially displacing the hypothalamic temperature of the animal in a neutral environment, I shall attempt to judge which view of the role of the hypothalamic temperature is the more tenable.

Natural variations in hypothalamic temperature.—Too few observations of this important temperature in animals exposed to a variety of thermal stresses have been made, and none in man. Many small fluctuations of the hypothalamic temperature within the range 38.4 to 39.1° C were typical of eight unanesthetized cats exposed to ambient temperatures from 0 to 34° C, but the mean hypothalamic temperature was not influenced by the environmental temperature, even though shivering was typical at the low temperatures (146). Two of these cats showed heat polypnea (respiration rates up to 200/min) and panting (mouth open, tongue out, and rates over 200 /min) at hypothalamic temperatures not significantly above the control temperature. The mean hypothalamic temperature of five cats was 0.6° C higher than the control value during heat polypnea and 0.9° C higher during panting at an ambient temperature of 40° C. There was no correlation between the vasomotor tone, as indicated by ear pinna temperature, and hypothalamic temperature (146). During sleep, the hypothalamic temperature was less than the control temperature when the animal was awake (3, 146).

In the dog, similarly, the hypothalamic temperature is variable in any environment, but the mean and the variability were the same in 35, 25, and 10° C environments; intermittent panting and shivering were activated at the high and low air temperatures respectively (192). During sleep, and at night, the hypothalamic temperature was 0.5 to 1.0° C lower in the dog (172, 314). Hypothalamic temperature in the rhesus monkey is not affected by ambient temperature during the daytime when the animal is awake, but it is affected by sleep and feeding and may be 1 to 2° C less at night (167, 172). Rats show similar large effects of feeding and sleeping upon the hypothalamic temperature in a neutral environment (1, 2, 304). Cold-acclimatized and normal rats exposed to 6 and −8° C environments tended to *increase* their hypothalamic temperature above the level measured at 26° C (274). In this case, the cold-acclimatized rats had lower (0.4 to 0.7° C) hypothalamic temperatures than did normal rats at all ambient temperatures. The brain temperature of an individual rabbit varied over a range of 1.2° C from day to day with no consistent correlation between this temperature and oxygen consumption or the clinical state of the animal (127). Panting can occur in calves in a warm environment with little or no change in brain temperature (143). Likewise, shivering can occur in sheep in a cold bath with little or no change or even an increase in brain temperature (194). Two generalizations follow from these observations: in a neutral environment, the hypothalamic temperature may vary over a range of 0.5 to 1° C, depending on the species, but within this range no thermoregulatory responses are activated; and the mean hypothalamic temperature and its variability do not depend on the environmental temperature, whether low with accompanying shivering or high with evaporative heat loss.

Artificial variations in hypothalamic temperature.—Many thermoregulatory responses have been activated in many species by displacing the hypothalamic temperature from its normal value. Only responses activated in unanesthetized animals will be considered. The most successful tests were accomplished by heating or cooling the whole brain using thermodes around the internal carotid arteries, or by local heating or cooling of the preoptic-hypothalamic tissue with a single large thermode placed in the midline or several small thermodes surrounding the preoptic-hypothalamic tissue.

The single most important advance in the study of body temperature regulation started with local thermal probing of the central nervous system.

These probings may be divided into four phases. Phase I was to explore the CNS to localize those regions which activate a response when their temperatures are displaced. Phase II was to discover what thermoregulatory responses are activated when the temperatures of the hypothalamus and other parts of the CNS are displaced. Phase III was to obtain the quantitative relationship between the response and the sign and magnitude of the temperature displacement. Phase IV was to investigate the unit activity of neurons within the controlling system in response to temperature displacement of thermal receptors providing inputs to the controlling system.

Phases I and II, with different objectives, are inseparable in their execution and will be reviewed together. The preoptic-hypothalamic region has been the center of attention from the beginning. An increasing number of thermoregulatory responses are described as activated by short-term hypothalamic heating and cooling. If the brain temperature of at least one species of lizard is artificially increased to 41° C, it exits from a hot environment at a lower colonic temperature than normal. Conversely, the colonic temperature at exit can be arised by cooling the brainstem (169). In several mammals investigated, moderate, short-term heating of the hypothalamus up to 40° C for less than thirty minutes also produces behavioral responses such as drowsiness (152, 375), extending the appendages (152), reduced metabolic rate (4), and fur wetting (164). Greater hypothalamic heating up to 42° C activates physiological responses such as vasodilatation, polypnea, and panting (4, 22, 152, 172, 192, 223, 236), and increase in cutaneous evaporative water loss (222) and in heart rate and blood pressure (224). Heating the hypothalamus also reduces or inhibits cold-induced vasoconstriction and shivering (17, 22, 152, 172, 173, 192, 223) and can activate panting in a cold environment (17, 22, 192).

Short-term preoptic-hypothalamic cooling increases the rate of bar pressing for radiant heat in a cold environment (26, 76, 292, 318, 329). Conversely, heating the same tissue in the same environment decreases the rate of bar pressing for heat (292, 318). Hypothalamic cooling activates vasoconstriction alone (157, 184) or with shivering (4, 12, 69, 127, 172, 173, 192). Short-term hypothalamic cooling may also inhibit panting and vasodilatation (12, 26, 172, 173, 192), and activate shivering (127, 173, 192), in a hot environment.

Shivering was not observed in the goat at an air temperature above 18°C (12). However, even in a 34°C environment, the ear pinna dropped from 39 to 34° C in less than ten minutes after start of hypothalamic cooling; during the first ten minutes, the vena caval blood temperature increased from 38.9 to 39.4° C (rate of increase = 2.9°/hr) ; during the next thirty-eight minutes it increased to 41.1° C (rate of increase for the last twenty-five minutes = 1.7° C/hr). The latter rate, equivalent to storing heat at 1.4 kcal kg^{-1} hr^{-1}, equals the imbalance between the resting heat production and heat loss. The loss consists of two components: insensible evaporative heat loss estimated at 10 per cent of resting heat production; and dry heat loss at a rate estimated to be that fraction of the rate of loss at 17° C equivalent to the ratio of the differences of core to air temperatures at 34 and 17° C. The inference is that the difference between the initial rate of increase of core temperature and the final rate was due to thermogenesis of about 1.0 kcal kg^{-1} hr^{-1}, or about one-half the resting metabolism. The same conclusion pertains to the 28° C environment (12). In another report, shivering was often observed in the goat at external temperatures above 18° C for an initial short period (17). Thus, vasoconstriction and increased heat production can be activated by preoptic hypothalamic cooling in the absence of any cold stimuli applied to the cutaneous thermoreceptors in the goat as in the dog and rabbit.

Hormonal responses in mammals are affected by preoptic-anterior hypothalamic cooling and warming for one-half hour or more, and have been especially well studied in the goat (19, 20). Cooling the preoptic-anterior hypothalamic tissue (17), even with a 36° C environmental temperature (14), releases protein-bound iodine (PBI[131]) from the thyroid gland, a result indicating a release of thyrotropic hormone. Warming the same tissue retards release of PBI[131] in the goat exposed to cold environment (16, 17). Prior intravenous injection of thyroxine blocked the release of PBI[131] by preoptic-anterior hypothalamic cooling, which indicates that during this time release of thyrotropin was suppressed (23).

Cooling the preoptic-anterior hypothalamic region of goats for two to three hours in an 18° C environment increased the levels of norepinephrine and epinephrine in the urine by 48 and 117 per cent respectively (22). When this tissue was cooled in one goat, after forty days without cooling, the response was considerably augmented. It was much reduced after repeated hypothalamic cooling in the same goat, ten times in thirty days, as was the rise in rectal temperature for the same level of hypothalamic cooling. After this repetitive procedure, the goat's fur was noticeably thicker than that of control animals, and PBI level was increased. These changes suggest an acclimatization to cold.

Warming the preoptic-hypothalamic tissue of goats inhibited the appearance of urinary catecholamines in a 5° C environment even though the rectal temperature fell markedly during two hours. On cessation of hypothalamic warming, a large increase in both catecholamines occurred (22). An adrenergic blocking agent greatly increased the control level of urinary catecholamines and reduced, but did not block, their release into the urine during brain cooling; under the influence of this agent, brain cooling led to enhanced shivering, but the increase in rectal temperature was diminished (22). A ganglionic blocking agent did, however, reduce the level of both catecholamines before, and prevented any increase during, hypothalamic cooling (15). Some shivering occurred, but the rectal temperature fell 1° C in four hours in an 18° C room. Shivering and the increase in urinary excretion of catecholamines in response to external cold and to hypothalamic cooling were accentuated in markedly hypothyroid goats (18). Blood glucose of the hypothyroid goat increased by 300 per cent during acute cold exposure compared with 20 per cent in controls. Bilateral splanchnicotomy in the euthyroid goat eliminated the excretion of epinephrine in the urine and blocked the hyperglycemic response, but did not prevent shivering during hypothalamic cooling (18).

Forcing the rectal temperature of the ox to over 40.5° C in a hot humid environment increased the plasma epinephrine level by 300 to 500 per cent and sometimes the norepinephrine level by 50 per cent; the effect was blocked by bilateral splanchnicotomy. Plasma catecholamine levels were unaffected by exposure to dry environments, cold or hot, or by heating the anterior hypothalamus (317).

Cooling the preoptic-hypothalamic region did not significantly change the plasma cortisol level in the goat (22). In the dog 40 to 90 per cent increase in the plasma cortisol level occurred in response to both preoptic cooling and acute environmental cooling (87), and to both preoptic heating and environmental heating (86); the largest increase caused by preoptic cooling or heating occurred in the first fifteen-minute period. Gradual environmental heating and cooling did not produce significant changes. An injected bacterial pyrogen also increased the plasma cortisol level in the dog in phase with the rising body temperature (86).

Cooling of the preoptic-anterior hypothalamic region of the rhesus monkey by 1–3° C in a cool (20–25° C) environment produced a water diuresis with a rise in plasma osmolality (184). As the rising blood temperature leveled off at an elevated steady-state value, the urine flow dropped toward control value. Rewarming the hypothalamus produced an antidiuretic response.

Thermal probings of the hypothalamus belonging to Phase III will yield the quantitative relationships between the thermoregulatory response and the sign and magnitude of the temperature displacement. In this phase the thermal physiologist requires the language and insight and some of the techniques of the control systems analyst. When the investigator can open the important feedback loops and manipulate these inputs to the controlling system independent of the response, then he can obtain the characteristics of the controlling system for each of the thermoregulatory responses available to the species under study and for all the thermal and metabolic states to which it is exposed. Too few studies of this type have been undertaken, but the number will no doubt increase.

When the preoptic temperature is artificially displaced for a few minutes at a time in the resting-wakeful dog in a neutral environment, no change occurs in the basal rate of evaporative heat loss for hypothalamic temperatures below about 39° C. Above this threshold temperature, however, an increasing amount of evaporative heat loss is activated by panting, in proportion to the temperature displacement. The response for panting appears to be linear with a slope or proportionality constant α_{EHL}, equal to 2–3 kcal kg^{-1} hr^{-1} °C^{-1} (192). This slope is apparently unaffected by the temperature of the environment, the skin, or the body core, but the threshold is increased by either a low skin or a low core temperature and is decreased by a high skin or high core temperature. The resting metabolic rate is constant for all hypothalamic temperatures above about 37.5° C in the neutral environment, but as the temperature is forced below this threshold, heat production by shivering increases approximately in proportion to the temperature displacement. The slope of the shivering response curve α_{HP} in the dog is about 1–2 keal kg^{-1} hr^{-1} °C^{-1} (173, 192). Again, the slope does not appear to be affected by skin or core temperature; the threshold is increased by low skin and core temperatures or decreased by high skin and core temperatures. In the resting-wakeful rabbit, α_{HP} = 1.5 kcal kg^{-1} hr^{-1} °C^{-1} and, as in the dog, the shivering threshold is raised in a cold environment and lowered in a hot environment (127).

Although the accomplishment of Phase III will contribute importantly to the analysis of body temperature regulation, only inferences can be drawn from it as to the circuitry of the CNS controlling system; the same can be said for Phase IV. There exists the enormous handicap of exploring in a region of the CNS where neurons subserving many kinds of regulatory processes comingle. Even more troublesome is the comingling of neurons subserving several kinds of thermoregulatory activity, rendering uncertain the position of the neuron under study in the chain of neurons activating the response. Studies belonging to Phase IV will be reviewed in the section entitled The Regulated Temperature—A Tenable Answer.

Artificial temperature displacement of spinal cord and other core organs.—Cooling of the body core of dogs under light barbiturate anesthesia induced shivering and increased oxygen consumption up to double the resting rate even though the brain and cutaneous temperatures were maintained at or above normal values (166, 311, 312, 344); during exposure to low air temperature, shivering and oxygen consumption increased further as the internal temperature was lowered (310). These reports indicate that extracranial thermoreceptors in the body core are involved in activating at least one thermoregulatory response.

One of the thermally sensitive core sites was found to be within the vertebral column between C_2 and L_7 in the dog (309, 343, 345, 346). Lightly anesthetized dogs were caused to shiver, to increase oxygen consumption by 30 per cent, and to show vasoconstriction in the paws when the spinal column was cooled while the skin and core temperatures were held 1° C above normal (346); the effects were greater when the air or core temperature was low than when the cutaneous and core temperatures were elevated (309). Warming the spinal column decreased shivering induced by low ambient temperature or by low core temperature (309). Shivering in these lightly anesthetized dogs did not appear to be different for internal cooling or local cooling of vertebral column (285); nor was shivering by internal cooling blocked or affected by bilateral cervical vagotomy (225). In these anesthetized dogs, cooling the core alone seemed to activate shivering more consistently than did cooling the brain alone (311, 312, 344). Cooling the spinal column of lightly anesthetized cats usually resulted in either an increase in the frequency of spontaneously firing gamma-motoneurons or activation of new gamma-motoneurons (260). Alpha-motoneurons could also be activated if the anesthesia were not too deep, but only after the gamma-motoneurons were activated. Warming the column to between 39–41° C reversibly suppressed gamma-motoneurons which were spontaneously firing.

Cooling the spinal column of *unanesthetized* dogs to about 34° C, ambient temperature 23° C, induced vigorous shivering in fore and hindlegs as recorded electromyographically (343). Thus, there is abundant evidence that the temperature of this portion of the central nervous system can, and very likely does, play a role in activating increased heat production and possibly also vasoconstriction. Whether the thermal sensitivity of this region is due to thermoreceptors that send afferents to the hypothalamus and facilitate heat production while inhibiting heat loss, including panting, is not known. From available evidence in the dog, it seems also possible that the activation of shivering is a local effect of cooling the spinal cord and would occur even without connections to the hypothalamus even though connections from the hypothalamus are essential (81, 193).

Heat production can also be affected in unanesthetized guinea pigs by warming and cooling the vertebral column (65–67). In unanesthetized guinea pigs three to four weeks old, shivering could be suppressed by moderate local warming of the cervical vertebral canal, but less effectively by local warming of the lumbar vertebral canal and of the hypothalamus (65). Later it was reported that shivering in the guinea pig is influenced by temperature changes in the cervical vertebral canal and in the skin, but not by the hypothalamic temperature. In animals four and eight weeks old, the shivering threshold was related to both the cervical spinal cord temperature (C_5-Th_2) and the skin temperature: the higher the temperature at either site the lower the threshold temperature at the other site for inducing shivering. It was concluded that the mean body temperature, rather than any local temperature within the body core, may be thought of as the controlled variable (66).

Cold-acclimatized guinea pigs had a 1° C lower shivering threshold for both skin and cervical spinal cord temperatures (67). After sectioning of the cord at C_5, cold-induced tremor in the head and neck muscles above the section (presumably caused by hypothalamic and head skin temperatures, certainly not by cervical cord temperature) could no longer be inhibited by warming the thermosensitive region of the cervical spinal cord (394). Warming the anterior and posterior hypothalamus of both newborn and cold-acclimatized guinea pigs reduced the amount of cold-induced nonshivering thermogenesis and oxygen consumption in proportion to the amount of heating (62).

Both shivering and nonshivering heat production in the guinea pig, affected by changing the cervical spinal cord temperature, seem to depend upon intact connections with the hypothalamus. Thus the temperatures of both the hypothalamus and the cervical cord are normally utilized to activate an increased heat production. To what extent an activated heat loss also depends upon the cervical cord temperature has not been reported.

Local heating of the lateral reticular formation within the medulla oblongata of both decerebrate cats and cats under urethane-anesthesia elicited decreases in respiratory rate and tidal volume, and bradycardia with little or no change in systolic pressure and slight increase in pulse pressure (80). Threshold temperature for these effects was 40–41° C and maximal effects were produced by 43–44° C. Local diathermy to the paws elicited either no response or one with less intensity. Respiratory inhibition by local diathermy to the medulla showed about the same temperature sensitivity as respiratory acceleration by diathermy to the rostral hypothalamus in urethane-anesthetized cats (80).

There are indications that the kidney and heart possess a kind of thermosensitivity which also can influence a thermoregulatory response. Cooling the blood flowing through the renal artery, external jugular vein, and inferior vena cava in unanesthetized rabbits produced an increase in oxygen consumption in proportion to the amount of cooling. The sensitivity was less than that demonstrated for cooling the internal carotid blood but greater than that for cooling blood flowing through the aorta and external carotid artery (127).

Effects of displacing cutaneous temperature of specialized areas.—Increasing to above 36° C the scrotal skin temperature of an unshorn ram in an 18° C environment evoked polypnea and falling body temperatures (386, 387), whereas warming an area of flank skin of the same size by the same amount had much less effect. If the scrotum was cooled to 15° C, shivering would sometimes ensue, and the core temperature would be restored rapidly. Shorn rams, whose flank skin temperatures were 30–34° C, 3–7° C lower than that of fully fleeced rams in air at 15° C, no longer panted when the scrotal temperature was increased to 40° C. However, rectal temperature fell 0.5 to 1° C in thirty minutes so that shivering was activated when scrotal heating stopped (387).

The skin of the udder of the goat, with essentially the same sensory innervation as the scrotum, when heated with 45° C air, could also bring about an increase in respiratory frequency from 20–40/min to 100–120/min, uncorrelated with a rising rectal temperature (273).

Increasing the surface temperature of the upper respiratory tract in sheep (48) and in dogs (249) by raising the relative humidity of warm inspired air, increases the breathing rate without additional change in the core or skin temperature. These observations indicate the presence of thermoreceptors in the evaporating surfaces of the mouth and nasal surfaces.

Panting in gulls stopped within a few seconds upon immersing the legs in cold water (363).

Intrahypothalamic and intraventricular injection of drugs.—A pharmacological agent injected or released into the preoptic-hypothalamic tissue which affects the membrane potential and firing rate of either the temperature-transducing neurons or those interneurons in the pathway for a thermoregulatory response may affect directly either the regulated temperature or a thermoregulatory response. It would be difficult, if not impossible, to predict the net effect upon the core temperature of such an injection, which would presumably depend upon which of the thermal receptor neurons and response interneurons are most facilitated, inhibited, or depressed. Many recent reports describe these effects, but do not indicate clearly that any of the agents are involved in normal thermoregulatory activity.

A small dose of an anesthetic agent injected into the cerebral ventricles produces changes in the core temperature similar to those produced by the same anesthetic administered systemically: less than 1 mg chloralose into the ventricle of an unanesthetized cat produced vasodilatation and a drop in rectal temperature of 2.5° C over two to three hours, followed by vasoconstriction, shivering, and a return to initial temperature in three to four hours; 2 mg pentobarbital sodium, similarly injected, produced a smaller drop in temperature followed by an earlier shivering response and a rising temperature to a hyperthermic level (139); 0.01 to 0.03 mg chloralose injected into the anterior hypothalamus of the cat dropped the rectal temperature by 1 to 6° C (141). Microinjections of pentobarbital sodium into the posterior hypothalamus of the unanesthetized cat failed to induce vasodilatation, reduced metabolism, or decreased colonic temperature, all of which were produced by injection of 0.06 mg into the caudal preoptic and anterior-most hypothalamic region (233). What neurons were depressed (or excited) by these agents cannot be stated unequivocally.

An exogenous bacterial pyrogen (typhoid vaccine or *Shigella dysenteriae*) injected in micro amounts into the cerebral ventricle of an unanesthetized cat produced a fever of 2° C after a delay of an hour or so (138, 384). Typhoid vaccine injected directly into the anterior hypothalamus induced a fever with a five to twenty minute latency (140, 231, 384). The hyperthermia, which lasts for up to twenty hours, results from vasoconstriction and shivering in a neutral environment. An intraventricular injection of pentobarbital sodium in an unanesthetized cat with fever produces a transient drop to normal in rectal temperature followed by a hyper-fever, then normal fever (139). Four hours after a state of general anesthesia and hypothermia is induced by intravenous chloralose, an intraventricular injection of typhoid vaccine hastens the return to normal temperature and goes on to produce a fever (139).

Injection of 200 μg of 5-hydroxytryptamine complexed with creatinine sulfate into the cerebral ventricle of an unanesthetized cat in a neutral environment induced shivering and vasoconstriction and caused the rectal temperature to rise by 2–3° C in three to four hours and remain elevated for more than fifteen hours (138). Conversely, if 50 μg of epinephrine or of norepinephrine were similarly injected, there followed a vasodilatation and a 0.5 to 1° C drop in rectal temperature during the first hour; then light shivering, vasoconstriction, and a rise in rectal temperature to control level in two to three hours (138). These catecholamines produced a similar or greater drop in rectal temperature if the unanesthetized cat was already hyperthermic as a result of a pyrogen fever or a previous injection of 5-HT.

Similar results were produced by injecting smaller amounts of these monoamines into the anterior hypothalamus of the unanesthetized cat (140), but injections of these monoamines (140) or of bacterial pyrogens (140, 384) into the posterior or the ventromedial hypothalamus had no effect. In another laboratory, injecting 15 μg of 5-HT into the preoptic ante-riohypothalamic region of unanesthetized cats reduced oxygen consumption, induced vasodilatation, and increased respiratory rate and evaporative water loss. When the 5-HT was complexed with creatinine sulfate, equal concentrations had no consistent effect on thermoregulatory responses (234).

Injecting 500 μg of 5-HT into the cerebral ventricle of a dog under pentobarbital anesthesia produced shivering and an increase of rectal temperature of about 1° C (136). Injecting 25 μg of epinephrine in the cerebral ventricles stopped shivering, when present, and produced vasodilatation and a 1.5° C drop in rectal temperature.

Norepinephrine injected into the lateral ventricle or anterior hypothalamus of an unanesthetized rabbit either caused vasoconstriction and a rise in rectal temperature or had no effect (93). When 200 μg 5-HT was injected into the lateral cerebral ventricle of the rabbit, the rectal temperature dropped by 0.3–0.7° C in four tests and did not change in two. In every test, a bacterial pyrogen caused a fever. Two to 20 μg 5-HT injected into the anterior hypothalamus had no effect in the rabbit unless a fever had already been induced by an endogenous leucocyte pyrogen or by epinephrine, when the effect of 5-HT was to dilate ear pinna vessels with intact innervation and to cause a drop in rectal temperature (93).

An intraventricular injection of 0.2–1.0 mg 5-HT complexed with creatinine sulfate into the conscious sheep most frequently caused a drop in body temperature which was sometimes accompanied by changes in ear pinna temperature and breathing rate (49). Injecting 0.05–1.0 mg epinephrine and norepinephrine into the lateral ventricle of the sheep caused an increase in body temperature up to 1.2° C for one to two hours accompanied by constriction of ear vessels, a reduction in breathing rate but no evidence of shivering (49). In conscious goats, either with normal temperature or with a pyrogen-induced fever, injections of 0.1–0.5 mg 5-HT into the third ventricle induced peripheral vasodilatation, polypnea, and a gradual drop in rectal temperature (24). Epinephrine and norepinephrine, on the other hand, produced no significant effect upon rectal temperature when injected into the goat's third ventricle (24).

In cats anesthetized with pentobarbital, the effluent from the third ventricle perfused with artificial cerebral spinal fluid was found to contain small amounts of 5-HT (130, 142). When an inhibitor of amine oxidase, tranylcypromine, was added to the perfusion fluid, the output of 5-HT increased and was accompanied by a transient shivering and rise in rectal temperature (130). Injection of 0.1–1 mg tranylcypromine into the cerebral ventricles caused an increase in rectal temperature of cats but not of rabbits (137).

Infusion of 0.9 μg acetylcholine, 5 μg eserine, or 12 μg histamine into the hypothalamus of conscious rabbits did not affect the rectal temperature, whereas a leucocyte pyrogen into the same site produced a fever (93). On the other hand, infusion of 10 μeq KCl into the hypothalamus caused an immediate rise of 1.3° C in rectal temperature, in less than one hour (93). Saline, plasma, and rabbit cerebral spinal fluid similarly injected had no effect. Injection of α-OH-sodium butyrate into the preoptic region or anterior hypothalamus of unanesthetized cats slowed the metabolism and lowered the colonic temperature accompanied by vasodilatation (361), as did injections of α-aminobutyric acid into the medial preoptic region. Similar injection of 2.5–6 μg picrotoxin had the opposite effect in the cat, increasing the metabolism and the temperature by as much as 1.5° C (357).

These observations give the strong impression that the neurons directly affected by anesthetics, pyrogens, monoamines, etc., reside in the preoptic-anterior hypothalamic tissue. The agents appear to act directly upon the neurons which interact to generate the set temperature, that is, they either excite or depress the activity of those neurons with a high temperature coefficient for transducing temperature to neural impulses or they depress or excite those neurons which transduce with a low temperature coefficient. It seems less likely that the efferent interneurons, which activate a specific thermoregulatory response, are directly affected by the agents. These impressions could be more firmly held if, for each agent, observations of the changes in the thermoregulatory responses had been made at three ambient temperatures—hot, neutral, and cold. For example, if an injection of an endogenous pyrogen (or 5-HT) into the preoptic tissue of an unanesthetized cat reduced panting in a hot environment—to increase the core temperature—then the more likely interpretation would be that the agent acted directly upon those neurons generating the set temperature. The question would still remain as to whether the neurons with the high or with the low temperature coefficient were depressed or excited respectively. There is an indication that the neurons with the high temperature coefficient are depressed by a pyrogen and those with the low temperature coefficient are unaffected, while the efferent interneurons which activate a specific thermoregulatory response are apparently not directly affected by the pyrogen

(128a). Injection of 200–500 μg 5-HT creatinine sulfate into the third ventricle of dogs under light chloralose-urethane anesthesia reduced the unit discharge rate of both temperature-sensitive and temperature-insensitive neurons (105, 106). Injecting 5–50 μg epinephrine into the third ventricle usually reduced the activity of warm-sensitive units while the temperature-insensitive units responded more variably (105, 106).

On the basis of the presence of catecholamines and 5-hydroxytryptamine in high concentrations in the hypothalamus and of their antagonistic actions in changing the core temperature when injected into the anterior hypothalamus, a recent suggestion was made, to account for the regulation of body temperature (135). According to this, when thermal stress increases one of the rates of exchange—heat loss or heat production—above the basal level, the concentrations of these monoamines in the hypothalamic tissue are presumed to change to favor an increase in the other rate of heat exchange and establish balance at a new level for the same core temperature. Presumably the changes in the concentrations of these agents are achieved by neural secretory elements within the anterior hypothalamus; these elements are acted upon by nervous inputs from peripheral thermal receptors, and by local temperature acting directly on the secretory elements or indirectly through adjacent temperature-sensitive neurons. In essence, this thesis proposes a humoral link in the complex of neural connections which regulate body temperature.

No compelling evidence favors this *ad hoc* thesis over the more typical synaptic chemistry linking neuron to neuron, nor does any evidence rule out a specialized humoral linkage at least in part. However, the slow recovery from the effects of an injection of these monoamines negates the thesis as a general account of regulatory processes. An amount of 5-HT required to affect a change in the core temperature sustains that effect for many hours, whereas thermoregulatory responses may be activated within seconds of a change in hypothalamic temperature. When extended cooling of the hypothalamus producing shivering and hyperthermia is terminated, panting and increased rate of heat loss are promptly activated to drive the body temperature back to normal. If 5-HT were released in sufficient amount to drive the body temperature up, all the evidence indicates that it would sustain the hyperthermia for many hours.

Other consequences of hypothalamic heating or cooling and their implications of negative feedback.—An inevitable consequence of hypothalamic heating accompanying either the reduction in heat conservation and heat production or the increase in heat loss is a reduction in the heat content and the core temperature of the animal, followed, in every species studied, by other consequences. As the core temperature falls, the magnitude of the effects first induced by sustained heating of the hypothalamus decreases. Finally, the animal balances heat loss and heat production, now at a lower steady-state core temperature, by making about the some responses (or only slightly less) that it was making before the hypothalamus was heated. The size of this induced steady-state hypothermia depends upon how much the hypothalamus was heated and, apparently, upon the species, being less in the dog (172, 192) than in the goat (12, 17, 19) and in some cats (132) but not others (4). Further, if, after steady-state hypothermia is achieved, the hypothalamic temperature is released and allowed to fall to some low value dictated by the core hypothermia, a large response, opposite in sign to that first induced by hypothalamic heating, now restores (rapidly at first) the heat content and body temperature to the levels they initially had prior to hypothalamic heating. Thus it is in the dog (152, 172, 192) and goat (12, 17, 22). The mirror images of these events are produced by hypothalamic cooling in the dog (172, 192), goat (12, 17, 22), and baboon (157).

Three important deductions may be drawn from these observations: first, the hypothalamic temperature is involved in determining what the response and its magnitude shall be; second, the hypothalamic temperature alone is not enough to determine what the response and its magnitude shall be; and third, changes in the core temperature secondarily induced by hypothalamic temperature displacement are transduced and fed back to the controlling system with a negative sign to reduce the response first produced by the change in hypothalamic temperature. Changes in the skin temperature over the core of the furred animal may be involved with the core in the negative feedback signal, but changes in the temperature of the appendages are not involved for they are of the opposite sign and would be transduced as a positive feedback signal.

One additional important deduction must be recognized. When the preoptic-hypothalamic region in a resting-wakeful animal is heated or cooled in a thermal neutral environment, the change in hypothalamic temperature required to activate evaporative heat loss, shivering, or other neural or humoral thermoregulatory response, except the vasomotor response, is always more than occurs naturally when the animal pants vigorously in a hot environment or shivers vigorously in a cold environment. In fact, under natural conditions, when the animal is exposed to moderately high or low environmental temperatures, hypothalamic temperature does not vary from that observed in the neutral environment.

Man—a special case.—Since there is no way of dissociating hypothalamic temperature from other core temperatures in man, activation of thermoregulatory responses in man will be reviewed separately. If the hypothalamic temperature were the only core temperature affecting the regulation of body temperature, if the levels of exercise, rest, and sleep had no effect, and if the skin temperatures and their time derivatives could be measured and weighted in proportion to their thermal sensitivity, then the thermoregulatory responses of man would be ideal material to review since no other species has been studied so extensively and with such indifference to these conditions. Partial control over the core and cutaneous temperatures has been achieved by taking advantage of the induced variations during steady-state stress, transfer from one environment to another, or exercise at several work loads in different environments. An unusual way to control body temperature was first to elevate the core temperature rapidly in a very hot humid air stream and then to maintain it at the desired level during the test period by variable ventilation of a vapor-barrier suit in which the subject was dressed (148).

The simplest account of the activation of a thermoregulatory response has been a correlation of the sweat rate with the mean body temperature (354). When thermal load was varied by different levels of work in a range of ambient temperatures from 20 to 35° C, the sweat rates of two young men increased linearly with slopes of 6.6 and 8.6 g min^{-1} for a 1° C increase in mean body temperature above a critical value for each man.

There is a consensus that sweating in man may be affected by changes in the intracranial temperature, by steady-state and time-dependent changes in cutaneous temperature, or by some combination of both. An intense heat stimulus (47° C water) applied to one leg up to the knee and one arm to the elbow elicited sweating within a minute on the dorsum of the other foot before the sensation became painful, and on the thigh, forearm, and chest after pain was sensed (306). No change in tympanic membrane temperature occurred during the four-minute exposure; however, the participation of the cutaneous C-fibers (pain fibers) in the sweating response was suggested by these observations. Either core or skin temperatures may affect cutaneous vascular and sweating responses in transition from one environment to another (41, 42, 88, 179, 280, 365, 395). When a resting nude man is moved from a neutral (25–30° C) to a hot (50–68° C) environment, the number of active sweat glands on various areas (280, 395) and the total evaporative water loss (41, 179, 365) may increase in correlation with an increasing mean skin temperature before core temperature begins to increase. Sweating may continue to increase as tympanic membrane temperature increases and without further increase in skin temperature. On return to the neutral environment, all sweat glands may become inactive in less than one minute in association with a high but falling skin temperature and with no change in or even a rising tympanic temperature (280, 395). Immediate vasoconstriction in the palm occurred in transition from hot to neutral, but other cutaneous sites showed little or no evidence of vascular change (280, 395).

Walking at 4.5 km hr^{-1} for one hour at 35° C, then one hour at 50° C, and, finally, one hour at 35° C produced rates of evaporative water loss that paralleled those of the resting man similarly exposed (41). In going from hot to warm, sweat rate sharply dropped but did not return to the level of the first hour until well after the skin temperature had returned to control level. The declining sweat rate could be correlated with the changes in tympanic membrane temperature. Heat-acclimatized subjects, in transition from a 35 to 50° C environment, showed an increase in sweat rate without a concurrent increase in core temperature and a further increase in sweat rate which did correlate with the rising core temperature (88). In this same study, however, nonacclimatized subjects appeared to sweat in correlation with the rising core temperature but not with skin temperature.

Without more knowledge of the interactions between hypothalamic temperature, extrahypothalamic core temperatures, and the several cutaneous thermal sensory sites subject to both steady-state and time-rate changes, it is difficult to formulate an accurate quantitative description of a thermoregulatory response even in a resting, wakeful man subject only to external thermal stress. Two recent attempts to predict evaporative heat loss have been made:

$$1.\ E_{HL} = 5 + 80\ (T_e - 37.18) + 18\ (T_s - 33) \tag{365}$$

and

$$2.\ E_{HL} = 10 + 70\ (T_e - 36.60)\ (T_s - 33.5) \tag{179}$$

where E_{HL} equals the total evaporative heat loss in kcal m^{-2} hr^{-1}, T_e is the tympanic membrane or head core temperature, and T_s is the mean of skin temperatures weighted according to the representative surface area.

The two equations were derived from common data at least in part, but they do not predict the same answer for the same temperatures for evaporative heat loss in excess of about 80 kcal m^{-2} hr^{-1}. For example, Equation 1 predicts 125 kcal m^{-2} hr^{-1}, and Equation 2 predicts 255 kcal m^{-2} hr^{-1} for $T_e = 38°$ C and $T_s = 36°$ C.

When exercise is added as an independent variable, predicting a thermoregulatory response becomes even more hazardous and no one has attempted to do so in terms of core and mean skin temperatures. However, several relevant observations have been made of sweat rate, thermal conductance, and body temperatures at several levels of exercise and external thermal stress (42, 261, 271, 272, 396). When sweat rate and conductance were plotted as functions of rectal temperature for the same mean skin temperature, both responses were minimal up to a rectal temperature of about 36.5° C for all skin temperatures (396). For a low mean skin temperature (26° C), there was a gradual and accelerating increase in both responses as rectal temperature increased with larger work rates. Both responses increased more rapidly with increasing rectal temperatures at a mean skin temperature at 33° C, and even more so at 36.5° C. Response curves for both conductance and sweat rate for each skin temperature tended to become parallel, with saturation becoming evident for the highest skin temperature at a high rectal temperature (396).

Acclimatized men were exposed to graded combinations of exercise and environmental temperature to test the relative effects of internal and external thermal stress upon rectal temperature and heart rate (261). Internal heat stress was about twice as effective on heart rate as external heat stress, whereas they were equally effective on rectal temperature. Rectal temperature at all work levels increased with increasing environmental temperature. Also, the higher the work level, the greater was the rectal temperature at all environmental temperatures. For ambient temperatures less than 33° C, the equilibrium rectal temperature was practically independent of the environmental temperature over a wide range (271).

Men walking at 5.6 km hr⁻¹ were alternately exposed to 55 and 30° C environmental temperatures. The average hourly sweat rate, heart rate, and skin and rectal temperatures during the pulsed exposures were similar to those observed in steady-state exposures at a midway environmental temperature (42). When the same subjects walked alternately at 5.6 km hr⁻¹ and 2.0 km hr⁻¹ in a 46° C environment, their average responses were not different from those observed at a steady-state pace with a midway metabolic rate. These results are similar to those of comparisons of intermittent with continuous work in moderate heat and of intermittent with continuous heat at a continuous level of activity over an eight-hour period, in both of which the physiological cost was similar as judged by rectal temperature, pulse rate, and water loss (277).

Exercise imposes an internal heat load on the body which produces an imbalance between the rates of heat loss and production and, therefore, an increasing body temperature in any environment. In man, as in other animals, there must be feedback loops to the controlling system from thermal transducers in the hypothalamus, and perhaps also in the body core, which respond to this temperature increase. There is increasing evidence that exercise, in man as in dog, affects thermoregulatory responses not only by these thermal feedback loops but also by a nonthermal feedback loop. This latter loop acts as if to decrease the set temperatures for all thermoregulatory responses. Thus, in a hot environment, evaporative heat loss is promptly increased; in a warm environment, it may be promptly initiated; and in a cold environment, shivering is probably promptly reduced, although the total heat production will be increased by the added work load. Since the decrease in set temperature by exercise is never enough to balance the rates of heat exchange promptly, core temperature rises in all environments.

By the technique of controlled hyperthermia (148), the body temperature of men was elevated to a given level while the sweat rate was measured at different levels of exercise (54). The sweat rate was higher during work than at rest for the same internal temperature (38.5° C aural), in spite of a lower mean skin temperature during work. These results confirm earlier observations on the total sweat rate in man (287, 319) and sweat rates at local skin areas (38, 39, 262).

The onset of a change in sweat rate at a local skin area in a hot environment occurred within a few seconds after the start of work (38, 39), and the rate of evaporative water loss diminished in less than two minutes after the end of work (38, 39). The level of sweating seemed to correlate with the level of work (38, 54), but not with passive movement of the limbs alone (39, 319). The most effective stimulus appeared to be a combination of muscle contraction and limb movement since isometric contraction against a heavy load augmented sweating less than did dynamic contraction (39). The abrupt decrease in total sweat rate at the end of exercise has been correlated with an abrupt decrease in femoral vein temperature, an observation indicating involvement of thermal receptors in these veins (322). However, the decrease in femoral vein temperature correlates with an abrupt increase in saphenous vein temperature. If the latter veins also had thermoreceptors, the combined thermal effect of blood temperature changes in all veins draining muscle and skin would be diminished.

Acclimatization to external heat loads produces a well-studied effect on the sweat rate. Heat acclimatization may be produced by exposure to an environment of saturated air at mouth temperature until the mouth reaches 38.5° C on twelve successive days. The rate of increase in sweating per 0.4° C increase in oral temperature is augmented nearly fivefold, almost linearly with time (56). When heat acclimatization was induced by controlled elevation of oral temperature to 37.3, 37.9 and 38.5° C for periods of varying durations on each of eleven days, the extent of increase in sweat rate occurring throughout the acclimatization depended upon both the elevation in oral temperature and the duration of the daily exposure (148). Tests with a two-hour standard heat exposure showed an increase in sweat loss after acclimatization ranging from 10 to 120 per cent, depending on duration and extent of the elevated temperature during acclimatization. Sensations of discomfort during controlled hyperthermia were worse after than before acclimatization.

After artificial heat acclimatization, induced by working two to four hours in a hot environment for seven to fourteen days (36, 148, 158, 200, 398, 401), sweat, whose concentration of NaCl may be low, is secreted at a higher rate for a given core temperature. The core temperature increases less during work in the heat, the pulse rate is lower, and discomfort is less than before acclimatization. Unacclimatized women are more severely strained than men when exposed to the same severe heat and work conditions (398), but on repeated exposure they acclimatize (200) and react to thermal stress about as men, although with less sweating (398). The natural heat acclimatization of Caucasian men living in hot and humid, or hot and dry climates was about halfway between that of unacclimatized and highly acclimatized men (401). Working in a hot, humid environment leads to acclimatization manifested by higher sweat rate with less electrolyte, but with reduction in neither the pulse rate nor the rise in core temperature. (158). These results resemble those of heat acclimatization produced by the controlled hyperthermia method wherein the subject is always in a hot humid climate inside his suit (148). Bantu men have a degree of natural heat acclimatization, but their maximum level of induced acclimatization is no greater than that of highly acclimatized Caucasians (400).

In heat acclimatization the increase in the sweat rate per degree of rise in core temperature (56) and the increase in the maximum sweat rate (56, 399) may be due to changes in the controlling system, the controlled system, or both. No clear evidence indicates how heat acclimatization modifies the controlling system. It might do so by shifting downward the threshold for the sweating response, thereby increasing the activating signal for the same core temperature, or it might increase the sensitivity; i.e., yield a larger controlling signal for the same activating signal. Heat acclimatization may be, in part, an increased responsiveness of the sweat glands to the same controlling signal (89, 147). Sweat secreted by an arm immersed daily in 43° C water for two hours, while heat acclimatization in the body was induced by controlled hyperthermia, was greater than in the control arm. Sweat secreted by an arm immersed daily in 13° C under the same conditions was not above the insensible level, while the control arm in the 13° C test yielded the same as the control arm in the 43° C test (147). Sweat rate increased a little in an arm immersed in 43° C water daily for fifteen days in subjects who were not concurrently heat acclimatized; no change occurred in the control arm. Thus heat acclimatization in the body produced the larger effect which could be enhanced or suppressed by increased or decreased local arm temperature. Also, the glands apparently must be activated to show the effects of acclimatization; the increase in sweating after acclimatization correlates with the total sweat loss incurred during the induction of acclimatization (148).

Raising the oral, esophageal, and tympanic temperatures to 37.5° C by radiant heating of the body above the waist, while the body below the waist was immersed in 10° C water for 100 minutes daily for ten days, did not produce acclimatization, but at the same core temperatures with the bath at 36° C sweating was activated daily and acclimatization occurred (89). Thus, daily elevation of core temperature alone does not yield heat acclimatization. The threshold concentration of intradermally injected acetylcholine required to activate the sweat glands in a neutral environment was the same before and after heat acclimatization (89). However, the sweat output induced by injection into the wrist of methacholine at a suprathreshold concentration was 60–100 per cent greater after heat acclimatization (89). This increase is comparable to that in total sweat rate due to heat acclimatization; the increase from the arm alone may be as much as 400 per cent (147). Repeated intradermal injections of methacholine into the arm for twelve days in a neutral environment also increase the local sweat rate by 30–100 per cent (89).

Heat acclimatization evidently does not increase the number of active sweat glands (89). The increase in thermal sweating is apparently associated with and is perhaps the cause of a concurrent increase in blood flow to these areas due to vasodilator activity (275, 340); this increase is greater relative to the core temperature after heat acclimatization (149). Release of vasoconstrictor tone to the hand and ear (149) or from the arm (275, 340) does not correlate with onset of sweating, nor is the increase in hand blood flow relative to the core temperature as great after heat acclimatization as in the arm (1/10 for the hand compared with 1/3 for the arm)

(149). Glycogen is depleted from the secretory part of the sweat gland on the first day of heat exposure; the loss decreases to zero by the tenth day (89, 116). In salt-depleted subjects, glycogen was lost from the secretory coil of the gland on each day of acclimatizing heat exposure, but only on the first day on salt-loaded subjects (119). The sweat rate is not affected by salt depletion, but the rate of sodium excretion progressively falls (118).

Recently, it has been shown that the fluid secreted by the secretory coil of the gland is probably isotonic with plasma (75, 335), which suggests that the gland secretes sodium, and that water passively diffuses into the gland lumen (117). The reabsorption of sodium, thought to be accomplished in the duct membrane which appears to be relatively impermeable to water (117), is controlled by adrenal corticosteroids (91). The low water permeability is not influenced by antidiuretic hormone (308). It has been suggested that acclimatization to heat is accompanied by an increased circulating level of aldosterone induced initially by rapid sodium depletion accompanying sweating (117). Subsequent to the first day, the renal tubules are thought to escape the influence of the aldosterone, and renal excretion of sodium increases to normal. Aldosterone acts only on the ductal portion of the sweat gland (74) which apparently does not escape from the effects of the corticoids as do the renal tubules (117).

Another feature of sweat gland activity in both acclimatized and unacclimatized subjects, termed hidromeiosis (61), is that the amount of sweating tends to decrease during the second, third, and fourth hour of heat exposure following an early increase to peak level. This is true for exposure in hot water (201), in dry heat (398, 401), and in humid heat (56, 147, 148); for a single arm, the decrease is less in dry heat (55) than in humid heat. Sweat output from the arm, during a two-hour heat exposure, increased fourfold after acclimatization, whereas that of the total body increased 2.5-fold. Furthermore, the arm sweat rate decreased less during the second hour than did the total sweat rate (147). The decline in sweating in freshwater always occurred regardless of the level of thermal stress (201). The decline in sweat rate in hot water and in humid heat may be attributed to soaking of the skin rather than "sweat gland fatigue". When diffusion of water into the skin was reduced by adding 10 to 15 per cent NaCl to the bath water, the decline was greatly reduced (90, 201).

The reduction in sweat rate from fully wetted skin proceeds exponentially for more than 300 minutes from the time of wetting with a time constant of 105–135 minutes (55). The reduction appears not to be due to any decrease in controlling signal from the central nervous system, since the sweat rate from a continuously dry arm surface does not decay (55). The indication is that wetting the skin does not interfere with the cutaneous temperature transducers although this possibility requires more direct exploration. It also appears that the neural-glandular junction does not fail under prolonged stimulation (90). The consensus is that hydration of the skin, possibly the stratum corneum, is an important factor in reducing the sweat rate from wetted skin; this may be due to obstruction of the duct of the gland (61, 90, 201).

Sweat glands are said to fatigue during the last hours of prolonged work in heat. When heat-acclimatized subjects worked at any of several levels for five hours, the sweat rate at the end of the fifth hour was lower than at the end of the first and second hour; under the severest stress, it was only one half (399).

Oral administration of salicylates did not affect the rise in body temperature in unacclimatized men exercising at six times BMR at 22° C and 50 per cent RH (124). In men working in hot-humid and hot-dry environments salicylate did not affect skin temperature or pulse rate; however, the rectal temperature and sweat rate were increased by salicylate in the hot-humid environment and the sweat rate increased in the hot-dry environment (232). Since salicylate does not increase oxygen consumption in exercise (125), it is puzzling that the higher sweat rate did not lower the core temperature. Salicylate did not affect acclimatization to heat although the rectal temperature was higher during acclimatization when salicylate was administered (37). Overhydration during heat acclimatization did not affect the pattern of acclimatization, although before and during acclimatization, overhydration increased the sweat rate and decreased the rectal temperature (289). Forced breathing suppressed sweating from the forehead at rest; the suppression was attributable to respiratory alkalosis (11).

Reflex reduction of vasoconstriction in the hand by warming the trunk skin with radiant heat does not occur unless the core temperature is greater than 36.5° C; for core temperature above 37° C, vasoconstriction of the hand was progressively increased as trunk skin temperature fell below 33° C and was maximum at 29° C (95). Dehydration during a twelve-hour exposure to a hot-dry environment decreased the cutaneous pulse amplitude by 20 per cent, but the heart rate increased by 26 per cent which indicates that the cutaneous blood flow was not affected by dehydration (339). The sweat rate was not significantly less in the dehydrated subjects nor did the rate decrease significantly throughout the exposure in hydrated or dehydrated subjects although the oral temperature was slightly higher (0.1° C) in the dehydrated men (339).

Heating the forearm increases the blood flow not only in the heated area but also in adjacent skin areas at about the same time. Involvement of a spinal reflex mechanism was excluded, since a subcutaneous ring of local anesthetic proximal to the heated area did not affect the response, whereas a ring of anesthetic or of epinephrine between the heated and unheated skin areas blocked the spread of increased blood flow to the unheated area; moreover, in patients with cervical sympathectomy or complete brachial plexus tears, blood flow increased normally in heated and adjacent unheated skin (102). The suggestion was made that an axon reflex or any nervous mechanism was unlikely and that the wave of relaxation was conducted to the vessels of the unheated area by the smooth muscle of the cutaneous arterial plexus (102). Locally applied cold to the skin induces increased blood flow at all of thirty-four sites tested, but was greatest in areas of the body likely to be exposed to severe local cooling in cold climates (150). Repeated exposure to cold augments the increase in blood flow to the severely cooled extremity (5, 145, 191, 266).

Valuable observations have been made on men with spinal cord sections. Patients with cervical and high thoracic transections exposed to gradual increase of ambient temperature from 25 to 52° C all showed a progressive increase in number of active sweat glands on most of the body surface and an increased amplitude of cutaneous pulse (307). The sweating was distinct but sparse, and would not have been sufficient to prevent hyperthermia on prolonged exposure. Sweating appeared to be greater during heat exposure when the initial core temperature was high, although sweating gradually declined and stopped as the air temperature was cooled to control level (within ten to twenty minutes) even though the rectal temperature continued to increase. Skin temperature or, perhaps more importantly, the rate of change of skin temperature appears to be involved in this response (307). The level of excitability of the sweat glands appears to be set, in part, by their own temperature or by the excitability of preganglionic sudomotor cells in the cord which in turn may be in part directly influenced by the cutaneous temperature (307).

The inhibition of general body sweating in normal man when localized cooling is applied to the skin requires the intact somatic sensory afferents. A low-level paraplegic (T-12) whose sympathetic innervation was intact but who was without somatic senation in the legs, a normal man, and a lumbar sympathectomized man were heated to a steady-state sweating rate of 65–85 cal m^{-2} hr^{-1} and their legs were cooled while circulation was arrested. Trunk sweating was depressed in the normal and in the sympathectomized man but not in the paraplegic (313).

The core temperature of patients with cervical spinal transections was decreased by cooling the part of the body innervated by spinal nerves below the section. Shivering and increased metabolism were induced when the tympanic membrane temperature fell below about 35.5° C, and the response increased in proportion to further decrease in temperature even though the temperature of the sentient skin was held above 34° C in a 29–25° C environment (123, 246). Similar cooling of the core in an environment of 19–24° C, at which the sentient skin temperature was about 30° C, again produced shivering (247) with about the same threshold temperature (35.5° C), and about the same relation of oxygen consumption to tympanic temperature below 35.5° C (123). Thus shivering could be activated without a contributing signal from the sentient skin. The role of the skin was not clearly indicated in these tests; however, in one patient shivering was readily elicited in the cooler environment but was not activated in the warmer environment even when the tympanic temperature dropped to 34.4° C. Intense cooling of the insentient skin below the section apparently had no direct effect on shivering below the section, since oxygen consumption did not increase during the first hour of cooling but only after the tympanic temperature fell below 35.5° C and visible shivering and EMG activity appeared in muscles innervated by nerves above the section (123).

The Regulated Temperature—A Tenable Answer

The preoptic-hypothalamic tissue is like no other part of the nervous system in being essential for regulation of internal body temperature. If de-afferented, this tissue can activate appropriate thermoregulatory responses and thereby minimize changes in internal body temperature induced by external thermal stress. However, the change in internal temperature cannot be rendered zero, for a small change is required to activate the response in the de-afferented preparation. The preoptic-hypothalamic tissue does, of course, require intact efferent pathways to function and does require its afferent inputs to function normally.

A normal animal resting in a neutral environment is also functionally deafferented insofar as inputs from surface temperatures are concerned, yet its hypothalamus can activate appropriate responses if the hypothalamic temperature is displaced no more than 1 to 2° C up or down. The goat may be different in this regard (12). It is said to require a cold stimulus to its skin before it can be made to shiver, that is, it has not been made to manifest vigorous shivering in a neutral, warm, or hot environment by cooling its preoptic-hypothalamic tissue. Dogs, rabbit, ox can all be made to shiver in a 35° C environment with sufficient hypothalamic cooling (to 34° C). The difference in the goat may be more in degree than in principle and the difference does not apply to the converse stimuli, that is, the goat need not be in a warm or hot environment to activate vigorous panting by heating the hypothalamus. Even in a cold environment, the goat, dog, ox, etc., can be made to pant by a sufficient short-term increase in hypothalamic temperature.

Man is said to depend on his hypothalamic temperature for driving evaporative heat loss, and the role of the skin temperature is only to inhibit that response when cooled (44, 45). At the same time it is claimed that the essential drive for shivering comes from a cold skin and the only effect of cooling the hypothalamus would be to reduce the inhibition of the signal derived from the skin (45). Accordingly, man could not be made to shiver in a hot environment in the absence of drive from the skin, no matter how much the hypothalamic temperature was decreased. A more recent suggestion implies that if the hypothalamic temperature of man were held at 36.6° C, he could not be made to sweat or shiver no matter what his skin temperature. Conversely, if his skin temperature were held somewhere between 33.6 and 34.1° C, he could not be made to sweat or shiver no matter what his hypothalamic temperature (179, 366). These two views on man's regulation of body temperature are disputed and probably do not represent the majority view. A conservative view might be that if man is fundamentally different from other species with regard to the manner in which peripheral and central temperatures are combined to activate a thermoregulatory response, then that difference must rest on more certain proof than is currently available. Ideally, techniques for a controlled dissociation of hypothalamic temperature from other body temperatures are needed or, in lieu of this, studies of artificially controlled hypothalamic temperatures in apes would be extremely useful.

There remain the questions: is the hypothalamic temperature the regulated temperature in most species under all conditions, or is it only a coarsely controlling temperature revealing its effects only under extreme thermal stress and serving only as a protective or safety capability? Does this leave the fine regulation of body temperature up to the nicely evolved but, nevertheless, fortuitous influences of other core and cutaneous receptors where the cutaneous receptors are subject to the vagaries of the transformed thermal disturbances and regulatory responses? The answers to these questions depend upon knowledge, not yet available, of the linkage between the afferent inputs and the controlling neurons.

At present, I can only indicate what I think the inputs to the controlling neurons are doing, as indicated schematically in Figure 1. The basic requirement of the controlling system of an endotherm is that it generates a nervous signal to activate (a) a graded rate of evaporative heat loss when its temperature rises above some temperature designated $T_{\mathrm{set_{EHL}}}$; (b) a graded increase in rate of heat production when its temperature falls below some temperature designated T_{set_M}, where $T_{\mathrm{set}_M} < T_{\mathrm{set_{EHL}}}$; ($c$) a graded reduction in the flow of heat by control of blood flow from the core to the skin when its temperature falls below some temperature designated $T_{\mathrm{set_{VC}}}$, where $T_{\mathrm{set_{VC}}} \leq T_{\mathrm{set_{EHL}}}$; and ($d$) possibly graded hormonal and behavioral responses.

Before suggesting how the inputs have their effect, it seems to be in order to indicate how the requirements of the controlling system may be achieved. The basic requirements appear to be (a) a class (I) of neurons in the preoptic-anterior hypothalamic tissue possess a spontaneous firing rate that increases with increasing temperature; (b) the neurons of class I link with and facilitate a second class (II) of neurons which can activate evaporative heat loss but which lack both a spontaneous and temperature-dependent activity by themselves; (c) a third class (III) of neurons in the preoptic-anterior hypothalamic tissue possess a spontaneous firing rate with little or no temperature dependence; (d) the neurons of class III link with and facilitate a fourth class (IV) of neurons which can activate heat production but which lack both a spontaneous and temperature dependent activity by themselves; (e) at the same time, neurons of class I also inhibit those of class IV, and neurons of class III also inhibit those of class II; (f) between temperatures slightly above and slightly below normal internal temperature, neurons of both class II and class IV are inhibited more than they are facilitated so between these temperatures there is neither panting nor shivering as in the dog; thus only above a certain temperature $T_{set_{EHL}}$ is panting activated and only below a certain temperature T_{set_M} is shivering activated; (g) neurons of all four classes comingle, especially in the preoptic tissue, but the greatest density of class IV neurons is more caudal in the hypothalamic tissue, since it has been shown that electrical stimulation in the dorsomedial region of the posterior hypothalamus consistently initiated and maintained shivering (370); and (h) classes of neurons affecting other thermoregulatory responses may also be found in the preoptic-hypothalamic tissue or elsewhere in the brain. With these basic neurons and connections, the deafferented controlling system may be supposed to function like the deafferented preoptic-hypothalamic tissue of several animal species.

The unanswered question is how the afferent inputs from cutaneous thermal receptors, core thermal receptors, proprioceptors, the cortex, the ascending reticular activating system (ARAS), etc. feed into and affect the basic controlling neurons. The simplest schema is that all inputs facilitate or inhibit neurons of class I, or class III, or both; i.e., those neurons which interact to transduce hypothalamic temperature into an activating nervous signal of appropriate sign. Any or all inputs would then properly affect the set temperatures for all of the thermoregulatory responses without an effect upon the slope of the response curve, and in accordance with what seems to be a fair summary of current knowledge. A low skin temperature could facilitate class III neurons, thereby raising the set temperatures for all the responses. Reduced facilitation to the class III neurons from the ARAS or increased facilitation to class I neurons from proprioceptors could reduce all set temperatures in sleep and in exercise respectively. Two pathways to the summing circle of the controlling system shown in Figure 1 appear to be possible. Afferent inputs to the thalamus may continue on to the cortex and be reflected there either as a common integrated signal or as separate signals to the primary summing circle in the preoptic tissue. Alternately, afferents from the thalamus may go more directly to the primary summing circle. In either case, the effect of the afferent inputs to the controlling system would be as already described. If either of these suggestions were to pertain to the actual pathway, then the hypothalamic temperature would, at all times, be in control of internal body temperature. Its temperature would be transduced and compared with set temperatures which are adjusted by all peripheral information, and the response would then be in accordance with the sign and magnitude of the difference.

The other possibility is that some one or all of the afferent inputs may go directly to the neurons of class II and class IV. Afferents from the thalamus relaying cold reception at the skin may go directly to the class IV neurons and facilitate shivering. If they do, they must also go to and inhibit class II neurons, since the threshold for panting has at the same time been raised by the cold. Connections from the warm receptors of the skin may go directly to and facilitate class II and inhibit class IV neurons, so that the thresholds for both panting and shivering be decreased. This schema is represented in Figure 1 by the direct links from the thalamus to the small summing circles which provide the input to each of the transformation boxes for the thermoregulatory responses within the controlling system. By this scheme, the hypothalamic signal serves to enhance the signal already derived from the skin if and when the hypothalamic temperature is displaced. This scheme can also account for the observed characteristics of the controlling system and the effects of peripheral receptors upon it.

Since the afferent connections to the controlling system have not been described, there is no way to judge which scheme actually pertains in any one species. However, animals with lesions in the preoptic-anterior hypothalamic tissue exhibit a major deficit in their shivering response when exposed to cold (21, 235, 237, 238, 251, 359, 369). This indicates that afferent connections from peripheral cold receptors to the posterior hypothalamus are either lacking or insufficient to activate shivering, and that an intact afferent flow from the periphery to the preoptic neurons is essential for normal vigorous shivering. For these reasons, I favor the view that the afferent inflow to the controlling system affects the neurons of classes I and III. Thus, these neurons generate the sole activating signal for each of the controlled responses and are influenced in this process by the afferent inputs from several thermal and nonthermal sources.

Some units in the preoptic region show activity which increases strongly (Q_{10} up to 8) with local heating in the urethanized cat (128, 129, 293, 294, 393), dog (178, 291), and rabbit (73). These could conceivably be class I or class II neurons, or both. Other units in the same region which show spontaneous activity, but little or no temperature dependence in urethanized cat (128, 129, 293, 294, 393) and dog (178, 291), may possibly be class III neurons. Units in the preoptic tissue having activity which increases with decreasing temperature were found in the dog (178), rabbit (73), and cat (128a, 129) and these may possibly be class III or, more likely, class IV neurons, or both (128A, 129). Units have been found in the septal region of urethanized cats which have a high activity which decreases with increasing temperature (128, 129) and are thought to be class IV neurons. Units have been found in the hypothalamus caudal to the preoptic region of the rabbit, and in the thalamus, as well, which show increasing activity with cooling in the same region (73); these may be neurons of class IV, class III, or both. Units in the hypothalamus of the rabbit increased activity with decreasing temperature in the preoptic region (personal communication from Cabanac); these could be class IV neurons. In the urethanized cat are preoptic units which show low activity up to a threshold temperature and then increase their activity with temperatures above threshold (128, 129); these are possibly class II neurons.

Units in the preoptic-hypothalamic region of a urethanized cat have been described whose activity increases with rising local and ambient temperature (393); these may conceivably be class I or class II neurons, or both. Spontaneous unit activity was found among the neurons in the hypothalamus, septum, and preoptic area of the urethanized female rat (269, 270). Forty to 60 per cent of the units had firing rates of less than 1 spike/sec, and only 10–15 per cent had rates exceeding 6/sec. Units with a mean discharge rate of 2–4/sec contributed most to the total spike activity. The level of spontaneous activity in the anterior hypothalamus, preoptic, and septal areas was greater in ovariectomized rats than in rats in estrus. The reverse was true in the lateral hypothalamus (269). The majority of the spontaneously active units in the lateral hypothalamus were excited by pain, cold, and cervical stimuli, whereas in the lateral septal area most were inhibited. In the anterior hypothalamic and preoptic areas, units that were excited were about equal in number to those that were inhibited by these peripheral stimuli (270). The time-course of the responses to peripheral pain, cold, and cervical stimuli of most hypothalamic and septal units closely corresponded to that of the associated EEG activation of the frontal cortex; this suggested that they were nonspecific arousal effects (270). From these descriptions of single-unit activity in the preoptic-hypothalamic tissue, it is not yet possible to decide how the afferent links are made with the controlling system. Finally, cortical neurons increase their spontaneous firing rate by local cooling of the surface of the cerebral cortex in the rat under urethane anesthesia (159). Cooling the surface for more than five minutes produced an aftereffect; the firing rate remained elevated above control for up to three and a half hours. There is no evidence to indicate whether these neurons are involved in body temperature regulation, but their existence points up the difficulties of unequivocal interpretation of neurophysiological observations.

CHARACTERISTICS OF THE CONTROLLING SYSTEM

I shall postulate that the hypothalamic temperature is the regulated temperature, and then describe the characteristics of the controlling system by stating the input-output relationships for each of the thermoregulatory responses. Each relationship may be directly obtained by measuring the magnitude of the thermoregulatory response as a function of the hypothalamic temperature, when the hypothalamic temperature is uncoupled from its normal feedback value and caused to range for short periods from well below to well above the normal value (34 to 42° C in a typical endotherm) (4, 127, 173, 192, 236). The input-output relationship for each of the thermoregulatory responses is required not only for the resting, wakeful, unacclimated animal in a neutral environment, but for every combination of sleeping, waking, resting, exercising, and acclimatization in hot, neutral, and cold environments. For comparative interest, these results are needed for many ectothermic and endothermic species representing adaptations of the many diversified thermoregulatory responses. At present, there are only meager results on a few species.

Proportional control.—Burton has suggested that temperature regulation is achieved by a proportional controller (68). Hardy has discussed other possible types of control in connection with regulation of body temperature (175, 177). There is increasing evidence that the dominant type of control possessed by the hypothalamic controller is proportional for at least some of the physiological responses. Proportional control means that the regulatory response is proportional to the difference between the hypothalamic temperature and a threshold or set temperature T_{set_R}, for that response. Thus,

$$R - R_0 = {_\alpha}_R \ (T_{hypo} - T_{set_R}), \text{ where } R - R_0 \gtreqqless 0$$

R_0 is the inactive level of response R, and α_R is the proportionality factor for response R. The sign of the difference determines which responses are activated; if T_{hypo} exceeds T_{set_R}, then R increases the rate of heat loss, or if T_{hypo} is less than T_{set_R}, the response reduces the rate of heat loss, or increases the rate of heat production, or both. If, in addition, the controller for any of the thermoregulatory responses had the capacity to differentiate the error signal, $\varepsilon = (T_R - T_{set_R})$, and generate a response in proportion to the time derivative of ε, i.e., $\beta_R \ (d\varepsilon/dt)$, then the controller would be termed a proportional plus derivative controller. Derivative or rate control enhances the output forcing function in anticipation of an error in the immediate future, and the enhancement goes to zero in steady state. Derivative control reduces the tendency of the proportional controller to overshoot or hunt, rendering a system with proportional plus derivative control more stable when exposed to a transient stress. If, in addition to proportional control, the controller had the capacity to integrate the error signal and generate a response in proportion to the time integral of ε, i.e., $\gamma_R \int \varepsilon \ dt$, then the controller would be termed a proportional plus integral controller. By adding integral control, the steady-state error which is essential for activating a proportional controller can be eliminated.

There is no evidence that any of the proportional controllers of thermoregulatory responses include derivative or integral control. Nor is there evidence that the transducer of hypothalamic temperature is rate dependent, that is, the thermoregulatory effects of (dT_{hypo}/dt) appear to be zero (168, 192). However, if T_{set} were adjustable by inputs from thermoreceptors in the periphery and if the sign of the adjustment were opposite to the sign of the peripheral temperature change, then the output forcing functions from the proportional controllers would respond as if the controllers also possessed integral control. If, as the peripheral temperatures decrease, T_{set} were to increase accordingly, then T_{hypo} need not drop as much in order to generate the signal to activate the required proportional response to balance heat loss and heat production. This sequence achieves the same end as does proportional plus integral control, which is to minimize the change in the regulated temperature. The latter controller does it by adding a response which is proportional to the time integral of the error signal ε, and drives ε to zero. The actual controlling system for body temperature seems to function by adjusting the hypothalamic set temperature so that the error signal, which is never zero and on which the proportional controllers act, is achieved with minimal change in hypothalamic temperature.

Likewise, if the peripheral thermal transducers generate a rate-dependent or phasic component and this component is included with the steady-state component in the input to the controlling system, and if this input adjusts the set temperature, then the output forcing function from each proportional controller would respond as if the controller also possessed derivative control. There is evidence that this kind of derivative control does occur during the transition from one environment to another when the skin temperature is changing rapidly (57, 179, 280, 365, 395).

An occasional voluntary interruption of some regulatory responses such as panting or shivering may be considered a form of on-off control, but here too this may be more in the nature of a cortical disturbance to proportional control rather than an additional type of control.

Apparently because of the complexity of inputs to the controlling system, it is difficult to maintain constant all inputs to the controlling system while the hypothalamic temperature alone is artificially caused to change. As a consequence, the experimental data may fit only approximately to the zero-order proportional control equation even in a resting-wakeful animal in a constant environment. Likewise, the proportionality factor α_R and the set temperature T_{set_R} may be only approximate values. The quantity α_R appears to be constant, that is, the proportional equation appears to be linear over a wide range of response for the dog (173, 192), rabbit (127), and possibly man (45) if the activated response does not approach saturation at the maximum possible value.

Adjustable set temperatures.—Accepting the hypothalamic temperature as the regulated temperature, then other inputs to the controlling system may be considered to effect a change in the set temperatures, that is, a change in the thresholds for the thermoregulatory responses. The effect of skin temperature has clearly been shown to be a change in the set temperature of panting, vasoconstriction, and shivering in the dog. Both in air (173, 192) and in water (71, 84), the higher the ambient temperature, the lower the set or threshold temperatures for panting and shivering; conversely, the lower the ambient temperature, the higher the threshold or set temperatures for both responses. In a similar way, the core temperature, apart from the hypothalamic temperature, affects the set temperatures for panting and shivering in the dog (192). Both core and cutaneous temperatures in the dog appear to change only the set temperatures without changing the value of α_R for both panting and shivering (173, 192). The effect of ambient and skin temperatures upon the threshold or set temperature for shivering or panting appears to be the same in the rabbit (127), goat (12, 22), and ox (223) as in the dog. The higher the skin and air temperatures in all these species, the lower the thresholds for shivering and panting, since in the warmer environment more hypothalamic cooling and less hypothalamic heating was required to produce shivering and panting respectively.

Although hypothalamic temperature has not been artifically dissociated from other core temperatures in man, there has been some success in dissociating these from skin temperatures (41, 45, 57, 88, 179, 280, 365, 366, 395, 396). These results may be interpreted as if a low or falling skin temperature raised the threshold for sweating and shivering and, conversely, a high or rising skin temperature lowered the threshold for sweating and shivering in man.

Other inputs to the controlling system seem to change the set temperatures for the thermoregulatory responses. At the onset of sleep, the set temperature for vasoconstriction appears to decrease in the monkey (172) so that the cutaneous vessels dilate and body heat is actively dissipated until the hypothalamic temperature drops to a lower sleeping level (167, 172). At the onset of sleep, the sweating threshold drops in man and heat is actively dissipated to bring the internal temperature to a lower level (160, 262), and the rate of thermogenic sweating is associated with the EEG depth of sleep in the daytime (330) and at night, early in the sleep cycle (300). Many species maintain a lower hypothalamic or internal body temperature when asleep (52, 53, 187, 284, 298, 301, 302, 314, 315, 328). On arousal from sleep, shivering may be activated to restore the body temperature to the waking level (187).

Regulation of internal body temperature appears to be normal in all regards during sleep except that the internal temperature is lower. Vasomotor responses and sweating (160) and mild shivering (203) may be activated in sleeping man. Even vigorous shivering may occur in sleeping birds (390). In a drowsy goat a smaller increase in the preoptic hypothalamic temperature was required to elicit panting than in the same animal when alert (17), which suggests a lower set temperature during sleep.

Lightly clothed men, exposed to 4° C for one hour, shivered less in a hypnotic trance than they did in control exposures (259). Their rectal temperature fell more under hypnosis, although their average skin temperature fell by the same amount in both states. A hypnotic trance does not affect the metabolic rate in a basal condition while the metabolic rate during natural sleep was 8.7 per cent less than the BMR (205).

The modification in temperature regulation during hibernation probably should not be characterized as just a reduction in the set temperatures as was done for sleep, although the animal is asleep at the onset of hibernation and actively dissipates body heat by vasodilatation. The body temperatures and oxygen consumption passively follow the ambient temperatures over a wide range during deep hibernation (170). The response during hibernation is more like a reversible inactivation of temperature regulation which can be reactivated by a number of thermal and nonthermal stimuli.

Dogs running on a treadmill in a water bath at bath temperatures ranging from 17 to 44° C and with just the head out of water do not appear to have a lower brain temperature at the threshold of panting compared with the threshold temperature when just standing on their hindfeet (83). At the onset of exercise in air, there is an immediate increase in panting in the dog in a warm or hot environment, followed by a further increase in evaporative heat loss by panting to a constant high level as the hypothalamic temperature gradually increases to a constant and higher than resting level (229, 230). At the end of exercise, panting immediately decreases and then gradually declines as the hypothalamic temperature slowly returns to the resting level (229, 230). These observations are readily interpreted by suggesting that the set temperature for panting decreased at the onset of exercise and increased at the end of exercise. The same observations have been made for sweating in man at the onset or end of exercise, or both (38, 40, 262, 288, 296, 320), and have been (40) or may be interpreted in the same way.

The impression persists that the hypothalamic set temperature rises and remains up during exercise in man (295, 296, 297, 320). This deduction is said to follow from the well-established fact that the core temperature gradually rises to a higher level, depending on the work load, and to about the same level for the same work load in a warm, neutral, or cold environment. If the set temperature for sweating were to increase as much as the hypothalamic temperature during work in a hot environment, then it is unclear to me what signal is activating the greatly increased sweat rate during work. Only by postulating a very large increase in the gain of the sweating controller α_{sw} during exercise can this thesis be made tenable. There is no evidence that α_{sw} does increase greatly or even slightly during exercise, although a slight increase seems plausible (230). The correlation of changes in femoral vein temperature with changes in sweating rate in transition from work to no work is the basis for suggesting that thermoreceptors capable of reflexly exciting the sweat glands may be located in the veins which drain warm blood from the working muscle (319, 320). The record on which this suggestion was based contains evidence that temperature changes alone in the femoral vein were not sufficient to account for the changes in sweat rate with no change in set temperature, and certainly not if the set temperature were presumed to increase.

There is good evidence in man that the higher the walking or running rate, the lower the set temperature for sweating (295). A man running in steady state on a $+10°$ grade at 6 km hr^{-1} had the same metabolic rate, 826 kcal hr^{-1}, as the same man running on a 0° C grade at 13 km hr^{-1}. On the 0° grade, he had to dissipate all of this as heat; and on the 10° grade, he had to dissipate only 675 kcal hr^{-1} because the rest of his energy expenditure was manifested as external work. The man's sweat rate was about 480 kcal hr^{-1} on the 0° grade, and only about 350 kcal hr^{-1} on the 10° grade even though his internal temperature was 0.2–0.3° C less at the higher sweat rate and his skin temperature was the same. The higher sweat rate is to be attributed to a lower set temperature at the higher running rate; no other clue was reported which could account for these results.

Steady-state sweat rate increases linearly with the rise in rectal, esophageal, and tympanic temperatures obtained by increasing work intensity at a constant environmental temperature (20° C) and the same mean skin temperature; this indicates that the controller for sweating responds proportionally in man (296). However, the slope of the response line does not equal the proportionality constant for hypothalamic control of sweating, since other core temperatures and the rate of running varied and both these may feed back to the controller and affect the set temperature. For given work intensity and esophageal and rectal temperatures, increase in steady-state sweat rate increased nearly linearly with rising mean skin temperature in environments ranging from 5 to 30° C (296). This could mean that the set temperature for sweating decreases with increasing skin temperature with all other inputs remaining the same, thereby activating sweating in a hot environment. During work at 30° C, the sweat rate was high although the skin temperature was 2–3° C lower than when sweat was elicited at rest (296). If the lower skin temperature should raise the set temperature, then the effects of exercise and the higher core temperature must be to decrease the set temperature that much, or even more, to activate sweating by the small increase in hypothalamic temperature. Raising the steady-state rate of heat loss to five times the basal level by heating the body with short-wave diathermy, or by producing internal heat through work, increases the core temperature (rectal) to about the same level for all environments between 10 and 27° C and for all skin temperatures (297). Both the conductances and the sweat rates during body heat loading were many times greater for all skin temperatures between 30 and 36° C than were these values for the same skin temperatures at rest. The somewhat higher sweat rate during heat loading by exercise suggests that the drive for sweating was derived in part directly from the exercise in addition to the indirect effect of increasing the hypothalamic and other core temperatures.

For men and women subjects with widely different maximal oxygen uptakes, the increase in esophageal temperature with submaximal work accorded more with the individual's work load relative to his maximum capacity rather than with the absolute work load. The quadriceps temperature was about 0.7° C above esophageal temperature for each work level. The sweat rate was related to the external work load even though the increase in esophageal temperature was related to the relative work load (327). In another study, the temperature of the vastus lateralis increased from a resting level of 33.5–35° C up to 37.8–39.7° C after fifteen minutes of work at 900, 1200, and 1500 kpm/min, and the esophageal temperature increased to 37.0–39.0° C, while the biceps brachii increased by no more than 0.5° C from its resting temperature of 34.5–36.0° C (6).

To say that the set temperature increases as the internal temperature increases and then to suggest that evaporative heat loss and vasodilatation are activated reflexly by a "work factor" or more specifically by mechanoreceptors or thermoreceptors in thermal association with the working muscle seems to be a misuse of the set-point concept. Since at present the concept of set-point is based only on the performance characteristics of the controlling system, and since the controlled responses perform as if the set temperatures for panting, sweating, and vasodilatation are decreased during exercise, why say the opposite? Common experience is enough to suggest that the set temperature for at least one other thermoregulatory response in man also decreases at the onset of exercise. If one is chilled and shivering while reclining, it is sufficient to rise and exercise in order to reduce immediately the shivering and the discomfort accompanying it.

The regulation of body temperature is modified by endogenous pyrogens during fever. It is as if the set temperatures for all thermoregulatory responses are increased in fever, and the effects of all other inputs to the controlling system induced by external heat loading (68a, 94) and exercise (162, 279) are as in the normal state. Responses to hypothalamic heating and cooling in the dog are normal, but at a higher temperature reference (13). The rise in body temperature in exercise is in no sense a fever, but is to be interpreted as a load error. The increase in body temperature in fever, but not that in exercise, may be blocked by acetylsalicylic acid (124).

Open-loop gain.—An important static characteristic of a controlling system is its open-loop gain. To determine this in a feedback control system with a single feedback loop, the loop is opened and a change is applied to the forward side of the break in the loop, designated the input; the magnitude of the change in the returning side of the break, the output, is observed. The open-loop gain is the ratio of the observed change in output to the induced change in the input. For example, the open-loop gain of the controlling system that regulates hypothalamic temperature might be determined by placing thermodes around the preoptic-hypothalamic tissue, fixing its temperature at two levels, and observing the steady-state change in the returning blood temperature induced by the change in the hypothalamic temperature. If there were no other feedback loops providing input to the controlling system, then the ratio of the change in blood temperature to the change in hypothalamic temperature would be the open-loop gain. In many species these other feedback inputs are important, so that this simple experiment cannot yield a valid estimate of the gain.

On the other hand, if for any species these inputs are shown to be small, then an approximate value for the open-loop gain may be determined by this procedure. Uniformly increasing temperature of the pre- and supraoptic tissue of a cat from 38.6 to 38.9° C with 1 Mc r-f heating caused the rectal temperature at first to fall rapidly from 38.4° C, then more slowly during the first hour until it became steady at 35.8° C during the second hour; air temperature was 18° C (132). From these results, the calculated open-loop gain was 8.7. For two other tests, a 0.2 and a 0.5° C increase in hypothalamic temperature dropped the rectal temperature by 1.6 and 3.8° C for a calculated open-loop gain of 8.0 and 7.6 respectively. These calculations were based on the assumption that the feedback loops derived from core and cutaneous thermoreceptors have negligible effect upon the controlling system. This appears to be approximately so in the cat; however, there is in the record evidence that they are not negligible. When the hypothalamic temperature was increased, panting was at first vigorous. The rate of breathing increased from a control level of 40/min to 220/min; vasodilatation increased the temperature of the ear pinna from 28 to 36° C. Thereafter, however, the breathing rate and ear pinna temperature gradually subsided as the rectal temperature fell so that during the second hour the breathing increased from a control level of 40/min to 220/min; vasodila-24–26° C. These responses suggest that the lower core temperature was fed back to inhibit the response activated by the hypothalamic heating. Without these negative feedback loops, the heat-loss responses should have remained uninhibited throughout the hypothalamic heating, with heat loss balancing with heat production at a still lower temperature.

In a species for which the feedback from core and cutaneous receptors is too important to be neglected, another procedure is required to obtain the open-loop gain. The value of the proportionality constant for evaporative heat loss, α_{EHL}, may be obtained by controlled short-term displacements of the hypothalamic temperature above threshold and measurement of the rates of evaporative heat loss. In a warm environment, the resting heating production or metabolic rate M_0 will equal the heat loss in steady state. Thus,

$$M_0 = K \ (T_{core} - T_{amb}) + EHL_0 + \alpha_{EHL} \ (T_{hypo} - T_{set_{EHL}})$$

where K, the coefficient for nonevaporative heat transfer from core to environment, depends on shape, vasomotor state, air movement, and other factors. With this equation, a small steady-state change in core temperature $(T_{core} - T'_{core})$ may be computed for a small increase in hypothalamic temperature ΔT_{hypo}, on the assumption that $T_{core} = T_{hypo} \geq T_{set_{EHL}}$ and that $T_{set_{EHL}}$ is invariant for a very small change in T_{core} or T_{skin}. From this,

$$K \ (T_{core} - T'_{core}) = \alpha_{EHL} \ \Delta T_{hypo}$$

or by definition,

$$\text{open-loop gain }_{EHL} = (T_{core} - T'_{core})/\Delta T_{hypo} = \alpha_{EHL}/K$$

here designated as the open-loop gain for evaporative heat loss.

Similarly, the steady-state equation for increased metabolism by shivering is

$$M_0 + \alpha_M \ (T_{set_M} - T_{hypo}) = K \ (T_{core} - T_{air}) + EHL_0$$

By similar assumptions, the open-loop gain for shivering becomes

$$\text{open-loop gain}_M = \alpha_M/K$$

Of course, K is not always the same, and will be higher in a hot environment than in a cold one. In a thinly furred dog (Wt = 10 kg, S.A. = 0.51 m²) in a hot environment, $K_{hot} = 2.1$ kcal hr⁻¹ °C⁻¹ whereas in the cold it was equal to 1.3 kcal hr⁻¹ °C⁻¹ or even less if the dog could have curled up (174). With measured values of α_E and α_M for a 10 kg dog (173, 192), open-loop gain$_{EHL}$ $\simeq 3.0 \times 10 \div 2.1 = 14$ and open-loop gain$_M \simeq 1.5 \times 10 \div 1.3 = 12$. Thus, the open-loop gains for these two responses are approximately the same even though the proportionality constant for shivering is only about one-half that for panting.

CHARACTERISTICS OF THE CONTROLLED SYSTEM

The output-forcing functions from the several controllers of the controlling system become, along with the disturbances, the inputs to the controlled system. The transformation of these inputs into the temperatures of the body is extraordinarily complex and cannot be considered in any useful detail in this review. The complex shape of the body which is subject to behavioral modification; the body size; the uneven thickness and quality of insulation external to the skin surface which can be modified by piloerector activity; the variable distribution of blood flow to and from the skin and muscle by way of specialized vascular heat exchangers; the uneven distribution of constant and variable heat-producing organs; the variable physical factors of the thermal environment such as radiation, air or water medium, air or water convection, wet and dry bulb temperatures—all render even the best analysis of the transformation an approximation.

Perhaps the most useful analytical approach has been to create an analog of the physical, anatomical, and physiological characteristics of the body and its environment. With sufficient tampering, adjusting of components, and increase in complexity, the analog can be made to simulate approximately the real body and its environment (59, 60, 103, 154, 239, 341, 348, 366, 391, 392, 397). These analog models, especially of man, have the practical value of predicting the response of the body in an untried stressful exposure. Those who make these models also have another expectation—to gain insight into the nature of the controlling system.

LITERATURE CITED

1. Abrams, R. M., Hammel, H. T. Hypothalamic temperature in unanesthetized albino rats during feeding and sleeping. *Am. J. Physiol.*, **206**, 641–46 (1964)
2. Abrams, R. M., Hammel, H. T. Cyclic variations in hypothalamic temperature in unanesthetized rats. *Ibid.*, **208**, 698–702 (1965)
3. Adams, T. Hypothalamic temperature in the cat during feeding and sleep. *Science*, **139**, 609–10 (1962)
4. Adams, T. Body temperature regulation in the normal and cold-acclimatized cat. *J. Appl. Physiol.*, **18**, 772–77 (1963)
5. Adams, T., Smith, R. E. Effects of chronic local cold exposure on finger temperature responses. *J. Appl. Physiol.*, **17**, 317–22 (1962)
6. Äikäs, E., Karvonen, M. J., Piironen, P., Ruosteenoja, R. Intramuscular, rectal and oesophageal temperature during exercise. *Acta Physiol. Scand.*, **54**, 366–70 (1962)
7. Albers, C. Der Mechanismus des Wärmehechelns beim Hund. I. Die Ventilation und die arteriellen Blutgase während des Wärmehechelns. *Arch. Ges. Physiol.*, **274**, 125–47 (1961)
8. Albers, C. Der Mechanismus des Wärmehechelns beim Hund. II. Der respiratorische Stoffwechsel während des Wärmehechelns. *Ibid.*, 148–65
9. Albers, C. Der Mechanismus des Wärmehechelns beim Hund. IV. Die Wechselwirkung zwischen Blutgasregulation und Temperaturregulation. *Ibid.*, 184–91
10. American Society of Mechanical Engineers. *Terminology for Automatic Control* (Am. Soc. Mech. Eng., New York, 45 pp., 1963)
11. Albert, R. E. Sweat suppression by forced breathing in man. *J. Appl. Physiol.*, **20**, 134–36 (1965)
12. Andersen, H. T., Andersson, B., Gale, C. Central control of cold defense mechanisms and the release of "endopyrogen" in the goat. *Acta Physiol. Scand.*, **54**, 159–74 (1962)
13. Andersen, H. T., Hammel, H. T., Hardy, J. D. Modifications of the febrile response to pyrogen by hypothalamic heating and cooling in the unanesthetized dog. *Acta Physiol. Scand.*, **53**, 247–54 (1961)
14. Andersson, B., Brook, A. H., Ekman,

L. Further studies of the thyroidal response to local cooling of the "heat loss center". *Acta Physiol. Scand.*, **63**, 186–92 (1965)
15. Andersson, B., Brook, A. H., Gale, C. C., Hökfelt, B. The effect of a ganglionic blocking agent on the thermoregulatory response to preoptic cooling. *Acta Physiol. Scand.*, **61**, 393–99 (1964)
16. Andersson, B., Ekman, L., Gale, C. C., Sundsten, J. W. Blocking of the thyroid response to cold by local warming of the preoptic region. *Acta Physiol. Scand.*, **56**, 94–96 (1962)
17. Andersson, B., Ekman, L., Gale, C. C., Sundsten, J. W. Control of thyrotrophic hormone (TSH) secretion by the "heat loss center". *Ibid.*, **59**, 12–33 (1963)
18. Andersson, B., Ekman, L., Hökfelt, B., Jobin, M., Olsson, K., Robertshaw, D. Studies of the importance of the thyroid and the sympathetic system in the defence to cold of the goat. *Acta Physiol. Scand.*, **69**, 111–18 (1967)
19. Andersson, B., Gale, C. C. Role of the CNS in thyroid response to cold in mammals. In *Proc. 2nd Intern. Congr. Endocrinol.*, 495–98 (*Excerpta Med. Intern. Congr. Ser. No. 83*, 1964)
20. Andersson, B., Gale, C. C., Hökfelt, B. Studies of the interaction between neural and hormonal mechanisms in the regulation of body temperature. In *Major Problems in Neuroendocrinology*, 42–61 (Bajusz, E., Jasmin, C., Eds., S. Karger, Basel/New York, 1964)
21. Andersson, B., Gale, C. C., Hökfelt, B., Larsson, B. Acute and chronic effects of preoptic lesions. *Acta Physiol. Scand.*, **65**, 45–60 (1965)
22. Andersson, B., Gale, C. C., Hökfelt, B., Ohga, A. Relation of preoptic temperature to the function of the sympathico-adrenomedullary system and the adrenal cortex. *Acta Physiol. Scand.*, **61**, 182–91 (1963)
23. Andersson, B., Gale, C. C., Ohga, A. Suppression by thyroxine of the thyroidal response to local cooling of the "heat loss center." *Acta Physiol. Scand.*, **59**, 67–73 (1963)
24. Andersson, B., Jobin, M., Olsson, K. Serotonine and temperature control. *Acta Physiol. Scand.*, **67**,

50–56 (1966)

25. Ashby, W. R. Mathematical models and computer analysis of the function of the central nervous system. *Ann. Rev. Physiol.*, **28**, 89–106 (1966)

26. Baldwin, B. A., Ingram, D. L. Effects of cooling the hypothalamus in the pig. *J. Physiol. (London)*, **186**, 72P (1966)

27. Bard, P., Woods, J. Central nervous region essential for endotoxin fever. *Trans. Am. Neurol. Assoc.*, **87**, 37–39 (1962)

28. Bartholomew, G. A. A field study of temperature relations in the Galapagos marine iguana. *Copeia*, **1966 (2)**, 241–50

29. Bartholomew, G. A., Hudson, J. W. Hibernation, estivation, temperature regulation, evaporative water loss, and heart rate of the pigmy possum *Cercaertus nanus*. *Physiol. Zool.*, **35**, 94–107 (1962)

30. Bartholomew, G. A., Hudson, J. W., Howell, T. R. Body temperature, oxygen consumption, evaporative water loss, and heart rate in the poor will. *Condor*, **44**, 117–25 (1962)

31. Bartholomew, G. A., Lasiewski, R. C. Heating and cooling rates, heart rate and simulated diving in the Galapagos marine iguana. *Comp. Biochem. Physiol.*, **16**, 573–82 (1965)

32. Bartholomew, G. A., Leitner, P., Nelson, J. E. Body temperature, oxygen consumption, and heart rate in three species of Australian flying foxes. *Physiol. Zool.*, **37**, 179–98 (1964)

33. Bartholomew, G. A., Tucker, V. A. Control of changes in body temperature, metabolism, and circulation by the agamid lizard. *Amphibolurus barbatus*. *Physiol. Zool.*, **36**, 199–218 (1963)

34. Bartholomew, G. A., Tucker, V. A. Size, body temperature, thermal conductance, oxygen consumption, and heart rate in Australian varanid lizards. *Ibid.*, 341–54

35. Bartholomew, G. A., Tucker, V. A., Lee, A. K. Oxygen consumption, thermal conductance, and heart rate in the Australian skink. *Tiliqua scincoides*. *Copeia*, **1965 (2)**, 169–73 (1965)

36. Bass, D. E. Thermoregulatory and circulatory adjustments during acclimatization to heat in man. In *Temperature: Its Measurement and Control in Science and Industry* (See Ref. 176), 299–305

37. Bass, D. E., Jacobson, E. D. Effects of salicylate on acclimatization to work in the heat. *J. Appl. Physiol.*, **20**, 70–72 (1965)

38. van Beaumont, W., Bullard, R. W. Sweating: its rapid response to muscular work. *Science*, **141**, 643–46 (1963)

39. van Beaumont, W., Bullard, R. W. Non-thermal sweating in exercise. *Fed. Proc.*, **23**, 472 (1964)

40. van Beaumont, W., Bullard, R. W. Sweating exercise stimulation during circulatory arrest. *Science*, **152**, 1521–23 (1966)

41. Belding, H. S., Hertig, B. A. Sweating and body temperatures following abrupt changes in environmental temperature. *J. Appl. Physiol.*, **17**, 103–6 (1962)

42. Belding, H. S., Hertig, B. A., Kraning, K. K. II. Comparison of man's responses to pulsed and unpulsed environmental heat and exercise. *J. Appl. Physiol.*, **21**, 138–42 (1966)

43. Bentley, P. J., Schmidt-Nielsen, K. Cutaneous water loss in reptiles. *Science*, **151**, 1547–48 (1966)

44. Benzinger, T. H. The diminution of thermoregulatory sweating during cold-reception at the skin. *Proc. Natl. Acad. Sci.*, **47**, 1683–88 (1961)

45. Benzinger, T. H. The thermal homeostasis of man. In *Les Concepts de Claude Bernard sur le Milieu Interieur*, 327–79 (Masson, Paris, 423 pp., 1967)

46. Bligh, J. The synchronous discharge of apocrine sweat glands of the Welsh mountain sheep. *Nature*, **189**, 582–83 (1961)

47. Bligh, J. Possible temperature-sensitive elements in or near the vena cava of sheep. *J. Physiol. (London)*, **159**, 85P (1961)

48. Bligh, J. The receptors concerned in the respiratory response to humidity in sheep at high ambient temperature. *Ibid.*, **168**, 747–63 (1963)

49. Bligh, J. Effects on temperature of monoamines injected into the lateral ventricles of sheep. *Ibid.*, **185**, 46P (1966)

50. Bligh, J. The thermosensitivity of the hypothalamus and thermoregulation in mammals. *Biol. Rev.*, **41**, 317–67 (1966)

51. Bligh, J. A thesis concerning the processes of secretion and discharge of sweat. *Environ. Res.*, **1**, 28–45 (1967)

52. Bligh, J., Harthoorn, A. M. Continuous radio telemetric records of the deep body temperature of some unrestrained African mammals under near-natural conditions. *J. Physiol. (London)*, **176**, 145–62 (1965)

53. Bligh, J., Hartley, T. C. The deep body temperature of an unrestrained ostrich *Struthio camelus* recorded continuously by a radio-telemetric technique. *Ibis*, **107**, 104–5 (1965)

54. Bradbury, P. A., Fox, R. H., Goldsmith, R., Hampton, I. F. G. The effect of exercise on temperature regulation. *J. Physiol. (London)*, **171**, 384–96 (1964)

55. Brebner, D. F., Kerslake, D. McK. The time course of the decline in sweating produced by wetting the skin. *J. Physiol. (London)*, **175**, 295–302 (1964)

56. Brebner, D. F., Kerslake, D. McK., Soper, D. G. Some effects of exposure to an environment of saturated air at mouth temperature. *J. Physiol. (London)*, **162**, 244–58 (1962)

57. Brengelmann, G., Patton, H. D. Acute cold exposure and the variable set point model. *Fed. Proc.*, **25**, 1833 (1966)

58. Brockway, J. M., McDonald, J. D., Pullar, J. D. Evaporative heat-loss mechanisms in sheep. *J. Physiol. (London)*, **179**, 554–68 (1965)

59. Brown, A. C. Analog computer simulation of temperature regulation in man. *Rept. AMRL-TDR-63-116*, 1–108 (Aerospace Med. Res. Lab., Wright-Patterson A.F.B., Ohio, 1963)

60. Brown, A. C. Further development of the biothermal analog computer. *Rept. AMRL-TDR-66-167*, 1–58 (Aerospace Med. Res. Lab., Wright-Patterson A.F.B., Ohio, 1966)

61. Brown, W. K., Sargent, F. II. Hidromeiosis. *Arch. Environ. Health*, **11**, 442–53 (1965)

62. Brück, K., Gallmeier, H., Wünnenberg, W. Einfluss der Temperatur des vorderen Hypothalamus auf die zitterfrei Thermogenese des Meerschweinchens. *Arch. Ges. Physiol.*, **294**, 86 (1967)

63. Brück, K., Wünnenberg, B. Untersuchungen über die Bedeutung des multilokularen Fettgewebes für die Thermogenese des neugeborenen Meerschweinchens. *Arch. Ges. Physiol.*, **283**, 1–16 (1965)

64. Brück, K., Wünnenberg, B. Influence of ambient temperature in the process of replacement of nonshivering by shivering thermogenesis during postnatal development. *Fed. Proc.*, **25**, 1332–37 (1966)

65. Brück, K., Wünnenberg, W. Beziehung zwischen Thermogenese im "braunen" Fettgewebe, Temperatur im cervicalen Anteil des Vertebrakanals und Kältezittern. *Arch. Ges. Physiol.*, **290**, 167–83 (1966)

66. Brück, K., Wünnenberg, W. Die Steuerung des Kältezitterns beim Meerschweinchen. *Ibid.*, **293**, 215–25 (1967)

67. Brück, K., Wünnenberg, W. Eine kälteadaptative Modifikation: Senkung den Schwellentemperaturen für Kältezittern. *Ibid.*, 226–35

68. Burton, A. C. The pattern of response to cold in animals and the evolution of homeothermy. In *Temperature: Its Measurement and Control in Science and Industry* (See Ref. 176), 363–71

68a. Buskirk, E. R., Thompson, R. H., Rubenstein, M., Wolff, S. M. Heat exchange in men and women following intravenous injection of endotoxin. *J. Appl. Physiol.*, **19**, 907–13 (1964)

69. Cabanac, M. *Démonstration expérimentale de l'existence dans l'hypothalamus d'une sensibilité au froid*, 1–127 (Doctoral thesis, Univ. Lyon Med. School, 1961)

70. Cabanac, M., Chatonnet, J., Duclaux, R. Influence de la température centrale sur le choix de l'ambiance thermique chez le chien. *J. Physiol. (Paris)*, **57**, 574–75 (1965)

71. Cabanac, M., Chatonnet, J., Philipot, R. Les conditions de températures cérébrale et cutanée moyènnes pour l'apparition du frisson thermique chez le chien. *Compt. Rend. Acad. Sci.*, **260**, 680–83 (1965)

72. Cabanac, M., Duclaux, R., Chatonnet, J. Influence d'une élévation passive de la température interne sur le comportement thermorégulateur

du chien. *J. Physiol. (Paris)*, **58**, 214 (1966)

72a. Cabanac, M., Hammel, H. T., Hardy, J. D. Temperature sensitive neurons in a reptilian brain. *Physiologist*, **10**, 137 (1967)

73. Cabanac, M., Hardy, J. D. Effect of temperature and pyrogen on unit activity in the rabbit's brain stem. *Fed. Proc.*, **26**, 1672 (1967)

74. Cage, G. M., Dobson, R. L. Effect of a steroid, diuretics and pitressin on sodium excretion by the sweat gland. *Fed. Proc.*, **24**, 280 (1965)

75. Cage, G. W., Dobson, R. L. Sodium secretion and reabsorption in the human eccrine sweat gland. *J. Clin. Invest.*, **44**, 1270–76 (1965)

76. Carlisle, H. J. Behavioral significance of hypothalamic temperature-sensitive cells. *Nature*, **209**, 1324–25 (1966)

77. Chaffee, R. R. J., Allen, J. R., Brewer, M., Horvath, S. M., Mason, C., Smith, R. E. Cellular physiology of cold- and heat-exposed squirrel monkeys (*Saimiri sciurea*). *J. Appl. Physiol.*, **21**, 151–57 (1966)

78. Chaffee, R. R. J., Allen, J. R., Cassuto, Y., Smith, R. E. Biochemistry of brown fat and liver of cold-acclimated hamsters. *Am. J. Physiol.*, **207**, 1211–14 (1964)

78a. Chaffee, R. R. J., Horvath, S. M., Smith, R. E., Welsh, R. S. Studies on the cellular biochemistry and organ mass of cold- and heat-acclimated monkeys. *Fed. Proc.*, **25**, 1177–81 (1966)

79. Chaffee, R. R. J., Pengelley, E. T., Allen, J. R., Smith, R. E. Biochemistry of the brown fat and liver of hibernating golden-mantled ground squirrels (Citellus lateralis). *Can. J. Physiol. Pharmacol.*, **44**, 217–23 (1966)

80. Chai, C. Y., Mu, J. Y., Brobeck, J. R. Cardiovascular and respiratory responses from local heating of medulla oblongata. *Am. J. Physiol.*, **209**, 301–6 (1965)

81. Chatonnet, J. Nervous control of metabolism. *Fed. Proc.*, **22**, 729–31 (1963)

82. Chatonnet, J., Cabanac, M. The perception of thermal comfort. *Intern. J. Biometeorol.*, **9**, 183–93 (1965)

83. Chatonnet, J., Cabanac, M., Jeddi, E. Le niveau de réglage de la temperature interne est-il modifié par le travail musculaire? *Compt. Rend. Soc. Biol.*, **159**, 1576–78 (1965)

84. Chatonnet, J., Cabanac, M., Mottaz, M. Les conditions de températures cérébrale et cutanée moyenne pour l'apparition de la polypnée thermique chez le chien. *Compt. Rend. Soc. Biol.*, **58**, 1354–56 (1964)

85. Chew, R. M., Dammann, A. E. Evaporative water loss of small vertebrates, as measured with an infrared analyzer. *Science*, **133**, 384–85 (1961)

86. Chowers, I., Hammel, H. T., Eisenman, J., Abrams, R. M., McCann, S. M. Comparison of effect of environmental and pre-optic heating and pyrogen on plasma cortisol. *Am. J. Physiol.*, **210**, 606–10 (1966)

87. Chowers, I., Hammel, H. T., Strømme, S. B., McCann, S. M. Comparison of effect of environmental and preoptic cooling on plasma cortisol levels. *Am. J. Physiol.*, **207**, 577–82 (1964)

88. Colin, J., Houdas, Y. Initiation of sweating in man after abrupt rise in environmental temperature. *J. Appl. Physiol.*, **20**, 984–90 (1965)

89. Collins, K. J., Crockford, G. W., Weiner, J. S. Sweat-gland training by drugs and thermal stress. *Arch. Environ. Health*, **11**, 407–22 (1965)

90. Collins, K. J., Weiner, J. S. Observations on arm-bag suppression of sweating and its relationship to thermal sweat-gland fatigue. *J. Physiol. (London)*, **161**, 538–56 (1962)

91. Conn, J. W. Aldosteronism in man. *J. Am. Med. Assoc.*, **183**, 775–81 (1963)

92. Cooper, K. E. Temperature regulation and hypothalamus. *Brit. Med. Bull.* **22**, 238–42 (1966)

93. Cooper, K. E., Cranston, W. I., Honour, A. J. Effects of intraventricular and intrahypothalamic injection of nor-adrenaline and 5-HT on body temperature in conscious rabbits. *J. Physiol. (London)*, **181**, 852–64 (1965)

94. Cooper, K. E., Cranston, W. I., Snell, E. S. Temperature regulation during fever in man. *Clin. Sci.*, **27**, 345–56 (1964)

95. Cooper, K. E., Johnson, R. H., Spalding, J. M. K. The effects of

central body and trunk skin temperatures on the reflex vasodilatation in the hand. *J. Physiol. (London)*, **174**, 46–54 (1964)

96. Cowles, R. B. Fur and feathers; a result of high temperature? *Science*, **103**, 74–75 (1946)

97. Cowles, R. B. Possible origin of dermal temperature regulation. *Evolution*, **12**, 347–57 (1958)

98. Cowles, R. B., Bogert, C. M. A preliminary study of the thermal requirements of desert reptiles. *Bull. Am. Mus. Nat. Hist.*, **83**, 261–96 (1944)

99. Crawford, E. C., Jr. Mechanical aspects of panting in dogs. *J. Appl. Physiol.*, **17**, 249–51 (1962)

100. Crawford, E. C., Jr., Schmidt-Nielsen, K. Temperature regulation in the ostrich. *Fed. Proc.*, **24**, 347 (1965)

101. Crawford, E. C., Jr., Schmidt-Nielsen, K. Temperature regulation and evaporative cooling in the ostrich. *Am. J. Physiol.*, **212**, 347–53 (1967)

102. Crockford, G. W., Hellon, R. F., Parkhouse, J. Thermal vasomotor responses in human skin mediated by local mechanisms. *J. Physiol. (London)*, **161**, 10–20 (1962)

103. Crosbie, R. J., Hardy, J. D., Fessenden, E. Electrical analog simulation of temperature regulation in man. In *Temperature: Its Measurement and Control in Science and Industry* (See Ref. 176), 627–35

104. Cross, B. A., Silver, I. A. Electrophysiological studies on the hypothalamus. *Brit. Med. Bull.*, **22**, 254–60 (1966)

105. Cunningham, D., Hardy, J. D. Unit activity in the preoptic region following intraventricular injection of serotonin and epinephrine. *Physiologist*, **8**, 144 (1965)

106. Cunningham, D., Stolwijk, J. A. J., Murakami, N., Hardy, J. D. Responses of neurons in the preoptic area to temperature, serotonin and epinephrine. *Am. J. Physiol.* (In press)

107. Davies, M. On body size and tissue respiration. *J. Cellular Comp. Physiol.*, **57**, 135–47 (1961)

108. Dawkins, M. J. R., Hull, D. Brown adipose tissue and the response of new-born rabbits to cold. *J. Physiol. (London)*, **172**, 216–38 (1964)

109. Dawkins, M. J. R., Scopes, J. W. Non-shivering thermogenesis and brown adipose tissue in the human new-born infant. *Nature*, **206**, 201–2 (1965)

110. Dawson, W. R., Templeton, J. R. Physiological responses to temperature in the lizard *Crotophytus collaris*. Physiol. Zool., **36**, 219–36 (1963)

111. Dawson, W. R., Templeton, J. R. Physiological response to temperature in the alligator lizard *Gerrhonotus multicarnatus*. Ecology, **47**, 759–65 (1966)

112. Dawson, W. R., Tordoff, H. B. Relation of oxygen consumption to temperature in the red and white-winged crossbills. *Auk*, **81**, 26–35 (1964)

113. Dawson, W. W. Thermal stimulation of experimentally vasoconstricted human skin. *Perceptual Motor Skills*, **19**, 775–88 (1964)

114. DeWitt, C. B. Precision of thermoregulation and its relation to environmental factors in the desert iguana, *Dipsosaurus dorsalis*. *Physiol. Zool.*, **40**, 49–66 (1967)

115. Dill, D. B., Ed. *Handbook of Physiology, Sect. IV, Adaptation to the Environment* (Am. Physiol. Soc., Wash., D.C., 1056 pp., 1964)

116. Dobson, R. L. The effect of repeated episodes of profuse sweating on the human eccrine sweat glands. *J. Invest. Dermatol.*, **35**, 195–98 (1960)

117. Dobson, R. L. The human eccrine sweat gland. *Arch. Environ. Health*, **11**, 423–29 (1965)

118. Dobson, R. L., Abele, D. C. The correlation of structure and function in the human eccrine sweat gland. *Trans. Assoc. Am. Physicians*, **75**, 242–52 (1962)

119. Dobson, R. L., Abele, D. C., Hale, D. M. The effect of high and low salt intake and repeated episodes of sweating on the human eccrine sweat gland. *J. Invest. Dermatol.*, **36**, 327–35 (1961)

120. Donhoffer, S. The regulation of energy metabolism and van't Hoff's rule in the homeotherm animal. *Helgoländer Wiss. Meeresuntersuch.*, **14**, 541–58 (1966)

121. Donhoffer, S., Sardy, F., Szegvari, G. Brown adipose tissue and thermoregulatory heat production

in the rat. *Nature*, **203**, 765–66 (1964)

122. Donhoffer, S., Szelenyi, Z. The role of brown adipose tissue in thermoregulatory heat production in the non cold-adapted adult rat, guinea pig, ground squirrel and in the young rabbit. *Acta Physiol. (Hung.)*, **28**, 349–61 (1965)

123. Downey, J. A., Chiodi, H. P., Darling, R. C. Central temperature regulation in the spinal man. *J. Appl. Physiol.*, **22**, 91–94 (1967)

124. Downey, J. A., Darling, R. C. Effect of salicylates on elevation of body temperature during exercise. *J. Appl. Physiol.*, **17**, 323–25 (1962)

125. Downey, J. A., Darling, R. C. Effects of salicylates on exercise metabolism. *Ibid.*, 665–68

126. Downey, J. A., Darling, R. C. Thermotherapy and thermoregulation. *Intern. Rev. Phys. Med. Rehab.*, **43**, 265–76 (1964)

127. Downey, J. A., Mottram, R. F., Pickering, G. W. The location by regional cooling of central temperature receptors in the conscious rabbit. *J. Physiol. (London)*, **170**, 415–41 (1964)

128. Eisenman, J. S. Thermosensitivity of septal and preoptic neurons in cats. *Physiologist*, **8**, 158 (1965)

128a. Eisenman, J. S. Pyrogen induced changes in thermo-responsiveness of septal, preoptic and hypothalamic neurons. *Ibid.*, **10**, 160 (1967)

129. Eisenman, J. S., Jackson, D. C. Thermal response patterns of septal and preoptic neurons in cats. *Exptl. Neurol.* (In press) (1967)

130. El Hawary, M. B. E., Feldberg, W., Lotti, V. J. Monoamine oxidase inhibition: effect on 5-hydroxytryptamine output from perfused third ventricle and body temperature. *J. Physiol. (London)*, **188**, 131–40 (1967)

131. Euler, C. von. Physiology and pharmacology of temperature regulation. *Pharmacol. Rev.*, **13**, 361–98 (1961)

132. Euler, C. von. The gain of the hypothalamic temperature regulating mechanisms. In *Progr. Brain Res.*, **5**, *Lectures on the Diencephalon*, 127–31 (1964)

133. Evans, C. L., Smith, D. F. G. Sweating responses in the horse. *Proc. Roy. Soc. B*, **145**, 61–83 (1956)

134. Fay, F. H., Ray, C. The influence of climate on the distribution of walruses, *Odobenus rosmarus* Linnaeus. I. Evidence from thermoregulatory behavior. *Zoologica* (In press) (1967)

135. Feldberg, W. A new concept of temperature control in the hypothalamus. *Proc. Roy. Soc. Med.*, **58**, 395–404 (1965)

136. Feldberg, W., Hellon, R. F., Myers, R. D. Effects on temperature of nonoamines injected into the cerebral ventricals of unanesthetized dogs. *J. Physiol. (London)*, **186**, 416–23 (1966)

137. Feldberg, W., Lotti, V. J. Body temperature response in cats and rabbits to the monoamine oxidase inhibitor tranylcypromine. *J. Physiol. (London)*, **190**, 203–20 (1967)

138. Feldberg, W., Myers, R. D. Effects of temperature of amines injected into the cerebral ventricles. A new concept of temperature regulation. *J. Physiol. (London)*, **173**, 226–37 (1964)

139. Feldberg, W., Myers, R. D. Temperature changes produced by amines injected into the cerebral ventricles during anesthesia. *Ibid.*, **175**, 464–78

140. Feldberg, W., Myers, R. D. Changes in temperature produced by microinjections of amines into the anterior hypothalamus of cats. *Ibid.*, **177**, 239–45 (1965)

141. Feldberg, W., Myers, R. D. Hypothermia produced by chloralose acting on the hypothalamus. *Ibid.*, **179**, 509–517

142. Feldberg, W., Myers, R. D. Appearance of 5-hydroxytryptamine and an unidentified pharmacologically active lipid acid in effluent from perfused cerebral ventricles. *Ibid.*, **184**, 837–55 (1965)

143. Findlay, J. D., Ingram, D. L. Brain temperature as a factor in the control of thermal polypnea in the ox (Bos taurus). *J. Physiol. (London)*, **155**, 72–85 (1961)

144. Findlay, J. D., Robertshaw, D. The role of the sympatho-adrenal system in the control of sweating in the ox (*Bos taurus*). *J. Physiol. (London)*, **179**, 285–97 (1965)

145. Folkow, B., Fox, R. H., Krog,

J., Odelram, H., Thorén, O. Studies on the reactions of the cutaneous vessels to cold exposure. *Acta Physiol. Scand.*, **58**, 342–54 (1963)

146. Forster, R. E., Ferguson, T. B. Relationship between hypothalamic temperature and thermoregulatory effectors in unanesthetized cat. *Am. J. Physiol.*, **169**, 255–61 (1952)

147. Fox, R. H., Goldsmith, R., Hampton, I. F. G., Lewis, H. E. The nature of the increase in sweating capacity produced by heat acclimatization. *J. Physiol. (London)*, **171**, 368–76 (1964)

148. Fox, R. H., Goldsmith, R., Kidd, D. J., Lewis, H. E. Acclimatization to heat in man by controlled elevation of body temperature. *J. Physiol. (London)*, **166**, 530–47 (1963)

149. Fox, R. H., Goldsmith, R., Kidd, D. J., Lewis, H. E. Blood flow and other thermoregulatory changes with acclimatization to heat. *Ibid.*, 548–62

150. Fox, R. H., Wyatt, H. T. Cold induced vasodilatation in various areas of the body surface of man. *J. Physiol. (London)*, **162**, 289–97 (1962)

151. Fry, F. E. J. Animals in aquatic environments: Fishes. In: *Handbook of Physiology, Sect. IV, Adaptation to the Environment,* (See Ref. 115), 715–28

152. Fusco, M. M., Hardy, J. D., Hammel, H. T. Interaction of central and peripheral factors in physiological temperature regulation. *Am. J. Physiol.*, **200**, 572–80 (1961)

153. Gagge, A. P. Comfort: New concepts and applications. *Building Res.*, July-Aug., 8 pp. (1966)

154. Gagge, A. P., Stolwijk, J. A. J., Hardy, J. D. A novel approach to measurement of man's heat exchange with a complex radiant environment. *Aerospace Med.*, **36**, 431–35 (1965)

155. Gagge, A. P., Stolwijk, J. A. J., Hardy, J. D. Comfort and thermal sensations and associated physiological responses at various ambient temperatures. *Environ. Res.*, **1**, 1–20 (1967)

156. Gale, C. C., Jobin, M. Further studies on CNS-Endocrine responses to hypothalamic cooling in unanesthe-tized baboons. *Fed. Proc.*, **26**, 3 (1967)

157. Gale, C. C., Ruch, T. C. CNS-Endocrine response to hypothalamic cooling in unanesthetized baboons. *Fed. Proc.*, **25**, 123 (1966)

158. Garden, J. W., Wilson, I. D., Rasch, P. J. Acclimatization of healthy young adult males to a hot-wet environment. *J. Appl. Physiol.*, **21**, 665–69 (1966)

159. Gartside, I. B., Lippold, O. C. J. The production of persistent changes in the level of neuronal activity by brief local cooling of the cerebral cortex of the rat. *J. Physiol. (London)*, **189**, 475–87 (1967)

160. Geschickter, E. H., Andrews, P. A., Bullard, R. W. Nocturnal body temperature regulation in man: a rationale for sweating in sleep. *J. Appl. Physiol.*, **21**, 623–30 (1966)

161. Grant, R. T. Vasodilatation and body warming in the rat. *J. Physiol. (London)*, **167**, 311–17 (1963)

162. Grimby, G. Exercise in man during pyrogen-induced fever. *Scand. J. Clin. Lab. Invest.*, **14**, Suppl. 67, 1–112 (1962)

163. Grodins, F. S. *Control Theory and Biological Systems* (Columbia Univ. Press, New York, 205 pp., 1963)

164. Hainsworth, F. R., Epstein, A. N. Necessity of saliva spreading in rats for body temperature regulation in the heat. *Fed. Proc.*, **26**, 599 (1966)

165. Hales, J. R. S., Webster, M. E. D. Respiratory function during thermal tachypnoea in sheep. *J. Physiol. (London)*, **190**, 241–60 (1967)

166. Hallwachs, O., Thauer, R., Usinger, W. Die Bedeutung der tiefen Körpertemperatur für die Auslösung der chemischen Temperaturregulation. *Arch. Ges. Physiol.*, **274**, 115–24 (1961)

167. Hamilton, C. L. Hypothalamic temperature records of a monkey. *Soc. Exptl. Biol. Med.*, **112**, 55–57 (1963)

168. Hammel, H. T. The regulator of body temperature. *Brody Memorial Lecture VI, Univ. of Missouri Spec. Rept. 73,* 1–34 (1966)

169. Hammel, H. T., Caldwell, F. T., Jr., Abrams, R. M. Regulation of body temperature in the blue-tongued

lizard. *Science,* **156,** 1260–62 (1967)

170. Hammel, H. T., Dawson, T. J., Abrams, R. M., Andersen, H. T. Total calorimetric measurements on *Citellus lateralis* in hibernation. *Physiol. Zool.* (In press) (1967)

171. Hammel, H. T., Houpt, T. R., Lange Andersen, K., Skenneberg, S. Thermal and metabolic measurements on a reindeer at rest and in exercise. *Rept. AAL-TDR-61-54* (Arctic Aeromed. Lab., Fort Wainwright, Alaska, 1962)

172. Hammel, H. T., Jackson, D. C., Stolwijk, J. A. J., Hardy, J. D., Strømme, S. B. Temperature regulation by hypothalamic proportional control with adjustable set temperature. *J. Appl. Physiol.,* **18,** 1146–54 (1963)

173. Hammel, H. T., Strømme, S. B., Cornew, R. W. Proportionality constant for hypothalamic proportional control of metabolism in unanesthetized dog. *Life Sci.,* **12,** 933–47 (1963)

174. Hammel, H. T., Wyndham, C. H., Hardy, J. D. Heat production and heat loss in the dog at 8–36°C environmental temperature. *Am. J. Physiol.,* **194,** 99–108 (1958)

175. Hardy, J. D. Physiology of temperature regulation. *Physiol. Rev.,* **41,** 521–606 (1961)

176. Hardy, J. D., Ed. *Temperature: Its Measurement and Control in Science and Industry,* **3,** Part 3 (Hardy, J. D., Ed., Reinhold, New York, 683 pp., 1963)

177. Hardy, J. D. Central and peripheral factors in physiological temperature regulation. In *Les Concepts de Claude Bernard sur le Milieu Interieur,* 247–83 (Masson, Paris, 423 pp., 1967)

178. Hardy, J. D., Hellon, R. F., Sutherland, K. Temperature-sensitive neurones in the dog's hypothalamus. *J. Physiol. (London),* **175,** 242–53 (1964)

179. Hardy, J. D., Stolwijk, J. A. J. Partitional calorimetric studies of man during exposures to thermal transients. *J. Appl. Physiol.,* **21,** 1799–1806 (1966)

180. Hart, J. S. Seasonal acclimatization in four species of small wild birds. *Physiol. Zool.* **35,** 224–36 (1962)

181. Hart, J. S. Physiological responses to cold in non-hibernating homeo-

therms. In: *Temperature: Its Measurement and Control in Science and Industry* (See Ref. 176), 373–406

182. Hart, J. S. Insulative and metabolic adaptations to cold in vertebrates. *Symp. Soc. Exptl. Biol.,* **18,** 31–48 (1964)

183. Haslag, W. M., Hertzman, A. B. Temperature regulation in young women. *J. Appl. Physiol.,* **20,** 1283–88 (1965)

183a. Hayashi, H., Austin, G. Temperature effects on neuronal membrane potentials. *Physiologist,* **10,** 198 (1967)

184. Hayward, J. N. Diuretic response to hypothalamic cooling in the monkey. *Fed. Proc.,* **26,** 555 (1967)

185. Hayward, J. S., Ball, E. G. Quantitative aspects of brown adipose tissue thermogenesis during arousal from hibernation. *Biol. Bull.,* **131,** 94–103 (1966)

186. Heath. J. E. Temperature-independent morning emergence in lizards of the genus *Phrynosoma. Science,* **138,** 891–92 (1962)

187. Heath, J. E. Temperature fluctuation in the turkey vulture. *Condor,* **64,** 234–35 (1962)

188. Heath, J. E. Reptilian thermoregulation: evaluation of field studies. *Science,* **146,** 784–85 (1964)

189. Heath, J. E. Temperature regulation and diurnal activity in horned lizards. *Univ. Calif. Publ. Zool.,* **64,** 97–129 (1965)

190. Heath, J. E. Reptilian thermoregulation. *Science,* **148,** 1251 (1965)

191. Hellstrøm, B. Local effects of acclimatization to cold in man. *Norwegian Monograph on Medical Science* (Universitets Forlaget, 156 pp., 1965)

192. Hellstrøm, B., Hammel, H. T. Some characteristics of temperature regulation in the unanesthetized dog. *Am. J. Physiol.,* **213,** 547–56 (1967)

193. Hemingway, A. Shivering. *Physiol. Rev.,* **43,** 397–422 (1963)

194. Hemingway, A., Robinson, R., Hemingway, C., Wall, J. Cutaneous and brain temperatures related to respiratory metabolism of the sheep. *J. Appl. Physiol.,* **21,** 1223–27 (1966)

195. Hensel, H. Electro physiology of thermosensitive nerve endings. In

Temperature: Its Measurement and Control in Science and Industry (See Ref. 176), 191–98

196. Hensel, H., Boman, K. K. A. Afferent impulses in cutaneous sensory nerves in human subjects. *J. Neurophysiol.*, **23**, 564–78 (1960)

197. Hensel, H., Iggo, A., Witt, I. A quantitative study of sensitive cutaneous thermoreceptors with C afferent fibers. *J. Physiol. (London)*, **153**, 113–26 (1960)

198. Herreid, C. F. II. Temperature regulation, temperature preference and tolerance, and metabolism of young and adult free-tailed bats. *Physiol. Zool.*, **40**, 1–22 (1967)

199. Herreid, C. F. II. Schmidt-Nielsen, K. Oxygen consumption, temperature, and water loss in bats from different environments. *Am. J. Physiol.*, **211**, 1108–12 (1966)

200. Hertig, B. A., Belding, H. S., Kraning, K. K., Batterton, D. L., Smith, C. R., Sargent, F. II. Artificial acclimatization of women in heat. *J. Appl. Physiol.*, **18**, 283–86 (1963)

201. Hertig, B. A., Riedesel, M. L., Belding, H. S. Sweating in hot baths. *J. Appl. Physiol.*, **16**, 647–51 (1961)

202. Hertzman, A. B. Regulation of cutaneous circulation during body heating. In *Temperature: Its Measurement and Control in Science and Industry* (See Ref. 176), 559–70

203. Hildes, J. A. Sleep and muscle activity during a night of moderate cold exposure. Part V. *Acta Univ. Lund II*, No. 14, 1–10 (1966)

204. Hildwein, G. Evolution saisonniere de la thermoregulation chez le tenrec (*Centetes ecaudatus*). *Compt. Rend. Soc. Biol.*, **158**, 1137–39 (1964)

205. Hrishikesh, J. Energy metabolism in hypnotic trance and sleep. *J. Appl. Physiol.*, **20**, 308–10 (1965)

206. Hudson, J. W. Temperature regulation in the round-tailed ground squirrel *Citellus tereticaudus*. *Ann. Acad. Sci. Fennicae, A4*, **71**/15, 219–33 (1964)

207. Hudson, J. W. Temperature regulation and torpidity in the pygmy mouse, *Baiomys Taylori*. *Physiol. Zool.*, **38**, 243–54 (1965)

208. Hudson, J. W., Bartholomew, G. A.

Terrestial animals in dry heat: estivators. In *Handbook of Physiology, Sect. IV, Adaptation to the Environment* (See Ref. 115), 541–50

209. Hudson, J. W., Bertram, F. W. Physiological responses to temperature in the ground skink, *Lygosoma laterale*. *Physiol. Zool.*, **39**, 21–29 (1966)

210. Hudson, J. W., Kimzey, S. L. Temperature regulation and metabolic rhythms in populations of the house sparrow *Passer domesticus*. *Comp. Biochem. Physiol.*, **17**, 203–17 (1966)

211. Hull, D., Segall, M. M. The contribution of brown adipose tissue to heat production in the new-born rabbit. *J. Physiol. (London)*, **181**, 449–57 (1965)

212. Hull, D., Segall, M. M. Sympathetic nervous control of brown adipose tissue and heat production in the new-born rabbit. *Ibid.*, 458–67

213. Hull, D., Segall, M. M. Heat production in the new-born rabbit and the fat content of the brown adipose tissue. *Ibid.*, 468–77

214. Hutchison, V. H., Dowling, H. G., Vinegar, A. Thermoregulation in a brooding female Indian python, *Python molurus bivittatus*. *Science*, **151**, 694–96 (1966)

215. Iggo, A. Cutaneous heat and cold receptors with slowly conducting (C) afferent fibres. *Quart. J. Exptl. Physiol*, **44**, 362–70 (1959)

216. Iggo, A. New specific structures in hairy skin. *Acta Neuroveg.*, **24**, 175–80 (1963)

217. Iggo, A. An electrophysiological analysis of afferent fibers in primate skin. *Ibid.*, 225–40

218. Iggo, A. Temperature discrimination in the skin. *Nature*, **204**, 481–83 (1964)

219. Iggo, A. The peripheral mechanisms of cutaneous sensation. In *Studies in Physiology*, 92–100 (Curtis, D. R., McIntyre, A. K., Eds., Springer-Verlag, Berlin, 276 pp., 1965)

220. Ingram, D. L. Stimulation of cutaneous glands in the pig. *J. Comp. Pathol.*, **77**, 93–98 (1967)

221. Ingram, D. L., McLean, J. A., Whittow, G. C. Increase of evaporative loss of water from the skin of the ox in response to local heating of

the hypothalamus. *Nature,* **191,** 81–82 (1961)

222. Ingram, D. L., McLean, J. A., Whittow, G. C. The effect of heating the hypothalamus and the skin on the rate of moisture vaporization from the skin of the ox (*Bos taurus*). *J. Physiol. (London),* **169,** 394–403 (1963)

223. Ingram, D. L., Whittow, G. C. The effect of heating the hypothalamus on respiration in the ox (*Bos taurus*). *J. Physiol. (London),* **163,** 200–10 (1962)

224. Ingram, D. L., Whittow, G. C. Changes of arterial blood pressure and heart rate in the ox (*Bos taurus*) with changes of body temperature. *Ibid.,* **168,** 736–46 (1963)

225. Iriki, M., Meurer, K. Der Einfluss der Vagusausschaltung auf die Temperaturregulation bei innerer Kühlung. *Arch. Ges. Physiol.,* **283,** 203–12 (1965)

226. Iriuchijima, J., Zotterman, Y. Specificity of afferent cutaneous C fibers in mammals. *Acta Physiol. Scand.,* **49,** 267–78 (1960)

227. Irving, L. Terrestial animals in cold : birds and mammals. In *Handbook of Physiology, Sect. IV, Adaptation to the Environment* (See Ref. 115), 361–77

228. Irving, L., Peyton, L. J., Bahn, C. H., Peterson, R. S. Regulation of temperature in fur seals. *Physiol. Zool.,* **35,** 275–84 (1962)

229. Jackson, D. C. *Set point temperature as a factor in temperature regulation in the exercising dog* (Ph.D. thesis, Univ. of Pennsylvania, Philadelphia, Pa., 1963)

230. Jackson, D. C., Hammel, H. T. Hypothalamic "set" temperature decreased in exercising dog. *Life Sci.,* **8,** 554–63 (1963)

231. Jackson, D. L. A hypothalamic region responsive to localized injection of pyrogens. *J. Neurophysiol.,* **30,** 586–602 (1967)

232. Jacobson, E. D., Bass, D. E. Effects of sodium salicylate on physiological responses to work in heat. *J. Appl. Physiol.,* **19,** 33–36 (1964)

233. Jacobson, F. H. Hypothalamic site of the metabolic reduction by pentobarbital. *Fed. Proc.,* **25,** 515 (1966)

234. Jacobson, F. H. "Warmth response" evoked by injections of serotonin. *Ibid.,* **26,** 555 (1967)

235. Jacobson, F. H., Squires, R. D. Effect of preoptic lesions on oxygen consumption of the cat. *Fed. Proc.,* **22,** 223 (1963)

236. Jacobson, F. H., Squires, R. D. Thermoregulatory responses to varied preoptic temperature during heat and cold exposure. *Ibid.,* **23,** 566 (1964)

237. Jacobson, F. H., Squires, R. D. Decrease of metabolic rate by preoptic lesions as cause of hypothermia in cats. *Rept. NADA-MR-6605* (U.S. Naval Air Develop. Center, Johnsville, Pa., 1966)

238. Jacobson, F. H., Squires, R. D. Decrease of metabolic rate in chronically hypothermic cats with preoptic lesions. *Rept. NADA-MR-6616* (U.S. Naval Air Develop. Center, Johnsville, Pa., 1966)

239. James, E. W., Jr., Smith, P. E. II, Broucha, L. Analog simulation of the thermoregulatory system of men at work. *Fed. Proc.,* **22,** 284 (1963)

240. Jansky, L. Adaptability of heat production mechanisms in homeotherms. *Acta Univ. Carolinae-Biol.,* **1,** 1–91 (1965)

241. Jansky, L., Hart, J. S. Participation of skeletal muscle and kidney during nonshivering thermogenesis in cold acclimated rats. *Can. J. Biochem. Physiol.,* **41,** 953–64 (1963)

242. Joel, C. D. The physiological role of brown adipose tissue. In : *Handbook of Physiology, Sect. V, Adipose Tissue,* 59–85 (Renold, A. E., Cahill, G. F., Jr., Eds., Am. Physiol. Soc., Washington, D.C., 824 pp., 1965)

243. Joel, C. D., Treble, D. E., Ball, E. G. On a major role for brown adipose tissue in heat production during arousal from hibernation. *Fed. Proc.,* **23,** 271 (1964)

244. Johansen, K. Heat exchange through the skin in the tail of the muskrat (*Ondatra zibethica*). *Fed. Proc.,* **20,** 110 (1961)

245. Johansen, K. Temperature regulation in the nine-banded armadillo (*Dasypus novemcinctus mexicanus*). *Physiol. Zool.,* **34,** 126–44 (1961)

246. Johnson, R. H., Spalding, J. M. K. The role of a central temperature

receptor in shivering in man. *J. Physiol. (London)*, **184**, 733–40 (1966)

247. Johnson, R. H., Smith, A. C., Spalding, J. M. K. Oxygen consumption of paralyzed men exposed to cold. *J. Physiol. (London)*, **169**, 584–91 (1963)

248. Kahl, M. P. Thermoregulation in the wood stork, with special reference to the role of the legs. *Physiol. Zool.*, **36**, 141–52 (1963)

249. Kappey, F., Albers, C. Der Einfluss der relativen Feuchte auf die Auslösung des Hechelas beim-wachen Hund. *Arch. Ges. Physiol.*, **278**, 262–72 (1963)

250. Kayser, C., Heusner, A. A. Le rythme nycthéméral de la dépense d'énergie. Étude de physiologie comparée. *J. Physiol. (Paris)*, **59**, 3–116 (1967)

251. Keller, A. D., McClaskey, E. B. Localization, by the brain slicing method, of the level or levels of the cephalic brain stem upon which effective heat dissipation is dependent. *Am. J. Phys. Med.*, **43**, 181–213 (1964)

252. Kenshalo, D. R. The temperature sensitivity of furred skin of cats. *J. Physiol. (London)*, **172**, 439–48 (1964)

253. Kenshalo, D. R., Duncan, D. G., Weymark, C. Thresholds for thermal stimulation of the inner thigh, foot pad, and face of cats. *J. Comp. Physiol. Psychol.*, **63**, 133–38 (1967)

254. Kenshalo, D. R., Nafe, J. P. A quantitative theory of feeling—1960. *Psychol. Rev.*, **69**, 17–33 (1962)

255. Kenshalo, D. R., Nafe, J. P. Cutaneous vascular system as a model temperature receptor. *Perceptual Motor Skills*, **17**, 257–58 (1963)

256. Kenshalo, D. R., Nafe, J. P. The peripheral basis of temperature sensitivity in man. In *Temperature: Its Measurement and Control in Science and Industry* (See Ref. 176), 231–38

257. Kenshalo, D. R., Nafe, J. P., Brooks, B. Variations in thermal sensitivity. *Science*, **134**, 104–5 (1961)

258. Kimura, S., Aoki, T. Functional activity of the apocrine sweat gland in the goat. *Tohoku J. Exptl. Med.*, **76**, 8–22 (1962)

259. Kissen, A. T., Reifler, C. B., Thaler, V. H. Modification of thermoregulatory responses to cold by hypnosis. *J. Appl. Physiol.*, **19**, 1043–50 (1964)

260. Klussmann, F. W. The influence of temperature on the activity of spinal α- and γ- motoneurons. *Experientia*, **20**, 450–52 (1964)

261. Kraning, K. K. II, Belding, H. S., Hertig, B. A. Use of sweating rate to predict other physiological responses to heat. *J. Appl. Physiol.*, **21**, 111–17 (1966)

262. Kuno, Y. *Human Perspiration* (Thomas, Springfield, Ill., 1956)

263. Lasiewski, R. C. Oxygen consumption of torpid, resting, active, and flying hummingbirds. *Physiol. Zool.*, **36**, 122–40 (1963)

264. Lasiewski, R. C. Body temperature, heart, and breathing rate, and evaporative water loss in hummingbirds. *Ibid.*, **37**, 212–23 (1964)

265. Lasiewski, R. C., Dawson, W. R. Physiological responses to temperature in the common nighthawk. *Condor*, **66**, 477–90 (1964)

266. Le Blanc, J. Local adaptation to cold of Gaspé fishermen. *J. Appl. Physiol.*, **22**, 937–39 (1963)

267. Lee, A. K., Badham, J. A. Body temperature, activity, and behavior of the agamid lizard *Amphibolurus barbatus. Copeia*, **1963** (2), 387–94 (1963)

268. Licht, P., Dawson, W. R., Shoemaker, V. H., Main, A. R. Observations on the thermal relations of Western Australian lizards. *Copeia*, **1966** (1), 97–110 (1966)

269. Lincoln, D. W. Unit activity in the hypothalamus, septum and preoptic area of the rat: characteristics of spontaneous activity and the effect of oestrogen. *J. Endocrinol.*, **37**, 177–89 (1967)

270. Lincoln, D. W., Cross, B. A. Effect of oestrogen on the responsiveness of neurones in the hypothalamus, septum and preoptic area of rats with light-induced persistent oestrus. *J. Endocrinol.*, **37**, 191–203 (1967)

271. Lind, A. R. A physiological criterion for setting thermal environmental limits for every day work. *J. Appl. Physiol.*, **18**, 51–56 (1963)

272. Lind, A. R. Physiological effects of continuous or intermittent work in

the heat. *Ibid.*, 57–60

273. Linzell, J. L., Bligh, J. Polypnoea evoked by heating the udder of the goat. *Nature*, **190**, 173 (1961)

274. Lomax, P., Malveaux, E., Smith, R. E. Brain temperatures in the rat during exposure to low environmental temperatures. *Am. J. Physiol.*, **207**, 736–39 (1964)

275. Love, A. H. G., Shanks, R. G. The relationship between the onset of sweating and vasodilatation in the forearm during body heating. *J. Physiol. (London)*, **162**, 121–28 (1962)

276. Lucas, E. A., Reynolds, W. A. Temperature selection by amphibian larvae. *Physiol. Zool.*, **40**, 159–71 (1967)

277. Macfarlane, W. V. Terrestrial animals in dry heat: ungulates. In *Handbook of Physiology, Sect. IV, Adaptation to the Environment* (See Ref. 115), 509–39

278. MacMillen, R. E., Trost, C. H. Thermoregulation and water loss in the inca dove. *Comp. Biochem. Physiol.*, **20**, 263–73 (1967)

279. MacPherson, R. K. The effect of fever on temperature regulation in man. *Clin. Sci.*, **18**, 281–87 (1959)

280. McCook, R. D., Wurster, R. D., Randall, W. C. Sudomotor and vasomotor responses to changing environmental temperature. *J. Appl. Physiol.*, **20**, 371–78 (1965)

281. McGinnis, S. M., Dickson, L. L. Thermoregulation in the desert iguana *Dipsosaurus dorsalis*. *Science*, **156**, 1757–59 (1967)

282. McLean, J. A. The partition of insensible losses of body weight and heat from cattle under various climatic conditions. *J. Physiol. (London)*, **167**, 427–47 (1963)

283. McNab, B. K., Morrison, P. R. Temperature regulation and metabolism in subspecies of *Peromyscus* from acid and mesic environments. *Ecol. Monogr.*, **33**, 63–82 (1963)

284. Mendel, V. E., Raghavan, G. V. A study of diurnal temperature patterns in sheep. *J. Physiol. (London)*, **174**, 206–16 (1964)

285. Meurer, K., Iriki, M., Bauman, C., Jessen, C. Kältezittern bei zentroler und peripherer Kühlung. *Arch. Ges. Physiol.*, **285**, 63–72 (1965)

286. Milhorn, H. T., Jr. *The Application of Control Theory to Physiological Systems* (Saunders, Philadelphia, Pa., 386 pp., 1966)

287. Minard, D. Sweat rate during work and rest at elevated internal temperatures. *Fed. Proc.*, **22**, 177 (1963)

288. Minard, D., Copman, L. Elevation of body temperature in health. In *Temperature: Its Measurement and Control in Science and Industry* (See Ref. 176), 527–43

289. Moroff, S. V., Bass, D. E. Effects of overhydration on man's physiological responses to work in the heat. *J. Appl. Physiol.*, **20**, 267–70 (1965)

290. Mount, L. E. Basis of heat regulation in homeotherms. *Brit. Med. Bull.*, **22**, 84–87 (1966)

291. Murakami, N., Cunningham, D., Stolwijk, J. A. J., Hardy, J. D. Interneurons in the temperature sensitive preoptic region. *Physiologist*, **9**, 250 (1966)

292. Murgatroyd, D. Central and peripheral factors in behavioral thermoregulation in the rat. *Physiologist*, **9**, 251 (1966)

293. Nakayama, T., Eisenman, J. S., Hardy, J. D. Single unit activity of anterior hypothalamus during local heating. *Science*, **134**, 560–61 (1961)

294. Nakayama, T., Hammel, H. T., Hardy, J. D., Eisenman, J. S. Thermal stimulation of electrical activity of single units of the preoptic region. *Am. J. Physiol.*, **204**, 1122–26 (1963)

295. Nielsen, B. Regulation of body temperature and heat dissipation at different levels of energy and heat production in man. *Acta Physiol. Scand.*, **68**, 215–27 (1966)

296. Nielsen, B., Nielsen, M. On the regulation of sweat secretion in exercise. *Acta Physiol. Scand.*, **64**, 314–22 (1965)

297. Nielsen, B., Nielsen, M. Influence of passive and active heating on the temperature regulation of man. *Ibid.*, 323–31

298. Ogata, K., Sasaki, T. On the causes of diurnal body temperature rhythm in man, with reference to observations during voyage. *Japan. J. Physiol.*, **13**, 84–96 (1963)

299. Ogata, K., Sasaki, T., Murakami, N. Central nervous and metabolic as-

pects of body temperature regulation. *Bull. Inst. Constitutional Kumamoto Univ., XVI Suppl.,* 1–67 (1966)

300. Ogawa, T., Satoh, T., Takagi, K. Sweating during night sleep. *Japan. J. Physiol.,* **17,** 135–48 (1967)

301. Palmai, G. Diurnal and seasonal variations in deep body temperature. *Med. J. Australia,* **2,** 989–91 (1962)

302. Peiponen, V. A. The diurnal heterothermy of the nightjar (*Caprimulgus europaeus L.*). *Ann. Acad. Scien. Fennicae, A. IV,* **101,** 1–35 (1966)

303. Pirlet, K. Die Verstellung des Kerntemperatur-Sollwertes bei Kältebelastung. *Arch. Ges. Physiol.,* **275,** 71–94 (1962)

304. Rampone, A., Shirau, M. Temperature changes in the rat in response to feeding. *Science,* **144,** 317 (1964)

305. Randall, W. C. Sweating and its neural control. In *Temperature: Its Measurement and Control in Science and Industry* (See Ref. 176), 275–86

306. Randall, W. C., Rawson, R. O., McCook, R. D., Peiss, C. N. Central and peripheral factors in dynamic thermoregulation. *J. Appl. Physiol.,* **18,** 61–64 (1963)

307. Randall, W. C., Wurster, R. D., Lewin, R. J. Responses of patients with high spinal transection to high ambient temperatures. *J. Appl. Physiol.,* **21,** 985–93 (1966)

308. Ratner, A. C., Dobson, R. L. The effect of antidiuretic hormone on sweating. *J. Invest. Dermatol.,* **43,** 379–81 (1964)

309. Rautenberg, W., Simon, E. Die Beeinflussung des Kältezitterns durch lokale Temperaturänderung im Wirbelkanal. *Arch. Ges. Physiol.,* **281,** 332–45 (1964)

310. Rautenberg, W., Simon, E., Thauer, R. Kältezittern unter äusserer und innerer Kältebelastung beim Hund in leichter Narkose. *Arch. Ges. Physiol.,* **277,** 214–30 (1963)

311. Rautenberg, W., Simon, E., Thauer, R. Die Bedeutung der Kerntemperatur für die chemische Temperaturregulation beim Hund in leichter Narkose. *Ibid.,* **278,** 337–49 (1963)

312. Rautenberg, W., Simon, E., Thauer, R. *Ibid.,* 350–60

313. Rawson, R. O., Hardy, J. D. Sweat inhibition by cutaneous cooling in normal, sympathectomized, and paraplegic man. *J. Appl. Physiol.,* **22,** 287–91 (1967)

314. Rawson, R. O., Stolwijk, J. A. J., Graichen, H., Abrams, R. Continuous radio telemetry of hypothalamic temperatures from unrestrained animals. *J. Appl. Physiol.,* **20,** 321–25 (1965)

315. Regal, P. J. Voluntary hypothermia in reptiles. *Science,* **155,** 1551–53 (1967)

316. Roberts, J. C., Smith, R. E. Time-dependent responses of brown fat in cold-exposed rats. *Am. J. Physiol.,* **212,** 519–25 (1967)

317. Robertshaw, D., Whittow, G. C. The effect of hyperthermia and localized heating of the anterior hypothalamus on the sympatho-adrenal system of the ox (*Bos taurus*). *J. Physiol. (London),* **187,** 351–60 (1966)

318. Robinson, J. J., Hammel, H. T. Behavioral thermoregulation in response to heating and cooling of the hypothalamic preoptic area of the dog. *Rept. AMRL-TR-67-144* (Wright-Patterson A.F.B., Ohio, 1967)

319. Robinson, S. The regulation of sweating in exercise. *Advan. Biol. Skin,* **3,** 152–62 (1962)

320. Robinson, S. Temperature regulation in exercise. *Pediatrics,* **32,** 691–702 (1963)

321. Robinson, S. Circulatory adjustments of men in hot environments. In *Temperature: Its Measurement and Control in Science and Industry* (See Ref. 176), 287–97

322. Robinson, S., Meyer, F. R., Newton, J. L., Ts'ao, C. H., Holgersen, L. O. Relations between sweating, cutaneous blood flow, and body temperature in work. *J. Appl. Physiol.,* **20,** 575–82 (1965)

323. Roe, F. C. Fever and energy metabolism in surgical disease. *Monogr. Surg. Sci.,* **3,** 85–132 (1966)

324. Rosenmann, M., Morrison, P. Some effects of water deprivation in reindeer. *Physiol. Zool.,* **40,** 134–42 (1967)

325. Rozin, P. N., Mayer, J. Thermal re-

inforcement and thermoregulatory behavior in the goldfish *Carassius auratus*. *Science*, **134**, 942–43 (1961)

326. Rubol, R. Thermal relations of five species of tropical lizards. *Evolution*, **15**, 98–111 (1961)

327. Saltin, B., Hermansen, L. Esophageal, rectal, and muscle temperature during exercise. *J. Appl. Physiol.*, **21**, 1757–62 (1966)

328. Sasaki, T. Effect of rapid transposition around the earth on diurnal variation in body temperature. *Proc. Soc. Exptl. Biol. Med.*, **115**, 1129–31 (1964)

329. Satinoff, E. Behavioral thermoregulation in response to local cooling of the rat brain. *Am. J. Physiol.*, **206**, 1389–94 (1964)

330. Satoh, T., Ogawa, T., Takagi, K. Sweating during daytime sleep. *Japan. J. Physiol.*, **15**, 523–31 (1965)

331. Schmidt-Nielsen, K., Crawford, E. C., Jr., Newsome, A. E., Rawson, K. S., Hammel, H. T. Metabolic, rate of camels: effect of body temperature and dehydration. *Am. J. Physiol.*, **212**, 341–46 (1967)

332. Schmidt-Nielsen, K., Dawson, T. J., Crawford, E. C., Jr. Temperature regulation in the echidna *Tachyglossus aculeatus*. *J. Cellular Physiol.*, **67**, 63–71 (1966)

333. Schmidt-Nielsen, K., Dawson, T. J., Hammel, H. T., Hind, D., Jackson, D. C. The jack rabbit—a study in its desert survival. *Hvalrådets Skrifter*, No. 48, 125–42 (1965)

334. Schmidt-Nielsen, K., Dawson, W. R. Terrestrial animals in dry heat: desert reptiles. In *Handbook of Physiology, Sect. IV, Adaptation to the Environment* (See Ref. 115), 467–80

335. Schulz, I., Ullrich, K. J., Frömter, E., Holzgreve, H., Frick, A., Hegel, U. Mikropunktion und elektrische Potentialmessung an Schweissdrüsen des Menschen. *Arch. Ges. Physiol.*, **284**, 360–72 (1965)

336. Scopes, J. W. Metabolic rate and temperature control in the human body. *Brit. Med. Bull.*, **22**, 88–91 (1966)

337. Segrem, N. P., Hart, J. S. Oxygen supply and performance in *Peromyscus*. Metabolic and circulatory responses to exercise. *Can. J. Physiol. Pharmacol.*, **45**, 531–41 (1967)

338. Segrem, N. P., Hart, J. S. Oxygen supply and performance in peromyscus. Comparison of exercise with cold exposure. *Ibid.*, 543–49

339. Senay, L. C., Jr., Christensen, M. L. Cutaneous circulation during dehydration and heat stress. *J. Appl. Physiol.*, **20**, 278–82 (1965)

340. Senay, L. C., Jr., Prokop, L. D., Cronau, L., Hertzman, A. B. Relation of local skin temperature and local sweating to cutaneous blood flow. *J. Appl. Physiol.*, **18**, 781–85 (1963)

341. Sibbons, J. L. H. Assessment of thermal stress from energy balance considerations. *J. Appl. Physiol.*, **21**, 1207–17 (1966)

342. Silverman, W. S., Zamelis, A., Sinclair, J. C., Agate, F. J., Jr. Warm nape of the newborn. *Pediatrics*, **33**, 984–86 (1964)

343. Simon, E., Rautenberg, W., Jessen, C. Initiation of shivering in unanesthetized dogs by local cooling within the vertebral canal. *Experientia*, **21**, 477–80 (1965)

344. Simon, E., Rautenberg, W., Thauer, R. Die Bedeutung der Kerntemperatur für die chemische Temperaturregulation beim Hund in leichter Narkose. *Arch. Ges. Physiol.*, **278**, 361–73 (1963)

345. Simon, E., Rautenberg, W., Thauer, R., Iriki, M. Auslösung thermoregulatorischer Reaktionen durch lokale Kühlung im Vertebralkanal. *Naturwissenschaften*, **8**, 337–39 (1963)

346. Simon, E., Rautenberg, W., Thauer, R., Iriki, M. Die Auslösung von Kältezittern durch lokale Kühlung im Wirbelkanal. *Arch. Ges. Physiol.*, **281**, 309–31 (1964)

347. Smalley, R. L., Dryer, R. L. Brown fat: thermogenic effect during arousal from hibernation in the bat. *Science*, **140**, 1333–34 (1963)

348. Smith, P. E., Jr., James, E. W. II, Human responses to heat stress. *Arch. Environ. Health*, **9**, 332–42 (1964)

349. Smith, R. E. Thermogenic activity of the hibernating gland in the cold-acclimated rat. *Physiologist*, **4**, 113 (1961)

350. Smith, R. E. Thermoregulation by brown adipose tissue in cold. *Fed. Proc.*, **21**, 221 (1962)

351. Smith, R. E. Brown fat in the rat: adaptive changes in cold. *Helgolaender Wiss. Meeresuntersuch.,* **9,** 187–96 (1964)

352. Smith, R. E., Hock, R. J. Brown fat: thermogenic effector of arousal in hibernators. *Science,* **140,** 199–200 (1963)

353. Smith, R. E., Roberts, J. C. Thermogenesis of brown adipose tissue in cold-acclimated rats. *Am. J. Physiol.,* **206,** 143–48 (1964)

354. Snellen, J. W. Mean body temperature and the control of thermal sweating. *Acta Physiol. Pharmacol. Neerl.,* **14,** 99–174 (1966)

355. Soulé, M. Aspects of thermoregulation in nine species of lizards from Baja, California. *Copeia,* **1963** (1), 107–15 (1963)

356. Soulé, M. Reptilian thermoregulation. *Science,* **148,** 1250–51 (1965)

357. Squires, R. D. Thermoregulatory effects of injections of γ-aminobutyric acid (GABA) and picrotoxin (PT) into medial preoptic region (MPR) of cats. *Fed. Proc.,* **26,** 555 (1967)

358. Squires, R. D., Jacobson, F. H. Further observations of unstable hypothermia due to lesions in the preoptic region of cats. *Fed. Proc.,* **21,** 225 (1962)

359. Squires, R. D., Jacobson, F. H. Further observations on chronic deficits of temperature regulation produced in cats by preoptic lesions. *Rept. NADA-MR-6626* (U.S. Naval Air Develop. Center, Johnsville, Pa., 1966)

360. Squires, R. D., Hale, L. L., Byrne, S. Abolition of the metabolic response to cold. *Fed. Proc.,* **25,** 515 (1966)

361. Squires, R. D., Hale, L. L., Jacobson, F. H. Decrease of metabolism by intrahypothalamic injection of α-OH-butyrate (Na). *Fed. Proc.,* **24,** 346 (1965)

362. Steen, I., Steen, J. B. Thermoregulatory importance of the beaver's tail. *Comp. Biochem. Physiol.,* **15,** 267–70 (1965)

363. Steen, I., Steen, J. B. The importance of the legs in thermoregulation of birds. *Acta Physiol. Scand.,* **63,** 285–91 (1965)

364. St. Girons, H., St. Girons, M. C. Cycle d'activité et thermorégulation chez les reptiles (lézards et serpents). *Vie Milieu,* **7,** 133–226 (1956)

365. Stolwijk, J. A. J., Hardy, J. D. Partitional calorimetric studies of responses of man to thermal transients. *J. Appl. Physiol.,* **21,** 967–77 (1966)

366. Stolwijk, J. A. J., Hardy, J. D. Temperature regulation in man—a theoretical study. *Arch. Ges. Physiol.,* **291,** 129–62 (1966)

367. Stuart, D. G. Nervous control of shivering—a review. *Rept. AAL-TDR-62-11,* 1–23 (Arctic Aeromed. Lab., Fort Wainwright, Alaska, 1962)

368. Stuart, D. G., Eldred, E., Hemingway, A., Kawamura, Y. Neural regulation of the rhythm of shivering. In *Temperature: Its Measurement and Control in Science and Industry* (See Ref. 176), 545–57

369. Stuart, D. G., Freeman, W. J., Hemingway, A. Effects of decerebration and decortication on shivering in the cat. *Neurology,* **12,** 99–107 (1962)

370. Stuart, D. G., Kawamura, Y., Hemingway, A. Activation and suppression of shivering during septal and hypothalamic stimulation. *Exptl. Neurol.,* **4,** 485–506 (1961)

371. Stuart, D., Ott, K., Eldred, E. Effects of cerebellar lesions and stimulation on the shivering tremor. *Am. J. Physiol.,* **209,** 1261–66 (1965)

372. Stuart, D., Ott, K., Ishikawa, K., Eldred, E. The rhythm of shivering: I. General sensory contributions. *Am. J. Phys. Med.,* **45,** 61–74 (1966)

373. Stuart, D., Ott, K., Ishikawa, K., Eldred, E. The rhythm of shivering: II. Passive proprioceptive contributions. *Ibid.,* 75–90

374. Stuart, D., Ott, K., Ishikawa, K., Eldred, E. The rhythm of shivering: III. Central contributions. *Ibid.,* **45,** 91–104 (1966)

375. Tanabe, K., Takaori, S. Effects of cooling and warming of the common carotid arteries on the brain and tympanic membrane temperatures in the rabbit. *Japan. J. Pharmacol.,* **14,** 67–79 (1964)

376. Tanche, M., Chatonnet, J., Cabanac, J. Exclusion élective de la sensibilité "centrale" hypothalamique au

froid. *Excerpta Med. Intern. Congr. Ser. No. 48* (1962)

377. Taylor, C. R. The vascularity and possible thermoregulatory function of the horns in goats. *Physiol. Zool.,* **39,** 127–39 (1966)

378. Thauer, R. Mécanismes périphériques et centraux de la régulation de la température. *Arch. Sci. Physiol.,* **15,** 95–123 (1961)

379. Thauer, R. Der nervöse Mechanismus der chemischen Temperaturregulation des Warmblüters. *Naturwissenschaften,* **4,** 73–80 (1964)

380. Thiele, P., Albers, C. Die Wasserdampfabgabe durch die Atemwege und der Wirkungsgrad des Wärmehechelns beim wachen Hund. *Arch. Ges. Physiol.,* **278,** 316–24 (1963)

381. Thorington, R. W., Jr. The biology of rodent tails—A study of form and function. *AAL-TR-65-8* (Arctic Aeromed. Lab., Fort Wainwright, Alaska, 1966)

382. Veghte, J. H. Thermal and metabolic responses of the gray jay to cold stress. *Physiol. Zool.,* **37,** 316–28 (1964)

383. Vendrik, A. J. H., Vos, J. J. Comparison of the stimulation of the warmth sense organ by microwave and infrared. *J. Appl. Physiol.,* **13,** 435–44 (1958)

384. Villablanca, J., Myers, R. D. Fever produced by microinjection of typhoid vaccine into hypothalamus of cats. *Am. J. Physiol.,* **208,** 703–7 (1965)

385. Wang, G. H. *The Neural Control of Sweating* (Univ. of Wisconsin Press, Madison, Wis., 1964)

386. Waites, G. M. H. Polypnoea evoked by heating the scrotum of the ram. *Nature,* **190,** 172 (1961)

387. Waites, G. M. H. The effect of heating the scrotum of the ram on respiration and body temperature. *Quart. J. Exptl. Physiol.,* **47,** 314–23 (1962)

388. Waites, G. M. H., Voglymayr, J. K. The functional activity and control of the apocrine sweat glands of the scrotum of the ram. *Australian J. Agr. Res.,* **14,** 839–51 (1963)

389. Weiss, B., Laties, V. G. Behavioral thermoregulation. *Science,* **133,** 1338–44 (1961)

390. West, G. C. Shivering and heat production in wild birds. *Physiol. Zool.,* **30,** 111–20 1965)

391. Wissler, E. H. An analysis of factors affecting temperature levels in the nude human. In *Temperature: Its Measurement and Control in Science and Industry* (See Ref. 176), 603–12

392. Wissler, E. H. A mathematical model of the human thermal system. *Bull. Math. Biophys.,* **26,** 147–66 (1964)

393. Wit, A., Wang, S. C. Effects of increasing ambient temperature on unit activity in the preoptic-anterior hypothalamus (PO/AH) region. *Fed. Proc.,* **26,** 1672 (1967)

394. Wünnenberg, W., Brück, K. Untersuchungen über die Funktionsweise thermoreceptiver Strückturen im Cervicalmark des Meerschweinchens. *Arch. Ges. Physiol.,* **294,** 84 (1967)

395. Wurster, R. D., McCook, R. D., Randall, W. C. Cutaneous vascular and sweating responses to tympanic and skin temperatures. *J. Appl. Physiol.,* **21,** 617–22 (1966)

396. Wyndham, C. H. Role of skin and core temperatures in man's temperature regulation. *J. Appl. Physiol.,* **20,** 31–36 (1965)

397. Wyndham, C. H., Aitkens, A. P. An approach to the solution of the human biothermal problems with the aid of an analogue computer. *Proc. Intern. Conf. Med. Electronics, 3rd, London, 1960,* 32–38

398. Wyndham, C. H., Morrison, J. F., Williams, C. G. Heat reactions of male and female caucasians. *J. Appl. Physiol.,* **20,** 357–64 (1965)

399. Wyndham, C. H., Strydom, N. B., Morrison, J. F., Williams, C. G., Bredell, G. A. G., Peter, J. Fatigue of the sweat gland response. *J. Appl. Physiol.,* **21,** 107–10 (1966)

400. Wyndham, C. H., Strydom, N. B., Morrison, J. F., Williams, C. G., Bredell, G. A. G., Von Rahden, M. J. E., Holdsworth, L. D., Van Graan, C. H., Van Rensburg, A. J., Munro, A. Heat reactions of Caucasians and Bantu in South Africa. *J. Appl. Physiol.,* **19,** 598–606 (1964)

401. Wyndham, C. H., Strydom, N. B.,

Munro, A., MacPherson, R. K.,
Metz, B., Schaff, G., Schieber, J.
Heat reactions of Caucasians in
temperate, in hot, dry, and in hot,
humid climates. *J. Appl. Physiol.*,
19, 607–12 (1964)

402. Yamamoto, W. S., Brobeck, J. R.,
Eds. *Physiological Controls and
Regulations* (Saunders, Phila-
delphia, Pa., 362 pp., 1965)

AUTHOR INDEX

Harris, E. J., 60, 61
Harris, G. W., 214, 218, 246, 563, 574, 590, 607, 620, 621
Harrison, F. A., 35
Harrison, G. K., 539
Harrison, J. M., 328, 329
Harsing, L., 447
Hart, A., 114
Hart, J. S., 651, 659
Hartcroft, P. M., 194
Harthoorn, A. M., 688
Hartley, T. C., 688
Hartline, H. K., 298
Hartmann, J. F., 558
Hartshorne, D. J., 410, 411
Harvey, A., 443
Harvey, N., 489, 490
Harvey, R. B., 448
Haselbach, C. H., 616
Hasen, J., 231, 234
Hashimoto, K., 160, 450
Hasselbach, W., 21, 23, 42, 423
Hatcher, G., 34
Hatt, P. Y., 452
Hauge, A., 159
Haun, C. K., 574
Hausmans, J., 387
Havel, V., 120
Hawk, H. W., 254, 257, 258
Hawkins, L. H., 123
Hawkins, N. M., 500
Hayano, M., 187
Hayashi, H., 644
Haydon, D. A., 28
Hayes, C. P., 480
Hayhow, W. R., 334
Haynes, R. C., 181, 264
Haynes, R. C., Jr., 176, 180
Hays, R. L., 559, 563, 564
Hays, R. M., 22
Hayward, J. N., 603, 608, 662, 664
Hayward, J. S., 659
Heald, P. J., 604
Healy, J. K., 475, 499
Heard, B. E., 116
Hearn, W. R., 250, 259, 260, 261, 262, 573
Heath, J. E., 651, 652, 688
Heath, W. C., 544
Hechter, O., 173, 176, 183, 187
Hecker, E., 231
Hedge, G. A., 595
Hefner, L. L., 533, 541
Hegel, U., 455, 456, 467, 678
Hehl, U., 468
Heilbrunn, L. V., 423

Heim, T., 162
Heine, H., 156
Heinemann, H. O., 466
Heintz, R., 489
Helbock, H. J., 42
Held, U., 487
Hellam, D. C., 421
Heller, H., 490, 557, 560, 561
Heller, J., 489, 490
Hellig, H., 264, 266
Hellman, D., 469
Hellon, R. F., 644, 669, 679, 680, 684
Hellstrøm, B., 647, 648, 661, 662, 665, 672, 680, 685, 686, 687, 693
Helmreich, M. L., 188
Hemingway, A., 643, 649, 659, 661, 666, 683, 684
Hemingway, C., 661
Hempling, H. G., 31, 52
Hems, D. A., 25
Henderson, I. W., 95
Henderson, J. A. M., 118
Henderson, W. J., 213
Hendricks, D. M., 261
Hennen, G., 220
Hennenman, E., 340
Henricks, D. M., 261, 604, 612
Henry, J. P., 561, 562
Henry, R. J., 230
Hensel, H., 319, 320, 644
Herbert, S. J., 117
Herbst, A. L., 603
Herd, J. A., 160, 445
Heric, T. M., 336
Herlyn, U., 613
Herman-Giddens, S., 537
Hermansen, L., 690
Hern, J. E., 367, 368
Hernandez, R. R., 539
Heroux, D., 214
Herreid, C. F. II, 651
Herron, M. A., 191
Hershberger, L. G., 600
Hershey, S. G., 577
Hertig, B. A., 673, 674, 675, 676, 678, 679, 688
Hertzman, A. B., 654, 677
Herz, R., 42, 418, 422
Hess, A., 424, 426, 427, 428
Hess, M., 250
Hess, W. N., 91
Heston, W. E., 184
Heuman, H.-G., 403
Heusner, A. A., 643
Heymann, M., 113
Heywood, S. M., 223
Hickman, C. P., 93, 94
Hidalgo, C., 52

Hierholzer, K., 463, 496, 497
Higashino, S., 418
Higasi, B., 550
Higgins, J. T., Jr., 193
Higgs, B. E., 114, 120, 122
Higinbotham, N., 37, 43
Hildes, J. A., 688
Hildwein, G., 651
Hilf, R., 171
Hill, A. F., 413
Hill, A. V., 412, 413, 414
Hill, R. M., 333, 336, 337
Hill, R. V., 122, 549
Hill, T. L., 31
Hille, B., 39
Hilliard, J., 255, 256, 602, 603, 608
Hills, A. G., 478, 480
Hilton, J. G., 181, 195, 572
Hilton, R., 541
Hilton, S. M., 134, 162
Hind, D., 651, 655
Hind, J. E., 324, 325, 326, 327, 329, 330, 331
Hindmarsh, J. T., 51, 57
Hines, M., 377
Hines, M. F. M., 590, 591, 592, 593, 594
Hines, R. A., 56
Hinke, J. A. M., 33, 567
Hinman, J. W., 452
Hinsey, J. C., 590
Hiroi, M., 604
Hiroshige, T., 575
Hirsch, L., 159
Hirsch, P. F., 213, 469
Hirsch, R. L., 485
Hirshfield, I. N., 178
Histand, M., 538
Ho, P. M., 50
Ho, R. J., 182
Hobson, H. D., 30
Hoch, F. L., 236
Hochster, R. M., 49
Hock, R. J., 659
Hodgkin, A. L., 296, 323, 324
Høedt-Rasmussen, K., 158
Hoeppner, D. L., 161
Hofert, J., 184
Hoff, E., 230
Hoff, H. E., 122
Hoffman, J. F., 33, 52
Hoffman, J. I. E., 549
Hoffman, W. W., 237
Hofmann, F. G., 192
Hökfelt, B., 648, 649, 662, 663, 664, 672, 684, 687
Hokin, L. E., 18
Hokin, M. R., 18, 52
Holden, J. T., 50
Holderness, M., 218

SUBJECT INDEX

647-49, 659, 662-63, 665-
67, 669, 681, 687-88,
692-93
equation for open-loop gain,
692
Shock
alpha-adrenergic blockade
in, 141
hemorrhagic
nervous control of, 155
synthetic vasopressin use
in, 577
mesenteric microcirculatory
adaptations to, 141-
42
treatment of
beta-adrenergic stimula-
tion, 137
Sialic acid
in membrane synthesis,
57
Singing
voluntary intercostal control
in, 106
Skin
afferent nerve system of
inputs of, 361
control of circulation in,
161
glabrous
dermal ridge innervation,
339
hairy
afferent supply to, 338
temperature receptors of,
644-45
thermoregulatory role of,
667, 679-81, 687-90
see also Sweat
Sleep
thermoregulation during,
688
Sniffing
diaphragm movement during,
106
Sodium
active transport of
split-droplet method of
study, 459
aldosterone effects on, 54-
55
balance maintenance
juxtaglomerular apparatus
in, 453-55
calcium competition with,
54
excretion
neurohypophyseal hormone
effects on, 566
intracellular binding of,
460
invertebrate regulation of,
80-90
localization of activity of,
73-74
in membrane excitation, 37-
41

membrane transport of
energetics of, 51-53
and oxygen consumption,
52-53
protozoal regulation of,
79
pump
in striated muscle, 32
receptor potential dependence upon, 319
and renal circulatory control, 160
renal reabsorption of
angiotensin effects on,
500-1
oxygen cost of, 451
thermoregulatory effects,
678
renal transport of, 457-
66
aldosterone effects on,
496-97
Henle's loops, 483-84
for renal tubular glucose
transport, 469-70
renal tubular permeabilities
for, 459
and renin secretion, 453-
54
for sugar and amino acid
transport, 50-51
transport
bulk-phase limitations of,
33
in epithelial systems,
35
in erythrocytes, 34
mitochondrial, 60-61
in other mammalian cells,
34
in plants, 37
sites of, 74
in striated muscle, 32-
33
transverse tubule localization of, 42, 419
urinary excretion of, 463-
66
vascular reactivity to, 140-
41
vertebrate regulation of, 91-
99
Sodium bicarbonate
renal effects of, 477
Sodium dodecyl sulfate
on ATPase, 24
Sodium-potassium adenosine
triphosphatase
corticosteroids' effect on
levels of, 55
inhibitors of, 24
isolation and purification
attempts, 24
and lipid turnover, 18-
19
of plasma membrane, 22-
25

renal membrane transport
of, 457, 470
Somatosensory system
afferent mechanisms of,
337-44
Sorbose
membrane transport of,
48
Sound
localization of, 330
Spectrometry
practical hints on, 249
Sperm
transport of
oxytocin role in, 563,
570
Spermidine
on FHS secretion, 610
Spherocytosis
enzyme activity in, 22
Spinal cord
afferent pathways in, 340-
43
motor fiber tracts in, 381-
85
thermoregulatory role of,
665-67, 680
transection
and respiration, 109
ventral funiculi
motoneuron excitation by,
381-82
Spinocervical tract
afferent mechanisms of,
340-42
response characteristics,
341
unit inhibition of, 342
distinguished from dorsal
column, 341-42
Spirometry
clinical use of, 115
Spleen
circulation in, 136-37
Squid
axon of
model of, 31
see also under Nerve fiber
Squirrel
afferent visual mechanisms
in, 333-34
Staining techniques
negative staining, 16-
17
Starling hypothesis
re-evaluation of, 150, 163
Starvation
intestinal response to,
57
Steroidogenin
physicochemical behavior of,
178-79, 182, 184-85
Steroidohibin
physicochemical behavior,
179, 183-85
Steroids
nomenclature of, 171

CUMULATIVE INDEXES

VOLUMES 26-30

INDEX OF CONTRIBUTING AUTHORS

INDEX OF CHAPTER TITLES

VOLUMES 26-30